MODERN SCIENCE
AND
TECHNOLOGY

MODERN SCIENCE AND TECHNOLOGY

ROBERT COLBORN, Chief Editor

and the Editors of *International Science and Technology*

D. VAN NOSTRAND COMPANY, INC.

PRINCETON, NEW JERSEY

TORONTO NEW YORK LONDON

D. VAN NOSTRAND COMPANY, INC.
120 Alexander St., Princeton, New Jersey (*Principal office*)
24 West 40 Street, New York 18, New York

D. VAN NOSTRAND COMPANY, LTD.
358, Kensington High Street, London, W.14, England

D. VAN NOSTRAND COMPANY (*Canada*), LTD.
25 Hollinger Road, Toronto 16, Canada

Published simultaneously in Canada by
D. VAN NOSTRAND COMPANY (Canada), LTD.

Preface

This book is a selection of eighty-one articles on various phases of modern investigation of the physical world. The immense scope of this field gives, necessarily, the appearance of randomness to choice of subjects. Nevertheless, the present collection does have a coherence, I believe, and perhaps some explanation of the things that bind it together can be helpful to a reader.

One attitude that holds these articles together is that the sciences, even the most remote, and technology, even the most familiar, are all parts of one enterprise. They are all concerned with understanding and controlling the physical world, even though some put more emphasis on understanding and some more on control. There is a constant flow of ideas from one part of the enterprise to another. And—nowadays particularly—there is an increasing flow of people from one specialized field to another. That is why it seems to make sense to include in the same collection Wheeler's discussion of the geometry of space-time (page 11) and Park's account of new ways of shaping metal parts (page 397). The two articles do share a common attitude toward the physical world and, in a strange way, a common manner of talking about it.

That common way of talking is itself another element which holds this collection of articles together. The articles all speak in a particular voice—one which is not often heard. It is not the voice of the popularizer who tries to give a lay reader a tourist's view of the world of science. Neither is it the voice of the expert talking to his fellow experts. These articles were written for professional scientists and engineers to read when they want to inform themselves about technical progress outside their own particular field of specialization. Each writer assumed that his readers would have a vigorous professional interest in technical matters. He assumed a familiarity with the fundamental principles of science and the better known mathematical tools. Furthermore, each writer, with varying degrees of success, has tried to translate the narrow jargon of his own field into the basic technical vocabulary shared by nearly all technical men.

Moreover, it is obvious that this particular voice happens also to be one which can be as useful to the serious student as it is to the professional. It allows the student to share in the shop talk of his future colleagues. In other words, the student can profit from the fact that the basic principle of selection has been that of professional usefulness.

That principle is still another strand uniting these articles. All of them are intended to present news. Each was written to describe and explain recent happenings in some particular field to a man outside that field, who ought to know about these occurrences, but who, quite likely, does not. New discoveries have been made, perhaps, or old knowledge has taken on new meaning; the professional background of the scientist or engineer must be expanded to take account of this.

The underlying reason for this unity is that all these articles are taken from a single magazine, *International Science and Technology.* As editor of that magazine, I have a peculiar advantage over most editors; I know exactly who my readers are. The reason is that ever since Conover-Mast Publications established *International Science and Technology,* it has been circulated only to professional scientists and engineers. These articles were conceived, written, and edited to meet the professional needs of those particular readers.

I would like to say a word about the way these articles were produced. The choice of topics represents the collective judgment of two groups of people. One group consists of the editorial staff. The other is an advisory group, the Editorial

Board, which meets periodically to consult with the editorial staff. During the period when the articles in this volume were produced, these were the members of the Board: E. U. Condon, its chairman, physicist, teacher, and former head of the U.S. Bureau of Standards; Sir Harrie Massey, another distinguished physicist, adviser on space activity to the British government, and Quain professor of physics at London University's University College; Ernst Weber, president of Brooklyn Polytechnic Institute, and also the first president of the recently merged Institute of Electrical and Electronics Engineers; Louis P. Hammett, a notable worker in inorganic chemistry, professor emeritus at Columbia University, and past president of the American Chemical Society; Hugh Odishaw, a geophysicist, secretary of the Space Science Board of the National Academy of Sciences, and a moving spirit in the organization of the International Geophysical Year.

Out of the deliberations of this group, out of the incessant consultations of the editorial staff, and most likely, out of the private musings of one of the editors will emerge the conviction that some particular topic ought to become the subject of an article. One of the staff editors takes charge of the idea. He scouts the field to determine who is the most logical author on this subject and induces that man to write an article. Then it becomes the responsibility of the editor to work closely with the author in the formulation of a piece adapted to the needs of a broad audience of technical men from many fields.

Primary credit for the authority and quality of the articles in the volume must go, naturally, to the authors who wrote them—and I am grateful that busy and responsible men have been willing to put long hours into formulating and refining the essence of their fields of work. But the contribution of the staff editor is too large to let it be entirely anonymous. Each article, therefore, carries at the end of its introductory abstract the initials of the editor who worked with its author. Here is the code: *D.C.* is Daniel Cooper, executive editor of the magazine. The others, all associate editors, are as follows: *D.A.* is David Allison; *E.H.* is Evan Herbert; *C.J.L.* is Charles Lynch; *H.W.M.* is Howard Mattson; *F.P.* is Ford Park; *S.T.* is Seymour Tilson. Three former members of the staff, also associate editors, also appear: *S.B.* is Sheila Bouwman; *T.M.* is Theodore Melnechuk; and *R.G.N.* is Ronald Neswald. Also, though you will not find their initials, I should say here that art director Gerald Ferguson is responsible for the illustration and the general visual effectiveness of the articles, and that Regula Davis, assistant editor, has contributed largely to the grace and consistency of the style.

As for myself, I have been a useful voice, I hope, in the consultations that led to the selection of these particular topics. But the contribution which makes me willing to have my name appear as editor of this volume is that it was I who found and brought together these thoughtful and enthusiastic people.

ROBERT COLBORN

New York, New York
January, 1965

Contributors

ISIDORE ADLER
U.S. Department of the Interior

ROBERT BAKISH
Consulting Engineer

LOUIS J. BATTAN
University of Arizona

A. E. BRAIN
Stanford Research Institute

ROBERT M. BRUGGER
Phillips Petroleum Co.

SHELDON A. BUCKLER
Polaroid Corp.

A. G. W. CAMERON
Goddard Space Flight Center

B. S. CHANDRASEKHAR
Western Reserve University

HONG-YEE CHIU
Goddard Institute for Space Studies

LEWIS C. CLAPP
Bolt, Beranek and Newman, Inc.

BERNARD L. COHEN
University of Pittsburgh

WILLIAM COHEN
National Aeronautics and Space Administration

KENNETH R. COLEMAN
U.K. Atomic Energy Authority

DANIEL I. COOPER
International Science and Technology

C. CHAPIN CUTLER
Bell Telephone Laboratories

R. H. DICKE
Princeton University

GEORGE DIETER
Drexel Institute of Technology

GEORGE E. DUVALL
Washington State University

IRA DYER
Bolt, Beranek and Newman, Inc.

STANTON L. EILENBERG
Electro-Optical Systems, Inc.

HENRY EYRING
University of Utah

DAVID FALCONER
University of Texas

ANTONIO FERRI
General Applied Science Laboratories, Inc.

R. E. FINNIGAN
Electronic Associates, Inc.

A. THEODORE FORRESTER
Electro-Optical Systems, Inc.

G. E. FORSEN
Stanford Research Institute

HAROLD L. FOX
Sperry Utah Co.

ROBERT C. FRANK
Augustana College

PETER FRANKEN
University of Michigan

ROBERT A. FROSCH
Office of the Secretary of Defense

FELIX J. GERMINO
American Machine and Foundry Co.

V. I. GOLDANSKII
Institute for Chemical Physics of U.S.S.R.

SOLOMON W. GOLOMB
University of Southern California

RALPH GOMORY
International Business Machines

HAROLD M. GORDY
Giannini Controls Corp.

IRVING GRUNTFEST
General Electric Co.

PAUL GUGLIOTTA
Juster and Gugliotta

JACK K. HALE
Brown University

LOUIS P. HAMMETT
Columbia University (retired)

EVAN HERBERT
International Science and Technology

WILMOT N. HESS
Goddard Space Flight Center

JOEL HILDEBRAND
University of California at Berkeley

T. P. HOAR
Cambridge University

ALAN HOFFMAN
International Business Machines

DOUGLAS L. HOGAN
U.S. Department of Defense

J. K. HULM
Westinghouse Electric Corp.

MELVIN J. HUNTER
Dow Corning Corp.

JOHN D. ISAACS
Scripps Institution of Oceanography

LEONARD JAFFE
National Aeronautics and Space Administration

ROWLAND E. JOHNSON
Texas Instruments

HERBERT L. KAHN
Perkin-Elmer Corp.

AHARON KATCHALSKY
Weizmann Institute of Science (Israel)

BRIAN KAYE
IIT Research Institute

W. W. KELLOGG
National Center for Atmospheric Research

J. KING
University of Michigan

LUDWIG KOCH
Continental Oil Co.

BÖRJE LANGEFORS
Svenska Aeroplan Aktiebolaget (SAAB)

JOSEPH P. LaSALLE
Brown University

A. E. LEE
Stanford Research Institute

EDWARD V. LEWIS
Webb Institute of Naval Architecture

T. LIMPERIS
University of Michigan

CHARLES J. LYNCH
International Science and Technology

R. K. MacCRONE
University of Pennsylvania

THOMAS F. MALONE
Travelers Insurance Co.

HERMAN F. MARK
Polytechnic Institute of Brooklyn (retired)

SIR HARRIE MASSEY
European Space Research Organization

THEODORE MELNECHUK
Massachusetts Institute of Technology

J. MORGAN
University of Michigan

YUVAL NE'EMAN
Tel-Aviv University

R. R. NEIMAN
Interphase-West

RONALD G. NESWALD
International Science and Technology

GALE NEVILL
University of Florida

N. J. NILSSON
Stanford Research Institute

BERNARD M. OLIVER
Hewlett-Packard Co.

WILLIAM G. OSMUN
Space/Aeronautics

FORD PARK
International Science and Technology

E. G. D. PATERSON
Bell Telephone Laboratories (retired)

OGDEN R. PIERCE
Dow Corning Corp.

F. POLCYN
University of Michigan

T. M. QUIST
Lincoln Laboratory, MIT

THOMAS B. REED
Lincoln Laboratory, MIT

STUART RICE
University of Chicago

H. RIEMERSMA
Westinghouse Electric Corp.

P. G. ROLL
Princeton University

C. A. ROSEN
Stanford Research Institute

LAWRENCE G. RUBIN
National Magnet Laboratory, MIT

CARL SAGAN
Smithsonian Astrophysical Observatory

WALTER R. SCHMITT
Scripps Institution of Oceanography

HAROLD SCHONHORN
Bell Telephone Laboratories

RAYMOND W. SEARS, JR.
U.S. Department of Defense

LOUIS H. SHARPE
Bell Telephone Laboratories

LAWRENCE SHENKER
General Electric Co.

WALTER SLAVIN
Perkin-Elmer Corp.

JOHN L. SPEIER
Dow Corning Corp.

JOHN L. SPRAGUE
Sprague Electric Co.

CHAUNCEY STARR
Atomics International

S. DONALD STOOKEY
Corning Glass Works

BENSON R. SUNDHEIM
New York University

SEYMOUR TILSON
International Science and Technology

P. M. UTHE
Electronic Associates, Inc.

BERNARD L. WALSH
Hughes Aircraft

J. WEBER
University of Maryland

JOHN A. WHEELER
Princeton University

RONALD L. WIGINGTON
U.S. Department of Defense

W. WOLFE
University of Michigan

O. LEW WOOD
Sperry Utah Co.

HUSEYIN YILMAZ
Arthur D. Little Co.

CLAUDE E. ZoBELL
Scripps Institution of Oceanography

Contents

6 MATHEMATICS, COMPUTERS, AND CONTROL

Color Illustrations

In encountering in the text a reference to a Color Figure, the reader may wish to consult this listing to determine quickly the page number of that specific Color Figure.

Chapter 1

Physics and Electronics

GRAVITY EXPERIMENTS

by R. H. Dicke, P. G. Roll, and J. Weber *

IN BRIEF: *Meaningful experiments concerning the nature of gravity are few and far between—for two reasons: gravitational forces are woefully weak, so data sufficiently precise to be meaningful are hard to come by; and the essential nature of gravity lies hidden in the theoretical labyrinth of relativity, in which it's easy to lose your way, assuming you have the courage to enter in the first place. But to the intrepid, three experimental paths lie open.*

The first is in null checks of extreme precision—accuracies of 1 part in 10^{11} and a few parts in 10^{23} are involved in two such experiments discussed here—which seek to balance against each other two quantities that are expected from existing theory to be equal. The magnitude of any inequality discovered sets clear limits to theory. A second kind of experiment seeks more accurate checks than presently available for the three famous predictions of Einstein's theory of general relativity which ties gravitation to curved space— the gravity-induced red shift, bending of light, and precession of Mercury's orbit. The third experimental approach has generated most industrial interest lately, because it seems to point to the possibilities—remote ones—of communication by gravity and of shielding against gravity. This approach assumes the existence of gravity waves analogous to electromagnetic radiation, as predicted by Einstein, and seeks to find them.—S.T.

* R. H. Dicke currently engages in gravitation and relativity experiments at Princeton University. P. G. Roll, Assistant Professor of Physics at Princeton, is associated with Dicke's research program. J. Weber, Professor of Physics at the University of Maryland, has recently completed his second period of residence at the Institute for Advanced Study, Princeton, New Jersey.

■ There has been until recently what we might term a psychological lull in matters gravitational. Perhaps this was only to be expected after the early great labors in the long history of gravity studies. Our present ideas about it are most completely crystallized in Newton's law of universal gravitation and his three laws of motion, and in Einstein's theory of general relativity and its modern extensions (see "The Dynamics of Space-Time," page 11). Yet this lull would be easier for us to understand if the field really was "cleaned up" by these theoretical achievements. It is not, of course. In many fundamental respects gravitation still offers all the exploratory challenges of a field that's just beginning.

The feeble force called gravity

The nature of the challenge and the main barrier to possible rewards arises from the fact that gravity is the weakest force now known. The ratio of the gravitational force to the electrostatic force between a proton and an electron in an average atom is only about 5×10^{-40}. If the diminutive size of this number is hard to comprehend, here's another analogy that may help. The electrostatic force of repulsion between two electrons 5 meters apart—a scant 10^{-24} dynes—approximately equals the gravitational force exerted by the *entire* earth on one of the electrons. The extremely small magnitude of gravitational forces has led many technical people to feel that, while gravitation may be interesting from a philosophical standpoint, it's unimportant either theoretically or experimentally in work concerned with everyday phenomena. This feeling may be justified, of course. In fact, on a slightly more sophisticated level, application of the strong principle of equivalence seems at first to reinforce this point of view.

This principle tells us that the effects of gravitational forces on observations can be transformed away by making the observations in a laboratory framework that is properly accelerated. The best concrete example of this still is Einstein's original freely falling elevator in a gravity field, in which an experimenter and all his apparatus are placed. Since he and his apparatus fall with the same acceleration, gravitational effects apparently disappear from phenomena observed in the elevator. Gravitational forces, in other words, sometimes simulate inertial ones. From this it's easy to conclude that gravitation is of little or no concern.

This is probably too provincial a point of view. Our little laboratories are embedded in a large universe and thinking scientists can hardly ignore this external reality. The universal character of gravitation shows that it affects all matter, in ways we have yet fully to comprehend. For all we know now, gravitation may play a dominant role in determining ultimate particle structure. And our laboratories—freely falling or otherwise—may be tossing about on "gravitational waves" without our knowing it.

Gravitational waves represent the energy which should be radiated from a source—any source—composed of masses undergoing accelerated motion with respect to each other. Such waves—if they exist as called for in Einstein's theory of general relativity—should exert forces on objects with mass, just as elastic waves do in passing through an elastic medium, or as ocean waves do when striking the shore. An athlete exercising with dumbbells or riding a bicycle, however, would radiate away an incredibly small amount of such energy. A pair of white dwarf stars, on the other hand, with a total mass roughly equal to that of the sun, and with each star rotating at enormous speed with respect to the other in a binary or double-star system, might radiate about 2×10^{37} ergs/sec of energy as gravitational waves. This is 5000 times the amount of energy contained in the sun's optical luminosity, and far from negligible if it occurs, but in order to decide whether gravity and gravitational waves are significant or not we must learn more about them. And to do this we must subject our most profound physical theories concerning them to critical scrutiny. The moment we do we find that these theories rest upon an exceedingly small number of sig-

nificant experimental measurements, and that many of these measurements are of dubious precision.

Profound theories with shaky foundations

Einstein's theory of general relativity (usually abbreviated by physicists as GTR, to distinguish it from many other relativistic theories of gravitation) is, of course, the prime example. The key idea expressed by the theory, relating gravitation to a curvature of space, is an elegant one despite the tensor language which makes it difficult for many to understand. It reduces to the more generally comprehended Newtonian form in most cases where measurements can be made. And further contributions to its tacit acceptance by most present-day physicists have come from the experimental checks of Einstein's three famous predictions made on the basis of it: the gravitational redshift of light, the gravitational bending of light, and the precession of the perihelion of the orbit of the planet Mercury. We have in GTR a widely accepted theory, elegant beyond most others, based on very little *critical* evidence.

Strategy and tactics in experimentation

How can we remedy this lack? What can the earth-bound experimenter do to investigate the nature of gravitation? Most often, in view of the extreme weakness of the force, he will need to use as his power source astronomical bodies which have sufficiently strong gravitational fields. Instead of a laboratory experiment in which all of the significant variables are under his control, some or all of the effects he seeks may be associated with planetary systems, stars, galaxies, or the universe as a whole. Two examples of this approach (to which we'll return) are the Princeton group's recent refinement of the classic Eötvös experiment, which used the sun as a source of a gravitational field, and Weber's suggested study of elastic oscillations in the earth, on the idea that they may be caused by gravitational waves coming, perhaps, from an exploding supernova.

There are roughly three categories into which experiments on gravitation may be placed. First and most important are highly precise null experiments, such as the classic experiment devised by the Hungarian nobleman and physicist Baron von Eötvös. By balancing on a torsion balance the inertial forces arising from the earth's rotation against gravitational forces due to the earth's mass (Fig. 1-1) he was able to show to a precision of a few parts in 10^9 that all materials and masses fell with the same acceleration. This was an amazing accuracy for his day, and one that two of us (Roll and Dicke) have had to work hard for several years to improve by just two orders of magnitude! Null checks of this sort seek to balance against each other two quantities, which are expected from GTR to be equal or almost equal, in order to obtain an upper limit on the magnitude of any inequality and thus place clear limits on the applicability of the theory.

The second experimental category seeks to improve the accuracy of the three experimental verifications of the predictions of GTR mentioned above. These values can and should be improved as we'll show later. But limited as they are, they do provide valuable insights into the kind and number of fields associated with the all-pervading force called gravity.

The third class of experiments deals with gravitational radiation. In 1916 Einstein studied the approximate solutions of his gravitational-field equations and concluded that gravity waves ought to exist. But only recently has it become technologically possible even to attempt to detect the minute effects of such waves in the laboratory, as is being done by the Maryland group with equipment like that shown in Fig. 1-2.

What we've said so far suggests that experimental programs in gravity and relativity exist at only two places—Princeton and Maryland. That very nearly is the case. Miscellaneous experiments, some highly important, have of course been carried out elsewhere; we'll mention one of them later on. And the air in recent years has turned thick with glamorous proposals for "critical" one-shot experiments. But— to our knowledge—no other institutions in the world are following a consistent and continuing *experimental* program guided by the rigorous theoretical framework which guides our efforts.

The null-experiment program at Princeton, for instance, considers Einstein's GTR as only *one* theory in a large class of relativistic theories, any one of which can account for gravitational effects equally well with the limited, low-quality experimental evidence presently available. Our program aims at narrowing down possibilities in this large class.

What gravity seems to be

All relativistic requirements suggest that gravitational effects—like electromagnetic ones —are due to the interaction of matter with one or more of three kinds of classical field. (1) Matter could interact with a *scalar* field. Perhaps the most familiar such field is the sound field associated with fluctuations in air pressure. The air pressure itself is a scalar quantity, a number whose value at any point is independent of the coordinates used to label the point. (2) Matter could interact with a

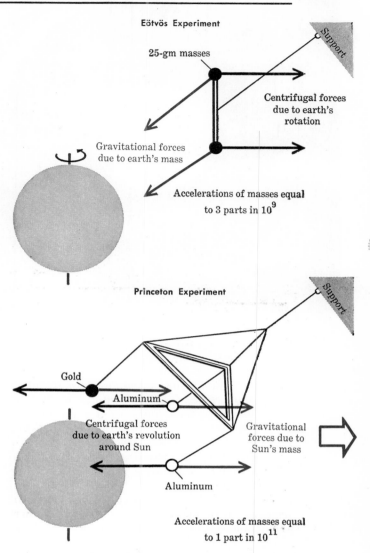

Fig. 1-1. *The classic Eötvös experiment and the recent Princeton version of it that raised its accuracy two orders of magnitude, both shown above, prove that all masses fall with the same acceleration to within the accuracies achieved. This result is necessary—but not sufficient by itself—to validate the theory of general relativity which ascribes gravitational interactions to tensor field interactions in curved space.*

vector field. A familiar three-dimensional example of this is a flowing fluid, in which the streaming velocity at each point is a vector quantity. (3) Matter could interact with one or more *tensor* fields. The stress distribution in an elastic body is one example of a simple three-dimensional tensor field. The stress at any point in the body has no single value, but varies with the direction considered. For this reason we must specify six quantities to characterize the stress at each point. More exactly, the scalar, vector, and tensor fields which concern us are all in *four*-dimensional space, and

Fig. 1-2. Group at the University of Maryland hopes to detect oscillations in the gravitational field reaching earth—gravity waves—with the solid 1½-ton aluminum cylinder shown mounted in the hollow cylindrical vacuum chamber. Detection cylinder is 2 ft in diameter × 6 ft long, and is suspended on acoustic bricks to null out extraneous vibration. Wiring leads to piezo-electric quartz sensors embedded in detector, that convert its oscillations to voltages. The hope is that if gravity waves with frequencies near the natural frequency of the detector (1657 cps) impinge upon it, its natural frequency will be reinforced.

they cannot be as readily visualized as in these three-dimensional examples.

In the experimental effort at Princeton we hope to eliminate one or more of these four-dimensional fields—scalar, vector, and tensor—as possible contributors to gravitation. If we could demonstrate, for example, that all fields could be eliminated except a single tensor field with suitable properties, Einstein's GTR would receive strong support. As of this writing, null experiments which have been performed at Princeton and other places do seem to drastically narrow down the number of possible combinations of fields permitted by relativistic theories—and hence the possible theories themselves—to a smaller class which still includes the GTR. Vector fields of any appreciable strength, for example, can be excluded from the gravitational interaction by the Princeton Eötvös experiment. And the same experiment appears to exclude more than one scalar field from gravitational interactions. Arguments based upon another experiment, performed by Vernon Hughes and collaborators at Yale University, appear to exclude more than one tensor field from contributing to gravitational interactions.

Thus, by this unspectacular process of experimental elimination, gravitation is being increasingly revealed as primarily due to a single tensor field, as the GTR requires, although a substantial contribution from a scalar field, which some other relativistic theories permit, cannot yet be excluded.

Null experiments don't prove "nothin"

Of the various null experiments, perhaps the most important is the Eötvös experiment con-firming that all masses and all materials have the same gravitational acceleration. A null result is necessary (but not sufficient) for GTR (and Newton's law of universal gravitation) to be valid. The most precise version of this experiment, completed recently at Princeton University (Figs. 1-1 and 1-3), showed that the acceleration toward the sun of test masses of gold and aluminum differs by no more than 1 part in 10^{11}, an improvement of two orders of magnitude over Eötvös' original experimental precision of 3 parts in 10^9.

The results of this experiment are highly significant for ascertaining that various forms of *energy* (which are related to the inertial mass of a body via Einstein's well-known formula $E = Mc^2$) are indeed equivalent to the gravitational *mass* of the body. (The gravitational mass is defined as that property of matter on which gravity acts.) To see this, consider the energy associated with the strong nuclear forces which bind the atomic nuclei of our gold and aluminum test masses against the disruptive effects of electrostatic repulsive forces. Nuclear binding energy makes up 11.0×10^{-3} of the total mass of a gold atom and 9.7×10^{-3} of the total mass of an aluminum atom. Hence, recalling the accuracy of 1 part in 10^{11} of the new Eötvös experiment, its result says that—to within about 1.3 parts in 10^8—the gravitational acceleration of the inertial mass (which is equivalent to nuclear binding energy) is the same as the gravitational acceleration of *all* the other mass-energy contributions to the total masses of gold and aluminum. The other contributions come from neutrons, protons, electrons, electrostatic energy, and other still smaller contributors to the total mass of an atom. Moreover, since gold and aluminum atoms differ not only in nuclear binding energy and total mass, but also in many other significant respects—such as total electron mass, electron binding energy, nuclear electrostatic energy, and energies concentrated in the electron-positron pair field surrounding the nucleus—similar arguments may be advanced to set small upper limits on any nonequivalence among *all* of these different forms of energy in their gravitational interactions.

So the Eötvös experiment establishes with considerable precision a different form of the principle of equivalence than the strong one we discussed earlier; it establishes a *weak* form which states that gravitational acceleration is the same for all important contributions to the mass-energy of a small body like an atomic nucleus.

But what of the strong version of this same principle, upon which GTR is founded? This requires that the form and numerical content of *all* physical laws be the same in all freely falling, nonrotating laboratories. The more precise null result of our Eötvös experiment verifies the *strong* principle of equivalence, too, for *strongly interacting* particles and fields such as the electro-magnetic and nuclear-force fields and their associated particles, positron-electron pairs, and pi mesons. But the experiment *fails* to verify the strong equivalence principle for interactions as weak as the universal Fermi interaction (involved in the beta decay of atomic nuclei) or the gravitational interaction itself.

Tactics of the Eötvös experiment

One of the fundamental differences between the Princeton experiment and that of Eötvös was our use of the gravitational acceleration toward the sun, balanced by the corresponding centrifugal acceleration due to revolution of the earth in orbit about the sun (Fig. 1-1, bottom). Although these accelerations are somewhat less than those which Eötvös used—his were due to the earth's mass and its rotation on its axis, remember—ours had the great advantage of appearing with a 24-hour period because, in effect, the sun moves around the earth once each day. Thus any gravitational anomalies on our torsion balance would have appeared with a sinusoidal 24-hour periodicity. By recording the rotation or torque on our balance remotely and continuously, then using a digital computer to analyze the record for a 24-hour periodicity with the proper phase, all of the extraneous effects which can produce small torques with other periods or the wrong phase could be discarded.

One additional difficulty with which Eötvös had to contend was the sensitivity of his torsion balance to gradients in the gravitational field, such as those produced by the good Baron himself sitting at the telescope. The Princeton experiment minimized such problems not only by remote observation (Fig. 1-3) but by making the torsion balance triangular in shape, with the two aluminum weights and one gold weight suspended from the corners of a triangular quartz frame. This threefold symmetry made it insensitive to nonuniformities in the gravitational field.

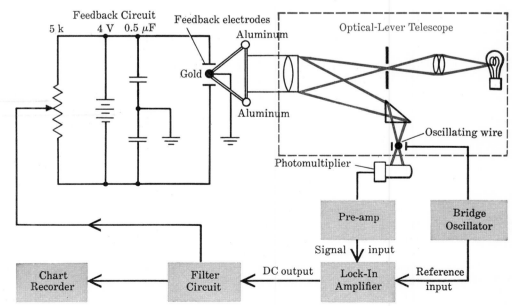

Fig. 1-3. The optical-lever system shown here was used to detect rotation of the triangular torsion balance used in Princeton version of the Eötvös experiment, shown in Fig. 1-1. Output of the detector had to be fed back to the torsion balance, through an appropriate filter network, in order to damp out long-period non-gravitational disturbances of the torsion balance caused by ground vibrations. Because balance was suspended in high-vacuum chamber (10^{-8} mm) there were no natural mechanisms to damp such extraneous oscillations in periods of time less than several months.

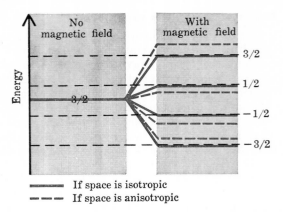

Fig. 1-4. In Yale experiment shown schematically above, the single ground-state energy level of a Li⁷ nucleus splits into four substates when the nucleus is placed in a magnetic field. Energy levels of these substates are extremely sensitive to isotropy of gravitational fields in space; they would shift as experimental apparatus was rotated, if space were anisotropic. But they don't shift—at least not to a few parts in 10^{23}. This excludes more than one tensor field as contributor to gravity, a tremendous simplification and one to be grateful for.

Our torsion balance evolved to its final form over a period of several years, and the final data were obtained between July 1962 and April 1963 in some 39 runs, lasting from 38 to 86 hours each. We could detect angular rotations of about 10^{-9} radians, corresponding to a torque of about 2.5×10^{-10} dyne cm, which in turn was 1×10^{-11} times the gravitational torque of the sun on one of the balance weights. As you may have discerned, we're rather proud of our results. They were not easy to get; but they buttress our fragile theoretical edifice a bit more firmly.

Is inertia the same in all directions?

A second important kind of null experiment is the recent measurement of the anisotropy of space carried out at Yale University by Hughes, Robinson, and Beltran-Lopez and independently by Drever at the University of Glasgow. The principle of this experiment is simply illustrated in Fig. 1-4. A Li⁷ nucleus, when placed in a magnetic field, has its ground-state quantum-energy level split into four different energy levels because of the interaction between the magnetic field and the magnetic moment of the nucleus. The energy levels of these magnetic substates are extremely sensitive. They would have shifted as the experimental apparatus was rotated—but only if the inertial masses of particles comprising the nucleus varied with the direction in which the particles were being accelerated. The apparatus used could have detected any such effect of

space anisotropy on the energy levels of the Li⁷ nucleus' magnetic substates to as little as a few parts in 10^{23}. But the significant thing is that even such minute shifts were not detected. In other words, the inertial mass of a nucleon is independent of the direction in space in which the nucleon is accelerated to this remarkable accuracy. This experiment's negative result is most important because—as we said earlier—it excludes more than one tensor field from the total effect we know as gravitation.

Experimental checks of general relativity

This still leaves the essential nature of gravitation hidden, however, in the theoretical lair of that class of theories—now more thinly populated—called general relativity.

So let's turn our attention from the null-type experiment, which endeavors to set the smallest possible upper limit on a critical quantity, to the experimental verifications of that *particular* theory in the class called GTR.

In these experiments the magnitude of a (very small) quantity is measured and compared with the predictions of the theory. The first of these tests, and one which has received much attention in the last five years, is the gravitational red shift. The best-known recent experimental measurement of the gravitational red shift is that of Pound and Rebka at Harvard and, independently, Cranshaw and Schiffer at Harwell, England. Using the Mössbauer effect (see "Using the Mössbauer Effect," page 31), the Harvard group was able to measure the incredibly small shift in frequency between a Co⁵⁷ source and Fe⁵⁷ absorber produced by a difference in gravitational potential corresponding to a 74-ft height difference on the earth. The Mössbauer effect has been capable of measuring this minute gravitational frequency shift to five parts in 10^{15}, with an accuracy of about 10%.

A less well-known, but probably more accurate and reliable measurement, has been carried out recently by J. W. Brault in a thesis at Princeton. He measured the wavelength of a spectral line coming from the sun and compared it with the wavelength of the same line coming from a laboratory standard. According to the GTR the shift in sunlight's wavelength toward the red end of the visible spectrum should be about 12.5 milliangstroms or about 2 parts in 10^6. This predicted solar red shift has been crudely verified in the past, in a similar way by several observers—as early as the 1920's—but Brault's measurement is the first precise and reliable one. Previous observers used narrow solar spectral lines for their determinations because of the difficulty in fixing the exact center of a broad spectral line. Such narrow lines, however, arise from deep down in the solar atmosphere where complex convection currents cause frequency shifts—variably towards the red *or* the blue—of the Doppler kind, not the gravitational kind. Brault developed a photoelectric spectrometer that permitted him to determine the center of a broad spectral line—the D_1 line of sodium—which arises from higher in the sun's atmosphere, above the main convective complications. He finds a shift agreeing with that predicted by GTR to well within the 5% noise-limited accuracy of his spectrometer.

Although these results are pleasing, of course, we must point out that these experiments do *not* represent a critical test of GTR. A red shift comparable to that predicted by GTR can be derived simply from the principles of energy conservation and mass-energy equivalence, making use of the precise null results of the Eötvös experiment. The gravitational redshift experiment, in other words, no matter how it is done, cannot be used to distinguish between Einstein's GTR—which treats gravitation as a pure tensor interaction—and alternative mixed scalar-tensor theories.

Neither does the observed fact that photons —like baseballs—fall as they pass the sun, help to make this critical distinction. The deflection of light expected from GTR is perhaps 10% greater than that expected on the basis of scalar-tensor theories of gravitation.

Unfortunately the expected light deflection is very small—it's just 1.75 sec of arc for light just grazing the edge of the sun—and this stellar mass just brings it to the threshold of observation with conventional astronomical techniques. These techniques, refined to the utmost, have yielded a wide variety of results. After applying a series of intricate corrections to hundreds of individual observations and then averaging all of them, the result does agree satisfactorily with the 1.75 sec prediction of general relativity. But the low quality of the data, together with a general lack of confidence that the results are entirely free of systematic errors, make it rashly optimistic to ascribe an accuracy of better than 20% to the currently available light deflection measurements. And this accuracy is insufficient to resolve the pure-tensor GTR from scalar-tensor theories.

The precession of Mercury's perihelion

The third of the three famous tests of GTR involves the precession of the perihelion of Mercury, as illustrated by Fig. 1-5. This is the most significant test from the theoretical standpoint, because it involves all of the components of the gravitational field. Furthermore, if there is an elusive scalar field interacting with matter in addition to the tensor field, it will affect the value of the perihelion's precession rate; the amount of deviation of Mercury's observed precession rate from that predicted by the pure-tensor GTR thus can set limits on the contribution, if any, of a scalar field.

Many observations of Mercury's orbital precession have been made, and after being suitably corrected for the perturbing effects upon the orbit by other planets—particularly Venus —the remaining precession is 43.11 ± 0.45 sec of arc per century. Comparing this with the prediction of GTR—43.03 sec of arc per century—it would appear that Einstein's theory has been checked to about 1% by its most significant test.

One real possibility which cannot be excluded on the basis of available evidence, however, is the perturbing influence of any oblateness of mass distribution in the sun itself. If the polar diameter of the sun were shorter than the equatorial diameter by as little as 0.1 sec of arc —or one part in 10^4—the perihelion precession rate of Mercury would increase by 20% of the GTR's prediction! And a lesser oblateness of only 2 parts in 10^5 would mark the threshold of significance; it probably would result in enough of a discrepancy between the prediction of GTR and the corrected observations to require rejection of Einstein's GTR, and to favor a modified relativistic theory of gravitation based on tensor and scalar interactions.

Because of its critical importance to the general theory of relativity, and to the possible existence of a scalar field interaction in gravitation, an attempt is underway at Princeton to measure the oblateness of the sun.

As of this writing the sun's figure is *not* accurately enough known for the perihelion rotation of Mercury to provide a precision check of general relativity. We hope that the new Princeton measures will change the situation in the next two years. The Maryland group searching for the gravity waves predicted by GTR also hopes for early answers.

Strategy in the search for gravity waves

A gravitational wave can be thought of as a propagating gravitational field. As such, it should exert forces on objects with mass whether the objects are electrically charged or not. In the familiar interactions between electrically charged particles, as we go to higher time derivatives, forces between charges at rest describe an electrostatic field, forces that depend on the velocity of charges describe a magnetic field, and when charged particles are accelerated, radiation of electromagnetic energy in the form of waves results.

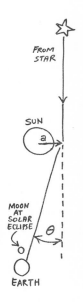

FROM STAR

SUN
a

MOON AT SOLAR ECLIPSE

θ

EARTH

$\theta = 4GM/c^2a$
G = GRAVITY CONST.
C = VELOCITY OF LIGHT

Predicted precession = 43.03 sec of arc/10^2 yr

Line of Apsides

Mercury

Sun

Perihelion

Fig. 1-5. The theory of general relativity ascribes gravity to purely tensor types of interaction, and on this basis predicts that Mercury's orbit will precess as shown here. But if a scalar field also contributes to gravity, it will cause the precession rate to depart from that predicted by general relativity. To measure any such scalar contribution, all other astronomical sources of mass which might perturb the orbit must be accounted for, and they have been, except for a possible oblateness in the distribution of mass in the sun itself, which needs checking.

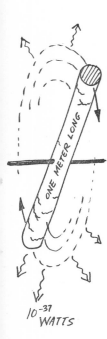

ONE METER LONG

10^{-37} WATTS

These electromagnetic forces all have gravitational analogs. The static gravitational force of attraction between two masses at rest departs only very slightly in GTR from the force called for by Newton's inverse-square law. And velocity-dependent gravitational forces between masses in motion depend on a form of the product of their velocities, as in magnetism, but no special name is given the "magnetic" components of the gravitational field. They simply appear as components of the tensor expression which describes the gravity field, in much the same way that magnetic fields appear in tensor formulations of electromagnetism. Finally, when masses—instead of charges—accelerate relative to each other, the gravitational field is disturbed and propagation of the disturbance results in the radiation of gravitational energy as gravity waves.

Einstein, with Eddington, evaluated the gravitational energy that would radiate from a hypothetical rod one meter long, spun rapidly about its center, as sketched in the margin. If the rod were spun so fast that it was on the verge of breaking up from centrifugal stresses, the power radiated would be roughly 10^{-37} watts—which isn't much! At this trivial rate, the rotational energy would be radiated away in about 10^{35} years! Our chances of de-

tecting gravity waves from such a laboratory source are obviously poor. Can we do better? Maybe, along three general directions: (1) We can search for the much more powerful gravitational radiation that may be coming from astronomical sources such as a pair of closely spaced white dwarf stars or neutron stars rotating in a binary system. (2) We can try to boost the output of laboratory gravity-wave generators. (3) We can improve methods of detecting gravity waves. The need for improvement in detection methods is underscored by the fact that gravity waves have never been observed; their existence for the time being remains a prediction of GTR.

How can we detect a gravitational wave? In relativity language, it exerts an undulatory effect on the geometry of space. In any language, it changes the distance between objects and such changes are what we must detect.

An antenna for gravity waves

Suppose we borrow from the ideas for detecting radio waves. In radio communication relative motions produced in an antenna by the waves are greatest in the plane transverse to the wave's propagation direction. Gravity waves are also transverse waves. Suppose then that we have an incident gravitational wave front and let this fall upon a particle with mass, as at A in the marginal sketch. The particle would oscillate of course. What would an observer see? Nothing, because *all* bodies in a gravity field fall with the same acceleration regardless of their mass, and our observer would oscillate in unison with the particle. Putting a second particle at B, as shown in the sketch, might help; the phase of its oscillations might differ from that at A because of an acceleration retardation effect, and we might observe the relative motion of the two particles. Such an effect is really there, but for particles A and B it is exactly canceled by a simultaneous effect on the geometry of the space. But if we move particle B to C, the geometry effect persists and the acceleration retardation effect is zero, so we get a real net effect, that we *can* observe.

This motion could be used to transfer energy to a load. An enormous improvement in sensitivity results if the two masses are connected by a spring (see marginal sketch) so that resonance storage of energy is possible. This too is analogous to antenna work in the radio region as any present or ex-EE will know, where we can transfer maximum power from an antenna if we can tune out all its reactance and couple it to a load which just matches its radiation resistance. This also turns out to be the condition for most efficient operation of a gravitational-wave antenna. But in a gravity-wave antenna, unfortunately, the gravitational-radiation resistance is fantastically small. It is so small that the ordinary internal friction of the finest materials utterly swamp it by at least twenty-five orders of magnitude. It is impossible to match the gravitational-radiation resistance because we never see anything other than the internal frictional resistance.

Furthermore, a detector made up of masses coupled by a spring has cumbersome and complex mechanical properties. Instead we might use a neater elastic body such as a solid cylinder or a sphere. Such an elastic body has natural frequencies of oscillation. In the parlance of electrical engineering, it corresponds to using a system with distributed constants instead of lumped constants. In the language of relativity, we might say that an elastic body is deformed when placed in a gravitational field. If the gravitational field is time dependent—as it must be if gravity waves ripple through it—and if its frequency is near one of the natural resonant frequencies of such an elastic body, the natural oscillations of the elastic body will be driven or reinforced. This is the detection strategy we're following at Maryland, where David Zipoy, Robert Forward, and Joe

Weber have constructed such an elastic body (Fig. 1-2).

It is an aluminum cylinder, two feet in diameter and about six feet long, weighing about a ton and a half. It's suspended in a vacuum chamber, and rests on acoustic filters. This device is a directive gravity-wave antenna. The earth rotates it. Piezoelectric quartz sensors embedded in it convert its oscillations to voltages which are amplified by low-noise amplifiers. If gravity waves with a white-noise spectrum that has components in the vicinity of 1657 cps (the tuning frequency of our antenna) are incident on earth from some given direction, we will see a diurnal change in noise output from the antenna. We "chose" this frequency because it corresponded to that of the largest installation we could build with the funds we had available.

We will dwell no further on the instrumentation, except to note that it's highly influenced by a theorem attributed to Dr. Dayhoff of the Naval Ordnance Laboratory—that a simple experiment cannot be done without several rackfuls of electronic apparatus. And what could be more simple than a cylinder suspended in a vacuum?

This antenna represents a major advance in the gravitation art, an improvement in sensitivity over previous devices by nine or ten orders of magnitude. Nonetheless it is extremely insensitive by radio antenna standards. It will find gravity signals only if they are extremely powerful by electromagnetic standards.

The earth as a gravity antenna

The sensitivity of any such antenna is proportional to its mass; the larger the mass the better. We happen to have available an unusually large mass—the earth itself. The natural frequency oscillations of the earth can be used to search for gravity waves. These oscillations have a long-period mode of 54 minutes, and many shorter period modes. The great Chilean earthquake some years ago excited these modes of oscillation and permitted them to be positively identified. After the earthquake effects subsided, there was only earth-strain noise resulting from winds, ocean-loading effects, and tidal irregularities. If gravitational waves of large intensity had been present, with periods varying from one cycle in 54 min to one cycle every minute or so, this would have been evident in the fact that modes of certain symmetry were excited and modes of other symmetry were not excited. But no such evidence was found. This failure, of course, does not mean that gravity waves were completely absent. It only proves that the gravitational wave flux during the period of observation, and over the bandwidth of the earth's 54-min mode, was less than

GRAVITY WAVE FRONT

PROPAGATION →

A   B
•   •

•
C

Mass
Spring
Mass

10^{-4} W/cm². A number like 10^{-4} W indicates how poor the sensitivity of a gravitational antenna is. A radio receiver, in contrast, using synchronous detection at room temperature with a noise figure of 2, averaging over one minute, can detect 10^{-22} W.

Can we make bigger waves?

Can we ease the detection problem by improving laboratory sources of gravitational waves? We started our discussion by pointing out that the spinning rod is an incredibly poor radiator. Can we do better in the laboratory?

We can do very much better indeed, but nowhere nearly good enough even to consider gravity waves for communications, as suggested by some.

For example, to test our 1½-ton gravity-wave detector at Maryland we use a gravitational field whose frequency lies in the audio range. This field is generated by the acoustically driven oscillations of a second, smaller cylinder—also visible in Fig. 1-2—built by J. Sinsky. This second cylinder, driven by a force of one ton at 1657 cycles, should generate a gravity field that can be detected by our large cylinder, when the two cylinders are a few inches apart in a vacuum. But even if this field is detectable, this still does not represent "communication" via gravity waves. The effect is rather more like telephone communication than it is like radio communication, in that it uses static-type fields rather than radiation-type fields.

From the standpoint of verifying GTR this is not a significant experiment. But from the standpoint of gravitational technology—if it succeeds—it will compare with stepping from the amber-and-cat's fur stage of electricity to the telephone stage.

Recent research has improved the total generation-detection picture in gravity waves by about fifty orders of magnitude. Even this is still quite far short (by about 10^{12}) of what is needed to generate and detect gravitational waves in a small laboratory. A national effort comparable to development of high-energy particle accelerators or space exploration would be needed to achieve this.

Can gravity be nulled out?

The same pessimistic answer must be given to questions about nulling out gravity, or shielding against it. Since our 1½-ton detector at Maryland absorbs gravitational energy, for instance, it does act as a kind of gravity shield. Gravitational waves incident on it would indeed be very slightly attenuated due to absorption. The cross section of the detector for absorption is 10^{-17} cm², and its area is about 10^5 cm². As a gravity shield it absorbs just about 10^{-22} of the gravitational flux incident upon it. It is obvious that gravitational shielding is not a technique which will be useful in the immediate future.

What other sort of experiments would we like to do in the field of gravitational radiation? The classic example of radiation experiments was that of Hertz. He not only was able to generate and detect electromagnetic waves in the same laboratory, he showed that they were polarized and that they exhibited interference and diffraction phenomena. These also are experiments we should very much like to do with gravitation—someday.

Further reading

The best point of departure for the nonexpert is *Gravitation and Relativity*, edited by Chiu and Hoffmann (Benjamin, 1964, $16). It was developed from a series of seminars (organized by Dicke) for the newcomer, and it stresses concepts rather than mathematics. Then you might try Weber's *General Relativity and Gravitational Waves* (Interscience, 1961, $2.50) which gives a complete but concise account of Einstein's theory of general relativity, its experimental tests, and the wave phenomena which it implies. Physical ideas are stressed, although tensor calculus is used freely. For a brief understandable treatment of the effects which might arise from deviations from Einstein's gravitational theory, and their all-important magnitudes, see the article by Dicke, "New Possibilities for Fundamental Experiments and Techniques," in *Quantum Electronics*, edited by Townes (Columbia U. Press, 1960, $15). Rougher mathematical going is involved in *Evidence for Gravitational Theories*, Proceedings of the International School of Physics "Enrico Fermi," Varenna, 1961, edited by C. Moller (Academic Press, 1962, $10). In this volume Dicke's rather dry mathematical-physical explanation of a body's inertia by gravity interactions with distant matter, "Mach's Principle and Equivalence," is relieved by a delightful short study about what could have happened if A. H. Lorentz knew about the gravitational deflection of light back in 1906. The same volume offers Weber's more detailed and mathematically difficult exposition of some ideas touched on in this article, "Theory of Methods for Measurement and Production of Gravitational Waves." Also coming up is an article by Dicke covering some of the material in this article on a considerably more advanced level: It will appear in the *Proceedings of the 1963 Les Houches Summer School of Physics* (Gordon & Breach, in press).

Gravitation: An Introduction to Current Research, edited by Witten (Wiley, 1962, $15), offers a collection of summaries of the active research edge—as of that time—in each of the theoretical and experimental areas of the field. Finally, if you have some familiarity with the ideas of classical field theory (electromagnetics) *and* special and general relativity, see Dicke's article "Cosmology, Mach's Principle and Relativity," *Am. J. Phys.* **31**, 500 (1963), which relates physical ideas to scalar and tensor fields generated by distant matter in the universe.

THE DYNAMICS OF SPACE-TIME

by John A. Wheeler and Seymour Tilson *

IN BRIEF: *Is space-time only an empty arena within which real fields and particles move; or is it all there is? Recently recognized implications of Einstein's long-dormant 1916 theory of general relativity suggest it may indeed be all there is. The geometry of space, originally the slave of matter and only curving in response to the gravitational field created by matter, turns out to manifest curvature even in the absence of matter. And this curvature must evolve through time. Which means that curved empty space is a dynamic entity, as competent to store and carry energy as are ordinary elastic materials and electromagnetic waves. Catalyzed by energy, and precisely guided by Einstein's field equations, empty space evolves: Into a gentle curve that apes a gravitational field; Into ripples indistinguishable from an electromagnetic field; Into regions of intense curvature—infested by "wormholes" 20 orders of magnitude smaller than elementary nuclear particles. Bunched together, these wormholes may be what elementary particles are—S.T.*

■ Is the physical universe made of matter, or is it made of mathematics? To put the question another way—is space-time only an empty arena within which real fields and particles play out their drama; or is the four-dimensional continuum of space-time all there is? No questions are more central than these to the master plan of physics, the plan which seeks to unify into one harmonious whole phenomena so apparently diverse in scale and kind as elementary particles, neutrinos, electromagnetic fields, gravitation, and galaxies.

The answer to such questions suggested by striking new developments in general relativity is that empty space may indeed be all there is. Fields, particles, galaxies, and stars truly may not be independent entities immersed within the static, vapid geometry of space. In

* John A Wheeler, a prominent consultant in the nation's nuclear program, is Professor of Physics at Princeton University, Princeton, New Jersey. Seymour Tilson is Associate Editor of *International Science and Technology.*

the end they may prove to be nothing but geometry—but geometry of an unexpectedly rich and dynamic kind. And it was Einstein's general relativity that gave geometry a life of its own.

Only one line suffices to write Einstein's equation in the highly compressed language of tensors, telling how much gravitational attraction a given concentration of matter and energy produces in space:

$$R_{\mu\nu} + \tfrac{1}{2}g_{\mu\nu}R = (8\pi G/c^4)T_{\mu\nu}$$

But how much more this line has been made to tell! Where Newton's gravitation was a force depending on matter for its existence, Einstein's giant step forward liberated gravitation from matter by describing it geometrically instead—as a curvature of space-time. Curved space-time is not a complicated idea; more about it later. What's important now is this. The geometry of space-time, originally the slave of matter and told by Einstein's equation merely how to represent the gravitational field created by matter, manifests curvature even in the absence of matter. And this matter-free curvature must, of mathematical necessity, evolve through time.

Unexpected riches in general relativity

In a matter-free universe the stuff of space-time, literally nothing but geometry, turns out to be a remarkably malleable primordial dough. Catalyzed only by energy and by the fertile yeast of mathematical imagination, it rises—here into a slowly curving section that has all the attributes of a gravitational field, there into a rippled configuration indistinguishable from an electromagnetic field, and elsewhere into knotted regions of intense curvature that manifest concentrations of charge and of mass-energy and behave like particles.

What does this seemingly abstract triumph of general relativity mean? Can it only delight the heart of a topologist? Definitely not! From this "geometrodynamic" interpretation of general relativity has come a satisfying specific array of experimental and theoretical riches. And beyond these is the possibility of tying up

the large-scale structure of the universe with the small-scale structure of so-called "elementary" particles.

Elementary particles are not elementary

To mention elementary particles in the same sentence as cosmology may seem at first sight to connect issues that have very little to do with each other. The dynamics of the universe deals with distances of the order of 10^{28} cm. Elementary particles within atomic nuclei, in contrast, average 10^{-13} cm in size. And yet both of these distances are enormous in contrast to the lowest limiting distance for quantum fluctuations in geometry, the lowest limiting dimension to the phenomenology of the universe, sometimes called Planck's length. It depends upon Planck's quantum of action or angular momentum, Newton's constant of gravitation, and the speed of light, and is only about 10^{-33} cm. The gap in scale of some 61 powers of ten between the cosmos and Planck's length—and 20 powers of ten between elementary particles and Planck's length—would seem to imply that quantum effects in geometry are negligible in the larger scale phenomena of cosmology and particle physics. Yet to draw this conclusion would be a mistake. A closer look shows inescapable connections between the disparate worlds of very small distances and very great distances.

To see this connection, compare the geometry of the universe with the shape of a great ocean wave (Fig. 1-6). As the wave moves into shallow water it curves up more and more strongly. Finally it develops a crest—a zone of infinite curvature—at which point it breaks up into foam. What happens thereafter? In the case of the ocean wave the usual simple hydrodynamical equations lose their power to predict beyond the moment of infinite curvature of the crest. Only when the equations include a new effect—capillarity—having to do with physics at small distances, do they reveal that the curvature does not become infinite along the crest. And only then can one analyze the development of droplets at the crest and the further dynamical evolution of the wave.

When a closed model universe similarly endowed only with large-scale curvature evolves in time in accordance with Einstein's equations, like the wave it too develops a highly localized region of infinitely sharp curvature. And a new effect comes into being at this "wave crest" of the evolving universe, an effect which involves Planck's quantum of action and Planck's miniscule limiting length. Is this effect the creation of matter? No one knows. But no alternative is evident.

Before going further it is hardly out of place to at least ask a larger question. What of value can possibly come out of geometrodynamics extrapolated down in scale, as it will necessarily have to be when quantum effects are allowed for, to far below the range of distances directly accessible to experiment?

Some questions of validity and worth

Conceivably nothing! Then the whole effort will have turned out to be only an academic exercise. Or perhaps only a few considerations fundamental for thinking about the elemen-

Fig. 1-6. The lowest limiting dimension to the phenomenology of the universe, sometimes called Planck's length, is only about 10^{-33} cm. This is 20 orders of magnitude smaller than the elementary particles of nuclear physics (10^{-13} cm) and 61 orders of magnitude smaller than the large-scale structure of the universe (10^{28} cm). Yet it may prove to be the crucial connection between the latter two. To see this, compare the evolving geometry of the universe with that of the ocean wave shown. As the wave moves into shallow water its curvature increases until finally it develops a crest—a zone of apparently infinite curvature—at which point it breaks up into foam. Beyond this point the wave's further evolution cannot be predicted with the usual hydrodynamic equations. Only when the equations include a distinctly new effect— capillarity—dealing with the physics at small distances, does it become clear that curvature does not become infinite along the crest. And only then can the development of droplets at the crest and the further evolution of the wave be analyzed. Similarly, when a closed model universe that's only gently curved evolves through time in accordance with Einstein's equations, like the wave it too develops highly localized regions of apparently infinite curvature. And at these "wave-crests" of the evolving universe a new effect enters, one that involves Planck's miniscule limiting length. Is this effect the creation of matter? No one knows, yet. But no alternative is evident, as suggested in more detail in Fig. 1-13. (Courtesy Heka)

tary particle problem will emerge. But best of all, at the end may come an insight into the structure of space at small distances so nearly correct, and so penetrating, as essentially to explain how elementary particles are built out of pure geometry and nothing more. For general relativity—already extraordinarily successful on the cosmic scale—to be of any use in discussing such a question, Einstein's equations must make sense not merely down to the 10^{-13} dimensions of elementary particles but to distances 20 orders of magnitude smaller! Yet such an outcome would not be completely surprising in view of the unexpected extrapolatory power discovered for another simple physical law, that of electromagnetism, associated with the names of Coulomb, Faraday, and Maxwell. In 1833, it was experimentally validated from 10^3 cm to 10^{-1} cm; in 1913, it was verified down to 10^{-8} cm (stopping power and atomic structure); and in 1933, it was found, still to hold at 10^{-13} cm (nuclear structure).

Checks for the hand and the intellect

Happily, tests of the idea of a world of pure geometry need not wait for that day, perhaps far distant, when quantum effects have been incorporated into relativity. There are several concrete reasons right now why interest in general relativity has more than doubled in the last decade, by any measure—people, papers, money—after a lapse of 40 years. On the experimental side there is wider awareness of the precision with which four major con-

sequences of general relativity predicted by Einstein have been confirmed:

(1) The prediction that light which just grazes the sun will be deflected 1.751 sec of arc by the curvature of space caused by the sun's gravitation has been confirmed; two typical recent observations are 2.01 ± 0.27 sec and 1.70 ± 0.10 sec of arc.

(2) The predicted precession of a planet's perihelion—or point of closest approach to the sun—which, for Mercury, called for 43.03 sec of arc precession per century, was confirmed as long ago as 1947 to be 42.56 ± 0.94 sec.

(3) The predicted "red shift," caused by gravitation and analogous in character to the Doppler effect, which called for a rising photon to drop in frequency ("tired light") at a rate of 2.19 parts in 10^{16} per meter of rise on earth —or a falling photon to increase in frequency by a like amount—was confirmed by a beautifully precise experiment in 1960. Using the Mössbauer effect, Pound and Rebka found that photons falling 22.5 m, the height of their experimental shaft at Cambridge, Mass., *did* increase in frequency by (2.28 ± 0.23) parts in 10^{16} per m.

(4) The prediction that a universe of uniform curvature will expand and ultimately recontract calls for a continual slowing down of the rate of expansion, measured in current practice by the red shift of light coming from distant galaxies. "Slowing down," used in this sense, implies that the ratio between the *extrapolated* time back to the start of expansion (as deduced from the present rate of expansion) and the *actual* time back to the start (as deduced from radioactive dating of terrestrial rocks and meteorites from space) must be greater than 1.5. And, indeed, observations give for the extrapolated time 14 × 10^9 years (±50%) and for the actual time 7 × 10^9 years (± perhaps 50% or more). The ratio of these values can range anywhere from 1 to 4, with a most probable value of 2—clearly compatible with the 1.5 lower limit predicted.

Impressive as are these "concrete" accomplishments, they do not dwarf comparable progress at the theoretical level:

(1) The concept of "gravitational radiation" has become better understood. Gravitational radiation arises whenever a mass is accelerated, just as electromagnetic radiation comes off when a charge is accelerated. Such acceleration of a mass necessarily disturbs the surrounding gravitational field. The disturbance propagates to the farthest reaches of the universe—as a force in Newton's sense, as a warp in the curvature of space in Einstein's sense. Extremely sophisticated experiments are now under way to detect this radiation. This search

—with good luck—may turn out to be as successful as that which confirmed in 1956 the existence of the neutrino, now so central in the scheme of physics.

(2) The problem of "unifying" electromagnetism and gravitation under one geometric roof, which so preoccupied Einstein and in his later years made him doubt his own standard 1916 theory, is no longer a problem. Closer study of that theory revealed that it is an "already-unified" field theory, in that complete knowledge of the geometry of space-time afforded by geometrodynamics reveals all that one wants to know, all that one ever can know about the electromagnetic field.

(3) Electricity itself, or electric charge, also has been successfully interpreted as resulting from nothing more mysterious than endless and uncharged electric lines of force trapped in the topology of what is called multiply connected space. In fact, it was the explanation of electromagnetism and electricity in terms of geometry in 1956 that generated much of the new interest in general relativity.

In spite of such progress, the prospect of much immediate guidance out of experiment is far less in the dynamics of geometry than it was and is, for instance, in the dynamics of fluids. To be sure, it is interesting and important to study with increased detail such relatively gross effects as the correlation of clocks, the bending of light, the gravitational red shift, and the precession of gyroscopes and planetary orbits. However, the physics of dramatically new character already predicted by general relativity (and the new phenomenology undoubtedly still to be predicted) comes at distances as far removed as can be from the domain of everyday experimentation. Therefore, geometrodynamics will be forced to evolve by a pattern extraordinarily hard to find among any of the other branches of physics. It will require a long and arduous effort assisted by only a few immediately relevant critical experiments. Furthermore, the *Gedanken*—or ideal but nonperformable experiment—has as crucial as ever a role to play, especially when one deals with something as esoteric as curved empty space.

So what *is* "curved empty space"?

What does it mean for space to be curved? How dismaying is one's first meeting with this idea! How can we establish a concept on something as ethereal and as devoid of anything to grab hold of as just empty space? Even more upsetting, it is not merely 3-dimensional space which is curved—Riemann's original concept—but 4-dimensional space-time, Einstein's deeper insight.

It is clear enough what one means by the curvature of the hull of a beached ship that lies over on her side. We can at least drive nails into the wood, measure distances between these nails, and verify by these distance measurements that the surface is curved. But how can we drive nails into space-time?

Perhaps an analogy will make the concept easier to think about. Nothing illustrates the concept of curved space so well as one of those little diaries that lists airline distances between the principal cities of the world. These tabulated distances spell out a rigid framework of points, fully defining the curved shape of the earth—and even its radius of curvature. Try to plot distances between more than three of these points, to scale, on a flat sheet of paper. It can't be done, of course. But go to a globe of proper curvature and the problem is solved.

The same simple idea applies to Einstein's space-time. Given a table of distances in the 4-dimensional world, between each "event" and every other "event," all the data are at hand to define the entire geometry of space-time.

An event effectively serves as the nail in the curved hull of space-time. It is defined quite simply, as in Fig. 1-7, as either a point in space-time where two particles in motion meet; or a point where a particle's path intersects a light ray; or even as a point where two light rays intersect. The 4-dimensional continuum itself can be compared to a giant haystack, each straw of which represents the path of either a particle or a light ray. Space-time is filled by such "straws," and by their intersections—Einstein's events.

Between any two events there is a well-defined distance in space-time, the Einstein "interval." And such intervals can be compared, one with another. But in this comparison the two traditional tools of compass and ruler must be abandoned. They are replaced by light rays and the tracks of material particles, used as indicated in Fig. 1-8. With these tools we can find the unknown interval separating any two events in space-time, in terms of a previously defined standard interval between any other two chosen events.

The two events which define the standard interval—the "geometrodynamic standard meter"—can be, for example, merely two successive sparks, or two successive flashes of light, that took place fifty years ago.

Moreover, *and most important*, such a comparison can be carried out over *any* route through space-time between the unknown interval and the standard interval, regardless of the curvature of the space that intervenes between the two intervals: in other words, the ratio of the intervals will be the same regard-

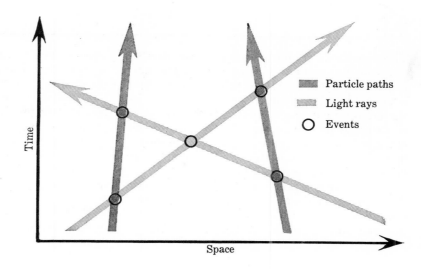

Fig. 1-7. Just as a table of airline distances between cities rigidly defines the curvature of the earth's surface, so a table of the Einstein "intervals," or distances between "events" in the four-dimensional world, fully defines the curved geometry of space-time. Events are simply the intersections, as shown, of the ubiquitous particle paths and/or light rays that fill space-time. But also essential to defining the curvature of space-time is the condition described in Fig. 1-8.

less of the route followed through space-time in their intercomparison.

A real world of Riemannian geometry

The abstract-sounding statement that the ratio of two intervals between pairs of events in space-time is independent of the route followed in comparing them is a statement of enormous content. It means that the real physical world is a "Riemannian 4-dimensional manifold," in the ideal or geometric sense of the term. This is a hypothesis fundamental to general relativity. And it is a *testable* hypothesis. Many experiments could be done to check it, but they have not been done.

The best test to date is indirect. It tests the identity, not of intervals, but of electrons, brought by different routes to a common point of comparison. Relativity assigns to every mass a length, so that in comparing masses such as electrons we are in essence comparing lengths. And an atom can be regarded as a piece of experimental equipment for comparing electrons.

Each additional revolution the electrons make within an atom increases the precision with which we know them to be identical. If they were not identical, they would escape the action of the Pauli exclusion principle and they would fall to the ground state, to the lowest orbit around the atom's nucleus. The atom would collapse! Imagine, then, that we have an atom of iron, for instance, with its electrons taken from widely scattered parts of the universe. Iron-containing meteorites and terrestrial rocks are known whose age is greater than 3×10^9 years. In this time, the electrons in one of their iron atoms have made 10^{35} revolutions around the nucleus—without collapsing. In this sense, at least, the identity of electrons which came originally from different parts of the solar system is checked—to the fantastic accuracy of one part in 10^{35}!

So far as one can tell, Riemannian geometry does hold in the real world, and with high precision. This conclusion is essential, because it means that the Einstein intervals between events in space-time are strictly comparable to the airline distances between points on earth that were mentioned earlier. Just as the latter define the curvature of the earth, so the former define the curvature of space-time. Thus, if space-time is curved, what is the physics of this curvature and how does it change with time?

Intrinsic geometry versus extrinsic geometry

The first step into this new era of dynamic geometry that changes with time asks and answers the question: How much information has to be given about the geometry at one instant —or in relativistic language, on "one space-like three-dimensional hypersurface," or on one "slice" through space-time—to make it possible to predict the entire past and future of the geometry? In still other words, what are the *initial data* for geometrodynamics? The corresponding question had long before received attention in particle dynamics and in electromagnetism. In particle dynamics, to predict the entire future and past of a particle moving in a known field of force, it is sufficient to specify only its initial position and its velocity. Similarly, to forecast the complete evolution in time of the electromagnetic field it is sufficient to give at the initial moment—everywhere on a slice through space-time—the values of the electric and magnetic field strengths. And, similarly, in geometrodynamics! One must give not only the three-dimensional geometry *intrinsic* to the initial three-dimensional space-like surface (the analog of the magnetic field), but also the *extrinsic* curvature of this space-like surface (the analog of the electric field), telling how it is to be embedded in the not-yet-calculated four-dimensional geometry of space-*time*.

The distinction between intrinsic and extrinsic geometry is best illustrated, as in Fig. 1-9, by drawing a right triangle on a sheet of paper and then bending this piece of paper.

15

The Euclidean or plane geometry *intrinsic* to the triangle remains the same; lengths and angles are unchanged; the *intrinsic* curvature happens, in this example, to be zero. Not so the *extrinsic* curvature! Its value at any point is governed by the radius of curvature of the crumpled paper at that point. It tells, in effect, how the two-dimensional plane geometry is embedded in three-dimensional space.

Our problem is analogous. But to tell how three-dimensional space is embedded in four-dimensional space-*time*—or to specify both the intrinsic and extrinsic curvature of a slice of

space-time—is a mathematically complex task. Fortunately, it is not insurmountable; and once this initial information—or pair of curvatures —is specified, Einstein's ten field equations completely predict the evolution of the three-dimensional geometry through all of time— past, present, and future. The initial information, in other words, determines the entire *four*-dimensional geometry of the Riemannian manifold.

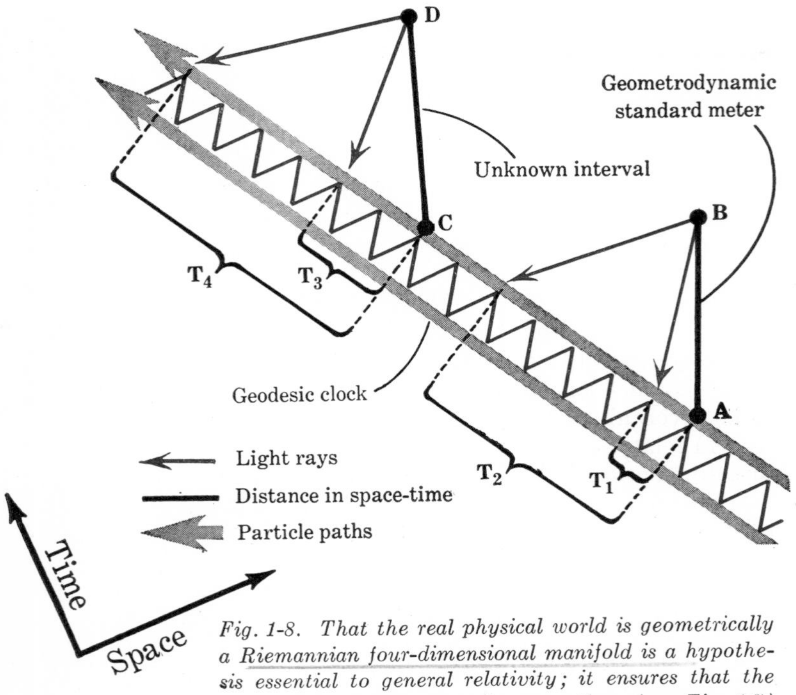

The essence of general relativity

Let's pause for another look at this "space-time" whose curvature merits so much attention. Let space-time be symbolized by the space in a room. Let "up" represent the direction in which time is increasing. Then a plane parallel to the floor makes a slice through space-time. The directions of travel on the plane—left and right, forward and backward—are space-like directions; motion up from the plane is time-like. The distinction between space and time is, however, one which makes sense only to us. A second set of observers, for instance—in motion with respect to us—will define differently the distinction between space and time. What to these moving observers is a space-like slice through space-time (parallel to the floor) will appear to us as a plane not parallel to the floor. Time, in other words, is really a length, not an independent concept.

To appreciate the falseness of the usual distinction between space and time, consider the inconsistent use of feet to measure the width of a highway and miles to measure its length. Yet it is equally inconsistent to measure intervals in one direction in space-time in seconds, and to measure them in three other directions in centimeters. The conversion factor that changes one metric unit of length (cm) in the "space" directions to the other metric unit (sec), *still of length*, in the "time" direction is the speed of light—numerically 3×10^{10}. And this factor is just as historical, indeed accidental, in character as the conversion factor 5280 that changes feet to miles! There is no more need to "explain" 3×10^{10} than there is to "explain" 5280!

Time, mass, and length are all equally matters of pure geometry. So are electromagnetic fields. In brief, classical physics—gravitation plus electromagnetism—deals with *nothing but lengths*, however much historical terminology conceals this fact from view.

So a slice through space-time defines a 3-dimensional geometry, one which is unique to that slice. And every point on the slice has both an intrinsic and an extrinsic curvature. Now, according to Einstein, where the density

Fig. 1-8. That the real physical world is geometrically a Riemannian four-dimensional manifold is a hypothesis essential to general relativity; it ensures that the intervals between events in space-time (see Fig. 1-7) do, in fact, fully define the curvature of space-time. Although the hypothesis can be observationally confirmed to 1 part in 10^{35}—as explained in the text—it also can be ideally or geometrically confirmed, absolutely. This involves comparing any unknown interval between events C and D, above, to a previously defined standard interval between events A and B. For Riemannian geometry to hold, the measured ratio of the two intervals must be invariant, regardless of the curvature of space intervening between the two intervals. To fulfill this condition a "geodesic clock" can be used. It consists of three elements: (1) an ideal test particle that passes through events A and C; (2) a second nearby particle whose path parallels that of the first; (3) the light scattered back and forth between particle paths—this provides a fixed repeat unit of time. Projecting both the free end (B) of the standard interval and (D) of the unknown interval on to the clock with light rays permits direct comparison of the two intervals in terms of their respective time intercepts—T^1, T^2, T^3, and T^4.

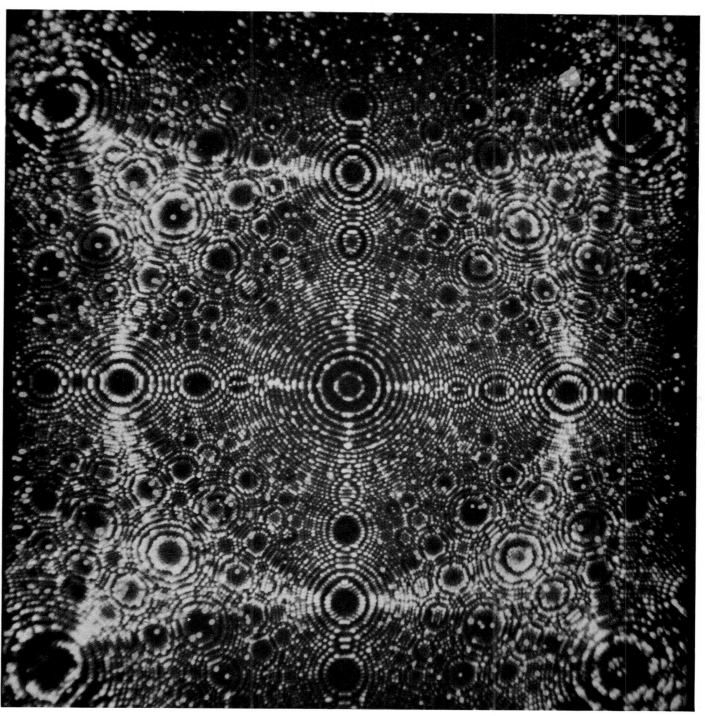

Color Fig. 1. Individual atoms show up clearly in this field-ion microscope image of a platinum-iridium alloy point. The microscope provides an unparalleled magnification of greater than one-million times (see photo of "invisible" point in Fig. 1-42) which allows detailed studies of surface structure never before possible. At this magnification, the sharp point is found to be a hemisphere that cuts the metal's crystal planes to form an array of small, circular crystal facets. To show the effect of surface treatment, two field-ion microscope images are superimposed here. The first was printed as a red transparency; the second, taken after particle bombardment, was printed as a green transparency. Therefore, unaffected atoms appear yellow, atoms that were removed appear red, atoms in new positions appear green. See "Solid Surfaces," in Chapter 1. (Courtesy E. W. Müller)

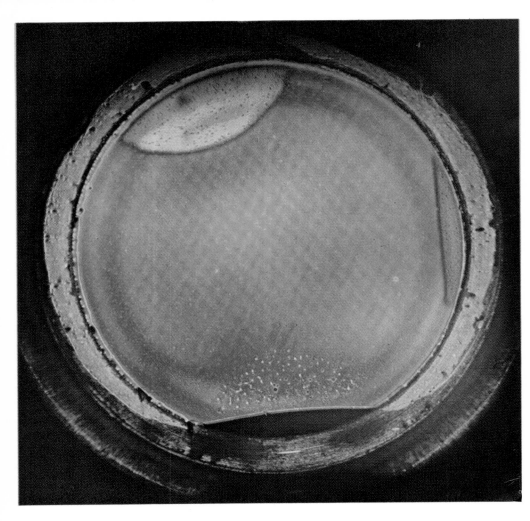

Color Fig. 2. Thermal image of honeycomb structural material was taken using evaporograph imaging system. Material is made by bonding thin metal skins on each side of honeycomb. Sample is heated on one side, and other side is imaged by evaporograph onto oil-covered membrane. Thickness of oil film varies with local radiation intensity. Optical interference in film thus provides color map of sample's skin temperature. Honeycomb structure is clearly visible as region of high conductivity. Honeycomb would not be visible at point where bond was defective. See "Infrared," in Chapter 1. (Courtesy Baird Atomic)

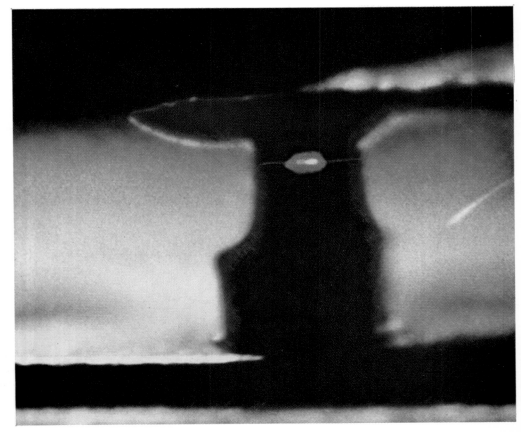

Color Fig. 3. Looking end-on into this semiconductor laser beam, the only thing that shows clearly is the beam itself. The semiconductor crystal (ink-well shaped blob) and the upper contact (spoon-shaped blob) are both fuzzed-out on green background. The semiconductor material is gallium arsenide phosphide, the only compound yet developed that emits light in the visible spectrum (7,000 angstroms). Despite its yellow color on film, beam is actually pure red. This laser was made by N. Holonyak, Jr. of General Electric's Advanced Semiconductor Laboratory in Syracuse, N.Y. See "Semiconductor Lasers," in Chapter 1. (Courtesy N. Holonyak, Jr., General Electric)

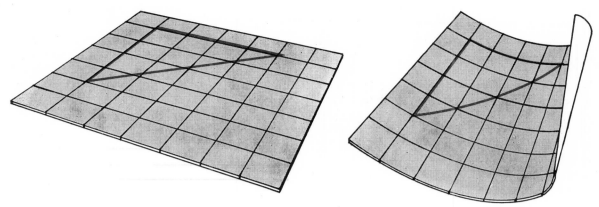

Fig. 1-9. In order to predict the evolution of curved space throughout all of time, it is necessary to specify as initial data both the intrinsic and extrinsic curvature of the geometry. The distinction between the two is illustrated above. The two-dimensional geometry intrinsic to the triangle drawn on the piece of paper remains the same no matter how the paper is bent; lengths and angles are unchanged; the intrinsic curvature is zero. Not so the extrinsic curvature! It is fixed at any point by the radius of curvature of the paper at that point; and it tells, in effect, how the intrinsic two-dimensional geometry of the triangle is embedded in three-dimensional space. The problem in geometrodynamics is analogous, but mathematically more difficult, because it is necessary to specify not only the geometry intrinsic to three-dimensional space, but also to specify the extrinsic curvature of three-dimensional space, telling how it is to be embedded in the not-yet-calculated four-dimensional geometry of space-time. Once both curvatures are specified, however, Einstein's field equations can completely predict the evolution of three-dimensional space through all of time.

of mass-energy is zero, there the difference between intrinsic and extrinsic curvatures is also zero. But when mass-energy is available to curve space, the difference between the two curvatures equals the constant, 16π, times the density of mass-energy, expressed in purely geometric units. When we impose this same condition of equality

Intrinsic curvature—Extrinsic curvature
$= 16\pi$ (Density of mass-energy)

not merely at every point on *one* slice through space-time, but at every point on *every* slice, we have stated the entire content of Einstein's geometrodynamical law of the structure of space-time. In fact, all the field equations of general relativity are derived from this same condition—*and that's all there is to general relativity!*

But this structural law of space-time has a most important consequence for all of physics. It means that geometry is a dynamic entity in itself, with the same kind of ability to store energy and to carry energy as that which belongs to elastic materials and electromagnetic waves!

The total mass of the universe

In checking this dynamic relativity on a large scale, attention today has turned from questions of whether the universe is expanding to the issue of the total density of mass-energy in the universe. With a given time for the expansion and recontraction of the universe goes a definite radius at the moment of maximum expansion. Equally determinate is the effective density of mass-energy at every phase of the expansion, because a lesser density would not be adequate to curve the universe into closure. The predicted effective density in turn depends upon the values adopted both for the extrapolated time back to the beginning of expansion and for the actual time. It also depends upon what fraction of the mass-energy is in the form of "real matter" and what fraction is in the form of radiation. Considering these uncertainties, it is reasonable to think of a 75% probability for the predicted total density of mass-energy to lie between 7×10^{-30} g/cm³ and 100×10^{-30} g/cm³. In contrast, the present best figure for the actual density of mass-energy averaged over volumes of space containing many galaxies is much lower, and lies between $(\frac{1}{3}) \times 10^{-30}$ g/cm³ and 3×10^{-30} g/cm³.

But this kind of discrepancy does not lead in today's state of thinking to the doubts about relativity which were common in earlier decades. Instead, it leads to questions about the figures used in the comparison, and to work designed to improve these numbers. The extrapolated age and the actual age, for instance, both need to be known with more precision so that one can narrow the rather broad limits for the predicted density of mass-energy. And the sources contributing to the actual effective density must be better identified. The best known of these, the mass contained in the stars and dust clouds of galaxies, will be better known as a consequence of work now in progress. Three other potential sources of mass-energy are also receiving increasing attention:

dispersed neutral hydrogen, neutrinos, and gravitational radiation.

It may be that all three will prove negligible in the bookkeeping of Einstein's equations. However, it is impossible with present knowledge to exclude the possibility that any one of the three will contribute more to the effective mass-energy—and thus more to satisfying the relation between actual density and that predicted from the curvature of space—than all of the matter seen in galaxies.

Making the energy budget balance

How important is gravitational radiation in the energy balance of space? What if numerous experiments currently under way should show that gravitational radiation contributes substantially to the cosmic energy balance? What sources can be conceived which could set free as radiation an amount of mass-energy comparable to or greater than the amount of mass in the galaxies themselves? No known double star will do as a source; the pair radiates gravitational radiation at a rate fantastically smaller than the rate at which it pours out heat energy. However, a close pair of highly compact neutron stars—if such stars exist—should emit at an enormous rate; and the pair should convert a large fraction of its total mass into gravitational radiation. Such a process has never been detected. But if by any chance it occurs often enough to be important in the dynamics of the universe, it should ultimately be observable.

But gravitational radiation produced today is not the only source for any radiation that may be observed today. If the expansion and re-contraction of the universe are asymmetrical —something like the implosion and re-explosion process followed by undersea bubbles (rising to the surface, as sketched in the margin) which turn inside out, one prong and spike at a time —great amounts of gravitational radiation must have been generated automatically at various times in the past, at the points of the prongs and spikes produced in space-time, where curvature approached infinity.

Presumably such "primordial" gravitational radiation—if there is much of it—came into being with a scale of wavelengths comparable to distances separating the large clusters of matter in the universe, the galaxies. Indeed, in the simplest models of a closed, empty universe, free of all matter or electromagnetic radiation—where the complete evolution has been traced with all mathematical accuracy— a gravitational wave with enough energy will curve space into closure even when it has a wavelength the size of the universe itself!

SURFACE

Such gravitational radiation would be so weak and so diffused through time as to be impossible to measure. (The oscillation period of such a long-wave disturbance in the geometry is about the total time for expansion and contraction of the universe—hopelessly long and slow for experiments bounded by a human lifetime.) However, such a long gravitational wave may be detected by an observation that reaches over a great distance. Over great distances a closed universe has optical focusing properties. These properties are greatly modified by the presence of a strong gravitational wave. As a consequence, distant galaxies that are receding at the same rate—and which therefore lie at comparable distances—will appear to the observer as of very different brightness, according as they are in one quarter of the sky or another. The striking reality of this effect in the model universe obviously makes it worth looking for in the actual universe!

The search for gravitational radiation promises to be a challenging one, whether undertaken on a cosmic scale or in the laboratory. In sharp contrast, electromagnetic radiation already has been well explored experimentally. And it too now can be described as one aspect of curved space-time.

Electromagnetism without electromagnetism

"Maxwell's second-order differential equations of electromagnetism can be combined with the second-order differential equations of general relativity to give one set of purely geometrical equations of the fourth order." Let's translate this idea into physics (Fig. 1-10)! The electromagnetic field, in a sense, leaves "footprints" on the geometry of space-time so characteristic that from them one can read back to the electromagnetic field. Thus, in effect, these footprints *are* the electromagnetic field. Lines of electric or magnetic force vary in spacing, regions of closer spacing corresponding to regions of greater density of energy and stress in space-time. Energy, however, implies mass; and mass is the source of a gravitational field, or a bending of space. Thus arises a distortion in space-time, the curvature of which can in principle be detected by purely *geometrical* measurements. From such measurements one can deduce the electromagnetic field. In other words, the full content of Maxwell's equations for the electromagnetic field can be expressed in terms of statements about the curvature of space—and the derivatives of that curvature—and nothing more. If we summarize the earliest achievement of general relativity as gravitation without gravitation, then we can count this analysis

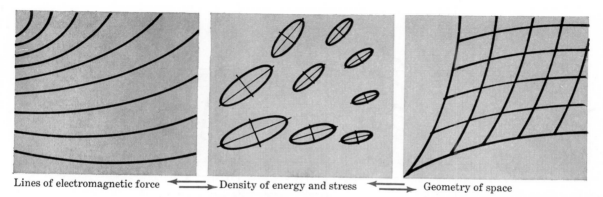

Lines of electromagnetic force ◄════► Density of energy and stress ◄════► Geometry of space

Fig. 1-10. The electromagnetic field distorts space by creating regions of greater density of energy and stress—shown by ellipsoids—where lines of force are more closely spaced. But energy implies mass; and mass is the source of a gravitational field which, in relativity, is identical with a curvature of space. So, in essence, the curvature in space created by the electromagntic field is the electromagnetic field; and this curvature can in principle be detected by purely geometric measurements.

as giving us "electromagnetism without electromagnetism," and can turn now to "charge without charge."

Keep your eye on the hole, not the doughnut

Let the geometry as it changes with time lead to a direct joining together (Fig. 1-11) of two regions of space previously not immediately contiguous. Then electric lines of force which thread through this region may become trapped in the topology of a "multiply-connected geometry." As shown in the margin, a doughnut is a simple example of such a geometry. Stretch a rubber string from a point on the outside circumference of the doughnut, through the hole, and back to the starting point; now tie a knot in the string. Then try to remove the string from inside the doughnut to outside. There is no way to transform one route for the string into the other. The surface is doubly connected, in contrast to the singly connected or Euclidean surface (see margin) on which one route easily transforms into any other route.

Electric lines of force (which in empty space have neither beginning nor end) similarly are trapped in any "wormhole" or "handle" of the geometry (see Fig. 1-12) as effectively as the rubber string is trapped in the hole in the doughnut. Into the wormhole from all directions converge electric lines of force, their number in any particular wormhole unchanging with time. This number represents the charge associated with the wormhole: To an observer on one side of the wormhole—the inlet side—this number represents negative charge; to an observer counting lines of force that emerge from the other side of the wormhole, the same number represents positive charge. Thus, in this geometrodynamic conception the zero total charge of the universe is automatically guaranteed. Yet nowhere is any

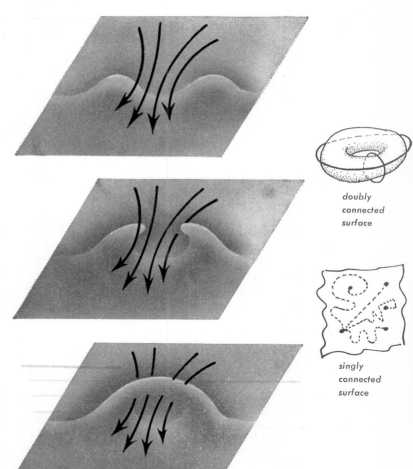

doubly connected surface

singly connected surface

Fig. 1-11. A topological "wormhole" can develop in the geometry of space, as shown above, when the geometry's evolution leads to direct joining of two regions of space not previously immediately contiguous to each other. In a wormhole, the endless and uncharged lines of force of classical electricity—which have no relation to the quantized electrical charges of elementary particle physics—may become trapped, creating electric charge on either side of the wormhole, as shown in Fig. 1-12.

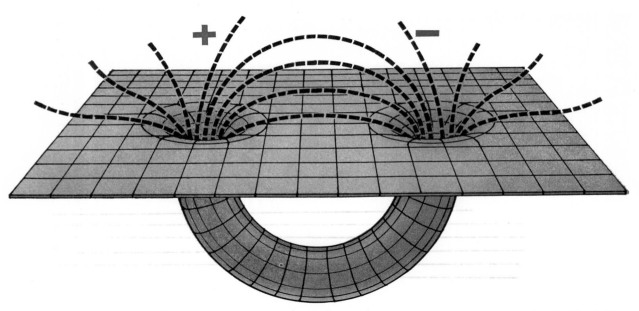

Fig. 1-12. When the two sides or mouths of a single wormhole such as that in Fig. 1-11 are geometrically separated—as above—so they appear as two mouths connected by a "handle," the geometric explanation of classical electric charge follows. Electric lines of force (which in empty space have neither beginning nor end) are trapped in the wormhole. They converge into it from all directions, their number in any particular wormhole unchanging with time. This number is the charge associated with the wormhole: to an observer at one end of the handle this number represents negative charge; to an observer counting lines of force emerging from the other end of the handle the same number represents positive charge. And the total charge of the universe is zero.

call made upon the idea of a mystical, magical jelly to explain electricity.

Electrical evidence for space with wormholes

But this simple picture of electric charge is out of the question in a world free of wormholes. So it's natural to ask—is the physical world singly connected or is it multiply connected?

In answer, imagine the history of physics relived in another order. The new race is extraordinarily interested in distance measurements of enormous precision. They find spacetime is curved. They discover the two independent kinds of curvature, one describing electromagnetic waves, the other gravitational waves. They find the Einstein-Maxwell equations—all the laws of geometrodynamics—but they have never heard of the idea of charge. However, their topologists become interested in their equations. These mathematical friends point out that in a space endowed with many wormholes the electrical flux through each is constant regardless of the wormhole's motion, and despite all the other changes that go on in the geometry as time advances. They also know that no one has yet seen the mouth of a wormhole. Nevertheless they explain that they have a way to search for wormholes, even if they are much too small to be seen.

It is only necessary, they point out, to draw a sphere—even a large sphere—around the region where one is searching; to measure at each point on the sphere's surface a certain property that can be found from the curvature of space (the normal component of the electric field, they call it); and to integrate the values of this field over the entire surface. If the integral differs from zero then inside the sphere there is the mouth of a wormhole.

The suggested experiment is performed, and the electric flux *is* found to be different from zero. Everyone concludes that space is multiply connected, as the topologists suggested *might* be possible. In other words, from this point of view *the existence of electric charges in nature can be taken as experimental proof that space is multiply connected.* The existence of electric charge is the most compelling reason we have today to believe that the "real" physical world is made of curved empty space. This conclusion, however, is far too general in character to reveal anything specific about the constitution of electrons and nucleons. Though the mouth of a wormhole is endowed with charge and energy—and therefore with mass—it has not the slightest direct connection with an elementary particle.

Quantized geometry and the making of matter

When one surveys the consequences of quantizing general relativity, one realizes that wormholes can be regarded as a property, not of elementary particles, but of all space. Space is like an ocean which looks flat to an aviator who flies high above it, but which is a tossing turmoil to the hapless butterfly fallen upon it. Regarded more and more closely, it shows more and more agitation, until—so quantum geometrodynamics predicts—at distances of the order of 10^{-33} cm the entire structure is impermeated every which way with wormholes. If geometrodynamic law is correct at such distances, it forces on all space this foam-like character, suggested schematically in Fig. 1-13.

The multiply-connected foam-like structure is virtual, in the sense of quantum theory, in that there is no unique topology at any given time. Instead, there is a certain—and predictable—probability of this degree of multiple connectedness, a certain probability of that one, and so on. The flux of lines of force, being trapped as new wormholes are formed, and being released as the local topology momentarily simplifies, describes pairs of positive and negative charges being created and annihilated. This goes on throughout all space. The submicroscopic agitation everywhere is violent. If these consequences of the quantum version of geometrodynamics have any relevance to the problem of elementary particles, the disturbances in the geometry must be compared and identified with the so-called "vacuum fluctuations" of Dirac's well-tested relativistic quantum theory of the electron.

In that description of nature, too, all space is the scene of virtual creations and annihilations—going on all the time—of pairs of so-called "undressed electrons," the artificially overcharged and overheavy electrons that Dirac's theory had to assume to account for experimental electrons of the normal charge and mass. Thus, the undressed electron must be identified—so far as can be judged—with the elementary wormhole of quantum geometrodynamics. According to this identification, the experimental or everyday "real" electron is to be understood as a region of space where the concentration of undressed electrons—or of wormholes—is percentagewise just a tiny bit more than the average. On this view the dynamics of the vacuum is even more central to physics than the constitution of elementary particles; particles represent, so to speak, only regions where the virtual foam-like structure of empty space is a little denser than elsewhere.

Where can matter be made?

Where in the universe can we expect to see the geometrodynamical analog of storm conditions at sea? Where can we expect to see the sharpening crest of a large-scale gravitational wave—like the ocean wave of Fig. 1-6—transmuted into foam, into the microstructure known as matter? In the chaos of the primordial universe? Yes. But such events offer little scope for the tactics of observational science. A much more accessible location, strangely enough, is the interior of a collapsing star. There, to be sure, the issue is not matter's creation but its destruction, the crushing of it out of existence under immense gravitational pressure.

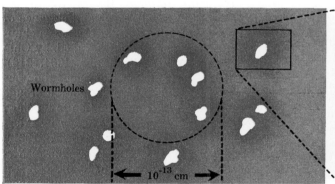

Elementary particle

Wormholes

10^{-13} cm

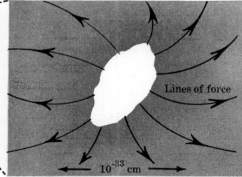

Elementary wormhole

Lines of force

10^{-33} cm

Fig. 1-13. The seemingly inescapable consequence of quantizing general relativity—broadly suggested back in Fig. 1-6—is that wormholes like those described in Figs. 1-11 and 1-12 are a property, not of elementary particles, but of space. When space is regarded more and more closely, it shows more and more violent agitation. Finally, at distances of about 10^{-33} cm (the lowest limit to quantum fluctuations in geometry, or to the phenomenology of the universe) the entire structure of space is so impermeated with wormholes that it takes on a foam-like character, analogous to that of the breaking wave of Fig. 1-6. Associated with each wormhole is not only a great curvature of space—suggested above by the color tint—but also an intense electromagnetic field. On this quantum geometrodynamic view, the dynamics of the vacuum is even more central to the makeup of matter than is the constitution of elementary particles. Particles only represent, so to speak, regions where the foam-like structure of empty space is a little denser than elsewhere.

But the principle of reversibility rules in all domains of physics: if a process can go in one direction, it can also proceed in the other. The creation and annihilation of a pair of positive and negative electrons, for example, have both been observed. The two particles literally disappear, leaving behind nothing but an electromagnetic wave—or, in principle, a gravitational wave—or in either case only curved empty space. At issue here is not this often observed kind of annihilation, but a process in which *ordinary* matter—composed of protons, neutrons, and negatively charged orbital electrons—is crushed out of existence by a mechanism intimately connected with gravitation and with the curvature of space.

A star collapses when it accrues sufficient mass or cools to a low enough temperature so that the inwardly directed gravitational pull exceeds the outwardly directed pressure that sustains the star. Once it starts shrinking it collapses faster and faster. At the end lies the mysterious fate which also awaits Einstein's collapsing universe.

There is no difference in relativity theory between the star's collapse and the collapse of the universe. In both cases the curvature of the geometry increases without limit; in both cases quantum effects must come in before curvature reaches infinity. In both cases the conclusion seems unavoidable that matter must be crushed out of existence, whatever our ignorance about the quantum details of the mechanism. And there's new cause for hoping we can fill in the details.

Unprecedented outbursts of radio energy, observed from three distant galaxies within the last few years, on closer study just this past spring, have raised widespread hopes that eventually it may be possible to photograph the process of gravitational collapse. But not only light and radio waves come off during collapse; neutrinos and gravitational radiation must also come off. Happily, some physicists already have been preparing special equipment to search for unusual cosmic effects. Weber is testing his detector for gravitational radiation at the University of Maryland. Reines at Case Institute already has a neutrino detector in operation. We are homing in on those key spots in nature where a "storm" in space-time is most likely to be observed.

Imagine having on hand, some years from now, a motion picture of a collapsing star. And imagine we can see the neutrinos and gravitational radiation streaming out as matter dissolves away. It presents a fantastic scene when run backwards. Sufficiently many neutrinos of the right helicity, and enough gravitational radiation, coming together from all directions—into one region of space over a short time interval—magically materialize into nuclear matter!

Many surprises are undoubtedly in store for us as we seek to fill in the frames of this motion picture. But at least—and at last—we seem to be looking in a reasonable direction when we raise up our eyes to the ancient vision of a universe of pure geometry.

Further reading

Classic in the field and still by far the most intelligible point of entry into it is Einstein's *The Meaning of Relativity* (Princeton, 4th ed., 1953). To brush up on developments that have taken place since 1955, especially the electromagnetic theory and introductory tensor analysis essential to close tracking of these newer developments, try *The Classical Theory of Fields* by Landau and Lifshitz, translated by Hamermesh (Addison-Wesley, 1951). Then home in on Wheeler's *Geometrodynamics* (Academic Press, 1962), a collection of the critical papers in the field since 1955, including a valuable, brief, new survey and summary.

Gravitation: An Introduction to Current Research, ed. by Witten (Wiley, 1962), offers summaries of the active edge in each of the areas in the field. The level is advanced enough to serve as a starting point for someone planning to tackle research. Rationale for experimental work on gravitational waves is *General Relativity and Gravitational Waves* by Weber (Interscience, 1961). The rigor and elegance of the geodesic clock is more fully treated in chapter 3 of *Gravitation and Relativity*, ed. by Chiu and Hoffman (W. A. Benjamin, 1964, $16). Chapter 10 in the same book develops the issue of gravitational collapse in a more thorough way. An excellent brief introduction to topology is *Elementary Concepts of Topology* by Alexandroff (transl. by Farley, Dover, 1961). Longer, but no less incisive, is Eisenhart's *Riemannian Geometry* (Princeton, 1926).

English language journals which carry most of the important work in these areas are *Phys. Rev.* and *Rev. Modern Phys.* Look for authors such as DeWitt, Dirac, Deser, Arnowitt, Misner, Bergmann, and, of course, John Archibald Wheeler.

PARTICLE SYMMETRIES

by Yuval Ne'eman *

IN BRIEF: *The elementary particles, especially those that take part in strong interactions, pose one of the most intriguing puzzles in modern physics. No attempt to build a consistent theory, which would account for their behavior and properties, has had more than a limited success. And the recent deluge of particle-like entities created by high-energy accelerators seems to have complicated matters considerably.*

An old approach that is gaining new interest seeks to bring order into this chaotic situation by studying the symmetries respected by the strongly interacting particles. What is really new here is the use of higher symmetries, involving a large number of dimensions to describe particles.

This approach has produced a number of schemes. While none of them are wholly satisfactory, their success in predicting new particles lends appeal to this line of development. In particular the octet model predicted the omega-minus particle, which was discovered at Brookhaven National Laboratory after the original publication of this article. (The omega-minus corresponds to the empty circle at the bottom of the R(3, 0, 0) diagram in Fig. 1-17.) —S.B.

■ As physicists continue to probe the nature of matter, a flood of new particles is appearing on the scene. Some of them are welcome, for they help to fill gaps in existing theories. Others, at first, only seemed to create bewilderment; their properties and behavior did not fit into any orderly scheme.

The strongly interacting particles were the most confusing of all. These included the K- and π-mesons, and the baryons, whose properties are given in Fig. 1-14. But we also have to contend with a more recent deluge of extremely short-lived entities called resonances. It is not clear whether these are new, ultra heavy particles, or bound states of existing particles.

The present state of strong-interaction theory is extremely messy. Indeed, no one attempt to establish a relatively complete theory has been successful. We will look at one approach that is based on a study of the symmetries respected by strong interactions. It is not an entirely new approach; some of the results were successfully integrated into the theory in the thirties. But the use of "higher"

* Yuval Ne'eman is Scientific Director of the Israeli AEC Laboratories in Rehovoth, and Head of the Physics Department at Tel-Aviv University.

symmetries seems to have just crossed a threshold—it is now providing physically interesting results, and may contain answers to parts of what we described as a mess—which is just our state of ignorance.

The basic interactions

Let us first examine the nature of the four kinds of interaction that modern physics regards as the basis of all natural forces. These interactions take place between basic constituents that are called either particles or fields. Both terms refer to the same things, but spring from different aspects of these constituents— the "corpuscular" and the "wave-like." In physics, we are dealing with discrete entities, or particles, that travel around individually but are characterized by a wave-field which describes their statistical behavior. Both matter and radiation exhibit such duality. Just as an electromagnetic field can be treated as an ensemble of photons, so may a meson be regarded as a meson field.

The four kinds of interaction among these entities are: (1) the familiar electromagnetic forces; (2) the extremely weak gravitational forces; (3) the so-called weak forces that show up in many kinds of particle decay; and (4) the strong forces that hold atomic nuclei together. These four interactions differ widely with regard to their interaction, or coupling, strengths.

For example, the electrostatic attraction between an electron, with a charge $-e$, and a proton, with a charge $+e$, is

$$F = (-e^2/4\pi)(1/r^2)$$

(The 4π is a consequence of the system of units used.) The interaction is thus characterized by the constant $e^2/4\pi$; it is called the electromagnetic coupling constant, and equals $\frac{1}{137}$.

In the same units, the gravitational interaction is characterized by a coupling constant of about 10^{-39}, which is extremely small. Just as the electromagnetic interaction is mediated by a flow of photons, the gravitational interaction is believed to be mediated by a flow of gravitons. Both the photon and the hypothetical graviton have zero mass and move at the speed of light, which accounts for the extremely long range of electromagnetic and gravitational forces.

Between these two lie the weak interactions, with a coupling strength of 10^{-13}. These include decays like beta decay, which is a neu-

	Particle		Anti-particle	Mass (MeV)	Spin	Charge no. Q	Baryon no. B	Lepton no. L	Strangeness no. S	Mean life (sec)
Photon	Photon	γ	γ	0	1	0	0	0	0	Stable
Leptons (light particles)	Neutrino	ν	$\bar{\nu}$	0	½	0	0	+1	0	Stable
	Electron	e^-	e^+	0.51	½	−1	0	+1	0	Stable
	Muon	μ^-	μ^+	105.66	½	−1	0	+1	−1	2.2×10^{-6}
Mesons (medium particles)	Pion	π^0	π^0	135.00	0	0	0	0	0	2.2×10^{-16}
		π^+	π^-	139.59	0	+1	0	0	0	2.6×10^{-8}
	Kaon	K^+	K^-	493.9	0	+1	0	0	+1	1.2×10^{-8}
		K^0	$\bar{K}^0$	497.8	0	0	0	0	+1	$K_1^0 : 1.0 \times 10^{-10}$ $K_2^0 : 6.1 \times 10^{-8}$
Baryons (heavy particles)	Nucleon	p	$\bar{p}$	938.21	½	+1	+1	0	0	Stable
		n	n	939.51	½	0	+1	0	0	1.0×10^3
	Λ hyperon	Λ	$\bar{\Lambda}$	1115.36	½	0	+1		−1	2.2×10^{-10}
	Σ hyperon	Σ^+	$\bar{\Sigma}^+$	1189.40	½	+1	+1	0	−1	0.8×10^{-10}
		Σ^0	$\bar{\Sigma}^0$	1191.5	½	0	+1	0	−1	$<0.1 \times 10^{-10}$
		Σ^-	$\bar{\Sigma}^-$	1195.96	½	−1	+1	0	−1	1.6×10^{-10}
	Ξ hyperon	Ξ^0	$\bar{\Xi}^0$	1311	?	0	+1	0	−2	1.5×10^{-10}
		Ξ^-	$\bar{\Xi}^-$	1318.4	?	−1	+1	0	−2	1.3×10^{-10}

Fig. 1-14. Table of elementary particles as of 1961, before the flood of unstable "resonances," the elementarity of which is in question, were produced. Classification for the mesons and baryons is based on a scheme proposed by Gell-Mann and Nishijima in 1953. Lepton- and baryon-number assignments and strangeness number assignments lead to conservation laws that help determine particle interactions.

tron decaying into a proton by emitting an electron and an antineutrino. There are many weak interactions, some of them responsible for such tremendous effects as novae (see "Neutrino Astronomy," in Chapter 4).

The strong interactions have a coupling strength between 1 and 15. This means that strong forces are about a thousand times stronger than the Coulomb electrostatic force. The interaction that binds protons and neutrons in nuclei is one strong force that has been studied extensively. It has a very short range —some 10^{-13} cm—so that each particle interacts only with its nearest neighbors.

H. Yukawa suggested, in 1934, that the interaction between nucleons is mediated by a massive particle of about $300m$, where m is the electron mass. This mass—or inertia—would explain the short range of nuclear forces. The π meson, or pion, which fits that description, was discovered in cosmic rays in 1947.

There are three kinds of pions: positively or negatively charged, and neutral (π^+, π^-, π^0). All have about the same mass—$273m$ and $264m$ for the charged and neutral pions respectively. Other particles mediating strong interactions have been discovered since; the best known are the K-mesons or kaons with masses in the neighborhood of $965m$.

The large coupling strength of strong interactions is the reason that "orthodox" field theory, invented in the thirties by W. Pauli and V. Weisskopf, cannot be applied in the same way as in electromagnetism, where it scored beautifully in the early fifties. Its methods are based on a mathematical expansion in terms of the coupling strengths. A process like the electric attraction mentioned is analyzed into the effects of the exchange of one, two, three, etc., photons between the proton and the electron. This yields a series of terms with coupling strengths of

$$e^2/4\pi, \quad (e^2/4\pi)^2, \quad (e^2/4\pi)^3, \ldots$$

Since $e^2/4\pi$ is a very small number, higher-order terms can be disregarded, and extremely accurate calculations can be made without going beyond the first two terms. For strong interactions, the coupling constant is of the order of 10, and succeeding terms just get larger and larger. Thus, the method does not work for strong interactions.

Another technique, dispersion theory, was introduced by M. Gell-Mann, M. L. Goldberger, and W. Thirring in 1954, and developed by F. Low, H. Lehmann, and others, but even after a major contribution by S. Mandelstam, only general qualitative results have come out of the method. New hopes have now been raised by a further advance along the same lines, due to T. Regge, but the goal is still not in sight.

Symmetries and conservation laws

Where do symmetries come in? Their importance derives from the principle that for every symmetry displayed by nature, there is a corresponding conservation law. There is no need to emphasize the importance of conservation laws, if we remember the role played by the conservation of energy, momentum, and angular momentum in classical mechanics, or the conservation of matter in chemistry.

The relationship between symmetries and conservation laws is not a new concept; it has its roots deep in classical physics. The key to this relationship may be found in the concept of invariance. Consider, for example, a snowflake. How would you describe its symmetry? One way would be to enumerate all the spatial transformations that bring the snowflake back into itself. A 60° rotation is one such transformation; in fact, so are all rotations through angles that are integral multiples of 60°. We say that the snowflake is invariant to such transformations.

Now consider a coordinate system in empty, three-dimensional space. It doesn't matter how you translate the origin or rotate the axes; the new system is equivalent. Thus, we say that space is homogeneous and isotropic. If you include time as a fourth dimension, the system is also homogeneous in time. These symmetry properties are reflected in the fact that the dynamical equations that describe the behavior of a physical system are invariant to these transformations.

Moreover, it can be shown that invariance to rotation means that the system's angular momentum is conserved. Similarly, invariance to translation implies conservation of linear momentum, and invariance to a change in the origin of the time coordinate implies conservation of energy. Thus, our search for new symmetries is, in fact, an attempt to discover new conservation laws, new physically measurable quantities that remain constant in a closed system. In modern physics, conserved quantities are often represented by quantum numbers.

These are all continuous symmetries; that is, you can perform the transformations gradually, in small additive steps. There are also discrete symmetries; the snowflake is one example. Another is involved in going over from a system to its mirror-image; no series of small changes can turn a man's right hand into his left. Still, reflection does conserve distances and angles as in the original.

A symmetry of that type happened to become famous in 1957; to everybody's surprise, Lee and Yang showed that the weak interactions were not invariant under reflection with respect to a point. If a system is invariant to such reflection, the physical observable that is conserved is parity. Thus a break in the symmetry is termed parity nonconservation.

Internal degrees of freedom

What about other conserved quantities? There have been various attempts to discover transformations in space-time leading to electric charge conservation, but none were satisfactory. We are compelled to assume the existence of internal degrees of freedom, in addition to space and time which are external ones. These are needed to account for aspects of a particle that are not amenable to an explicit mathematical relationship with space and time, though they probably are space-time manifestations. For example, we have no way to introduce notions like particle shapes.

To introduce notions like electric charge, we invent an isospace. This is a mathematical construct that provides us with additional coordinates. A particle in isospace is thought of as having new coordinates $\alpha_1, \alpha_2, \ldots$, in addition to the four coordinates of space-time. There is nothing mysterious about such a space, it is simply a device which enables us to include the above-mentioned evasive aspects in our mathematical description of the particle. The particle's "position" in the isospace is a reading of some of its internal parameters.

To get an invariance principle that corresponds to electric charge conservation, we start with the simplest isospace, a plane. In fact, we do not need a full plane—we only need one variable; the dial shown in the margin is an ideal isospace for electric charge.

Suppose we set it so that the hand reads off the value α_e for the particle's charge. For a neutral particle, it points at the zero. If we now move the zero mark by an angle β_e, all the readings change by the same amount. This corresponds to a redefinition of the zero level of electric charge; we call it a gage transformation. The trouble is that it could produce unwarranted physical effects: neutral particles would acquire a charge and be attracted by a charged particle.

This is where our invariance principle will come in—the theory should not produce such effects. To insure this, we introduce a second hand at $-\alpha_e$, symmetric with the first hand and require that any transfer of the zero level from which α_e is read brings about an opposite resetting of the second hand. The neutral particle will now acquire an opposite charge of the same amount due to the new hand, and the two effects cancel. We could also describe the revised readings by ascribing to one hand a clockwise rotation, identifiable with negative charges, while the other, describing positive ones, goes counterclockwise.

We see that we have had to construct the theory so that every particle will have an antiparticle—a particle with the same dynamical qualities but opposite charge—to achieve electrical gage invariance.

The electric charge isospace is called a $U(1)$ symmetry. The 1 denotes the single coordinate

Electric charge dial
Positive particle
αe
$-\alpha e$
Negative particle

When dial is disturbed
positive particle
new αe
new $-\alpha e$
Negative particle

required by the symmetry; the U refers to the dial-like aspect of this isospace, mathematically termed a unitary space.

We will encounter other conserved quantities that can be described with a $U(1)$ gage invariance. In the various isospace we shall discuss, antiparticles will always emerge as a necessity. The operation of replacing a particle by its antiparticle (equivalent to inverting the direction of the angle of rotation under all gage transformations) is a discrete symmetry, like that involved in parity conservation. It is called charge conjugation and produces a conserved quantity, charge-parity.

After the 1932 discovery that atomic nuclei are composed of protons and neutrons, it was clear that, since neutrons do not carry electric charge, some other interaction must be responsible for the strong binding energies in the nucleus. Moreover, it was found that this new interaction was the same between two protons, two neutrons, or a proton and a neutron; this was termed charge-independence. It requires about equal efforts to tear either kind of nucleon from a nucleus. W. Heisenberg therefore noted that one could regard the proton and the neutron as different states of a nucleon.

Isospin

This led to the introduction of a new conserved quantity—isospin—to distinguish the two nucleon states. We are saying, in effect, that if the electromagnetic interaction were turned off, the difference between neutrons and protons would disappear, and they would simply be different isospin states of one particle. (In mathematical language, we say that they form a single representation.) Isospin is not related to ordinary spin, although it is the same kind of mathematical quantity.

A $U(1)$ isospace would be insufficient to describe the symmetry, as the neutron is not the proton's antiparticle; the antiproton and the antineutron have to be included. The minimum isospace must thus contain two double-dials, one for the proton and one for the neutron. We are thus led, like B. Cassen and E. U. Condon in 1936, to assume a $U(2)$ symmetry.

What is the meaning of this new $U(2)$ gage invariance? Consider our two dials, the proton's and the neutron's. We have two new angles, α_1 and α_2, to add to our particle coordinates. Since we can introduce two independent "disturbances" (or resettings of the zeros), β_1 and β_2, we have four possibilities, as each can be applied to either dial.

We find that applying β_1 to the α_1 dial and β_2 to the α_2 is equivalent to our previous operation on a $U(1)$ dial and is separable from the rest of the $U(2)$ gage. Treating it separately, we are left with the conservation of a three-component quantity; this is isospin.

Isospin conservation thus reflects invariance to three variations: adding β_1 to the α_2 dial; adding β_2 to the α_1 dial; and adding β_1 to α_1 and β_2 to α_2 but in opposite directions.

Measuring isospin is a twofold operation; to describe a particle's isospin, we give both the absolute value I and one component, I_z. Thus, if we look at the nucleon isospin diagram in Fig. 1-15, we see that $I = \frac{1}{2}$ for both neutron and proton, but $I_z = +\frac{1}{2}$ for the proton and $-\frac{1}{2}$ for the neutron. There are no other particles belonging to this representation, because for any I, there are always $2I + 1$ states, with I_z changing by unit intervals. Here, $I = \frac{1}{2}$, $2I + 1 = 2$.

What does this tell us about the π-mesons that mediate nucleon-nucleon interactions in nuclei? In scattering experiments, it was found that when a target proton is struck by a neutron, there is a high proportion of cases where the particle emerging forward is a proton, while the target has turned into a neutron. This is obviously an exchange reaction, where scatterer and scattered particles exchange a charged particle. This particle had to carry one negative unit of isospin lost by the energetic neutron in the reaction

$$n^0 + p^+ \rightarrow p^+ + \pi^- + p^+ \rightarrow p^+ + n^0$$

We see that to conserve I_z, the π^- has $I_z = -1$. The π^+, its antiparticle, has $I_z = +1$. The rule for I_z values makes us expect a third particle with $I_z = 0$. This will be the π^0, responsible for the strong attraction between two protons or two neutrons. Thus the mesons also become three isospin states of a single particle, or representation, with $I = 1$, as in Fig. 1-15.

So-called strange particles

Just as pion physics was becoming semi-respectable, cosmic rays and accelerator experiments started throwing upon the stage a series of particles which seemed to complicate the picture. The name "strange particles" was given to these "heavier nucleons," or baryons, and K-mesons. And with these particles came the need for new conserved quantities.

A strong process lasts less than some 10^{-22} sec. The hyperons (Λ, Σ, Ξ) and K-mesons, although produced in strong interactions, subsequently undergo extremely slow decays, of the order of 10^{-10} sec or longer. The decay processes are thus weak interactions. (The π^0 and the Σ^0 decay faster, through an electromagnetic interaction.)

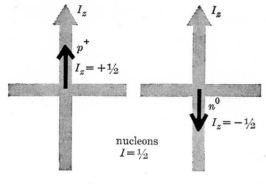

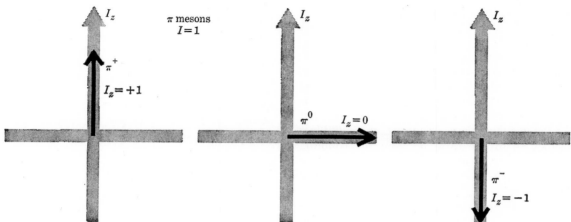

Fig. 1-15. Isospin states of nucleons and pions are shown. Both proton and neutron have $I = \frac{1}{2}$, but isospins point in opposite directions, giving I_z values shown. Pions have $I = 1$, and isospin can assume three possible directions. Note that in both cases, I_z changes always by 1 unit.

When baryons decay, they leave behind them a proton and a number of light particles (electrons, muons, neutrinos and their antiparticles). Protons do not decay. On the other hand, when they absorb an antiproton they annihilate into π or K-mesons. Experiments have shown that the number of baryons minus the number of antibaryons is constant. This becomes the law of baryonic charge conservation when we assign a baryon "charge" B of $B = 1$ to baryons and $B = -1$ to antibaryons. It can be described by a further $U(1)$ dial, an isospace like the electric charge isospace, with a coordinate α_b and opposite rotation directions for baryons and antibaryons.

A principal feature of the strong processes that produce baryons is "associated production." This means that a strange particle is never produced by itself. They come in pairs, as in

$$\pi^- + p^+ \rightarrow \Lambda^0 + K^0$$

This implies a new conservation law; there must be some conserved quantity that does not appear in the nonstrange pair on the left and yet does exist in strange particles. For the interaction to conserve this quantity it must cancel on the right as well; therefore two strange particles are needed.

This new quantity is strangeness, introduced in 1953 by M. Gell-Mann and K. Nishijima; they gave one unit of S to K^0 and minus one unit of S to Λ^0. They attached isospin assignments to the various strange particles to account for strong processes, and also postulated a relation

$$\text{electric charge} = I_z + (B + S)/2$$

which proved extremely useful.

Several of the particles required by these assignments—and most antiparticles—were missing at the time. All have since been discovered, the latest being the Ξ antiparticle, produced in the spring of 1962 at Brookhaven and at CERN at the same time. The Gell-Mann-Nishijima scheme tamed the particle jungle for about eight years. Most textbooks—and about a dozen of them appeared in 1960–61—include the table of the elementary particles, reproducing these assignments, that is shown in Fig. 1-14.

It was assumed that strangeness, baryon charge, and isospin are conserved in all strong interactions. This still holds, even though the number of known strong interactions has grown tenfold since. Baryon charge is conserved in electromagnetic, weak, and probably gravitational interactions as well; strangeness and the z-component of isospin are conserved in electromagnetic interactions, but the full isospin invariance is broken. Weak interactions destroy both S and I conservation entirely, but respect electric charge conservation.

The need for higher symmetries

These developments were followed by a period in which theoreticians tried to find more inclusive symmetries. These higher symmetries were sought because a number of serious problems remained.

For one thing, the systematics for further growth of the table of particles were lacking. The first pion-nucleon resonance—one of those short-lived "particles" we spoke of in the introduction—had an isospin of $I = \frac{3}{2}$, the next one had $I = \frac{1}{2}$, like the nucleon. Why just these values?

Moreover, by regarding the proton and neutron as different isospin states of one particle, a relationship between nucleon coupling strengths had been obtained. But as long as the rest of the baryons remained as distinct and independent representations, one could say nothing about the ratio between the coupling forces. The nucleons, the lambda, the sigma, and the xi hyperons all had to be allowed "private forces."

Also, with so many particles around, physicists were again looking for a basic set from which to construct the rest. As early as 1949, E. Fermi and C. N. Yang had tried to look at a pion as a "bound state" of a nucleon and an antinucleon. This would provide the right values for all conserved quantities (spin, isospin, hypercharge, baryon number), but would require a tremendous binding energy (the nucleon-antinucleon combination has 13.5 times the mass of the pion). M. Goldhaber and others tried to adapt such models to the new growth particles.

Then there was the tantalizing fact that the electromagnetic interaction allowed a perfect symmetry, yet to be found elsewhere. If you try to turn your dial by an angle β while you move in space-time, and make β a function of your space-time displacement, you mix the internal symmetry with external effects. But the computations produce momenta (remember the connection between translations and momenta) that are never actually observed; it is only if you postulate the existence of an electromagnetic field, with spin $j = 1$ (the photons), that you cancel out these unobserved phenomena.

C. N. Yang and H. Mills tried to do the same with isospin, that is, to introduce variations β_1 and β_2 in the dials with a space-time dependence. As a result, it became necessary to look for new mediating particles, with the pion's isospin, but with one unit of ordinary spin. Such particles, resembling the photon, are called vector-mesons or vectons. In fact, experiments probing the nucleons' structure seemed to require the existence of vectons in the meson cloud around the nucleon core.

Physicists had a feeling for rotations and spins, and tried first to find a way out of some of these difficulties by looking for a higher rotation symmetry. A. Pais in 1954, A. Salam and J. Polkinghone in 1955, and J. Schwinger in 1957 tried four-dimensional symmetry schemes. Then came global symmetry, introduced by M. Gell-Mann and J. Schwinger; to describe this symmetry, one needed rotations in seven dimensions. To connect the theory somehow with the weak interactions, this was even pushed to eight and then nine dimensions. The trouble was that these schemes had to disregard the difference between the Σ and Λ hyperons, mixing them up as two nucleon-like doublets, and disregarding their "proper" isospin assignments. Moreover, they were invalidated by some experimental results.

Unitary symmetry

Sometime in 1959–1960, M. Ikeda, S. Ogawa, and Y. Ohnuki in Japan and Y. Yamaguchi at CERN gave mathematical substance to a model suggested by S. Sakata in 1956. To build any desired particle, Sakata had suggested using the proton, neutron, and lambda and their antiparticles as building bricks. With half a unit of isospin of either sign supplied by the two nucleons, and one negative unit of strangeness possessed by the lambda, you could create any necessary combination. A K^+-meson, for instance, has one positive unit of strangeness and isospin of one-half, with $I_z = +\frac{1}{2}$. You can get these values from $p + \bar{\Lambda}^0$, since the baryon charge will cancel out, the p^+ will supply the right isospin (Λ^0 has none, and neither does $\bar{\Lambda}^0$ of course), and the $\bar{\Lambda}^0$ provides the strangeness.

The symmetry principle one uses brings us back to that set of double-dials we were using for $U(2)$, the isospace that describes isospin. If we add a third double-dial, we have a $U(3)$ isospace, which contains isospin, strangeness, and baryon charge, and thus electric charge as well, by the Gell-Mann-Nishijima formula. In the Sakata model, you may associate p, n, and Λ with the 3 dials respectively.

What does $U(3)$ give us? Again we have to vary the three dials, hands at angles α_1, α_2, and α_3 by imposing three "disturbances," β_1, β_2, β_3. This creates nine possible variations.

One combination of three variations can be reduced to a simple $U(1)$ symmetry, corresponding to baryon charge conservation. Another combination gives hypercharge (a quantity related to strangeness by the formula $U = B + S$ and often used in its stead). Three other variations reproduce isospin. Altogether,

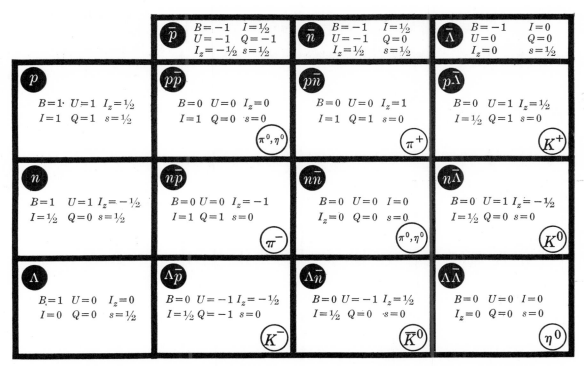

Fig. 1-16. Table shows how p, n and Λ, and their antiparticles can be combined, in the Sakata model, to give π-mesons, K-mesons, η⁰, and a vacuum-like particle. B, U, Q, and I_z are additive quantum numbers; I and s add vectorially. Vacuum-like particle and η⁰ particle differ in that former is invariant to all exchanges of p, n, and Λ, while η⁰ is not invariant to exchanges of Λ with either n or p. U is the hypercharge (see page 30) and s is the spin. The combination $p\bar{p} + n\bar{n} + \Lambda\bar{\Lambda}$ is vacuum-like because all charges and quantum numbers cancel in it.

the symmetry involves eight arbitrary operations, leading to an eight component conservation law.

Figure 1-16 shows how a model works when "sakatons" (p^+, n, Λ^0) are combined with "antisakatons" ($\bar{p}^+$, $\bar{n}$, $\bar{\Lambda}^0$). The result in the 3 diagonal squares requires computation too cumbersome to relate here, but the six off-diagonal squares are simple enough.

What we got are just the three pions, the two kaons, and the two antikaons. But we also got an η⁰; this missing particle should have the same space-time properties as the others (spinless, negative parity) and zero isospin and hypercharge (like the lambda). It should be its own charge conjugate, like the π⁰. It is possible to continue this process by combining two sakatons and one antisakaton, etc.

In 1961, M. Gell-Mann and the author offered an alternative model, the octet model shown in Fig. 1-17, based on the same higher symmetry. Just as isospin assignments grouped particles differing only by I_z into multiplets, the higher symmetry models group together several isospin and strangeness multiplets into one supermultiplet. There is one important difference between the two cases, however; the mass differences among particles within the isospin multiplets are small, and can possibly be attributed to electromagnetic effects resulting from electric charge differences. The particles grouped by a higher symmetry model differ greatly in mass, a fact to be accounted for.

However, the octet has the advantage of putting all 8 baryons on the same footing. One of the crucial tests we await is the final measurement of the spin of the Ξ⁰ or Ξ⁻, still uncertain. In the octet, it should be $j = \frac{1}{2}$; in the Sakata model, it should be $j = \frac{3}{2}$.

Gell-Mann has also shown that the symmetry allows one to derive a relationship between the masses in the octet model. This comes out as $3M_\Lambda + M_\Sigma = 2(M_N = M_\Xi)$, where N stands for nucleon. This equation is accurate experimentally to less than one percent difference.

The same method gives for the bosons, $3(M_\eta)^2 + (M_\pi)^2 = 4(M_K)^2$. The use of this formula enables one to predict a mass of about 570 MeV for the η⁰.

These were some of the theoretical models. Shortly after their publication, experiments at Berkeley, Brookhaven, CERN, and elsewhere produced a deluge of new particles or resonances. Without the higher symmetries one would have felt submerged. As it happened, they started filling up the gaps nicely.

The η⁰ is with us. Its mass is about 560 MeV.

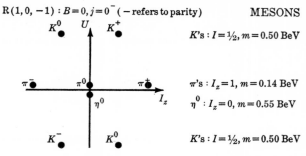

R(2,1,0) : B=1, j=½, (fundamental octet) **BARYONS**

n   U   p

Σ⁻   Σ⁰   Σ⁺ I_z

Λ

Ξ⁻   Ξ⁰

$n, p : I=½, m=0.94$ BeV

$Σ's : I=1, m=1.19$ BeV
$Λ : I=0, m=1.11$ BeV

$Ξ's : I=½, m=1.32$ BeV
(spin uncertain)

R(1,0,−1) : B=0, j=0⁻ (− refers to parity) **MESONS**

K⁰   U   K⁺

π⁻   π⁰   π⁺ I_z
η⁰

K⁻   K⁰

$K's : I=½, m=0.50$ BeV

$π's : I_z=1, m=0.14$ BeV
$η⁰ : I_z=0, m=0.55$ BeV

$K's : I=½, m=0.50$ BeV

R(0,0,0) : B=1, j=?

U

$Y_0^{(*)}$ I_z $I=0, m=1.40$ BeV

R(0,0,0) : B=0, j=?

F⁰

$I=0, m=1.3$ BeV

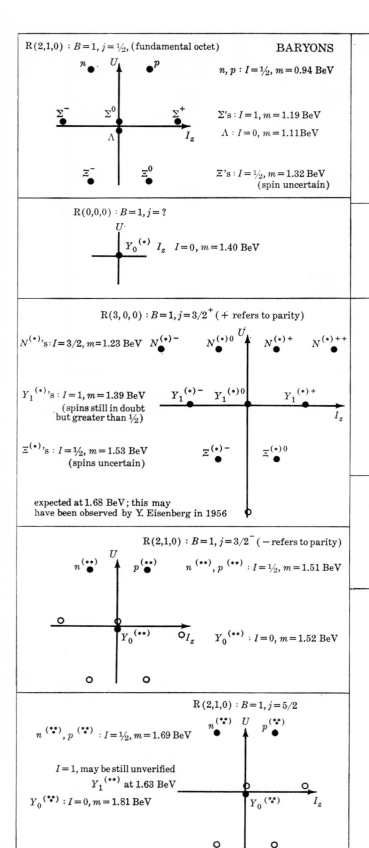

R(3,0,0) : B=1, j=3/2⁺ (+ refers to parity)

$N^{(*)}'s : I=3/2, m=1.23$ BeV   N^{(*)−}   U   N^{(*)0}   N^{(*)+}   N^{(*)++}

$Y_1^{(*)}'s : I=1, m=1.39$ BeV $Y_1^{(*)−}$ $Y_1^{(*)0}$ $Y_1^{(*)+}$ I_z
(spins still in doubt but greater than ½)

$Ξ^{(*)}'s : I=½, m=1.53$ BeV   Ξ^{(*)−}   Ξ^{(*)0}
(spins uncertain)

expected at 1.68 BeV; this may have been observed by Y. Eisenberg in 1956

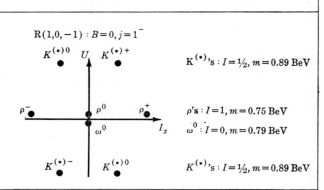

R(1,0,−1) : B=0, j=1⁻

K^{(*)0}   U   K^{(*)+}

$K^{(*)}'s : I=½, m=0.89$ BeV

ρ⁻   ρ⁰   ρ⁺ I_z
ω⁰

$ρ's : I=1, m=0.75$ BeV
$ω⁰ : I=0, m=0.79$ BeV

K^{(*)−}   K^{(*)0}

$K^{(*)}'s : I=½, m=0.89$ BeV

Other unidentified particles that have recently been observed:

ω⁰' : U=0, I=0, j=?, m=1.02 BeV
this ω⁰' may replace ω⁰ in the above
R(1,0,1⁻), j=1⁻;
the isolated ω⁰ or ω⁰' is a
R(0,0,0) singlet

R(2,1,0) : B=1, j=3/2⁻ (− refers to parity)

n^{(**)}   U   p^{(**)} $n^{(**)}, p^{(**)} : I=½, m=1.51$ BeV

$Y_0^{(**)}$ I_z $Y_0^{(**)} : I=0, m=1.52$ BeV

R(2,1,0) : B=1, j=5/2

$n^{(**)}, p^{(**)} : I=½, m=1.69$ BeV   n^{(**)}   U   p^{(**)}

I=1, may be still unverified
$Y_1^{(**)}$ at 1.63 BeV
$Y_0^{(**)} : I=0, m=1.81$ BeV $Y_0^{(**)}$ I_z

Fig. 1-17. Gell-Mann-Ne'eman octet model groups particles in various representations, labeled R(a,b,c). Baryons are shown on the left, mesons on the right. Each particle is charted by isospin component, I_z, and hypercharge, U. Solid dots are observed particles, white dots are expected particles. Apart from mass differences and their dynamical effects, strong interactions should be unable to distinguish between particles in the same representation. A BeV is 1000 MeV or about 2000 electron masses.

The whole octet of vector mesons is here; it contains a K-like set (called K*) at 888 MeV, a π-like triplet ρ at 750 MeV, and an $η^0$ like $ω^0$ at 788 MeV. The last figure is a bit too small if the mass formula is to be believed; the particle should lie near the nucleon mass or slightly above it. The symmetries do have room for one extra such $I = 0$ particle; two mesons with masses near and above the nucleon mass have been reported lately. These may set the count right.

The laboratories have also supplied high-spin particles. For people who like the Sakata model, there is a nice "higher Sakaton" at $j = \frac{5}{2}$; this would be the beginning of a new octet to the partisans of the octet. At $j = \frac{3}{2}$ things seem to go relatively well for the octet, where a ten-particle multiplet is almost full, only one particle still unreported, although a forgotten, unexplained event found by Y. Eisenberg some six years ago might be it.

The number of observed particles is nearing fifty, with some thirty more "certain" antiparticles, and another ten more doubtful cases. Is a $U(3)$ symmetry the answer to our quest for order? Personally, I think it will at least supply an approximation; the exact symmetry may be much more involved, although I do believe that it should be derivable from some further simple notions. Anyhow, we shall have advanced one step further, although an incomplete step. When Bohr produced his model of the atom, it did provide a useful tool for predicting and identifying the various electron shells; but it was only with the advent of quantum mechanics that the mechanism could really be understood and carried further.

The same applies here. We shall need a dynamical theory to explain how "composite" particles are bound. We also have to look for a symmetry-breaking mechanism, linking the supposedly tamed, strong interactions with the electromagnetic and weak ones. In fact, some sort of fundamental derivation will even have to tell us why our isospace and octet models have three and eight dimensions respectively.

The story is apparently just starting to un-fold. Altogether, the present situation seems comparable to the situation in 1870, when D. I. Mendeleev was writing, "When I arranged the elements according to the magnitude of their atomic weights . . . it became evident that there exists a kind of periodicity in their properties. . . ."

Further reading

The ideal place to begin is with a book by Weyl called *Symmetry* (Princeton U. Press, 1952, $4.50). It starts with the geometrical concept of symmetry as it occurs in art and nature, and then develops the abstract mathematical ideas underlying the various forms of symmetry. The reader should also see *Elementary Particles* by Yang (Princeton U. Press, 1961, $2.75), which is a historical account of the discoveries of the elementary particles.

A clear and simple discussion of the well-established concepts, including strangeness and isospin, can be found in "Elementary Particles" by Gell-Mann, *Scientific American*, **197**, 72 (July 1957). For those with the background to dig still deeper, there have been a number of books published in the last few years. One good one is *Introduction to Elementary Particle Physics* by Marshak and Sudershan (Interscience, 1961, paperback $2.50, hardcover $4.50). Another is *High Energy Nuclear Physics* by Lock (Methuen-Wiley, 1960, $4.00), which covers the physics of pions and nuclear interactions.

"Resonance Particles" by Hill, *Scientific American*, **208**, 38 (Jan. 1963), provides a phenomenological description of these newcomers on the scientific scene. Aside from this, information on the latest developments is confined to the professional journals. Those who would like to sample the flavor of current work might look at the following references, dealing with the Sakata and Gell-Mann-Ne'eman models: Sakata, *Progress of Theoretical Physics*, **16**, 686 (1956); Gell-Mann, *The Physical Review*, **125**, 1067 (1962); Ne'eman, *Nuclear Physics*, **26**, 222 ('61), and **30**, 347 ('62).

USING THE MÖSSBAUER EFFECT

by V. I. Goldanskii *

*V. I. Goldanskii heads the nuclear and radiation chemistry laboratory of the Institute for Chemical Physics of U.S.S.R. in Moscow.

IN BRIEF: *Gamma rays can be resonantly absorbed just as sound and light waves are. However, gamma-ray resonances are remarkably well tuned: the ratio of the cen-ter frequency of the resonance to its width at half-maximum can be as high as 2×10^{15}. Practical use can be made of these resonances because, in a crystal lattice, gamma rays can be emitted (or absorbed) without recoil of the emitting atom, which would otherwise destroy the match. One class of applications involves* *measuring small changes in the position of the resonance caused by internal electric or magnetic fields. What is measured is the steady velocity (on the order of 1 mm/sec, it turns out) that must be imparted to the absorber relative to the emitter so that the Doppler shift in frequency compensates for the change. These measurements can be interpreted to give information about chemical structure, about nuclear electric and magnetic properties, about ferromagnetic domains. For example, the author has confirmed the polymer-like structure of SnF_4 this way.*

There are potential applications of engineering interest. One stems from the use of the Doppler shift idea as a sensitive noncontact motion indicator. Another would use the technique for mineral assay.—D.C.

■ There is great unity in physics. For example, the phenomenon of resonance, which is familiar from many common acoustic and electrical phenomena, has its analog in optics and in the scattering and absorption of gamma rays. Thus phenomena of the macroscopic world, governed by classical mechanics, have their parallels in the microscopic world of atoms and nuclei, governed by the laws of quantum mechanics.

But this parallelism is sometimes obscured by quantitative differences. Thus it was that though acoustic resonance has been known since Galileo, and though optical resonance was predicted by Lord Rayleigh and was discovered experimentally by R. W. Wood in 1904, it was not until Rudolf Mössbauer's remarkable discovery of 1958 that it became possible to observe gamma-ray resonances with the same ease and clarity.

The difficulty was that recoil of the emitting and the absorbing nuclei took away part of the energy of the gamma ray and thus destroyed the resonant condition. Mössbauer's essential contribution was to discover (at first, quite accidentally) that it was possible for gamma rays to be emitted or absorbed practically without any recoil of the emitting or absorbing nucleus. This opened up to experimentation and application the extreme precision of frequency inherent in the gamma rays emitted by nuclei. When emitting gamma rays, nuclei are perhaps the most sharply tuned resonant systems in nature—up to 1 part in 2×10^{15}. (See Figs. 1-18 and 1-19.)

This precision makes the gamma-ray resonance a superb tool for studying the influence of external factors on nuclear electric and magnetic properties. For example, we can readily observe the interaction between nuclear electric charge and electron shells, between nuclear magnetic moments and external or intramolecular magnetic fields, between nuclear electric quadrupole moments and external or intramolecular inhomogeneous electric fields. We can even detect the influence of the earth's gravitational field on gamma-ray energies.

We are accustomed from school years to the statement that radioactive decay properties are independent of pressure, temperature, or the chemical state of a substance. Mössbauer's discovery brings the magnificent evidence that the correctness of this statement is quite restricted. Indeed, the nuclear resonance is so sharp (see Fig. 1-18) that we are able to see effects on it of even the outermost electrons of the atom. This leads to a vast and varied scope of application in chemistry and the physics of solids.

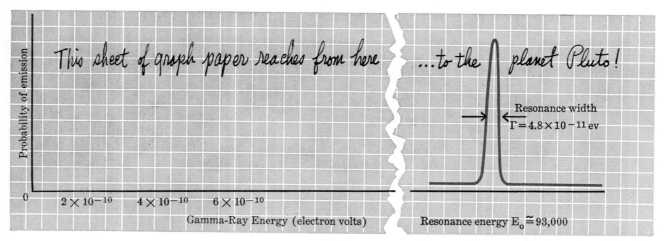

Fig. 1-18. *The sharpness of gamma-ray lines (here that of zinc-67) is such that a plot on a linear scale that displays the resonance only ⅛ in. wide must stretch from Earth to Pluto if the origin is to be included. Note that resonance energy (~93,000 ev) is not known to 15 places; Mössbauer techniques have great sensitivity not great accuracy.*

Some of the large-scale properties of matter that can be studied include the electric and magnetic fields within crystals, the effects of atomic impurities on crystal lattices, and the vibrational spectra of solids. And then there is a wide range of applications in technology. The Mössbauer effect can be used, for example, to study defects in materials, to record extremely weak vibrations and changes in acceleration, and as an assay tool for elements like iron, tin, and gold.

I myself have been exploring its use to study problems of chemical bonding; even the early results show we have here an important tool for the chemist, too. Thus the Mössbauer effect is growing in usefulness in the same way as quadrupole resonance and nuclear magnetic resonance; all these started out as investigations in pure physics and proved to have a wide range of application.

Resonances and their half widths

To trace again the path from acoustic to optical to nuclear resonance that I mentioned in my introduction, consider the familiar example of a tuning fork. When struck, it emits a note whose frequency depends on the dimensions and material properties of the fork. If the fork is stilled and a source of sound of that same characteristic frequency (it might come from an identical tuning fork) is brought nearby, the fork will be set into vibration at its characteristic frequency. This is the phenomenon of resonance—and examples of it abound in physics and in engineering.

Now the two frequencies do not need to be *exactly* the same—every resonance is characterized by varying degrees of response depending on the departure of the frequency from that marking the peak of the resonance curve. The usual way to describe this situation is to speak of the width of the resonance, this being the difference between the two frequencies at which the response is half that at the peak of the resonance. The more sharply tuned the system, the narrower the resonance relative to its center frequency; radio engineers speak of this sharpness as the quality factor or Q of a resonance.

The phenomenon of resonance, then, depends on having a pair of systems with nearly the same characteristic frequencies. Note that it is necessary to have an emitter, an absorber, and radiant energy that passes between them.

Atoms have frequencies associated with them; these are the frequencies of light emitted by the atom. The emission is due to transitions of electrons from one orbit to another, and the characteristic frequencies are given by the differences in energy levels of the atom, divided

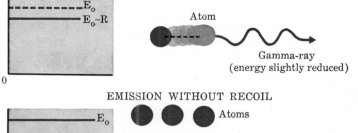

EMISSION WITH RECOIL

EMISSION WITHOUT RECOIL

Fig. 1-19. If emitting atom is in a gas it can recoil freely, robbing energy R from the energy E_0 available in the excited nucleus. But in a crystal, recoil-free emission—the Mössbauer Effect—produces full-energy gamma ray.

by Planck's constant $h = 6.62 \times 10^{-27}$ erg sec. That is, $\nu = E/h$.

Because energy and frequency are directly proportional in the atomic case, it is common to speak in terms of the *resonant energy* and to give the width of the resonance in energy units. The energy unit that is customarily used is the electron volt, reflecting the fact that the forces within an atom are electrical and the potential differences are of the order of a volt.

As suggested schematically in the margin, an excited atom emits a light photon of energy E, which has a high probability of being absorbed by another atom of the same sort which becomes excited thereby. This second atom will emit a photon after a brief while, a phenomenon that is known as resonance fluorescence. For a typical atom the resonance energy is of the order of 1 electron volt and the width of the resonance, designated Γ, is of the order of 10^{-8} ev; so the ratio E/Γ is of the order of 10^8. That's why the lines in an optical spectrum are so sharp; the atom is a very high Q oscillator. Recently ways have been found to increase the effective Q to of the order of 10^{13} by getting an ensemble of excited atoms to emit in unison in what has come to be known as the laser. But the gamma-ray resonances with which the Mössbauer effect is concerned are even sharper, have an even higher Q.

Just as atoms can emit light, so nuclei can emit gamma rays. And just as atoms are more likely to absorb light with which they are resonant, so nuclei can absorb strongly gamma rays with which they are resonant. The energy of these gamma rays is of the order of 10^4 electron volts (same unit as before, but now the energy is much larger, reflecting the fact that the forces involved in this resonant system are more nuclear than they are electrical). The widths of the resonances are about the same as the widths of atomic (light) resonances, but, the energy being so much higher, the resonance is correspondingly sharper: $E/\Gamma = 10^{15}$ and even higher. Thus in the resonance between gamma rays and nuclei we have one of the most sharply tuned systems in all of nature.

The recoiling nucleus can't resonate

But this higher energy leads to a basic difficulty. Some of the energy of the gamma ray is dissipated in recoil of the nucleus; this destroys the resonant condition. Such recoil has not been quantitatively important in any of the systems we have discussed previously because the energy of recoil was not great compared with the width of the resonance. Now it is.

Let us consider this recoil effect. Basically it is similar to the situation whereby a portion of the energy released by a bullet fired from a gun goes into the recoil of the gun barrel. For the nuclear case, a simple calculation shows that the recoil energy increases with the square of the transition energy; $R = E^2/2Mc^2$, where M is the mass of the emitting (or absorbing) nucleus and c is the velocity of light. Putting numbers in, $R \cong 10^{-3}$ ev—which is tiny compared with $E (= 10,000$ ev in this case) but large compared with $\Gamma (= 10^{-8}$ ev, say). As a result, direct observation of the resonance used to seem impossible—the recoil would take so much energy from the gamma ray, that it would no longer have the same resonant energy upon absorption as it did upon emission.

To make matters even more complicated, the recoil energy combines with the normal thermal motion of the nuclei to broaden the resonance still further. The resonance takes on a new shape and the effective width is now the so-called Doppler width given by $D = \sqrt{8RE_{Th}}$ where E_{Th} is the energy per degree of freedom of the thermal motion $(= \frac{1}{2}kT$, for those who are familiar with the uses of Boltzmann's constant, k).

By way of illustration here is a numerical example, describing the particular case of the isotope used in most of the studies that will be discussed in the sections which follow. It is the radioactive isotope tin-119, for which there is a gamma-ray level at $E = 23.8$ kev and $\Gamma = 2.4 \times 10^{-8}$ ev. It works out that the recoil energy $R = 2.5 \times 10^{-3}$ ev and $D = 1.6 \times 10^{-2}$ ev (when $T = 300°K$).

The spectrum of the *emitted* gamma-quanta is now characterized, not by the familiar resonance curve, but by a broadened Doppler distribution having its maximum at $E - R$, the

resonance energy less the recoil energy. But, for absorption, the analogous resonance spectrum has its maximum at $E + R$. That is, the incoming quantum must provide energy R over and above the resonance energy if there is to be resonant absorption. Resonance can take place only in the small overlap region of these spectra, a rather discouraging situation.

Cooling the source and the absorber to reduce the Doppler broadening doesn't help; in fact, it worsens things by narrowing the two peaks so that the overlap region is reduced. Therefore, the usual procedure used to be to heat up the emitter and absorber to several thousand degrees so as to broaden further the region of overlap. Another method was to use rapid rotors and similar devices to move the source relative to the absorber at a speed of $(R/E)c$—hundreds or thousands of meters per second—to compensate at least in part for the recoil.

Eliminating the recoil

Rudolf Mössbauer's discovery, which earned him the Nobel prize in physics, was that if the emitting and absorbing atoms were each part of crystal lattices, emission and absorption could take place without recoil. The secret lies in the fact that the recoil energy, while large compared with the width of the gamma-ray line, is nonetheless small compared with the typical binding energy of atoms in lattices. What this means is that the recoiling atom breaks no bonds, but merely moves a short distance out of its equilibrium position. This sets up vibrational waves within the lattice that carry away the energy, eventually distributing it as part of the over-all thermal vibration of the atoms in the lattice. But these vibrational waves are themselves quantized; they are called phonons (see "Neutrons and Phonons"). With such a quantized system it is possible that in a certain fraction of the events *no* phonon is emitted. What it amounts to in this case is that the recoil momentum is taken up by the lattice as a whole. This is the Mössbauer Effect (Fig. 1-19).

The expression for the recoil energy under such conditions contains, not the mass of an individual nucleus, but the total mass of the crystal lattice with its huge number of atoms (there are 8×10^{19} atoms in a 1 mm cube of iron). Thus the recoil energy drops to a quite negligible value—much less than the natural resonance width Γ. Recoil can no longer interfere with observations of this sharp resonance line. The absence of Doppler broadening can also be explained in terms of thermal motion of lattice as a whole instead of the motion of a given nucleus. Actually, we have in the solid state not

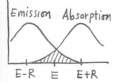

the translational, but only the vibrational motion of the source and the absorber, without the change of the average position of one of them in respect to another. Therefore, we have here no Doppler broadening unless the state of lattice is changed.

So sharp is the resonance that any influence which changes the energy of the emitting (or absorbing) nucleus by even so little as one part in 10^{12} will cause a detectable shift from resonance. Indeed, in an extreme case a shift of one part in 10^{16} has been detected.

Such minute changes can be readily measured by compensating for them by steady motion of the absorber relative to the emitter. The resulting Doppler shift changes the frequency—and, therefore, the energy—of the gamma ray sufficiently to restore resonance. It is remarkable how slight a velocity will suffice—it is of the order of $(\Gamma/E)c = 10^{-12} \times 3 \times 10^{10}$ cm/sec or a few hundred microns per second. This is why the Zn^{67} resonance, which is even sharper, is little used—it's too sharp to be practical; even small vibrations mask the slow Doppler velocity called for. Typical experimental setups are shown in Figs. 1-20 and 1-21.

As an aid in consolidating the points made so far, consider an acoustic analog of the basic Mössbauer technique just described. Imagine two identical tuning forks, one of which was put out of tune by attaching some wax to one of the prongs. Its characteristic frequency would drop because of the greater load that needs to be moved, and the forks would no longer resonate. But resonance could be re-established by putting the fork with lower pitch onto a train that moved *toward* the normal fork at a velocity such that the Doppler shift in frequency raised the pitch of the sound waves impinging in it back to the resonant point. (Using numbers in this little experiment, you find that the train needs to go at about 30 miles per hour if the piece of wax were such as to drop the frequency of a 256 cps fork by 10 cps.) This is completely analogous to what is done in Mössbauer experiments. Some effect shifts the position of an energy level in the nucleus, and one can tell just how far it is shifted by measuring the velocity he must impart to the emitter (or absorber) to restore resonance.

How heavy is a photon?

One early application that demonstrated the great sensitivity of the Mössbauer effect was to measure the pull of the earth's gravitational field on gamma rays. A gamma ray has no rest mass, but by Einstein's $E = mc^2$ it has an effective mass equal to E/c^2. This mass is acted on by the earth's gravitational field—if a pho-

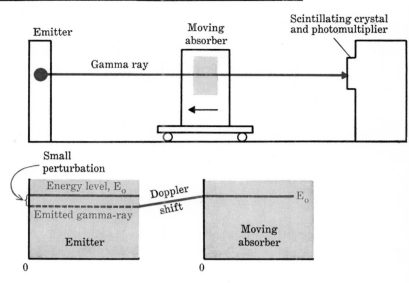

Fig. 1-20. *Essentials of a Mössbauer experiment: Owing to some perturbing effect the energy levels of the emitting nuclei are depressed. The resulting gamma rays can be restored to resonance with the unperturbed absorbing nuclei by moving the absorber towards the emitter, thanks to the same Doppler Effect that makes the pitch of an approaching train whistle sound higher. Greater absorption at resonance shows up as a decreased counting rate at the detector, right.*

Fig. 1-21. *Mössbauer apparatus developed as teaching tool by Alan J. Bearden of Cornell. Source is at end of cross arm that extends from post in left foreground. Detector is in cylindrical housing at right. Neat trick is rotating absorber disk; increasing speed of rotation increases component of velocity along emitter-detector line. (Courtesy S. Tramm)*

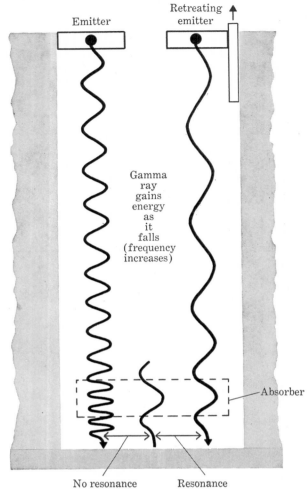

Emitter

Retreating emitter

Gamma ray gains energy as it falls (frequency increases)

Absorber

No resonance   Resonance

Fig. 1-22. How heavy is a photon? Just as heavy as Einstein's M = E/c² says it should be. Proof came in Pound-Rebka experiment that measured velocity at which emitter must retreat from absorber so that Doppler Effect just compensates the gain in energy as gamma ray "falls" in Earth's gravitational field. Stationary emitter results in no resonance, lessened absorption.

ton falls through a distance d its gravitational potential energy will decrease by an amount $mgd = Egd/c^2$. This decreased potential energy shows up as a corresponding increase in the energy (and therefore the frequency) of the gamma ray itself. Thus a gamma ray traveling from an emitting nucleus *down* to an identical absorbing nucleus, a sufficient distance *below* it, will fall out of resonance—its energy will be too *high*. But we can compensate for this by moving the absorber away from the emitter at a steady velocity such that the Doppler shift just compensates for this effect and resonance is restored (Fig. 1-22).

But the effect is small. The fractional change in energy is gd/c^2, about 10^{-16} per meter. This

difference is so minute that its existence was not expected to be observable until many years hence, when the frequencies of atomic clocks in a satellite and on earth were to be compared. Thanks to the Mössbauer effect, however, Pound and Rebka of Harvard University, using a 21-meter-high tower, were able to detect a gravitational resonance shift in good agreement with Einstein's theoretical predictions.

Putting the effect to work

By now it should not be difficult to visualize possible applications of this effect in technology. Here are a few examples:

Suppose we are using a crystal combined with a photomultiplier as a detector of gamma-quanta—measuring the electric current produced by the multiplier. If the source of gamma-quanta is recoil-less and resonant with respect to the detector, then the current taken off the multiplier will vary with the slightest motion of the source and detector relative to each other.

Thus, if the detector is placed in a fixed position and the source is installed on the surface of an object, we can readily determine whether the object is in motion. In fact, we can determine the speed of this motion, provided the relationship of current to velocity has been calibrated before the experiment.

It is thus possible to observe extremely slow displacements such as the shifting of machine components relative to one another, or of the walls of a building relative to the earth, or the relative motion of various areas of the earth. This suggests that a highly sensitive, noncontact device could be designed for observing various types of vibrations.

The Mössbauer technique can also be used for mineral assay. Assume a sample of an unknown rock has been placed between detector and source in order to determine whether shifting the rock has any effect on detector readings. If the counting rate of the detector is affected, it means that the Mössbauer resonance is present. This implies that the rock sample contains some nuclei of the same isotope that provides our source of gamma-quanta. It follows that tin, iron, gold, and many other elements (see Fig. 1-23) can be detected and quantitatively evaluated.

There are extensive possibilities associated with the so-called splitting of Mössbauer spectral lines.

Both energy levels involved in an emission of radiation—the ground and the excited—are characterized by a specific value of the complete nuclear spin I. The projection of this spin upon a given direction can assume any of several specific quantized values. If no electric or

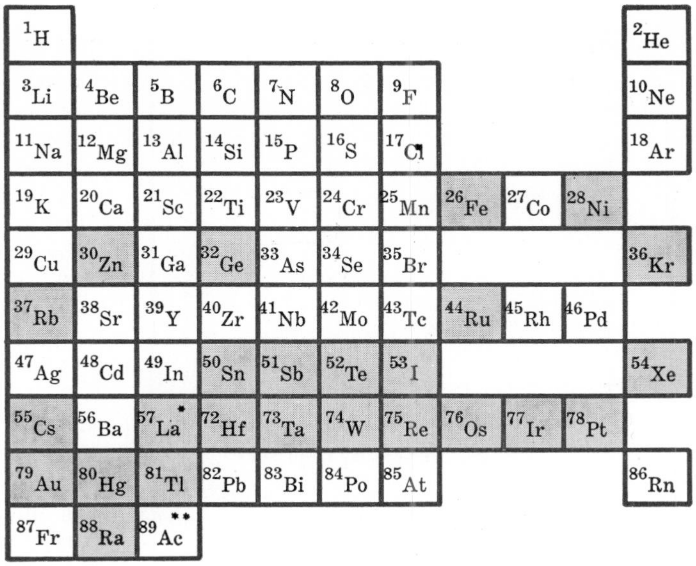

Fig. 1-23 periodic table:

^{1}H																	^{2}He
^{3}Li	^{4}Be											^{5}B	^{6}C	^{7}N	^{8}O	^{9}F	^{10}Ne
^{11}Na	^{12}Mg											^{13}Al	^{14}Si	^{15}P	^{16}S	^{17}Cl	^{18}Ar
^{19}K	^{20}Ca	^{21}Sc	^{22}Ti	^{23}V	^{24}Cr	^{25}Mn	^{26}Fe	^{27}Co	^{28}Ni								
^{29}Cu	^{30}Zn	^{31}Ga	^{32}Ge	^{33}As	^{34}Se	^{35}Br											^{36}Kr
^{37}Rb	^{38}Sr	^{39}Y	^{40}Zr	^{41}Nb	^{42}Mo	^{43}Tc	^{44}Ru	^{45}Rh	^{46}Pd								
^{47}Ag	^{48}Cd	^{49}In	^{50}Sn	^{51}Sb	^{52}Te	^{53}I											^{54}Xe
^{55}Cs	^{56}Ba	^{57}La*	^{72}Hf	^{73}Ta	^{74}W	^{75}Re	^{76}Os	^{77}Ir	^{78}Pt								
^{79}Au	^{80}Hg	^{81}Tl	^{82}Pb	^{83}Bi	^{84}Po	^{85}At											^{86}Rn
^{87}Fr	^{88}Ra	^{89}Ac**															

Fig. 1-23. Mössbauer elements, those with suitable gamma ray lines, are shaded in color. Light elements are unsatisfactory because gamma ray energies E tend to be high, increasing the recoil energy ($\sim E^2$). But elsewhere in the periodic table possibilities abound, including lanthanides and actinides.

*Lanthanides: (Rare earths) 58-71 **Actinides: 90-103
Mossbauer effect expected to be observable for all of these

magnetic field is acting upon the nucleus, its energy does not depend on the projection of the complete spin—so all the sublevels merge. This leaves only a single line in the gamma-ray spectrum, produced by the transition from one level to the other. Should the nucleus, however, be acted upon by an external magnetic field, the energy would depend upon the projection of the full nuclear spin along the direction of this field. Corresponding to each quantized value of this projection, therefore, is a sublevel of energy. The levels, along with the Mössbauer spectral lines, undergo splitting.

From the extent of such magnetic (or Zeeman) splitting in a specified external magnetic field, it is possible to determine the values of nuclear magnetic moments for both the ground and excited states. Knowing these values, we can evaluate the intramolecular magnetic fields, describe the interaction of atoms in magnetic alloys, or show how magnetic domains behave.

In cases where the nuclei possess electric quadrupole moments, similar splitting of levels takes place in inhomogeneous electric fields. (For present purposes the quadrupole moment can be regarded as a measure of the departure of the nuclear electric charge distribution from simple spherical symmetry.) Knowing the strength of these fields one can infer the molecular structure; of this more later.

Another possible application: At room temperature the probability of a nucleus being in any one of the split substates is practically equal for all substates. Over the very-low-temperature range, however, close to absolute zero, the probability is considerably greater for the lower than the upper sublevels. It follows that the ratio of the number of transitions be-tween the various sublevels will now depend strongly on temperature. Thus, a possibility exists for measuring the temperature by following up the pattern variations of the Mössbauer spectrum. It appears quite feasible, therefore, that an accurate Mössbauer thermometer could be designed in the temperature region around 10^{-3} degree Kelvin.

The properties of intramolecular electric and magnetic fields vary with temperature and pressure and the action of various mechanical agents. Observation of the corresponding changes in the patterns of Mössbauer spectra creates new possibilities for observing defects in various materials. We will be able to detect not only internal cavities but also stresses.

Applications in chemistry

To see how the Mössbauer effect can be applied in chemistry we need to ask how the electron clouds surrounding an atom, and especially those outer electrons that participate in chemical bonding, can affect the energies of the emitting and absorbing nuclei. One effect arises from the density of the electron distribution at the nucleus. Another way in which electrons can affect the nucleus, even at a distance, is through the electric field they set up; this will be discussed later.

Quantum theory says that atomic electrons are not confined to one path but are spread throughout the atom with definite probability distributions. The specifics of these distributions will not be gone into here: suffice it to say that there is a certain probability that some of the so-called s-electrons (those with zero angular momentum) will be at the center of the atom, where the nucleus is located.

37

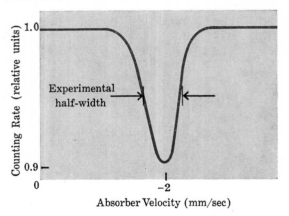

Fig. 1-24. *A Mössbauer spectrum, in this case that of tin tetrachloride (SnCl₄) as absorber relative to metallic beta tin as an emitter. Fact that absorber had to retreat from emitter for maximum absorption shows electron density at nucleus is lower for SnCl₄, hence that its bonding is more ionic in character.*

Quantum theory denotes this probability $|\psi(0)|^2$. This probability is greatest for the inner s-electrons, of course, but it is nonzero even for the outermost s-electrons. Its exact value is determined by the arrangement of electrons within the atom. In particular, as between two atoms of the same element that differ only in respect to the molecule or crystal in which they are bound, the difference in the electron density at the nucleus will reflect these differences in chemistry. While we do not always have exact theories for calculating $|\psi(0)|^2$, chemists are clever at combining such theories as we do have with trends observed as many different compounds are tried. Thus the chain is from Mössbauer experiments to electron densities at the nucleus $|\psi(0)|^2$ to semi-quantitative descriptions of chemical bonds.

If the nucleus were a point charge, changes in the electron distribution would not affect gamma-ray energies: The effect of the electron charge on the excited nucleus and the ground-state nucleus is the same, so the difference in energy levels is unchanged. Actually, however, the nuclear electric charge is also distributed in space, though over a fairly well-defined volume. Now the important point is that the radius of the nuclear charge distribution in its excited state is slightly different from its radius in the ground state. The extent to which the electron and nucleus overlap and neutralize each other is different for the two states—and, therefore, the transition energy, the gamma-ray frequency, is changed by the electron distribution, which is to say, by the chemical state of the atom.

If the emitter and the absorber in a Mössbauer experiment are both in the same chemical state, we do not need to move them to obtain

maximum absorption. But when the absorber and emitter differ in their chemical nature, there appears a difference, δ, in their transition energies, and this has to be compensated for by a relative motion with velocity $v = c\delta/E$.

The quantity, δ, is known as the chemical or isomer shift of the Mössbauer spectral line. The first observation of the chemical shift was made by Kistner and Sunyar at Brookhaven National Laboratory when they looked for Mössbauer spectra using Fe^{57} in stainless steel as emitter and Fe^{57} in Fe_2O_3 as absorber.

In the theoretical expression for the chemical shift there appears a product of two terms —one of them reflecting the percentage change in nuclear radius and the other reflecting the difference between the values of $|\psi(0)|^2$ for the emitter and for the absorber. It is quite easy to make a set of similar measurements with different substances and compare the differences in $|\psi(0)|^2$ values without knowing the values themselves. But sometimes it is even possible to determine these values when one uses theory to sort out the effects.

Some chemical experiments

Consider first an example of the first sort of chemical effect where differences in the electron concentrations at the nucleus in the absorber and the emitter result in different values for the resonance energy. In this experiment the emitter was metallic tin in the beta phase; most of the atoms were nonradioactive tin but a few (1 in 10^6) were Sn^{119} in an excited state (decay scheme is shown in the margin). Similarly the absorber contained tin, some of it Sn^{119} in its ground state, in the form of the tetrachloride, $SnCl_4$. As can be seen from Fig. 1-24 it was necessary for the absorber to move away from the emitter at a velocity of a little under 2 mm/sec to compensate for the lower energy of the absorbing system.

To what can we attribute lowered energy of the tin nucleus in $SnCl_4$? It results from the fact that the bonding of the tin atom to its chlorines is partly ionic in character (as in NaCl); thus the tendency is for the bonded tin to lose electrons, becoming something between Sn and Sn^{4+}, while the four chlorines each gain an electron, becoming more like Cl^-. This decreases the electron concentration at the nucleus, because one of the outer electrons in tin is in an s-state. (More strictly, each of the four outer electrons behaves 25% as an s-electron and 75% as a p-electron—the phenomenon known as sp^3 hybridization of chemical bonds. Still more strictly, the β tin used as emitter and reference, commonly called white tin, is not entirely covalent in its bonds.)

Studies of other tin-halide compounds show a regular correlation between the degree of ionic bonding and the Mössbauer shift, as is shown in Fig. 1-25. This permits us to extrapolate the curve to get the change in shift corresponding to the change from purely covalent to purely ionic bonding. It comes to -5.6 ± 0.5 mm/sec, and we can easily compute that this Doppler shift corresponds to an energy change of $-(4.4 \pm 0.4) \times 10^{-7}$ ev. On the other hand we have theories of atomic structure that permit us to calculate the change in $|\psi(0)|^2$ for the addition of one $5s$ electron; this is equal to $1.5 \times 10^{26}/cm^3$. Now we can also determine the relative change of radius in the emitting and absorbing states; it comes to $(1.9 \pm 0.2) \times 10^{-4}$. Knowing this ratio for Sn^{119}, we can use it to derive $|\psi(0)|^2$ values for all the tin compounds under study, given their Mössbauer spectra. The data on the chemical shifts are quite important to modern theories of chemical structure. Sometimes they can also bring information on the nature of compounds formed in intermediate stages of chemical reactions.

Quadrupole splitting of spectral lines

If the charge in the nucleus is not distributed completely symmetrically (and this is usually the case, see "Nuclear Orbital Structure," page 41), the nucleus will have what is called a quadrupole moment as pointed out earlier.

The interaction of this nonuniform nuclear charge distribution with an inhomogeneous electric field leads to small shifts in the energy of the nucleus. (The field is that produced by all the electrons in the atoms close to the nucleus and will be homogeneous or not, depending on how the nearby atoms are arranged.) The shift is different depending on the relative orientation of nucleus and field. But, as always in quantum mechanics, not all nuclear orientations are allowed. So if a quadrupole moment is present, the basic energy level is split into several closely spaced sublevels—and the number of sublevels depends on the quantum value of the spin of the nucleus.

The presence and the extent of such splitting is therefore a rapid and qualitative indication of a nonzero quadrupole moment, and also gives the spin of the nucleus. A nice thing about Mössbauer experiments is that even if the electric charge distribution in the absorbing nuclei (which are in the ground state) is spherically symmetrical and they have no quadrupole moment, the emitting nuclei (which are in the excited state) are likely to have one. This makes possible observations of quadrupole splitting in Sn, Fe, Te, W, and other elements. (Of course, if both emitter and absorber have quadrupole moments the experimental curves of the Mössbauer spectra get complex as each energy of gamma rays from the emitter is brought into resonance

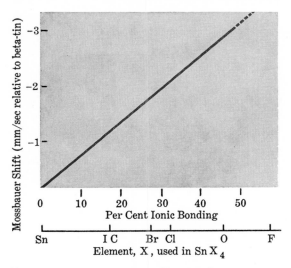

Fig. 1-25. Measuring spectra like that in Fig. 1-24 for several tin compounds of the form SnX_4 permits correlation of Mössbauer shift with degree of ionic bonding (from other experiments) and extrapolation to fully ionic bonding.

with each of the levels of the absorber, but I won't trouble you with those complexities, which can, I assure you, be handled.)

Inorganic polymers; SnF₄ for one

As one example consider the compounds of the type SnX_4, where X is any element with the proper valence to make this compound. The spectra of several such compounds are shown in Fig. 1-26. Note that, in addition to having the greatest shift because it has the greatest electronegativity, the compound SnF_4 is the only one showing quadrupole splitting of the lines. This information is of definite importance to chemists. It indicates that not all the Sn-F bonds in SnF_4 are equivalent to one another. This new evidence confirms the assumption, generally accepted by inorganic chemists, that SnF_4 has a form like a polymer chain, with some of the fluorine atoms joined on at right angles to the chain while others form bridge bonds joining the tin atoms. SnF_4, that is, looks like the representation in Fig. 1-27.

It is apparent that this compound, like many other inorganic compounds, occurs in a polymer-like form. But, in addition to such either/or answers (the electric charge distribution in the molecule is symmetrical or it isn't) gamma-resonance spectroscopy can also give us quantitative information. Consider, for example, the organic halides of tin, compounds of the type $(C_6H_5)_3SnX$—where X can be F, Cl, Br, or I.

Our results on organic halides permit us to characterize the (largely ionic) bond between the tin and the halide atom. They also permitted us (on the basis of chemical considera-

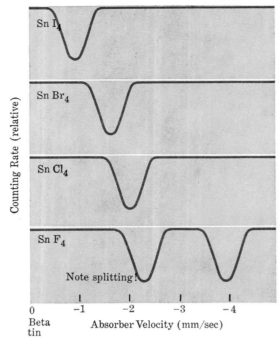

Fig. 1-26. *Mössbauer spectra can contain more than one line, if energy levels are split by interaction that depends on nuclear orientation. In this case SnF_4 spectrum is doublet because Sn^{119} electric moment interacts with inhomogeneous field of surrounding F atoms.*

tions) to get a refined value for the quadrupole moment of the excited state of Sn^{119}.

Some other new horizons

But this is only the beginning of what we can do with this technique in chemistry. We can, for example, learn about the structure of molecules when they are present as a minority

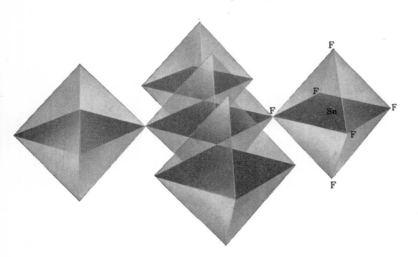

Fig. 1-27. *Splitting of lines in Mössbauer spectrum of SnF_4 implies that its structure must be less symmetrical than sphere or cube. Tin atoms are at centers of asymmetric octahedra defined by four F atoms that it shares, two it does not.*

ingredient in a solid solution with some host matrix. We have also obtained evidence on a question of great interest to organic chemists and biochemists: the effects of relatively distant atoms on a bond in an organic molecule. For example, we have shown that it's all the same to a tin atom whether it's part of triethyl tin acetate $(C_2H_5)_3SnOCO$—CH_3 or of a polymer having triethyl tin methyl methacrylate as a base:

$$(C_2H_5)_3 Sn\ OCO - C \overset{\displaystyle CH_3}{\underset{\displaystyle CH_2}{}}$$

On the other hand, there are detectable differences between this polymer and the seemingly similar:

$$(C_6H_5)_3 Sn\ OCO - C \overset{\displaystyle CH_3}{\underset{\displaystyle CH_2}{}}$$

In both of these systems, the tin atoms have the same four neighbors: three C's and one O. But in the first case, one of the carbon atoms is part of the aliphatic radical C_2H_5 and in the second case it is part of the aromatic ring radical C_6H_5—and these distant carbon and hydrogen atoms change the nature of the carbon-tin bond.

Similarly, study of Mössbauer spectra of tin-organic oxides of the form R_2SnO (where R stands for an organic radical) shows that these so-called polymer oxides do not have a simple structure like this:

$$-Sn-O-Sn-O-Sn-O-Sn-O-$$

but have this more complicated structure in which, however, the atoms are the same:

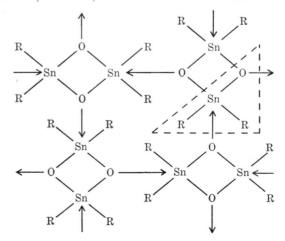

Mössbauer spectra may also permit the study of some of the chemical aftereffects—disrupted chemical bonds, free radicals—of the particle or gamma-ray emission that directly precedes the emission of the low-energy, resonant gamma ray in most Mössbauer nuclei. (Incidentally, this effect would make the application of Mössbauer techniques much more difficult were it not for the fact that most of the time the atom settles down to its normal state before the second, resonant gamma ray is emitted.) Also one can study radiation chemistry, many questions of chemical kinetics, the physical chemistry of polymers, and many other problems. I hope what little I've been able to say is sufficient to give some idea of the vast possibilities implied in the use of the Mössbauer effect—a discovery of nuclear physics unique in its inspired simplicity.

Further reading

V. I. Goldanskii has just published a slim paperback that extends the ideas given in his article. It is entitled «Эффект Мёссбауэра и его применения в химии» (Publishing House of the Academy of Sciences of the USSR, Moscow, 1963, 34 kopeks, or about 35¢). An English translation is available from Consultants Bureau.

Some of the actualities surrounding the discovery of the Mössbauer effect were related by the discoverer in a speech accepting the Research Corporation Award for 1961. Mössbauer reviewed present art in *Annual Review of Nuclear Science*, **12** (Annual Reviews, Palo Alto, Calif., 1962, $8.50).

Another good way to review the field is through a book *The Mössbauer Effect* (W. A. Benjamin, New York, 1962, $7.75 cloth, $4.95 paper). It consists of reprints of the principal papers in the field along with an admirable review by the editor, H. Frauenfelder.

The proceedings of the 1963 symposium on the Mössbauer effect and its applications, held at Cornell University, appeared in the January, 1964 issue of *Reviews of Modern Physics*.

A good bibliography of the subject is contained in a "resource letter" for physics teachers by G. Wertheim, *Am. J. Phys.* **31**, 1 (1963).

NUCLEAR ORBITAL STRUCTURE

by Bernard L. Cohen *

IN BRIEF: *The translation from quantum mechanics to the pith-balls and wire so familiar to students of elementary atomics has its analogue in the shell theory of nuclear structure. And it's just as appropriate one place as the other.*

Just set the neutrons and protons spinning in quantum-allowed orbits around their center of mass, endow them with four quantum numbers to define their speed, orientation, and spin. Then postulate a short-range mutually attractive meson field (in which π-mesons act like droplets of glue), and bring the Pauli exclusion principle into play (so that no two particles can be in identical states).

Voilà, you have a model with which you can understand nuclear behavior: You can calculate energy levels, and you can show how collisions among nucleons complicate nuclear structure, leading to distorted shapes and to a multiplicity of vibration modes. And you can see how the plot—of the whereabouts and interactions of the nucleons—thickens.—R.G.N.

■ Present puzzles in particle physics notwithstanding, we can understand nuclear structure fully as well as we understand atomic structure: It turns out that, in many ways, the two systems are quite similar. In fact, they are similar enough to permit an explanation of the structure of the nucleus on the level of balls moving in orbits—a nuclear counterpart to the atomic model so dear to the hearts of high school chemistry teachers.

To make such a model, we must, of course, translate from the quantum mechanical description of nuclear systems. But that translation is every bit as valid as the one so commonly used for explaining the electronic structure of atoms. Besides, while the picture we present cannot be taken completely literally, it is certainly very much closer to the truth than the usual picture of the nucleus as a glob of neutrons and protons in a random motion, like the ramblings of unintroduced guests in the early stages of a cocktail party (speeded up some 10^9 or 10^{10} times).

In the more orderly shell model, shown in Fig. 1-28, the nucleons (a collective term for neutrons and protons) orbit about the center of the nucleus.

Shell models and their rules

Just as with electrons in an atom, the nucleons can assume only certain orbits. And here again, each allowed orbit is characterized by four quantum numbers—the three dimen-

* Bernard L. Cohen is Professor of Physics at the University of Pittsburgh, Pittsburgh, Pennsylvania.

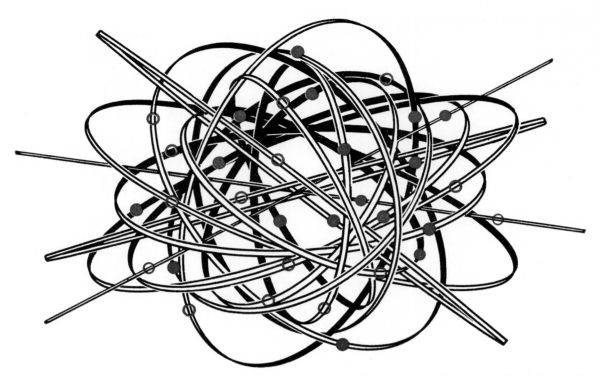

Fig. 1-28. In nuclear shell theory, as in electron shell theory, terms like orbits, angular momentum, etc., are common; everybody in the nuclear shell game uses them. Here are those notions incorporated in a model in which one neutron and/or one proton can occupy each orbit around the common center of mass. Although these orbits resemble those of electrons in atoms (reduced in size about 10^4 times), there are many differences in detail. Note, for example, that the sizes of these nuclear orbits are similar, whereas the electron orbits in an atom vary greatly.

The neutrons and protons in this model move with velocities between $\frac{1}{10}$ and $\frac{1}{3}$ the speed of light, and are held in their orbits by the combined forces of all the other neutrons and protons in the nucleus. In most nuclei, some of these nucleons may change orbits by collisions, but only if certain very stringent conditions are satisfied.

sions lead to three quantum numbers; the fourth number is just a characteristic of spin-½ particles, particles such as electrons, protons, and neutrons.

These quantum numbers, designated N, l, j, and m, give, respectively, the total energy, the orbital angular momentum, the total angular momentum (including spin), and the orientation of the orbit with respect to any arbitrary direction (say the top of this page). The rules for finding the values they can assume are listed, with their meanings to the model in Fig. 1-28, in Table I. (Incidentally, the quantum number m does not completely specify the orientation of the orbit; but, since it gives all the information possible under the laws of quantum mechanics, one may consider that N, l, j, m do completely specify an orbit. The situation for electrons in atoms is analogous.)

Using all the allowed values of Table I, Table II lists all the allowed orbits for $N = 1$, 2, and 3. The total number of orbits for each j is also shown in Table II. If you add the number of orbits for each allowed j, you get the total number of orbits for each shell, so that (as shown on the last row of Table II) the shells

$N = 1$, 2, and 3 can have a total of 2, 6, and 12 orbits respectively.

The origin of the word "shell," referring to a group of orbits with the same energy, offers an interesting sidelight to this business: Of the four quantum numbers which characterize the orbits of electrons around the nucleus of an atom, the quantum number N largely determines the energy of an electron. In addition, the average radius of the orbit is also determined by N. Thus, the electron orbits for a given N not only have the same energy, but the same size, so they lie in something resembling a spherical *shell*. Electron orbits with the next higher value of N have a considerably larger radius; they lie in a *shell* of a larger radius.

In nuclei, it turns out that the radius depends only slightly on N, so that all orbits have about the same average radius. Only the *energies* of the nucleons in these orbits occur in groups (as shown in the first sketch of Table I). Nevertheless, the "shell" has carried over from the atomic case.

The energies and exclusiveness of orbits

I said that the energy of a particle in one of the allowed orbits depends primarily on the

Table I. THE FOUR QUANTUM NUMBERS

	Quantum number	Quantum number	Value of quantum number Allowable	Value of quantum number Typically
Energy level ($N=4$, $N=3$, $N=2$, $N=1$)	N	approx. total energy of nucleon in orbit	any positive integer,	$+1, 2, 3\ldots$
$l=N-1$ $l=N-3$ $l=N-N=0$	l	orbital angular momentum (orbit ellipsicity)	$N -$ (any positive odd integer N)	when $N = 5$, $l = 4, 2,$ or 0
$j=l+\frac{1}{2}$ $j=l-\frac{1}{2}$	j	total angular momentum (l + spin)	$l \pm \frac{1}{2}$	when $l = 2$, $l = \frac{5}{2}$ or $\frac{3}{2}$
$m=5/2$, $m=3/2$, $m=1/2$, $m=-1/2$, $m=-3/2$, $m=-5/2$	m	spatial orientation of orbit with respect to any arbitrary direction	all half-integers from $+j$ to $-j$	when $j = \frac{5}{2}$, $m = \frac{5}{2}, \frac{3}{2}, \frac{1}{2}, -\frac{1}{2}, -\frac{3}{2},$ or $-\frac{5}{2}$

Table II. ALLOWED ORBITS IN N= 1, 2, AND 3 SHELLS

Quantum number	Allowable values					
N =	1	2		3		
l = (N-1...) =	0	1		2		0
j = (l±1/2) =	1/2	3/2	1/2	5/2	3/2	1/2
m = (+j) ... (−j) =	+1/2, −1/2	+3/2, +1/2, −1/2, −3/2	+1/2, −1/2	+5/2, +3/2, +1/2, −1/2, −3/2, −5/2	+3/2, +1/2, −1/2, −3/2	+1/2, −1/2
Total number of orbits with this j	2	4	2	6	4	2
Total number of orbits with this N	2	6		12		

Table III. NUMBER OF ORBITS WITH VARIOUS VALUES OF N, l, j,

N	1	2	3		4		5				6				7				
l	0	1	2	0	3	1	4	2	0	5	3	1	6	4	2	0	7		
j	$\frac{1}{2}$	$\frac{3}{2}$ $\frac{1}{2}$	$\frac{5}{2}$ $\frac{3}{2}$ $\frac{1}{2}$		$\frac{7}{2}$ $\frac{5}{2}$	$\frac{3}{2}$ $\frac{1}{2}$	$\frac{9}{2}$ $\frac{7}{2}$	$\frac{5}{2}$ $\frac{3}{2}$	$\frac{1}{2}$	$\frac{11}{2}$ $\frac{9}{2}$	$\frac{7}{2}$ $\frac{5}{2}$	$\frac{3}{2}$ $\frac{1}{2}$	$\frac{13}{2}$ $\frac{11}{2}$	$\frac{9}{2}$ $\frac{7}{2}$	$\frac{5}{2}$ $\frac{3}{2}$	$\frac{1}{2}$	$\frac{15}{2}$ $\frac{13}{2}$		
Number of orbits with j	2	4 2	6 4 2		8 6	4 2	10 8	6 4	2	12 10	8 6	4 2	14 12	10 8	6 4	2	16 14		
Number of orbits in shell	2	6	12	8	22		32				44				58				
Accumulative number	2	8	20	28	50		82				126				184				
Shell	First	Second	Third	Fourth	Fifth		Sixth				Seventh				Eighth				

Vertical colored lines show the shell groupings.

Note that some orbits (e.g. $N=5$, $j=9/2$) are grouped in shells of next lower N.

quantum number N, and these energies are distributed in groups as shown in Tables I, II, and III. The two $N = 1$ orbits have the lowest energy, the six $N = 2$ orbits have the next lowest energy, etc. Actually, the energy does depend somewhat on l, j, and m, so that, for example, the six orbits with $N = 2$ do not have exactly the same energy, but all orbits with $N = 2$ are much closer to each other in energy than they are to orbits with $N = 1$ or $N = 3$. That is, there are large energy gaps between different shells.

I have grouped some orbits from $N = 1$ to $N = 7$ into shells of like energy in Table III. (The shells are separated by the wide vertical lines.) You can see that for values of $N > 3$, the orbit energies depend heavily on j. In some cases an orbit is grouped not in the shell with its own value of N, but in the shell with the next lower N. Still, the orbit energies occur in well separated shells.

There is still another important ingredient to be introduced into the picture, namely the celebrated Pauli Exclusion Principle which plays an important role in the structure of atoms. The principle is that there can be no more than one proton, and no more than one neutron in each allowed orbit. Since all particles in nature tend to get to their lowest possible energy (for example, water collects in valleys rather than on hill tops), the nucleons in a normal nucleus go into the lowest-energy orbits available.

The lowest-energy orbits are those with $N = 1$, but there are only two of these available for each kind of particle. Thus (we see that in the margin) all four nucleons of He⁴ can be in $N = 1$ orbits. But in Li⁵, which has two neutrons and three protons, one proton must be in an $N = 2$ orbit. In O¹⁶, which has eight neutrons and eight protons, all nucleons are in $N = 1$ and $N = 2$ orbits, but in O¹⁷ one neutron must be in an $N = 3$ orbit. Nuclei, like He⁴ and O¹⁶, which have some shells completely filled and all other shells completely empty, are known as "closed shell" nuclei; nuclei, like Li⁵ and O¹⁷, which have only one nucleon outside a closed shell are known as "single particle" nuclei. Both these types of nuclei have especially simple properties; they play roles in nuclear structure analogous to those of the noble gas (closed-shell) and alkali metal (single-particle) atoms in atomic structure. However, it is important to remember that the orbits of nucleons are more nearly the same size than the orbits of electrons. For instance, in Fig. 1-28, the largest orbits have mean diameters only about $1\frac{1}{3}$ the size of the smallest ones.

Since all nucleons in a nucleus have orbits

of about the same size, you might wonder whether they collide. Collisions between nucleons can occur, provided that (1) angular momentum is conserved, (2) the nucleons go into allowed orbits after the collision, and (3) energy is *approximately* conserved. (The reason why energy is only "approximately" conserved is that we are considering only the orbit energies. There is a small correction to this energy which arises from the collisions themselves.)

These conditions forbid collisions between two nucleons in a filled shell, since the only allowed orbits which are not already occupied are in a higher energy shell, and thus cannot be reached consistent with condition 3. Similar arguments preclude collisions between a nucleon in a filled shell and one in the lowest unfilled shell. The only possible collision in this case is where two neutrons or two protons exchange orbits, but then nothing is changed and so this is not recognized as a collision between nucleons.

When nucleons collide

The simplest collisions of importance are between two nucleons in an otherwise empty shell. An especially important example of this is when two nucleons traveling in opposite directions on the same orbit collide and end up going in opposite directions in another (allowed) orbit. The total angular momentum is zero both before and after the collision, since the individual angular momenta of the two nucleons have equal magnitudes but opposite signs in both cases; thus condition (1) is fulfilled. Actually, this is a probabilistic situation (the confronting nucleons need not necessarily collide each time around the circuit shown in the margin sketch), but that is one of the limitations this kind of model has for describing a statistical situation.

If the before and after orbits are in the same major shell, their energies are close enough so that condition (3) is satisfied. Collisions of this type occur frequently, and are very important in the normal (i.e., ground) states of many nuclei. We can both calculate and measure the fraction of the time two such nucleons spend in each orbit.

For example, the two neutrons outside of the 28-neutron closed shell of Ni⁵⁸ spend 62% of the time in the $j = \frac{3}{2}$ orbit, 30% in the $j = \frac{5}{2}$ orbit, and 4% each in the $j = \frac{1}{2}$ and $j = \frac{9}{2}$ orbits (and for each j their time is shared equally among all the m orbits). In all cases, the two outer Ni neutrons are in the same orbit but moving in opposite directions so the total angular momentum is always zero. This type of collision is also important for nuclei

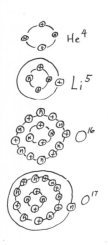

He⁴

Li⁵

O¹⁶

O¹⁷

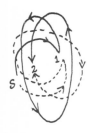

S — start
1 — 1ˢᵀ collision
2 — 2ᴺᴰ collision

with many more than two neutrons in the un-filled shell. At any instant, each participating neutron must have a partner moving in the same orbit but in the opposite direction.

However, when many nucleons are involved it is simplest to determine the time-average number of neutrons in each orbit. For example, in the ground state of tin-120 (with 20 neutrons outside its 50-neutron closed shell), on an average there are 7.2 neutrons with $j = \frac{7}{2}$, 5.2 with $j = \frac{5}{2}$ and 4.2, 2.2, and 1.2 neutrons with $j = \frac{11}{2}$, $\frac{3}{2}$ and $\frac{1}{2}$, respectively; these have been calculated and experimentally verified.

While collisions between nucleons moving in the same orbit but in opposite directions have been the most widely studied, any other collisions consistent with the three rules given can occur, and condition (3) is sufficiently satisfied if all orbits involved are in the same shell. Other examples are illustrated in Fig. 1-29. Here again, the fraction of the time spent in each of these situations can be calculated and, to some extent, measured experimentally.

In nuclei in which many nucleons are changing orbits by collisions, the motion is generally very complicated. However, in a few special cases, the orbit-changing occurs in such a systematic way that some very simple types of nuclear vibrations (i.e., of cyclical changes of nuclear *shape*) have been identified. Those shown in Fig. 1-30 are easily excited experimentally. But one of the greatest recent triumphs in nuclear-structure theory has been the calculation of the details of the orbit-changing, which give these oscillations the energies needed to excite them, etc.

Simple or complex, all these phenomena of orbit-changing through collisions without changing the energy are known as "configuration mixing." Configuration mixing occurs between electrons in atoms too, but there it is not so widespread.

The limits of the analogy

By now, you are probably very much impressed by the strong similarities between atomic and nuclear structures. But all analogies end somewhere, and it might be useful to pause for a more detailed comparison of the two. In size, atoms are larger (some 10^{-8} vs. 10^{-12} cm for nuclei). The binding energies of nuclei are very much larger: 10^7 electron volts vs. 10 ev for (the least-bound particles of) nuclei and atoms, respectively.

Some of the quantum numbers for the two systems are different, and even where they are the same, there are differences in the allowed values. Therefore, the number of orbits in the various shells are different. As mentioned earlier, the orbit radii differ radically for dif-

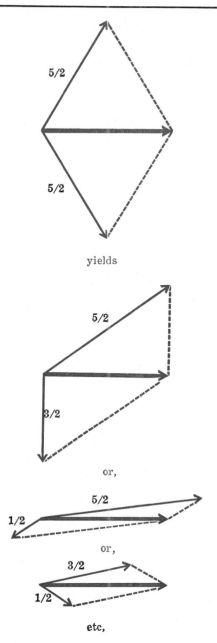

Fig. 1-29. *Various situations can arise from nucleon collisions without energy change. For example, we might have two colliding nucleons, each with angular momentum $j = \frac{5}{2}$ (light vector arrows at top), whose total angular momentum (heavy vector) is 2. The collision can result in any of the succeeding situations, provided that the total angular momentum vector remains unchanged, and that there are available orbits (of about the same energy) with $j = \frac{1}{2}$, $j = \frac{3}{2}$, and $j = \frac{5}{2}$.*

ferent values of N in atoms, but only slightly in nuclei. Also, the energies of orbits in different shells differ much more in atoms than in nuclei—by a factor of 10^4 in a heavy atom, but only by a factor of 5 or 10 in the heaviest nuclei.

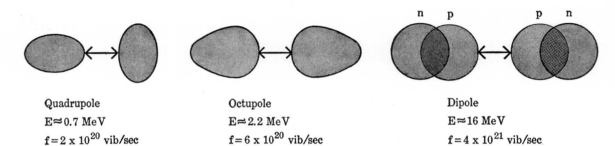

Quadrupole	Octupole	Dipole
$E \approx 0.7$ MeV	$E \approx 2.2$ MeV	$E \approx 16$ MeV
$f = 2 \times 10^{20}$ vib/sec	$f = 6 \times 10^{20}$ vib/sec	$f = 4 \times 10^{21}$ vib/sec

Fig. 1-30. In these common vibrations of the nuclear shape, each pair of shapes connected by $\longleftrightarrow$ shows the extremes of a vibration mode. The nucleus assumes all shapes between the two extreme shapes shown. Energies listed are the energies involved in the vibrations; dividing these energies by Planck's constant gives the frequencies shown, the number of vibrations per second for each vibration mode.

Perhaps the most spectacular difference is in the force that holds the particles in orbit. In the atom, this is the well-known electrostatic attraction between the negatively charged electrons and the positively charged nucleus. However, it is well known that the nucleus is held together by the nuclear force, the meson force as it is sometimes called. This is a very strong force acting between any two nucleons when they are very close together—it must be strong, to overcome the mutual repulsion of positive protons.

At large distances, the meson force is proportional to $(e^{-r/r_0})/(r/r_0)$ where r is the distance between nucleons. By large distances, I mean distance of the order of r_0, which is the Compton wavelength of the meson (the elementary binding particle).

Whereas orbital electrons surround a large nucleus, nucleons are held in orbit only by the combined attractions of all the other nucleons in the nucleus. This fact has a very interesting consequence—it causes may nuclei to be distorted into an ellipsoidal shape.

How distorted nuclei get that way

For a closed shell nucleus, orbits of all m values must be filled, so that all orbit orientations are equally represented; thus, a closed-shell nucleus is spherical. However, let us consider what happens as we add nucleons to the system. They must go into orbits in the next-higher shell, and since that shell is empty, there is a wide variety of orbits to choose from.

Suppose the first nucleon added beyond a closed shell goes into an $m = 5/2$ orbit. Since this orbit lies near the horizontal plane, it is most likely that the next nucleon added will also go into a horizontal orbit rather than into an orbit near the vertical planes, because of the attraction of the first nucleon. Since there are now two nucleons in horizontal orbits, it is even more likely that a third added nucleon go into a horizontal orbit: Now two nucleons attract it to such an orbit. Things continue thus as more nucleons are added.

Now we must reconsider the nucleons in the closed-shell orbits. I said, they are kept in these orbits by the combined attraction of all the other nucleons in the nucleus, but by now a majority of these other nucleons have orbits which lie near the horizontal plane. Thus, even the orbits of the nucleons in the closed shells are distorted so as to lie closer to the horizontal plane, and the whole nucleus assumes the shape of an ellipsoid of revolution.

As more nucleons are added, all the orbits which lie near the horizontal plane become filled, and additional nucleons must either go into orbits which lie near the vertical planes (e.g., $m = 1/2$ in Table I) or go into horizontal orbits in the next shell. But the latter course requires more energy. So the former is chosen; as more nucleons are added, they continue to go into vertical orbits. The nucleus becomes less and less distorted; by the time the shell is filled, all values of m are equally represented and the nucleus is again spherical.

The three principal regions of the periodic table where nuclei are distorted are near atomic weights 25 (magnesium & aluminum), 170 (the heavy rare earths and tantalum, and tungsten), and 240 (uranium and plutonium). In some of the most distorted nuclei, the longest axis of the ellipsoidal shape is some 20% longer than the shortest axis.

How the model deals with radioactivity

Our model can be useful in understanding nuclear decay, if we remember that, in *all* physical systems, any exothermal transformation (one in which potential or mass-energy is changed into kinetic energy) will take place—provided there is a mechanism available. A ball on a hill or an electron in an electric field will accelerate, but a proton does not change into a positive electron (positron) because there is no mechanism in nature to cause such a transformation. Now in those nuclear cases where there *is* a mechanism, the rate of nuclear transformation depends on four things: the characteristic rate of the mechanism, R_0; the

$r_0 = \dfrac{\hbar}{M_\mu c} \approx 1.4 \times 10^{-13}$ cm = (large distance!)

amount of kinetic energy released, E; the amount by which the orbit(s) change, M; and the ease with which any hindering potential barriers can be penetrated, P. The last factor, the quantum-mechanical tunneling of nucleons through potential barriers, is too large a topic to be treated here, but it is analogous to the tunneling of electrons in tunnel diodes and such.

The factor M depends on the structure of the nucleus; it is a measure of how many nucleons must change orbits in the transformation, how different the initial and final orbits are. It is clear that a transformation in which many nucleons must change orbits takes more time than one in which only one nucleon must change, so that in most of the commonly observed transformations, the initial and final nuclei differ only in the orbit of one nucleon. This important contribution to the M is readily calculated once the populations of nucleons in the various orbits are known. Another important consideration is how much the orbit must change: If the orbit changes from a very circular to a very ellip-

tical one, the transformation is much slower than if only a slight change of ellipticity is required. Thus, the transformation slows down as the change in l increases.

Let us consider some exothermal transformations in nuclei.

In the simplest case, we have a nucleon in a high-energy orbit while a lower-energy orbit is unfilled. In this case, the principal energy-dissipating process available is the emission of electromagnetic radiation. It is just as with atoms whose electrons drop from a higher- to a lower-energy orbit with the emission of light, but in the nuclear case the change in energy is much larger. Since $E = h\nu$, the "light" emitted consists of gamma rays.

The characteristic rate, R_0 is such that the time required for γ-decay can be as short as 10^{-14} sec (and is almost always less than 10^{-8} sec). But if the orbit must change from a very circular to a very elliptical one, and if the kinetic-energy release is rather small, the γ-ray emission may take seconds, days, or even years.

Another transformation that can lower the

Fig. 1-31. The answer end of the University of Pittsburgh's cyclotron sorts out nuclear particles of various energies by refraction; with it, the author experimentally confirmed calculations of nucleon populations in various energy-states in several nuclei, and found vibration modes such as the octopole mode in Fig. 1-30. (Courtesy University of Pittsburgh)

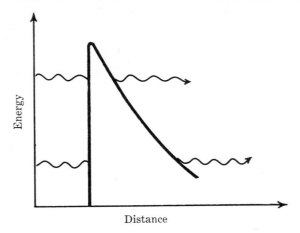

Fig. 1-32. Like electrons tunneling through thin films, the decay particles in α-decay must tunnel through potential barriers to escape their nuclei. Observed times range from less than 10^{-22} sec to more than 10^{15} years, depending on the form and height of the barrier, and on the energy available.

energy in some nuclei is for a proton to change to a neutron, or vice versa. For example, if a nucleus has 9 neutrons and 7 protons (i.e., N^{16}), Table II indicates that the ninth neutron must be in an $N = 3$ orbit. But the table also shows that if the neutron were changed to a proton, it could be in a lower-energy $N = 2$ orbit. That is, we would have an exothermic reaction if the neutron in the $N = 3$ orbit changed into a proton, releasing a lot of potential energy as kinetic energy.

It so happens that there *is* a mechanism in nature whereby a neutron can change into a proton (or vice versa); it is the beta-decay process. (Although the details of this process are very interesting, they have nothing to do with nuclear structure and so will not be treated here; they are, however, a suitable matter for supplementary reading.) The important point is that a neutron *is* changed into a proton, and that an electron and a neutrino are instantaneously formed in the process. This β-decay always occurs if there are too many neutrons and not enough protons in a nucleus. If the situation is reversed (too many protons and not enough neutrons) the β-decay process allows a proton to change into a neutron with the emission of a positron (a positive electron) and a neutrino. The characteristic rate, R_0, for the β-decay process is rather slow: In the most favorable cases it requires a fraction of a second, but if the change of orbit shape is great, it may take billions of years.

Quite often, the orbit shape is less drastically changed if the transition is not to the *lowest* unfilled orbit of the final nucleus, so that the β-decay transition is to some other orbit. The

nucleon will then drop down to the lowest unfilled orbit by gamma-ray emission. Thus, γ-ray emission frequently accompanies β-ray decay. Since γ-ray emission is such a rapid process, it often appears to occur simultaneously with the beta decay, but the time delay between the two has been measured (and shown to agree with calculations of γ-ray decay times) for a great number of cases.

In still another radioactive transformation, a nucleus breaks up into two separate nuclei. The most familiar example of this is alpha decay, where a nucleus breaks up into a He^4 nucleus and a nucleus with two fewer neutrons and two fewer protons than the original one. This is especially favorable energetically because the He^4 nucleus is very tightly bound (i.e., all its four nucleons are in low-energy $N = 1$ orbits). Another example of nuclear breakup is fission, where the decay yields two nuclei of approximately equal mass.

The mechanism for reactions of this type is the elementary one of two energetic fragments moving apart, so the characteristic time is just the size of the nucleus divided by the velocity of the fragments. ($1/R_0$ is typically about 10^{-22} sec.) However, the controlling element in these cases is the time required for the fission fragments to tunnel through a potential barrier (see Fig. 1-32). This leads to fission times (for known cases) varying from 10^{-20} sec to 10^{+15}

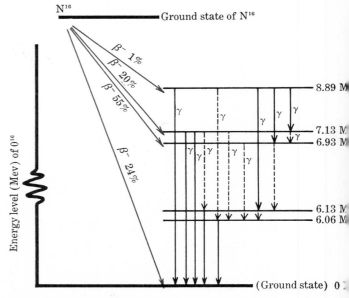

Fig. 1-33. Nuclei of N^{16} in the ground (lowest energy) state bec ground-state O^{16} by a combination of β- and γ-decays. First, the nucleus emits an electron (β−), becoming O^{16} in the 8.89 Mev s 1% of the time, 7.13 Mev O^{16} 20% of the time, etc. (That takes a 7.4 sec.) Then the excited O^{16} nuclei emit energy in the form of γ until they reach O^{16} ground state (unobserved, but allowed transit are dashed).

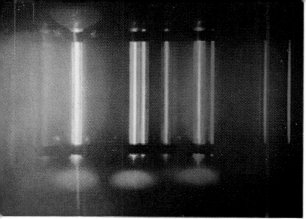

Color Fig. 4. Colors that identify helium are produced in a discharge tube as atoms excited by electrical energy emit radiation with characteristic wavelengths. When the bright yellow helium emission was distinguished from the yellow incandescence of sodium vapor, helium was discovered in the sun twenty-six years sooner than on earth. (Courtesy National Bureau of Standards)

Color Fig. 5. The heart of an emission spectroscope is the arc that excites the elements in a sample to emit the characteristic spectra by which they can be identified. The highly stable arc shown here has a temperature of 8000° C. It burns in a chamber between a graphite anode and a water-cooled tungsten cathode, and is stabilized by a gas stream to ensure that the spectral intensities will be highly reproducible. The setup shown is for the direct spectroscopic analysis of materials in solution. To analyze such a specimen, a capillary atomizer introduces the solution into the arc at a steady rate. The energy of the arc instantly vaporizes the sample and makes it incandescent at specific wavelengths. (Courtesy National Bureau of Standards)

Color Fig. 7 (below). In a determination of alkali metals by flame photometry, an air-hydrogen flame at a temperature of 2500° C. is almost invisible (left) before the addition to it of a small vaporized sample of sodium, calcium, and strontium in solution, after which the flame changes color (right). Like the other branches of spectrochemical analysis, flame photometry exploits the emission of characteristic electromagnetic radiation. The wavelengths, isolated with a monochromator, determine the identity of the unknown, while the intensities, measured photoelectrically, determine its concentration. For details of Color Figs. 4, 5, 6, and 7, see "Tools for Analytical Chemistry," in Chapter 2. (Courtesy National Bureau of Standards)

Color Fig. 6 (above). Wet chemical methods can isolate chemically similar metals in the same or adjoining groups of the Periodic Table. Here, anion-exchange columns separate soluble metal complexes formed by eluting samples of a high-temperature alloy with specific concentrations of hydrochloric acid. The orange-yellow color in the columns indicates the retention of iron, the turquoise that of cobalt. The light blue solution in the beakers indicates nickel, the dark blue solution nickel and chromium. (Courtesy National Bureau of Standards)

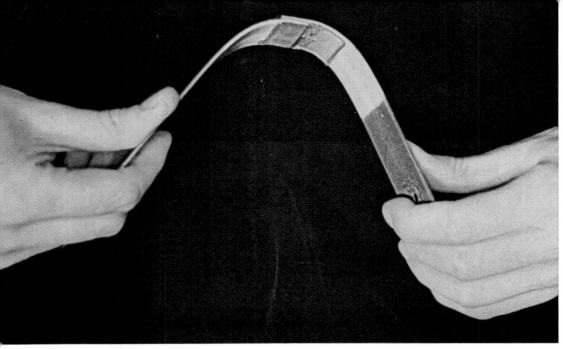

Color Fig. 8. *Polyethylene is a strong adhesive if it's treated right. This is a polyethylene-epoxy lap joint made by melting the polyethylene between two epoxy-coated aluminum strips (epoxy can be seen around the joint; polyethylene is not visible). Strips of hard aluminum (2024-T3, 1/16 in. thick) can be bent almost full circle before the joint will break. Hands show the direction of the applied load. See "Adhesives," in Chapter 2. (Courtesy Bob and Heka Davis)*

Color Fig. 9. *To vaporize and ionize solid samples for mass spectroscopy, they are used as electrodes for high-energy radio-frequency sparks. The power to start and maintain the spark reaches a peak voltage of about 100 kv at a frequency of 1 megacycle. The rf is pulsed, both to allow the electrodes to lose heat between pulses and to reduce the duty cycle of the spark. Sample electrodes are held in small vises that can be adjusted to maintain the spark while keeping the electrodes aligned behind the object slit through which the resulting beam of ions passes. Ions are sent through a combination of electric and magnetic fields so arranged that a spectrum of different ion masses is produced. See "Tools for Analytical Chemistry," in Chapter 2. (Courtesy Consolidated Electrodynamics)*

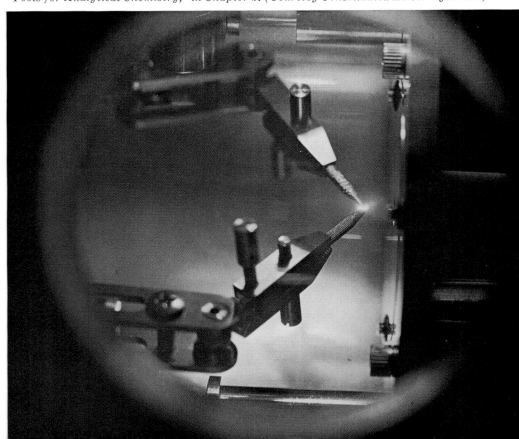

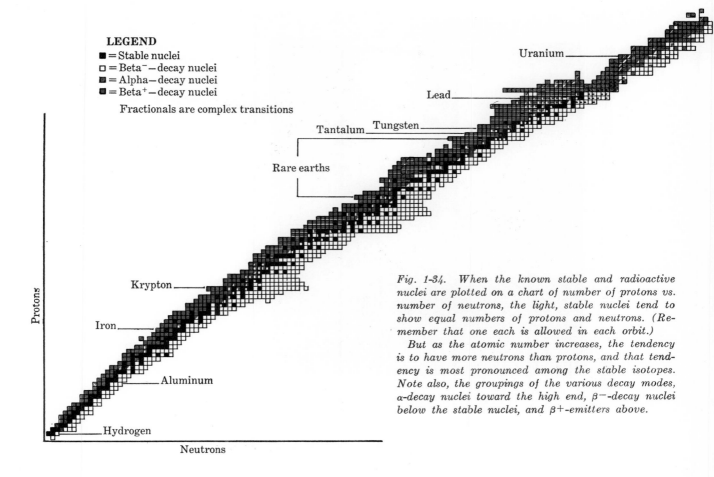

Uranium

Lead

Tantalum   Tungsten

Rare earths

Krypton

Protons

Iron

Aluminum

Hydrogen

Neutrons

Fig. 1-34. When the known stable and radioactive nuclei are plotted on a chart of number of protons vs. number of neutrons, the light, stable nuclei tend to show equal numbers of protons and neutrons. (Remember that one each is allowed in each orbit.)

But as the atomic number increases, the tendency is to have more neutrons than protons, and that tendency is most pronounced among the stable isotopes. Note also, the groupings of the various decay modes, α-decay nuclei toward the high end, β⁻-decay nuclei below the stable nuclei, and β⁺-emitters above.

years, and it is easy to show that much longer times are common but difficult to observe experimentally. The factor M, which depends on how much orbit changing occurs, is also present, but is very difficult to study because of the overwhelming importance of P. Recently, however, there has been considerable success in comparing calculated and experimental values of M for α-delay. Our understanding of the more complicated fission processes has not yet reached this stage.

Further reading

Some very readable elementary treatments of nuclear matters, including shell theory, are to be found in Halliday's *Introductory Nuclear Physics* (Wiley, 1955, $7.95), which is also interesting in that among its descriptions of various experiments and apparatus, used to elucidate nuclear structure, are the specifications of the cyclotron used at the University of Pittsburgh by the author's group. Another relevant reference is Eisberg's senior-level college text ("These days everybody takes a course out of Eisberg"), *Fundamentals of Modern Physics* (Wiley, 1961, $10.50). If your major was more chemistry-oriented than physics, try Friedlander and Kennedy's *Nuclear and Radiochem-*

istry (Wiley, 1955, $7.50). (It's amazing how close nuclear physics and radiochemistry now are.)

Less elementary and more particularly concerned with shell theory (and including some quantum mechanics) is *Elementary Theory of Nuclear Shell Structure* by Mayer and Jensen (Wiley, 1955, $8.75), while an advanced treatment of the subject awaits you in de Shalit and Talmi's *Nuclear Shell Theory* (Academic Press, 1963, $14.50).

In this field perhaps more than in most, the professional literature [found in such places as *Nuovo cimento, The Physical Review, the Journal of Experimental and Theoretical Physics* (USSR), etc.] has become increasingly unapproachable by the uninitiate, but several good popular articles on nuclear structure have appeared in *Scientific American* over the past few years. The most directly related to our article, and our author's recommendation as the next article to read, is Mayer's "The Structure of the Nucleus" (March 1951). Two other pieces, which also discuss other ways to look at the nucleus, are "A Model of the Nucleus" by Weisskopf and Rosenbaum (Dec. 1955) and "The Atomic Nucleus" by Peirels (Jan. 1959).

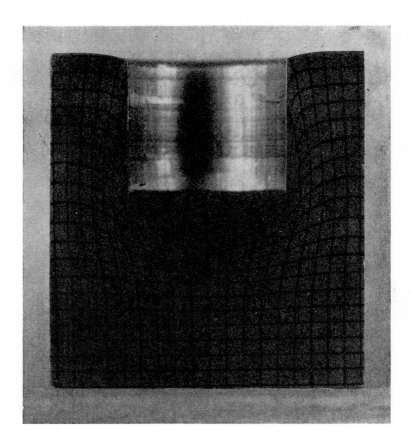

Fig. 1-35. The effect of plastic deformation on this lead cylinder is clearly evident in the distortion of the grid pattern. The test specimen was prepared by dividing a lead cylinder along its axis. After the grid was applied to one face, the two pieces were put back together and a rod pushed part way through the specimen while it was confined in a container. (Courtesy International Research in Production Engineering, ASME)

PLASTIC DEFORMATION

by R. K. MacCrone*

IN BRIEF: *Plastic deformation is as common as a dented fender, but more difficult to explain. It begins with a defect in the lattice of an otherwise perfect crystal—a line defect that moves under stress to permit one crystal plane to slip with respect to its neighbor. These defects—called dislocations—occur in almost numberless quantities in the crystals of a typical metal specimen. Their movement, their multiplication, and their interactions with each other and with impurities in the crystal lattice account for much of the mechanical behavior summarized in the stress-strain diagram. At stresses below the elastic limit, the interwoven network of dislocation lines merely stretches like a fishing net. At higher stresses, the dislocations begin to move, easily at first and then more stubbornly as they begin to encounter obstacles, to multiply, and to pile up. Exactly what happens during the last stages of plastic deformation is not well understood except that it clearly depends on the detailed motion of dislocations.—C.J.L.*

■ I vividly remember being confronted as a student with the stress-strain curves of metals

*R. K. MacCrone is Assistant Professor in the School of Metallurgical Engineering at the University of Pennsylvania, in Philadelphia.

beyond their elastic limit. My reaction to endless curves with various kinks and bends was completely and utterly negative. Yet only a few years later, these very same curves took on a new meaning; they became alive and fascinating.

My reaction changed because I began to look at the curves from a new point of view, one in which I was mentally inside the metal wondering about the microscopic atomic processes that give the curves their characteristic shape. The stress-strain curve became a source of information about these atomic processes. Today there is still much that remains to be explained about the shape of the curve, but we have learned enough about the atomic processes to gain some control over the mechanical properties of materials.

One of the reasons the stress-strain curve is interesting is that it doesn't seem to make sense in terms of a perfect single crystal, or even a body composed of many perfect single crystals. For although a typical curve begins with the expected linear stress-strain relationship, it eventually bends over and enters the plastic region of the diagram, a region where strains remain after the stress is removed.

Intuition tells us that a perfect crystal with

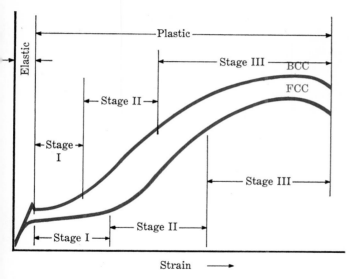

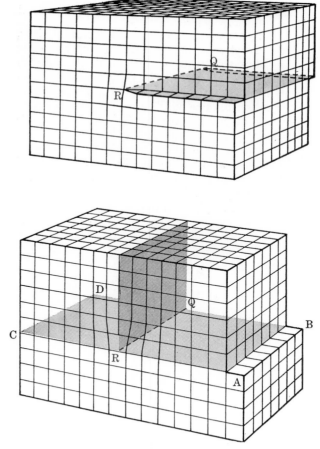

Fig. 1-36. *Dislocation movements account for the characteristic shape of stress-strain curves in both the elastic and plastic ranges. Principal difference between the body-centered cubic curve and the face-centered cubic curve is the "yield drop" at the peak of the BCC elastic range. It is caused by the release of anchored dislocations. BCC curve has longer elastic range principally because BCC metals are usually stronger (stronger interatomic bonds) than FCC materials.*

Fig. 1-37. *Geometry of dislocations permits crystal planes to slip a little at a time, rather than all at once, thus reducing the stress needed to deform the material. Edge dislocation, RQ, at bottom, moves in slip plane ABCD. Screw dislocation, at top, may glide on any plane containing the axis of the dislocation.*

its perfectly ordered planes of atoms stacked one on the other would not behave this way. Under stress, the bonds between atoms should stretch linearly, and elastically, until the stress exceeded the strength of the bonds, at which point the crystal should fracture. Indeed, calculations show that the theoretical stresses needed to break the bonds are enormous—about 10 times larger than those that produce fracture in a real material. Moreover, it is difficult to see how a perfect crystal could become permanently deformed by stresses so much lower than those needed to slide one crystal plane over another.

As a direct consequence of this discrepancy between the theoretically calculated stresses and the very much smaller stresses observed in practice, lattice defects called dislocations were first invented and later verified to exist as the mechanism by which crystals deform when subjected to an applied load. The motion and interaction of dislocations explains why there are kinks and bends in the stress-strain diagram. It is, in fact, the behavior of dislocations that ultimately determines whether a material will be strong or weak, soft or hard, ductile or brittle.

Recent insights into the details of dislocation processes have yielded significant advances in the technology of materials. Today, it is possible to make materials that maintain good mechanical properties at temperatures that would have been described as unbelievably high a few years ago. Eventually, it may be possible

to tailor materials to any application by controlling dislocation movements.

Like shifting a carpet

First, let us look at a simplified model of a crystal containing dislocations. One of the simplest forms of a dislocation is shown in Fig. 1-37. This is an edge dislocation and can be considered to have been formed by a shearing motion that has moved only partway through the crystal. In effect, the shearing motion has created a line defect in the crystal at a point where there is an extra half plane of atoms and hence a local mismatch between the atoms in the upper half of the crystal and those in the lower half. The plane where the partial shearing action has occurred is called the slip plane.

To illustrate how such a dislocation enables one plane of atoms to move bodily over another plane at stresses much smaller than those needed to break all bonds between planes simultaneously, consider the practical problem of shifting a carpet some distance across a floor. The carpet may be dragged bodily across the floor, but this requires a large force. A much easier way is to form a linear bulge in the carpet by rucking up one end of it and pushing the ruck from one end to the other. As the ruck sweeps across the carpet, it shifts the whole carpet a small distance.

Another kind of dislocation is the pure screw dislocation also shown in Fig. 1-37. This kind of dislocation has no extra half plane associated with it; instead, it has connected the crystal planes into a spiral, so that by traveling around

the dislocation line, it is possible to travel throughout the crystal without leaving the original crystal plane. The screw dislocation has no unique slip plane and may glide on any plane parallel to its axis.

Notice that a certain displacement (represented by the ledge in the illustration) was required to form both the edge and screw dislocation. This displacement defines the Burgers vector—a property of dislocations that enters into most of the theoretical calculations and is characteristic of the material's crystal geometry. In both examples above, the magnitude

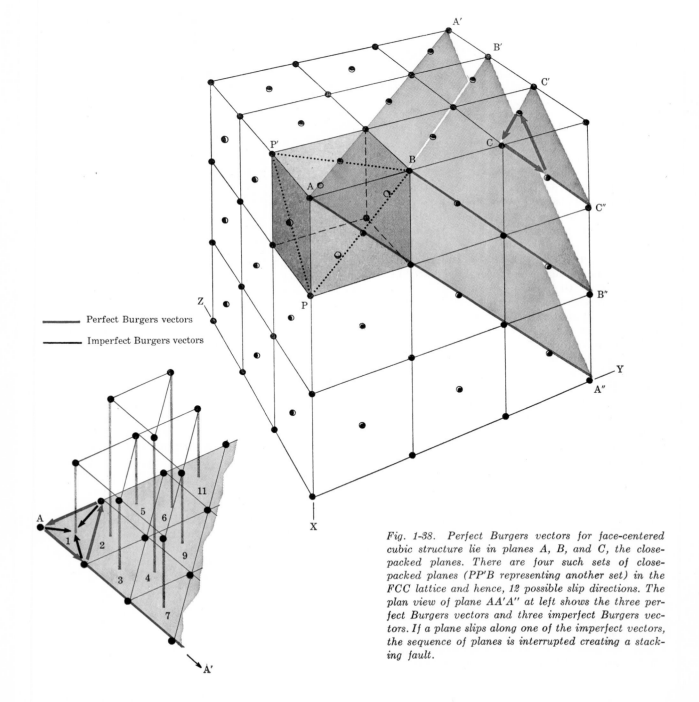

Fig. 1-38. *Perfect Burgers vectors for face-centered cubic structure lie in planes A, B, and C, the close-packed planes. There are four such sets of close-packed planes (PP′B representing another set) in the FCC lattice and hence, 12 possible slip directions. The plan view of plane AA′A″ at left shows the three perfect Burgers vectors and three imperfect Burgers vectors. If a plane slips along one of the imperfect vectors, the sequence of planes is interrupted creating a stacking fault.*

of the vector, **b,** is equal to the lattice spacing of the crystal and its direction, for edge dislocations, is perpendicular to the dislocation line, while for screw dislocations, the vector is parallel to the dislocation line. Energy considerations show that dislocations having the shortest Burgers vectors are favored since these have the lowest energy. For this reason, dislocations generally move on the planes in which the atoms are most closely packed.

The face-centered cubic structure, the crystal habit of gold, silver, copper, aluminum, and most of their alloys, can be considered to consist of an orderly stacked sequence of close-packed planes. One such close-packed plane is $CC'C''$ shown in Fig. 1-38; $BB'B''$ is another, $AA'A''$ another, and so on. (Notice how a close-packed plane contains hexagonal arrangements of atoms with one atom in the center. An experiment with peas on a table will verify that atoms cannot be packed more closely in any other arrangement.)

Logically, the shortest lattice vectors will be found in close-packed planes. There are three such vectors in this plane, all equivalent, and they are shown in the figure. However, the plane $PP'B$ represents another set of close-packed planes crystallographically equivalent to the A, B, and C planes. All together, there are four different close-packed planes in the face-centered lattice, each with three vectors, giving $4 \times 3 = 12$ slip systems.

Reshuffling the stack

So far, we have succeeded in identifying the set of perfect or shear Burgers vectors in the face-centered cubic lattice. Besides these, there is another set of Burgers vectors called imperfect Burgers vectors. To locate these, we look now at the stacking sequence of the close-packed planes. It is found that all the atoms in the close-packed plane $BB'B''$ are directly above the center of the odd numbered triangles of plane $AA'A''$ (see auxiliary sketch in Fig. 1-38), while the atoms of plane $CC'C''$ are directly above the centers of the even numbered triangles of plane $AA'A''$. The atoms of the next plane above C are directly above the atoms of plane $AA'A''$, so this plane is again an A plane. Thus, the stacking sequence can be represented as . . . ABC ABC ABC . . .

A perfect or shear dislocation, as it sweeps across the plane, will shift the atoms in plane B, say, from above 1 to above 3, from above 5 to above 9, etc. This does not disrupt the stacking sequence.

An imperfect dislocation would shift the atoms in plane B from above 3 to above 4, from above 5 to above 6, etc., changing a B

plane into a C plane. The old C plane—the plane above the B plane before the dislocation swept over—changes to an A plane, and so on upwards. The stacking sequence is now . . . $ABCA$ C $ABCAB$ . . . This irregularity in the orderly sequence of planes is called a stacking fault. If another partial or twinning dislocation sweeps across just above the plane where the stacking fault occurs, the sequence becomes . . . $ABCA$ CB $CABC$ . . . Continuing this process on successive close-packed planes leads to this stacking sequence:

$$\text{ABCA} \quad | \quad \text{CBACBA}$$

Original crystal		Twin
$\longleftarrow$	$\uparrow$	$\longrightarrow$

In a face-centered cubic structure there are three possible imperfect or twinning Burgers vectors associated with each close-packed plane. One set of imperfect vectors is shown on the auxiliary sketch in Fig. 1-38 along with the perfect vectors for that plane.

It is evident that any one of the shear Burgers vectors would give the same shear as two twinning Burgers vectors according to the ordinary rules of vector addition. Thus it is possible for a perfect shear dislocation to split physically into two dislocations with Burgers vectors whose vector sum is equal to the original Burgers vector. Whether or not it will split depends on the energy before splitting compared with the energy after splitting.

The elastic energy of a dislocation line per unit length may be calculated by elastic theory. It is found to be proportional to the square of the Burgers vector. Hence, Frank's rule, which states that a dislocation with Burgers vector **b** will split into two other dislocations of Burgers vector b_1 and b_2 provided $b^2 > b^2_1 + b^2_2$. Similarly, two dislocations will combine to give one if $b^2 < b^2_1 + b^2_2$.

Applying Frank's rule to the splitting of a shear dislocation into two twinning dislocations, we find that it is generally favorable for the splitting to occur. The two twinning dislocations repel each other with a force that decreases linearly with the distance between them. At the same time, there is a constant force drawing them together that attempts to minimize the energy of the stacking fault created between the two twinning dislocations. This force is proportional to the stacking fault energy of the material. The equilibrium distance is obtained when these forces balance.

A similar set of shear and twinning Burgers vectors will be found in the body-centered cubic structure, the crystal habit of iron, molybdenum, tungsten, and other metals. In this case,

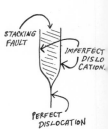

STACKING FAULT

IMPERFECT DISLOCATION.

PERFECT DISLOCATION

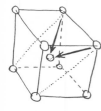

however, the close-packed plane is the one shown in the margin. There are six such planes in the crystal and two shear Burgers vectors in each plane making, again, a total of 12 slip systems. The stacking sequence and the twinning Burgers vectors are somewhat more complicated in the body-centered cubic lattice, but the principles of dislocation, formation, and movement are the same.

A more complex model

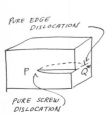

The simple geometry of edge and screw dislocations accounts for some of the behavior observed during plastic deformation. It explains why the stress-strain curve for a crystal is not a straight line to the point of fracture. But the crystal model is still not a very good analog of a real crystal structure. With the simple dislocation movements described above, the stress-strain curve would be expected to follow a steeply sloping straight line until the stress became large enough to overcome the frictional forces holding the dislocations in place. At that point, the curve should bend over and follow a nearly horizontal line to the point of fracture. As we know, real stress-strain curves are more complex than this. Ac-

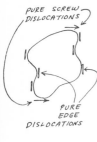

cordingly, we will have to improve our simple model to include a more complex array of dislocations. Also, we need a group of mechanisms by which dislocations can interact with each other and with other crystal defects.

Neither the geometry of dislocations nor their Burgers vectors are as simple as I have implied. The pure edge and pure screw dislocations just discussed are particular cases. In general, the Burgers vector (which is the only invariant of a dislocation) lies at some angle other than 0° or 90° to the dislocation line, and this angle need not even be constant along the length of the dislocation. Suppose, for example, one end, Q, of the screw dislocation shown in Fig. 1-37 were pulled around to a new point, Q^*, on the side, as shown in the margin. The dislocation would then be the line RQ^*. At R the dislocation is pure screw, at Q^* it is pure edge, and it is mixed everywhere else, the screw character decreasing from R to Q^*. It is also clear from this that dislocations cannot end within the crystal. They must begin or end at free surfaces or form closed loops inside the material (see margin).

From little acorns . . .

Examination of crystals after plastic deformation shows that there are many more dislocations than there were before the crystal was deformed. This indicates that there is some mechanism within the crystal by which dislocations can multiply. We will now examine one such proposed mechanism.

The shorter a dislocation line is, the lower the energy of the crystal will be. Therefore, unless forces are acting, dislocation lines will be as short as possible and hence, straight. We can describe this property of dislocations by calculating their effective line tension T, a dislocation then becoming the two-dimensional analog of the three-dimensional soap film.

Consider a force acting on the initially straight dislocation segment shown in Fig. 1-39. The segment is anchored at A and B so the force bows it into the arc $AC'B$. If the stress is removed, the dislocation will snap back into the straight line AB. If the stress is increased, the bulge will grow. When the bulge reaches a radius equal to half the distance between the anchor points A and B, the stress needed to support the dislocation falls off. Thus, the loop will grow rapidly, assuming momentarily the shape $AC''B$.

The dislocation segments Q and Q' are dislocations of opposite sign (since they are moving in opposite directions under the action of the same stress) and when these segments meet, a length RR' of dislocation will be annihilated. The cusp-shaped portion ARB will straighten

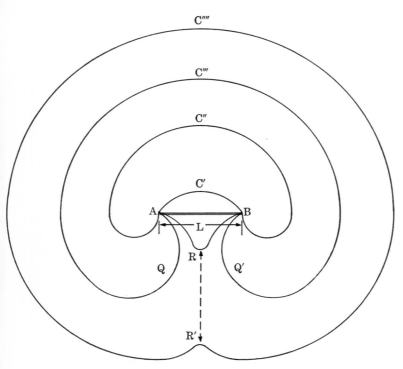

Fig. 1-39. One dislocation can become many dislocations under stress by following the pattern of this Frank-Read source mechanism. It begins with a dislocation AB anchored at both ends. Under stress, it bows out, then circles round, finally colliding with itself to annihilate section RR'. C'''' continues to grow while AB repeats the process.

out to give *AB* again, while the loop *C''''* continues to grow in size. This section *AB* can then go through the whole process over and over again. This is the Frank-Read source for dislocation multiplication.

Intersecting dislocations

What happens when two dislocations intersect with one another? The most interesting case is the intersection of a screw dislocation and an edge dislocation at right angles to one another. (Often, two perpendicular dislocations do not exist in the structure, but the example to be quoted is easy to visualize.) Figure 1-40 shows a screw dislocation and an edge dislocation which has completely glided across the plane *KLMN*, having intersected at *J* with the dislocation *RQ*. In so doing, the dislocation has shifted all the material behind *KLMN* up by an amount *b*, and a segment of dislocation *JJ'* = *b* was formed to prevent *RJ* and *J'Q* from ending inside the crystal.

Now, this little segment *JJ'*, called the intersection jog, is the whole point. It is a small length of edge dislocation, in a containing screw dislocation, and has associated with it an extra plane of atoms. If *RJJ'Q* now moves as indicated by the arrow, the half plane of the intersection jog will get longer (or shorter), thus producing vacancies (or interstitials). This is one of the actual mechanisms by which vacancies and interstitials are formed in real crystals, namely, the nonconservative motion of an intersection jog, which is dragged along by the screw dislocation.

Another type of dislocation configuration is the array. When one portion of a crystal is rotated through a small angle with respect to another portion of the crystal, an array of dislocations forms in the bounding surface between the two portions. Because the boundary is similar in many respects to a grain boundary, it is called a sub-boundary.

Two examples of sub-boundaries are shown in the margin. The first is a set of pure edge dislocations, one above the other, forming a simple kink boundary. The second is a simple twist boundary, consisting of two sets of pure screw dislocations perpendicular to one another. This was achieved by twisting the crystal above the plane of the paper around an axis perpendicular to the paper. (Using a typewriter, this array of dislocations may be verified by typing a square array of *O*'s, representing the atom positions below the sub-boundary, then typing a smilar square array of *X*'s on a sheet of tracing paper to represent the atom positions above the sub-boundary. A little manipulation of the two sheets when the patterns are rotated

by small angles will show that a crossed grid of screw dislocations where the moiré pattern is most muddled is just the answer to get the minimum overall atomic misfit.)

There is one final complication to be added to our model of dislocation behavior. All of the mechanisms I have described have been discussed in terms of single crystals. But most metallic objects around are not in the form of single crystals; they are polycrystalline. The plastic properties of a crystalline body are the average plastic properties of single crystals, in all possible orientations, with the constraint that each crystal must take its neighbor's deformation into account.

An elastic fishing net

With the additional refinements in our model, let us see if it is sufficient to explain the behavior of a material under stress. Assume we have a material containing many dislocations "grown in," 10^6 being a typical value for most metals. These dislocations arrange themselves into stable networks and sub-boundaries.

If we apply a small stress to a material containing such a network of dislocations, the network will stretch and distort, just as a fishing net would stretch and deform. This represents the straight line or "elastic" segment of the stress-strain diagram. On removing the stress, the line tension of the dislocations in the network will pull the network back

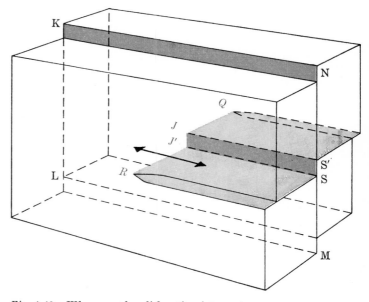

Fig. 1-40. When an edge dislocation intersects a screw dislocation, it must form an additional plane of atoms, JJ'SS'. If the screw dislocation then moves in the direction of the arrow, it will produce vacancies and interstitial atoms in the lattice, depending on whether the additional plane becomes shorter or longer.

as best it can. Associated with this dislocation network distortion is a reversible strain. This strain is far larger than the pure elastic strain associated with the stretching of bonds between atoms.

However, there is a limit to which the dislocation network will stretch before new dislocations are formed by the Frank-Read mechanism or generated at the surface. This limiting stress is called the "critical resolved shear stress," or "yield stress."

We now look at mechanisms that effect this critical shear stress—hardening mechanisms that make it difficult for dislocations to move before strong dislocation interactions occur.

An atmosphere of impurities

Imagine a spherical cavity, produced by removing an atom from the crystal of radius r, whose distance from an edge dislocation is given by R and θ. The spherical cavity is positioned so that it is under the influence of the local stress field created by the edge dislocation. Suppose, now, an impurity atom of radius $r' > r$ is placed inside the cavity. The elastic strain is $\epsilon = r' - r/r$. The result is the interaction energy between an impurity solute atom and an edge dislocation, given by $U = 4Gb\epsilon r^3 \sin \theta/R$. The sign of the interaction energy depends on the sign of ϵ and $\sin \theta$. Thus, both larger and smaller atoms ($\epsilon > 0$ and $\epsilon < 0$) can always find a θ to make U negative by diffusing towards the dilated or compressed side of an edge dislocation. This results in an attractive force between the impurity atoms and the dislocation, which decreases with increasing distance. In this way impurities can pin down dislocations very effectively when they are very close to or in the core, since at ordinary temperatures the diffusion of impurities is very slow compared to dislocation velocities. Because diffusion creates an atmosphere of impurities around the core of a dislocation, this mechanism is called Cottrell atmosphere hardening.

An impurity content of 0.001% is sufficient to allow 10^7 impurity atoms per unit length of dislocation line in a specimen containing 10^{10} dislocations/cm³. Consequently, small amounts of impurities have a considerable effect. Atmosphere hardening is common in iron and other body-centered cubic materials.

At sufficiently high stresses, the force on the dislocations becomes sufficient to tear some of them away from their atmospheres. Once a dislocation has been torn away, the stress required for its continued movement is lower than before. This accounts for the spike or "yield drop" seen in the stress-strain diagrams of body-centered cubic materials.

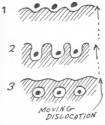

YIELD DROP

BCC

FCC

σ

ϵ

1

2

3

MOVING DISLOCATION

Precipitation hardening

The principal hardening mechanisms in face-centered cubic materials is precipitation hardening. At about 600°C, aluminum will dissolve about 4 atomic percent copper, whereas at 20°C the solubility is very much less. If a 4% Cu-Al alloy is quenched from 600°C to room temperature, the excess copper atoms precipitate out. At first, the atoms are randomly dispersed. This configuration is, however, thermodynamically unstable so copper atoms begin to coagulate, forming many small precipitates.

When the precipitates are small, they have very little effect on the dislocations and, consequently, on the yield stress. As they grow, they begin to block dislocations locally, mainly for geometrical reasons. The dislocations bow round precipitate particles in a manner similar to that of the Frank-Read source mechanism. As before (see marginal sketch) dislocation segments of opposite sign attract each other, and on meeting, annihilate a section of dislocation line. This leaves a small loop of dislocation around each precipitate passed by a dislocation.

As some precipitates grow at the expense of others, the distance between them increases and, consequently, the stress needed for a dislocation to pass by them decreases. In this condition, the alloy is overaged.

An improved understanding of the precipitation hardening process has recently led to the development of alloys that retain their hardness at very high temperatures. One such alloy is a material called TD Nickel, developed by DuPont, in which fine particles of thorium oxide (amounting to about 2% weight) are dispersed uniformly within the structure of the nickel base material. Because the thorium oxide does not dissolve or diffuse (appreciably) through the lattice at high temperatures, the alloy retains its strength to temperatures as high as 2400°F.

Three stages of plastic flow

Once the material is stressed beyond the critical resolved shear stress, it enters the plastic portion of the stress-strain diagram. Typically, this portion of the curve is divided into three segments. In Stage I (see Fig. 1-36), strain increases at nearly constant stress—the curve is nearly a horizontal line. In Stage II, the curve bends up and enters a nearly linear portion where large increases in stress produce only small increases in strain. Finally, in Stage III, the curve rolls over gently, each increment of stress producing successively larger increments of strain, until the sample fractures.

There is, as yet, no acceptable theory of dislocation behavior that explains the shape of the curve in the plastic region. During the past twenty years, several models have been proposed. But today, for a variety of reasons, none of them are believed to give a very accurate picture of dislocation behavior during plastic deformation.

Despite the lack of a proper theory, we can gain a conceptual appreciation for the shape of the curve by applying what we know about the geometry and mechanics of dislocations. In the hardening mechanisms just discussed, we have seen that the stress required to move a dislocation (and therefore, the stress-strain relationship) can be changed by blocking the dislocation with particles and interstitial atoms in the lattice. Likewise, the dislocation can be blocked by another dislocation intersecting with it. These geometrical obstructions are responsible for one part of the stress required to move a dislocation. The other part is an elastic part whose magnitude depends on the opposing stress fields created by other dislocations in the vicinity of (but not interacting directly with) the dislocation that is attempting to move. It is the combined effect of these two opposing forces that accounts for the shape of the stress-strain diagram. But exactly how the magnitudes of these forces vary with strain is not yet clear.

However, suppose we look at a pure single crystal—one that has not been subjected to artificial hardening treatments and has been made as free from impurities as is technologically possible. Initially, we will assume that it contains a typical number of "grown in" dislocations. Once the stress on the crystal exceeds the frictional forces holding the dislocations in place, the stress-strain curve bends over and enters Stage I. During this stage, it is believed that the number of dislocations is so small that deformation is carried on by a few dislocations moving large distances. If one of these should become blocked, even slightly, it may be replaced (in a way that is not well understood) by another that continues the plastic deformation elsewhere. Eventually, it is thought, most of the dislocations reach a point near the end of Stage I where they can no longer move as easily as they did at the beginning of Stage I. All the experimental evidence collected to date seems to agree with this superficial picture.

A conflict of theories

In Stage II and Stage III it becomes more difficult to formulate even a superficial picture that agrees with all the experimental data. The complexity of the problem is best illustrated by looking at Fig. 1-41.

The top photo is what one expects to see. The

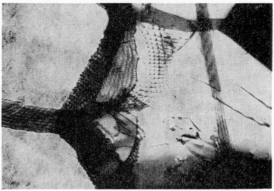

Fig. 1-41. The outside of a crystal gives little hint of what is happening inside. Regular slip bands on the surface of the crystal at top (magnification: 100×) imply well-behaved dislocation movements (dark spots are specks of dirt on the specimen). At bottom, the electron micrograph of a foil cut from a strained sample shows that dislocations inside a similar crystal are tangled and disordered. Nets in center of bottom photo are sub-boundaries; vertical ribbon in right part of photo is a twin. (Courtesy R. K. MacCrone)

lines are slip lines, the steps on the surface left by the movement of dislocations. These steps are quite large, involving hundreds of Burgers vectors, whose many dislocations have glided on a stack of adjacent slip planes. It is reasonable to suppose that these dislocations have come from Frank-Read sources inside the crystal. These dislocation sources have been seen in decorated ionic crystals and actually observed operating in the electron miscroscope.

Now look at the bottom photo. This electron microscope image of a foil obtained from strained specimen reveals a totally different behavior of dislocations *inside* the specimen. The dislocations are simply not gliding on well-defined slip planes. Instead, they are collecting into "cells," three-dimensional irregular shaped networks that apparently become smaller and better defined with increasing strain.

Clearly there is a difference between what is happening on the surface and what is happening inside the crystal. The difference shows up in experiments when a thin surface layer (amounting to as little as 1% of the cross-sectional area) of a previously strained crystal is stripped off by electropolishing. On reloading, the flow stress is observed to decrease by 5 to 10%. One explanation is that the surface layer was carrying a large share of the stress and that electropolishing removed the blocked dislocations in this region. But a completely different and equally plausible explanation is that stripping off the outer surface enabled new dislocations to be formed at a lower stress than before, and these then moved into the crystal on reloading.

Within the crystal, experimental evidence suggests that the tangling of dislocations is caused, in many cases, by point defects (vacancies and interstitial atoms). A very topical question is: Where do the defects that produce tangling come from? There are various possibilities. For instance, some believe that the vacancies exist as clusters, "grown in" during the growth of the crystal, and that there are relatively few clusters near the surface, which is a sink for vacancies. Alternatively, the operative vacancies may arise during the plastic flow as intersection jogs move nonconservatively. It is known that vacancies are formed during plastic deformation, a result deduced from annealing experiments first performed twenty years ago.

Thus, work-hardening theories of the future must necessarily be schizophrenic in outlook. In some materials, "surface type" configurations seem to be more important, whereas in others, "volume type" configurations predominate. No satisfactory solution seems near, as continuously new and unexpected dislocation reactions and behavior are observed.

Further reading

There are a number of excellent books that offer a more detailed account of the mathematics and physics of plastic deformation and dislocation behavior. You might begin with Cottrell's *Dislocations and Plastic Flow in Crystals* (Oxford, 1953, $4.50). It is relatively easy reading and presents a rather complete summary of the mechanical aspects of dislocations. For a less mathematical and somewhat less rigorous coverage of nearly the same areas, see Read's *Dislocations in Crystals* (McGraw-Hill, 1953, $5). *Imperfections in Crystals* by van Bueren (North Holland, 1960, $16.75) is probably the most complete treatise on the subject. It is textbooky, but discusses dislocations in metals and nonmetals and describes their role in diffusion, crystal growth, electrical properties.

For a survey of typical research work concerning dislocations and plastic flow, look up the proceedings of these two conferences: *Dislocations and Mechanical Properties of Crystals* (Wiley, 1959, $15) edited by Fisher and others, and *Imperfections in Nearly Perfect Crystals* (Wiley, 1952, $11.50), edited by Shockley and others. The effect of dislocations on other properties (conductivity, corrosion, catalysis, magnetism) is described in *The Defect Solid State* (Interscience, 1957, $11), a collection of papers by a number of authors, edited by Gray. For a more detailed view of the puzzling phenomenon of work hardening, see "Work Hardening of Metals" by Clarebrough and Hargraves in *Progress in Metal Physics*, Vol. 8, Chalmers and King, eds. (Pergamon, 1959).

SOLID SURFACES

by Charles J. Lynch *

IN BRIEF: *Traditionally, surfaces have been described and studied largely in terms of their chemistry. Recently, physicists have joined the party. As might be expected, they take a different view of the subject. They want to know where the surface atoms are, how they are arranged, the details of their electronic interaction with other atoms. The answers, they feel, lie in the atomically clean surface—a surface that reveals the unique personality of the material.*

Surfaces can be made atomically clean, they find, by heating, cleaving, ion bombardment or *by chemical means. And they can be kept that way in a vacuum of 10^{-9} or better. When these clean surfaces are examined with field-ion or field-electron microscopes, or probed with low-energy electrons, they reveal a variety of unexpected properties. Surface atoms often are not arranged as are atoms in the bulk, and they sometimes move from place to place with surprising ease. When gases are adsorbed, on the surface, they bind tenaciously in some places and loosely in others. Such studies are laying the groundwork for new theories that will eventually help to solve practical surface problems.—C.J.L.*

* Charles J. Lynch is Associate Editor of *International Science and Technology*.

■ Complicated as the pattern in Color Fig. 1 is, it is probably one of the simpler pictures of surface atoms you are likely to see. Only the damage done by ion bombardment (denoted by the red and green atoms) mars the structure of the pattern. Not a single foreign atom upsets the regular spacings of the lattice. No step or grain boundary breaks the orderly arrangement of circles and rows.

Most of the surfaces we ordinarily deal with are more complex than this. Surface atoms are often disorderly, show no detectable pattern, and are usually intermingled with a variety of other kinds of atoms. But by studying simple surfaces, surfaces stripped of their customary crust like that in Color Fig. 1, physicists are now hoping to learn something about the fundamental nature of a surface.

Surfaces are rewarding things to study because a surface is the place where things happen, the place where a solid material interacts with the outside world. It's where chemical reactions occur, where glue sticks, where metals corrode, where bearings are lubricated, where electrons are emitted. More important, a surface is different from its own bulk. It is not just the place where a piece of material stops; it has unique properties of its own. Surface atoms are caught between the rigid world of the solid and the free world of the gas. Because they are bound on only one side, surface atoms can move to positions that upset the regular geometry of the crystalline solid. In many respects, a surface is simply a giant crystal flaw.

For over forty years, beginning with the classic work by Langmuir and Taylor in the early 1920's, the study of surfaces has been largely a study of surface chemistry. The questions we have asked have been questions of gross surface properties, questions of thermodynamics, with answers stated in terms of surface free energies, adsorption isotherms, wetting contact angles. These studies have taught us (and are still teaching us) a great deal about how specific surfaces behave. But the science has lagged behind technology, and technology has struggled on without it. We now know how to make the glue stick, the catalyst catalyze, the electron emitter emit. At this applied level, the scientist knows a great deal about surfaces, but he doesn't understand all he knows. His problems are eventually solved with empirical rules, and an after-the-fact explanation. He has learned that surface problems, like so many problems, never really get solved; they just go away.

The approach of surface chemists has been largely a thermodynamic approach, and thermodynamics, by definition, ignores detail. In

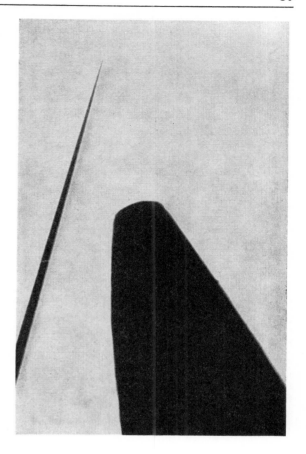

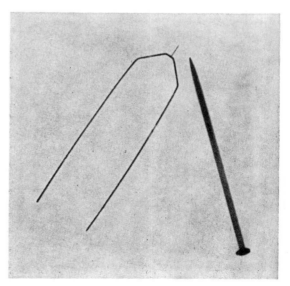

Fig. 1-42. The area shown in Color Fig. 1 is literally invisible by optical means. The fine point of an ion-microscope tip has a radius of about 500 angstroms, which is one-tenth the wavelength of green light, and is, therefore, invisible even when magnified as in the upper photograph. The other object, on the right in both photographs, is an ordinary straight pin. Magnification is about 2✕ below, 70✕ above. (Courtesy E. W. Müller)

the past few years, surface science has begun to move in a new direction, to ask new questions. These are questions of detail: How do electrons in surface atoms behave? How are surface atoms arranged? And from answers to these questions, what can we learn about surfaces? These are questions of physics rather than chemistry, so it is natural that the researchers in this branch of surface science are predominantly physicists. They seek to explore the problem at its most fundamental level, to attack it at its source.

But to ask a surface a fundamental question, you first have to get to it. Any surface is piled high with the debris of uncounted collisions with atoms from the atmosphere and atoms rubbed off other surfaces. In a word, the surface is dirty. And the dirt masks the surface's true properties. Getting the dirt off is only half the battle; keeping it off is the other half. In a vacuum of 10^{-6} torr (mm of Hg) it usually takes only about 1 sec for a monolayer of foreign atoms to form. To keep a surface clean long enough to study it requires a vacuum of 10^{-9} or better.

From tools to brass tacks

There are many reasons why this interest in the properties of clean surfaces has developed within the last 10 years. One, undoubtedly, is the new-found ability to achieve and measure vacuums in the 10^{-9} range. Before the development of the Bayard-Alpert ionization gage, and, more recently, the Redhead magnetron gage, such vacuums were questionable; the pumps were probably capable of it, but the gages couldn't measure it. Another reason can probably be traced to the interest in surface properties of semiconductors. It was fundamental studies of semiconductor surfaces that led to the discovery of the transistor in 1948, and it was surface problems that kept them from becoming commercial products until 1954. And surface problems are still the most critical problems in semiconductor research.

But most of all, the interest in clean surfaces arose with the development of tools capable of probing the atomic structure of surfaces. The field-ion microscope that made the image for Color Fig. 1 is an invention of the last 10 years. And low-energy-electron diffraction, a powerful tool for revealing the structure of a surface, didn't come along (in its more tractable form) until 1959.

With the development of these tools and capabilities, it suddenly became possible to study the surface itself, and the study of clean surfaces has since become an active and important field of research. The clean surface is of interest to science because it is the most

simple surface, has the least number of uncontrolled parameters, is most likely to yield answers to fundamental questions. "The clean surface," as the University of Chicago's Robert Gomer likes to describe it, "is closest to brass tacks."

But brass tacks are not necessarily the fastest way to get a carpet laid. While clean surfaces are of most interest to science—and of most appeal to pure scientists—they are certainly of least interest to technology. Indeed, much of technology depends on a surface being messy. No one is going to make a bearing surface atomically clean if he can help it; the two surfaces would weld tight the moment they were put together. Clean semiconductor surfaces would be far too reactive and unstable; they are purposely and painstakingly oxidized to preserve their stability. And clean catalysts that can still catalyze are rare beasts; except for a few metals, catalysts must be messy if they are to work.

Despite this, there is one place where clean surfaces exist in nature and where the findings of clean surface research may prove to have a direct application. In the vacuum of outer space, surfaces are frequently as clean as those produced in the laboratory, and this cleanness is often a source of trouble. Knowing what to do about gear teeth that weld together, brushes that stick to slip rings, lubricants that evaporate, would be a welcome addition to space technology. Equally welcome would be information about how to make the most effective use of clean surfaces in space vehicles: in electrical contacts, for example, or in fastening and joining.

Problems in search of solution

Further off is the hope that this fundamental spadework will lay the foundation for solutions to many of the surface problems now facing technology. For example:

In semiconductors the problem is to explain the existence of surface electron traps called surface states. Surface states are energy states at the surface of semiconductors that are forbidden in the bulk, but energetically attractive to electrons. Surface states degrade the performance of transistors, diodes, and solar cells because they act as recombination centers for holes and electrons, thus reducing the number of precious charge carriers. And at a junction between an N-type and a P-type semiconductor they can cause a high reverse current to flow. Today the problem is handled by careful oxidation of the surface—etch it in this, expose it in that, wash it in this (pray over it)—to keep the density of surface states constant and,

Surface

Conduction electrons

Forbidden energy band

Valence electrons

Energy

Surface states

hence, the electronic properties of the device stable.

In catalysis the problem is to find out how the structure of chemical A is changed by adsorption on a catalytic surface so that it reacts with chemical B. The key is thought to lie in the adsorption mechanism. There are a number of theories—the most recent of which involves the electronic properties of the solid—but none of the theories seems to fit all the experimental evidence. Though some physicists have studied catalysis on clean surfaces to shed some light on the adsorption mystery, catalyst chemists prefer to work with a normally dirty surface because that's where catalysis occurs in practice.

In thin films the problem is to make them thin enough to take advantage of the properties thinness has to offer. Additionally, there is the problem of making the thin film fashion itself into a single crystal, so that it can be used for transistors, diodes, and solar cells. To some extent, the two problems are the same. When atoms are deposited on a substrate they cluster together in little clumps all over the surface and grow upwards as well as sideways. Each clump develops its own crystal orientation so that by the time they grow together to form a continuous film, the film is neither thin, nor single-crystal. Both thin films and single-crystal films have been made experimentally, but the theory of nucleation is not yet worked out.

In adhesives the problem is to understand, in detail, why they stick—what kind of interatomic forces are involved. Technologically, the question is not of much importance because, according to present theory, even the weakest interatomic forces are stronger than needed, providing they can be used to full advantage. And they can be used to full advantage if the adhesive "wets" the solid it is to adhere to. But the question of interatomic forces, if answered, might help solve the practical problem of making adhesives stick to wet or moist surfaces, which is one of the most pressing problems in adhesives today.

The clean surfaces that are being studied with the hope of cracking some of these problems are made clean in a variety of ways. Usual practice is to start with a small, single-crystal specimen of a metal or semiconductor. Single crystals are chosen because their structure is simple and well understood.

How clean is clean?

Removing the accumulated layers of dirt without disturbing the surface is something of a scientific achievement itself. It is complicated by the fact that whatever is done must be done in an ultrahigh vacuum. There are several ways it can be done successfully, depending on the material and the nature of the surface layer. If the chemistry of the contaminating layer is known (and it seldom is) it can sometimes be removed by combining it with some other chemical to form a volatile product. A more common way is simply to heat the surface and drive off the contaminants. But this too is limited because many metals will melt before the foreign atoms are driven off.

One of the most effective cleaning methods—although a bit brutal—is to bombard the surface with positive ions. This is simply the method of sputtering, often used to evaporate metals in forming thin films. Ion bombardment is a process that removes contaminant atoms by simply knocking them out with a heavy projectile. The projectile is usually an argon atom which has been ionized (and thus become positively charged) by an electron beam. It is accelerated into the crystal surface by placing a negative charge on the crystal. Although the sputtering process leaves a roughened and pitted surface, this damage can be repaired by annealing the crystal at a temperature well below its melting point but high enough to allow surface atoms to migrate back to their normal positions. Annealing also drives off argon atoms embedded as much as two or three atomic layers beneath the surface.

A more direct, but more difficult way to expose a fresh surface is simply to break the crystal. It is not used very frequently because of the difficulty of mounting the cleaving gadgetry inside the vacuum chamber in such a way that it can still be operated from outside. The usual way is to notch the specimen on opposite sides of the crystal plane to be exposed. After it is in the vacuum chamber, a pair of wedges is magnetically driven into the notches as in the margin sketch.

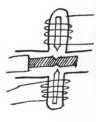

A few dollars' worth of glass

Fermi once said, "Surfaces are very interesting, but there is so little of them." This is the problem in studying any surface, whether it is clean or not. It is a job for sensitive tools that can make surface measurements without accidentally measuring the bulk as well.

Such a tool is the field-ion microscope. It was invented by E. W. Müller of Pennsylvania State University in 1955. A number of these instruments are now in use in research laboratories all over the world and a commercial model has been placed on the market within the last year.

Considering the unparalleled results it gives, the field-ion microscope is a remarkably simple device. A clever glass blower could probably rig one up in less than a week, using only

Fig. 1-43. The first commercial field-ion microscope on the market is an adaptation of an instrument designed by E. W. Müller as an exercise in simplifying his original laboratory apparatus. With its demountable specimen holder, emission tips can be changed and the system pumped down in less than one hour. Price of the instrument: $2400. (Courtesy Cenco Instruments)

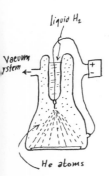

ful for studying clean surfaces because it has a built-in surface-cleaning mechanism. The 450-million-volt/cm field exerts a force of about 1 ton/mm², which is sufficient to pull off even the most tenaciously attached gas atoms. In an ion microscope, this field desorption process takes only a few seconds, at most, to strip a metal bare. And once clean, it will stay clean, even if the vacuum is no better than 10^{-6} torr. Any other atoms that happen to be wandering about in the vacuum system will be ionized before they can stick to the surface.

A world magnified a million times or more is a strange world, even to a scientist who has spent much of his life peering through a micro-

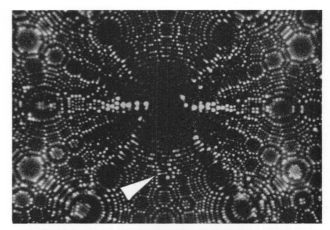

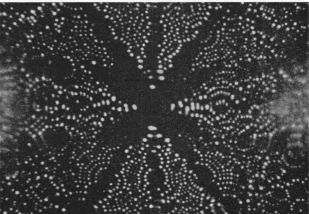

Fig. 1-44. Interpretation of a field-ion-microscope image requires experience and close scrutiny. The effect of alpha radiation on the tungsten surface at top can be seen (arrow point) only by comparing this slightly disorderly array of atoms with the orderly array in the corresponding portion at the other side of the central circle. Photo below is an image of a typical molybdenum surface. There is not yet any explanation for the clean paths across the molybdenum surface and the string of brighter spots on both sides of the center circle in the tungsten surface. Both effects are frequently observed with these materials. (Courtesy E. W. Müller)

a few dollars' worth of glass. The two active elements are an extremely sharp single-crystal needle of metal, which is the specimen to be studied, and a fluorescent screen opposite the needle tip. The space between contains a small quantity of an inert gas such as helium or neon. When a voltage is applied between the tip and the screen, with the polarity arranged that the tip is positive, an extremely high electric field—450 million volts/cm or more—is developed around the tip. When an electrically neutral helium atom diffuses to a point just above an atom in the tip, the intense electric field strips off an electron. This ion, now having a positive charge, is propelled toward a point on the screen corresponding to the position of the atom over which it was ionized.

The image is one of unprecedented resolution. Because ions are heavy particles, their wavelength is so short that diffraction effects, which might be expected to occur where the quantum waves interact, are not noticeable at the screen. Moreover, the tip is cooled with liquid hydrogen and this, along with the mass of the ion, keeps thermal motion transverse to the line of flight to a minimum. Maximum resolution of the microscope is about 2.5 angstroms, which is significantly better than the resolution of the best electron microscope, and about equal to the spacing between atoms in a metal surface.

The field-ion microscope is particularly use-

scope. Look again at Color Fig. 1. To the trained observer, each dot is readily identifiable as an atom lying in a certain crystal plane. A missing atom is easily spotted, not by looking at the edges of the circles (these are atoms on the edge of a plane), but by looking instead at the atoms in the center of the plane where their absence cannot be explained by an accidental removal during surface cleaning.

The trained analyst can also spot surface defects, unusual surface structures, interstitial foreign atoms. But some effects are too subtle even for him to follow. Minute changes in a surface, before and after radiation exposure, or before and after ion bombardment, are not so easily detected. In these cases, he can turn to the method of superimposed color transparencies, shown in Color Fig. 1.

At fields higher than those needed to ionize the imaging gas, the stress on surface atoms in the metal tip becomes greater than the strength of their bonds and the metal begins to peel away like the layers of a submicroscopic onion. This is a dramatic and somewhat surprising effect since it occurs at liquid hydrogen temperatures and works even with the most refractory metals. Such field evaporation, as it is called, can be a useful way to excavate subsurface defects. Because the peeling process can be controlled by controlling the field strength, atomic layers can be examined one at a time to determine the density of defects in the bulk of the crystal.

The ion microscope is most useful for studying defects in the crystal lattice. It has been used, for example, to measure the density of defects and relate this measurement to the conductivity of the metal. In an interesting experiment still in process in Müller's laboratory, the microscope is being used to study the structure of iron whiskers—those exceedingly strong single crystals of metal that grow spontaneously under certain conditions. Whiskers, it has generally been assumed, are strong because they are free of the usual imperfections except for a single dislocation about which the crystal grows. Preliminary results indicate otherwise; Müller finds the tiny filaments contain a number and variety of imperfections.

From ions to electrons

Powerful as the ion microscope is, it cannot reveal the structure of foreign atoms arrayed on the surface of the tip, nor can it examine materials of low melting point. The culprit is the intense ionization field. At 450 million volts/cm, only the most durable metals (tungsten, tantalum, molybdenum, iridium, chromium, platinum and, to some extent, iron and nickel) can withstand the abuse of the field

forces; others are literally wrenched apart. Some weaker materials (silicon and germanium, for example) can be examined with the ion microscope using gases that ionize at fields of 350 to 400 million volts/cm, but resolution suffers.

Besides this limitation, the high field prevents the study of adsorbed gases and their binding habits, an investigation of great fundamental importance. It is possible to adsorb gases on the tip with the field off and look at them momentarily after it has been turned back on, but the desorption rate is very high.

For these experiments we turn to an older, simpler, and less powerful tool—the field-electron-emission microscope. As its name implies, it is similar to the ion microscope except that the projectiles which form the image are electrons rather than ions.

The field-electron-emission microscope was invented in 1937, and represents Müller's original idea for examining a fine metal tip. In this case, the field is applied so that the tip is negative and the projectiles are electrons snatched away from surface atoms. The field needed at the tip varies from 20 to 80 million volts/cm depending on how easily the metal surrenders its electrons.

The image formed by the field-electron emission microscope is a pattern of bright and dark areas looking a little like a reversed Rorschach.

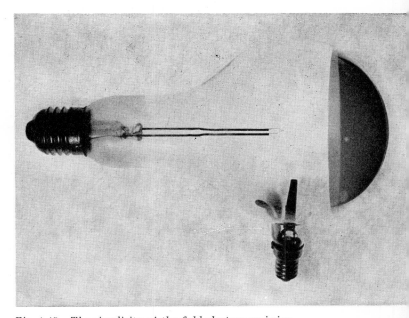

Fig. 1-45. The simplicity of the field-electron-emission microscope is demonstrated by this device, designed for classroom demonstrations. When a voltage is applied between the base and the side electrode, an emission pattern appears on the screen. The gadget is made by E. Leybold's Nachfolger of Cologne, Germany. (Courtesy E. W. Müller)

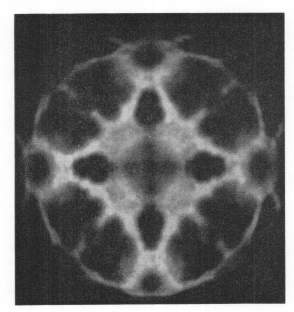

Fig. 1-46. Field electron emission patterns do not show the detailed structure typical of field-ion pattern, but they are useful for studying the bonding of adsorbed gases and their movement across the surface. This one shows the structure of a silicon surface cleaned by heating. The photo was made by F. G. Allen of Bell Laboratories. (Courtesy F. G. Allen)

Because the electrons do not travel in straight lines from the source, and because the quantum mechanical wavelength of an electron is longer than that of the heavier ions, dispersed-electron and diffraction effects spoil image clarity. Maximum resolution is only about 25 angstroms, which, for all its coarseness, is still about the same as that of a conventional electron microscope.

Besides its poorly resolved image, the field-electron-emission microscope has a further disadvantage. The intensity of the image depends on the amount of energy needed to pluck an electron out of the tip (the work function of the metal) and the strength of the applied electric field. Both of these vary uncontrollably: work function is usually different for different crystal planes of the same material and field strength varies from point to point on the surface depending on the local radius of curvature. Whether a bright spot in the pattern is caused by a small local radius, or by a low work function, is a problem for the observer to sort out. By plotting the geometry of the surface, it is possible to separate the two effects, but image interpretation is still more complex than for ion microscopy.

The low field in the field-electron-emission microscope creates only a comparatively small stress on surface atoms and consequently, the method can be used to study a variety of metals.

Cleaning the tip, however, is something of a problem. Refractory metals can be cleaned with a high field, as in the ion microscope, and high-melting-point metals (platinum, tantalum, rhenium, niobium, nickel, etc.) can be cleaned by heating. But with most softer metals, the metal melts before the surface oxide. One method for making a clean surface—although admittedly not one that is easily accomplished—is to fashion a tip by growing a whisker of the material in the microscope. This method has been used to make clean tips of silver, copper, zinc, and a variety of softer metals, even mercury.

The electron stew

Despite its limitations, the field-electron-emission microscope is an extremely valuable tool for examining the interaction between a clean surface and an adsorbed gas. The question of how an atom bonds to a clean metal surface is one of the most challenging questions in clean-surface research. No amount of hand-waving or of muttering words like "covalent" or "ionic" will serve for an answer. The problem is deeper than that.

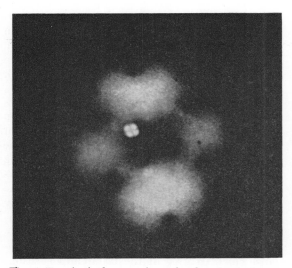

Fig. 1-47. A single organic molecule adsorbed on a field-electron emitter tip often forms this four-lobed pattern. At first, it was thought that the pattern was a direct image of the molecule (the first studies were done with phthalocyanine, which has four benzene rings arranged in the form of a four-leaf clover). But then it was found that a three-lobed molecule (triphenylene) also gave a four-lobed pattern. It is now thought that the adsorbed molecule acts as a small waveguide for electrons and, like an optical fiber whose diameter is smaller than the wavelength of light it carries, the waves interact creating two- and four-lobed diffraction patterns. This theory, first proposed by E. Komar of Leningrad, accounts for the fact that some molecules give both a four- and two-lobed pattern depending on whether they stack upon one another. (Courtesy R. Gomer)

The metal surface, like the bulk, is a sea of nonlocalized electrons, none of them specifically attached to any surface atom. What happens when a hydrogen atom attaches itself to such a surface? Does it form a localized bond with one surface atom, or does it take advantage of the electron reservoir at the surface to interact with several surface atoms? In a restricted sense, this is the same question that physics and chemistry have been asking for many years: What is the detailed electronic structure of the chemical bond?

Studies aimed at answering these questions with the field-electron-emission microscope are in progress in several laboratories. Among the most active investigators are Gert Ehrlich at General Electric and Robert Gomer at the University of Chicago. They have both been extensively engaged in the problem for several years. In general, the technique is to selectively adsorb a gas on one side of the needle tip at low temperature, then raise the temperature and watch its progress as it migrates across the tip. The adsorbed molecules increase the work function of the surface, causing the gas to appear as a dark area on a bright field—an effect that could not be observed with the ion microscope since brightness of its image does not depend on work function. These studies reveal that the temperatures for migration vary with the crystal plane over which the atoms move; on some planes, the atoms move easily, on others they migrate only at temperatures close to the desorption temperature. By measuring these migration temperatures it is possible to compute the energy required to disrupt the surface bonds.

Another source of clues lies in the desorption of adsorbed atoms by applying a large reverse field. Gomer has found, for example, that by controlling the desorption field, he can measure and plot the binding energy for an adsorbed atom as a function of its distance from the surface. Such experimental data, combined with the data from other experiments, may eventually yield a satisfactory description of the bond. In fact, Gomer feels that there may already be enough data and that the next step may be a job for the theorist.

Meanwhile, there are a number of other problems to be tackled. Studies of the clean surfaces themselves are of much interest. How much energy is required to cause atoms of a metal or semiconductor to migrate over their own lattice? F. G. Allen, of Bell Laboratories, has produced clean surfaces of germanium and silicon (a difficult feat itself, because of the tenacious oxide layer) and watched migration of their surface atoms at various tip temperatures. He finds that surface migration begins to occur at about $\frac{1}{3}$ to $\frac{1}{2}$ the melting temperature of the material, which is in agreement with similar studies on clean metals. Contaminated surfaces are a different matter. Müller finds that tungsten atoms migrate more easily when there is a small amount of oxygen present. On the other hand, when a molybdenum tip is covered with a layer of silicon, oxygen inhibits migration of the molybdenum atoms.

Müller has also found that the presence of the field in the instrument apparently triggers some reactions that would not normally occur. Tungsten is normally unaffected by the presence of water vapor or nitrogen, but in the high fields of the electron-emission microscope, these molecules become strongly bonded to a tungsten surface and cannot be removed without taking a piece of the surface with them. Similar effects have been observed when hydrogen adsorbs on copper, zinc, silicon, and a variety of other materials.

Two-dimensional crystallography

In terms of sheer magnifying power, the field-ion and field-electron microscopes have no peers. Even so, they are not powerful enough to reveal subtle changes of surface structure, slight displacements of atoms from their regular crystalline lattice. For this, we must turn to another means for examining the clean surface, one that, although it does not reveal the atoms themselves, reveals their relative placement, one with the other: the method is low-energy-electron diffraction, which is to surfaces what x-ray diffraction is to bulk solids.

In low-energy-electron diffraction, a surface is bombarded with electrons that have been accelerated by a potential of only 50 to 150 volts. These electrons do not have sufficient energy to penetrate deeply and are therefore scattered back by the first layer of surface atoms or, at most, the first few layers. At 150 volts, the quantum mechanical wavelength of electrons is about 1 angstrom, which is close enough to the interatomic spacing to make them useful for diffraction studies.

To an electron, the surface of a single crystal with its ordered rows of atoms, looks like the lines on a pair of crossed diffraction gratings. Consequently, the back-scattered electrons from one atom interact in an orderly way with those scattered from other atoms. At some points the scattered electrons reinforce each other, at other points they interfere and this creates the characteristic diffraction-pattern spots. Because each spot represents the combined reinforcement from many surface atoms (more atoms than the entire field of a field-emission-microscope image) the method is useful for determining the character of the

Fig. 1-48. The business end of this direct-view low-energy-electron diffraction apparatus is the circular face plate at the intersection of the three tubes. The specimen is the small rectangle mounted at the apex of the two supports that enter from the left. Electrons pass through a hole in the viewing screen from an electron gun hidden behind the specimen and travel in a direction perpendicular to this page. When they strike the specimen, they are scattered back against the fluorescent screen to form the diffraction pattern. The instrument was built under the direction of L. H. Germer at Bell Laboratories. (Courtesy Bell Laboratories)

long-range order in a surface, and for detecting deviations from that order.

Experimentally, there are two methods for determining the pattern of the diffracted electrons. The oldest of these dates back to the original Davisson-Germer experiment that confirmed the wave nature of the electron in 1928 (and, incidentally, brought Davisson the Nobel prize in physics in 1937). It does not give a traditional diffraction pattern at all, but instead, reveals a series of curves from which the pattern could be derived, if desired. It consists of a simple box to catch electrons and a way of measuring the number of electrons entering the box. In the low-energy diffraction apparatus, this Faraday cage is mounted inside the vacuum system so that, by rotating the crystal in the axis of the incident electron beam, and by swinging the cage from side to side, a solid angle of nearly 180 degrees can be scanned as in the marginal sketch. The curves are generally plotted to show the angle of the cage versus the electron current.

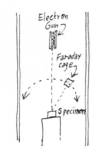

The second method, a more convenient one experimentally, has been perfected over the last nine years by a group at Bell Laboratories. It is a modification of a method originally developed by W. Eherenberg, a German scientist, in 1934 but unexplainably abandoned shortly thereafter. With this equipment, the pattern is displayed directly by placing a fluorescent screen in the path of the back-scattered electrons. This is an obvious modification, perhaps, but not one that is easily implemented because

the electrons move too slowly to excite even the most sensitive fluorescent materials. To make the pattern visible, the electrons are accelerated by a potential difference of several kilovolts as they move between the crystal and the screen. Although this direct-view apparatus speeds up data collection, it is not as precise as the Faraday cage scheme, for spot intensities must be measured with a photometer rather than by measuring electron current directly.

In the past two years, a number of laboratories have begun to explore surfaces by low-energy-electron diffraction. However, the bulk of the work to date has been done by two groups: L. H. Germer's group at Bell Laboratories and H. E. Farnsworth and his associates at Brown University. Farnsworth relies principally on instruments built around the Faraday-cage design and has been active in the field for nearly 30 years.

Transplanted atoms

The two groups have uncovered a remarkable number of interesting effects that occur in the surface structure of various materials. Farnsworth has found, for example, that the arrangement of atoms on the surface of semiconductors is not the same as that in the bulk material. The regular arrangement of atoms in the diamond lattice characteristic of these materials apparently stops about two atomic layers below the surface and another structure begins. This rearranged structure is different

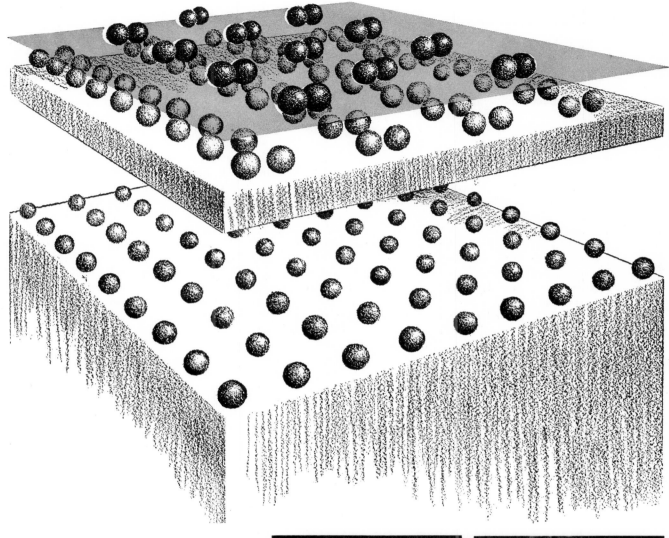

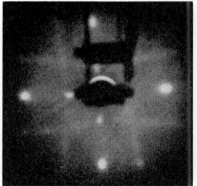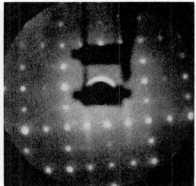

Fig. 1-49. From the two diffraction patterns of a germanium surface at right (and several dozen others taken at different voltages and using different crystals) J. J. Lander and J. K. Morrison of Bell Laboratories have concluded that the surface of one crystal plane of germanium looks like the sketch above. The sketch shows the first two surface layers and a typical layer of atoms in the bulk. Notice that many surface atoms are missing and that there is also some disorder in the second atomic layer. (Courtesy Bell Laboratories)

for each crystal face and, moreover, it depends on the method used to clean the surface; a cleaved clean surface has one characteristic structure while a surface cleaned by ion bombardment and annealing has another. However, if the cleaved surface is also annealed, the diffraction patterns are then identical, indicating that the freshly cleaved surface is not in its lowest energy state. Farnsworth has also observed that when a monolayer of oxygen is adsorbed on the clean surface, the disordered structure disappears and an ordered structure characteristic of the bulk appears. Displaced atoms have not been observed on clean metal surfaces and it is thought that this effect occurs in semiconductors because of the directional character of their tetrahedral bonds.

Metal surfaces containing foreign atoms can become rearranged, however. Atomic disordering of nickel surfaces containing adsorbed oxygen has been observed by L. H. Germer and A. U. MacRae of Bell Laboratories. They studied the least densely packed crystal plane of nickel and found that the adsorption of a fractional monolayer of oxygen caused the nickel atoms in the surface to migrate to new positions. Most surprising in this result was the fact that migration occurred at room temperature whereas surface migration in nickel would not normally occur below 300°C. When Farnsworth studied adsorption of oxygen on nickel, he found that this disordering took the form of a place-exchange between the oxygen and nickel atoms. By measuring the work function, he was able to show that when the surface oxygen reached a certain concentration, the surface is predominantly made up of nickel atoms and the oxygen atoms apparently disappear beneath the surface.

Adsorption of gases on semiconductor surfaces also produces some strange effects. Iodine atoms, which need one electron to complete their outer shell, apparently do not form a covalent bond with one of the dangling bonds of a germanium surface atom. Instead, they seem to attach themselves in such a way that they are equally distant from three germanium atoms as shown in the margin. Such a bond seems to have more of an ionic flavor than the usual (and expected) covalent structure.

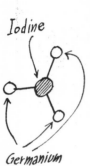

The effect of unbalanced forces on surface atoms is a difficult thing to detect experimentally but it seems reasonable to expect that, because of their one-sided bonds, there would be a larger spacing between the first and second layer in a surface, than between two equivalent layers in the bulk. Germer and MacRae turned their low-energy electron diffraction apparatus on this question and found that these expectations are justified. Close examination of the spots in their diffraction patterns revealed an intensity in the spots that they interpret as a coherence between electrons scattered from surface atoms and electrons scattered from the second layer. From the position of this intense region, they estimate that the spacing between surface atoms and the second layer is about 5% greater than the spacing between bulk atoms.

The seeds of controversy

Like any diffraction technique, low-energy-electron diffraction is a difficult way to make nature tell her secrets. Diffraction patterns are merely an array of spots related in some way to the structure doing the diffracting. The problem is to discover that relationship. Collecting the data is relatively easy; interpretation is a difficult and tedious job requiring much imagination and insight. This, as much as anything

else, probably accounts for the limited number of people working in the field.

Because diffraction patterns are uncommonly difficult things to interpret, there is not universal agreement about the results. Scientists working with dirty surfaces and other instruments get results incompatible with these. And, in some cases, there are differences in interpretation between the group at Brown and the group at Bell. But the potential importance of the work cannot be denied. The results to date represent a creditable record for a science without a glamour-incentive and with so few man-hours recorded in the log.

One of the points of controversy revolves around the cleanness of the surface. For some scientific critics, it is yet to be proven that the surfaces are as clean as they are claimed to be. In the field-emission-microscope studies there is little question; the surface must be clean if surface atoms can be peeled away layer by layer to reveal essentially the same pattern. But the cleaning methods used in the low-energy diffraction apparatus cannot be tested so easily. It is doubtful that the instrument is sensitive to contamination amounting to less than 5% of a monolayer. This is approximately 5×10^{13} atoms/cm^2, which can hardly be considered insignificant. In ion-bombardment cleaning, argon ions become embedded in the surface and there is the possibility that some remain after annealing. There is also the possibility that adsorbed gases assume a structure so similar to the substrate lattice that they cannot be detected. But the fact that freshly cleaved surfaces, which are surely clean for a short time at least, give results that are for the most part identical with results for surfaces cleaned by other methods is a strong argument in favor of cleanness of surfaces in the diffraction chamber.

Some answers, many questions

It is not clear what impact, if any, clean-surface research will have on technology or the more applied branches of science. Certainly, the scientist attempting to grow an epitaxial layer of silicon on a silicon wafer will find it of interest to know that the atomic arrangement in the surface of his substrate bears no relation to the crystal structure in the bulk or to the crystal structure he wants to grow. Certainly, a man wishing to sinter tungsten or molybdenum powder will be interested to learn that oxygen inhibits surface migration on a silicon-coated molybdenum while it promotes it on tungsten. Similarly, room-temperature migration of nickel atoms in the presence of oxygen should be of interest to the catalyst chemist. And field-induced reactions between tungsten and water vapor may be helpful to the corrosion chemist. But to some extent, any of these effects might have been predicted from what we already knew; no one working close to the physics and chemistry of surfaces finds them very surprising.

It remains that the justification for clean-surface research is not technology but science. The results accumulated to date have answered a few questions, but have added many new ones to the list. Although clean-surface research is only the first step, it may be the thin end of a very thick wedge—a wedge that will one day pry open the box containing the secrets of surface behavior.

Further reading

Most of what is known about clean surfaces resides in the heads of those doing the research, and in the papers they have published. Fortunately, they are a tidy lot; in many cases they have collected the papers and published them as a group between soft covers.

One such volume, representing the most up-to-date review of research, is the proceedings of the clean-surface conference, early in 1962. Titled, *Conference on Clean Surfaces with Supplement: Surface Phenomena in Semiconductors (Symposium)*—the supplement being a series of papers given at a Section of the American Chemical Society also early in 1962 —it is published by the New York Academy of Sciences and is available from them. Also worth looking at are the four hardbound proceedings of previous conferences on surface chemistry and physics. The first, a 1952 conference arranged by the National Research Council, is titled *Structure and Properties of Solid Surfaces*, ed. by Gomer and Smith (U. of Chicago Press, 1953, $11.50). The second, *Semiconductor Surface Physics*, ed. by Kingston (U. of Pa.

Press, 1957, $8), is a compendium of papers presented at a conference that met in Philadelphia in 1956 and contains two papers on clean surfaces. The third, a collection of papers presented at the 1959 Columbus meeting of the Electrochemical Society, is *The Surface Chemistry of Metals and Semiconductors*, ed. by Gatos (Wiley, 1960, $12.50). The fourth is titled *Semiconductor Surfaces—Proceedings of the Second Conference*, ed. by Zemel (Pergamon, 1960, $25).

For more about the tools of clean-surface research, see *Field Emission and Field Ionization* by Gomer (Harvard Press, 1961, $6.75) and a longish chapter by Müller in *Advances in Electronics and Electron Physics*, Vol. 13 (Academic Press, 1960, $14), which, taken together, give a good picture of the field-electron and field-ion microscopes and what they can do. The only comprehensive volume on low-energy-electron diffraction—and it's not very comprehensive—is a monograph published by Bell Laboratories, which includes reprints of a number of important papers: *Low-Energy Diffraction* (No. 4364 Bell Telephone System Technical Publications) by Germer, Hartman, MacRae, and Schiebner. Due out soon but three years out of date because of compilation problems, is a several-volume effort called *Perspectives in Materials Research*, ed. by Gomer (Govt. Printing Office). It includes a 200-page-plus review of surface phenomena compiled by a committee of experts.

For more about surfaces of all kinds, liquid as well as solid, you will find Adamson's textbook, *Physical Chemistry of Surfaces*, a thorough and eminently readable volume (Interscience, 1960, $12.75). Also in this class, although somewhat biased toward the liquid surface, is *Interfacial Phenomena* by Davies and Rideal (Academic Press, 1961, $14).

SOLIDS UNDER PRESSURE

by Seymour Tilson *

IN BRIEF: *Now attainable with neither undue difficulty nor expense, pressures of 10,000 to 500,000 atmospheres offer vast research opportunity to every discipline.*

Acting on solids, such extreme pressures can reduce atomic spacing and size, perturb an atom's electron shell structure, and alter atomic bonding. Such pressure, therefore, provides a powerful means to study the many solid-state phenomena that relate to these basic parameters. Studies using pressure—on semiconductors,

in superconductivity, and over a wide range of optical, electrical, magnetic, and structural effects—are increasing rapidly.

In all chemical processes, where the thermodynamics and kinetics of phase equilibria and phase transformations are crucial, pressure offers the possibility of significantly shifting such equilibria. This clears the path to syntheses, reactions, and substances never before attainable.

To the metallurgist and materials engineer, high pressure affords a new tool for studies in diffusion mechanisms and rates, atomic mo-

* Seymour Tilson is Associate Editor of *International Science and Technology*.

bility, defect structures, grain boundary energies, and the ultimate effects of these upon mechanical properties.

And in the earth sciences, many problems of the most fundamental nature are yielding to studies of mineral phase equilibria under pressure conditions that simulate those existing deep within the earth.—S.T.

TABLE 1. HIGH-PRESSURE ORIENTATION

Phenomenon	*Pressure (atm)*
Gas cylinder	100
Chemical process	1,000
Mohorovicic discontinuity	15,000
High-pressure laboratory *	10,000–500,000
Earth's core	3,000,000
Explosive shock	3,000,000
White-dwarf stars	10^{13}–10^{15}

* Some Examples:

Resistance drops in Bi	25,000
Coesite synthesis	35,000
Diamond synthesis	55,000–100,000
Metallic selenium	135,000
Metallic iodine	250,000
Metallic sulfur	400,000
Resistance peak in rubidium	450,000

■ When solids enter the realm of high pressure now attainable in the laboratory, man takes a short step towards emulating conditions that exist at depths within the earth, and inside the stars. Though laboratory pressures are limited compared with those known in nature, as shown in Table 1, they are sufficient to create a new environment for matter—a harsh environment that imposes unaccustomed discipline and restraint upon matter's ultimate constituents. But matter, obdurate and perverse, seeks freedom in new directions. And it finds such freedom in directions that are precisely afforded to it by no other circumstances. The maneuvers of matter under high pressure open a new dimension of research opportunity to every science that deals with solids.

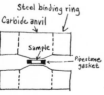

For the mechanical sciences that make possible the apparatuses for reaching very high pressure, there's been a dividend in the form of new insight into how to design for high stress. For chemistry, high pressure has made possible previously unrealized reactions. For metallurgy, it's meant extending the range and variety of possible alloys, some of which can be preserved by quenching to room temperature. For physics, and for fundamental investigation in the preceding two fields, high pressures have been a unique tool for studying matter, for only that way can interatomic distances be changed without heating effects.

The seeming magic of phenomena at high pressure—insulators becoming like metallic conductors, gases turning to liquids and then to dense solids, graphite turning into diamond—reflects the profound sensitivity of macroscopic properties to changes in lattice spacing. It also portends a range of applications only some of which are now visible to us.

Twice the room for chemical maneuver

Suppose, for instance, one wants to induce a chemical reaction in a system that is otherwise reluctant to react, under any conditions of catalysis or temperature. A case in point is the long search for a way to synthesize diamond from other crystalline or amorphous forms of carbon.

The vital clue that led to commercial success in transforming ordinary graphite into diamond is clearly visible in Fig. 1-50. This phase diagram for carbon shows the conditions of temperature and pressure at which the two crystal forms, and the various physical states of the element, are thermodynamically stable. It seemed reasonable that efforts to accomplish the desired graphite-to-diamond reaction should concentrate in those temperature and pressure regions where diamond is the thermodynamically stable form. And in 1955, this approach succeeded. Diamonds of industrial grade, up to 1 carat in size, surpassing the natural stone in some properties, are being routinely produced under suitable conditions of temperature and catalysis—and at pressures between 55,000 and 100,000 atmospheres.

Glamorous as the diamond synthesis is, its greatest value is to highlight the power of the added experimental dimension which pressure provides to achieve chemical reactions, phase changes, and syntheses in the solid state.

Another way to look at this new dimension for chemical exploration is shown in Fig. 1-51. The limited region of pressure and temperature formerly accessible was opened to exploration by the Nobel Prize winning work of P. W. Bridgman of Harvard. Bridgman's several modifications of his early deceptively simple "anvil" apparatus, shown in the margin, led to apparatus capable of getting pressures as high as perhaps 400,000 atm, but only at modest temperatures. It took another decade of effort—by groups such as those at the General Electric Company, the Geophysical Laboratory of the Carnegie Institute, and the National Bureau of Standards—to develop the simultaneous capability of attaining high pressure plus high temperature.

Squeeze an insulator—make a metal

Instead of chemical synthesis, suppose your aim as a student of the solid state is the understanding of insulating and semiconducting ma-

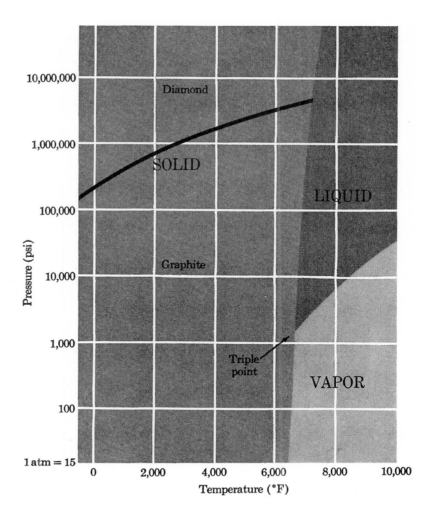

Fig. 1-50. Phase diagram for carbon shows the ranges of temperature and pressure over which the diamond and graphite polymorphs are thermodynamically stable. All known commercial methods for making diamonds use pressures that lie well within the field of diamond's stability—plus appropriate temperatures, and suitable catalytic agents.

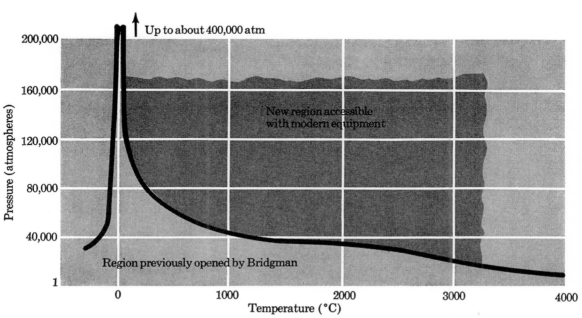

Fig. 1-51. Schematic curves indicate graphically the greatly enlarged domain of temperature and pressure now available to research with modern high pressure equipment. Prior to General Electric Research Lab's development of the "belt" apparatus, shown in Fig. 1-55, high pressures were attainable with various modifications of the simple Bridgman anvil, but only over limited range of temperature. Several other types of modern apparatus now have combined pressure-temperature capability similar to that of the belt.

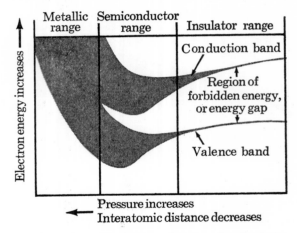

Fig. 1-52. Increasing pressure broadens bands of electron energy. As valence and conduction bands approach each other and finally overlap, insulating solid passes through semiconducting interval, then goes metallic. Such transitions are reversible, of course.

terials. Whether a particular substance will behave as an insulator, semiconductor, or metal depends chiefly on one basic quantum property —the interval of forbidden energy between levels of allowed electron energy within the interacting atoms of the material. Figure 1-52 and the discussion that follows will help make this clear.

In the solid state the discrete electron energy levels of a material's isolated atoms are broadened into bands of energy, because the electron orbits around the individual atoms overlap and interact to some extent in the close confines of the solid crystal's lattice structure. According to the band theory description of the electronic structure of solids, a semiconductor or an insulator is characterized by the fact that the highest level of energy available to the electrons—termed the "conduction" band—is empty; on the contrary, the next lower energy band—the "valence" band—is completely filled with electrons. And lying between the conduction and valence bands is the "energy gap," or region of forbidden energy, which is disallowed to the electrons. Characterizing any particular substance, the width of this zone of forbidden energy is greater for an insulator than for a semiconductor, as indicated in Fig. 1-52.

When pressure upon a solid that is an intrinsic insulator is increased, the interatomic spacing is reduced, and several things start to happen. The discrete energy levels—or narrow energy bands—of the atoms which are relatively far apart are broadened into wider bands of permitted energy. As a result, the width of the zone of forbidden energy may diminish, and the material, which entered the pressure

domain as an insulator, becomes a semiconductor.

Finally, at some critical interatomic distance, the valence and conduction bands will overlap as their broadening entirely eliminates the energy gap. When this occurs, the electrons at the higher-energy end of the valence band gain access to a state of even higher energy—that of the conduction band. They then become capable of moving freely in response to an applied potential. Lo and behold, the insulator, after passing through an interval of semiconducting behavior, has become semimetallic in conductivity. Such transition to the metallic state will presumably occur in any insulator at high enough pressure, i.e., at sufficiently small interatomic distances.

Recent experimental work at the University of Illinois by H. Drickamer has demonstrated metallic transitions of this kind for selenium and iodine. Selenium's electrical resistance drops rapidly but continuously, as pressure is increased to about 128,000 atm. At this pressure, the resistance plummets with sharp discontinuity—some three orders of magnitude. And selenium's resistivity after the sharp transition is estimated to be $50–100 \times 10^{-6}$ ohm-cm—definitely in the metallic range. Iodine similarly crosses the threshold to a metallic resistivity of about $60–120 \times 10^{-5}$ ohm-cm at pressure above about 235,000 atm.

Such manipulation of matter's fundamental electrical properties opens the way to a clearer understanding of insulators and semiconductors. It even suggests, speculatively, using pressure as an alternative to the widespread practice of doping semiconductor materials in order to obtain desirable continuous rather than stepwise variation in semiconductor properties. And, less speculatively, experiments undertaken by W. Paul at Harvard on the pressure dependence of the energy gaps in silicon and germanium promise to clarify the properties of tunnel diodes and to provide a critical test for the quantum-mechanical theory of tunneling.

Putting a subtle squeeze on steel

Another example of the possibilities in high pressure comes from the metallurgy of steel. The schematic phase diagram in Fig. 1-53 shows the effect of pressure on the phase boundaries within an iron-based alloy system, such as in the important iron-chromium or iron-aluminum systems, for example.

The phase diagrams of some such alloys exhibit a feature known as the "gamma loop," crescent shaped in Fig. 1-53. Gamma and alpha iron differ in crystal structure: gamma iron is face-centered cubic; alpha iron is body-centered cubic. When a steel is heated to the appropriate temperature, the body-centered alpha iron converts to the gamma structure, and the substance that the metallurgists call austenite is formed. Austenite is denser than the lower-temperature-annealed form of steel, and, furthermore, it has the virtue of taking up in solid solution all of the carbon present in the steel. This means that to the degree that austenite can be preserved upon quenching of the heated steel to room temperature, that steel is simultaneously made both harder and tougher (or less brittle).

Now the effect of pressure on such iron-alloy systems is to extend both the temperature range and the compositional range over which the desirable gamma type of iron is stable. Thus, when heat treatment is conducted under pressure, the quenched experimental sample volume (a few mm³) behaves as shown in Fig. 1-53. Compositions to the right of the alpha plus gamma field remain body-centered cubic (alpha) at all temperatures. But pressure of about 75,000 atm shifts the gamma loop to the position shown on the right. In the iron-chromium system, for instance, the alloy composition range over which the gamma form is stable is increased from a maximum of 12.5% (by weight) chromium content to 20%. For the iron-aluminum system, the shift in the gamma loop under the same pressure is from 0.6% to more than 3.0% maximum aluminum content.

The practical interest in this pressure-induced extension of the gamma (or austenitic) region is that it widens the compositional range over which such alloys can be successfully heat-treated.

But such shifts in phase equilibria are just one way that metallurgy and the other materials sciences can find new research riches in high pressure. As with temperature in the past, we can expect that in the future metallurgical studies will systematically determine the effects of pressure on basic properties of various alloy systems—atomic mobility, diffusion phenomena, rate-controlling mechanisms, defect structures, grain boundary energies, and so on. Even the straightforward mechanical properties have scarcely been studied at all.

The chief reason for this paucity of research into such basics as mechanical properties is the very small size of specimen chambers in present pressure apparatus. It is difficult to perform mechanical tests, other than hardness determinations.

This sample-size limitation is serious too in another important way. The would-be commercial synthesis of new substances of any category, in such small volumes, means that such syntheses necessarily are restricted to materials

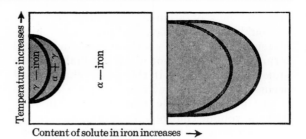

Fig. 1-53. Gamma loop separates the stability fields of the gamma and alpha forms of iron. Pressure enlarges the stable domain of the desirable gamma iron; may permit heat treatment of a steel over a wider range of compositions.

that have high value per unit volume—such as diamonds. Thus while small sample volume is only a moderate drawback in research application of pressure, commercial production is another matter.

Let's leave specific examples at this point and see why pressure offers such peculiar and powerful research capabilities.

Pressure and temperature: pro and con

The unique influence of high pressure can best be understood by comparing its effects upon solids with the more familiar ones of temperature. In most respects, of course, temperature and pressure are opposed to each other in the demands they make upon matter. Thus, for example, decreasing the temperature of most solids increases their density and lowers their volume and entropy. The same effects can be achieved by *raising* the pressure.

Table 2 shows the thermal energy that is equivalent to certain values of pressure as applied to a few common materials. It is obvious that ordinary chemical reactions at atmospheric pressure involve much greater energy changes than can be conveniently produced by applying pressure alone. Indeed, a pressure of even 100,000 atm might almost be ignored, from the

TABLE 2. ENERGY EQUIVALENTS OF PRESSURE

Pressure (atm)	Substance	Energy (cal/mole)
1,000	gas	3,000
1,000	solid	1
10,000	solid	5
100,000	Fe	20
100,000	H_2O	1,000
100,000	K	1,600
1	Ordinary chemical reaction	20,000
100,000	Solid in which phase change occurs	25,000

point of view of a single atom. But to ignore it would be to overlook the promise of high-pressure work. Phase changes from one crystal form to another are not at all unusual in solids under pressure. And if the phase change that occurs is associated with a volume change of 1 cm³ per gram mole (this is approximately half the volume change in the graphite-diamond reaction) at a pressure of 100,000 atm, the free-energy difference between the two states is about 25,000 calories per gram mole. Such a driving energy is decidedly neither trivial nor is it to be ignored as a reaction driving force. It is quite comparable with chemical bonding energies. Thus, pressure offers the distinct possibility, almost totally unexplored, of shifting chemical and physical equilibria, in appropriate systems where appreciable volume changes are involved.

Another way to look at pressure is in the mechanical sense. Either temperature or pressure can be used to manipulate the interatomic distances in solids. Lowered temperature, or increased pressure, each can bring the atoms of a solid closer together, as was noted earlier. But temperature change alone can vary interatomic distances only within strict limits and then only as a secondary effect of the lattice vibrations that are the primary microscopic link to temperature. One such limit at the upper extreme is the melting point of the solid. And, the lower limit is immutably fixed by the absolute zero of temperature. This in turn sets bounds to the degree of atomic proximity, interaction, and consequent perturbation that can be achieved by lowering the temperature. But no such limits exist with pressure.

In fact, even rather modest pressure (10,000–20,000 atm or so) literally not only squeezes the atoms closer together but, tantamount to saying the same thing—it also perturbs the individual atom's electron shell structure, altering it in various measurable ways.

Theoretically there is no limit to the pressure that can be imposed, but practical limits are set by the failure of the pressure-producing apparatus. However, under the very highest pressures estimated to exist in the universe—10^{13} to 10^{15} atm within white dwarf stars (extremely remote from any pressure that can be reached experimentally)—electrons are stripped from their nuclei, matter becomes completely degenerate, and the nuclei themselves are brought close enough together to permit nuclear fusion.

There is another crucial distinction to be made between temperature and pressure effects upon solids. Temperature variation simultaneously affects two quantities: (1) the kinetic energy of vibration of the atoms in the lattice;

(2) the distance between them. High pressure, on the other hand, even more competent than lowered temperature to reduce atomic spacing, has an added advantage. It is free from the extraneous complicating effects upon the behavior of atoms within a lattice caused by changes in kinetic energy when temperature is used as the manipulative variable.

Therefore, the advent of experimental capability in high pressures brings to solid state research and development a surer, sharper means of probing interatomic—and intra-atomic—forces and the effects of perturbations upon them. And in many laboratories studies are accelerating into the effects of pressure on insulators, semiconductors, and metals. Other studies shed light on such diverse matters as: melting-point behavior, superconductivity phenomena in helium and hydrogen, valence theory, charge transfer, atomic and molecular bonding, electrical and magnetic properties of materials, color centers in alkali halides, vacancies, interstitials, and other defect structures, optical phenomena, and more.

Finally, consider briefly how pressure can help simulate conditions in the physically inaccessible depths of the earth.

A pressure probe for the depths of the earth

Research into phase equilibria and chemical kinetics at high pressure has attracted earth scientists for a very long time. Those portions of the planet below a few miles in depth are inaccessible to direct observation. Yet hidden there are the answers to many intriguing questions: What are the sources for volcanic lavas? What temperatures exist at the earth's core? What is the nature of the mountain building, rock metamorphism, and crustal deformation that seem to be so closely related to the growth of the continental land masses?

The obvious recourse to remedy the lack of information on conditions deep in the earth has been duplication in the laboratory.

The 10,000–500,000-atm range of today's high-pressure apparatus at least duplicates conditions characteristic of depths well into the earth's mantle—several hundreds of miles —even as it falls short of the 3,000,000-atm pressure at the earth's core. But, of course, temperature rises along with pressure as depth increases. And the best apparatuses now available can maintain sustained high temperatures —in the order of 2000°C—only at pressures in the vicinity of 100,000 atm.

Still, even such limited studies of mineral stability suggest that some of the rocks now exposed at the earth's surface were formed at surprisingly great depths. Such data crudely indicate that vertical displacements in the crust of the earth over long periods of geologic time are much greater than was previously suspected. In fact, vertical displacements of rock masses on the order of magnitude of the crust's total thickness itself—about 20 miles—seem to be not at all unusual.

The cost of high pressure

When asked to explain the almost total neglect, until recent years, of research on solids under high pressure, a leader in the field replied, "High-pressure work is rough, dirty, and potentially dangerous. You have to be willing to get your hands dirty on occasion. In fact, in pressure research, the instincts of a good plumber or blacksmith are as essential as scientific sophistication."

His reply is at once both one possible answer to the original question, and an equally accurate portrayal of the equipment situation. Most of the equipment used for investigation above 10,000 atm is both home-made and custom-made for specific research and development purposes. There is little in the way of equipment that is available from the catalog, although there are a few suppliers of packaged high-pressure units. In this respect, the situation is entirely analogous to similarly early phases in the development of other research techniques such as x-rays or infrared.

Ultrahigh-pressure apparatus, in other words, is some years away from the production line. On the other hand, whether newcomers to the use of pressure in research applications must build their own apparatus depends very largely on the kind of research program they want to pursue. Getting capability in the high-pressure domain can be quite expensive—in the order of tens to hundreds of thousands of dollars—or as inexpensive as a few hundred or thousand dollars.

Referring to basic parameters once again, cost in pressure work seems to depend upon two key variables. One is the volume of specimen that is to be handled. In a crude way, cost is roughly proportional to specimen volume—for a very simple reason, the nature of pressure. The absolute unit of pressure is, of course, force divided by area. And as the surface area or volume of a sample enclosure increases, the force needed to achieve the desired pressure also goes up—along with the concomitant difficulties we will discuss shortly.

This factor, however, is relatively less important in fixing experimental difficulty and cost than is the second—the temperature capability that is desired along with the pressure. The higher the pair go, the greater in general the cost becomes.

Three classes of pressure apparatus

There are nearly as many kinds of pressure-generating equipment as there are kinds of research to be done—and very nearly as many as there are groups or individuals doing research. But this diversity of apparatus can be reduced to three major classes: (1) Fluid (or hydraulic) pressure media; (2) Solid piston-and-cylinder units; (3) Anvil bearing arrangements. The capability of each of these is indicated in Fig. 1-54, which shows the useful regions of temperature and pressure for each class of equipment.

Each category of equipment has its particular capability. The highest static pressures are attainable with some surprisingly simple modifications of the old Bridgman anvil idea—at, however, some cost in temperature capability.

For the combination of pressure with the highest attainable temperatures, no other class of equipment touches the supported or confined piston devices. Their temperature capacity puts them into a class of their own.

Not evident from Fig. 1-54 is the fact that the relatively routine and commercially available fluid pressure generators also have a particular advantage for applications such as semiconductor or superconductivity studies, where the highest possible precision is essential. This is because the pressure they offer, though relatively low, is at all times completely defined in value, and certainly hydrostatic in nature. Pressure transmitted by the fluid is accurately defined by resistance changes in highly refined manganin wire gauges. On the contrary, in apparatus using solid pressure transmitting media, both piston and anvil, the precision with which pressure is defined is considerably lower, for reasons we will explain below. Furthermore, the solid pressure trans-

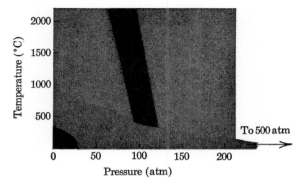

Fig. 1-54. Solid area at lower left shows pressure-temperature capability of commercially available fluid-pressure generators. Dark area next to it indicates region accessible with various anvil apparatuses. Vertical area is the domain of piston-cylinder types of equipment. Overlaps are not shown.

mitters develop and support shearing or differential stresses which are impossible in the fluid media, and therefore the degree to which stresses on the sample in these is truly hydrostatic is uncertain at present stages of development.

In spite of this advantage, fluid pressure generators are limited in the pressures and temperatures they can attain. At pressures beyond 25,000–30,000 atm the fluids commonly used—argon, helium, nitrogen, or isopentane—either become too viscous for use, or else they freeze in the pressure lines. Combining them with higher temperatures requires elaborate and clumsy plumbing arrangements. And a further practical disadvantage with hydraulic equipment is the need for sealing and resealing against leakage each time the specimen chamber is opened to change a run.

In general, then, solid pressure-transmitting devices are finding most favor for both lower- and higher-temperature work. Uncertainty in the precise value of the pressure acting on a sample and the unavoidable and difficult-to-evaluate presence of some shearing stress components in the pressure distribution on the sample are problems, to be sure. But at the moment, such problems are outweighed by the twin advantages of much greater pressure and temperature, particularly for much raw first exploration of the high-pressure realm where the highest precision is not required by the investigation.

Solid pistons, anvils, in a wide variety

The few types of equipment that we will consider in this brief survey merely illustrate some of the general principles and problems which, with only slight modification in details, apply to all types of equipment. Many other examples would serve as well.

Probably the most impressive apparatus around, from the dual standpoint of its size and its combined temperature-pressure capability, is the so-called "belt" apparatus. It was developed for the diamond-synthesis and general high-pressure program at General Electric's research laboratory. This setup is shown in Fig. 1-55. In this unit, pressures of about 100,000 atm, at temperatures in excess of 2000°C, can be maintained for several hours.

The equipment functions rather simply, as do

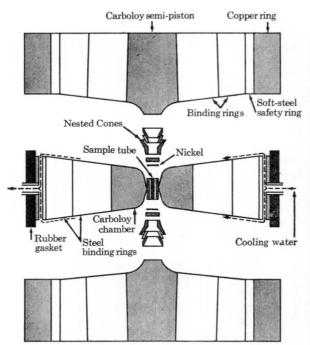

Fig. 1-55. Exploded view of GE belt apparatus shows how pistons and confining chamber are tapered to reduce stress concentrations. Massive support is provided by binding rings which are prestressed and press fitted into place. Nest of conical sections—alternately pyrophyllite and steel—collapses as press at right applies load, and provides smooth pressure gradient, flash gasket, pressure seal, and insulation. (Courtesy General Electric Co.)

all pressure generators. The two semi-pistons enter each side of the Carboloy chamber, impelled by a hydraulic press. The Carboloy chamber, together with its steel binding rings, forms a toroidal belt around the sample chamber, hence the name of the apparatus. Pressure is transmitted to the sample within the nickel sample tube by a pyrophyllite sleeve which encloses the sample tube. (More about pyrophyllite, appropriately called "wonderstone" by high-pressure workers, in a moment.) The pyrophyllite conical cylinders in the nest serve not only as the pressure-transmitting medium, but also as flash gaskets and pressure seals, and as electrical and thermal insulators too. Samples are heated by passing electrical current through the nickel sample tube via the steel-and-nickel end discs adjacent to the sample tube. The binding rings of hardened steel, which are strained near their elastic limits by forced-on taper fits (analogous to the old trick used in naval gun barrels), back up and greatly strengthen the pistons and the toroidal chamber. Safety rings are of soft steel, and offer protection from fragments when binding rings fracture, as they sometimes may.

An example both of the variability in design geometry possible, and of an apparatus that is really in a position between the supported piston type and the unconfined anvil equipments is shown in Fig. 1-56. This unit is the National Bureau of Standard's modification of a tetrahedral multipiston unit developed by H. T. Hall at General Electric.

The unit essentially consists of four pistons or anvils, each of which is shaped as a truncated three-sided pyramid. The truncating terminal face has the shape of an equilateral triangle. When the four pistons are brought together, their terminal faces enclose a tetrahedral volume, as shown in the bottom part of Fig. 1-56. In the NBS design, one piston is actively brought down by a press into a nest of the other three. These in turn are set into a nesting ring that has a tapered inside surface. In the positions shown occupied by paper in Fig. 1-56 are normally placed thin Teflon sheets. These separate the lower three pistons from the nesting ring, and provide electrical insulation. They also serve as a lubricant to the motion of the three lower pistons when the advancing active piston forces them down into the conically tapered inner surface of the nesting ring retainer.

The pyrophyllite tetrahedron shown in the lower part of Fig. 1-56 is about 10% larger in edge dimension than the edges of the equilateral-triangle faces of the pistons. Thus, when the ram piston is advanced, all of the pistons are separated from each other slightly along

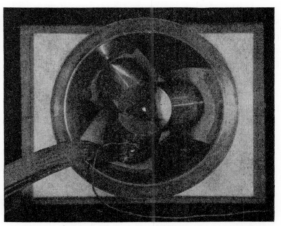

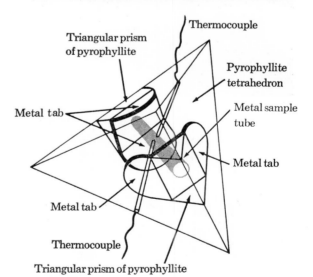

Fig. 1-56. Modification of tetrahedral apparatus at National Bureau of Standards uses one active piston, top, which is brought down into nest of three others enclosed in internally tapered retainer, as shown in middle photo. Four pistons confine tetrahedral volume of pyrophyllite cell shown at bottom. Pyrophyllite extrudes under pressure to form gasket and seal and transmit pressure to sample cell enclosed within it. (Courtesy National Bureau of Standards and S. Tilson)

their pyramidal faces. And as the pistons compress the tetrahedral sample cell, some of the pyrophyllite is extruded along the piston flanks to form a flash gasket and seal, quite analogous in function to its behavior in the belt machine. This unit's capability is similar to that of the belt.

A remarkably simple apparatus which differs quite a bit from the rather hefty devices just discussed is shown in Fig. 1-57. This anvil-type unit was developed at NBS for conducting infrared studies of samples under pressure. Its claimed pressure capability is about 160,000 atm. And that high pressure is obtained simply by turning the loading screw by hand. Force is accurately determined from knowledge of the constants of the calibrated loading spring. The sample is pressed between the anvils, which can be of diamond or sapphire depending on the infrared transmission range desired for a study. One anvil face is ground smaller than the other,

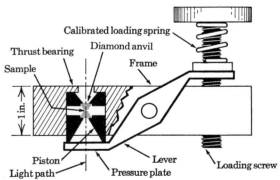

Fig. 1-57. Simple device developed at National Bureau of Standards for optical and infrared studies at high pressure. Pressure is applied to the anvil surfaces by turning hand screw against calibrated loading spring. This unit can reach pressure of about 160,000 atm, at room temperature. Higher temperature capability would require extensive modification. (Courtesy S. Tilson)

and its area is assumed to be the bearing area for the purpose of calculating pressure. Its use at present is limited to the lower temperature ranges of a few hundred degrees centigrade, which can be obtained either by forcing heated air past the anvil area or by placing the whole gadget, suitably modified within a furnace.

Problems in apparatus multiply, of course, when high temperatures are added to the requirements. The strength of the steels and sintered tungsten carbides used drops sharply with rising temperatures. To a degree this can be circumvented by provision for internal heating of the sample only. However, this raises a number of additional problems such as insulating the heated zone from the pressure vessel itself, transmitting the pressure from vessel to sample, preventing chemical reaction between vessel, sample, and insulator, and accurately determining temperature and pressure within this small, relatively inaccessible area.

Here is where the pyrophyllite, or other gasket materials become important.

Pressure transmitters and gaskets

The requirements of the perfect pressure transmitting medium and the ideal gasket material are, fortunately, complementary in many ways. Ideally, a perfect pressure transmitter would support no shearing stresses at all. It would transmit the uniaxial compressive stress applied to it by piston or anvil as an isotropic, hydrostatic pressure throughout the sample zone. In addition to hydrostatic transmission of the pressure, the ideal medium would be only slightly compressible, have low electrical and thermal conductivity, and would be chemically and thermally stable.

Similarly, a pressure gasket must be simultaneously capable of yielding to pressure induced by the advancing pistons, and yet resisting the outwardly directed thrust of the sample material being compressed. And it must smooth the extremely high pressure gradient from within the sample area to the external surfaces of the extruded gasket. That gradient must be free of abrupt transitions that would permit the buildup of excessive stress concentrations upon the metal pistons or anvils.

Such unusual materials do not exist. But substances such as talc, pyrophyllite, and boron nitride (itself created in the high-pressure laboratory) at least approximate these requirements. In research on super-conductivity at cryogenic temperatures, another important area where the pressure factor is quite helpful, pressure-transmitting media such as indium are most useful.

A question that should become apparent at this point is this: with the sample, the piston or anvil, and the gasket material all either deforming or extruding under the applied press force, how can one really know the area over which the applied load is acting on the sample? Or, in other words, how does one determine the pressure?

Calibration—few absolutes on the way up

Pressure calibration is still up for grabs. At this point it is an intralaboratory art subject to interlaboratory checks.

In general, a laboratory calculates its pressure from the known applied force, and from its best estimate of the working area, the latter subject to the design geometry of the equipment and the uncertainties indicated above. The nominal pressures are then determined for several physical transition phenomena—such as volume or resistance changes—for a number of agreed-upon reference substances. Finally, cross checking among laboratories leads to continual refinement of the pressure values that are assigned to the reference transitions. The present state of the calibration art is such that pressures in the 100,000-atm range can be measured to within an accuracy of better than one percent.

Figure 1-58 shows the volume and resistance changes that occur at agreed-upon values of pressure for the four materials most commonly used for such calibration—bismuth, thallium, barium, and cesium. The calibration procedure in a new apparatus setup simply requires the running of these materials, and the detection of the resistance changes which occur. For this, conventional thermocouple materials are used, although most of them require a correction for the effect of pressure on their emf.

If the pressure range of experimental work in a new apparatus is considerably above the calibration range established by these transitions, a number of additional materials and transition phenomena have been reasonably well fixed. These include transition events such as a resistance increase of 350% in iron at about 130,000 atm, and a rather broad peak in the resistance of rubidium at around 420,000 atm.

Another striking check of the calibration scale at these higher pressures has become available recently. Much research is being carried on using the detonation front of an explosive shock wave as the pressure-producing mechanism. And determinations of the iron resistance peak's pressure value by static loading methods we have discussed is very closely confirmed by a shock-wave velocity change at nearly the same pressure in the dynamic experiments.

We can anticipate further refinement of pressure calibration in the future. We can also expect slow but steady upward progress

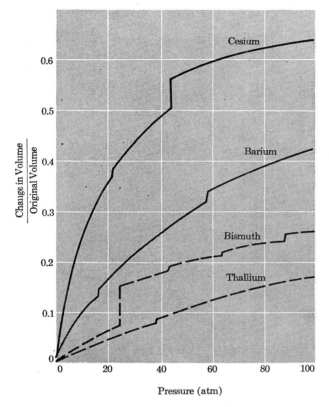

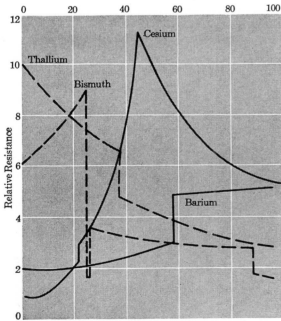

Fig. 1-58. Curves illustrate the changes in volume and resistance which occur in bismuth, thallium, cesium, and barium over the pressure range up to 100,000 atm. Such discontinuous changes are the basis for calibration of new pressure apparatus.

in combined pressure and temperature capability, perhaps to 200,000 atm at temperatures of 2000–3000°C. We can look forward to rapid extension of the data-gathering possibilities under high-pressure conditions as problems of sample accessibility are overcome. And we can confidently expect the completely unexpected to emerge, as pressure is brought to bear in an ever-widening variety of practical and theoretical investigations.

Further reading

Still the basic introduction to the pathways of high pressure, after all these years, is P. W. Bridgman's *Physics of High Pressure* (Bell, London, 1949). But two new books have recently been published. Together, they should provide a comprehensive and up-to-date picture of this vast heterogeneous field.

One is *Modern Very High Pressure Techniques*, edited by Wentorf, Jr. (Butterworths, London, 1963, $8.40). This is a collection of chapters by active researchers emphasizing apparatus, instrumentation, and calibration problems of the high-pressure laboratory.

Quite different, in that it concentrates on research goals and is much more comprehensive in scope, is *High Pressure Physics and Chemistry*, edited by Bradley (Academic Press, 1963).

A collection of papers that were presented at a 1960 conference on high-pressure work, uneven in tone and content but containing a mass of useful information, is available in *Progress in Very High Pressure Research*, edited by Bundy, Strong, and Hibbard, Jr. (Wiley, New York, 1961, $12). "A Survey of High Pressure Effects of Solids," by DeVries et al., offers a summary of the known high-pressure work done on solids from 1947–1959. It also has selected references to work with liquids and gases. It is available as Order PB 181 096, from the Office of Technical Services, Department of Commerce, Washington 25, D.C., $6.

Useful review articles on the application of pressure to solid state research can be found in Volumes 6, 11, 12, and 13 of the serial publication *Solid State Physics*, edited by Seitz and Turnbull, Academic Press, New York. Scattered additional material occurs in the *J. Chem. Phys.*, *J. Geophys. Research*, and *Rev. Modern Phys.*

SHOCK WAVES IN SOLIDS

by George E. Duvall *

IN BRIEF: *Although an explosion is both sudden and violent, the energy it releases can be controlled to generate a shock wave of almost any desired magnitude. Pressures range from about 15 to perhaps 9 thousand kilobars in solids. Such almost-instantaneous pressures change levels of electron energy in solids, redistribute atoms in lattices, and alter the internal energy balance of a solid. Thus, shock waves can cause phase changes, yield equation-of-state data currently obtainable in no other way, drastically alter electrical, mechanical, and thermal properties, harden metals, bond dissimilar materials, elucidate the kinetics of fast chemical reactions, and yield data of prime interest to solid-state physics, metallurgy, and geophysics.*

Drawbacks, however, are high cost—$25,000 minimum for an experimental facility, and no less than $1,000 for each shot, difficulty of using explosives, and present limits to understanding of how shocks interact with matter. Improving time resolution from 10^{-8} to 10^{-9} sec would help.—S.T.

* George E. Duvall, for ten years Senior Physicist, Scientific Director, and Director of Stanford Research Institute's Poulter Laboratories, is now Professor of Physics at Washington State University, Pullman, Washington.

■ Shock waves have been important in military and industrial technology at least since the invention of blasting powder. And theorizing about them dates as far back as Rankine's classical memoir of 1870. Yet only now, with improved techniques and instrumentation, are the interactions between shock waves and matter beginning to play a serious research role. The reasons for such long delay in exploiting a potent research avenue are not difficult to understand.

Requirements on instrumentation for shock-wave research are rigorous indeed; and carrying out work with high explosives calls for both isolation and considerable expense (Fig. 1-59). But probably the most serious barrier has been the paralysis that overtakes the inexperienced mind when it is faced with an explosion. This prevents many from recognizing an explosion as the orderly process it is. Like any orderly process, an explosive shock can be investigated, its effects recorded (Fig. 1-60), understood, and used. The rapidity and violence of an explosion do not vitiate Newton's laws, nor those of thermodynamics, chemistry, or quantum mechanics. They do, however, force matter into new states quite different from those we customarily deal with. These provide stringent

Fig. 1-59. Typical shock experiment uses shot setup at left, placed in front of armor-plated instrument bunker at right. Streak camera inside bunker views mirror at top of setup through glass ports. Light source for camera is in rectangular box next to mirror. Just below it is specimen assembly, in cylinder with hose attached to vacuum line; below this is second cylinder with explosive and plane-wave generator. The shot reduces entire setup to rubble.

tests for some of our favorite assumptions about matter's bulk properties.

Broad accomplishments and applications

Although the laboratories devoted to shock-wave work are very few, their research accomplishments in the last dozen years already are impressive, and the range of applications opened to further development is astonishingly broad. Transient pressures as high as 9 million atmospheres have been achieved: this is three times greater than the pressure at the earth's core, and about 18 times higher than the pressure that can be reached in static pressure-generating equipment (see "Solids Under Pressure," page 69). Shock pressures of such magnitude drastically change electronic energy levels in solids, rearrange atoms in lattices, and

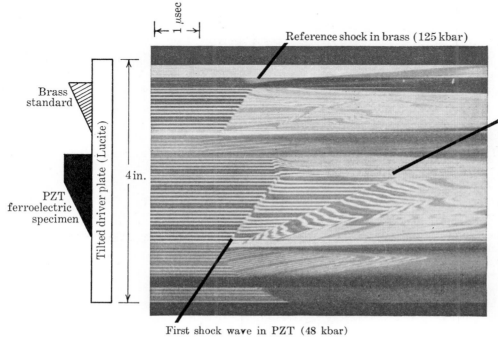

Fig. 1-60. Streak camera record shows shock arrival preceded by an elastic wave. Reference shock in brass gives needed data on state in the driver plate. Record of this kind yields both shock velocity and the velocity of free surface on specimen. Either one can be used to determine the material's (here PZT) equation-of-state when the state in the driver plate is known.

alter the equilibrium partition of energy in substances.

Thus, such pressures—applied almost instantaneously, and under controlled conditions—have yielded fundamental thermodynamic data essential to every science—known as equation-of-state data—for over a hundred materials in a pressure range where thermodynamic parameters could not be obtained by any other means. Changes in crystal structure (such as the familiar graphite-diamond transition)—perma-

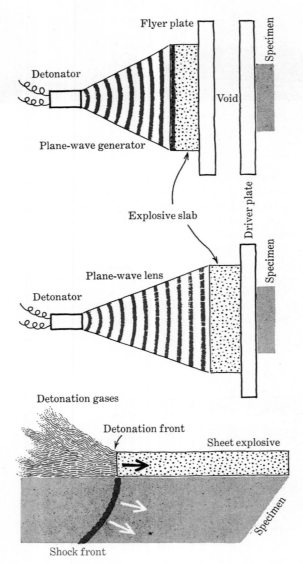

Fig. 1-61. Methods to deliver shock to a specimen differ in cost, pressures they can attain, and ease of interpretation: (Top) Flying plate is most difficult, usually most costly, but attains highest pressures; contact explosive reaches intermediate pressures at comparable or slightly lower cost; oblique shot is least expensive of methods shown, achieves only low pressures, requires large sample, and geometry complicates interpretation.

nent in some materials, transient in others—have been induced by shock.

Shocks change electrical conductivity too, almost magically making conductors out of such insulators as sulfur and paraffin. Shocks also release electrical charges from piezoelectrics, ferroelectrics, and many insulator materials, producing measurable currents in an external circuit; this effect is already the basis of new developments in transducer materials and applications.

Shocks harden metals, create and alter vacancies and dislocations in lattices, and shock-induced impact bonding of metals is now commercial (see "High Energy Rate Metalworking," page 421).

In geophysics, shock-wave research in the laboratory has provided some of the first data ever gained on phase changes that may occur deep in the earth's mantle; and in chemistry shock waves have contributed uniquely to understanding kinetics of fast reaction in gases.

But applications and accomplishments thus far, though impressive, are modest and tentative, compared with what shock research may accomplish—if certain of its inherent difficulties can be overcome.

Great future promise, but problems galore

There are several serious obstacles to the rapid expansion of shock-wave research. One is the shortage of skilled personnel at all technical levels in the field. Another is the violence of strong shock waves—particularly in solids and liquids. Shocks are usually generated by explosives, and the resulting hazards and noise traditionally force operations to remote sites. Ingenuity and forethought may relax this condition; for example, gas guns for producing shock by impact have already been successfully used near office areas, and enclosed shooting chambers may, in the future, permit the detonation of high explosives in relatively populous areas.

Another limitation is that techniques for measuring the details of shock-wave structure are now being pressed to their limits and the best time resolution attainable is about 10^{-8} sec. If this could be decreased to 10^{-9} sec or less, the added details of wave structure that would be discernible could contribute substantially to knowledge of compressive response of shocked materials.

Last, shock-wave research on solids and liquids is relatively expensive. A minimum installation for making quantitative, dynamic measurements probably costs on the order of $25,000 to $50,000. This is aside from the cost of a remote location; and, because experimental assemblies are complicated and require precision manufacture and assembly, the cost of each fully instrumented shot is at least about $1000, including data analysis. Moreover, the thought of an elegant and precise assembly being destroyed in each experiment is almost more than some scientists can bear, and this approach to experimentation calls for a profound psychological readjustment on the part of many experimenters.

Promising as they are, applications are just one aspect of my interest in shock-wave work. Applications depend largely on the effects a shock wave has on the material through which it passes. However, the material reciprocally affects the structure of the shock wave itself, altering and complicating it. One of the chief goals of our work at the Poulter laboratories is to unravel the connections between the original structure of a shock, the properties of the material through which it travels, and the effects upon the shock of its brief journey through the material. The better we understand these relationships, the more likely become applications that we cannot now foresee.

What's a shock wave? More than a big boom!

We all know what a shock wave is, in a sense —it is the boom from a supersonic aircraft, the crack of a bullet, or the blast from an explosion. Yet a precise definition of a shock wave is not so easy to formulate. We commonly use the term to refer to any almost-instantaneous increase in the value of stress or pressure in a material, so long as the velocity with which the stress transition travels through the material is greater than the velocity of sound in the substance. Also essential to our definition is the idea that the stress transition retains its characteristic abruptness as it travels through the medium. As shown in Fig. 1-62, the abrupt transition itself is called the shock front, or shock; it is the compressive phase of the entire shock wave; behind this, where pressure tails off rapidly from its peak value to its pre-shock ambient value, is the wave's rarefaction phase.

Immediately ahead of the shock front at any instant, the material through which the shock is propagating remains undisturbed, blissfully unaware of what's to come. But an infinitesimal distance behind the shock front the material is in the shocked state: it's compressed to a higher density, and its constituent particles are accelerated. This additional particle velocity behind the shock, added to the wave's propagation velocity, permits the rarefaction portion of the shock wave to travel faster than the shock front itself. Therefore, the rarefaction part of the wave gradually overtakes the shock front and, as suggested by Fig. 1-62, the entire shock wave simultaneously lengthens and decreases in am-

plitude as it travels. In a sense, the shock front —by accelerating particles as it passes—sets in motion the cause of its own ultimate undoing.

The details of shock-wave structure depend upon how the wave was generated, how far it has propagated, geometry of generation and of the medium, and upon the material properties of the medium itself. It is this last which is most often of interest, and in consequence, the attempt is made to generate incident shocks so that their detailed structure can be related to properties of the medium. This requires that the experimental geometry be simple and calculable: therefore shock waves for dynamic measurement are most often generated in plane geometry where the direction of propagation and the lapse of time since propagation are the two independent coordinates. This can be done in several ways.

How to make plane shock waves

One drives a flying plate against the specimen assembly (Fig. 1-61 top). Another, not shown in the figure, accelerates a flat-ended projectile in a gun barrel against the specimen. The flying plate arrangement is capable of achieving the highest shock pressures; its range is 300–9000 kbars, although it can be adapted for lower pressure. The data it yields are poorer in quality and higher in cost than those attainable with either the contact-explosive arrangement shown in Fig. 1-61 middle or the gun-launched projectile. The latter also is much more adaptable to conventional laboratory use, but its pressure capability is low; it lies in the range below 100 kbars.

In the flying plate setup, the plane-wave generator produces detonation in a slab of explosive, accelerating the plate to high velocity. It crosses the void, strikes the driver plate,

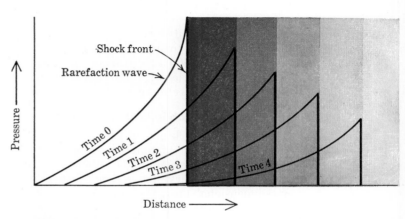

Fig. 1-62. Rarefaction phase of shock wave—where pressure tails off to ambient from its peak value in shock front—travels faster than shock front itself, progressively overtakes it. This causes entire shock wave to decay in amplitude.

and delivers its momentum to the driver plate and specimen.

Pressures as high as 2000 kbars have been reported in iron, in work in this country. And pressures as high as 9000 kbars have been reported in Soviet work on tungsten samples, using this method.

A different way to generate plane shock waves is shown in Fig. 1-61 middle. Here, as with the flying plate setup, a spherical detonation wave started by the detonator is converted into a plane wave by the lens. But then the detonation wave passes through the explosive slab to impinge directly on the driver plate-specimen assembly with no void or flyer plate intervening, as in Fig. 1-61 top. The pressure induced in the driver plate increases with its mechanical impedance. This factor, as we shall see, limits the peak pressure that can be achieved in the specimen.

Why not use the explosive shock directly?

Since the detonation wave in the explosive is itself a shock wave—driven by expansion of the chemically reacting gases behind it—one might reasonably ask, why not use this shock wave directly? Why interpose between this detonation shock and the specimen all the impedimenta shown in Fig. 1-61—especially the explosive slab and the driver plate? In essence, the answer is that the driver plate smooths the extreme dropoff in stress that occurs behind a detonation front; it thus stretches a shock's decay time, improving resolution.

Moreover, introduction of the driver plate and explosive slab into the array gives us three independent parameters for controlling the shock pressure finally induced in the specimen: (1) The kind of explosive in the explosive slab; (2) the material of the driver plate; (3) the ratio of driver-plate thickness to explosive-slab thickness. Thus, for example, the range of pressures that can be produced in a single material with the kind of setup in Fig. 1-61 middle is about four to one. Pressures attainable are in the 100–1500 kbar range, intermediate to those obtainable with the flying plate or gun-launched projectile discussed a while back.

How to make an oblique shock wave

A fourth shock-generating method, the method of oblique detonation shown in Fig. 1-61 bottom, differs from the others in geometry, yielding a curviplanar shock instead of a one-dimensional one. The chief advantages of this method are: first, it offers lower pressures than any other method (18 kbars in aluminum, for instance), making it useful in attempts to correlate shock work with static high-pressure studies; second, it offers a continuous record of both pressure and density from a single experiment, making it valuable for equation-of-state measurements; third, it is the least costly way to make shocks, because large, precise plane-wave generators are not required to initiate detonation. Disadvantages arise from the more complex geometry of the shock wave, which makes data interpretation more difficult than in other methods.

We now know what shock waves are, and how to generate them. Next, let's trace the energy delivered from explosive to specimen further along its path to dissolution.

Old shocks never die—they just fade away

Back in Fig. 1-61 middle, for example, when the plane shock wave in the driver plate reaches the interface between driver plate and specimen, part of the wave is transmitted into the specimen, and part is reflected back into the driver plate. In order to determine the amplitude (and ultimately the energy) of the transmitted wave, we must use the equations which describe the effects of shock transition on both the mechanical and the thermodynamic states of the medium.

These equations express the fact that mass, momentum, and energy are conserved in the shock transition:

$$u_1 = \frac{p_1 - p_0}{\rho_0 U} \tag{1}$$

$$U^2 = V_0^2 \frac{p_1 - p_0}{V_0 - V_1} \tag{2}$$

$$u_1 = \left(1 - \frac{\rho_0}{\rho_1}\right) U \tag{3}$$

$$E_1 - E_0 = \tfrac{1}{2}(V_0 - V_1)(p_1 + p_0) \tag{4}$$

In these equations, which apply precisely to a shock which connects two uniform states —indicated by the subscript (0) for an initial unshocked state, and (1) for a subsequent shocked state—p is the component of compressive stress parallel to the direction of shock propagation. Density is denoted by ρ, and its reciprocal—the specific volume—by V. The velocity of propagation of the shock relative to the unstressed material just ahead of it is U. As mentioned earlier, the shock compresses material to a higher density, and simultaneously increases its particle velocity by u_1. The work done on a unit of mass by the force driving the shock thus shows up as an increase in the internal energy per unit mass of the shock, E, along with an increase in kinetic energy. Equation 4 represents this energy conserved with kinetic energy eliminated by means of Equations 1 and 3.

Equation 4 is most important for discussing the thermodynamics of the shock transitions. Since velocities have been eliminated, it is this equation which serves as basis for comparing the shock transition with better known transitions like the isothermals and adiabatics. Using this equation we can show that the shock transition is dissipative.

When the Rankine-Hugoniot relation is combined with the equation of state of any material, a unique relation between p and V is obtained. This relation is called the Rankine-Hugoniot (R-H) curve of the material (see Fig. 1-63). This curve expresses the locus of all states (p_1, V_1, E_1, and so on) that can be reached from an initial state (p_0, V_0, E_0) by shock compression. In an analogous way, the ordinary adiabat or adiabatic curve may be defined as the locus of all states that can be reached by adiabatic compression.

At the point B, which represents initial unshocked conditions in the material (p_0, V_0, E_0), the R-H curve and an adiabat have the same slope and curvature, but only at that point: at all higher pressures the R-H curve lies above the adiabat, because unlike adiabatic compression, shock compression dissipates energy, and is, therefore, irreversible.

As shown in Fig. 1-63, the increase in internal energy in a shock whose pressure amplitude is p_1 is represented by area ABCD. Loss of energy in a shock can be illustrated by comparing this area thermodynamically with that associated with a weaker shock, area $ABC'D'$, for example. It can also be shown by simple calculation that just as the internal energy increases or decreases as the shock is stronger or weaker, so the entropy of the final shocked state also increases with the shock strength. Although such calculations are valuable in computing the entropy of the shocked state, they are insufficient for calculating the total energy dissipation resulting from passage of the shock wave. However, referring again to Fig. 1-63, the gray area—bounded below by the Rankine-Hugoniot curve and above by the straight line connecting the initial, unshocked point B with the final shocked state C—is a fair approximation to the energy dissipated in the shock cycle. This area is sometimes called the waste heat of the cycle. It is difficult to determine an exact expression for energy dissipated because thermal stresses are left behind in the material, even after the shock pressure has been relieved. Therefore, a precise calculation of the true energy dissipation in a decaying shock must account for hard-to-evaluate effects of thermally induced after-flow in the material. In practice we often settle for the waste heat approximation.

We are now prepared to intelligently conclude our discussion of how a shock wave gets across an interface between two media—as from driver plate to specimen in Fig. 1-61. Such transmission phenomena determine the magnitude of shock we finally get in the specimen, for a given combination of explosive and driver plate characteristics. They are also basic to determining the equation-of-state for unknown materials, using shock data.

Propagation and transmission of shocks

Every unique Rankine-Hugoniot curve derived from relations between pressure and specific volume—as in Fig. 1-63—transforms to an equally unique relationship between pressure and the velocity of particles in the material. The sketch in the margin shows such unique modifications of the R-H curve for both the shock incident in the driver plate (OA), and the shock transmitted into the specimen (OB). But there's an all-important third wave in shock interactions that we also must consider. This is the wave *reflected* back into the driver plate from its interface with the specimen. This can be either a compression or a rarefaction—and the difference is critical—because if it's compressive the shock transmitted to the specimen will be even stronger than that originally incident in the driver. But if, instead, the reflection is a rarefaction, the transmitted shock will be weaker than the incident.

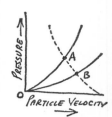

OA = R-H CURVE DRIVER PLATE
OB = R-H CURVE SPECIMEN
AB = CROSS-CURVE FOR DRIVER PLATE

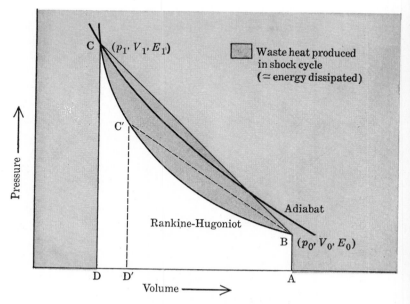

Fig. 1-63. The Rankine-Hugoniot curve defines states that can be induced in substance by shock compression in terms of pressure (p), specific volume (V), and internal energy (E). Shock compression from initial state B to shocked state C follows the straight line BC and dissipates energy shown by the gray area. Thus shock compression is not a reversible process—unlike adiabatic compression, which is, at least ideally. See story for details.

The nature of the reflected wave, therefore, is part of the answer to an important practical question—what experimental conditions are necessary for achieving in a specimen a shock of specified pressure?

In the marginal sketch on page 85, the reflected wave is represented by cross-curve (AB), approximately the mirror image of the R-H curve (OA). Such a cross-curve plays the same role for reflected waves as do R-H curves for direct waves: it defines conditions that exist in material as a result of a wave's passage.

For a given experimental arrangement, if conditions of pressure and particle velocity in the wave reflected back into the driver lie above point A on cross-curve (AB), the reflection is compressive. If, on the other hand, the reflection lies below point A, it is a rarefaction. Point B represents conditions common to both driver plate and specimen (at their interface only), and it is evident that the reflection illustrated is a rarefaction, and that the transmitted wave is weaker than the incident one.

This would be the case for a setup that combined a relatively harder driver—steel, for instance—with a relatively softer specimen such as lucite. Reversing the relative hardness of driver and specimen would, of course, reverse the relative strength of transmitted and incident shocks.

These transmission concepts underlie the curves of Fig. 1-64. This figure shows plane shock-wave pressures that can be reached in various materials with various explosives. The pressure that is attainable for a given combination of material and explosive lies at the intersection of the curve for the material with the curve for the explosive. For example, a plane

detonation wave in an explosive made up of 64% RDX and 36% TNT, incident normally on aluminum, induces a shock pressure of about 360 kbars in the aluminum; in water, the same explosive would induce a pressure of only about 190 kbars.

All well and good; now let's get some idea of the data that come out of a shock experiment, and of how to get these data.

The ideal shock transducer doesn't exist

Let's return to the experimental setup of Fig. 1-61 middle. As the shock passes from driver plate to specimen, either the shock's velocity, or the free-surface velocity in the specimen, or both, are to be measured. How?

One method uses the familiar principle of the optical lever. As the incident shock wave produces small rotational displacements in an inclined polished surface on the specimen, reflections of light—incident on the same surface from point sources—are displaced via appropriate reflection geometry. Reflections are recorded on film by a streak camera as a series of light streaks, against a base whose abscissa is time and whose ordinate is distance. Figure 1-60 shows such a record. Wave arrivals at points on both specimen and reference standard are indicated by abrupt displacements of successive traces.

The speed of the shock along the free inclined surface of the specimen is obtained from such a record by measuring the slope of the line that connects the same wave break in adjacent light traces.

An interesting feature of this record is that the first deflection of light traces in PZT is produced by an elastic wave that precedes the main shock wave. Since this elastic precursor travels with constant velocity, regardless of its amplitude, the first break in the light traces forms a straight line. But in the shock wave that follows it, the velocity is continually changing; and a trace-by-trace measurement must be made to determine the local slopes and velocity values in the decaying shock.

Another light-reflection technique for recording motion of shocked surfaces is based on the apparent change of reflectivity of polished or mirrored surfaces when they are struck by a shock wave. Figure 1-65 shows a streak camera record obtained from such a setup.

This technique allows the specimen's free-surface motion to be monitored continuously; hence, it is particularly useful where the wave in the sample consists of more than one shock front, as is the case in Fig. 1-65. But the method is sensitive to both tilt and nonplanarity of the shock, so that good plane-wave generators are essential to its successful use.

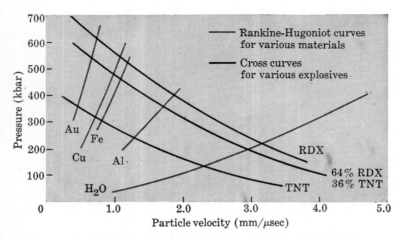

Fig. 1-64. Representative pressures that can be generated in various materials by different explosives are shown by points where curves cross. For example, a detonation wave in an explosive made up of 64% RDX/36% TNT, incident on aluminum, yields 360 kbar pressure.

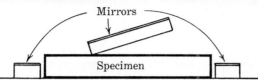

Fig. 1-65. Streak camera photograph of two shocks in $BaTiO_3$ (arrival times T_1 and T_2) affords both shock and free-surface velocities by measurement of the slope of successive shock fronts.

Nonoptical methods also can be used for measuring shock and free-surface velocities in specimens that are electrical conductors. One such is called the pin method, in which motion of a shock-accelerated surface closes a gap and strikes a pin. This short-circuits an RC network, which discharges through an oscilloscope. If the pin position is accurately known and the RC discharge recorded, the time at which the shock-accelerated surface reached that position is known. If several pins are used on a single specimen, an (x, t) plot of its motion can be made and its velocity obtained by differentiation. Such a pin record from a raster oscilloscope is shown in Fig. 1-66.

But none of these data-taking methods is ideal; all are relatively delicate to arrange; and all involve rather complex subsequent reduction of the data.

Specifications for the ideal shock recorder

Serious efforts have recently been made to measure stress or pressure in the shock wave directly; and the results show considerable promise. An ideal arrangement for making direct stress measurements would imbed in the sample a stress-sensing element that had the same impedance characteristics as the sample. The sensing element would be small enough in diameter to be uninfluenced by rarefaction

waves originating at the side of the sample; and it would be thin enough to give the minimum time resolution (which is roughly equal to thickness of the element divided by the shock velocity). Attempts to realize this ideal use the electrical transducing properties of various materials—sulfur, quartz, or manganin wire, for example. All have their deficiencies, and the better mousetrap among shock-pressure transducers is yet to be built.

More applications and some afterthoughts

At this point in our discussion, it will surprise nobody to hear that shock waves can alter the electrical and electronic properties of matter, often permanently. But studies of such effects have been less vigorously prosecuted than studies of mechanical effects.

One such mechanical effect that has far-reaching potential applications is the anelastic behavior of a solid under shock. At some sufficiently high value of pressure atomic bonds in the solid are no longer able to sustain such high stresses; the material either fractures, or it yields plastically, and measurement of the elastic precursor in a shocked solid provides value for dynamic yield strength.

Furthermore, shearing stresses acting in the shock front may cause martensitic transformations in metals; permanent structural changes can be created either by the shock pressure, or by the shock-induced rise in temperature, or both. Such changes are readily detected in

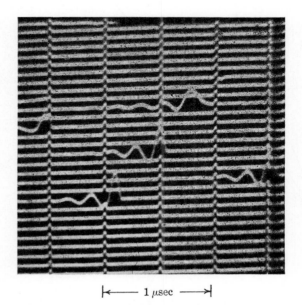

Fig. 1-66. Pin method for measuring shock and free-surface velocities in specimen uses motion of its shocked surface to close a gap and strike a pin, short-circuiting an R-C network which discharges through a raster oscilloscope to yield record.

metals as shock-induced twin effects, or as newly generated dislocations in the metal's lattice structure. Changes in microstructure show up as changes in macroscopic properties as well.

Figure 1-67 illustrates how the Vickers hardness of many metals increases as a function of shock pressure. Although hardness in the pressure range shown increases monotonically with pressure, it would be misleading to leave you with the thought that this can be extrapolated ad infinitum. Ultimately the curves must reverse in slope because of the annealing effect that would be produced by the high temperatures left by strong shock.

Another lively area of application of the shock wave art is one we mentioned earlier, bonding of dissimilar metals. Figure 1-68 shows an interface between hardened and annealed aluminum alloys, which was produced by firing the upper plate against the lower. Both atomic

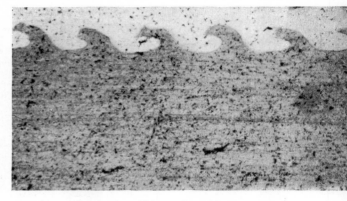

|←— 200 μ —→|

Fig. 1-68. Both size and shape of ripples at interface between explosively bonded aluminum alloys depend on velocity and impact angle of the two surfaces. Ripples increase area in contact, aid diffusion of atoms across interface by straining surfaces at high rate, provide interlock.

diffusion and simple mechanical locking probably play a role in this kind of bond.

The future role of shock research appears to me to be greatest in solid state physics and metallurgy. Here, in the broadest and most favorable terms, shock waves offer the opportunity to apply very large, known stresses, in a way that is geometrically well-defined. Observation of the response of the sample—mechanically, thermally, electrically, or however the scientist wishes—is limited only by his imagination, pocket book, and the hard facts of nature.

Further reading

For a starter take a look at *Shock Waves in Chemistry and Physics* by J. N. Bradley (Wiley, 1962); or try Chapter 9, entitled "Shock Waves," by Duvall and Fowles, in *High Pressure Physics and Chemistry*, R. S. Bradley ed. (Academic Press, 1963). Also in book form is the mathematical foundation for much later thinking about shock phenomena—*Supersonic Flow and Shock Waves*, by R. Courant and K. O. Friedrichs (Interscience, 1948).

The most recent review of shock effects, especially as applied to solids, is the article "Compression of Solids by Strong Shock Waves" by M. H. Rice, R. G. McQueen, and J. M. Walsh in Vol. 6 of Seitz and Turnbull's series *Solid State Physics* (Academic Press, 1958). To back off—or dig deeper, as the case may be—read "Studies in the Theory of Shock Propagation in Solids" by W. Band in *J. Geophys. Research* **65**, 695 (Feb. 1960), or "Concepts of Shock Wave Propagation" by G. E. Duvall in *Bull Seis. Soc. Am.* **52**, 869 (Oct. 1962). For a

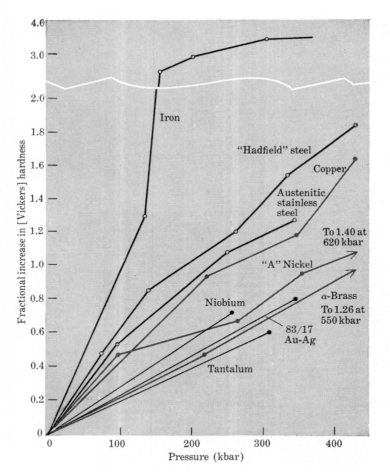

Fig. 1-67. Increase in hardness of shocked metals relative to their hardness in pre-shock, annealed condition is impressive. Curves cannot be extrapolated upwards indefinitely, however, because rapid rise in heat induced by shock would also have annealing effect. This would eventually surpass hardening effect, reversing slope of the curves.

briefer, less highly mathematical discussion of the same sort try W. Band and G. E. Duvall, "The Physical Nature of Shock Propagation" in *Am. J. Phys.* **29,** 780 (1961).

Some of the questions you have about apparatus will be answered in Chapter 11 of *Modern Very-High-Pressure Techniques,* ed. by R. H. Wentorf, Jr. (Butterworths, 1962). What may turn out to be the most comprehensive book on various aspects of technique is, unfortunately, still in the writing stage, but you can be on the lookout for it: *Dynamic High Pressure Techniques* (tentative title) by W. E. Deal, Jr.

For a compendium of information on explo-sives see *Science of High Explosives* by M. A. Cook (Reinhold, 1958).

Those seeking information on the explosive working of metals should see the book of that title by J. S. Rinehart and John Pearson (Macmillan, 1963).

Applications by the score must be hunted down in the appropriate periodical literature—among the more relevant journals are the *Journal of Applied Physics,* the *Journal of Chemical Physics, The Physical Review, Chemical Reviews, Proceedings of the Royal Society (London), Transactions of the American Geophysical Union,* and the *Journal of Geophysical Research.*

GASES-IN-SOLIDS

by Robert C. Frank *

IN BRIEF: *When gases enter solids, the resultant gases-in-solids may bear little resemblance to their origins. That's to be expected: The movements of small gas atoms (or molecules) are pretty well governed by their hosts, and such effects as the embrittlement of metals by gases were known (if not understood) before 1900.*

Even so, when modern techniques are trained on gases-in-solids, the results can turn out to be startling, for the simple diffusion equations are complicated by the many kinds of relationships gases bear to their hosts. These run the gamut, from inclusions of gas in voids to gas participation in crystal lattices.

In practice, the results can mean the failure of superalloys through "delayed brittle fracture" and the escape of radioactive poisons from reactors or the interesting attainment of higher concentrations of hydrogen (as a solution in palladium) than H_2 *exhibits alone under like conditions and the recovery of He from natural gas by permeation through fused quartz.— R.G.N.*

■ Gases-in-solids are not gases in solids. They are normally gaseous materials that are adsorbed onto and then absorbed into solids. Once these gases become gases-in-solids, their behaviors can no longer be described by the classical gas laws; they are controlled by the properties of their solid hosts. Depending on the natures of the gases and solvents involved, gases-in-solids can assume molecular or atomic forms:

* Robert C. Frank prepared this article while at General Motors Research Laboratories in Warren, Michigan. He continues his research on gases-in-solids as Head of the Physics Department at Augustana College, Rock Island, Illinois.

Type of solid	Gases absorbed	Form of gas
Metals	H, N, O	Atomic
Glasses	He, H_2, Ne, O_2, Ar	Molecular
Polymers	He, H_2, CO_2, CH_4 and many others	Molecular
Semiconductors	H, He, O, N	Atomic

and in these forms, the solute gases can relate to their host in various ways, ranging from the collection of pockets of gases in voids to the chemical combination of gases with the solids to form hydrides, nitrides, oxides, etc.

Because gas atoms are smaller (and much lighter) than the host molecules, gases have comparatively large mobilities; they move into and out of—and often times right through—their solid hosts rather freely. In fact, one of the clearest demonstrations of the discontinuous nature of solids is the permeation of gases through solid membranes, and commercial use is made of this permeability for the filtering of hydrogen through the walls of palladium and palladium-alloy tubing. For instance, in a representative filter, operating at about 400°C and with a differential pressure across the tubing wall of 140 psi, hydrogen permeates through the 4-mil wall of a ⅛-in.-diameter tube at the rate of 1½ ft³/hr, per foot of tubing.

In such cases the rates of permeation are so high that some early researchers believed that solids contained small fissures or channels through which the gas atoms were passing. However, in the last decade, studies have assured us that, although gases often tend to migrate to small voids and fissures and along grain boundaries, usually the small gas atoms simply diffuse among the atoms of the solids. We now also know that imperfections in the lattice structures of solids can retard as well as accelerate the migration.

Fig. 1-69. Aftermath of a gas. The center of this steel disk shows the permanent effect of hydrogen which entered the metal in atomic form, collected in voids within the metal, and recombined to form H_2 which then exerted pressure outward. The hydrogen was generated by exposing the metal to acid, and the process enhanced by electrolysis. The unaffected area of the disk was protected from the acid by an annular mask. (Courtesy General Motors Research Laboratories)

When World War II began there was already considerable literature on gases-in-metals. Most of it concerned how much gas metals absorbed and how fast the gases permeated through metal membranes, because this kind of data required only modest apparatus (mercury manometers, McLeod gages, etc.).

The war changed all that: It became fairly easy to get support for large and complicated experiments. Electronics and nuclear physics grew to prodigious proportions, while gases-in-solids, with its mundane mercury manometers, became unfashionable. However, almost unnoticed, a renaissance has occurred in gases-in-solids research in the last decade.

We are now applying advances in other fields to develop new sophisticated techniques. The number of investigations with the older methods has also increased. Besides their commercial applications, the reasons for all this activity and the results of the work are interesting in themselves. First a review of some of the basic measurements used in a study of gases-in-solids will be presented.

Measurements and meanings

In one very popular experiment, a solid forms a wall between an evacuated chamber and one filled with gas. As gas permeates through the solid, the pressure change in the evacuated chamber is measured. Since a quantity of gas is defined by its pressure, volume, and temperature, the temperature and volume of the nearly empty chamber is fixed and the change in pressure then becomes a direct measurement of the rate of permeation of the gas through the solid.

It is usually found that if the gas retains its molecular form while passing through a solid membrane (as it does in glasses and polymers), the permeation rate M is

$$M = \frac{PA(p_1 - p_0)}{l}$$

where A is the area of the membrane, l is its thickness, $(p_1 - p_0)$ is the difference in pressure on the two sides of the membrane, and P is a constant of proportionality called the permeability (sometimes called the permeation velocity constant and designated by K).

In contact with metals and semiconductors, diatomic gases usually dissociate at the surface, their diatomic bonds being broken by the influence of the proximate solid atoms. (This action is reversed when gases egress from a solid.) Once dissociated, the gas enters its host solid and moves about in atomic form. Under these circumstances, instead of M being dependent on the measured pressure difference $(p_1 - p_0)$, it varies with $(p_1^{1/2} - p_0^{1/2})$ because the pressures of *molecular* gases are the ones that are measured and permeation rates depend on the concentrations of gas *atoms*. The reaction rate for a dissociation reaction such as $H_2 \rightarrow 2H$ is a square root function of the concentration of H_2, which is itself proportional to pressure.

The permeation of a gas through a solid is a rather complex process. It involves the entrance and exit of the gas through the surfaces as well as the diffusion of the gas through the bulk of the solids. Sometimes the surface processes are so slow they control the permeation rate. In these cases the usual permeation-rate equations do not hold.

A better measure of the mobility of the gas atom in the solid is the diffusion coefficient or diffusivity (D), which is the proportionality constant that relates rate of diffusion per unit area to gas concentration gradient. Measurements of D are usually made by disturbing the gas-solid equilibrium, for example by suddenly changing the gas pressure and studying the (nonsteady) rate of release of the gas from the solid. Often these methods become quite complicated and involve solving the differential equations for diffusion and comparing the predicted behavior with the actual behavior of the gas in the solid.

One of the simplest is the so-called "time lag" method. When a membrane is suddenly exposed to a gas, the quantity Q which has diffused through over a time t can be plotted. If the straight portion of the curve Q vs. t is extrapolated to the line $Q = 0$, the value of t at the intercept is called the effective time lag t_0. This is related to the diffusion coefficient D:

$$t_0 = \frac{l^2}{6D}$$

where l is the thickness of the membrane.

Another useful quantity is solubility, the amount of gas a solid will absorb under equilibrium conditions. This is often measured by exposing a solid to a known quantity of gas and then measuring how much gas is left after the solid has absorbed as much as it can. Solubility is usually directly proportional to gas pressure if the gas enters the solid in the molecular form, but it is proportional to the square root of the gas pressure if a diatomic gas enters in atomic form, because the concentration of H atoms is a square root function of the concentration of H_2 molecules.

Sometimes gas atoms combine chemically with the atoms of the solid; in such cases, the simple laws of solubility hold only as long as chemical combination and precipitation don't occur. (Once chemical bonds are formed, the gas atoms are no longer free to move from place to place in the solid and are then not considered to be in simple solid solution.)

When the permeation rate is controlled by a simple diffusion process, the permeability constant P is related to the diffusion coefficient

and solubility by $P = DS$. The temperature dependence of all three quantities is very similar

$$P = P_0 e^{\frac{-Q}{RT}} \quad D = D_0 e^{\frac{-E}{RT}} \quad S = S_0 e^{\frac{-H}{RT}}$$

where Q and E are the activation energies. For Q this is the heat absorbed or released when a unit quantity of gas atoms or molecules goes from the gas phase on one side of a solid to the gas phase on the other side. E is the energy required for a unit quantity of atoms to jump to new sites and H is the heat of solution, P_0, D_0, and S_0 are constants, R is the universal gas constant, and T is the absolute temperature.

Plots of the log of any of these against $(1/T)$ should, therefore, yield straight lines. *Usually*, they do. But these apply only where the behavior of gases-in-solids is relatively simple. If chemical reactions or phase changes take place in the solid, or the gas atoms become trapped by lattice defects, the mathematical descriptions become much more complicated. (Sometimes they can't even be formulated.) A great deal of research has been done on some of these "anomalous" behavior patterns in the last few years.

Hardening/embrittlement in gassy metals

Metals are hardened when gases are dissolved in them. As hardening, this is often desirable, but it also takes the form of an unwanted tendency toward brittle-type fractures. Then it is called embrittlement. A classic example of desirable hardening follows from the introduction of nitrogen into steel. This is almost always done by heating the steel in an ammonia atmosphere. At the elevated temperatures, the NH_3 dissociates; the nitrogen enters the steel and the hydrogen probably eventually escapes. Depending on the further heat treatment, the nitrogen may cause the very hard martensite crystal structure to be formed, or it may react with the iron to form iron nitride which then precipitates and causes hardness by another means.

In some of the softer metals, like copper, oxygen can produce hardening in still a different manner. Internal oxidation occurs when an alloy contains a solute element that has a greater affinity for oxygen than does the solvent metal. Then the solute may form an oxide even when the concentration of oxygen is too low to form an oxide with the major constituent. For example if copper contains a small amount of aluminum, oxygen can diffuse into the alloy to produce aluminum oxide internally. The aluminum oxide then forms a finely dispersed precipitate which hardens the parent copper.

In the last few years, research has not only

$$J = -D \frac{\partial c}{\partial x}$$

$$\frac{\partial c}{\partial t} = D \frac{\partial^2 c}{\partial x^2}$$

Fick's Law

$1\,\text{Torr} = 1\,\text{mm Hg}$

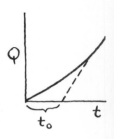

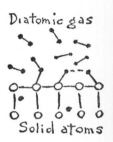

Diatomic gas

Solid atoms

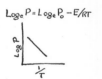

$\log_e P = \log_e P_0 - E/RT$

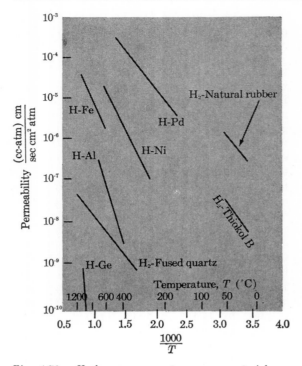

Fig. 1-70. *Hydrogen permeates some materials as atomic H, some materials as molecular H$_2$. Units of permeability are cc of gas (at normal temperature and pressure) per sec, per cm^2 of membrane, per cm thickness of membrane, per atm pressure difference across the membrane.*

The harrowing hydrogen haunt

Hydrogen embrittlement is now referred to as "low-strain-rate embrittlement" because the metal must be strained slowly for the hydrogen embrittlement to be observed. If the strain rate is too high (e.g., in an impact test) the steel does not appear brittle. This strain-rate dependence along with the over-all low solubility of hydrogen in iron has led most researchers to conclude that embrittlement occurs by a segregation of the hydrogen to certain areas and that this segregation is controlled by diffusion. And so, lately, there has been an intensive effort to correlate diffusion-rate with the strain-rate information.

The success of this venture has been only mediocre because it is hard to make good diffusion coefficient measurements. Apparently the hydrogen is easily trapped by almost every conceivable type of lattice imperfection. As a result, the diffusion-coefficient data published by different labs have not been very consistent, particularly data taken at low temperatures.

The embrittlement enigma is going to get worse before it gets better. As if forewarning this, a relatively new manifestation of hydrogen embrittlement called "delayed brittle fracture" has appeared in some ultrahigh-strength steels. When a normally safe static load is applied to parts made from these steels they will sometimes sustain the load for a while. Then suddenly they will fracture. This effect has been traced to hydrogen in the steel.

Many hardenable low-alloy steels show evidence of this catastrophic effect. Among the stainless steels, the martensitics seem to be susceptible to hydrogen embrittlement but the austenitics do not. Other metals suspected of susceptibility to this "low-strain-rate hydrogen embrittlement" are vanadium, columbium, molybdenum, tantalum, nickel, and titanium alloys. Hydrogen is usually introduced into metals during heat treatment in a hydrogen atmosphere or during metal finishing processes. Because of this, attempts have been made to either keep hydrogen out of metals or to drive it out by baking the metals after treatment.

Cadmium plating is well known for its ability to produce hydrogen embrittlement in ultrahigh-strength steels. The electrolytic action at the surface of the metal during plating yields a large amount of hydrogen which is readily absorbed by the metal, and the protective cadmium coating prevents the hydrogen from escaping. This can work wonders to ensure a long-lived embrittlement, should your interest be to demonstrate this intriguing phenomenon.

Several ways have been developed for getting around this problem. Two popular methods are

been establishing suitable gas-metal combinations for producing hardening effects but also examining in detail how the hardening takes place. Of particular interest has been the nucleation and growth of the precipitate particles. A notable discovery has been that these precipitates often nucleate on lattice imperfections such as dislocations or vacancies. Concurrently there have also been improvements in the mathematical descriptions of the factors affecting the growth of these potent precipitate particles.

One of the greatest enigmas of the steel industry has been hydrogen embrittlement. Despite a lot of research, the mechanism of embrittlement is still highly controversial. The main problem is that, due to its high mobility, hydrogen moves in and out of the steel so fast that it's difficult to get consistent data. The obvious corollary to this is that hydrogen embrittlement will diminish with time—if the hydrogen is allowed to escape. The time involved varies with specimen size and shape, ranging from a few minutes (for, say, a small 1/8-in.-diameter tensile test sample) to several weeks or even months for a very massive machine member.

to: (1) coat the surface with cadmium by vapor deposition rather than electroplating, or (2) electroplate a thin coat of cadmium, bake the hydrogen out of the metal, and then electroplate the final thicker coat of cadmium. The thin coat of cadmium seems to serve very effectively to prevent the further penetration of hydrogen into the metal during the second electroplating process.

Some metals such as titanium, zirconium, and hafnium exhibit another kind of hydrogen embrittlement. They absorb great quantities of hydrogen and form hydrides. In contrast to the embrittlement which occurs in steels, in these materials the embrittlement is manifest at high strain rates; accordingly, the affected metal has a lowered resistance to an impact or sudden blow.

The crystal structures of these metal hydrides have been investigated in some detail by Surain Sidhu and his colleagues at the Argonne National Laboratory using neutron diffraction techniques. Neutron diffraction is particularly valuable for this type of work because it reveals the positions of the light hydrogen atoms whereas x-ray diffraction is only useful for determining the positions of the heavy metal atoms. On the basis of the positions of the hydrogen atoms, it is believed that the embrittlement is largely caused by the directional nature of hydrogen-metal bonds.

Titanium is very useful in aircraft and rocket parts or for other structural applications where minimum weight is required. But the alpha phase titanium alloys are impact-sensitive when charged with hydrogen, because insoluble and brittle titanium hydrides form, and fracture occurs in these. Consequently recent research has been directed toward producing alloys which stabilize more of the beta phase, those which retain the hydrogen interstitially instead of forming hydrides. However, many of these α-β alloys are susceptible to low-strain-rate hydrogen embrittlement. Still, progress is being made in developing titanium alloys which have greater tolerance to hydrogen from the standpoint of both types of embrittlement.

The hiatus in vacuum

The absorption of gases by solids and the permeation of gases through solids are very important considerations in attaining high vacua. The attainment of a good vacuum in a chamber is largely governed by four factors: (1) the pumping capacity, (2) leaks in the system, (3) the outgassing of the components, and (4) the rate at which gas permeates through the walls of the evacuated vessel. The size of the vacuum pump is largely controlled by how much one can afford to pay. Leaks can

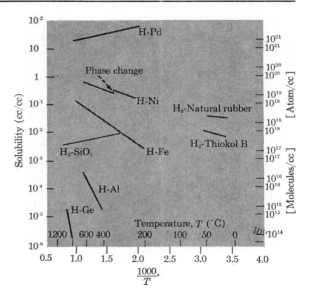

Fig. 1-71. *A curious consequence of hydrogen's great solubility in palladium is the high density which hydrogen can achieve when dissolved in that metal, compared to its density as a gas at normal atmospheric conditions. Solubilities on the left are in terms of cc of gas at normal temperature and pressure. To convert scale at right to atoms per atom or molecules per molecule, multiply by the formula in the margin.*

$\dfrac{M}{\rho N}$ = atoms of solid

M = mol. wt (solid)

ρ = density (solid)

N = Avogadro's const.

(6.025) $\times 10^{23}$
molecules/mole

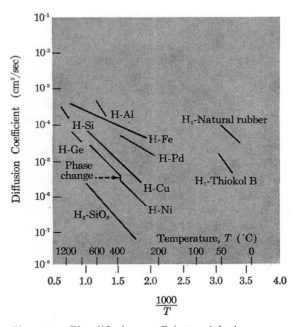

Fig. 1-72. *The diffusion coefficients of hydrogen in these solids cover only four orders of magnitude, whereas the solubilities of hydrogen in the same solids cover eight orders of magnitude under the same conditions. Notice that metals which have low solubilities often have high diffusion coefficients. Discontinuities in these curves (like the one in the H-Ni curve) occur when the host materials undergo phase changes.*

be found and closed. But when the pressure is limited by the latter two effects, the solution is not always so simple.

There are some interesting stories of how permeability can control a vacuum. In the first efforts to use water-cooled power-rectifier vacuum tubes made of steel, the cooling water corroded the steel and released hydrogen which then permeated through the steel and into the vacuum. This soon rendered the tube inoperable. All metal electron tubes are now painted to prevent corrosion, and those large tubes which have steel parts and are water-cooled must use water that has been treated to prevent corrosion.

The second illustration is found in the first efforts to attain ultrahigh vacua (10^{-10} to 10^{-12} Torr.). During their early experiments on ultrahigh vacua in 1953 and 1954, Daniel Alpert and his co-workers at Westinghouse found that one of the limiting factors was the permeation of helium from the atmosphere through the glass envelope of their vacuum system. Under other circumstances one might not consider this permeation rate very significant because the amount of helium in the atmosphere is only a few parts per million. However, it forced Alpert and his group to use special glasses, double-walled containers, and increased pumping rates.

The diffusion coefficients of gases-in-solids increase with increasing temperature. Therefore, most solids used in vacuum systems are preheated to drive off gas at temperatures well above those at which the system will normally be operating. If the evolution of the gas from the solid is inhibited by surface reactions, it is often necessary to choose the firing temperature carefully or to use a hydrogen atmosphere to help release the gas from the surface. Such outgassing procedures have been worked out for most metals and glass.

However, recently there has been considerable interest in the use of polymers for vacuum systems, particularly as a gasketing material. Here the outgassing problems are a little more difficult: Most polymers absorb hydrocarbon gases as well as the usual O_2, N_2, and CO_2, so when the temperature of many of these polymers is raised only slightly, copious quantities of gas issue forth. And, if the temperature is raised high enough, the polymer often begins to degrade and give off its own gaseous degradation products.

Until a few years ago Teflon was just about the only polymer useful in systems that had to be baked out or used at temperatures above 100°C. Recently though, several new elastomers have been developed which are useful to temperatures slightly above 100°C and which

can be outgassed fairly well. Among these are butyl rubber, the silicone rubbers, and the fluoroelastomers such as Viton.

The business of outgassing all types of components in vacuum systems has been greatly facilitated by mass spectroscopy. The spectrometer makes it possible to identify the residual gases in a vacuum system and thereby to establish what the various sources of these gases are.

Another area of interest to vacuum technology is the development of "getters." A getter is a substance that will remove molecules from a gas by adsorption, absorption, or chemical combination. These materials act like simple little vacuum pumps. Barium adsorbs gases prodigiously and is very popular for this purpose. Also among the many getter materials are metals like titanium and zirconium, which absorb very large quantities of gas. A small piece of one of these metals is placed in a vacuum system and the system is pumped down and sealed off. Then, when the metal is heated to a high temperature, it absorbs some of the gas still remaining in the vacuum chamber, thereby reducing the system pressure even further.

Ominous losses of gases

When gases are contained in pressurized systems they can permeate through the containing walls and escape if the materials are not chosen carefully. Ten or fifteen years ago this small loss of gas from a pressurized system would have perhaps been considered negligible. However, modern technology has created situations in which this small leakage of gas by permeation can be important.

For example, in nuclear power establishments, gas may be used in the heat exchangers, it can be produced as a fission product, or it can result from transmutations in some of the materials in the reactor. If the gas is or becomes radioactive, the containment problem becomes one of grave concern. Even a small amount of radioactive gas diffusing through the walls of its container can be a great hazard. This has stimulated research into the special problems of the diffusion of such radioactive gases in metals. In many of these cases the gas enters the surface of the metal by ion bombardment or the gas may be created inside of the metal so there is no possibility of the entrance surface acting as a barrier.

Another place where the loss of gas from pressurized systems will become increasingly important is outer space. This big vacuum poses a problem just the opposite of the one found in vacuum technology. Gas lost in space is irretrievable, and since it will also be in limited supply, even small losses are objectionable. In most metals, the permeation rates of all gases except hydrogen are extremely low at room temperature and therefore metal containing walls of pressurized systems can successfully hold gases other than hydrogen.

However, because of weight considerations and because of the occasional desire for flexibility, attention is necesarily drawn to the polymers. But polymers are usually permeable to oxygen, nitrogen, carbon dioxide, and other gasses. Losses by permeation can be quite large if the polymers are not chosen carefully.

Recent work has taken two directions: One is the development of new polymers less permeable to gases, and the other direction is the treatment of polymers that are already available to decrease their permeability. In the first case there are polymers such as Mylar, Saran, and polyvinyl alcohol, which have low permeabilities and are very likely suitable for some applications. As one approach to the second case, polymers have been impregnated with "fillers." Apparently the mechanism for this is simply the mechanical one of lengthening the paths of the migrating gas atoms.

In rubbers, such fillers as carbon black, powdered aluminum, and powdered mica have been used. Carbon black apparently has only a small effect whereas powdered aluminum and powdered mica can decrease the permeability by as much as 75%. Still another approach is to deposit a metal coating on the surface of the polymer. This is an attractive solution where the polymer does not require too much flexing.

Purification by permeation

Some solids are highly permeable to one gas but almost impermeable to other gases. This makes them very effective as filters for purifying gases. Palladium has a high permeability for hydrogen but a rather low permeability for other gases, so heated palladium tubes have been used (since 1866) for purifying hydrogen.

Palladium, however, deteriorates somewhat after a while if it is not used carefully. Therefore some people favor nickel as a hydrogen filter in spite of the fact that the rate of flow of hydrogen through Ni is considerably below that for Pd. Silver is fairly permeable to oxygen but not to other gases, so a heated silver membrane is a good filter for the purification of oxygen. Laboratory models of such filters for gas purification are now being made of palladium, nickel, and silver and are available commercially.

Another material, fused silica, is highly permeable to helium but only slightly permeable to other gases. The use of silica for separating helium from natural gas has been spearheaded by McAfee and his co-workers at Bell Labs. Since the permeation rate is directly proportional to membrane area, the high rates necessary for commercial purposes require very large areas. This was accomplished by using a bundle of long narrow tubes which are in-

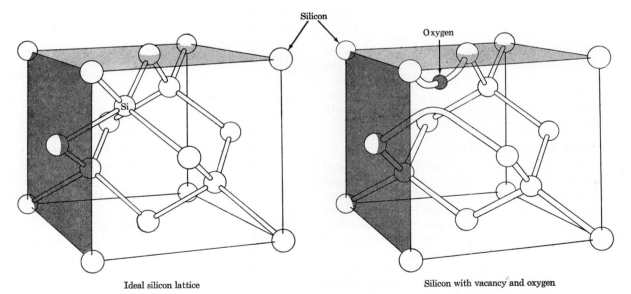

Ideal silicon lattice   Silicon with vacancy and oxygen

*Fig. 1-73. Gases-in-solids can even enter the crystal lattice structures of solids. For example, when the normal structure (left) of silicon develops a vacancy, an oxygen atom may enter the lattice as in this model proposed by G. Bemski. The oxygen atom does not enter in the vacancy, but is held by adjacent Si atoms. (Courtesy G. Bemski, J. Appl. Phys., **30**, 1195 (1959))*

dividually sealed shut at one end and joined to a common "header" at the other thus producing a membrane of very great area.

Solids as storage media for gases

The fact that the density of gas atoms dissolved in some solids exceeds the density of the gas atoms in the gas phase at normal temperatures and pressures suggests the possibility of using solids as storage media for gases. As an example, a cubic centimeter of titanium can retain so much hydrogen that when it is released it will nearly fill a thousand cubic centimeter volume with hydrogen gas at atmospheric pressure. There are certain advantages to having hydrogen dissolved in solids rather than having it in the gas form in a container. When it is in a solid, it is quite harmless. There is no fear of the container breaking because even if it broke the gas would remain dissolved in the broken parts. The gas is released by simply heating the solid. This method of storing and releasing hydrogen also appears to show some promise as a method of storing and releasing tritium. The gas can be stored safely and released in a pure form in a controlled manner.

A group of organic materials which occlude substantial quantities of gas are called clathrates. Actually the term "clathrate" is applied to the combination of the gas atom as a guest inside of the organic lattice which acts as the host. Some of these organic materials can occlude rather large gas molecules. The organic lattice has a kind of cage structure which tends to retain the gas molecule. An example is β-hydroquinone which can act as a host for such molecules as SO_2, H_2S, HCl, CH_3OH, CO, Ar, Kr, Xe, N_2, and O_2. This material could perhaps be used to store radioactive krypton or xenon. Therefore, the desirable radioactive properties of these gases could be used without having the undesirable handling problems normally encountered with radioactive gases.

Gases-in-semiconductors

The study of gasses-in-semiconductors is still a relatively new field, and there is not a great deal of information about the effect of dissolved gas on the properties of the various semiconductors. Only in a few cases is there enough information to decide whether the presence of the dissolved gas is detrimental.

Hydrogen and nitrogen apparently do not change the electrical resistivity of germanium or silicon when they are absorbed by these semiconductors, but there are indications that hydrogen may affect the lifetime of minority carriers by producing recombination centers for holes and electrons. On the other hand when hydrogen is absorbed by zinc oxide, the resistivity is changed.

The most well-known effect is that of oxygen on the resistivity of silicon. It was found that when silicon single crystals were grown from the melt in fused silica crucibles, the crystals became contaminated with oxygen from the fused silica. The oxygen-contaminated crystals were largely p-type but upon heat treatment between 300 to 700°C often became converted to n-type. The resistivity of the very pure silicon crystals grown by the crucibleless floating-zone method is often of the order of 1000 ohm-cm, while the oxygen-contaminated silicon varies from a few ohm-cm to 300 ohm-cm.

There are indications that the oxygen becomes polymerized in the lattice structure of the silicon, producing complexes of O_n. Whether these oxygen complexes act as donors or not depends upon how many atoms there are in the complex. Infrared studies show that oxygen diffuses interstitially (in between the Si atoms) in spite of the fact that the activation energy for diffusion is fairly high. It corresponds more to that expected for the much slower diffusion by substitution. This can be explained by other data which suggest that oxygen is readily associated with vacancies and forms oxygen-vacancy pairs.

The oxygen atom is believed to be covalently bonded to two neighboring atoms adjacent to the vacancy. This association with vacancies probably causes the similarity with substitutional diffusion, which also takes place by the migration of vacancies. There seems to be very little information about the solubility and diffusion of gases in the compound semiconductors but there will undoubtedly be more interest in this area as these materials become more important to the industry.

Further reading

The best book which covers the entire field is R. M. Barrer's book called *Diffusion in and Through Solids* (Cambridge U. Press, 1941). It has two failings however. One is that some of the data are obsolete and the other is that the book is out of print. But most good technical libraries have it and it is well worth reading. The chapter "Gases-in-Metals" by C. R. Cupp in *Progress in Metal Physics*, Vol. 4 (Interscience, 1953), is probably the best review of that subject.

A very good source of data on hydrogen embrittlement is *The Hydrogen Embrittlement of Metals* (Pergamon, 1961, $5.00) by Cotterill, which is one of the series *Progress in Materials Science*, edited by Chalmers. A book which is very helpful for actually solving hydrogen embrittlement problems is *Hydrogen Embrittlement in Metal Finishing*, edited by H. J. Read (Reinhold, 1961, $7.50). *Hydrogen in Steel* by Michael Smialowski (Addison-Wesley, 1962) is the most comprehensive collection of information about hydrogen in steel available.

Saul Dushman's very fine book on the *Scientific Foundations of Vacuum Technique* (Wiley, 1949, $19.50) has a great deal of useful information on gases-in-solids but some of the data are rather old and must be used cautiously. This situation has been improved somewhat in the recent revision by his colleagues. *Materials and Techniques for Electron Tubes* by Walter Kohl (Reinhold, 1960, $16.50) is a recent book which contains a great deal of information about gases-in-solids, but the data are again diffused throughout the book.

NEUTRONS AND PHONONS

by Robert M. Brugger *

IN BRIEF: *A new experimental technique is making it possible, for the first time, to reconstruct in detail the motions of atoms in a solid. Since neutrons have quantum-mechanical wave properties, they are diffracted, just as x-rays and electrons are, by the lattice of a crystalline solid or even by the local orderliness of an amorphous solid. But the energy of the scattered neutrons is detectably altered by the vibrational waves that course through the solid as a consequence of its thermal energy. (These vibrational waves are quantized, as are all things on an atomic scale, and the quanta are called phonons—even as the quanta of light are called photons.)*

In the experiments to date the source of neutrons has been a nuclear reactor. Neutrons in a narrow band of energies are selected either by diffraction from a particular set of planes in a single crystal or by passing the reactor beam through a pair of "choppers" rotating at the same rate but slightly out of phase so that only neutrons of a specified energy can pass. These monoenergetic neutrons are inelastically scattered from a sample, and the energies of the scattered neutrons are analyzed either by diffracting them from yet another set of planes in yet another crystal or by measuring electronically their time of flight over the fixed distance from the sample to a detector. The technique is expensive and complex, but the results are already forcing refinement of theoretical models of lattice dynamics and promising much deeper understanding of the internal dynamics of solids.—D.C.

■ Most technical men are familiar with the crystal lattice and with the fact that the atoms in a lattice vibrate as a consequence of their thermal energy. But more than familiarity is needed; advances in solid state theories and solid state devices are demanding a precise

* Robert M. Brugger, a nuclear physicist, heads the Solid-State Physics Section of Phillips Petroleum's Atomic Energy Division in Idaho Falls, Idaho.

picture of how atoms move around their equilibrium positions in a lattice. Fortunately a powerful, if complex, experimental tool that supplies this picture has become available in recent years. The technique of inelastic scattering of thermal neutrons, portrayed schematically in Fig. 1-74, has proved to be a unique probe for studying, in detail, the dynamics not only of crystalline solids but of amorphous solids, liquids, and molecules too.

These experiments provide a striking example of the unity that underlies the apparent wave-particle duality of quantum mechanics. Some of the time during this article the neutrons will be considered as waves; consequently, their wavelengths will be compared with those of x-rays, and their diffraction will be described by the grating-like lattices of crystals. At other times, the particle nature of the neutrons will be emphasized, and they will be described as passing this point in space at this time or as being detected by a counter, particle-like, at another time. In similar fashion, the lattice vibrations that are being probed with these neutrons will be looked at in two ways. At some times it will be easier to regard them as waves passing through the lattice. At other times the quantized nature of these waves will be emphasized, and they will be described in terms of particle-like "phonons," which are to vibrational elastic waves what photons are to light waves. But this seeming duality is superficial; there is a unity in the rigorous quantum mechanical description (avoided here) that underlies all this. The wave or particle aspects are emphasized for convenience in description.

Of course, it is not just aesthetics that gains us support for these rather expensive experiments. The main purpose in our laboratory is to understand better how neutrons interact with matter so that nuclear engineers can design better reactors. However, better understanding of lattice dynamics leads to all sorts of important results in other fields. On the one hand it connects very directly with such

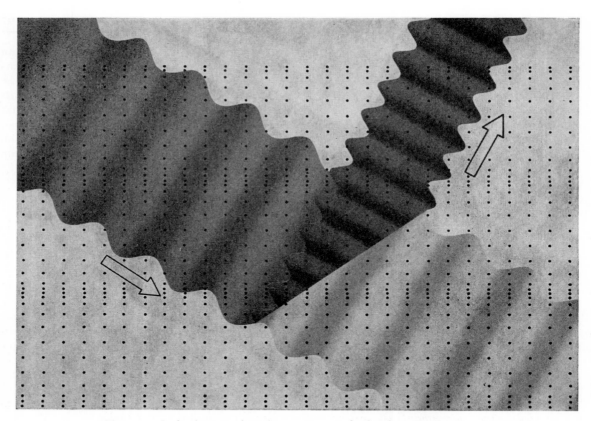

Fig. 1-74. Inelastic scattering of neutrons reveals the thermal vibrations in a lattice as suggested above. Neutrons enter from top left; quantum mechanically they can be described as a plane wave. This wave is reflected by the crystal lattice, just as x-rays are an x-ray diffraction. But, unlike x-rays, the neutrons have the right mass and energy to be able to get an observable contribution from the longitudinal wave shown moving through the lattice. As a result scattered neutrons come off with increased energy (hence shorter wavelength) and at a steeper angle than expected for specular reflection. By measuring angles and energies of scattered neutrons, the full spectrum of lattice vibrations can be derived. (Courtesy George Kelvin)

macroscopic properties of matter as specific heat, heat conductivity, and electrical conductivity. On the other hand our experiments make new demands on the theorists who seek to provide a mathematical description for how atoms combine in liquids and solids.

Within solids, our experiments measure properties which are microscopic, differential, detailed, and dynamic. Clearly these are a more exacting and fruitful challenge for theories that start from first principles than are macroscopic, integral measurements of such properties as the variation of specific heat with temperature.

It is not that such gross measurements are not important. Quite the contrary, they have sparked the development of the physics of matter for more than fifty years and occupied the talents of such giants as Dulong and Petit, Einstein, and Debye. It is just that, thanks to the efforts of such men, we have advanced to be concerned with the details of how matter "works." They long ago pointed out the connection between lattice vibrations and the internal heat energy of solids.

The vibrations in solids

A parallel but simpler connection exists in monatomic gases. Here the kinetic theory of gases affirms that we can account for the internal energy of a gas purely in terms of the kinetic energy of the individual atoms that comprise it. In a solid, the atoms are much closer together, on the average, and are, by the very definition of a solid, bound to each other. This has two consequences, at least. The first is that some of the internal energy now can be potential as well as kinetic. If we imagine the atoms bound to each other by springs, then some of the energy associated with an atom can be stored in the spring, the remainder in the motional energy of the atoms. The motions are no longer independent. The displacement of one atom affects its nearest neighbors, and they in turn move, affecting their neighbors, and so on. Rather than look at the motion of individual atoms we must look at the possible modes of collective motion of groups of atoms. In particular, we should explore what waves are possible in a lattice.

But this is a most complex problem. Imagine the many different kinds of jiggling possible in a collection of billions of atoms (even a crystal 1 mm on a side contains 10^{20} atoms) in a 3-dimensional array. All the more so since we do not know, precisely, the forces between these atoms, that being part of what we are trying eventually to determine.

The one-dimensional lattice

If the full complexity of the real 3-dimensional lattice is too much to face, consider first a simple analog that has many of the properties of the full lattice. Let us look at the vibrational properties of a 1-dimensional string of atoms.

Such a string of atoms is depicted as a line of masses distance a apart connected by massless springs with spring constant β. It turns out that waves can travel along this array if and only if their wavelength λ and their angular frequency ω are related as follows

$$\omega(\lambda) = (4\beta/M)^{1/2} \sin(\pi a/\lambda) \qquad (1)$$

For those who are accustomed to waves in continuous media this result is surprising. The wavelength and the frequency are not related through a simple constant velocity, rather the velocity is a function of frequency. This function $\omega(\lambda)$, to which we will refer often, is called the dispersion relation. One consequence of this relation is that for a given velocity, only waves with a fixed frequency or energy are possible. Note also that the force constant β of the spring enters the equation, and thus, if one measured the dispersion relation, one could determine the strength of the springs.

A second, less surprising, result is that waves with wavelength smaller than twice the spacing between atoms give nothing new—they appear as physically equivalent waves with a wavelength larger than $2a$.

If we check the formula for the case of wavelengths long compared with the interatomic spacing a, it is reassuring that (1) the velocity is constant, and (2) its value is the same as that which we obtain considering a uniform string of the same average density and elastic constant.

Fig. 1-75. The very complex vibrations of a three-dimensional crystal can be understood in terms of a simple model, the one-dimensional array of atoms. There are two significant differences from waves on a continuous string: waves with a wavelength shorter than two interatomic distances are not possible (i.e., give nothing new) and frequency and wavelength are not related through a constant velocity. Actual relations are shown in the margin. Note additional "optical" branch for case of two kinds of atoms. (Courtesy George Kelvin)

A SIMPLE MODEL FOR LATTICE VIBRATIONS

A linear array of bound atoms...

can support this sort of transverse wave...
(longitudinal waves are possible, too)

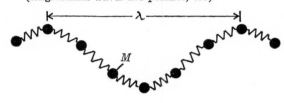

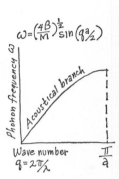

a wave similar to, but differing from, waves on a continuous string...

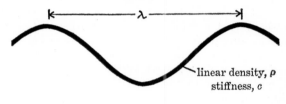

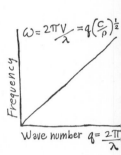

If the atoms are of two kinds, alternating...

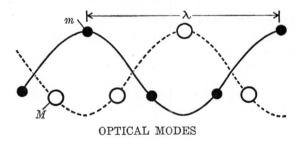

two modes are possible, as shown here...

OPTICAL MODES

ACOUSTIC MODES

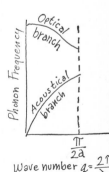

Before we return to real crystals, it is useful to consider a modification of the linear array. In the case where there are two kinds of atoms in the string, different in their mass, and alternating with each other along the string (Fig. 1-75), the dispersion curve now has two branches, an upper and a lower branch. As shown in Fig. 1-75, the upper branch represents modes of vibration in which the two kinds of atoms move in opposite directions, whereas in the lower branch, the atoms all move together, even as they did when there was only one kind of atom present.

This new set of modes, this new branch to the dispersion curves, is called the optical branch, because optical radiation, usually in the infrared, can excite these modes in certain crystals. All that is required is for the two kinds of atoms to be ions of different electric charge—one kind negatively charged, the other kind positively charged—so that they are pushed in opposite directions by the electrical field of an incident infrared light wave. The lower branch is called the acoustic branch, because in real crystals, it is the mode excited by acoustic waves. The frequency range for the interesting, nonlinear portions of both branches is approximately 10^{12} to 10^{13} cps. This is just the range that is so accessible to dynamic measurements by inelastic slow-neutron scattering experiments.

Of course, in a real crystal, forces extend beyond the nearest neighbors. Thus we should extend springs of a different strength from the first to the third atom, from the second to the fourth atom and so on. This modification changes the dispersion relations and introduces an even more complex relation than Eq. (1). Measurements of the dispersion relation give a method of discovery of this relation.

A crystal's full complexity

For an actual three-dimensional crystal, the dispersion relations are different for different directions in the crystal, but for any one direction they are similar in shape to the ones we have just been examining. There are additional acoustical or optical branches, depending on the number of atoms per unit cell of the crystal, but the general shape of the dispersion relation is the same. If we knew the positions of all the atoms in a crystal and the forces between them we could derive the dispersion curves. We do not possess that knowledge, but we do now have a technique for measuring the dispersion curve experimentally.

The technique that is used to place in evidence these thermal vibrations in a crystal is an extension of the techniques used to measure the undisturbed arrangement of atoms in the lattice—namely the diffraction of neutrons. Any wave which interacts with a periodic structure will be strongly reflected only at certain angles. These angles depend on the wavelength, the periodicity of the structure, and the angle of incidence of the wave. Quantum mechanics tells us that a particle of mass m moving freely with energy E can be described by a wave of wavelength

$$\lambda = h/(2mE)^{\frac{1}{2}}$$

where h is Planck's constant, 6.62×10^{-27} erg-sec. The wavelength is about 2×10^{-8} cm for neutrons with energies that are typical of those of the more populous "slow" neutrons in a reactor. Thus, a beam of neutrons from a reactor is an excellent source of probes of about the right wavelength to investigate crystal structure.

Neutron diffraction has, in fact, been used for some years to elucidate structures. Of course, so have x-rays; we just recently celebrated the fiftieth anniversary of x-ray diffraction. Why not use the older technique, since x-rays of the right wavelength are copiously available from x-ray tubes? The reason lies in the fact that x-rays of the right wavelength have so high an energy as to overpower the vibrations we want to detect. These x-rays have energy of the order of 10^6 times the energies (0.1–0.01 electron volt) of the phonons in the lattice. (Physicists measure energy on an atomic scale in electron volts—the energy gained by a particle with charge equal to that on an electron on falling through a 1-volt potential.) On the other hand, the neutrons have energies that are of the same order as the energies of the phonons and will be measurably affected. This is shown in Fig. 1-76.

Thus neutrons from a reactor are a natural probe for investigating lattice dynamics. To some extent this stems from the fact that the neutron has a mass like that of the atoms in the lattice. It is also closely related to the fact that the slowed-down, so-called "thermal" neutrons that we extract from our reactor for this experiment, are in thermal equilibrium with the solid material of the reactor. They come from an environment of the type we seek to probe.

Now it turns out that for certain energies and direction of the incident neutrons, there are favored directions for reflection from this periodic vibrating lattice. These preferred energies and directions tell us about the spacing and frequency of vibration. If we can measure these experimentally, we can determine how the lattice is vibrating. More precisely, we can measure the dispersion relations and from these

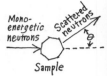

deduce the number and strength of the "springs" holding each atom in position.

What is done in this: A beam of neutrons of known (and controllable) energy, and, hence, of known wavelength is generated. This beam is directed in a known (and variable) direction at a single crystal sample of the material under study. Then the energy and the angle of the neutrons that come off are measured. Energy and momentum must be preserved in this process as in any scattering process. Formally, this can be expressed in the equations

$$\Delta E = E - E_0 = h\nu \qquad (2)$$

$$\Delta \mathbf{K} = \mathbf{k}_0 - \mathbf{k} = 2\pi\tau + \mathbf{q} \qquad (3)$$

Here the **k**'s are wave vectors—equal in magnitude to $2\pi/\lambda$ and in direction to the direction of the waves they represent. The reflecting properties of the lattice at rest are represented in the symbol τ and the waves in the lattice by the symbol **q**.

What the first of these equations says is that the final energy E of the neutron must equal its incident energy E_0 plus the energy, $h\nu$, gained from (or lost to) a phonon of frequency ν in the lattice. This loss or gain of energy is what makes the scattering inelastic; if there were no change we would say the scattering was elastic.

The second equation says that the momentum of the neutrons (remember momentum and wavelength are reciprocals, thus momentum is proportional to **k**) will be altered by reflection in the lattice (τ) and by momentum picked up from a phonon **q**.

In an experiment, we fix E_0 and $\mathbf{k}_0$ and we can measure E and $\mathbf{k}$, and we know τ from the known properties of the lattice of the sample. Thus, we are in a position to determine ν and **q**—the four unknowns (remember Eq. 3 is a vector equation) in our four equations.

The experimental instruments

Inelastic scattering experiments are low-intensity measurements because of the double energy selection that must be made and the angular dispersion of neutrons in scattering. Thus, it is necessary to start with the richest sources of thermal neutrons possible. Reactors with thermal fluxes greater than 5×10^{12} neutrons/cm²/sec are a necessity while the more precise equipment are at reactors with 10^{14} neutrons/cm²/sec. It was this limited source intensity that delayed neutron inelastic scattering experiments until the last 5–10 years when high-flux reactors became available and forced us to use automated equipment even then. Some of this equipment makes use of the wave properties of neutrons and selects them by diffraction in a crystal. Other equipment

emphasizes the particle aspect and measures neutron time of flight.

The triple axis spectrometer, an instrument that was developed by B. N. Brockhouse of Chalk River, Canada, who is a pioneer in this field, is shown in Fig. 1-77. The first crystal, called the monochromator, selects by coherent diffraction neutrons of a particular energy from the reactor beam. The energy of the diffracted beam is determined by the angle at which the neutrons are diffracted and the spacing of the crystal planes doing the scattering. This energy can be changed by changing the reflecting planes in the crystal and the angle of diffraction.

The diffracted beam of monochromatic neutrons is scattered by the sample. The angle of scattering and the energy of the neutrons after scattering depend upon the physical properties of the sample under study. At each angle of scattering, the intensity and energy of the neutrons are analyzed by a second crystal spectrometer, the analyzing spectrometer. The name "triple-axis spectrometer" arises because of the two axes through the crystals of the spectrometers and the axis through the sample.

Figure 1-78 shows another instrument, the phased-chopper velocity selector instrument. Here too, a beam of thermal neutrons is extracted through the reactor shielding. But, instead of a crystal monochromator, it is directed at a high-speed (about 15,000 rpm) rotor that has narrow slots which pass the beam only when they are in line with it. The first chopper chops this beam of neutrons into bursts

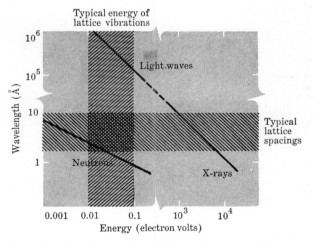

Fig. 1-76. Suitability of neutrons for studying lattice vibrations is shown by the fact that they have the right wavelength and the right energy. Wavelength is comparable with interatomic spacing, energy is comparable with the energy of lattice vibrations. X-rays have the right wavelength but energy is 10^5 too high; light waves have the right energy but wavelength is 10^5 too long.

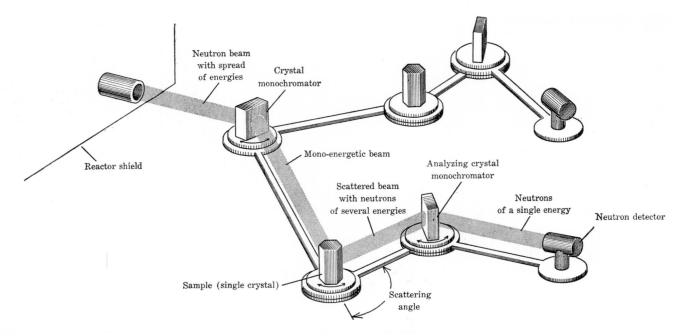

Neutron beam
with spread
of energies

Crystal
monochromator

Reactor shield

Mono-energetic beam

Scattered beam
with neutrons
of several energies

Analyzing crystal
monochromator

Neutrons
of a single energy

Neutron detector

Sample (single crystal)

Scattering
angle

GATE
OPEN

SLOWLY MOVING
Equipment
Do Not Touch
TAKE SWIPES

Fig. 1-77. Triple-axis spectrometer for measuring inelastic neutron scattering uses crystals (1) to make beam monoenergetic, (2) as scattering sample, (3) to analyze energy of scattered neutrons. Photo, left, shows embodiment at Canada's Chalk River Laboratory. Sample can be seen between magnet coils. Analyzing crystal is to right of it, just before heavily shielded counter with its warning sign. Stacked cartons of paraffin at left provide shielding. Big polyethylene sock at top of picture is filled with helium, to provide absorption-free path for neutrons in another experiment. (Drawing, courtesy George Kelvin; photograph, Atomic Energy of Canada)

of poly-energetic neutrons. Because of their different velocities, the neutrons in these bursts spread out in space as they travel down the flight path toward the second chopper. The second chopper spins at exactly the same speed as the first and is phased so as to open a predetermined time after the first. This second chopper allows only neutrons of one energy to pass, those neutrons that arrive at the second chopper when it is open. Some of the neutrons in the refined bursts of monoenergetic neutrons interact with the sample and scatter toward the detectors with a change in energy.

Timing signals are derived from the chopper. Therefore one can compute, electronically, the precise time these neutrons reach the sample. By the same token, time-of-flight methods are ideally suited to determine the energies of the scattered neutrons. Sensitive detectors are placed in an arc centered on the sample and 1–2 meters away. The signal from each detector is fed to a separate section of a multi-channel time analyzer. The analyzer sorts the pulse that marks a detected neutron according to its time of arrival relative to a trigger signal from the second chopper. Thus, the energies of

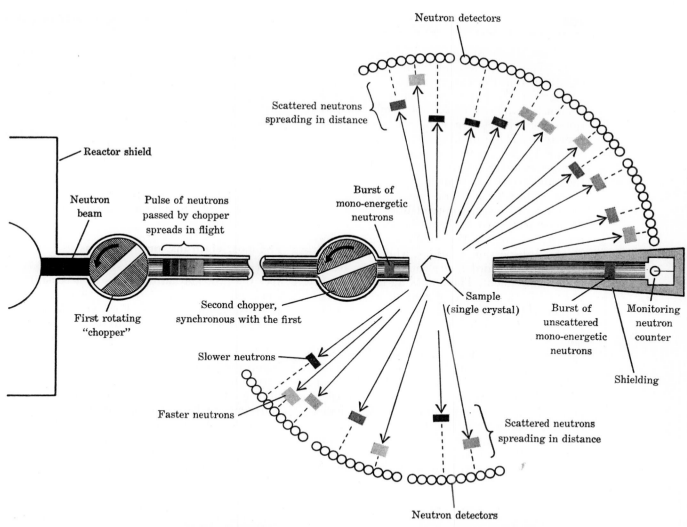

Fig. 1-78. *In the time-of-flight method only neutrons in a certain narrow band of energies can get through slots in pair of synchronous high-speed rotors. Neutrons strike sample in bursts lasting about 30 μsec. Some neutrons gain and some lose energy in the scattering process. Their speeds are affected correspondingly, and some reach detectors sooner than others. Thus it is possible to measure the time of flight of the scattered neutrons and thereby infer their energies. The measurement is done electronically. Counts from the detector are sorted according to their time of arrival and displayed on an oscilloscope or punched onto IBM cards for subsequent computer processing. Monitor counter at right keeps track of unscattered neutron intensity. (Courtesy George Kelvin)*

neutrons scattered at many angles are measured simultaneously. To obtain proper precision, the signals from each detector must be sorted into at least several hundred time channels. For 10 to 20 detectors, this means a total of some 4000 channels, but this can be done.

There are still other ways to carry out this type of measurement. For example, there is a scheme in which all but the very lowest energy neutrons (energies below 0.005 electron volt) are eliminated by passing them through a polycrystalline beryllium filter kept at liquid-nitrogen temperature. These "cold" neutrons gain energy when they interact with the sample, and this gain can be measured by time-of-flight or diffraction methods. Still other com-

binations and permutations of spectrometers and choppers are being employed in inelastic scattering measurements. But the two cited above are the most popular at this time.

Where it all leads

In neutron experiments, a single-crystal sample is placed at the sample position of one of the experimental instruments. The sample is oriented so that the initial neutron beam has some desired orientation relative to the crystal planes. When neutrons are scattered from the sample, only neutrons of certain discrete energies are observed at each scattering angle, those for which Eqs. 2 and 3 are satisfied. By calculating **k** for each of these peaks, the wavelength of the lattice waves can be fixed. The frequency of these phonons, ν, is obtained from Eq. 2.

Figure 1-79 shows a typical result: the dispersion relations in two of the symmetry directions for waves traveling in single-crystal beryllium. These data were obtained by R. E. Schmunk and co-workers with our phased-chopper velocity selector. These data show optical and acoustical branches because beryllium has two beryllium atoms per unit cell. There are only two distinct optical branches and two distinct acoustical branches because in one direction, two of the three expected modes have identical dispersion relations, while in the other direction, the third mode could not be excited in the experiment. These data agree reasonably well with the limited region of the acoustic branches that can be measured with ultrasonics. For the ultrasonics measurements, the frequency of sound wave is 10^7 cps, well below the interesting region where the curves are no longer linear.

Measured dispersion relations are becoming available for several cubic crystals such as germanium, aluminum, silicon, sodium iodide, sodium, copper, iron, and lead, and for several noncubic-structure crystals such as bismuth and pyrolytic graphite.

Theories of lattice vibrations incorporating different types of forces or interactions can be tested against the dispersion relation data. If the force between the atoms is assumed to act along the line between their centers and to be proportional to the distance between them, then results say these interactions must be extended to greater than 5th neighbors to get good but not perfect agreement. Data for other crystals indicate that interactions out to 14th neighbors may be evident or that other types of noncentral forces are required. Sufficient data are now available to present a challenge to the theoreticians.

Phonons, electrons, and magnons

Many physical properties of crystals can affect the propagation of waves in a crystal and thus can be measured through their effects on the dispersion relations. For example, the interaction between vibrations of atoms in the lattice and electrons in conduction bands in the solid modify the dispersion curves. Similarly, impurities in the crystal can shift the dispersion curves because of the change in mass of some of the atoms in the system. Mozer and his colleagues at Brookhaven National Laboratory have been able to see differences in samples of pure palladium and palladium with 5% nickel this way. If the experimental techniques can be refined to detect smaller quantities of impuri-

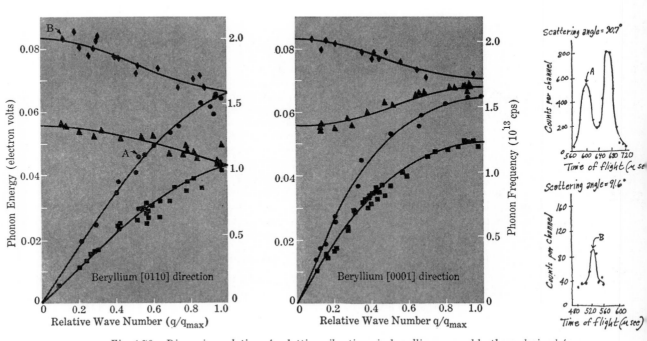

Fig. 1-79. Dispersion relations for lattice vibrations in beryllium resemble those derived from simple one-dimensional model (Fig. 1-75). Relation is different for different directions in the crystal. These are for principal symmetry directions of the hexagonal close-packed structure of beryllium. Every point on these curves represents a peak in a time-of-flight curve of the kind plotted of points A and B at right.

ties, say 0.001%, measurements of this type can play an important role in the study of impurities, radiation damage, and defects.

In crystals with atoms that have magnetic moments, a further modification of the dispersion relations is evident. The neutrons interact with the atoms both through the usual neutron-nucleus interaction and also through an interaction of the magnetic moment of the neutron with the magnetic moment of the atom. They are both little magnets and can exert a force on each other. When the first mode predominates, the waves excited are acoustic waves and dispersion relations characteristic of phonons are measured. But for scattering from some planes, the scattering can be predominantly by the magnetic interaction. Here, waves called spin waves are excited and propagate through the crystal by the interaction of the magnetic dipoles of the atoms (see margin). These quantized waves are called magnons. Experimental evidence of their existence is in Fig. 1-80. These results were obtained by Brockhouse and his co-workers, who measured the dispersion relations for magnons moving in a certain direction in a magnetite crystal.

To date, only the surface has been scratched of the possibilities of slow neutrons as dynamic probes of solid-state properties. Because of limited space the physical properties observed in single crystals have been only outlined, and all the interesting effects in amorphous solids, in liquids, and in molecules have been neglected. Even so, much new and challenging information has been produced. If as many advances in technique and precision are made in the next ten years as have been made in the last ten years, the neutron will take its equal place with microwaves and infrared radiation as a probe of the solid state. All indications are that these improvements and advances will be made.

Further reading

A good way to learn about things neutrons can do is to read the late D. J. Hughes' *Pile Neutron Research* (Addison-Wesley, 1960, $12.50). Neutron diffraction is covered in the book of that name by G. E. Bacon (Oxford, 1955, $5.60).

The fascinating analogies among waves in periodic structures, be they electrical, mechanical, or atomic, are brought out in Leon Bril-

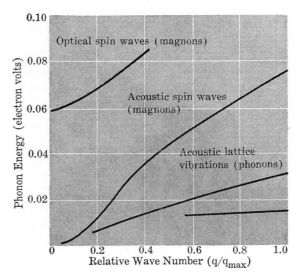

Fig. 1-80. *For a magnetic material, such as magnetite, the dispersion relations are altered because the magnetic moment of the neutron can now interact with the magnetic moment of atoms in the lattice and with waves involving these atoms. One characteristic of the dispersion curves for these spin waves is that they are quadratic rather than linear at long wavelengths (low q). Thus these curves provide direct evidence for the existence of spin waves and magnons in Fe_3O_4 lattice.*

louin's *Wave Propagation in Periodic Structures* (Dover, 1953, $1.75). More detailed discussion of the dynamical properties of solids is in Max Born and Kun Huang's *Dynamical Theory of Crystal Lattices* (Oxford, 1954, $8.80).

The text on solid-state physics is Charles Kittel's *Introduction to Solid State Physics* (Wiley, 1956, $12). Chapter 5 is particularly pertinent.

Detailed references to the specialized work on inelastic scattering are in the proceedings of an International Atomic Energy Agency symposium on the subject (IAEA, Vienna, 1961, $12). A second IAEA symposium was held in Chalk River, Canada, Sept. 10–14, 1962. A good review of the theory is Kothare and Singwi's article "Interaction of Thermal Neutrons with Solids" in *Solid State Physics Advances*, Vol. 8 (Academic Press, 1959, $13.50). A new book on this subject is *Inelastic Scattering of Slow Neutrons*, edited by P. A. Egelstaff (Academic Press, 1963). If you read Russian, try B. F. Turchin's *Slow Neutrons*.

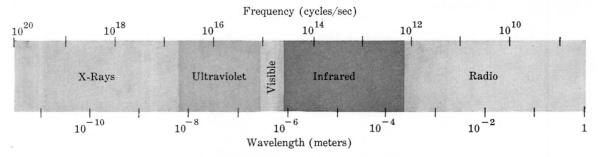

Frequency (cycles/sec)

10^{20} 10^{18} 10^{16} 10^{14} 10^{12} 10^{10}

X-Rays   Ultraviolet   Visible   Infrared   Radio

10^{-10} 10^{-8} 10^{-6} 10^{-4} 10^{-2} 1

Wavelength (meters)

Fig. 1-81. Infrared band occupies portion of electromagnetic spectrum between visible and very short radio-wave (microwave) regions. Here it extends from 0.75 μ to about 500 μ, but upper limit is quite arbitrary; many workers set 1 mm as the upper boundary.

INFRARED

by J. King, T. Limperis, J. Morgan, F. Polcyn, and W. Wolfe *

IN BRIEF: *Between visible light and microwaves stretches the band of radiation called the infrared. This portion of the electromagnetic spectrum is well known for its heating properties and for its importance in spectroscopy.*

Less familiar, perhaps, is the fact that the earth and most things on it, and many bodies in space, radiate large amounts of energy at infrared frequencies. Add to this recent advances in instrumentation—most notably faster, more sensitive detectors—and you get a rapidly growing, incredibly flexible technology.

Infrared guidance and warning systems are with us; communication and ranging systems are in the wings. Infrared data are teaching us new facts about our own atmosphere and those of other planets. New monitoring systems for industry, thermal diagnostic techniques for medicine, and new means of studying our environment, will all be provided by infrared technology—and that's just the beginning.—S.B.

■ If our eyes were sensitive to infrared rather than visible radiation, we would perceive a very different visual world. We normally see objects by the light they reflect, because most substances emit little, if any, light of their own. In the infrared region, the situation is almost reversed; most objects reflect little, but emit copiously.

The infrared world is a radiant world, a world almost without shadow. Warmer objects would appear brighter to our eyes, and the band of "colors" we would see might be much wider. Yet, although purists maintain a distinction between infrared and visible light, the differences are mainly biological—we sense infrared radiation as heat rather than light. To those working in optical technology, both fre-

quency bands are, along with the ultraviolet, part of the optical spectrum. Infrared equipment uses lenses, mirrors, and prisms; and, like visible light, infrared radiation can be detected by photoeffects.

The infrared spectrum was discovered in 1800 by the elder Herschel, Sir Frederick William, who used a thermometer to detect the energy beyond the end of a visible prismatic spectrum. In 1861, Richard Bunsen and Gustav Kirchhoff firmly established the underlying principles for infrared spectroscopy.

After a century of steady advances, the utility of infrared technology is no longer confined to spectroscopy, nor is it used just for devices for night vision and rifle sighting, or for infrared heating. There is developing a fascinating variety of applications of electromagnetic radiation constituting the spectrum from about 1 μ to about 1 mm—the three decades between visible light and very-high-frequency radars shown in Fig. 1-81.

The list of applications is long, ranging from missile defense and fire detection to meteorology and medical diagnostics. But however varied the applications, infrared systems can be broken down into four basic units: an infrared source, an optical system, a radiation detector, and an arrangement for presenting the data. Passive systems are used in most applications; the object of interest is in this case the source, which is seen by its self-emission. In active systems, a controlled source is used to illuminate the object under observation.

Figure 1-82 illustrates two representative infrared systems, both passive. The top typifies a guidance or tracking system. Its function is to provide error information for control purposes. The second, a scanning system, can be used for reconnaissance. Since a photo-like image is usually required, information is displayed on an oscilloscope screen or similar de-

* All five authors are members of the staff of the Infrared Laboratory at the Institute of Science and Technology, The University of Michigan.

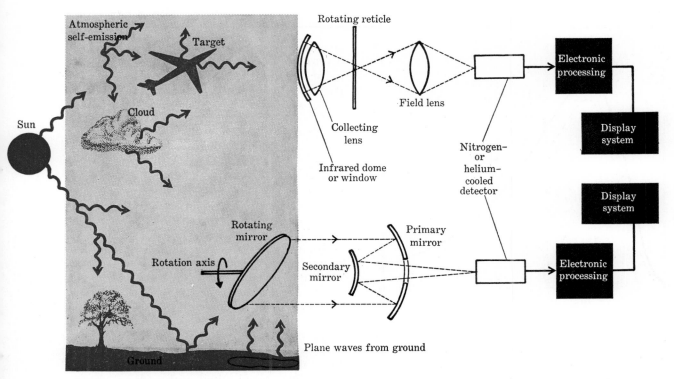

Fig. 1-82. Representative guidance system is shown at top. Background consists of radiation from sources both in and out of atmosphere (tinted area), and self-emission from atmosphere itself. Background and target radiation are partially absorbed and scattered by atmosphere. Collecting lens focuses radiation at reticle, which modulates it. Field lens then focuses radiation onto cooled detector. Signal is processed electronically and displayed. Display system may be cathode ray

tube, phototube, electromechanical system or magnetic tape. Second system represents typical reconnaissance device. Plane waves radiating from ground are intercepted by rotating mirror; background consists of scattered radiation from variety of sources, including sun. Radiation is focussed by primary mirror onto secondary, and then through hole in primary onto detector. Signal is then processed and can be displayed on cathode ray tube or recorded on magnetic tape.

vice. We have shown the guidance system using lenses and the scanner using mirrors, but other arrangements are possible with the wide variety of components available today. We will describe these components, and some applications they make possible, but it is necessary to review first the underlying physics.

Physics of infrared radiation

All substances emit electromagnetic energy. As we stated, most objects on earth radiate copiously in the infrared portion of the spectrum. The simplest emitters to describe are theoretically perfect radiators, or black bodies, which emit radiation with a spectral distribution shown in the marginal curves. Max Planck formulated the complicated law describing this distribution back at the turn of the century.

Earlier, Wilhelm Wien had found that the positions of the maxima of these curves are described by the relation $\lambda_{max}T \sim 3000\ \mu°K$. The radiation peak of the sun occurs at $0.5\ \mu$, in the visible part of the spectrum, because the sun's surface temperature is about $6000°K$. The earth has a spectral distribution with a peak at about $10\ \mu$, well in the ir, and corresponding to a temperature of about $300°K$; the radia-

tion from most earthbound objects has nearly the same distribution.

The total radiation, obtained by integrating Planck's equation over all possible wavelengths, yields the Stefan-Boltzmann law $W = \sigma T^4$, where σ is the Stefan-Boltzmann constant. The Stefan-Boltzmann law and that of Planck are both valid only for black bodies. Since few objects even approximate a perfect radiator, workers have introduced a multiplicative efficiency factor ϵ, called emissivity. Black bodies have an emissivity of 1. Other objects have an emissivity, ϵ_λ, which is either a constant less than 1 (gray body) or varies strongly with wavelength (non-gray body). Figure 1-83 illustrates the three types for a temperature of $300°K$.

Another important and famous law is also due to Kirchhoff: good absorbers are good emitters. If α_λ represents the percentage of power absorbed by a material per unit wavelength, then for that material at a given temperature, $\alpha_\lambda = \epsilon_\lambda$.

Infrared sources and atmospheric effects

The intensity and spectral distribution of radiation emitted from an infrared source are

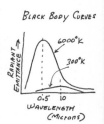

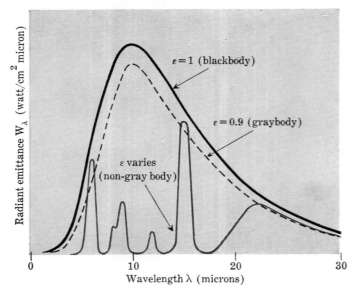

Fig. 1-83. Emitted radiation is plotted as function of wavelength for black body, gray body, and non-gray body, all at 300°K. Emissivity, ε, is an efficiency factor. Black body and gray body curves both peak at about 10 μ.

constituents and, as the blownup section from 3.4 to 3.5 μ shows, the spectrum is actually quite complex. The complete transmission curve has comparable structure. In addition, the atmosphere is not constant; it changes with season, altitude, time of day, viewing angle, etc. A calculation of transmission over any path must take all of these things into account.

For most system designs, the engineer requires a knowledge of the quantity and spectral distribution of radiation arriving at the collecting aperture (entrance pupil) or "dish" of his instrument. This spectral irradiance H_λ is usually specified as the number of watts per square centimeter per micron. For some problems it is known with great accuracy; for others an uncertainty of 200% is not unusual.

If this figure seems surprising, consider the nature of some sources—particularly exhaust gases from rocket plumes. Energy is emitted in a series of narrow spectral lines, bounded by a black-body envelope; the atmosphere operates like a comb filter on these lines, absorbing some frequencies, transmitting others. In addition, the atmosphere reradiates at the frequency of the absorbed power. Thus, the quantity and spectral distribution of the collected radiation is a complex combination of the filtered target radiation and the self-emitted atmospheric radiation. Moreover, not only does the atmospheric spectrum vary, but the spectrum of the source is not well known.

It is almost axiomatic to say that controlled sources—sniperscope beams, Nernst glowers and globars for use with spectrometers, communication sources like xenon lamps—are

determined by its physical characteristics (ϵ_λ) and by its temperature (Planck's law). This radiation usually passes through some medium, like the atmosphere, and the radiation impinging on any receiving device is thus a function of both the emission characteristics of the source and the absorption (or transmission) characteristics of the medium.

Figure 1-84 illustrates the over-all absorption spectrum of the atmosphere, made up of the superimposed spectra of all the atmospheric

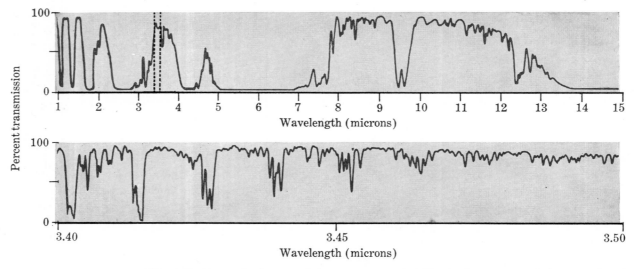

Fig. 1-84. Atmospheric transmission spectrum out of 15 μ is shown at top; it is composite of transmission spectra of all atmospheric components. Dotted section between 3 and 4 μ is shown in greater detail below it, revealing complex nature of spectrum.

understood quite well; stable, semicontrolled radiators like blast furnaces, rolling mills, and concrete surfaces are fairly well in hand; but targets like rockets, which are largely inaccessible, and some backgrounds, like suburbs and high-altitude clouds, which have sensitive weather-dependent properties, are only partially understood.

Sources for active systems

Whereas, passive infrared systems depend upon sensing the self-emission of the objects of interest, active systems depend upon sensing source radiation that is reflected by the object of interest. Consequently, the source problem is quite different. The nature of the source is known and controlled; the designer is plagued rather by a lack of good sources. The need for sources is acute because, although active systems sacrifice the advantages of secrecy, so important to the military, they can perform functions for which passive systems are just not naturally suited, particularly ranging, and communication.

Active systems have been restricted in range by power limitation because sources have not had sufficient spectral and spatial power densities. For example, only a small amount of the source power lies in the spectral region of interest. Sources must be relatively large to generate appreciable amounts of power, must be modulated externally, and are presently incoherent so that no use can be made of the information contained in the shape and phase of the waveform.

Laser sources may change the situation radically. Infrared laser beams share the advantages of visible coherent light for use as an information carrier for communication, ranging, and navigation systems. Infrared lasers provide good sources for night vision devices because of the high spectral and spatial densities possible. But, further advances are needed before these sources can be effectively utilized.

Detectors—the heart of the system

The increased usefulness of infrared radiation is primarily due to vastly improved detectors. The improvement is particularly striking in the wavelength region beyond 3 μ. Detector response times are shorter and sensitivity has been improved. Equally important, detectors are more rugged, and more resistant to aging and to attack by environmental factors.

Detectors fall into two broad categories: thermal detectors and photodetectors. The improvements we have listed above have been mainly in photodetectors. However, there have been improvements in thermal detectors, and many people feel that even greater improve-

ments are possible if more time and money are invested.

In thermal detectors, impinging infrared energy heats the sensitive element, and a temperature-dependent property of the solid is monitored. Generally, thermal detectors are slow, because it takes time for the sensing element to heat. Moreover, they are not particularly sensitive. Their chief advantage has been that they respond to long-wavelength radiation at ambient operating temperatures.

Although many photodetectors operate at wavelengths beyond three microns, most of them need to be cooled to the liquid helium or liquid nitrogen temperature range. Cooling devices occupy space and consume power. Consequently, thermal detectors are widely used whenever weight and power are important considerations as in the case of satellites carrying ir instruments.

A variety of thermal detectors is available. The oldest, aside from the thermometer, is the thermocouple. When several thermocouples are arranged in series, so that the voltages they produce add, a sensitive "thermopile" is formed. These have been used for some time in spectroscopy and other applications where room temperature operation is permissible and the time constant (a measure of speed of response) need not be shorter than several milliseconds.

In a Golay pneumatic cell, the energy of an ir beam is absorbed by the walls of a gas-filled chamber, increasing the temperature of the gas and the pressure it exerts on the chamber walls. This pressure can be used to distort some optical element, producing a means of detecting infrared radiation. Like the thermocouple, pneumatic cells are sluggish. However, they are equally sensitive at all ir wavelengths, and have been suggested as standards.

Outside of spectroscopy, bolometers are by far the most widely used thermal detectors. These devices take advantage of the fact that certain metals (like Ni and Pt) and some semiconductors (like mixtures of Mn, Ni, and Co oxides) exhibit a large change of resistance with a small temperature change over a considerable temperature range. The semiconductor bolometer is called a thermistor—thermally sensitive resistor. Bolometers are used extensively in infrared radiometers, satellite-borne horizon seekers, and other devices where either a flat, extensive, spectral response is required, or where little weight can be allowed for bulky cryogenics so that ambient temperatures must be satisfactory.

The sensitivity of bolometers has been increased in two ways. Smaller flakes of material are used which heat more quickly, and more recently, bolometers have been optically attached to condensing lenses.

Photodetectors have made the difference

As much as bolometers have been improved, the most important advances have been in photodetectors. One basic operational principle underlies all photodetection processes: Infrared photons react with bound electrons in the sensitive element, producing free charge carriers—unbound electrons and holes; some electrical property which depends upon the number of free charge carriers in the sensitive element is monitored to determine changes in flux density of the incident infrared radiation.

There are four different photoelectric phenomena which have been used successfully in infrared detectors: photoemission, photoconduction, the photovoltaic effect, and the photoelectromagnetic effect. Of the four, photoconducting and photovoltaic detectors are most frequently used. The sensitive element of both is a semiconductor, which has an electronic structure best described by the band structure sketched in the margin.

The valence band contains energy levels occupied by bound electrons; free electrons occupy energy levels in the conduction band. The gap between them, called the forbidden band, contains energy levels which the electrons cannot occupy. If the gap is not too large, the material is a semiconductor. Electrons can, by several processes, receive sufficient energy to cross the forbidden band. One important process is by the absorption of photons by the electrons.

Insulating materials which have large gaps that the electrons cannot readily cross, can be made semiconducting by the addition of impurities. This creates new occupied levels in the forbidden band, called impurity levels, from which electrons can readily cross to the conduction band. Such a material is called an extrinsic semiconductor. There are two types: *n*-types, in which the impurities contribute electrons (negative charge carriers); and *p*-types, in which the impurities contribute holes (positive charge carriers).

In photoconductive detectors, absorbed photons cause electrons in the valence band or impurity levels to jump into the conduction band, increasing the conductivity of the material. In photovoltaic detectors, photons create free carriers at a junction of *n*- and *p*-type materials, producing a potential difference. Indium antimonide is used in one of the best photovoltaic detectors made today. Its detectivity (a parameter used to designate sensitivity) is close to the theoretical limit, which is set by the random arrival of background photons. Unfortunately, this detector is sensitive only out to 5.5 μ, whereas available photoconducting detectors are sensitive out to 5 mm. (See curves in Fig. 1-85.)

Another drawback to using photovoltaic detectors is that, although their signal-to-noise ratio is high, the signal itself is small; this means that more sophisticated electronics are

---

BAND MODEL

CONDUCTION BAND

G = FORBIDDEN GAP

L = IMPURITY LEVELS (WHEN PRESENT)

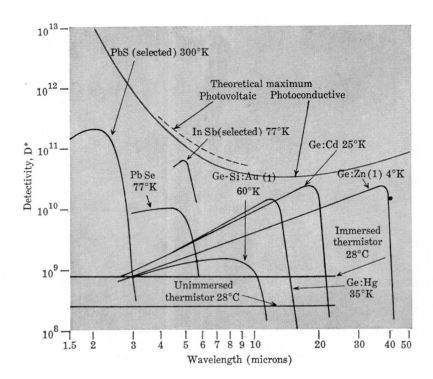

Fig. 1-85. Detectivity, D*, with which detector responds to radiation, is plotted as function of wavelength for variety of materials. Theoretical curves are included. PbS has been a mainstay for work in the 1 to 3 μ region. PbSe was one of first photodetectors sensitive out to 6 μ, and has highly reproducible properties. Doped Ge detectors are fast and sensitive at extremely long wavelengths, while Ge-Si is useful in 8 to 14 μ region because it operates at relatively high temperatures. InSb is also used a lot because of its speed and high D*.

frequently needed than with photoconducting detectors.

However, the primary limitation on photovoltaic detectors is their restriction to short wavelengths. This is a materials problem. The situation could change radically if materials were found that operate at long wavelengths. Meanwhile, photoconducting detectors remain dominant for most applications in which fast, sensitive detectors are needed.

Photoconducting detectors themselves still need some improving, however. Present extrinsic semiconductors used as long-wavelength detectors need to be cooled, and we have already mentioned the problems this entails. This problem would be mitigated considerably if we had intrinsic detectors that were sensitive in the 8 to 14 μ region. These need not be cooled as low (50°K vs. 35°K for extrinsic detectors), permitting a considerable saving in power and bulk. Other desirable improvements are increased resistance to shock, aging, and chemical attack.

Imaging devices are needed too

The detectors we have been discussing are all single-element, "point" detectors; all of the radiation falling on the detector at any moment gets combined into one output signal. Complementing point detectors are imaging devices. The oldest imaging devices are dye-sensitized infrared films, but these are sensitive only out to 1.2 μ. So far, no useful dyes exist which have sensitivities beyond 1.2 μ, and even if there were such dyes, the difficulty encountered in manufacturing and processing the films would be formidable. For instance, the infrared radiation from the walls of a standard darkroom can fog infrared film.

A wide variety of useful imaging devices is available. These are the image tubes. Like point detectors, they come in two types—thermal and photo—and share all of the advantages and drawbacks of point detectors.

The development of image tubes has been slow. A major problem has been extending the spectral response of image tubes. Like the point detectors, these image tubes must be cooled; the engineering involved is even more complex. Image distortion is a problem because it is difficult to get uniform sensitivity across a tube surface. Also, the basic physics is not as well understood as for point detectors.

Optics for ir systems

Whereas the detector is often called the heart of the infrared system, the optical device must be considered analogous to the eye. It collects the radiation from some region of space and then filters and focuses it onto the surface of the detector.

Optical systems for infrared use are, for the most part, telescopes with resolutions of a fraction of a milliradian, which often must perform well over the broad infrared spectrum from 1 to 15 μ. In size, the collecting mirrors or lenses range from about one inch in diameter for small laboratory equipments, and some missile systems to nearly two yards across for long-range detection and astronomical applications. Although there are special features for certain applications, most systems are folded reflecting types like the one in Fig. 1-82.

These designs have gained favor for many reasons. They are usually light compared with a lens system and are reasonably compact because of their folded configuration. More important, however, is the fact that materials like silver, aluminum, and gold, which have high reflectance in the infrared, are readily available.

Some designs have made use of the advantages of both reflecting (catoptric) and refracting (dioptric) elements, incorporating them in the so-called catadioptric designs patterned after Schmidt and Bouwers. Catadioptric and reflective designs are both limited to narrow field of view, but this has not been a restrictive limitation because the point detectors in current use integrate all incident radiation into one signal. Consequently, the only way to look at a large area is to scan it, using narrow field optics. As image tubes improve, increased call will be made for wide angle systems which also have large collecting power. It seems that the only way to accomplish this is to design better lens optics.

The biggest obstacle to such design improvements is the lack of satisfactory materials. Optical elements must be transparent in the infrared, strong and hard, unaffected by water and other environmental contaminants like ultraviolet radiation, must be heat and thermal-shock resistant, and for some applications, must even be cheap! In the visible portion of the spectrum, these stringent requirements are met rather well by a wide variety of glasses, but in the broader infrared spectral region the designer must seek a compromise from among many materials which are not ideal. Figure 1-86 lists some of the choices.

Almost all of the alkali and heavy-metal halides are transparent relatively far into the infrared. Unfortunately, the same molecular properties that impart desirable transparency usually cause low binding strength between molecules. If the binding is weak, the material is easily attacked, and almost all of the substances toward the bottom of the table, and a

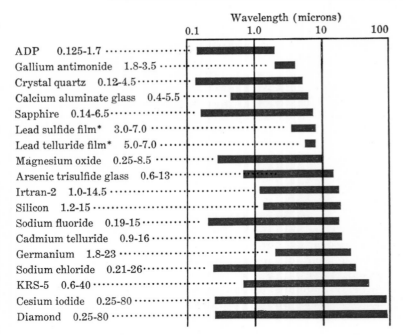

Wavelength (microns)

| | 0.1 | 1.0 | 10 | 100 |

ADP   0.125-1.7
Gallium antimonide   1.8-3.5
Crystal quartz   0.12-4.5
Calcium aluminate glass   0.4-5.5
Sapphire   0.14-6.5
Lead sulfide film*   3.0-7.0
Lead telluride film*   5.0-7.0
Magnesium oxide   0.25-8.5
Arsenic trisulfide glass   0.6-13
Irtran-2   1.0-14.5
Silicon   1.2-15
Sodium fluoride   0.19-15
Cadmium telluride   0.9-16
Germanium   1.8-23
Sodium chloride   0.21-26
KRS-5   0.6-40
Cesium iodide   0.25-80
Diamond   0.25-80

Fig. 1-86. Bars indicate regions of transparency for wide variety of optical materials. Cutoff wavelengths are those at which sample 2 mm thick has 10% transmission. Those marked with asterisks have less than 10% transmission throughout.

H = High REFRACTION LAYER

L = Low REFRACTION LAYER

great many we have not included, are very readily attacked by water—if not deliquescent. Silver chloride, one of the few exceptions, becomes opaque in strong sunlight, and Krs-5 (mixed thallium bromide and thallium iodide) will change its size and shape at room temperatures by slow plastic deformation under load.

In spite of all this, there are some useful and usable materials. Germanium and silicon in crystalline and cast forms, zinc sulfide or zinc selenide as hot-pressed compounds, certain mixed crystals, and arsenic-sulfur non-oxide glasses are all useful in the 8 to 20 μ region, some as windows or domes for reconnaissance sets or guidance units, some as field lenses in these or similar systems. Calcium aluminate glass, hot-pressed magnesium fluoride, crystalline magnesium oxide, and others can be used from 3 to 5 μ; and many materials, including silicate glasses, can be used out to about 2.7 μ where a molecular absorption band reduces transmission through the atmosphere intolerably. But there is still need for materials which have better optical and mechanical properties, and which have properties that relate to other materials properly so that multiple elements can be designed.

Processing the incoming radiation

Another important optical element is the spectral filter. A given detector will usually be

sensitive over a broader wavelength band than that in which the target radiates. Hence, background can be cut down considerably by filtering out radiation from all regions except the one of interest. Although there exists a wide variety of filter types for use in the infrared part of the spectrum, the simple absorption filter and the all-dielectric interference filter presently reign supreme. The first of these is conceptually simple: Every material is transparent in parts of the electromagnetic spectrum and opaque elsewhere; by selecting materials properly one can allow only the desired band of wavelengths into an instrument—if the right materials exist.

The all-dielectric filter, probably the most versatile and useful filter, is based upon the principle of interference rather than absorption. The transmission of optical elements can be improved by applying on their surface a thin coating of transparent material; the coating thickness and refractive index are chosen so that the waves reflected from the second surface interfere destructively with those from the first. The amplitude of the transmitted wave is larger. Because an arrangement like this can only be satisfied for a restricted, but not sharply defined, band of wavelengths, such a thin film is a filter, although a very unsatisfactory one. However, by combining a series or stack of such layers together in different arrangements, a great variety of filter characteristics can be obtained. The marginal sketch illustrates one arrangement.

The reticle, a small, patterned, rotating disk of sections which are completely transparent, completely opaque, or partially transparent, is often placed in a primary or secondary focus of the optical system. This remarkable device can be less than 1 cm in diameter yet can perform as many as three different operations simultaneously.

The first of these functions is the easiest to understand; the radiation, were the reticle not there, would be focused onto the detector at all times, and a steady source signal would generate a steady dc detector output signal; with the rotating reticle in position this steady light intensity is interrupted and a more manageable ac signal is generated.

In addition, particular types of modulation are accomplished as desired by the size and shape of the bars of the reticle. Amplitude modulation is accomplished, for instance, by the first reticle pattern shown in Fig. 1-87. A target spot can then be located circumferentially by measuring the time lag between a reference pulse and the first pulse from a point target. The reticle with nonradial spokes can provide radial position information by the pulse width.

Many other coding schemes are possible. These two bits of information can provide the two angles of a spherical coordinate system that are necessary for pointing.

The third function is independent of the first two, but naturally the reticle design is not. Most military targets—jet exhausts and rocket plumes—and many commercial ones are small, while backgrounds like clouds, lakes, and terrain are large. Therefore, if the spacings of the reticle are made small, the output waveform for a target remains well modulated, while that of a background becomes smoothed. In this way large objects can be discriminated from small.

Infrared in industry and medicine

Industry has barely begun to exploit the possibilities opened up by advances in infrared instrumentation, even though infrared radiation has long been used for industrial purposes. Early applications include the use of the infrared radiation as a heating mechanism, and infrared spectroscopy for chemical analysis. However, it is in the area of infrared sensing and control that improved instrumentation has made new applications possible.

One of the first industrial applications of infrared sensing techniques was the railroad "hot box" detector. The journal boxes must be kept in a satisfactory state of lubrication or they overheat and eventually fail, disrupting schedules and even causing wrecks. The trick is to detect the overheating before failure occurs. A small radiometer does this by collecting all the radiation in a broad spectral interval from a narrow field or view aimed at the level of the journal boxes. The amount of radiation is used to determine whether a box is hot or not. Such a device, introduced about five years ago, is now widely used by railroads throughout the country.

Another mode of temperature sensing uses a thermograph to photograph the thermal structure of objects. One application of such a device is the testing of structural "sandwiches" used in the construction of aircraft. One side of the structure is heated uniformly, and the heat is conducted through the structure. The thermal conductivity of flaws is lower than that of good bonds; the thermograph will pinpoint these regions of lower radiance (Color Fig. 2).

A different use has been made of the radiant properties of materials in industrial processes. In the manufacture of steel rods, the hot material is supposed to be of a designated diameter, within certain tolerances of course. The measurement of moving red hot steel rods is not an easy task by most methods, and a virtual impossibility by a contact technique. A simple radiometric technique does this very nicely by

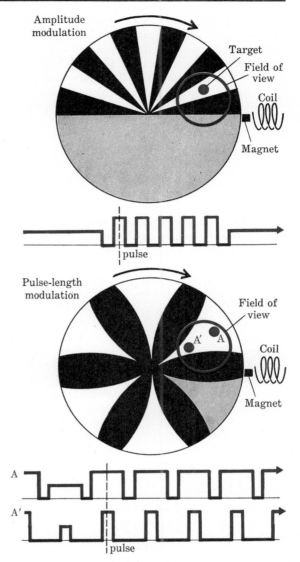

Fig. 1-87. *Two reticles are shown, consisting of opaque (black), 50% opaque (gray) and transparent sections. Signals they generate with each 360° rotation are shown. Small magnet attached to reticle at top generates reference pulse each time it passes coil; phase difference between reference pulse and end of 50% signal gives angular location of target. Reticle at bottom has spokes shaped to give radial location of target; pulse width differs for target at A and A'. This reticle also has semi-opaque section and magnet to supply angular position information.*

determining the area over which there is a radiation level considerably greater than the background.

Infrared instruments and ideas are also becoming useful in medicine. One direct application is the use of a thermograph for determining areas of unusual temperature variation on the body that usually indicate anomalies.

A second infrared diagnostic technique accurately and rapidly determines the percentage of CO_2 in the blood. The instrument uses a source of infrared radiation that is filtered so only a small band of light, centered at 4.3 μ, passes into the sample cell. The CO_2 molecule absorbs strongly at 4.3 μ. The percentage absorption can be related to the concentration of CO_2 in the sample cell, and is a sensitive function of the concentration. The key to techniques of this type is to find a line characteristic of only the substance in question.

Within the bounds of moderate restrictions, infrared techniques can be used to measure temperatures to within one thousandth of a degree in about one-millionth to one-thousandth of a second. Substances can be identified by their infrared spectra, and concentrations can be determined to within one part per million—or even per billion—in measuring times that depend upon the particular problem. What does this mean for future uses?

If we speculate a bit, we can foresee a great expansion of spectro-optical diagnostic laboratory techniques. Researchers may one day thermally map neural cells, providing activity indications; they may be able to correlate heat activity with dermatological disorders; or, they may determine better the relationship of local heat increases to incipient cancer, to phlebitis, and other pathological conditions. And industry will undoubtedly apply both spectrometric and remote temperature-monitoring techniques more extensively in the future.

Infrared in space

Infrared technology has been widely exploited for both military and scientific space

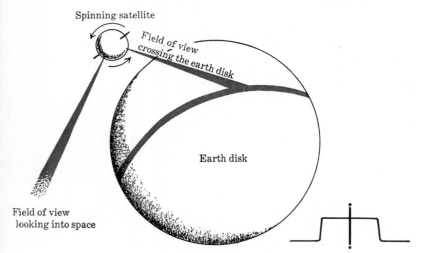

Fig. 1-88. Horizon scanner provides attitude control by finding direction to center of earth's disk. Since earth radiates more energy in the infrared than surrounding space does, scanner generates pulse shown as satellite rotates. By bisecting pulse, instruments determine vertical.

applications. Horizon scanners operating in the infrared region have been used for attitude control of vehicles in the US Manned Space Program, and in fact, for a good many satellites. While the mission of these devices is not to scan the horizon, but to determine the direction to the center of the earth, the local vertical, they in reality locate the direction to the center of the earth's disk (see Fig. 1-88).

Tiros meteorological satellites in orbit sent back a tremendous amount of data concerning the location and movements of great cloud masses which are indicative of the total weather situation. Pictures have been published showing embryo storm centers as well as full blown storms, and such information has been claimed by meteorologists as revolutionary in weather prediction and interpretation. The value of the Tiros instrumentation, however, is not just in the pictures but in information from several different spectral regions simultaneously. In fact, the Tiros instruments meter radiation in several spectral bands. The interpretation of this mass of data provided both visible imagery of cloud tops and infrared thermographs which could be interpreted in terms of temperature. The instrumentation for the projected Nimbus satellite is more specialized and more sophisticated. It includes, among other things, an infrared grating spectrometer which can provide a detailed spectral analysis of the earth's atmosphere from above. By carefully observing the radiation level in several spectral bands, located in regions of differing atmospheric absorption, a deduction concerning the temperature distribution can be made.

The Mariner included in its instrument payload an infrared radiometer which scanned the surface of Venus and provided an account of the radiance distribution and an indication of temperature. Measurements of Venus have been made from balloons 100,000 ft above the earth's surface to determine the water content by assessing the radiation in and near a water band. Such measurements are made from high-rising balloons because they are not accurate if they are modified to any significant degree by water vapor always present in the atmosphere of the earth.

Infrared guidance techniques are at least as useful in space as they are in the atmosphere. Although there still must be an adequate contrast between the target and the background, the effects of the atmosphere are no longer present. Important military functions can also be performed in space. The MIDAS system (Missile Infrared Defense and Alarm System) is based on the fact that ICBM's emit large quantities of infrared radiation from their plumes during their powered phase. The concept is simple: detect that radiation at satisfactory distances; substantiate that it is a military target; shoot it down. Undoubtedly the details are harder to work out than the concept! Less radiation is emitted by missiles and by satellites in midcourse, but in principle the same techniques can be used to intercept a missile or rendezvous with a satellite.

System performance can be improved considerably in all of these cases if a satisfactory solution is found to the cooling problem. And, both detectors and optical components must be made to operate flawlessly in the space environment, that is, in very high vacua, in intense radiation fields, and under micrometeorite bombardment. More powerful sources and larger diameter optics will be required for communication over interplanetary distances. One of the more difficult problems in space will be the acquisition problem. Unless precisely predictable orbits are used, the search times become staggering for long-distance tracking and communication.

Military uses are legion

Military applications of infrared technology have received increased emphasis since the early 1950's. Among the systems being studied are aerial reconnaissance devices, guidance sets, communicators, intrusion detectors, and night vision devices.

Aerial reconnaissance sets have been built for nighttime surveillance of enemy territory to detect troop activity, assess bomb damage, and even detect submarines. They have also been useful in daytime surveillance to obtain information with which to augment that obtained by standard photography, and for camouflage penetration, as Fig. 1-89 shows.

Guidance sets such as those employed in the terminal phase for certain missiles sometimes employ infrared sensors to supply the guidance error information; we might also include aiming devices, like those sometimes used in firing missiles and rockets, in this class of equipment. The success of these systems was well documented during the fighting over the Formosan Straits; even though severely outnumbered, the Chinese Nationalists, in aircraft armed with air-to-air missiles employing infrared terminal guidance, could win important sorties with the Chinese Communists with almost no losses to themselves.

Warning systems, too, have been built in diverse forms ranging from instruments for detecting intercontinental ballistic missiles during some portion of their flight, to intrusion devices for detecting the movement of enemy ground troops.

Most infrared ranging systems have been

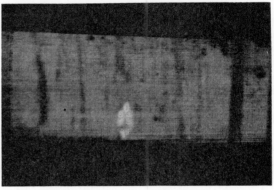

Fig. 1-89. This pair of pictures illustrates ability of infrared systems to penetrate camouflage. In upper photograph, man cannot be seen, although he is standing behind bushes in the background. Because he is warmer than his surroundings, man stands out clearly as a bright figure in the thermograph, made with a passive system. (Courtesy U.S. Army Engineer R & D Laboratories, Fort Belvoir, Virginia)

passive devices based on conventional geometric triangulation, inverse triangulation, or image position techniques. Infrared offers secrecy, due to the narrow, invisible, line-of-sight beam. Active infrared ranging systems have recently been used which operate in a manner similar in some ways to radar ranging devices, and the success of these active ranging systems has been widely acclaimed. Night vision devices include such things as filters to achieve a more favorable ratio of target to background signal as well as active systems for illuminating targets or scenes of interest. Night-driving aids and the sniperscope are successful examples of these devices.

The problems and limitations encountered in military applications of infrared technology seem to center around the inability of the various devices to discriminate between targets and backgrounds which look like the targets. At least a portion of this inability can be blamed on the fact that any equipment design decisions are based on either insufficient or inaccurate information. For example, descriptions of targets and backgrounds are usually not sufficiently good to permit the design of systems which take advantage of small but significant differences between them. The rest of the difficulty, however, must certainly rest with an inability to implement those techniques or methods which seem to promise increased discrimination capabilities. Filters have neither the sharp cut-offs nor the transmission efficiencies needed for certain spectral discrimination methods. The resolution, detectivity, and speed of response of various systems often limit what can be done.

Because there has never been an infrared equivalent of the MIT Radar Lab and because only a small fraction of the money devoted to radar advances has been allocated for infrared work, it is probably fair to say that the exploitation of the technology today is comparatively not much advanced from where radar development stood at the end of World War II. Advances should be rapid if advantage is taken of the large bodies of knowledge existing in the various pure and applied sciences.

The earth sciences—untapped potential

Among the exciting possibilities suggested by recent advances in infrared instrumentation are contributions to research in the earth sciences—geology, geophysics, oceanography, meteorology, and related fields. Many scientifically or economically interesting natural phenomena can be studied with infrared, and some interesting experimental results have already been obtained. Most of these new applications lend themselves to use of airborne techniques, although many could be done on a limited scale with ground-based equipment.

One large group of applications depends on detecting something under the ground by means of a temperature difference at the surface. For example, heat produced by exothermal processes could be detected this way, suggesting the possibility of thermal prospecting for mineral deposits, or mapping of submerged peat bogs along proposed highway routes. Underground explosions and fires might be detected this way. The technique has already been used to study underground hydro-thermal activity, and with notable success, to detect crevasses under the arctic snow.

Various oceanographic uses have been at least partly demonstrated, including iceberg detection and counting during hours of polar darkness, tracing of ocean currents, and sea ice reconnaissance. Forest fire detection has also been successful, as has the determination of temperatures of planetary atmospheres. Among the applications still in the speculative stage are studies of lunar geology based on the Moon's

thermal properties and the detection of diseased trees and fruit crops from emissivity changes.

In many cases, a limiting factor in infrared mapping techniques is the formidable problem of interpretation. In the case of aerial photography, long the supreme weapon for large area surveys of all kinds, we are greatly assisted in interpretation of photographs by the analogue of visual experience, whereas our sensory equipment for thermal radiation detection is primitive and our awareness of the self-luminous property of objects in daily experience is practically nil.

Extrapolation of the visual appearance of objects into the infrared is hazardous; color is strictly a visual property, and reflectivity values often change radically with wavelengths. Snow, for example, the brightest thing under the sun visually, has almost no reflectivity in the infrared beyond a few microns, behaving almost as a perfect black-body radiator. Interpretation is further complicated by the fact that thermal radiation is strongly influenced by a number of environmental parameters such as wind, rain, humidity, and sky conditions.

It seems clear that an infrared scanner could be used for detection of incipient forest fires and for surveillance of burned areas to make sure that fires have been thoroughly extinguished. A reliable technique capable of rapid search over large areas is urgently needed, especially in Alaska and similar large, sparsely populated areas. Both infrared and passive microwave techniques (forest fires emit microwave as well as ir radiation) have recently been tried with impressive results.

Figure 1-90 illustrates the use of infrared to delineate the edges of a burning area even in the presence of dense smoke. Smoke particles are about the right size to produce a lot of scattering of visible light, but too small to be effective at longer infrared or microwave wavelengths.

A forest fire is much hotter than the background, but those we wish to detect may be small, perhaps no larger than an ordinary campfire. Since rapid coverage of large areas and a map-like presentation are needed, whereas the information need only be qualitative, a strip mapping scanner is indicated. Peak radiation is at around 3μ, or longer if hot smoke is the target. An InSb detector, filtered for operation in the $4.5–5.5 \mu$ atmospheric window, should yield excellent results, and would also detect terrain features, so that the thermograph would show roads, rivers, and other details of convenience for map matching. Interpretation is fairly easy, as we are interested only in small hot spots against a forest background.

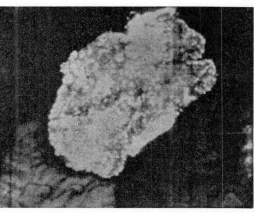

Fig. 1-90. Panchromatic photograph at right shows area in vicinity of fire densely covered by white smoke. Thermograph at far right was taken with high-speed airborne infrared scanner. Fire zone stands out as bright patch, with perimeter clearly defined. This is of considerable importance to fire fighters, who ordinarily experience considerable difficulty in deciding where to drop parachutists and extinguishing chemicals. (Courtesy Intermountain Forest and Range Experiment Station, Northern Forest Fire Laboratory)

Thermal detection of snow bridged crevasses which are often invisible to the eye and the aerial camera, depends on the fact that crevasses contain a volume of trapped air (see the marginal sketch), which may filter out through the porous snow of the bridge during barometric pressure changes. If this trapped air is appreciably warmer or colder than the ambient air, which is often the case, the surface temperature of the snow will be affected. Crevasses have been mapped with impressive reliability using airborne infrared equipment. Figure 1-91 shows a snowfield that has been mapped this way.

Parameters of the crevasse detection problem are quite different from those of forest fire detection. Expected temperature differentials are extremely small, and maximum sensitivity may be needed for positive detection. Snow approximates a good black body over a wide range of wavelengths, so nothing is to be gained by using more than one wavelength region. Since sub-zero temperatures are involved, the radiation peak is around 10 to 12 microns, and the energy difference associated with a small temperature difference is largest in this region. An impurity activated-germanium detector should be used, and it should be filtered for rejection of short wavelengths if detection is to be attempted in daytime. Experience has shown that interpretation is elementary, at least in Greenland; a long narrow warm (or cool) streak on the thermograph almost always delineates a crevasse.

All this serves to show that many problems of long standing may yield to a thoughtful application of the new and rapidly improving infrared technology.

Further reading

The great interest in infrared technology, and its state of maturity, is indicated by the recent publication of several textbooks on the subject: *Elements of Infrared Technology* by Kruse, McGlauchlin, and McQuistan (Wiley, 1962, $10.75), *Infrared Physics and Engineering* by Jamieson, McFee, Plass, Grube, and Richards (McGraw-Hill, 1963, $17.50), and *Fundamentals of Infrared Technology* by Holter, Nudelman, Suits, Zissis, and Wolfe (Macmillan, 1962, $12.50). Other recent texts at about the same level (first year graduate)

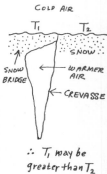

∴ T_1 may be greater than T_2

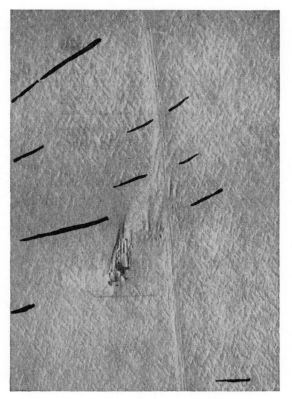

Fig. 1-91. Vertical aerial view of meteorological station known as Tuto East, located alongside a marked trail near the edge of the Greenland Icecap. Overlay has been constructed from radiometric data obtained from air. Dark streaks are crevasses under the snow. These show up clearly by infrared methods, but are not visible to eye or camera. (Under contract to U.S. Army Cold Regions Research and Engineering Laboratory)

include *The Detection and Measurement of Infrared Radiation* by Smith, Jones, and Chasmar (Academic Press, 1957, $11.20), which emphasizes the properties of detectors, and *Infrared Methods* by Conn and Avery (Academic Press, 1960, $6.80), which mainly treats the techniques and data that are useful in the laboratory.

There have also been two special treatments in the technical journals. The first of these, a special issue of the *Proceedings of the Institute of Radio Engineers*, published in Sept. 1959, is a comprehensive treatment, with fundamentals and applications presented in logical order and an extensive reference list appended. The second was a special issue of *Applied Optics*

published in Sept. 1962, which, to a large extent, brings the 1959 publication up to date.

Current articles appear in a host of journals, because of the diversity of both the fundamental science and its applications. Some of the more useful of these are the two just mentioned and *Infrared Physics, Journal of the Optical Society of America, Journal of the Physics and Chemistry of Solids, Journal of Quantitative and Molecular Spectroscopy, Optica Acta,* and *The Physical Review.*

In addition, many organizations (particularly those with security clearances) can obtain information about general and specific problems from IRIA, the Infrared Information and Analysis Center at The University of Michigan.

COHERENT LIGHT

by C. Chapin Cutler [*]

IN BRIEF: *Contrary to what you have heard, light from a laser is not coherent. It is simply more coherent than light from any other source. How much more coherent depends on how you define the word. For coherence can mean that waves are in step in the direction of propagation, or it can mean that they are in step in a plane perpendicular to the direction of propagation. Strictly speaking, both are necessary for complete coherence. But regardless of how you define the word, the laser beam is sufficiently coherent that it acts different from ordinary light. Because of coherence, it can be focused into an intense spot or radiated in narrow beams having unequalled signal-carrying capacity. A less familiar consequence of coherence is the appearance of the light when it is scattered off a surface. The waves interfere to make the surface appear to be covered with a multitude of scintillating spots. The effect may have novel applications.—C.J.L.*

■ Without coherence, the laser would be little more than another fluorescent tube. This one property of laser light is the principal reason for all the papers that have been written, all the research done, all the money spent. In view of this activity and excitement, it is a little surprising that there is still little understanding or agreement about what coherence is or how it affects the way light behaves.

For many people, I suspect, the word coherence brings to mind a train of waves that are all in step, like the orderly waves radiating from a rock thrown in a pool. There is nothing

wrong with this picture, but there is more to coherence than the simple picture conveys.

Coherence is not an absolute property; it exists in varying degrees and kinds. Not even the laser is perfectly coherent. Any useful definition of coherence, then, must include this idea of partial coherence and provide some qualitative way of specifying the degree of coherence between waves. As this implies, coherence, in its most rigorous sense, must be defined in mathematical terms. But before we look at that aspect of the subject, suppose we look first at some less precise conceptual definitions of the word.

It takes two to tangle

In Condon and Odishaw's *Handbook of Physics*, we find this definition for coherent sources and coherent waves: "Two or more wave sources are said to be coherent sources if the phase difference between a pair of points, one in each source, remains constant." Many different sets of wave trains will satisfy this definition. The waves may be two sine waves of identical frequency. To be coherent, the phase difference between them need not be zero but may have any value as long as it is constant (which it is if the frequencies are identical). Moreover, two waves of varying frequency (even two noise waves) are coherent if the two are identical.

The word "two" in this definition of coherence introduces a key point. It is not strictly meaningful to speak of the coherence of a single wave, as is so often done. What is implied in such cases is that there is a constant phase difference between any two points on the wave separated by a fixed time interval; the "two

[*] C. Chapin Cutler is Director of the Electronic Systems Research Laboratory at Bell Telephone Laboratories, Murray Hill, New Jersey.

Fig. 1-92. Familiar objects have a strange appearance under coherent light. Even a blank sheet of paper appears to be covered with thousands of tiny pinpoints of glittery light. The effect, caused by interference between light waves that reflect out of phase, is evident in the photo at bottom. Photo at top was taken with a focused beam of ordinary white light. (Courtesy C. Cutler, Bell Telephone Laboratories)

sources" in this instance are parts of the same wave. Used in this sense, a coherent wave is simply a wave having a single frequency.

Let us look a little more closely at this single-wave concept of coherence, sometimes referred to as temporal coherence. We are accustomed to think generally of electromagnetic radiation as periodic, being composed of continuous pure sine waves. Insofar as this is true, any single wave is coherent. But real waves are never exactly periodic and continuous, and many waves are very nonperiodic and discontinuous. Thus, coherent radiation is not necessarily common.

All real waves contain components with frequencies both above and below the wave's nominal frequency: they have a finite bandwidth (or spectral line width). Because the rate at which a wave changes phase is limited by its bandwidth, bandwidth is one measure of coherence. The minimum time in which a wave can be changed to an independent value of amplitude or phase is very nearly equal to the reciprocal of the bandwidth, B

$$\text{Coherence time} = 1/B$$

If a wave travels with a velocity c, the distance over which the wave may be coherent is:

$$\text{Coherence length} = c/B$$

or

$$\text{Coherence length in wavelengths} = c/B\lambda$$

It is interesting to consider the coherence dimensions of ordinary waves based on their bandwidth. The chart on page 120 gives the dimensions over which coherence may be observed for a number of common signal sources. The important parameter is the coherence length in wavelengths. This dimensionless ratio is a more suitable measure than coherence length itself, which could be large simply because the wavelength was large and not because the wave was particularly regular. Notice that some so-called incoherent optical spectral lines are coherent over many more cycles than common radio-frequency oscillators, which are generally considered to be coherent. It is also clear from the chart that the coherence of the laser is in a class by itself with coherence lengths up to 10^{14} cycles.

Modulated, but still coherent

Coherence measured in terms of bandwidth is strictly a measure of chromaticity. It represents only a lower limit on the degree of temporal coherence. That a wave can be more coherent than indicated by the bandwidth is apparent from consideration of a train of radio-frequency pulses. The pulse train has a spec-

COHERENCE OF TYPICAL SOURCES

Source	Bandwidth (cps)	Coherence time (sec)	Coherence length (km)	Coherence length (wavelengths)
Ordinary radio oscillator (1 Mc)	100	10^{-2}	3×10^3	10^4
Exceptionally stable oscillator (1 Mc)	10^{-3}	10^3	3×10^8	10^9
Visible spectrum	2×10^{14}	5×10^{-15}	10^{-9}	3
Mercury discharge (isotope-198 line)	10^7	10^{-7}	3×10^{-2}	6×10^7
He-Ne laser	between 3 and 10^4	between 0.3 and 10^{-4}	between 30 and 10^5	between 3×10^{10} and 10^{14}

Chopped sine wave freq = f

Spectral distribution

Coherence function

$$\Gamma(x_1, x_2, \tau) = \lim_{T \to \infty} \frac{1}{2T} \int_{-T}^{T} \left[V(x_1(t+\tau)) \right] V^*(x_2, t) \, dt$$

normalized

$$\frac{\Gamma(x_1, x_2, \tau)}{\sqrt{\Gamma(x_1, x_1, 0)} \sqrt{\Gamma(x_2, x_2, 0)}}$$

trum made up of a multitude of component lines spaced in frequency by an interval equal to the chopping rate and spread out over a band at least as large as the reciprocal of the pulse length (see marginal sketch). According to the bandwidth relationship, this should give a small temporal-coherence figure. However, it is clear that the coherence time and length of the wave is infinite since the phase relationship remains constant from pulse to pulse indefinitely.

Bandwidth, then, gives only a minimum value of temporal coherence. For a more rigorous measure—one that does not depend on the spectral purity of the radiation—we must turn to a mathematical treatment of the waves. If we write an expression for the wave at any time, t, and position, x_1, and another expression for the same wave after some time delay, τ, and at some new position, x_2, the degree of coherence can be determined by correlating the two waves. This correlation is called a mutual coherence function, Γ. It is defined mathematically in the margin along with an expression for normalizing the function. If the two waves are identical, the coherence function normalizes to unity. If there is no correlation, the coherence function will be zero. Notice that the coherence function is general; it applies to two waves from separate sources as well as to two parts of a single wave.

Coherence in 3-D

Strictly speaking, the coherence function applies to the radiation field in all three dimensions. Until now, we have spoken only of the coherence of waves as measured along their direction of propagation. However, waves can also be coherent in directions perpendicular to the direction of propagation. This is called lateral coherence. Lateral coherence and temporal coherence are sometimes considered to be two different kinds of coherence even though both are implied in the generalized definition of coherence. Of the two, lateral coherence is the less familiar and the most important to the usefulness of coherent waves. Lateral coherence

is usually expressed in terms of the maximum lateral dimension over which the phase relationships remain constant within some limit, say $\pi/2$ radians.

It is the existence of lateral coherence that makes the famous two-slit experiment of Young (first performed in 1801) possible. In that experiment, light from a nearly monochromatic (but incoherent) source is passed through a narrow slit and then through a pair of slits placed side by side. As the light from the two slits recombines on a white screen, the waves interfere to produce a series of light and dark fringes. In this case, a measure of lateral coherence was achieved by the first slit. Let us see how this is possible.

Suppose, for instance, we have an area covered with uncoupled, independent atomic radiators. This is an incoherent primary source of radiation and will radiate energy in all directions limited only by the purely geometrical limit of the cosine law (see Fig. 1-94). The radiation falling on a receiver near the source is coherent only over a very limited lateral dimension. But suppose we put an aperture in front of the source and monitor only that radiation passing through it. The further we place the aperture from the source, the more lateral coherence we find, since the effect of the aperture is to select only a part of the waves. If the distance is sufficiently great, the aperture subtends an angle equal to that subtended by the lateral coherence length, and the coherence of waves is then complete. When the separation between the aperture and the source is not large, geometrical optics suffices to describe the radiation field; when the separation is large, one must think in terms of diffraction effects.

In each case, radiation through the aperture can be described by assuming each point of the wave front to be a secondary source of waves, a centuries-old procedure first proposed by Christian Huygens. The differing character of the radiation field is caused by the relative phases, or coherence, of the Huygens sources.

In the case where the distance between the source and the aperture is large, the Huygens sources in the aperture have essentially a common origin. They may not be monochromatic, but their phasing remains constant.

The lateral dimension of coherence, S, in the field of an incoherent source is found by geometry to be

$$S = \lambda R/D = \lambda/\theta$$

where θ is the angle of convergence, R is the distance between the source and the receiver, and D is the linear dimension of the source.

Because stars subtend so small a solid angle when viewed from the earth, starlight has a high degree of lateral coherence, and these relationships are commonly used by astronomers to determine the dimensions of stars. Even though stars are too distant to be resolved by even the largest telescope, their dimensions can be computed by measuring the coherence distance (S) with an astronomical interferometer and combining this with an independent measurement on the star's distance from the earth.

Whence come the waves

Two important facts should be apparent from the foregoing discussion. The first is that we can gain in the temporal coherence of a wave by using frequency discrimination or filtering. The other is that we can gain in lateral coherence by aperturing. A coherent wave, therefore, may be nothing more nor less than a noise wave sufficiently filtered and apertured. If we examine the common sources of coherent waves, we find that this is what occurs.

In the last analysis, the primary source of electromagnetic radiation is noise caused by

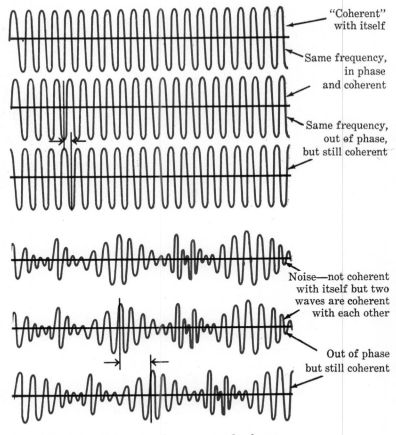

Fig. 1-93. When light waves have temporal coherence, the phase relationship between them, or between two parts of the same wave, is constant. Notice that the phase difference need not be zero, nor is it necessary that the waves be pure sine waves.

the random thermal motion of electrons or, in the case of the laser, the spontaneous emission from atomic transitions. Consider the so-called

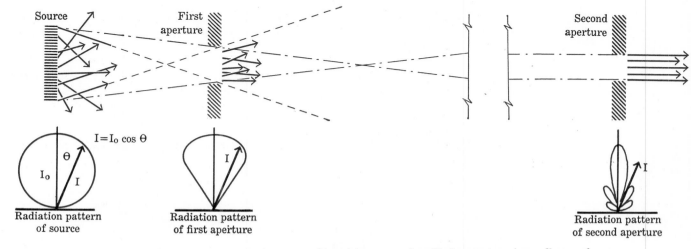

Fig. 1-94. Lateral coherence can be achieved by aperturing. If the aperture is small enough, and far enough away from the source, all the light passing through comes essentially from the same point on the wave front. It is therefore coherent and creates the interference effects shown in the radiation pattern of the distant aperture.

self-excited oscillator—a simple amplifier with its output fed back to its input in such a way that the feedback constitutes the input signal. In such an oscillator, there is always a source of noise and net loop gain must be slightly less than unity if the output is to be constant. The oscillator, then, is a narrow-band, high-gain circuit that amplifies the noise, however small, to the output amplitude.

In the self-excited oscillator, the amplifier output is filtered before it is fed back to the input. Spectral purity and coherence are produced by filtering, and the degree of coherence is determined partly by the degree with which this is done but also by the stability of the circuit components.

In the laser, there is also a random noise source, an amplifier, filter, and limiter. In this case, the circuit is multidimensional, but the result is similar to the classical oscillator. Amplification is provided by the stimulated decay of atoms from their excited energy states. The emission resulting from that decay mechanism, modified by Doppler shift and whatnot, provides a bandwidth that is sharpened and filtered by the resonance of the waves reflected between mirrors at the ends of the laser. This resonant cavity also provides aperturing of the radiation—radiation traveling off-axis is soon lost because of the finite size of the mirrors. These operations suffice to give both the lateral and temporal coherence observed in the laser output.

A loss that is a gain

It is important to understand that stimulated emission does not of itself make a coherent source. The resonant cavity to send radiation coursing back and forth past the assemblage of excited atoms is also needed. The chief difference between the laser medium and other transparent media is that the atoms are in excited states so that when the light waves interact with the atoms, the light does not lose energy as it would in any other medium, but gains energy instead. The released energy reinforces

that of the light wave, the amount of reinforcement depending on the number of atoms in excited states. In effect, the laser is simply a variable negative loss which compensates for the losses in filters, resonators, and apertures so that these elements can be used to clean up the wave, increasing temporal and lateral coherence.

Early observations of coherence in the laser were disappointing because lasers generally oscillate at several different frequencies. The difficulty lies in the dimensions of the resonant cavity. The distance between mirrors is necessarily large compared with the wavelength of light and, therefore, the frequencies of waves that can be accommodated between the mirrors are closely spaced. One can see this by considering the parameters of a typical laser as shown in the marginal sketch. Several of these closely spaced frequencies may fall within the emission spectrum of the laser medium causing several frequencies to occur in the output. Because of this, the first coherence measurements showed that the light from the laser, rather than being coherent for several hundred miles as expected, lost its coherence when the path length was only a few feet. If the experimenters had been able to make their measurements over very long distances, they might have reached a point where the various frequencies were back in phase and the coherence would again be evident.

Summarizing the elements that are important to coherence in an electromagnetic generator, we find that, first, inherent noise (random electron motion or spontaneous emission) must be small compared with the self-excited oscillations (stimulated emission). Second, the circuit constants must not change appreciably in the desired coherence time. And, third, the resonator bandwidth must be small.

The great feature of the laser, and particularly of the gaseous laser, is that it satisfies the first condition better than any previous oscillator. The spontaneous emission (noise) is low enough in most cases that it is the mechanical and electrical stability of the circuit constants that limit the monochromaticity or coherence of the output.

The consequences of coherence

Although coherence is not the only feature that makes the laser such a significant technological development, it is certainly the most important. It accounts for the laser's ability to be focused down so fine as to burn holes in diamonds and is essential to its eventual usefulness as a carrier of communications signals. It also makes the laser an unusual and valuable source of illumination and creates some remarkable visual effects, about which I will have

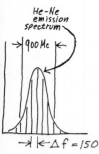

He-Ne emission spectrum

900 Mc

$\Delta f = 150\,Mc$

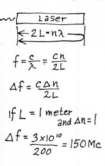

Laser

$2L = n\lambda$

$f = \dfrac{c}{\lambda} = \dfrac{cn}{2L}$

$\Delta f = \dfrac{c\,\Delta n}{2L}$

If $L = 1$ meter and $\Delta n = 1$

$\Delta f = \dfrac{3 \times 10^{10}}{200} = 150\,Mc$

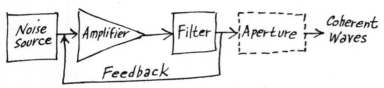

Fig. 1-95. A coherent source is simply a noise source with amplification, aperturing, and filtering. If the source is a radio-frequency oscillator, the feedback loop and resonant circuits provide the filtering and the aperture is essentially zero. In the laser, the mirrored cavity does the filtering and aperturing.

more to say later. Meantime, let us look at some of these other consequences of coherence.

Coherent light can be focused to achieve exceedingly high concentrations of energy because the usual limitations associated with ordinary light do not apply. When incoherent light is focused by an optical system, only a fraction of the radiation from the source can be concentrated into the image because of the geometrical limitations expressed in Abbe's sine law. This is the reason that the temperature of the image cannot be made greater than the temperature of the source in violation of the second law of thermodynamics: when the temperatures are equal, no more energy can be transferred from the source to the image. With a laser, focusing is limited by diffraction effects alone. Abbe's sine law and the second law of thermodynamics do not apply, and the temperature in the image can be made as high as the diffraction-limited focusing allows.

The power in a laser beam may be focused into a minimum cross section of about one square wavelength. If $\lambda = 1$ micron, 10 milliwatts from a gaseous laser gives a power density of 10^6 W/cm^2. A 100 megawatt pulsed output from a ruby laser (which is achievable today) gives 10^{16} W/cm^2. To be sure, the average powers are not yet large, but the concentration of power from a ruby laser is sufficient to vaporize any known material, and is already useful for cutting and welding in utterly new applications.

An even more exciting possibility is the use of these tremendous concentrations of energy to induce hitherto-impossible chemical reactions either by thermal excitation or by exploiting the exceedingly large electric and magnetic fields present in the beam.

A message-carrying vehicle

Much has been said about the usefulness of coherent radiation in communication without too much thought as to why coherence is important. Ordinary light waves, like the waves generated by the early spark radio transmitter, may be modulated, transmitted, and detected, and, indeed, are not too inefficient a medium for communication. But unlike coherent waves, ordinary light waves are not easily focused into narrow beams. Moreover, the energy is spread over a wide band, making it difficult to discriminate between the message-carrying beam and other light collected by the receiver.

By contrast, coherent light can be focused into an extremely narrow beam. The practical directivity is limited only by practical telescope apertures, required pointing accuracies, and possible atmospheric refraction. A 6328-angstrom visible beam only one centimeter in diameter diverges by only 15 seconds of arc and is essentially parallel for 150 meters. Ten milliwatts of light energy modulated to a 100-megacycle communication bandwidth has a spectral irradiance of 10^5 watts per cm^2 per micron, which is nearly a million times brighter than that of direct sunlight (0.2 watts/cm^2/micron).

There is, however, a more important reason why coherent waves are so promising for communication. Although incoherent waves may be amplitude-modulated the same as a coherent carrier, such "noise" carriers are extremely wasteful of bandwidth, do not lend themselves to such niceties as frequency modulation, and cannot be "beat" against other waves to produce sum and difference frequencies of narrow bandwidth. The great advantage of coherent light is that for the first time the light waves that serve as a carrier have a narrower bandwidth than the modulation. With this narrow bandwidth carrier, the effective bandwidth available for communication is perhaps 100 times as great as if one were limited to incoherent waves. Moreover, ordinary radio techniques can be used at light frequencies. With coherent waves, it is possible to multiply frequency efficiently and to heterodyne light waves, and parametric amplification (see "Parametric Amplification," page 160) of light is just around the corner.

Coherence is not sufficient for a good modulation carrier, however. The waves must also have a uniform amplitude. Without this, it would be impossible to discriminate between the amplitude-modulated signal and the random amplitude modulations of the wave. The laser's continuous-wave output is therefore at least as important to communications as is its coherence. The laser, fortunately, is more than a bandwidth-narrower for noise. Narrowing the bandwith alone would leave a signal of varying amplitude. It is therefore fortunate that besides this filtering feature, the laser also contains nonlinearities and saturation effects, which limit the maximum allowable amplitude and are therefore responsible for its continuous-wave output.

New light on the subject

Illumination will always be the most useful application of light to man, and many of the most interesting uses of the laser fall into this area. In Raman spectroscopy, for example, the Raman scattering effect is so subtle it requires a light source of extreme intensity and singular spectral purity. The laser promises to revolutionize this experimental technique making possible observations in seconds that used to take hours. The laser also promises undreamed-of chromatic resolution in other branches of spectroscopy and is making it possible to pursue spectroscopy to even longer wavelengths where efficient light sources were completely lacking. Also in the illumination category is the use of light as a yardstick for precise measurements. This technique has been much improved with the laser because coherent light makes diffraction and phase-interference effects much easier to detect.

In fact, probably the most distinguishing characteristics of coherent light are the striking diffraction effects. When continuous visible light from a laser was first observed in early 1962, even the inventors were unprepared for what they saw. Instead of a bright spot of light where the red pencil beam struck the wall, they saw a granular scintillating image. Although all observers could see the effect (and photographs later showed that the camera saw it too) they could not agree on what they were seeing. Some saw bright spots on a dark background, others dark spots on a light background. The granulations were of different size for different observers and appeared to move differently. Such effects are now known to be simply a result of diffraction caused by coherent light and have become a familiar trademark for laser light.

Most vision does not show diffraction effects because light sources are diffuse and far from monochromatic. Whether the illumination is coherent or otherwise, what the eye (or a camera) detects is the image formed on the retina (or film). The intensity of light at any point in the image is determined by the complex (vector) addition of all the components which reach the point in question by any possible path. In normal viewing there are innumerable paths from the light source to an image point. Because the light is incoherent (relatively), the multitudinous components add incoherently, and the vector resultant varies randomly at a rate which is fast compared with the speed of detection. Under these conditions, the eye or camera detects only an average brilliance. Thus it is that we get along in our everyday affairs without an awareness of diffraction optics.

When an object is illuminated by coherent light, however, the reflected waves have a fixed phase relationship so that any image point may have a small or large intensity depending on the chance addition of phase, as in the margin. Thus there is a difference; whether or not it is sufficient to explain the observations will now be seen.

$$l_1 - l_2 = \lambda n$$
$$l_3 - l_4 = \lambda n + \frac{\lambda}{2}$$

(1) *A film placed directly in a laser beam gives a smooth, unspeckled image.*

This is to be expected because the primary light is traveling nearly in a parallel beam and there is no interference between light rays traveling in two separate paths because only one path is associated with any point on the film.

(2) *The light scattered from a semi-smooth surface produces a speckled image.*

In this case, there are a large number of microscopic scatterers within an area smaller than can be resolved by the eye or the camera. These each contribute to the illumination of an area in the image plane, and since the distance along the line of sight is different for each element, the phases are all different and add randomly. Any adjacent area of resolution in the image has light from a different multitude of scatterers that add to a different brightness. The result is a reflecting surface that has a spangled appearance, as if the light were being reflected from a beaded screen.

(3) *The grain size in the image varies inversely with iris size. The effect is measurable with a camera and is very obvious when the light is viewed by eye through pinholes of various sizes.*

This observation is consistent with the fact that the resolution of an optical system is limited by diffraction and is proportional to the size of the aperture. As the aperture size decreases, resolution decreases, and the granulation in the image becomes larger. Indeed, the granularity of the image in a photograph corresponds closely to the calculated diffraction limited resolution of the camera. The angular resolution in naked-eye viewing is also consistent with this hypothesis.

(4) *The image appears to sparkle and scintillate, but when the observer is careful to remain stationary (and the laser is in a stable adjustment), the pattern is stationary.*

The reradiation pattern from a scattering surface is very complex, and as the observer moves from one point to another in the stationary-diffraction field, the observed intensity can be expected to change. Thus, one would expect that if the eye is moved a distance equal to the pupil diameter, a new, uncorrelated granular pattern would appear. When the eye is well focused, this is, in fact, what is seen.

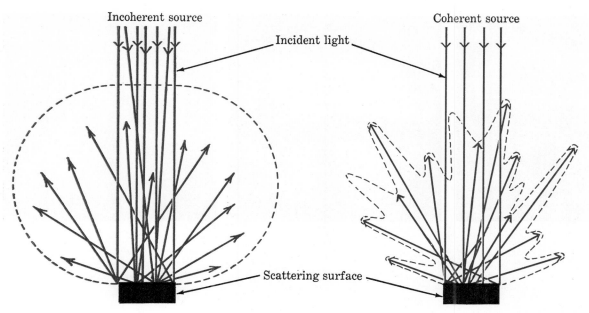

Incoherent source   Coherent source

Incident light

Scattering surface

Fig. 1-96. When coherent light is scattered from any rough surface, such as a sheet of paper, it produces a stationary diffraction pattern in space. To the eye, the pattern looks like a speckled pattern superimposed on the scattering surface.

(5) *When the viewing system is defocused, the granulations remain sharp even though the illuminated object loses definition.*

Myopics are startled to find that they can see sharply again. If they look at a sign illuminated by coherent light, the lettering in the sign may be out of focus but the characteristic granulations are just as sharp as if the image were in focus. An out-of-focus optical system does not change the focus of the granulations because the granulations are features of the light, not features of anything in the plane of the object. Even though a point on the object does not focus to a point on the image plane, the light that does fall on a point in the image plane arrives by many paths and comes from many points in the object. The sum of all these waves is either bright or dim depending on the chance addition of phase, as before. Changing the focus of the optical system changes the distribution of the granulations as one would expect, but does not change the sharpness.

(6) *Generally, when the observer moves his head, the granularity appears to move too. Sometimes it moves in the same direction the head moves, sometimes oppositely. Different viewers often see different motions.*

Most people have difficulty keeping an object in focus when it is illuminated by coherent light. Because the eye involuntarily focuses on detail, it tries to focus on the granulations but finds this impossible since the granular pattern is not located at any particular plane in space. So it focuses a little in

front or a little behind the plane of the object. When the observer moves his head, the granulations move one way or the other with respect to the object because of parallax between the object plane and the plane of focus.

(7) *When the object being illuminated is moved, the granulations move with it, even though there is no visible detail in the object. When the object is moved fast, the granularity disappears.*

A piece of ceramic glaze, opal glass, or paper, however smooth their surfaces, are rough compared with the wavelength of light. They all scatter light and the reradiation from any area of the surface has a characteristic phase and amplitude in space dependent upon the submicroscopic details of the multitude of scattering points within the area. The distant field pattern is a transform of the surface illumination modified by the phase variation due to surface irregularities. The reradiated light is just as complex as the surface, but the detailed variations are spread out in space so that the observer intercepts but a small part of the complex pattern. It takes a large lateral displacement of the scattering surface and observer to bring a different part of the reradiation pattern into view. However, if the motion is fast enough, the retentivity of the eye averages the resulting light fluctuation and the image appears smooth.

(8) *Solids in fluid suspension give a truly scintillating pattern that changes rapidly with time.*

This effect is striking with heavy suspensions (such as thoria or lead particles). Milk gives a

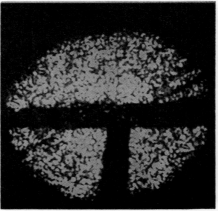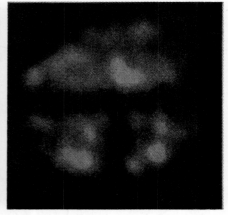

Fig. 1-97. The apparent size of the diffraction spots created by scattered coherent light depends on the size of the camera aperture. Here, a portion of the letter T was photographed through progressively smaller apertures. The striations in the image are caused by interference between several different frequencies in the laser beam. (Courtesy C. Cutler, Bell Telephone Laboratories)

more rapid, almost imperceptible, scintillation. Clearly, the variation is because the scattering points are in motion due to thermal agitation.

Possible applications

These visual effects are a result of the lateral coherence of waves, which, as has been noted, can be obtained merely by aperturing. It is not surprising, therefore, that such effects have been seen before. Carefully apertured sunlight, or light from certain gas discharges yield the same results, but the intensities are much lower and the effects are not as striking.

The foregoing observations seem peculiar because we are familiar only with a panchromatic world that we are admirably equipped to observe by what is essentially geometric optics. Our common observation of interference or diffraction effects are severely hampered by the poor frequency resolution of our light sources and the gross nature of our visual and illuminating apparatus. Although these diffraction effects are merely laboratory curiosities, there are a number of potential applications that come to mind. One might measure film resolution by observing the resolution of coherent-light diffraction patterns, which are of much finer detail than a lens can ordinarily resolve with ordinary light. Invisible movements, too tiny to be detected by any other means, are easily observed by watching the motion of the granular pattern. This effect might be useful in chemistry, for example, to measure the motion, and thus the mass, of colloid particles. Or it might be used to give a precise indication of the transition between the solid and the liquid state.

Today, with the development of the laser, things can be seen that have never been seen before. Surely this will lead to even more discoveries and applications for coherent light.

Further reading

The classical aspects of coherence of light have been reviewed in a few recent papers. Among these are: "On Coherence Properties of Light Waves" by Forrester, *Am. J. Phys.* **24,** 192 (1956), "Coherence Time of a Maser" by Neugebauer, *J. Opt. Soc. Am.* **52,** No. 4, 470 (1962), and "Spatial Coherence of Resonator Modes in a Maser Interferometer" by Wolf, *Phys. Rev. Letters* **3,** No. 4, 166 (1963). As background for these recent articles, a good general source, although written before the laser appeared, is *Principles of Optics* by Born and Wolf (Pergamon, 1959, $17.50).

Two letters in the correspondence sections of the *Proceedings of the IRE* describe the strange appearance of visible laser light. See: "The Granularity of Scattered Coherent Light" by Rigden and Gordon [**50,** 2367 (1962)] and "Sparkling Spots and Random Diffraction" by Oliver [**51,** 220 (1963)]. Although clear and accurate, these explanations add little to the remarkable treatise written by von Laue before any of these authors were born. In "Phenomena of Scattering from Many Disordered Distributed Particles" [*Sitzber. König. Preuss. Akad. Wiss.*, p. 1144 (1941)], von Laue beautifully explains the granular appearance of scattered coherent light. Furthermore, he credits the original observations to K. Exner, forty-three years earlier!

For more about lasers and applications of coherent light, see *Lasers* by Lengyel (Wiley, 1963, $6.95) and two recent review articles in the *Proceedings of the IRE*. Oliver's "Some Potentialities of Optical Masers" [**50,** No. 2, 135 (1963)], among other things, evaluates its capability for interstellar communications; Yariv and Gordon's "The Laser" [**51,** No. 1, 4 (1963)] is more technical.

SEMICONDUCTOR LASERS

by T. M. Quist *

IN BRIEF: *The semiconductor laser is to its predecessor what the transistor was to the vacuum tube. With the help of solid-state physics, all the functions of the laser are packed into a tiny crystal and the operation taken over by electrons and holes. In this case, the electrons and holes do what the excited atoms did in previous lasers—when stimulated, they fall from upper energy states emitting in-step photons of identical energy. Aside from this difference, the physical principles of semiconductor lasers are the same as other lasers. The device itself, however, is vastly different. It is extremely small. It is also a self-contained unit needing only a current to produce the coherent beam. Unlike other lasers, the amplitude of this beam can be modulated by modulating the current. And, most importantly, the device can be made in an infinite variety of wavelengths by varying the ingredients in the semiconductor.—C.J.L.*

■ With the appearance of the semiconductor laser, the generation of coherent light takes a giant step toward simplicity. This new addition to the laser family (known to some as an injection laser) has no mirrors to align, no gasses to deal with or glassware to break, and needs no bulky flashtube to drive it. To produce a beam of coherent light, it needs only a current through its terminals. For best efficiency, it should be cooled to liquid-nitrogen temperatures, but even this complication may soon be eliminated.

Besides its simplicity, the new laser has other attractive features. It can be made extremely small, the active element being scarcely larger than a letter "o" on this page. It can be operated with either a pulsed or a continuous output. Its beam will not drill holes through razor blades (only the pulsed ruby and glass lasers can do that) but it can deliver more power in a continuous wave than previously generated in any laser. It can be made in a broad range of frequencies and, best of all, the amplitude of the beam can be modulated by modulating the driving current.

The first success of the semiconductor laser in the fall of 1962 came about in a rather interesting way. The research apparently began by way of a careful re-examination of an experiment performed 7 years earlier and then

* T. M. Quist is an electrical engineer with the Lincoln Laboratory of Massachusetts Institute of Technology, Lexington, Massachusetts.

nearly forgotten. This initial work, done by R. Braunstein of RCA in 1955, had progressed to the stage where a beam of light (not a coherent one, of course) from a crystal of gallium arsenide could be used to carry music from one side of a room to another. In those days, however, the efficiency was low.

But, before discussing efficiency, let us examine the light-generating mechanism in a semiconductor.

Smeared-out levels

According to the restrictions of quantum mechanics, an electron in orbit about an atom is allowed only certain discrete levels of energy and the energy values between these specified levels are forbidden. This situation holds only for a free atom, however. When an atom is bound into a solid, its electrons interact with those of the neighboring atoms and the allowed energy levels get smeared out into allowed energy bands. These allowed bands are separated, as before, by bands of energy that are forbidden to the electrons.

This picture of allowed energy bands separated by forbidden energy bands explains why some materials conduct electricity and others do not. Because any system will always seek an equilibrium position at a condition of lowest possible energy, electrons fill the energy bands from the bottom up. The uppermost energy band will therefore either be completely filled or partially filled, depending on the type of material.

In a conductor, the upper band is only partially filled. This means that electrons can pick up that additional energy needed for conduction by merely moving to a slightly higher energy level in the allowed band. In a nonconductor, the uppermost energy band is filled and the slightly higher energy is not permitted. Therefore, electrons cannot be freed from atoms and the material cannot conduct.

In a semiconductor, the upper energy band is filled as in a nonconductor, but the forbidden band just above it is narrower than that of a nonconductor. Only modest amounts of energy are needed to boost an electron across this forbidden zone (called the band gap) and into the next highest allowed band. In semiconductor terminology, the allowed band above the forbidden band is called the conduction band for obvious reasons. The allowed band below the forbidden band is called the valence

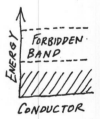

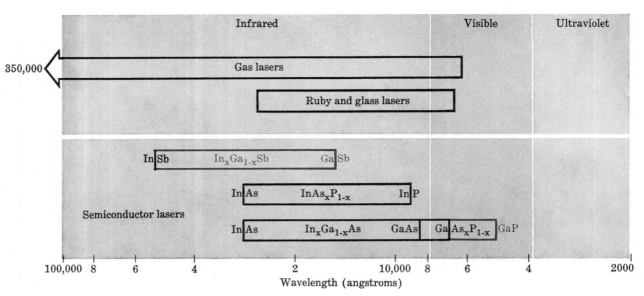

Fig. 1-98. *Output wavelengths of semiconductor lasers (lower bars) cover a broad range of the spectrum. All of the wavelengths between the ends of the bars can be achieved (black) or are expected to be achieved (color) by adjusting the composition of the semiconductor crystal. This is in contrast with other types of lasers (upper bars) where only a few specific wavelengths between the indicated limits can be achieved.*

band because the electrons in it are closely associated with their atoms.

Near absolute zero, most semiconductors behave as electrical insulators; all the electrons assume the lowest energy state and remain frozen in the valence band. At higher temperatures some electrons have enough energy to jump over the forbidden band into the conduction band. In so doing, they leave behind a vacancy in the valence band called a hole.

Now, suppose we momentarily excite electrons into the conduction band (say, by shining a light onto the semiconductor crystal) to create more electron-hole pairs than would ordinarily exist at that temperature. The excited electrons will eventually fall back into the valence band to recombine with holes. When they do, they will lose an amount of energy equal to the band gap by emitting either a photon or a phonon (or both). Energy lost by way of a phonon is transferred to lattice vibrations and ultimately appears as heat. Energy lost by way of a photon is radiated away in the form of light. Of the two, we are most interested in the photon emission, technically known as radiative recombination. It is the principal source of light from the laser.

Over the recombination barrier

In a pure semiconductor, there are an equal number of holes and electrons. This balance can be upset, however, by doping the crystal with impurities that create an excess of free electrons or an excess of holes. Materials with an excess of electrons are called n-type mate-

rials and those with an excess of holes are called p-type materials. Suppose that a single crystal is doped so that it is p-type at one end and n-type at the other with the two regions meeting at a planar junction somewhere between. Because of a potential barrier that is an inherent feature of such a junction, electrons and holes will not mix with each other.

Such a device is a p-n junction rectifier. It may also be a light-emitting diode. If a voltage is applied in the direction of easy current flow (p-type end positive with respect to the n-type end), electrons and holes may recombine after crossing the junction and the recombination energy may be radiated.

I have said "may" because radiative recombination will occur only in certain materials and under certain conditions. It depends to a large extent on a property of semiconductor materials called crystal momentum (see Fig. 1-100). Radiative recombination is much more probable with semiconductors in which electrons can recombine with holes without exchanging crystal momentum. These are called direct-gap semiconductors. In most indirect-gap semiconductors, the momentum of electrons in the conduction band is greater than that of holes in the valence band. Consequently, electrons must lose momentum to recombine with holes. This is accomplished by the emission of a phonon. Because this two-step transition is a much less likely process it is more difficult to make efficient light-emitting diodes from indirect-gap materials.

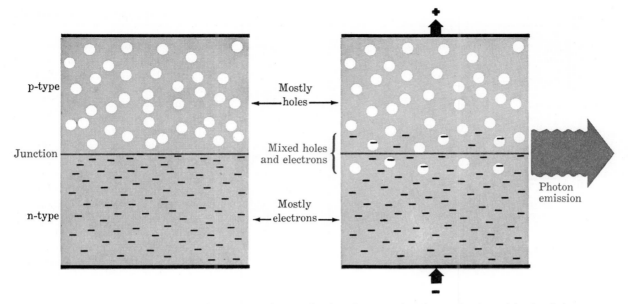

Fig. 1-99. The light-generating mechanism in a semiconductor begins with the holes on one side of the junction and electrons on the other. When a voltage is applied so that the p-type side is positive (direction of easy current flow) electrons and holes cross the junction where they recombine. The energy lost by recombination is emitted as photons.

Unexpected efficiency

As I mentioned earlier, light-emitting gallium arsenide diodes (not lasers, simply generators of incoherent light as shown in Fig. 1-101) were being studied as early as 1955. At that time, however, compound semiconductors were not as pure as they are today. The light they produced was not only dim, the energy of the radiation was much lower than the bandgap energy of the material. It was not until January 1962 that Pankove and Massoulie of RCA reported a narrow peak of infrared emission near the bandgap energy of gallium arsenide. In March of 1962, Mayburg and co-workers at General Telephone reported similar results. Finally, during the following July, Keyes and I reported on work done here at Lincoln Labs (with support from the Air Force) showing that the quantum efficiency of gallium arsenide diodes may be nearly 100 percent.

We were speaking, of course, of *internal* quantum efficiency—the ratio of the number of photons generated at the junction to the number of electrons injected. This efficiency,

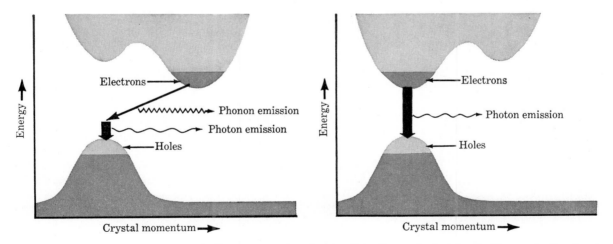

Fig. 1-100. In indirect-gap semiconductors (left diagram) electrons in the conduction band cannot recombine with holes in the valence band without first losing crystal momentum in the form of a phonon. In direct-gap materials (right diagram), holes and electrons can recombine directly, generally with the emission of a photon. Because direct recombination is much more probable, direct-gap materials (gallium arsenide) have received more attention for lasers than indirect-gap materials (germanium and silicon).

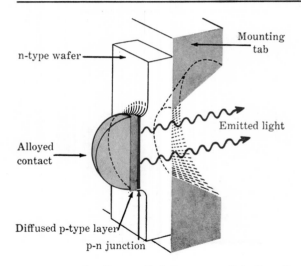

Fig. 1-101. Incoherent diodes generate light by the same mechanism used in the laser. They have applications where coherence is not required. Infrared light generated at the p-n junction passes through the wafer because it is nearly transparent to light of these wavelengths.

however, is almost impossible to measure because photon emission must be measured from outside the crystal and it is difficult to determine how many of the photons generated at the junction get lost on the way out. So, it is necessary to measure *external* quantum efficiency. The 100-percent figures quoted by Keyes and me were estimates calculated from this measurable external quantum efficiency and a knowledge of the semiconductor device itself.

With the realization of high-quantum efficiency in gallium arsenide, it was not surprising that in the fall of 1962, groups at General Electric, IBM, and Lincoln Laboratory reported coherent infrared radiation from gallium arsenide junctions almost simultaneously, with credit for the initial success going to R. N. Hall and co-workers at General Electric.

That step from the incoherent semiconductor diode to the semiconductor laser turned out to be a surprisingly short one; the physical differences between the two devices are remarkably few. But before I describe those differences, let us review some of the requirements for a device that emits coherent light.

Modifications for coherence

In general, there are three requirements for a laser. First, there must be an upper energy state to which the system can be pumped and from which the system can return with a high probability for the emission of a photon. Second, it is necessary that the lifetime of atoms or electrons in the upper energy state be long enough to permit the system to assume a con-

dition in which there are more atoms or electrons in the upper energy state than in the lower one. And third, there must be an optical cavity to produce coherent radiation.

The single incoherent semiconductor diode meets—or can be made to meet—all of these requirements. The first requirement is satisfied by the nature of the semiconductor material. The upper-energy state is the energy level of electrons in the conduction band and, as we have seen above, electrons pumped there will return to the lower state with a high probability for the emission of a photon.

The second condition is somewhat more difficult to satisfy. For direct-bandgap semiconductors such as gallium arsenide, the radiative recombination probability is very high. Consequently, it is difficult to establish a condition in which there are more electrons in the upper energy state than in the lower one because their lifetime in the upper state is so short. However, with very large currents, this population inversion can be achieved. For a typical gallium arsenide diode at 77°K, the required current density is in the vicinity of 1000 amp/cm^2.

On the surface, the third requirement looks like the most difficult of all. The optical cavity must be formed so that it will trap some photons in the region containing electrons at the higher energy levels. In a semiconductor laser, this region of population inversion is located in the plane of the junction and is estimated to be one to two microns thick. To reflect photons back into this layer, two of the faces perpendicular to the junction must be made perfectly flat, parallel to each other, and perpendicular to the junction plane. Although it is possible to grind and polish the optical flats, it is much easier and more perfect to cleave the crystal along parallel cleavage planes. Each semiconductor material has a preferred plane of cleavage; it is the plane where the interatomic forces are smallest. It is also the plane where the crystal usually breaks when it's dropped. Cleaved surfaces are parallel and perfectly flat (assuming the line of cleavage does not jump to a parallel crystal plane).

With this trick, the problem is now that of cutting the crystal so that after diffusion, the *p-n* junction will be perpendicular to the preferred cleavage plane. Fortunately, this is not difficult. Using x-ray crystallography, the appropriate diffusion face can be identified and the crystal cut so that the diffused junction will lie perpendicular to the desired cleavage plane. The sides of the diode are not polished and, indeed, may be intentionally roughened to prevent lasering in the short dimension.

First one, then two, then four . . .

Thus, the only difference in construction between the incoherent light-emitting diode and the laser diode is the optical cavity and the way the device is packaged. The laser package used at this laboratory, adapted from a microwave crystal-rectifier package, provides rugged construction along with a copper stud to dissipate the heat generated at the high current densities needed for laser operation.

Let us examine the operation of the laser step by step. When current passes through the diode, electrons and holes are injected into the junction region (whence comes the name "injection laser") creating the necessary non-equilibrium of holes and electrons. At low currents, many of the photons emitted by the radiative recombination process are absorbed in boosting valence-band electrons into the conduction band. At these currents, the diode does not function as a laser, but emits only incoherent light as before. When the current is further increased to establish a population inversion, this absorption process is reduced and, in fact, becomes smaller than the stimulated emission. Now the diode can operate as a laser. In the first stage of laser operation, however, spontaneous recombination occurs producing photons that are completely random in time and direction. They are also distributed over a relatively wide region of the spectrum depending on the temperature and current injection level.

Because most of the photons are emitted in directions other than in the plane of the junction, they soon leave the junction region and have no further effect on the behavior of the junction. There are, however, a few photons that happen to be traveling in the plane of the junction and will remain there for a considerable distance. These photons are within the population inversion region and, hence, excite additional photons. Significantly, these stimulated photons are exact duplicates of the exciting photons. They continue along the plane of the junction producing additional photons. Because photons of a certain energy will be most effective in producing stimulated emission, the radiation in the plane of the junction now becomes more intense and more narrow in its emission spectrum. This radiation is still incoherent.

It is the optical cavity that converts this amplifier into the oscillator needed for coherent radiation. The cleaved-end faces reflect some photons because of the difference in dielectric constant between the semiconductor material and the outside world. These reflected photons bounce back and forth through the inverted population region and thus receive further amplification on each reflection. Such positive feedback is necessary to establish an electromagnetic mode of oscillation, and coherent radiation now emerges from both faces of the diode. (One end can be coated with a dielectric to make it totally reflecting so that the diode radiates from one face only.)

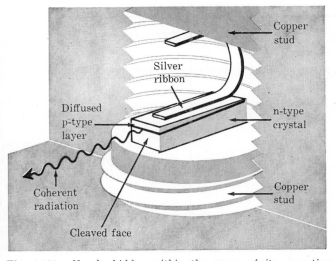

Fig. 1-102. Nearly hidden within the recess of its mounting is a tiny bar of semiconductor, the heart of the injection laser. This mounting is a modified crystal-rectifier package and is about the size of the ferrule on a lead pencil. Although it is not the only way to mount a semiconductor laser, it is a convenient one because the large copper stud at the bottom carries away the heat. (Courtesy T. M. Quist)

Beads with a narrow spectrum

When the current is first applied to the laser diode, a thin line of uniform radiation appears along the line of the junction. This radiation is incoherent. As the current is increased to the threshold value, a small intense spot of laser radiation appears at one point on the junction. This filamentary region of laser action passes all the way through the junction. As the current builds up, the number of these spots increases.

Besides the appearance of bright beads of light, there is a narrowing of the output spectrum. The radiation spectrum of an incoherent gallium arsenide diode at 77°K has an intense peak about 125 Å wide at a wavelength of about 8400 Å. A laser diode operating below its threshold current has a similar spectrum.

It is interesting to note that this radiation at 8400 Å is visible as a red glow even though it is outside the customary limits of visibility. We have studied the effect closely to determine whether the glow is a low-level emission of red light in the visible range. After a number of tests, we discovered that this was not the case. The eye "sees" 8400-Å light. This is either because of a small but detectable response in this range, or because the "invisible" light simply excites the eye as red.

When the laser is just above threshold current, the spontaneous peak narrows to a single line (see Fig. 1-103). At higher currents additional lines appear.

In previous discussions, we have assumed

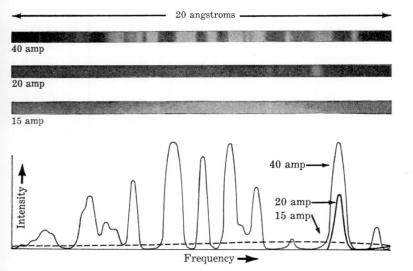

Fig. 1-103. Above threshold current, the laser changes from an incoherent to a coherent source. The first sign of this is the abrupt narrowing of the output spectrum as can be seen here by comparing the 15- and 20-amp spectra and associated densitometer traces. At higher currents (40 amp), additional laser lines appear.

that radiative recombination occurs between the lower level of the conduction band and the upper level of the valence band. However, in doped material there are additional energy states in the forbidden band: There are states immediately below the conduction band created by the n-type impurities, and there are states immediately above the valence band created by the p-type impurities. Because of a discrepancy between the photon energy and the bandgap energy (1.48 eV and 1.51 eV, respectively, for gallium arsenide at 77°K) it is tempting to conclude that recombination takes place by way of the impurity states. However, the exact mechanism of the recombination process is not yet clear. It could be that different processes take place depending on current density, doping level of the n- and p-type regions, and on how the junction is formed.

Less powerful, more versatile

Comparing the semiconductor laser with its cousins, the gas and ionic laser, we find a number of small but significant differences in its fundamental principles of operation. One of the most important differences is that in previous lasers, optical transitions take place between energy levels that are similar to those of free atoms. That is, the energy levels are sharply defined. To find if a population inversion exists in such lasers, one only needs to establish that there are more atoms in the upper state than in the lower state. In semiconductor junctions, however, the states available to the electrons are broadened into bands extending over an energy range. Thus, it is necessary to increase the current to the point where the occupancy at the bottom of the conduction band is greater than half, and the occupancy at the top of the valence band is less than half. If this condition is fulfilled, the population inversion is established.

Another difference is in the method of pumping. Ionic lasers are customarily pumped with a flash lamp and gas lasers are pumped from a source that delivers a high voltage at a low current. Semiconductor lasers, by contrast, are pumped from a source that delivers a high current at a low voltage. A third difference lies in the distribution of the population inversion region. In conventional lasers, the population is inverted throughout the entire volume of the laser material; in a semiconductor laser, only the region in the vicinity of the junction is inverted.

But more important than these differences are the differences in the features of the device itself. The semiconductor laser can be operated as either a pulsed source or as a continuous source. When cooled to 20°K or lower, semi-

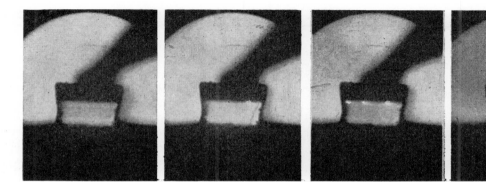

Fig. 1-104. *As current increases beyond threshold, first one point begins to emit a coherent beam, then, at higher currents, more join the chorus. These frames from a motion picture sequence taken by A. E. Michel and E. J. Walker of IBM show the output of an infrared laser, made visible by photographing it through an image converter. The lower (n-type) portion appears transparent because of infrared backlighting. (Courtesy A. E. Michel and E. J. Walker, IBM)*

conductor diodes have been made to deliver an output of more than two watts of continuous power, which is the most power yet produced by any continuous-wave laser. Maximum pulsed-power outputs of 200 W do not, however, compare with the giant 500 MW pulses obtained from ruby lasers and are not intense enough to do any of the drilling or burning stunts sometimes performed with other lasers. For continuous operation, the semiconductor laser must be operated at cryogenic temperatures, but some gallium arsenide lasers have been operated at room temperature by using very short pulses.

One unique feature of the semiconductor laser is that potentially, it can be designed to emit a range of wavelengths, between 52,000 Å and 5000 Å. The wavelength depends on the semiconductor material. In the discussion above, I have spoken only of gallium arsenide with its radiation peak at 8400 Å. Actually, there are a variety of semiconductor materials suitable for lasers. Indium antimonide, for example, emits radiation at 52,000 Å. Indium arsenide radiates at a wavelength of 31,000 Å, and indium phosphide at 9100 Å. Lasers have been made from all of these materials.

In addition, lasers have also been made from the mixed crystals of indium gallium arsenide and gallium arsenide phosphide. The radiation wavelength of these mixed crystals depends on the ratio of the elements in each compound. Indium gallium arsenide, for example, can be made to emit at any wavelength between 31,000 Å (InAs) and 8400 Å (GaAs). With these mixed-crystals it may one day be possible to tailor a semiconductor to any desired wavelength from 52,000 Å to about 6000 Å.

Temperature and magnetic fields can also be used to change the output wavelength. The wavelength of gallium arsenide, for example,

shifts from around 9100 Å at room temperature to around 8400 Å at liquid-nitrogen temperatures.

The magnetic-field effect is more subtle and is most pronounced for semiconductors with a small energy gap. I. Melngailis and R. H. Rediker have shown that indium arsenide diodes, for example, shift in steps to progressively shorter wavelengths as the magnetic field is increased (see Fig. 1-105).

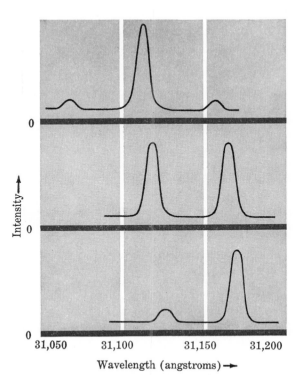

Fig. 1-105. *The emission line of an indium arsenide laser shifts from one cavity mode to the next as magnetic field increases. Slight shift of the modes themselves is caused by a decrease of the dielectric constant with increasing field. Measurements were made by R. H. Rediker and I. Melngailis.*

Light-beam transistor

The size, efficiency, narrow-radiation spectrum, and ease of modulation of the semiconductor lasers make them very attractive for many applications. At present the cost is high; experimental units are being offered by a number of manufacturers at prices ranging from $500 to $10,000. But these prices will surely fall as production techniques improve.

One of the most attractive features of the semiconductor device is the ease of modulation; the radiation can be amplitude modulated by simply modulating the diode current. The limiting speed of this modulation depends on the lifetime of electrons in the upper energy state. In an incoherent gallium arsenide diode, two-nanosecond bursts of radiation have been obtained. The ultimate speed has not been determined because of detector limitations. It should be possible to modulate diode lasers at higher frequencies since the radiative lifetime is much less when operated in the laser mode. Kilomegacycle infrared communication links should be possible.

To demonstrate their communications potential, we have successfully transmitted audio and video signals a distance of 30 miles via the infrared radiation emitted from an incoherent gallium arsenide diode. The diode was operated at liquid nitrogen temperatures and had an active radiating area about the size of a pinhead. For the TV-transmitting experiments, we intercepted the signal from a local TV station, separated the video part of it from the vhf carrier, and used this to modulate the diode. At the receiver, the signal was detected with a photomultiplier tube and displayed on a TV screen. In evaluating such a system, it is important to remember that light-beam communication is critically dependent on the weather and on other things that affect atmospheric visibility.

The tiny diodes have also been used to pump glass lasers. These lasers are capable of a much higher-pulsed output but are much less efficient than the semiconductor lasers. The low efficiency is largely traceable to the broadband light source customarily used to pump the crystal. Only a small portion of this light energy is converted to coherent radiation; the remainder is lost or is spent uselessly in heating the crystal. With a pump consisting of a laser diode having an emission line matched to the pump line of the ionic laser, most of the pump light is converted into coherent radiation. It is also possible to modulate the output of these lasers by simply modulating the diode pump source.

One of the more imaginative applications of radiative recombination is not an application for a diode laser at all. It is simply a scheme in which an incoherent diode functions as the emitter of a transistor. The reasoning runs this way: In a conventional transistor, amplification of currents depends on the (relatively) slow diffusion of charge carriers across the base from emitter to collector. Suppose the job of communication between emitter and collector were turned over to a beam of light. Such a beam-of-light-transistor would function as a conventional transistor except that photons would be used to transport the charge across the base region. Because of the speed of transport, it should be able to amplify at much higher frequencies than a conventional transistor.

High-speed light-emitting diodes (not necessarily coherent) will also find many applications in computers. For transmitting information from one part of the machine to the other, there is no faster method nor one with potentially greater bandwidth, than that of a light beam. Also a four-terminal device consisting of a diode light-emitter and a photodiode light-collector has many advantages over the three-terminal transistor. This component would be a four-terminal active device with input electrically isolated from output since the only coupling is via the light beam between emitter and collector.

In integrated circuits it may be very helpful to transmit the signal from one place to another using a beam of light. The incoherent infrared and visible light-emitting diodes may also be used in reading out information on punched tape and punched cards. This latter application may not require the very high-speed capability or very high efficiency of the diodes but will make use of their small size, near-monochromatic radiation, and expected reliability.

Further reading

There are two directions for additional reading, depending on whether you're more interested in the semiconductors or the lasers. The laser angle presents a more difficult approach. The only book, *Lasers* by Lengyel (Wiley, 1962, $7), is thorough and readable as far as it goes, but says nothing about the semiconductor variety. More theoretical is the special issue on quantum electronics from the *Proceedings of the IEEE* **51,** 1 (Jan. 1963), but again, the semiconductor laser gets little space. One recent article, "Semiconductor Lasers" by Lax, in *Science* **141,** 1247 (Sept. 27, 1963) adds a little to the present article.

A good starting place for the semiconductor

approach is *Introduction to Solid State Physics* by Kittel (Wiley, 1956, $12). It is a respected source and should answer most of your questions but is a textbook and, consequently, not light reading. For a thorough discussion of the light-generating mechanism in solids, there are two recent books. *Luminescence in Crystals* by Curie (Wiley, 1963, $8.50) is frankly more theoretical than practical and, although first published in 1963, was written before the laser (pre 1960). *Electroluminescence* by Hennish (Pergamon, 1962, $12.50) is aimed at the reader with a more practical interest in the light-generating mechanism.

HIGH-ENERGY LASERS

by Peter Franken *

IN BRIEF: *Among the properties that make the laser unique is the extremely high-energy-density light beam it can produce. With a high-energy laser, the beam can be focussed down to give an energy density of 10^8 watts/cm²; with special techniques, the figure can go as high as 10^{13} watts/cm²!*

These energy densities can be exploited in many directions: It is more than likely that the laser will provide an improved tool for micromachining and microwelding. Optical-ranging experiments will shed new light on geophysical problems. And the detectable, non-linear optical effects that lasers can generate open the way for the exploration of an entirely new host of optical phenomena.—S.B.

■ Since the first operating laser was announced in June 1960, these devices have become the focus of an enormous research effort. Countless articles have already been written about their construction and operation. I would like to discuss some of the applications of high-energy lasers, particularly in spectroscopy, micromachining, optical ranging, and nonlinear optics. For our purpose, then, we can regard them simply as black boxes and concern ourselves only with their output.

I would like to add that I am something of a devil's advocate in this field. It's probably fair to say that I've tried as hard as anyone to exploit lasers, but I don't think they constitute as much of a revolution as has been claimed. I find them very exciting as research tools; but where applications are concerned, the laser, in most cases, provides an improvement over existing methods rather than a radically new tool. One exception perhaps is mass communication over light beams, but personally, I doubt if this can be made economically competitive with current systems in the foreseeable future—although there are some very distinguished people in the field who would disagree with me.

* Peter Franken is Professor of Physics at the University of Michigan, Ann Arbor. As an industrial consultant, he is also involved in laser applications.

The laser as a microteaspoon

One development which comes under the heading of improvement rather than revolutionary device has to do with spectral analysis. Let's say you're sitting in your laboratory and you've got a small speck of material—a few micrograms—that you wish to analyze. For heaven's sake, don't use a laser! Just pick it up, carefully, and put it into any of dozens of available micro- or macrospectral arcs, flash it, and get a nice spectrogram.

There is, however, a peculiar problem that metallurgists run into all the time. For example, if they're examining an alloy of steel and find a small occlusion at the surface, it's well nigh impossible to dig it out for analysis without contaminating it. As a result, they use an x-ray microprobe, which just beams a high-intensity beam of electrons right on that spot, and they then examine the ensuing x-rays. This is a very nice device; it's quite easy to use, although it runs from $60,000 to $120,000 which is probably quite a lot, at least for a small laboratory to invest. And it has the technical disadvantage of being rather intractable for analysis of the light elements, because their x-rays are very soft.

Well, let's look at the laser as a possibility for doing this. The obvious approach is to focus a laser beam directly on the occlusion; the intense energy of the beam throws up a jet of material which burns in the presence of oxygen, producing a flame spectrum. However, there are two disadvantages to this technique. One is that the spectra are quite weak and require either a very fast spectrograph—of which there are few in the world—or repeated shots, and if you're working on one little occlusion, it's gone after the first shot. The other disadvantage is that these spectra occur only in the presence of air or pure oxygen, and in addition to the flame spectra of the elements that you wish to see, you get all sorts of other spectral bands—oxygen, nitrogen, cyanogen, and others.

A somewhat different approach, which seems to work, sprang from a suggestion by Fred

Brech of Jarrel Ash. The setup that was designed by John Ward and myself at Ann Arbor, is shown in Fig. 1-106. The glass tube contains a helium atmosphere and a piece of razor blade taped to the edge of a glass pedestal. You don't need very high energies for this; we used a 5-joule laser, aimed at the blade from above. The two copper electrodes are connected by the clip leads to a few-microfarad condenser charged up to 1000 to 1500 volts. When you fire the laser, a jet of steel is flung up between the electrodes, setting off a discharge, and it is possible to get the complete arc spectrum of iron, even with a very slow spectrograph. The helium atmosphere is inert and does not produce any additional spectra.

What you are doing here is using the laser in a somewhat unexpected way; you're using it as a microteaspoon; it reaches down, picks up a small piece of the metal, flings it up and sets off the discharge. This is something that might end up being a useful tool, and would probably be modest in cost.

How are you fixed for blades?

Using a laser to drill a hole through a razor blade has already become a classic experiment. The fact that you can drill a hole only a few microns in diameter in a razor blade suggests several areas of immediate technological interest. One of them is micromachining of difficult or refractory materials, such as a diamond. For example, I am told that refractory steel plates for the air spoilage flaps of supersonic aircraft need an enormous number of holes drilled in them. The cost in drills alone, for just one airplane, is staggering. It's possible—although it will require a lot of R&D—that the laser may provide a cheaper, more efficient way of doing this.

There are other areas, such as the fabrication of very small parts, where lasers will find application. One thing is clear, though; it's not an immediate, ready-to-go application.

Another possibility which has been mentioned by Bell Labs and others over the country is what is called micro-welding. The laser could certainly be used to melt, rather than vaporize, a very small amount of material, if the material is cooled while it is worked. This might provide a way to solve an increasingly sticky problem in transistor fabrication: trying to weld two or three different materials in one small juncture. Current methods employ a tiny soldering iron

Fig. 1-106. Elevation and discharge technique for analyzing occlusions in metal uses arrangement shown in top photograph. Laser (above and out of sight) is focussed by Bollex lens onto piece of razor blade, held on glass pedestal by strip of black tape. Front end of a Hilger spectrograph is seen in background. Clip leads connect copper electrode to charged condenser. When laser is fired, a jet of steel *particles is thrown up, setting off discharge shown in bottom photograph, and producing arc spectrum of iron. Glass tube contains helium, to prevent burning of steel particles.*

or cold-welding techniques, and it's possible that when the effects of laser beams on materials are better understood and controlled, they will play an important role in this connection.

A lot more data is needed

Let's look at some real data on drilling with light beams, given in Fig. 1-107. This is a sketch kindly provided by Fred Brech of a photomicrograph of a section of steel that he blasted with a 5-joule laser. The diameter of the pit across the top is about 300 microns.

There are a couple of features here that are interesting. There's a very fine, amorphous graininess to the steel that lines the cavity, suggestive of molten material that froze very quickly. There is also a curious bulge at the bottom of the cavity. The best explanation of the photo seems to be this: For the millisecond that the laser was operating, the cavity was lined with molten metal, which finally ran down and began to freeze. It overran a bit, producing that little bulge at the bottom. Notice also, that there is a region of rather large graininess, near the cavity, about 100 microns thick. This indicates grain growth, and correspondingly indicates that the material there during the time of the jet came pretty close to melting temperature. This kind of data is just the precursor of much data that must be taken before one can fully understand how to use lasers as machine tools.

More power by a clever technique

Another recent development permits a somewhat unusual laser performance: an output of a few tenths of a joule, but in a fabulously short time of the order of 10^{-8} seconds. An ordinary laser beam lasts for 10^{-3} or 10^{-4} sec.

Consider a ruby laser, pumped by a flash lamp. This excites the chromium ions in the ruby to a higher energy level. Ordinarily, as the ions start to emit, the light travels back and forth between the end mirrors, stimulating further emission, and produces the now familiar beam of red light.

Fred McClung, at Hughes Laboratories developed a technique which, in effect, prevents laser action from occurring until many more ions are excited than in normal operation. What he does is simply this: He takes a ruby laser, separates the polished end mirror from the ruby, and inserts a Kerr cell—basically, a very fast electro-optical shutter—between them. The shutter is kept closed, the flash lamp goes on and pumps the ruby until the ruby can barely stand it. Then the shutter is opened, the ruby sees its beloved mirror, and thereupon emits one vast, orgiastic burp of light which is all over in 3×10^{-8} sec.

Besides this amazingly short duration, the beam also has a good angular spread—about 10^{-3} radians. The beam is a centimeter in diameter, which means that you get 10^7 watts/

Fig. 1-107. Sketch made from photomicrograph shows cross section of pit, 300 microns in diameter, formed by aiming laser beam at piece of steel. Fine graininess lining the cavity indicates that lining of cavity was molten while beam was on; molten steel probably ran down sides, forming bulge at the bottom. Region of large grains indicates grain growth, which means that steel in that region was probably near melting temperature.

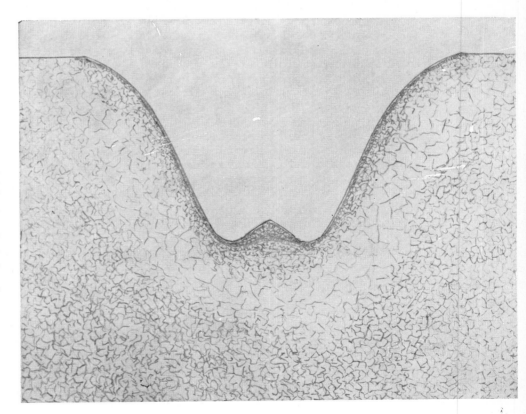

cm² *unfocussed!* If you focus the beam, you can perhaps get up to 10^{13} watts/cm²! I say "perhaps" because this is such an incredibly high power density that if you're using, say, air as a medium, you'll get electrical breakdown of the air unless you take a great deal of care, and you may not actually realize 10^{13} watts/cm².

A lot remains to be done with this technique. I don't have information on what kind of spectra you get from it; studies are still in an initial phase. But clearly, this opens up an entirely new realm of energy density.

First step—satellite ranging

This very fast, very powerful laser has led a group of us at Ann Arbor to contemplate the following satellite ranging experiments:

Suppose you have a satellite up at about 100,000 kilometers—a quarter of the way to the moon—and you put a 1-ft corner reflector on it. This reflector has the property of sending incident radiation back in the direction from which it comes. If you broadcast a tenth of a joule from McClung-type laser at the focus of a 36-in. reflector, you send out roughly 10^{18} photons and get about 100,000 back, which is more than enough to do very accurate optical radar. In fact, you only need a few hundred photons back, which indicates that there are parameters that you can relax.

So far, this is not terribly exciting. What you want to do, though, is send up a microwave pulse at the same time—and this is also within the art—and simultaneously do a microwave ranging of the satellite. The hope here is that you would get a comparison of the velocity of light and of microwaves in a vacuum to about one part in 10^8.

Two questions immediately come to mind. The first is, has this been done? The answer is that this comparison has been made in terrestrial experiments, but only to a part in a million, so this would represent an increase in accuracy of two orders of magnitude. The second question is, why do it? The answer is simply that this constitutes what could be described as a non-urgent fundamental experiment. It would provide a test of our current knowledge about the structure of the vacuum.

At present, it is known that even at absolute zero, the vacuum has a residual electromagnetic structure which actually provides observable effects. However, current theory has it that though the vacuum may provide some interesting effects in atomic physics, it should not exhibit dispersion—in other words, electromagnetic radiation should propagate through it with the same velocity at all frequencies. If you did an experiment and found that, in fact, light and radio waves did not propagate at the same velocity, it would imply that our understanding of the vacuum is not complete.

Another reason for exploring the satellite experiment has to do with things that might come after it. If you could get a one-ft corner reflector on the moon—subcontracted abroad, perhaps—you could do relative ranging of the earth-moon distance to within a few feet, which would enable you to explore several very interesting geophysical problems, for instance, the possibility that there is a secular, or temporal, variation in the gravitational constant, which would show up as a change in the earth-moon distance.

I would like to emphasize that this is only in the study phase. Even if everyone got very excited about it and decided to go full steam ahead, it would still be quite a few years before these things materialize. Nevertheless, we are very impatient and would like to do something, so we've decided to just bounce light off the moon with a laser. Of course, this is not a very original concept. Many have thought of it, and, as a matter of fact, Smullins and Fiocco at MIT have recently succeeded, using an arrangement not very different from ours. What I would like to do now is discuss the arrangement we are using and the numbers involved, and show you why it's not very easy to do.

Reaching for the moon

Consider first what happens if you simply beam the laser at the moon, using simple optics, and try to detect the returning signal with a photodetector placed at the focus of a 6-ft searchlight. If you use a 30-joule laser, you will get back only thirty photons, although you're sending out about 10^{20}! This is because the moon is a diffuse surface; we are assuming an average albedo, or reflectance, of between 5 and 10%.

That's still all right because you can count 30 photons in a millisecond, but here is the number that is discouraging: You get about 10^5 background photons in that millisecond, even in a narrow band of 20 Å. The dark side of the moon is just not dark, due to reflected light from the earth.

It's still not quite as bad as it sounds, because the signal-to-noise ratio is what you're interested in. If the background were constant you could just substract it out. But the background varies randomly, and that "noise" is just the square root of the background. Even so, the signal-to-noise ratio is $\frac{1}{10}$, which means that you'd have to take a hundred shots before you would have even 50% confidence that you were detecting the signal.

A more feasible approach is shown in Fig. 1-108. This is under way at Ann Arbor and has already produced results at MIT. We have coupled the 30-joule laser to a 37-in. astronomical telescope. With these optics, you get an emerging beam of only 30 sec angular spread, which is about a sixtieth of the angular diameter of the moon itself, and illuminates only ¼₀₀₀ of the area of the moon. You will get back only about 15 photons, but you have cut down the background enormously by looking at a small part of the moon.

We use one telescope, shown in Fig. 1-109, both to send and to detect the signal; the signal takes 2½ sec to go to the moon and return, which leaves enough time to flip a mirror into place and deflect the signal to the photomultiplier tube. At MIT they used two telescopes, a 12-in. instrument to transmit the signal from a 50-joule laser, and a 48-in. one to detect it.

The primary technical problem now is being fortunate enough to have the necessary crystal-clear night coincide with the right phase of the moon. Our main interest in the moon-bounce is as a precursor to the satellite experiments; we want to get our feet wet and see what the problems are. And of course, it's a lot of fun, in a frustrating way.

We have had a less frustrating time at Ann Arbor with our optical-harmonic experiments. These are nonlinear effects that we've been studying and, as such, they constitute a brand new area of optical research.

Nonlinear effects in optics

We have been working in Ann Arbor with what would now be called a medium-energy laser. It has an output of roughly 5 joules in ½ millisec. The 6943 Å beam can be focussed to an area of the order of 10^{-4} cm², giving a power density of about 10^8 watts/cm² at the focal plane. This is an enormous energy density, but more important, as we shall see, is that the optical electric field at that focus is about 10^5 volts/cm.

The harmonic experiments, basically, are very simple. You put a suitable crystal at the focal plane—the first one used was quartz—fire the laser, and analyze the emerging light with a spectrograph. You find that not only is there a copious amount of the red, 6943 Å, light, but also a detectable amount of ultraviolet light at just half the wavelength.

This is just the generation of a harmonic. In a way, it's quite analogous to what is seen very often in ordinary radio-frequency work, when you send a radio-frequency signal through a nonlinear circuit element such as a vacuum tube. It's those analogous harmonics in a radio circuit that trouble the hifi bug.

The efficiency with which the red light is converted into second harmonic is, in general, one part in 10^7 to one part in 10^9—perhaps

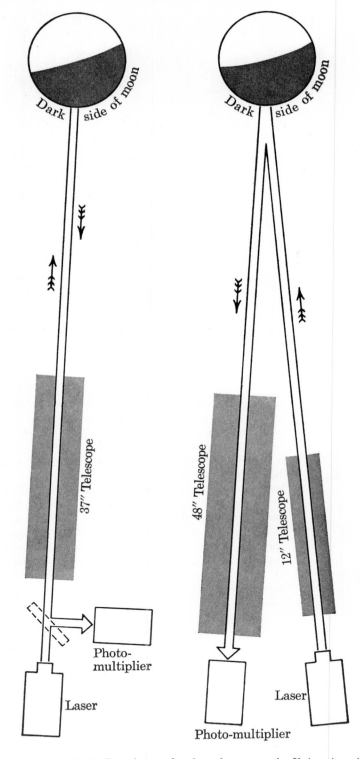

Fig. 1-108. Left: Experiment that is underway at the University of Michigan to bounce laser beam off moon uses 37-in. astronomical telescope to transmit signal from 30-joule laser. Same telescope is used to detect returning signal; during 2½ sec it takes for light to travel to moon and return, mirror (dotted lines) is swung into place and deflects returning light to photodetector. Right: Similar experiment at MIT used two astronomical telescopes: 12-in. telescope was used to transmit light from 50-joule laser. Returning signal was picked up by 48-in. telescope with photodetector placed at its focus, and displayed on oscilloscope screen.

Fig. 1-109. Photograph shows 37-in. astronomical telescope that is being used for moon-bounce experiment at University of Michigan. Chair near base of telescope gives indication of its size.

CALCITE

QUARTZ

as large as one part in 10^6, depending on the experiment. It's a very small conversion; on the other hand, it represents milliwatts, so it is not negligible and is easy to detect.

Here's how optical harmonics arise: Light, like any other electromagnetic radiation, consists of oscillating electric and magnetic fields. When you send light through a crystal, the oscillating electric field E causes a distortion of the electric charge distribution in the medium, which oscillates with the same frequency, ω, as the field E. This distortion effect is called the electrical polarization, P. Ordinarily, we assume that this is a linear effect, that is,

$$P = \chi E$$

where χ is the ordinary optical polarizability of the medium.

In any crystal, however, there will be higher order terms as well. In general,

$$P = \chi E + aE^2 + bE^3 + \cdots$$

These higher order terms give rise to polarizations which oscillate with frequencies of 2ω, 3ω, and on up, generating the second and higher harmonics.

Now the coefficients of these terms are extremely small: a is of the order of 10^{-9}, and the other coefficients get successively smaller, whereas χ is of the order of unity. But if you send a high enough electric field through the crystal, the higher order terms become significant. This is precisely what the laser does.

Finding the right material

I spoke before of using a suitable crystal to generate the harmonic. The problem, you see, is that there is a host of crystals for which the coefficient of the E^2 term, which generates the second harmonic, will be identically zero, by a symmetry argument. Those crystals which have a center of inversion, or are isotropic, like glass, can't tell up from down or left from right. The sketch of polarization versus field for calcite, which has a center of inversion, is shown in the margin. Specifically, if you apply an electric field and get some ensuing polarization, you should exactly reverse the polarization if you reverse the direction of the electric field.

Polarization in such crystals, is an "odd" function of field. This means that the coefficients of all the even terms must be zero, since if you reverse the sign of E, you reverse the sign of all the odd terms, but do not reverse the sign of the even ones.

There is, however, a class of materials that do have a preferred direction—the piezoelectric materials. If you put an electric field on a quartz crystal in a certain direction, it expands; if you reverse the direction, it contracts. This is the basis of the piezoelectric oscillator. Quartz has a preferred direction built into it because of the way ions are distributed in its lattice, and, as you might expect, the P versus E curve for quartz, sketched in the margin, is a little bit different to the left than it is to the right. Since it is not an odd function, P contains even terms in E, and quartz can produce second harmonic.

If you take a material like calcite and apply a strong bias electric field, you are effectively moving the center of coordinates up along the curve as shown by the dotted cross. In other words, you are applying the same bias externally that the quartz has internally, and P, in that case, would also contain even terms in E. This has been demonstrated recently by Terhune and Maker at Ford; they put a bias of several hundred thousand volts/cm on calcite and observed a copious production of second harmonic when they beamed a laser through it. I might also add that they recently observed some third harmonic production from calcite, as well.

Take two colors—get a third

If you can generate a second harmonic, that same E^2 term enables you to mix, or beat, two different frequencies in the crystal to get the sum and difference frequencies. This is easily done at radio frequencies, but has never been possible at optical frequencies before.

At Ann Arbor, we mixed the outputs of two

ruby lasers, one operated at room temperature and one operated at liquid-nitrogen temperature. Their outputs differ about 10 Å, which is enough to resolve with a resonable spectrograph. We beat them in a triglycine sulphate crystal, and observed three ultraviolet lines in the output: the second harmonic of both of the ruby lasers, and in between, the sum frequency of the two lasers. The experimental setup we used, and the resulting spectrum, are shown in Fig. 1-110. In a very recent experiment, by Smith and Braslau at IBM, a mercury green line was mixed with the ruby light to generate a sum frequency in the ultraviolet.

The difference frequencies have yet to be seen by anyone, although I understand there's quite an effort going on at Bell Labs and at other places. We would like to get the difference frequencies, because this would provide a very nice, although admittedly weak, spectroscopic source in the far infrared.

Finally, I would like to remark that the work in optical harmonics is a high-energy-laser application in this sense: The coefficients in the P versus E equation, as we saw, are so small that it is absolutely impossible to generate second harmonics and detect them with any believability with conventional light sources. This is one situation where the laser is not just an improvement over existing techniques.

Before I leave the subject, I want very much to give explicit recognition to my colleagues who have worked with me on these various experiments. The work on optical harmonics was performed by Michael Bass, Alan Hill, Wilbur Peters, Gabriel Weinreich, and myself at the University of Michigan. The group in Ann Arbor that has been working on the satellite-design and moon-shot program consists of Weston Vivian and Lee Evans of the Conductron Corp.; Lloyd Cross and William Fredrick of Trion Instruments; and Dean McLaughlin, Murray Miller, and myself of the University of Michigan. Finally, I would like to thank the technical staff of Trion Instruments, whose equipment we have used, for their continued technical advice.

Further reading

Those who have not yet acquainted themselves with the operating principles of the laser, and would like to do so, should read "Optical Masers" by Lewis, *Intl. Sci. and Tech.*, Prototype, 1961.

As far as applications are concerned, these are still very much in the research stage, and literature is mostly confined to the professional journals. If you wish to delve further, a good starting point is a recent bibliography published

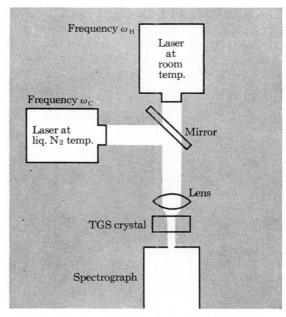

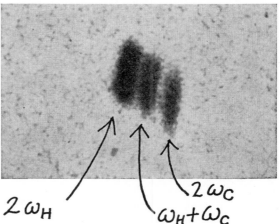

Fig. 1-110. Optical mixing experiment uses two ruby lasers. Since they are at different temperatures, their output wavelengths differ by 10 angstroms. Both beams are focussed by lens onto triglycine sulphate crystal. Resulting spectrum, as shown, consists of second harmonic from hot laser and from cold laser, and between them, a line at the sum frequency of the two lasers.

by the Office of Technical Services, covering the period from 1958 to 1962 (order UCRL-6769 from OTS, U.S. Dept. of Comm., Wash., D.C., 50¢). B. A. Lengyel's *Lasers* (Wiley, 1962, $7.00) combines background and applications of lasers.

Although the present article does not concern itself with optical communication, you may want to know more about this important aspect of laser technology. An excellent reference is a staff survey, "Coherent Light As Data Carrier," which appeared in *Space/Aeronautics*, Apr. 1962.

An extensive and inclusive market research report on masers and lasers has recently been published by Technology Markets, Inc., 509 Fifth Avenue, New York City. Entitled "Masers and Lasers: A New Market with Enormous Growth Potential," it does include descriptions of the technical aspects of the subject, but is concerned primarily with commercial opportunities. The price of the complete report, which runs to 70 pages, is $200; the table of contents may be obtained, at no charge, by contacting the company.

ORGANIC MATERIALS IN ELECTRONICS

by R. R. Neiman and Rowland E. Johnson *

IN BRIEF: *If you make a germanium transistor, you're pretty much stuck with germanium's properties. Plastic is something else again. If you don't like the properties you've got, you can mix up another batch, add a side chain here, an atom there, and you've got an entirely different material. What's more, you can manufacture the stuff at an awesome clip. That's what the interest in organic materials for electronics is all about. Semiconducting organic compounds, the raw materials for transistors, have proven difficult to make, however. Those that conduct, don't conduct like inorganic materials do, they're difficult to make in pure form, and no one has yet discovered an effective way to attach electrical contacts. Organic lasers and electro-optical materials have been more successful. The active element in the laser is a rare-earth ion locked in an organic molecule called a chelate. Successful lasers have been made with these chelates dispersed in plastic in one case, in alcohol in another. The electro-optical applications include successful laser modulating crystals and photodetectors. Organics also show promise as transducers and photo-sensitive coatings.—C.J.L.*

■ There's a peculiar similarity about all organic compounds. Consider a range of them—rubbers, plastics, textiles, leathers, papers, woods—and it soon becomes apparent that there's not a good electrical conductor in the lot. That's not a very promising beginning for materials that are to find applications in electronic circuitry.

But assuming there is something we can do about that (and it turns out there is) the organics have other features much too inviting to ignore. Few materials are easier to prepare or easier to manufacture in large quantities than the organics. The thought of a modern press rolling out sheets of solar cells, or an injection molding machine pressing out plastic

transistors by the gross, is extremely attractive. As for properties, a glance at a handbook of organic materials is sufficient to convince even the most skeptical that the number of organic compounds and the variety of properties is almost limitless. And if you can't find the properties you want, there are abundant guidelines to help tailor a new material. The state of organic chemistry is such that the structure and composition of a molecule can be precisely regulated and the properties of the materials "tuned" at the molecular level.

It is for these reasons that we feel organic compounds warrant serious consideration in electronics. So far, however, organic electronic devices have not been conspicuously successful; despite our best efforts, the plastic transistor, the thin-film organic solar cell, and a variety of other promising organic devices remain stubbornly out of reach. Somewhat more encouraging have been the results of research in optical devices. This includes organic lasers, organic photoconductive materials, and other optical and electro-optical devices. These qualify as "electronic devices" in the sense that they are part of a system that processes or displays a signal, whether the means be electrical, optical, or mechanical. That is the sense in which we will define "electronic devices" for this article.

Regardless of our eventual success in getting organic materials to behave as we want them to, we continue to be encouraged in our efforts by the overriding absolute assurance that the job is not impossible—the thing can be done. We know, for example, that a photo-sensor/electronic-computer combination exists and works and that it is made predominantly of organic compounds. Recall that you are reading this page with just such a device and that this eye-brain combination represents only a very small part of the total electronic system of man. An obvious success, even though nature has had millions of years to work on it, does much to keep the interest up.

The plastic-transistor gap

Although there have been scattered studies of the electronic properties of organic com-

---

* R. R. Neiman and Rowland E. Johnson, both chemists, surveyed organic materials while with Texas Instruments in Dallas, Texas, where Johnson heads an exploratory materials section. Neiman has since become head of the Materials Department at Interphase-West, Palo Alto, California.

Fig. 1-111. The organic ingredient in this flame laser is the organic gas burning brilliantly in the cavity between the two angled mirrors. When the device works—which it hasn't yet—it promises to generate a coherent beam much more powerful than that of a gas laser but equally as pure. (Courtesy R. Lorimer)

pounds for many years, efforts were sharply increased about four years ago when reports from the Soviet Union indicated that scientists there had succeeded in making a plastic transistor. Later, it developed that the reports were erroneous; the translators had mistaken the description of an organic semiconductor material, of which several had been known for some time, for the announcement of the plastic transistor. Nevertheless, it created quite a stir

in the electronics industry and set many companies on the search for organic semiconductor materials.

The search for organic materials suitable for semiconductor applications has been directed toward finding compounds that will offer the same properties as those of ordinary semiconductors. In particular, there are three properties it seems most essential to duplicate: First, the material should have an electronic (as opposed

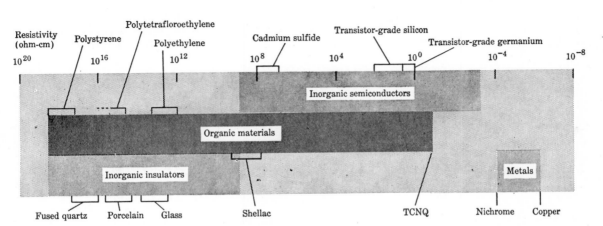

Fig. 1-112. There are no known organic compounds that conduct as well as metals. Most, in fact, are nonconductors with the exception of a few new materials such as TCNQ (tetracyanoquinodimethane).

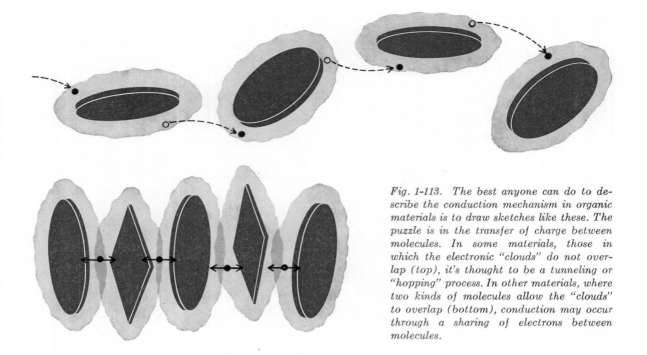

Fig. 1-113. *The best anyone can do to describe the conduction mechanism in organic materials is to draw sketches like these. The puzzle is in the transfer of charge between molecules. In some materials, those in which the electronic "clouds" do not overlap (top), it's thought to be a tunneling or "hopping" process. In other materials, where two kinds of molecules allow the "clouds" to overlap (bottom), conduction may occur through a sharing of electrons between molecules.*

to ionic) conduction mechanism. Second, it should have a resistivity between 10^8 ohm-cm and 10^{-4} ohm-cm—midway between metals and insulators. And third, it should have a resistivity that decreases with increasing temperature over at least part of the temperature range.

This last property—a negative temperature coefficient of resistance—is one of the identifying features of semiconductors. It is a result of their band structure (see margin). As the temperature increases, more and more electrons have enough energy to cross the forbidden band and enter the conduction band above it, thereby reducing the resistivity by increasing the number of charge carriers. In metals there is no "band gap"; there is already a generous supply of conduction electrons and the additional energy only increases the scattering of the electrons already present. Therefore, metals generally have a positive temperature coefficient of resistance.

In searching for an organic semiconductor, it was hoped that an organic material with electronic conduction and the right resistivity and energy band gap could substitute for the inorganic material in transistors and diodes. This has not yet occurred.

Nevertheless, a few materials have been found with properties at least superficially analogous to those of inorganic semiconductors. The perylene-iodine complexes—which are brittle, crystalline organic solids—have resistivities as low as 1 ohm-cm, and some tetracyanoquinodimethane (TCNQ) complexes (see Fig. 1-115) have resistivities around 10^{-2} ohm-cm. This is certainly in the semiconducting range and is a significant improvement over the resistivity of common organic materials, which are usually in the 10^{12}-ohm-cm range or greater. Many organics have also been shown to have a negative temperature coefficient of resistivity. And some materials have an apparent band gap of a magnitude suitable for electronic devices.

Fig. 1-114. *The longer the molecular chain, the fewer the number of charge transfers between molecules and, hence, the lower the resistivity. This, at least, is the suspicion. Extrapolated to the extreme, it has suggested to some experimenters that a fiber consisting of a single longchain molecule would be a room-temperature superconductor.*

But, for a variety of reasons, it is difficult to carry the development of organic devices further than this.

From cloud to cloud

In the first place, the conduction mechanism in organics is difficult to understand. There is no complete mathematical or physical description of electronic conduction in organics, and attempts to extend the band-structure theory to organic systems have not been completely successful. As for a physical description of the process, it seems likely that a charge is carried within the molecule by a mobile electron that moves along the molecular chain, but the question of charge transfer from molecule to molecule still remains. It has been proposed that the charge is passed between molecules by an electron that hops or tunnels across the potential barrier. The process is most likely different for different materials. In perylene-iodine, for example, there appears to be a physical overlap between the "clouds" of charge surrounding the molecules, and this undoubtedly aids the transfer. In anthracene, on the other hand, there is a gap between the surrounding charges, forcing the electron into some kind of tunneling or hopping process.

This rudimentary picture of the conduction mechanism draws some support from observations of resistivity in different kinds of materials. Materials that are made up of long-chain molecules generally have a lower resistivity than those with short molecules, indicating that resistivity is proportional to the number of charge transfers between molecules. This, combined with theoretical analyses that reveal a close resemblance between the charge flow in conjugated rings of aromatic molecules such as benzene and the charge flow in superconductors, has led to the conjecture that a fiber consisting of a single long-chain molecule would act like a superconductor—and at room temperature! But the contact problems and the experimental difficulties in preparing such a chain is something else again.

Whatever the mechanism, semiconducting properties of many organics seem to arise through the slowness of the charge transfer from molecule to molecule rather than through the scarcity of charge carriers, as in inorganic semiconductors. The difference is an important one. The resistivity of any material is inversely proportional to both the concentration of charge carriers in the material and the mobility of those carriers. Low-resistivity organic materials apparently get their low resistance from a high concentration of charge carriers rather than from a high mobility of electrons. In fact, mobility of electrons in many present

Fig. 1-115. TCNQ (tetracyanoquinodimethane) is an organic salt with a resistivity in the semiconductor range. This crystal, about 5 mm on a side, was grown by scientists at DuPont.

semiconducting organics is so small it can't be measured. This means it is less than 1 cm²/V-sec, which is considerably less than the typical values of 1000 cm²/V-sec for silicon and germanium. Mobility is important in making semiconductor diodes and transistors because it limits their maximum frequency response. A mobility of 1 cm²/V-sec would limit a conventional transistor to a frequency of about 10^3 cps, all other things being equal.

Modifying the conductivity of organic materials is another problem having no satisfactory solution. Control of electrical current in semiconductors depends on adjacent regions of a crystal having different amounts of the two charge carriers, holes, and electrons. Most organic materials act as if they were p-type; that is, they act as if the conductivity were due to holes. This is probably because of impurities or contact effects. Attempts to change the conductivity type have been unsuccessful with only minor exceptions. Current rectification has been observed at metal-organic interfaces, indicating the existence of a p-n junction, but this is probably a surface property rather than a bulk property of the organic.

Conductivity cannot be adjusted by adding small amounts of known impurities as is done in conventional semiconductor materials because the organics usually cannot be made sufficiently pure to begin with. Silicon and germanium, probably the purest materials known today, often have impurity concentrations as low as 1 part in 10^9. Such purity levels are completely unknown in the organic compounds. Indeed, no methods exist for the detection of some impurities, even at very much higher impurity levels. That leaves us with two alternatives. We will either have to develop high-powered methods of purification and analysis, or we will have to ignore the effect of impurities and find some other way to achieve the desired electrical properties.

The technology of making electrical contacts to organic materials has made the barest beginning. Low-resistance contacts are essential to the operation of diodes and transistors, for they represent the only practical way to get current in and out of the device. Alloying and soldering, two of the best ways to make low-resistance ohmic contacts, are unknown with organic materials. High-resistance contacts can sometimes give meaningful experimental results, but they are unsatisfactory for practical devices. Poor contact technology has probably held back application of organic material as much as any other factor.

Thin-film inductance?

If organic materials offer little hope, at present, for use in transistors or diodes, what are their potentialities for use as passive components such as resistors, capacitors, inductors, or transducers? Organic capacitors, in which the organic material serves as the dielectric, are, of course, common. Organic resistors, on the other hand, seem unlikely until the contact problem is licked.

Organic materials may also be piezoelectric. Of the 32 different crystal classes (classes of which body-centered-cubic and hexagonal-close-packed are two examples), 20 are piezoelectric due to their asymmetrical arrangements of atoms or molecules. Organic compounds occur in some of these asymmetrical crystal forms. A piezoelectric transducer doesn't require a low-resistance contact, which erases one of the disadvantages of the organics. Their advantages are comparative ease of growth, good coupling coefficients, and the possibility of making small adjustments in the resonant frequency by small chemical alterations in the molecule. And some organic materials have a higher melting point than some of the inorganic piezoelectric crystals.

The piezoelectric organics may solve a prob-

lem for the builder of integrated circuits. At the moment, there is no satisfactory means of making an inductance that can be deposited on the circuit wafer in the way that resistors and capacitors can—the inductance has to be a separate circuit element (see "Integrated Circuits," page 150). A piezoelectric element, on the other hand, acts, in certain ways, like an inductor; its equivalent circuit is formally that of a narrow bandpass filter. It is quite possible that some organic piezoelectric compounds could be deposited by sublimation to form an inductance in a truly integrated circuit.

Like a caged ion

We have been speaking of applications for organic materials where there appears to be great potential but where, so far, there has been little in the way of tangible results. Fortunately, this is not the case for all applications. One significant example is the organic laser. Several types of lasers, in the form of both organic liquids and plastics, have been built and successfully tested in a number of different laboratories.

In principle, organic lasers operate in much the same fashion as their inorganic counterparts. Atoms in low-lying energy states are excited to higher energy states to create an inverted population of energy states—inverted in the sense that there are more atoms in higher states than in lower states. This is accomplished thermally, chemically, or, most usually, by the absorption of a photon. When one of these excited atoms returns to the lower state, a photon is released, and this photon stimulates the release of photons from other excited atoms to generate coherent radiation.

In the case of the organic laser, the active ingredient is a rare-earth ion, such as europium, bonded to an organic molecule by coordinate bonds to form a chelate. The important thing about the chelate molecule is that it completely surrounds the rare-earth ion and chemically isolates it from its environment—it acts as a kind of chemical cage. This feature

Fig. 1-116. Plastic laser material can be drawn into a variety of shapes. It is made (in this case by RCA) by dispersing molecules consisting of chelated rare-earth ions in an acrylic plastic. This material fluoresces red when exposed to ultraviolet light.

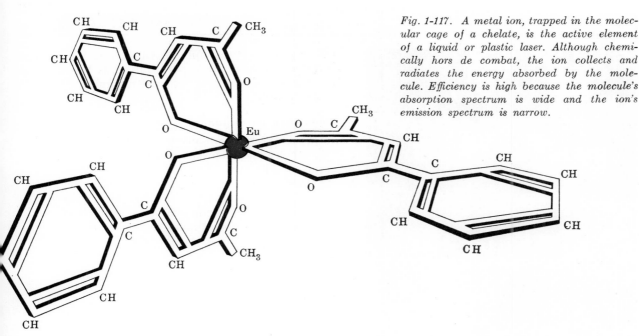

CH CH CH C CH₃
CH C
CH O
C
CH Eu CH₃
O O C
CH O CH
CH C C CH
O C CH
O CH
CH C CH
C CH
C CH₃ CH
CH C H
CH
CH
CH

Fig. 1-117. A metal ion, trapped in the molecular cage of a chelate, is the active element of a liquid or plastic laser. Although chemically hors de combat, the ion collects and radiates the energy absorbed by the molecule. Efficiency is high because the molecule's absorption spectrum is wide and the ion's emission spectrum is narrow.

gives the organic chelate laser certain advantages over lasers in which the rare-earth ions are simply distributed; without an organic overcoat, in glasses or other inorganic matrices.

The organic part of the molecule has two excited states above the ground state—a high-energy state and an intermediate state (see margin). When the molecule is illuminated with a mercury arc, it is excited to the high-energy state. Fluorescent decay back to the ground state ends the process, but there is good probability of a radiationless transfer of energy to the intermediate excited state. In this state, the molecule is metastable and decay to the ground state is forbidden. The lifetime in this state may be as much as milliseconds, which is a long time as excited-state lifetimes go. If this energy is transferred to the rare-earth ion, we then have all the conditions necessary for laser action. The calculations of the over-all transition probabilities are quite complex. But it can be shown that under certain conditions there will be an inverted population of rare-earth ions, and, under these conditions, laser radiation characteristic of the ion is generated.

One of the advantages of the rare-earth chelates is that the organic portion of the molecule is a large complex structure (compared with the ion it envelopes) and it therefore accepts pumping-light energy over a broad band of wavelengths. Although, initially, this energy is shared equally among all the atoms of the molecule, the ion eventually winds up with most of the energy because the energy transfer between molecule and ion is a one-way process —the ion can accept energy from the molecule but it can't give it back. This is because the excited state of the metal ion lies at a lower

energy than the excited state of the organic molecule.

The result of all this energy absorption and transfer is that the chelate laser is a very efficient device. It accepts much of the input light energy because of its broad-band absorption characteristics, and it delivers an output of exceptionally narrow linewidth because the long lifetime in the excited state reduces spontaneous emission to a minimum.

Another advantage is the isolation of the rare-earth ion by the chelating molecule. Regardless of the medium the compound is in, the ion sees the same atmosphere, namely, the organic part of the molecule. Such molecules are relatively insensitive to changes in the supporting medium and, indeed, chelate lasers have been made in which the molecules have been suspended in an acrylic plastic in one case, and alcohol in another (see Figs. 1-116 and 1-118).

Coherence in a flame

The method of stimulated emission in organic materials may also find applications at lower frequencies. There is widespread interest in the generation of coherent radiation in the millimeter and submillimeter regions—the regions between conventional microwave frequencies and optical frequencies. Rotational energy levels in some molecules lie in this region and, in fact, it was a study of these rotational energy levels that gave birth to the maser and quantum electronics.

In one of the simplest forms of such a system, an electrostatic field acts on a gaseous beam of molecules. The field separates the beam into two parts depending upon the rotational energy levels in the molecule. The higher en-

INTER-
MEDIATE   ION STATE

OUND STATE

Fig. 1-118. *Liquid laser apparatus at General Telephone looks pretty much like that of a ruby laser. The liquid-filled quartz tube rests in large tube extending from ends of open-sided square box. It is surrounded by an array of linear flash lamps.*

ergy group represents an inverted population; emission of coherent radiation occurs when a rotational quantum of energy is lost as the molecules return to a normal energy distribution. Although the beam-type maser is a very low-power device as a microwave generator, its attractiveness as a reliable frequency standard and low-noise amplifier continue to make it interesting for further research.

Another version of the organic laser—one that does not depend on chelates—is the flame laser. Conceptually, it is little more than a flame burning between two mirrors. The combustion reaction provides the energy needed to raise atoms to higher energy states and the non-equilibrium conditions occurring in the flame produce the necessary population inversion. The excitation and eventual decay of atoms in a flame is responsible for much of the light normally given off; the trick is to keep the spontaneous decay to a minimum so that the stimulated decay will have a chance to operate. The advantages of the device is that the amount of pumping energy available from a few liters of organic chemicals is equal to the energy stored in a large roomful of capacitors. The flame laser is therefore capable of delivering kilowatts of laser energy with the inherent advantages (coherence, narrow beam-spread) of the gaseous laser. So far as is known, no one

has yet built a successful one. Interphase-West of Palo Alto has been experimenting with one for several months now with encouraging preliminary results.

Photo-sensitive organics

One of the most promising areas of application for organic materials is that of the interaction of light with material, with or without the further interaction with an electrical signal. The emphasis on such phenomena is increasing rapidly; communications, computers, and visual displays all make use of optical interactions. With the wide range of energy transitions available in organic materials, we should expect organics to add considerably to this technology.

Photochromism is an example of a purely optical phenomenon; it is the color change produced in a material by exposure to light. The color change is usually produced by ultraviolet radiation and is due to an electronic rearrangement in the molecule to form an excited state with an absorption peak in the visible. The effect may be reversed by longer wavelength radiation or by thermal effects. (A trivial but interesting application is a pair of sun glasses with an organic coating whose optical density depends upon the light intensity and wavelength. In sunlight they have maximum absorption; on returning to shade, they clear to maximum transmission.)

The existence of a reversible change between two distinct states suggests bistable devices such as switches, computer elements, microfilm and display systems. National Cash Register Company has produced microfilm records with a process based in part on photochromic materials. The advantage is that there are no limitations on grain size. The same company and others have studied uv-sensitive photochromic glasses.

Another closely related effect is the color change that occurs in an organic material in the presence of an electric field, called electrochromism. The electrochromic effect will be useful for many of the same devices suggested for the photochromic effect but, in addition, may possibly be used as a modulator for laser beams. The time constant of the electrochromic shift is about 10^{-9} seconds, and could modulate a light beam at high frequencies. Although the shift is small—only 10 Å for a field of 10^6 V/cm on methyl red in polystyrene—this could be sufficient to modulate a laser beam that might have a bandwidth of 0.1 Å.

Organic compounds that change conductivity with changes in the intensity of the light to which they are exposed offer many device possibilities, again assuming that the problems of suitable contacts can be solved. Like the question of conductivity in organics, the mechanism of photoconductivity in organic materials is another controversial subject. Without speculating on that question, we can show that organic materials may have certain advantages over inorganic materials. For example, inorganic materials are usually most sensitive to the short waves. Recent work on several organic materials, particularly manganese phthalocyanine and the charge-transfer complex of perylene-fluoranil, has shown photoconductive responses to wavelengths as long as 1.3 microns, which is a region of active interest for infrared photoconductors.

Also, because organic infrared detectors have a high initial resistivity, a given change in radiation intensity would show up as a large change in resistance. For that reason, organic detectors, unlike inorganic detectors, should not have to be cooled to low temperatures to get a practical signal-to-noise ratio. With organics, there would also be the possibility of obtaining more uniform crystalline thin films. The need is increasing for large arrays of detectors with a uniform deposit and constant characteristics. And there is also the possibility of obtaining a wide spectral response by modifying the organic material.

Organic light modulators

An interesting effect shown by some organic materials is the linear electro-optical or Pockels effect. It is an analog of the Kerr effect, but is seen in solids rather than liquids or gases. As with the Kerr effect, an electrical field causes the plane of polarized light to rotate when passing through the material. Such materials serve as light modulators when placed between crossed polarizers; varying the electric field on the crystal varies the intensity of the light.

The Pockels effect occurs in all piezoelectric materials, organic and inorganic, but materials of the cubic crystal system make the most practical modulators. These materials are isotropic and because of this feature, the beam of light that passes through the material does not need to be collimated and the electric field can be applied perpendicular to the direction of light propagation. In other crystal systems, the light must pass through the electrical contacts.

At least two organic compounds meet the crystal requirements. Hexamethylenetetramine (HMTA) has been shown to operate as a light modulator to 10 Gc. Single crystals have been grown from the vapor at 70°C or from solution at 40°C. HMTA decomposes at its melting point of 260°C. A similar material, adamantane, should also show the effect, but no work has yet

Fig. 1-119. *HMTA (hexamethylenetetramine) is an organic compound that rotates a light beam's plane of polarization in response to an applied electric field. This crystal, set up for laser modulation, was grown at Aircraft Armaments Inc.*

been reported. We expect that one or both of these materials may be used in light-beam communications.

There are a number of other applications for organic materials that remain to be explored. It has been suggested that an injection luminescent device might be made from an organic system (see "Semiconductor Lasers," page 127). It is well known that some organic materials fluoresce in the visible region when excited. If a fluorescent material were combined with a good electrical conductor (such as TCNQ), the result might be an effective electro-luminescent material. Conduction electrons, accelerated by the electric field, would transfer their energy to the fluorescent material causing its excitation. The excited material would eventually decay with the emission of visible light.

Plastic wiring

Further work on the conduction mechanism in organics may lead to very low resistance material that could be used for electrical interconnections. (This may also be the answer to some of the contact problems.) The hope here is that the conductive plastics would offer a cheap and reliable method of interconnecting circuitry.

Undoubtedly, more electronic applications for organic compounds will be uncovered. Of those

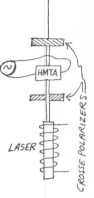

HMTA

LASER

CROSSED POLARIZERS

Fig. 1-120. Both these strips of glass are coated with a photochromic compound; the darker one has just been exposed to ultraviolet light. The material is being investigated by National Cash Register for use as a high-resolution microfilm.

described in this article, some seem very promising; others are decidedly chancy. For a time, organics were the new frontier of electronics. In many ways, they still are. We are just now beginning to find out how difficult it will be to cross that frontier.

Further reading

The idea of a plastic transistor has been around for several years and, consequently, there are a number of good reference sources; supplementary reading on the subject of optical

and electro-optical organic compounds is somewhat more scarce. Whichever way your interest turns, probably the best place to start is *Semiconductors,* edited by Hannay (Reinhold, 1959, $15). The book includes an excellent chapter on organic semiconductors by Garrett, still surprisingly current despite six years of intervening research. The other chapters are also well worth reading. The most recent book is *Physics and Chemistry of the Organic Solid State,* edited by Fox, Labes, and Weissberger (Interscience, 1963, $25). It's pretty rough going for the nonspecialist and deals largely with such matters as the growth and thermodynamics of organic crystals, purity of organic compounds, surfaces, and photochemistry, but is probably the most complete single-volume collection of information available on the subject.

For a more up-to-date review of the organic semiconductor business see "Organic Semiconductors" by Juster in *J. Chem. Educ.* **40,** 547 (1963). This article takes a close look at the conduction mechanism and reviews the various classes of electrically conducting materials. An earlier article, "Organic Semiconductors" by Gutmann and Netschey, in *Rev. Pure & Appl. Chem.* **12,** 2 (1962) offers a general discussion of the same subject.

Particular applications for organic materials are discussed in the following list of references: "How Rare-Earth Chelate Lasers Work" by Metlay, *Electronics* **36,** No. 46, 67 (Nov. 15, 1963); "Electro-optic Light Modulation with Cubic Crystals" by Buhrer, Bloom, and Baird, *Appl. Opt.* **2,** 839 (1963); "The Pockels Effect of Hexamethylenetetramine" by McQuaid, *Appl. Opt.* **2,** 320 (1963); "Electrochromism, a Possible Change of Color Producible in Dyes by an Electric Field" by Platt, *J. Chem. Phys.* **34,** 862 (1961); and the chapter titled "Photochromism" by Dessauer and Paris in *Advances in Photochemistry,* edited by Noyes, Hammond, and Pitts (Interscience, 1963, $16.50).

INTEGRATED CIRCUITS

by John L. Sprague *

IN BRIEF: *Just because you can really buy (and not just order) a whole circuit on a speck of dust, does not mean that conventional circuitry is on the way out. Not by a long mark. But it does portend far-reaching effects in this $10^{10} industry. For there comes a point beyond which shrinking pieces and crowding them just won't do.*

From there on, the active circuit elements

* John L. Sprague is Vice President in charge of engineering at the Sprague Electric Co.

(diodes, transistors, etc.), the passive components (resistors, capacitors, inductors), and the interconnections that give them meaning are all made together on (or in) a single chip of substrate. The component-maker and the circuit-builder become the same fellow. This vertical integration occurs whichever fabrication scheme you consider.

It holds for the thin-film approach of depositing alternating layers of conducting, insulating, and semiconducting materials to form cir-

cuit elements and it holds for the semiconductor-based approach of modifying the impurity-content of sites within a semiconductor chip to accomplish the same thing. Omen-like, finally there comes a stage where incidental circuit elements combine to make each resistor or capacitor or transistor all elements at once, where no piece is discrete, and the entire assemblage is an integrated unit.—R.G.N.

■ Integrated circuitry, microelectronics, molecular circuitry—whatever your terminology —these new and dramatic fabrication techniques that permit extreme miniaturization of electronic systems constitute *the* most important recent development in the history of the electronics industry. However, those words new and recent are themselves misleading, as misleading as it is to call these new technologies revolutionary. For, while their development has been much faster than anyone anticipated, and while these technologies may well cause far-reaching changes in the very nature of the electronics industry, research and development has been going on in this field for nearly twenty years.

Neglecting special packages of discrete components, there are two basic approaches to integrated circuitry. The so-called thin-film technique involves deposition of conducting and insulating films on substrates to form resistors and capacitors and the subsequent attachment of diodes and transistors. The second, or silicon-based microcircuit approach, involves the introduction of both active and passive elements into a single-crystal piece of silicon. Combinations of these two techniques are now under investigation in many labs.

The first benefit sought was small size. This was especially true in military electronics, and, in fact, the first systematic attack on the problem of circuitry size, was made during World War II by the National Bureau of Standards in the development of a mortar proximity fuze. They introduced the idea of depositing conductive and resistive inks on ceramic substrates, a concept which was to be the forerunner of printed circuits and, later, the more sophisticated ceramic-based microcircuits.

Those 1943 deposited networks did not, in most cases, involve active elements, such as vacuum tubes and rectifiers, which exhibit gain or control currents and voltages. A few of these early networks did have provisions for plugging in vacuum tubes, but it took the invention of the transistor in the late 1940's to make active elements a common feature of substrates containing passive elements, i.e., resistors, capacitors, and inductors.

Work on thin-film microcircuitry has devel-

oped rapidly since the early 1950's. On the other hand, attempts at the other major approach—introduction of a circuit into a piece of semiconductor—did not begin in earnest until after the middle 1950's. Again, small size was the desired result. For most of us, however, the primary motive was just the desire to see if we really could do it.

Easier said than done

Different approaches were tried in various labs utilizing both germanium and silicon as the semiconducting substrate. To produce some parts of the typical structure in the margin, we pulled single crystals from an appropriately doped melt while varying the rate of withdrawal just so. The results are called rate-grown junctions.

The transistor junctions we made by alloying impurities to thin webs previously etched into the Si substrate. As with all the early approaches, this one suffered from the major problem that the discrete circuit elements had to be interconnected by means of extremely fragile individual jumper wires.

This major stumbling block was overcome in 1960 with introduction of the silicon planar technology. The importance of this development can be seen in Fig. 1-121, which compares the planar structure with the mesa configuration, a common transistor structure. Both transistors can be formed—in multiplicity—on a slice of single-crystal silicon by diffusing minute amounts of dopant materials into the crystal. However, with the mesa structure each transistor is surrounded by a moat. Because of this moat, connecting one transistor to another, or

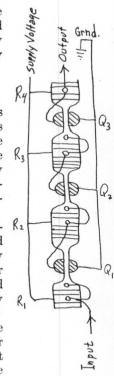

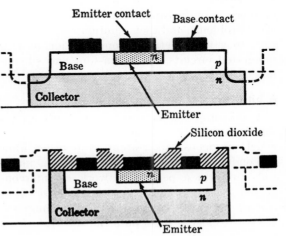

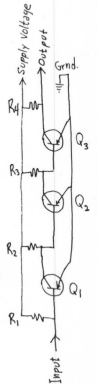

Fig. 1-121. Compare the common mesa (top) and planar transistor structures, and you'll see the advantage of planar technology: Connections to other components within the block don't require jumper wires, evaporated metal strips suffice. (Courtesy Sprague Electric Co.)

to a diode, resistor, or capacitor, on the same slice again requires jumper wires. And such interconnection between elements is exactly what one must have for a circuit.

On the other hand, with the planar structure, all contacts can be made on the surface of the device, no moat exists between adjacent structures, and interconnection becomes a seemingly simple matter of evaporating an appropriate metallic pattern over the surface of the silicon slice. As we shall see, however, this supposedly simple step is one of our major sources of difficulty.

Although small size is again inherent in this approach, two additional and even more important potential advantages soon become apparent: First of all, many circuits are made simultaneously by means of the same techniques and packaging of the individual components is eliminated, so low costs should ultimately be realizable, in some cases lower than equivalent combinations of discrete parts.

Secondly, the number of interconnections between dissimilar materials—a major source of equipment failures—is greatly reduced, so the inherent reliability of such a circuit should be appreciably higher than of discrete component assemblies. Similar arguments can be made for thin-film microcircuits. While these claims have yet to be proven out, there are strong indications that in many applications they will ultimately be true.

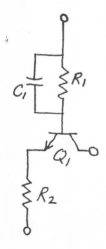

So there we have it. Integrated circuitry offers smaller size, potential savings in costs, and greater reliability. It also affords a multitude of problems, problems in technology, in circuit and systems design, and in the relationship between the components supplier and the systems manufacturer. To better understand these problems, and their solution, we must now turn to a more detailed consideration of how integrated circuits, both thin-film and silicon-based, are made.

A bit of how-to

A thin-film microcircuit starts with an insulating substrate (glass, ceramic, etc.), on which are deposited, in appropriate order, films of conducting, resistive, and insulating materials to form a passive network of interconnected resistors and capacitors. These films can be deposited by a variety of techniques: We can condense them onto the substrate from a vapor prepared by heating or by chemical reactions. We can also use printed-circuit methodologies, or possibly exotic machining methods, such as lasers or collimated electron beams. Then, if necessary, additional discrete capacitors, resistors, inductors, and finally the

diodes and transistors can be soldered or welded on.

Let's consider in particular the fabrication of an atypically simple ceramic-based microcircuit. I choose this technology because of its extreme flexibility and because the present state of the ceramic-circuit art is beyond that of most other thin-film techniques.

The synthesis of a ceramic-based microcircuit is based on silk screening and other graphic-arts processes. Typically, a precision mask is placed over the substrate, a paint or ink is forced through appropriate holes in the mask onto the substrate, the mask is removed, and the resulting printed areas are fired in a high temperature furnace. Although there are many types of paints, most commonly they consist of an electrically conductive or resistive material in powdered form, a finely divided glass, an organic binder, and some volatile solvent. Firing such a mixture leaves on the substrate a film of the conductive or resistive material dispersed in fused glass.

It is possible to deposit films with a wide variety of characteristics merely by varying the composition of the paint. That's one reason why the system is so flexible. Such paints are used to form over-glazes for resistors, the resistors themselves, capacitor electrodes, and interconnection patterns.

Now to our atypical microcircuit: The circuit in the margin is one logical element of a switching system used to control decisions within a computer. We are going to transform it into microcircuit form.

The first step is choice of the appropriate substrate. In our case that depends mainly on what value of capacitance we need, because the substrate will be used as the dielectric of C_1. If the circuit involves many capacitors of widely differing characteristics, the substrate could be made of several types of material. For low values (a few hundred micro-microfarads or less) a nonferroelectric BaTiO-based ceramic can be used, while for higher values (a few tens of thousands of $\mu\mu$F) a ferroelectric material or a stacked construction is usually necessary. In Sprague Electric's configuration, trademarked Monolythic, such a substrate is really a stacked ceramic capacitor block formed by alternately spraying dielectric and electrode materials and then firing the layered structure at high temperatures. This way, we can get 8 to 80 times as much capacitance as in the same volume of nonlayered construction. Finally, if more than 1.0 μF is needed, miniature tantalum capacitor sections can be attached directly to the substrate.

Having chosen our substrate, the next step is to deposit capacitor electrodes and intercon-

$capacitance = permittivity \times \dfrac{area}{distance}$

(a) Select insulating substrate to provide capacitor dielectric and glaze onto it the base for R_1 and R_2

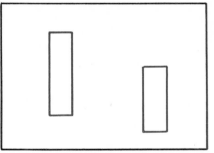

(b) Deposit metal capacitor electrodes, contact lands for transistor, and interconnections

(c) Deposit resistors and overglaze resistor areas only

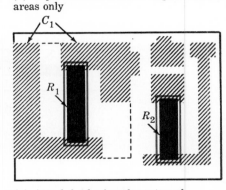

(d) Attach transistor by soldering or welding its leads to contact lands

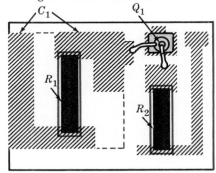

Or, place transistor with contact areas on its underside onto contact lands provided

Transistor contact land   Connection pad to Q_1

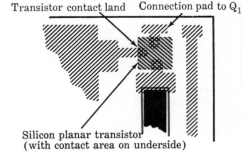

Silicon planar transistor (with contact area on underside)

(e) Attach lead wires for external connection and encapsulate the assembly

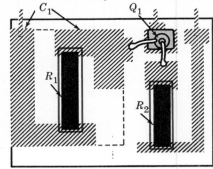

Fig. 1-122. In this thin-film circuit, the electrode deposited at left edge in step b continues around the dielectric chip to form the counterelectrode of C_1. (Courtesy Sprague Electric Co.)

nection patterns. The next step involves deposition of the resistor films and then covering these films with an overglaze for added protection. These resistors can be adjusted to closer than 1% by automatically abrading the film, using the resistor's value to control the operation until the desired resistance is reached. To finish the circuit, just attach Q_1 and the lead-wires and then encapsulate.

As I said, such a circuit can be formed by a variety of other thin-film techniques. Of these, vacuum deposition is the most often used, and the tantalum-based system has been the most extensively studied. Compared with silk-screening techniques, systems involving vacuum deposition suffer from less flexibility in materials choice.

However, vacuum techniques in conjunction with photolithographic masking give greater precision and control of the initial parameters of the deposited films and appear to offer the potential of greater automation, an important economic factor. And where high-precision resistors are needed in microcircuit form, the tantalum system is about the best. This is because tantalum or tantalum-nitride resistive films can be trimmed to a closer than 0.1% tolerance by selectively oxidizing their surfaces, thus accurately controlling their thickness and resultant resistance.

I have described the fabrication of an ex-

tremely simple circuit, but the flexibility of the thin-film approach can handle circuit complexity more easily than the alternate silicon-based approach. This is due to the great variety of materials available and to the possibility of adding discrete passive elements, including inductive ones such as chokes and transformers. As we shall see, the inability to achieve sufficient inductance in a silicon microcircuit is one of this technology's key problems. (There *are* inductive effects in transistors, but we just haven't been able to use them yet.)

The most serious problem with the thin-film techniques is with the active elements, most commonly diodes and transistors. Whereas the passive networks and interconnections can be made very cheaply and reliably on the substrate, adding extra components compromises this advantage. Today, the active elements usually are either a miniature case or in chip form with fragile protruding leads. Both these configurations are expensive. The cased transistors are too large; and the uncased chips are delicate. Furthermore, interconnection of the active elements onto the substrate is expensive and could raise reliability difficulties.

Obviously, the ideal answer would be to form the active elements at the same time and utilize the same materials as the passive elements. A number of attempts have been made to do just that. Early ones, such as the tunnel triode,

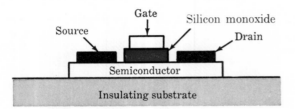

Fig. 1-123. The field-effect transistor, in which an electric field at the gate controls the conductivity of a channel between the source and drain electrodes, is one of the most promising thin-film active devices. (Courtesy Sprague Electric Co.)

involved trying to make amplifying devices, using the tunneling of electrons through very thin insulating films. Unfortunately, for the all-thin-film case, no one has yet succeeded. Some investigators are also looking at rectification and other effects in refractory metal oxides, such as niobium pentoxide. But there reproducibility and stability are great problems. Other people have deposited films of Si on insulating substrates and fabricated diodes and transistors in these films. However, these devices have been of inferior quality. As in nearly all thin-film active-element approaches, this one precludes pretesting of the active elements. And so it results in reduced yields.

Of all the deposited active element approaches, the vacuum deposition of field-effect devices looks the most promising. In a field-effect device the conductivity of a semiconductor is modulated between input (source) and output (drain) electrodes by applying an electric field to a control electrode (gate) normal to the semiconductor across an insulator (see Fig. 1-123). The electrical characteristics

of such devices are very similar to those of a vacuum tube. In vacuum-deposited elements of this type, cadmium sulfide, cadmium telluride, or similar materials are utilized as the semiconductor; typically silicon monoxide is the insulator, and any appropriate conducting metals may be the source, drain, and gate electrodes. Unfortunately, at this time these devices too suffer from lack of reproducibility, poor stability, and less than optimum operation.

Although a reliable and high-quality deposited active element may still be developed, the most promising looking approach to the problem of getting active devices onto the circuit seems to be a modification of the basic planar transistor. What we do is deposit a layer of glass over a silicon slice in which up to several thousand transistors have been formed—after the transistor slice has been metalized and connection pads laid down. This effectively seals the individual transistors. Then we bring contacts up through the glass to large contact areas on top of the surface. When the slice is separated into individual dies, each one is a hermetically sealed transistor with large contact lands on it. There are many ways to attach such a transistor to the thin-film circuit. One of the most attractive is to turn the die over and heat it while it is in contact with tinned lands on the thin-film substrate. At this point the dies are still very inexpensive, and the bonding operation is also cheap, so this approach looks very economical. Reliability still remains to be demonstrated, but several labs, including our own, are studying this approach.

All in all, we see that while thin-film microcircuits offer smaller size and potentially greater reliability than assemblies of discrete active and passive elements, and while they offer greater flexibility than silicon-based microcircuits, our realization of their full potential depends on developing an inexpensive, reliable and high-performance active element configuration. Happily, the method I outlined above appears to be a solution to this problem.

The active-element problem does not exist for the silicon-based microcircuit. Here, active and passive elements are made integrally and simultaneously within the block.

Silicon-based microcircuitry

Any silicon-based microcircuit begins with a conventional circuit diagram—an analog of the desired function in terms of discrete circuit elements. This analog is then transformed by a metaphysical process called design into a series of masks which will determine where circuit elements will be diffused into the silicon slice. Figure 1-124 shows a typical master mask about to undergo photographic reduc-

Fig. 1-124. A master pattern for an etching step is a few hundred times as large as the multiple replica mask used to expose the silicon. (Courtesy Sprague Electric Co.)

tion. These master masks are then photographically reduced to as little as $\frac{1}{400}$ of their original dimensions. During this reduction, the patterns are also repetitiously reproduced on a photographic plate. Through this reduction and "step-and-repeat" process we finally end up with a glass mask on which are many copies of the original master. A set of these glass masks can then be used to simultaneously fabricate up to several hundred microcircuits.

The patterns on these masks are translated to a silicon slice by photolithography. What takes place is the following: First of all the slice is thermally oxidized to form a layer of SiO_2 on it about one micron (10,000 Å) thick. Then a photosensitive emulsion, such as KPR (Kodak Photo Resist), is deposited on top of the oxide. This emulsion is sensitized in selected areas by shining a light through the glass mask. The resist emulsion is then immersed into a developer which removes the emulsion in the unsensitized areas, leaving a pattern of photoresist material on the oxide in the previously exposed places.

An appropriate etchant, such as hydrofluoric acid (HF), is used to selectively remove the SiO_2 not covered by the resist material. Thus the pattern originally on the glass mask is now etched into the oxide coating.

An SiO_2 layer will keep most gaseous impurities out of the semiconductor even at high temperatures. Therefore, when we place the slice in a furnace in which appropriate impurities are introduced at temperatures up to 1300°C, these impurities will diffuse into the semiconductor only in those areas where the oxide has been removed. For example, we might use P_2O_5 which, when diffused into the silicon crystal lattice, can contribute an excess electron for current-carrying purposes, to form n-type material. Or, we might make electron-deficient p-type (where the current carriers are electron deficiencies, called holes) material by doping with B_2O_3. This is how the diffused areas corresponding to circuit elements are introduced into the silicon slice.

To better understand the process, let us reconsider that same simple circuit I discussed—only this time as a silicon-based microcircuit. In Fig. 1-125, we start with a polished slice of silicon around 1 in. in diameter and 0.01 in. thick. Although my description will be in terms of fabrication of only one circuit, several hundred would actually be formed simultaneously on this single slice.

We first selectively diffuse in a highly doped n^+ region (the "plus" indicates a high impurity concentration, not electrical charge). Then we epitaxially deposit a less highly doped n layer on the p substrate. By epitaxial growth

I mean that we grow layers of Si atoms on top of the original substrate, as an extension of the original crystal lattice. This is done by the decomposition of silane:

$$SiH_4 \rightarrow Si + 2H_2\uparrow$$

or more often, by reduction of $SiCl_4$ or $SiHCl_3$. That leaves an n^+ pocket—which is highly conductive—within the resultant slice. Its purpose is to improve internal contact to the transistor to be fabricated over it and therefore the speed of the device.

The next step involves selective p diffusion down through the epitaxially grown n layer to the p substrate. This diffusion step forms pockets of n-type silicon in a p-type matrix. These pockets serve as R_1 (not shown) and R_2, as the collector region for Q_1, and are isolated from each other by the p-n junctions that exist between them (see Fig. 1-127).

Step e is a second p diffusion which forms the base region of Q_1 and the p region of C_1 and f introduces a further part of C_1, Q_1's emitter and the highly doped, highly conductive contact areas to the other n regions. Finally, holes (the donut kind, not the current kind) are etched in the oxide for contacts to the different diffused areas, and the interconnection pattern is deposited, using evaporative and photolithographic techniques.

At this point the circuit is complete. However, it must still be separated from the other circuits on the same slice, have leads attached, and be hermetically sealed in some kind of package. This has been the fabrication of a very simple circuit. Obviously much greater complexity is possible.

This capacity for complexity means you can be prodigal with components. The tiny oblong circuits in Fig. 1-126 each have many components—31 to be precise. These are diodes, transistors, resistors, and capacitors. Merely by changing the final interconnection mask, the components can be connected in a number of ways to serve different circuit functions. In this particular case we are using only 14 of the 31 components to make a flip-flop. That's one way to reduce the high design costs of individual circuit for each function.

The high cost for prototypes of silicon-based microcircuits (which can run into the $\$10^5$ range) is only one problem. There are many others. The very fact that the elements of such a device exist in the same single crystal block is a severe limitation. Today, most silicon microcircuits are direct analogs of their discrete-component counterparts: You can look at them and identify each resistor, capacitor, diode, and transistor. But where the electrical isolation of a circuit made up of discrete com-

To "grow" this four-component switch circuit...

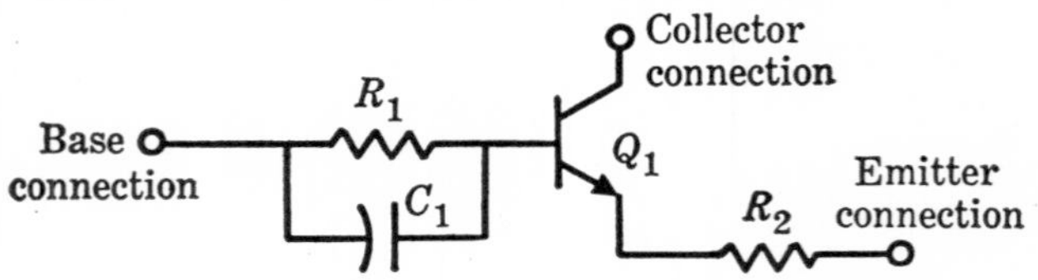

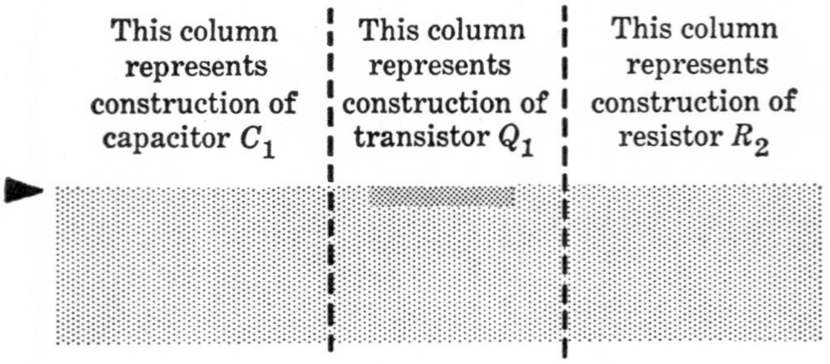

Base connection — R_1 — Collector connection — Q_1 — Emitter connection — R_2 — C_1

This column represents construction of capacitor C_1

This column represents construction of transistor Q_1

This column represents construction of resistor R_2

(a) Make a strongly n^+-type spot by diffusion into p-type silicon substrate

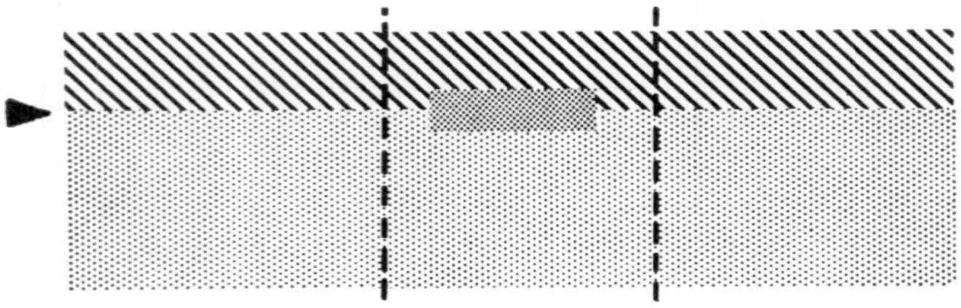

(b) Grow n layer epitaxially atop this; oxidize it

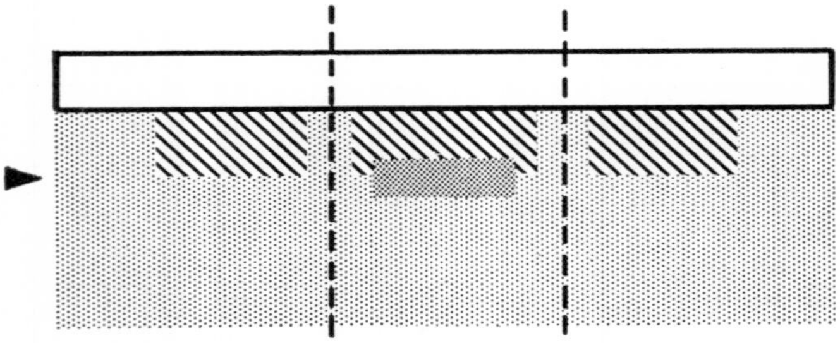

(c) Convert selected areas of the n layer to p-type by diffusion to provide component isolation. *You now have resistors R_2 and R_1 (not shown), collector of transistor Q_1 and the n material matrix of C_1*

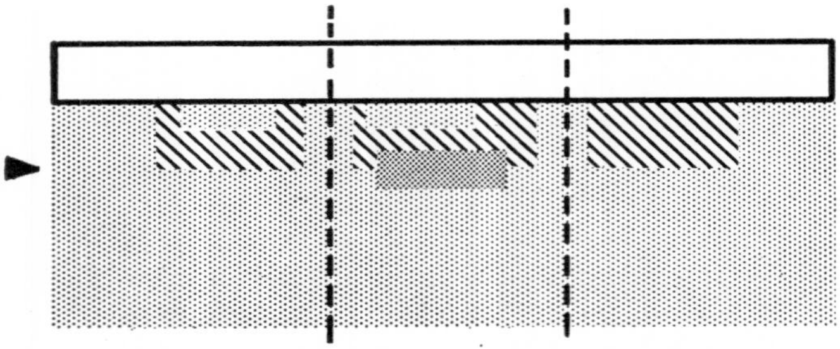

(d) Diffuse in p-dopant to form pockets of transistor base and other region of C_1

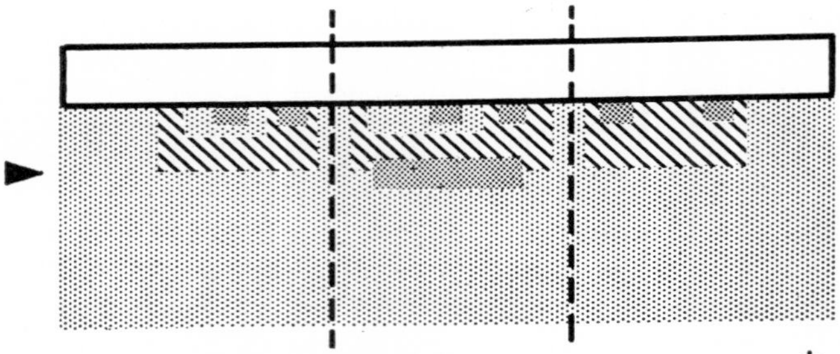

(e) Complete components by diffusing **in regions of** n^+ material as contacts

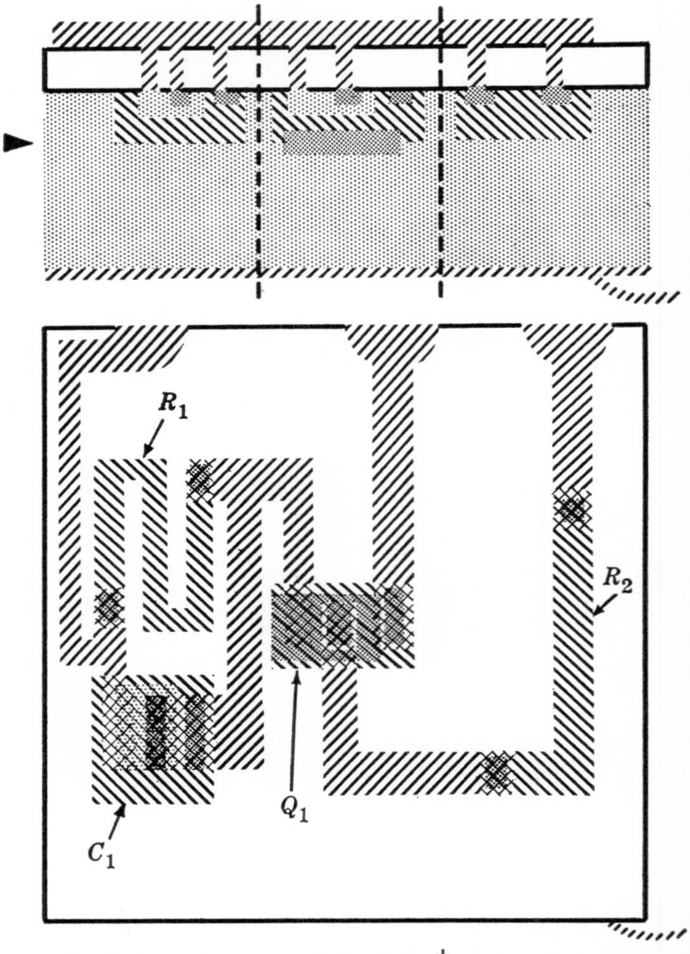

(f) Etch oxide layer to indicated n^+ and p regions and deposit metal to form component interconnections. Attach bias contact to substrate

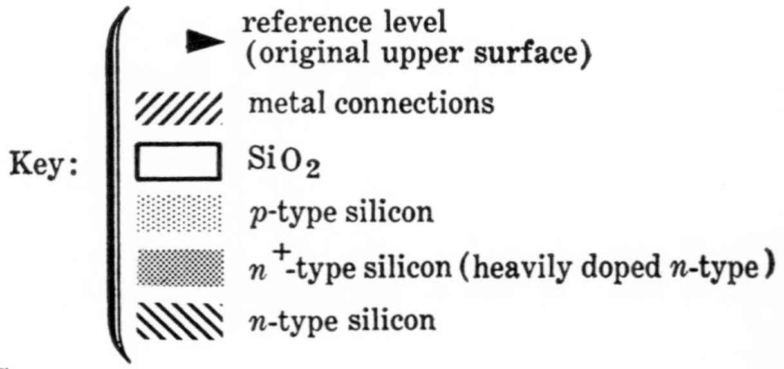

Key:

▶ reference level (original upper surface)

////// metal connections

☐ SiO$_2$

p-type silicon

n^+-type silicon (heavily doped n-type)

\\\\\\ n-type silicon

Fig. 1-125.

156

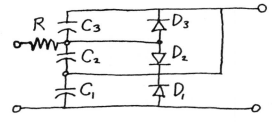

Fig. 1-126. *There are 36 partly completed circuits in this full-size view; resolution of this illustration as printed is 120 lines/in. (For any line counters, the engraver's lines are diagonal.) (Courtesy Sprague Electric Co.)*

ponents is excellent, isolation in the silicon circuit is by back-biased *p-n* junctions.

Macroproblems for microcircuits

This isolation isn't very good, because each such junction has associated with it various incidental equivalent circuit elements. (To a lesser extent, this happens with discrete-component circuits too.)

As a matter of fact, due to these so-called "parasitics" the equivalent circuits of seemingly simple components can be exceedingly complex. For example, the equivalent circuit for capacitor C_1 in Fig. 1-125 looks like:

These parasitics adversely affect the performance of any circuit, and further they greatly complicate the circuit designs. Coupled with this problem of parasitics is the additional one that diffused resistors and capacitors are rather inferior in performance. As a matter of fact, whereas we could say that with thin-film microcircuits the major problem is with the active elements, here our difficulties are with the passive devices.

First of all, it is almost impossible to fabricate diffused silicon resistors with initial tolerances closer than $\pm20\%$. Even this is stretching the limits of the diffusion technology but it really cramps the style of the circuit designer—in fact it makes most standard configurations for amplifiers, good quality radio detectors, etc., unfeasible. Further, these resistors are highly temperature sensitive, with temperature coefficients up to 2000 ppm/°C, depending upon the impurity concentration. Unfortunately the higher the resistance, the greater this temperature effect.

The commonly employed capacitors formed

by *p-n* junctions also suffer from similar limitations. These capacitors derive their capacitance from the so-called space-charge region created by the migration of current-carriers away from a junction when it is under the influence of an electric field, as shown in Fig. 1-127. Besides being limited to values below about 500 $\mu\mu$F, these capacitors are temperature sensitive and are a function of the voltage across them. Also, as follows from Fig. 1-127, the junction must be maintained with *p* material negative with respect to the *n*-material side.

Finally, in the present state of technology, effective inductive effects are not realizable in diffused-silicon bodies. These difficulties severely limit the tools which the circuit designer has to work with and tax his ingenuity. How are these problems overcome?

Compromises and hybrid circuits

One obvious way is to design for a minimum of passive components. This is relatively simple in the case of binary logic for computers. Here we are concerned basically with on-off applications, in other words, with a $\pm50\%$ situation. Still, close tolerances are important to power consumption, speed, and other considerations in most digital circuits.

There are several logic systems that utilize a minimum of resistors and no capacitor. However, they do require a number of active elements in each circuit, and this can cause a yield problem. It is also sometimes possible to compensate for change in one parameter by change in another. For example, the temperature increase of the current gain of a transistor can offset the increase in resistance of a resistor in the base circuit.

With linear or analog circuitry, where our needs are for a linear response by the circuit,

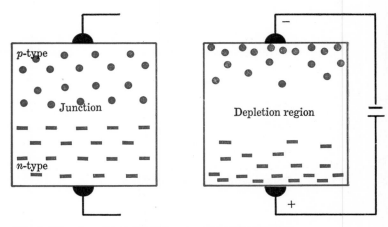

Fig. 1-127. *A voltage applied across a semiconductor junction with the polarity shown will sweep electrons (▬) and holes (●) away from the junction, creating an insulating zone.*

the limitations are much more serious. Here, passive component performance is much more critical and usually those elements cannot be designed out of the circuit. The most logical solution here is to combine thin-film and silicon-based techniques in the same microcircuit.

Referring again to Fig. 1-125, it is easy to visualize the sequence of steps involved in fabricating such a "hybrid" circuit. The early steps are the same except that no passive elements are formed during diffusion. In other words, at this point, only the transistor has been formed. Then contact holes for Q_1 are etched in the protective oxide and the interconnection pattern is formed. But we leave gaps in this pattern for subsequent deposition of R_1, R_2, and C_1, which are formed on top of the SiO_2 layer to complete the circuit.

The resistor deposition is relatively simple. For example, nichrome or tantalum nitride can be vacuum-deposited or formed in other ways. Compared to diffused elements, such resistors have much closer tolerances with lower temperature coefficients, and in general are far superior. However, forming capacitors is more complex, since they require three layers, a substrate electrode, dielectric, and counterelectrode. If the oxide coating on the silicon is used as the dielectric, then the semiconductor substrate serves as one plate and an evaporated area as the other electrode. Or an appropriate dielectric such as SiO, Al_2O_3, or Ta_2O_5 can be formed on a substrate area evaporated on top of the SiO_2 layer and the capacitor completed by evaporating the counterelectrode.

Such capacitors are far superior to their diffused counterparts. Still they are extremely limited in possible capacitance by the tiny area of a silicon chip (see margin).

Besides improved passive elements, hybrid microcircuits offer another advantage. Since the passive elements are on top of an oxide coating, their electrical isolation from each other and from the diffused active elements is much better than when all elements exist within the silicon block. Both of these advantages lead to improved circuit performance. Hybrid circuits, however, have one severe disadvantage. They require more fabrication steps, and these additional steps cause lower yields. So hybrid circuits are generally more costly than thin-film or silicon-based circuits.

Doing what comes naturally

Some of the cleverest new circuit techniques are built around what *is* available in a diffused silicon body rather than what *is not*. For example, in a direct-coupled amplifier (right) temperature drift presents a critical problem of shifting outputs for any given input. One way of reducing this problem is to provide a shunt feedback loop from the output to the input of the transistor. That way, although the load and feedback resistors may vary with temperature, their ratio does not, and we get temperature stabilization of the circuit.

Another typical case (see below) involves design of an audio power amplifier. "Design around" might be a better expression. The usually necessary transformer (which drives the output transistors 180° out of phase with respect to one another) can be eliminated by using transistor phase splitting stages or complementary *p-n-p/n-p-n* transistors in the same silicon block. Low rather than the usual high values of coupling capacitance will suffice if field-effect transistors are employed. Field-effect resistors permit adjustment of gain, volume, or output power. But what do we do with

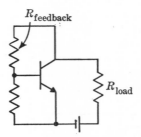

Direct-coupled amplifier with shunt feedback loop

This amplifier

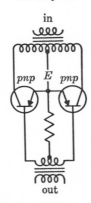

can be replaced by this one

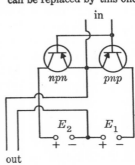

the L-C tuned circuits which require inductance as well as capacitance to achieve resonance? This is one of the most formidable and interesting problems in the field.

The best answer to date has been to design out the inductors and use distributed R-C networks which have filter characteristics. For example, the usually unwanted effective capacitance that shunts diffused resistors can be used to form such a network. Since the capacitance of a junction varies with the voltage across it, these networks can be used to tune oscillators and amplifiers. Such characteristics can be improved by varying the geometries of the diffused regions.

So we see that while there are a number of problems with silicon-based microcircuits, many are finding solutions; the situation will improve as the technology develops. But are the advantages of small size, greater reliability, and lower costs sufficient to warrant the expense involved in finding these solutions?

Shrinking—reliably and economically

There is no question about the small size of these circuits. This, in fact, can be a detriment since these tiny silicon chips are hard to get a handle on, that is, to get information into and out of. Packing densities of 10^8 equivalent parts/ft^3 are, in principle, possible with silicon-based microcircuits—as compared with 5×10^6 equivalent parts/ft^3 for thin-film circuitry and 10^5 for the most advanced discrete-component circuits. However, these figures, impressive and oft-quoted as they are, really have very little meaning; most such equipment size is limited more by considerations of internal connections and heat-dissipation than by component size.

The reliabilities of thin films and integrated blocks should be much greater than of discrete-component assemblies, because there are many less interfaces between different materials. Reliability data to date are impressive, but are still far from complete. And there are several potential trouble areas; the most serious one is the interconnection scheme. Almost universally, aluminum forms the internal connecting paths over the oxide layer—which has a certain density of faults in it created during processing or inherent in the oxide itself. During metallization, these can shortcircuit the interconnection areas to the substrate, or allow the aluminum metal to react with the SiO_2 insulator to cause failure during subsequent heat treatment. Such failures also, of course, lead to low yields. Other areas which need further study are the reliability of the different packaging techniques and the different methods of connecting these packages.

Finally we come to costs. The investment necessary to succeed financially (not just to demonstrate a laboratory capability) in this business is extremely high; annual budgets of several million dollars are not unusual at this point. And, since the initial costs in designing any single circuit are also very high, for inexpensive circuits we must need many of the same type, have circuits of limited complexity, and have high yields. One way is to get wide acceptance of a few standard circuits which, when used in various combinations, will satisfy a wide variety of electronic functions. This, however, can lead to poorer system performance, and it also robs the system designer of much of his flexibility.

Another answer is to produce a slice with a multiplicity of components interconnectable in a variety of ways to satisfy different functions. Here the main problem is that such circuits are large and complex. For high yields we need to make many circuits on the same slice. Further, since each slice has a certain number of faults, the larger and more complex the circuit, the greater the probability of such a fault causing a bad circuit and the lower the yields. This is an extremely important point. The low costs predicted for silicon-based microcircuits are based on improved yields as the technology develops. However, if greater complexity is also required, these improved yields may be hard to come by.

Phenomenology and blobtronics

Before leaving this subject I must mention the concept of "functional devices." Such a device performs a necessary electronic function, without involving the components of the conventional circuit which would perform the same function. It has no useful equivalent circuit, but rather operates by direct utilization of the basic properties of matter. The most classical example is the piezoelectric quartz-crystal resonator which directly combines and utilizes the piezoelectric effect and mechanical resonance to provide whole families of filters, delay-line elements, transducers, etc. Another is the elastic-wave amplifier which combines semiconduction with piezoelectric effects. Still another class are the Hall-effect devices, which are being used as multipliers, trig-function generators, and other things. Still another is the much-discussed 4-layer diode (with its equivalent, in the margin), a bistable semiconductor device which has great potential as a switching element in computer applications.

The concept of functional devices has received both ridicule and over-emphasis by those who do not believe in it or understand it. On one occasion I have heard it derided and described as "blob circuitry." On another, a group

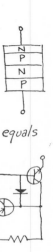

equals

of us were told to throw away all our classical concepts of circuits and component parts, return to our laboratories, and "invent." As new materials are introduced, as our understanding of the basic properties of matter improves, new types of functional devices will evolve. Many will find use in systems design and may even change certain of our design concepts. But it will be a very long time, if ever, before such devices can satisfy more than a small portion of our electronic needs.

Though all those approaches have their problems to be solved, the future in this field looks bright, bright enough for the electronics industry to be asking itself two important dollars and cents questions:

What is the future for discrete components if we expect more and more equipment to be designed using integrated circuitry? And who will make these integrated circuits?

Integrating in the industry

Many have predicted the death knell of the discrete component manufacturer. However, there are many things that cannot be done as well or at all by integrated circuitry. Several recent independent surveys have projected a market in 1972 of over 10^9 for thin-film and silicon-based microcircuits. On the other hand, these same surveys predict a 1972 market of more than $300 million in various types of discrete component assemblies, well over a billion in discrete passive elements, and a similar amount for discrete active elements. In 1962 these figures were $100 million, $900 million and $1.2 billion respectively. So it looks as though the component manufacturer will be around for a long time to come.

Besides, although some systems manufacturers—particularly the computer and communications companies with their own component divisions—are integrating downward to make their own microcircuits, I think the most logical arrangement will prove to be the classical relationship between component supplier and systems manufacturer, whether each chip of substrate contains a single transistor or resistor or capacitor or several of them.

The resistor and capacitor company has generally been working with thin films for many years and the planar transistor manufacturer already has nearly all the tricky technology needed for making silicon-based microcircuits. Ultimately, of course, those who remain will be those who do the best job, be they components manufacturers, integrated circuit specialists, or systems manufacturers.

Further reading

It's no mere coincidence that when the editor and the author met to iron out some fine points in this article, each was equipped with his own copy of Keonjian's *Microelectronics: Theory, Design and Fabrication* (McGraw-Hill, 1963, $12.50). It's the most complete collection of data in this field either one had seen, although the elements of this field are well-covered in Levine's *Principles of Solid-State Microelectronics* (Holt, Rinehart & Winston, 1963, $5.25), and the basic physics of the devices and effects involved are most thoroughly described in *Solid State Magnetic and Dielectric Devices*, edited by Katz (Wiley, 1959, $13.50).

See also the Selective Bibliography #444, "Electronic Miniaturization" (OTS, Washington, 1961, 10¢), which includes a subheading on microelectronics. OTS has also an up-to-date bibliography service.

The most valuable sources of data on this topic are the journals *Electronic Reliability, Microminiaturization,* and *Solid State Electronics* in addition to the general electronic publications. The microelectronics manufacturer's and plant operator's journal is *Semiconductor Products and Solid State Technology*. A tutorial seminar was held on this subject in 1963 by the Education and Research Association (NYC); the proceedings are $22.30.

PARAMETRIC AMPLIFICATION

by Bernard L. Walsh *

IN BRIEF: *As you well know if you have ever worked with them, the principal bugaboo of very sensitive amplifiers is noise. It's too bad, but the principles of operation of most available amplifiers inherently involve two of the worst offenders—thermal noise and shot noise, and these usually set the ultimate limits on sensitivity. However, there is, in principle, a way around this.*

* Bernard L. Walsh is a physicist-engineer with Hughes Aircraft in California.

Parametric amplifiers are a large class of circuits which, through variable reactance elements, transfer energy from "pump" power oscillators to signals. Many arrangements are possible: negative-resistance amplifiers, up-converters, down-converters, combinations and variations.

It all depends upon the frequencies involved (which range from 10^{-2} cps to about 10^{11} cps), the bandwidths required, the gain desired, the noise that can be tolerated, the devices avail-

able, and the ingenuity of the designers.—R.G.N.

■ In the middle 1950's, there was a sudden resurgence of interest in a principle that had been known at least since the last century, when there appeared papers on parametric equations (i.e., on linear equations with time-varying coefficients). These equations could, at least in theory, describe systems for amplification, but there were other, more straightforward, valve-like systems that could amplify small signals. So, although a paramp was used in radio-telephony before World War I, parametric amplication was generally neglected.

Why, then, the resurgence of interest? In the main, the answer is two-fold: the need for low-noise amplifiers and the availability of appropriate parametric devices with which to build them. What were needed were energy-storage devices whose properties could be varied with time so as to increase the signal energy stored in them.

But I'm getting ahead of my story. Let me back up and define what I mean by power-amplifier, so that we can particularize to the parametric amplifier.

Amplifying and parametizing

For my purpose, an amplifier is an input-output device whose output is an enlarged version of its input. Thus, a stiff beam with a fulcrum forms an amplifier; with it, enlargement of displacement *or* force is possible. Also, a transformer is an amplifier of voltage *or* of current. These and other such amplifiers meet the definition, yet they don't lead to more energy in their outputs than in their inputs.

An amplifier which increases the power—or, over time, the energy—of the output over the input I call a power amplifier. A vacuum tube (as used in, say, the last stage of a hi-fi set) is a power amplifier; so are many transistor and relay circuits. So are parametric amplifiers.

What's more, paramps are used as linear power amplifiers; over their operating ranges, the ratio of input to output is constant. A good many electronic power amplifiers are essentially (or sometimes ostensibly) linear power amplifiers. But the range of linearity of paramps is almost unlimited in theory, although it is somewhat limited in practice.

What sets the paramp apart from other linear power amplifiers is its extreme sensitivity. This comes from its very low internal noise. And the very low noise comes from its principle of operation. The rationale is this: The sensitivity of an amplifier is usually limited because the amplifier somehow degrades the input by generating signals similar enough to the input to be confused with it. These ambiguous signals (called noise) come from various sources within the amplifier, and its components. Thermal noise (the principal offender) is a consequence of the thermal agitations of electrons in thermal equilibrium and of the dissipation of energy within the circuit. In circuitry, the energy dissipators are termed resistances. Therein lies the important distinction between other power amplifiers and parametric amplifiers.

Most power amplifiers operate by causing signals to modulate some effective resistance, as does, say, the vacuum tube in the margin. The noise inherent in that resistance appears (amplified) in the output. In the case of electron emission devices (like vacuum tubes), there is also shot noise, i.e., the random fluctuation of current due to the fact that electrons are

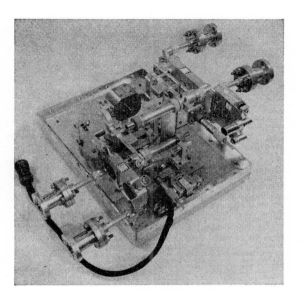

Fig. 1-128. From the depths of oceanography to the planetary probes, these low-noise amplifiers apply parametric principles from below 0.1 cps (seismic amplifiers, a above) to 950/2300 Mc (Mariner ground equipment, b right). (Courtesy Texas Instruments and Hughes Aircraft Co.)

emitted in random numbers and at random initial velocities.

The parametric amplifier has gained attention because signals are built up by modulating energy storage elements, and so paramps are inherently (I mean, theoretically and relatively) free from these noise effects. Paramps are sufficiently free from noise that many microwave systems, for example, use paramp-equipped receivers to get ten to a hundred times the sensitivity formerly available.

We said that a paramp works through modulation of energy storage devices (reactances). In electrical systems, the reactance can be a capacitance, which stores potential energy, an inductance, which stores kinetic energy, or a beam of electrons, which has both potential and kinetic energy. How can this time-varying reactance be made to amplify?

As an introduction to the idea, let me try an electro-mechanical analogy. We take a variable capacitor for the explanation since today it is the device most widely used and because it makes the explanation easy. Since it's just an analogy, let us imagine that the spacing between the plates of the capacitor can be varied, by an insulated rod attached between one of the plates and a reciprocating engine. We charge up the capacitor. Once one plate is positive and the other is negative, there is an attractive force between them.

Each time the engine pulls the plates of the capacitor apart it does work: it supplies some energy to the capacitor system. With no other electrical connection, the capacitor will return this energy to the reciprocating engine when the plates are brought closer on the return stroke.

However, in the illustration in the margin there is an inductor, L, connected to the capacitor. With the inductor connected to the charged capacitor, charges immediately begin to flow through the inductor to produce a current and, thus, magnetic energy. What was the potential energy of C is now all stored as the kinetic energy of charges flowing in L. Because of the currents through the inductor, a voltage is built up which re-charges the capacitor in the opposite polarity, and the process repeats itself. The rate of this oscillation is the familiar resonant frequency of the system; it is the frequency where the peak potential energy stored in C equals the peak kinetic energy stored in L.

Now if, during the very short interval when the capacitor is uncharged, or nearly so, the engine moves the plates in any way, capacitance changes without exchanging energy with our L-C circuit.

If we want to put energy into our system, therefore, we arrange to pull the capacitor

plate apart when they are fully charged. If we do so, the energy of the system will increase with time. This is the heart of the parametric process—the changing of one energy storage mechanism in a system which has at least two energy storage mechanisms.

One important point should be emphasized here. The reciprocating engine must pump the capacitor at a rate just twice the resonant frequency of our L-C system in order that energy be continually supplied to this system. A rate too slow or too fast or lacking the proper rhythm would not supply the system with energy efficiently. This requirement of timing or phasing of the pump, is important for parametric action. Because the oscillations in L and C will decay unless the phase of the pump falls within narrow limits, this arrangement is called a degenerate parametric amplifier. This phasing requirement is a stringent one; if this were the only way to get parametric action, there would be fewer paramps. Still, paramps have sometimes been used in this mode.

So far, we know how to enlarge a small oscillation in an L-C circuit by imparting to it energy from a pumped capacitor. However, we seem to have come up with more of a curiosity than a practical amplifier. One trouble is the awkward need for phasing between the signal and the pump. There is a way to circumvent this problem. We add another energy-storage device in Fig. 1-129a, a smaller inductor. And we mix the frequencies of our signal and our pumped capacitor.

Getting in step by mixing it up

The new circuit formed by inductor L_2 and the average value of our varying capacitor is resonant at a new higher frequency. This new frequency, f_i, will help us overcome the troublesome need for phasing the pump frequency, f_p, with the signal f_s.

We now have two circuits, L_1-C resonant at f_s and L_2-C resonant f_i. They are connected by our time-varying capacitor C. Now we cause the f_s circuit to oscillate by putting in a signal at its resonance from the outside. Then, if we change the capacity of C sinusoidally at a frequency $f_p = f_s + f_i$, we find that the f_i circuit also oscillates. It oscillates at its resonance, $f_i = f_p - f_s$.

This phenomenon is called the mixing of the pump (at f_p) and the signal (at f_s) in the time-varying capacitor. Mixing means the combination of two frequencies so as to produce additional frequencies which were not there to start with.

A way out of the phasing restriction now follows easily from the math. As we pump, the capacity of our condenser is given, at any moment by: $C = C_0 + C_1 \cos 2\pi f_p t$. Next we supply a signal voltage, $V = V_0 \cos (2\pi f_s t + \phi)$.

Then the instantaneous charge across C is the product of the varying voltage and the varying capacitance. A little analysis shows that new frequencies exist; these are the difference and the sum of those we started with as well as integral multiples of the sum and difference frequencies. The difference frequency is our f_i. The filters in Fig. 1-129b keep f_s and f_i in their respective loops and eliminate current at the sum frequency. We can now see how all this mixing takes up the slack in phase between the signal and our pump.

The result of the mixing (our so-called idle frequency, f_i) is phase coherent with f_s and f_p; if we shift the time at which peak current flows through L_1 by a quarter period's worth of f_s, the time at which peak current flows through L_2 will shift by a quarter period's worth of f_i. Thus the timing of events in the f_i circuit, comprised of L_2 and C, is dependent upon the phase of the pump, f_p and the signal, f_s. Another way to look at this "pulling" of f_i, is to say that we have defined the timing only of f_s and f_p, so f_i is free to take up the slack.

To have energy transfer from the pump to the f_s circuit, we need two things: (1) instants when the total charge, from f_s and f_i, on the plates of the time-varying capacitor is zero (so the plates can be collapsed without removing energy from the circuits at f_s and f_i), and (2), that these $q = 0$ times occur when the pump is exerting maximum force to collapse the capacitor plates. This second requirement demands that the intervals be of the proper length and the correct phase. Once again, a little math comes to the rescue to show we have both: We let the charge on time-varying C due to f_s be $q_s = \sin 2\pi f_s t$ and that due to f_i be $q_i = \sin 2\pi f_i t$. The total charge at any time is

$$q = \sin 2\pi f_s t + \sin 2\pi f_i t$$

or

$$q = 2 \sin \pi (f_s + f_i) t \cos \pi (f_s - f_i) t$$

Whenever the first term of this expression is zero, the total charge, q, is zero. This happens once each full period of pumping. So we have a situation here similar to the case of the degenerate paramp where the total charge on C was zero once every pump period. Further analysis shows that the pump closes the plates at these critical times.

The circuit in Fig. 1-129b which exhibits amplification *without* a phasing requirement between f_s and f_p is called a nondegenerate, 3-frequency paramp. We have f_p, the pump frequency; it supplies the energy to build up f_s, which is the signal. And we have f_i, which results from the mixing action of f_s and f_p and which supplies the necessary phase adjustment. Although f_i is called the "idle" or "idler" frequency (because in many actual amplifiers, it never leaves the confines of its resonant circuit), there are forms of paramps in which the idle frequency is not so idle, and in which power at f_i is the output delivered to an external load.

You may have noticed two disturbing things about the circuit so far. For one thing, there's no sign of how it connects to the outside world—no hint of an input or an output. Besides, the signal to be amplified grew across the same set of terminals where it was initially present.

To solve the first problem, we just insert a load resistor, R_l, between L_1 and the ideal filter and a signal generator (represented by an ac source and R_g). Fine.

Go in and out the paramp

However now the growing voltage across the varying reactor, C, is divided between the generator and the load resistors; that's not quite ideal. We want this growing voltage to be across R_1 alone so that the full output of our amplifier goes into the load. There are ways, and good ways (which we can't go into here), to achieve this kind of enhanced reflection of the signal. The methods vary with frequency and other design constraints, but the purpose of all of them is to ensure that the amplified signal is delivered entirely to the load rather

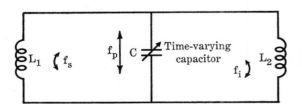

Fig. 1-129a. A major limitation of the degenerate circuit in the margin (its critical dependence on phasing between f_p and f_s) is circumvented in this nondegenerate circuit by adding inductor L_2.

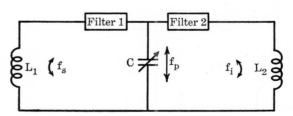

Fig. 1-129b. However, filters must be added to Fig. 1-129a to insure that the signal (f_s) and idler (f_i) currents remain in their respective loops and are coupled only by C. Next step is Fig. 1-129c.

than shared between the load and source re-sistances.

But there is still the fact that the signal grows across the same terminals where it was initially present. This type of amplification is different from that associated with a triode, for example, where the input is applied to the grid circuit terminals and appears amplified in the plate circuit. The amplification exhibited by the paramp is said to be due to a negative resistance, because the effect is just the oppo-site of the energy-dissipating effect of an ordinary resistor. There are other kinds of amplifiers (some tunnel diode circuits for ex-ample) which operate in the negative-resistance mode. Unfortunately, this mode has a reputa-tion for instability and criticality of adjust-ment. A slight change in either the load or the negative resistance itself will drastically change a paramp's gain or cause it to go into oscilla-tion, wildly generating renegade signals. It's tricky, but it's workable.

All of this brings us, at last, to consider the stability of parametric amplifiers. If the load resistance remains constant, we can confine our attentions to the negative resistance. The nega-tive resistance in a paramp depends upon sev-eral items: the nature of the pump power, the closeness of the idler and signal circuits to their resonance frequencies, and the nature of the varying reactor.

To stabilize the bouncing mirror

Working paramps tolerate little deviation in the frequency or the power of their pumps. Particularly in microwave systems, this entails some difficulties in actual service. There, the pump requires precise, stable dc supplies. The upshot is that the pump oscillator and parts of the dc supply must be temperature controlled and be mechanically rigid to minimize varia-tions of critical dimensions during vibration and shock. For a 10–20% gain stability require-ment, the necessary equipment becomes quite expensive; for a stability of 1% or less, the cost is almost prohibitive. Good amplifiers are

expensive. Some circuitry steps can be taken to relieve the burden on the pump and its dc supply—but they usually increase the noise of the paramp. However, those are the choices available, with the devices currently available.

At microwave frequencies where most of the present work is being done, we need devices that can be varied at 10^8–10^{11} cps. A reciprocating engine with a pair of metal plates would hardly do. There are two considerations—we need a variable reactor (varactor for short), and a pump capable of driving the reactance. For microwaves, several available oscillators nicely fulfill our pump needs. They all require that the varactor vary because of the applied voltage or current.

There is yet another restriction on varactors. They must have very little resistance at their operating frequencies. In our foregoing explana-tions, we assumed that the reactor had no re-sistance. You don't need a mathematical proof to see that adding an energy-dissipator to the varying reactance will reduce the output energy available and damp out the idler oscillation. In fact, if the resistance is too large, there can be no amplification. Resistance will also in-crease the noise of the paramp.

In the light of the foregoing, it is surprising that anything can be found with the right properties. However, I assure you that if there were no suitable varactors for high frequen-cies, this article would not have been written.

A solid-state reciprocating plate-puller

Long ago, people noticed that the capacitance of semiconductor rectifiers varied with applied dc voltage. In some circuits, these diodes ex-hibited negative resistance; the negative re-sistance was shown to result from the variable capacitance and the very low loss in the diode.

To see, in an elementary way, how this works, consider the semiconductor junction of a diode. Where the p-type and n-type ma-terials meet, there is a transition region, some-times called a depletion layer. When the junc-tion is formed, electrons migrate from the de-pletion layer to the p-region and holes to the n-region. So, the depletion region has relatively few charge carriers: it's an insulator.

The equilibrium charge distribution is not zero in a p-n junction as it is in the materials separately. Instead, the charge forms a dipole layer, positive on one side and negative on the other. Physically, it's like a parallel plate ca-pacitor. If we apply a voltage, the holes will be attracted to the $(-)$ potential and the elec-trons to the $(+)$. The resulting migration moves the net charge distribution away from the depletion layer. The capacitance decreases, as in a capacitor when its plates are separated.

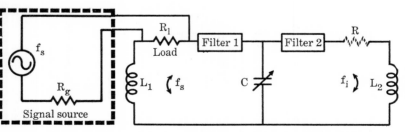

Fig. 1-129c. Connection with the outside world is now provided by a resistor between L_1 and the f_s filter. Now the signal grows across the same terminals through which it entered.

Reversing the voltage increases the capacitance of the junction.

Diodes used this way also have nonlinear resistance, the property that produces the rectification everyone thinks of when diodes are mentioned. However, in paramps, this resistance is usually very high (in the static case) and designers are careful to keep diode currents below a few microamps dc, so as to minimize the effects of this nonlinearity. Current across the depletion layer produces "shot noise." Shot effect (the discrete emission of carriers) is a very important nonthermal noise source. It is hoped (and generally confirmed) that these sources of noise are very small in paramps using varactor diodes to get low-noise amplification.

While in practical paramps there are noise sources other than the varactors, such noises can usually be reduced to the point where the diode junction is the dominant noise source. The minimum noise, contributed by a varactor diode, can be predicted. It turns out to be proportional to the diode junction temperature.

The answer: cool it

So far, we have considered the diode junction at room temperature (300°K). One way to reduce the noise from the diode is to lower its junction temperature—provided the diode isn't destroyed or degraded as the temperature is lowered. As a matter of experimental fact, junction temperatures have been lowered to the temperature of liquid nitrogen (78°K) and even liquid helium (4.2°K) with an observed reduction in noise. In fact paramps, using gallium arsenide varactors in a liquid helium bath, have recently shown noise levels comparable to those of ruby masers. I think this wedding of cryogenics and parametric amplifiers will lead to major advances in the important 1 to 10 Gc range.

Besides diodes which act as variable capacitors, ferrites can be used as variable inductors in paramps. Energy is transferred from a pump magnetic field to perpendicular signal and idler fields through the modulation of the precession angle between a bias field and the magnetization vector of the ferrite (see the margin sketch). A ferrite paramp built along these lines is shown in Fig. 1-130.

Unfortunately, the noise of ferrite paramps reported to date has been higher than predicted by simple theory and they have other practical problems. So they haven't yet been applied in systems. However, a great deal of effort is being directed at these problems because ferrites maintain their highly reactive properties over a very broad range of frequencies—up into the sub-infrared region. Besides, ferrites remain

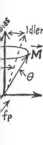

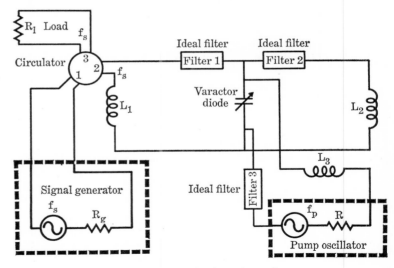

Fig. 1-129d. In some paramps, a circulator is used to direct f_s so that incoming signals go only to L_1-C circuit and outgoing amplified signals go to the load. In this circuit, a pump oscillator has been added, with its filter, to drive the variable capacitor at f_p.

almost pure reactances far from their pump frequencies and this could lead to a whole new class of low-noise amplifiers capable of covering a very wide band.

On gaining steadily over a band

In the previous explanation, we confined ourselves to two or three exact frequencies. What happens if one or all three frequencies change slightly? Does the amplifier quit working? The answer is no. The paramp does not operate as well as when the frequencies involved are those for which circuits are resonant, but it does work. By "not as well," I mean that the power gain is not as great as at resonance, and that the noise increases slightly. How far can we go before this power gain changes to half of

Fig. 1-130. An alternative to the diode junction used as a capacitor is a ferrite used as a variable inductor (small black cylinder at top). (Courtesy Hughes Aircraft Co.)

its former value? The actual number of cps is limited partly by the nonlinear reactor and partly by circuit design. In any event, this spread is called the bandwidth (expressed either in cps, or as a percent).

This does not necessarily mean that, for a particular application, the amplifier is of no use outside these points nor that it is useable everywhere inside these boundaries. The useful region is determined by the application. It is a property of the nondegenerate paramp circuit in Fig. 1-129b that the power gain times the percentage bandwidth is a constant for given circuit values; the higher we make the gain, the narrower the bandwidth becomes. (It is important to note that the foregoing relationship does not apply for more complicated circuits than we have considered here.) What gain-bandwidth product is achievable with no circuit restrictions is a question that has not yet been answered completely.

The dynamic range of a parametric amplifier is limited on the low side by the noise level and on the high side by the nonlinearity of the varactor. On the high side, the signal must be kept small enough so that if it alone were applied to the varactor diode, the capacitance of the diode would remain sensibly constant. Obviously, this depends on the nature of the nonlinearity and on what we mean by sensibly constant. In practice, it happens that when the signal input is some 10^{-5} to 10^{-6} watts, the gain decreases through a lack of energy transfer from the pump because of the diode's nonlinearity.

Finally, we have the nearness of the signal and idle frequencies to the resonance of the tuned circuits, as it affects gain. In most designs, signal frequencies pretty far from the exact resonance can still be handled quite well. In fact, the gain-bandwidth product is determined to a great extent by the idle frequency. If the idler is at 10^4 Mc and the bandwidth is 10 Mc, a change in the idle circuit, due either to temperature or vibration, of a part in 2×10^3 will change the gain by a factor of 2. This means signal and idler circuits must be mechanically rigid and temperature controlled.

Variations on a swing

Feedback circuits and comparison circuits have been tried in attempts to increase gain stability and so ease things for other components, but these are limited in application. We must face the fact that the gain stability is bought at a price; in those attempts, it's noise.

Another way to increase the gain-bandwidth product is with multiple varactors. Each varactor contributes a little to the total amplification over a broad band as the wave of signal energy progresses past it in what is called traveling-wave paramp. Multiple tuning has also resulted in single-diode paramps with gain-bandwidth products as high as 4500 Mc. In these cases, the penalty is in dollars.

We have discussed in fair detail just one degenerate paramp and one type of nondegenerate paramp, one which uses a single variable capacitor to couple its resonant circuits, has a single idler, and has identical input and output frequencies. There are as many other types of paramps as you can imagine by merely altering those characterizations. Parametric devices of various kinds have been operated at frequencies from a fraction of one cps to several gigacycles.

Usually still another mode (called quasi-degenerate) is employed, in which the signal and idle frequencies are slightly separated, and both are connected so that energy at either is amplified. This mode is quite useful for those applications where signals are present at both frequencies, e.g., radio astronomy, and where the phase of the signal input is unknown.

The mixing process, in which the pump and the signal create f_i by means of nonlinear elements, also leads to the formation of other frequencies. Those frequencies which are the sums of the signal and integral multiples of the pump frequency are called upper-sidebands. Those involving the difference frequencies are the lower sidebands. The lower sidebands (integral multiples of f_p, each minus f_s) enable us to surmount another restriction of our basic circuit—using them, we can build paramps in which f_p is below f_s.

Real live swingin' paramps

Another important use of varactors is sometimes considered as parametric amplification. The Manley-Rowe relationships between frequency and power (which sum up all these possibilities) tell us that, if power is converted in a pumped nonlinear reactance from a lower frequency to a higher one, the power out at the higher frequency will be increased by the ratio of the frequencies. Properly, a circuit using this mode is called a converter and it is used, with or without the negative resistance effect, to provide low-noise amplification. The noise levels are the same as those for the nondegenerate paramp, although the possible gains are not as large as with the paramp unless negative resistance is involved—which, of course, makes the device a combination converter-parametric amplifier. Such techniques have been applied to very low as well as high

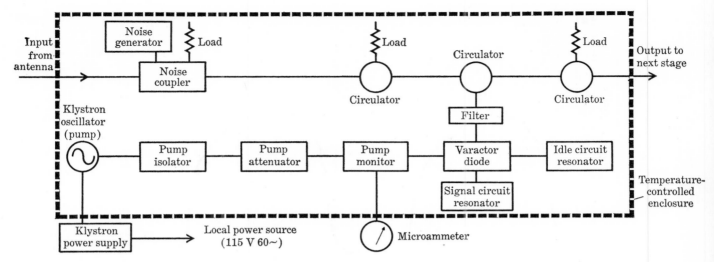

Fig. 1-129e. A paramp and its auxiliaries as it might be found in a ground antenna station. Blocks labeled circuit resonators are here to indicate their necessity, although at some frequencies, they may exist only as parts of the varactor package and the pump waveguide walls.

frequencies. Figure 1-128a shows an up-converter adapted for use on ocean-bottom seismometer covering the 0.1 to 200 cps range.

So far, not much has been said about actual hardware. In Fig. 1-129e we have a block diagram of a paramp as it might appear in a microwave system. First, there is a varactor. The important part is rarely visible in most designs—it's a semiconductor diode with a volume about 10^{-5} cubic inches, encased in a metal and dielectric package for mechanical protection and to provide electrical connections. The packages are generally cylindrical and range from ¾ to ⅒ in. long and ¼ to ½₀ in. in diameter. Unfortunately, these dimensions are comparable to the wavelengths involved and so the package contributes various non-negligible circuit elements, not always desired.

Since at microwave frequencies, inductors are rarely coils of wire, and capacitors rarely two parallel plates, it is hard to see circuit elements as actually existing in the hardware. However they are there, although they may exist only as part of the diode package and as boundaries of the hollow pump waveguide.

At any rate this varactor diode, encased in various hollow metal structures, is actually the parametric amplifier. In many cases there are mechanical adjustments for tuning over a wide range of signal and idle frequencies and to accommodate variations among varactors. Most often too, the filter in Fig. 1-129e isn't separate from the amplifier but it is built into it.

In Fig. 1-128b are two paramps adjusted to different frequencies but using a common pump and attached to a plate which temperature-controls all the microwave circuitry. These amplifiers improve the sensitivity of NASA's Deep Space Instrumentation Facility by a factor of

ten, allowing spacecraft to be heard from three times farther than before.

Besides being used in airborne and ground-based radars, and in spacecraft communication systems, microwave paramps are used in radio astronomy, in microwave radiometers, in point to point communications, and in troposcatter systems. Paramps have also been used for calibration of secondary "noise" or temperature standards. At much lower frequencies, paramps are just beginning to show up as very low noise amplifiers for seismograph, biomedical and other small signal applications. As new devices and techniques become available, these variable reactance amplifiers should find many (as yet, unanticipated) uses. Who knows? Someone may even invent that mechanical paramp, the playground swing.

Fig. 1-131. Here's a flyable paramp with its pump (in the temperature-controlled housing at the upper right) and its circulator (with its input and output ports showing at left). (Courtesy Hughes Aircraft Co.)

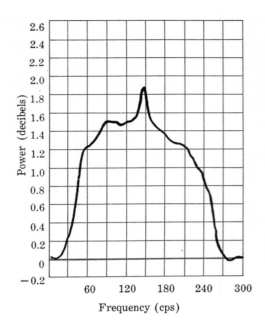 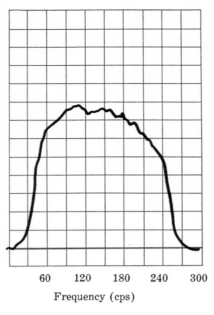 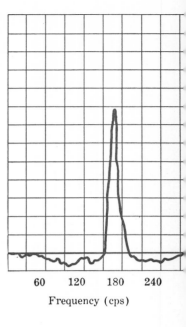

Further reading

One rarely comes across a serious publication on parametric circuits that doesn't reference the famous Manley and Rowe paper "Some General Properties of Nonlinear Elements—Part I, General Energy Relations," *Proc. IRE,* **44,** 904 (1956) or Rowe's "Some General Properties of Nonlinear Elements—Part II, Small Signal Theory," *Proc. IRE,* **46,** 850 (1958). There's a good reason why; these papers laid the foundation for much of the current work, most of which continues to find its way into that same journal. For example, see the Feb. 1963 issue, which has a very interesting article by Baird, "Low-Frequency Reactance Amplifiers."

A good, useful, but slightly dated, introduction to paramps appears in "Low-Noise, Solid-State Microwave Amplifiers" by Haun and Osial, which appeared in Vol. 64, No. 4 (1959),

of the old *Electrical Manufacturing* (now *Electro-Technology*). Reprints are still available, at $1.

Adashko has translated into English the Russian book *Nonlinear and Parametric Phenomena in Radio Engineering* by Kharkevich, which includes a nice description of the principles and is addressed to practical engineers (Rider, 1960, $6.50). A much more thorough treatment on a slightly more technical level is *Coupled Mode and Parametric Electronics* by Louisell (Wiley, 1960, $11.50), while a good treatment of how ferrites fit into paramps appears in *Microwave Ferrites and Ferrimagnetics* by Lax and Button (McGraw-Hill, 1962, $16.50).

Finally, if you've forsaken television uhf converters and other commercial mousetraps for a military contract, you'll probably find the hottest paramp data at the nearest ASTIA office.

FERRETING SIGNALS OUT OF NOISE

by Solomon W. Golomb *

IN BRIEF: *In principle at least, all problems of detection and measurement, all problems of seeking, sending, and sorting signals are problems in statistical communications theory. To handle such a gamut, the theory must be a very powerful and a very general one. It is.*

However, as with other general theories, simplifying (and restrictive) assumptions are usually made to fit it to specific applications, most of which have been in the electronic com-

munications and data-handling arts. Even though the significance of those simplifying assumptions has not always been fully appreciated in practice, the theory has given some surprisingly successful results. Now some non-electronic problems (and the non-electronic parts of some heretofore "electronic" problems) are being approached with the methods of communications theory.

Especially in the light of these new applications, it's time to go back to the general theory, and to reappraise the current forms of such basic notions as channels (and what they in-

* Solomon W. Golomb is Professor of Electrical Engineering and Mathematics at the University of Southern California, Los Angeles.

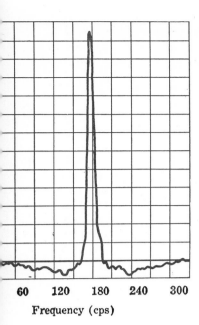

Frequency (cps)

Fig. 1-132. In this case, the signal is a radar echo of about 10^{-20} watts, being used by JPL's Goldstone radar facility to measure the distance to Venus to within about 5 parts in 10^8. To determine how fast Venus rotates, the 10kW transmitter was repeatedly pulsed on and off. Five minutes later, the returning signal auto-correlated (i.e., matched against itself) and passed through a filter, presented the spectrum at extreme left for the transmitter on-times.

When Richard Goldstein subtracted the noise-only spectrum (of the transmitter off-times), he got a spectrum less than 10 cps wide at a radio frequency of 2388 Mc. Since a rough, rotating planet would have Doppler-spread the reflection more than that, and since other measurements had indicated some surface roughness, he concluded that Venus rotates less than once each 100 days. The experiment also demonstrates how the echo—and its story— emerges more and more clearly as the integration time (the time over which the signal is gathered and processed) increases. (Courtesy CalTech Jet Propulsion Laboratory)

clude), bits and error rates (and their significance), and noise (and the appropriateness of the statistical procedures being applied to it). —R.G.N.

■ A reader peruses the verbiage in this article, looking for useful data; a control commissioner processes a seismograph record for evidence of nuclear explosions hidden in earthquake noise; a bacteriological-warfare officer examines a liter of air for dangerous organisms amid inorganic dust, organic waste particles, and innocuous bugs. Each requires the extraction of a needle of "signal" from a haystack of "noise." Just as a weed is a plant out of place, noise is the wrong signal or the right signal out of place. (And of course, one man's weed is another man's petunia.)

So, it is understandable that researchers in many areas have been looking desperately for solutions to their problems of detecting and identifying weak phenomena hidden in formidable backgrounds. That search has led to statistical communications theory, which has been so widely hailed as the answer to certain signal and noise problems in electronic communications.

The newcomer from another field reasonably expects the terminology to reflect this background. What he may not expect is that (especially for his individual purposes) most of the recent published results in this field are themselves noise, in the particular sense I mentioned above. Special pieces of the general truths (and special techniques) have been developed for restricted classes of problems—sometimes in disregard of the larger, more general problems and theory.

Some of this will become apparent as we abstract a general pattern—one which applies more or less to all problems of this type. This we can do by considering a few basic ideas as they have emerged from the background of the literature.

Shannon's channel, and others

One of the most basic of these is the idea of the noisy channel in a general signal-handling system (i.e., in a general communications system). It can be represented like this:

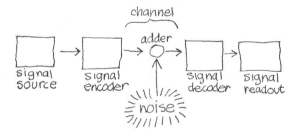

The signal starts at a "source," and goes to a device that prepares it for transmission over the channel. Preparatory devices take various forms—modulators in radio transmitters, semaphore flags on ships—but the essential feature is the interface between the source and the channel. The significance of the channel is that in the channel itself, some form of noise (sometimes called the background) is added to the signal. At the receiver, we detect the signal-plus-noise, extract the signal from the noise as best we can, and send it to its final destination.

Gradually, the art has evolved this realistically appropriate (though negative-sounding) definition: The channel is that part of any system which the experimenter doesn't control— the part he is unable or unwilling to change. (An obvious but inadequately appreciated consequence: The dimensions of that channel vary markedly from one experimental situation to another.)

When Shannon revolutionized our thinking about information and communication in 1948, he talked about a channel the way it might appear to a telegraph company. Customers come in with messages. We analyze them statistically, and send short codewords for the frequent messages and long codewords for the infrequent ones. So we might end up sending 73 to mean "Best Regards" and 88 for "Love and Kisses" (as did the ham radio operators in the days before Shannon made it all quantitative and rigorous). But the problem is quite different from the customer's point of view.

Long after the telegraph company has solved its problem of efficient channel utilization, the customer must still solve *his* problem of economical and unambiguous channel utilization. That customer has further problems: The company's efficient coding and error-correcting schemes for *typical* messages might have a distorting (a noise-introducing) effect on cleverly contrived messages; also, the company's message-handling and coding systems, a part of the customer's channel, are largely unknown to him. Clearly, different parts of the same system are the channel for people in different situations.

To the telephone subscriber, everything between his mouthpiece and his listener's earphone is the channel. His only option is to speak more distinctly, or repeat his message, or take other measures outside of what for him is the channel. For example, if he knows the characteristics of the telephone system, he can alter his message to increase its chances of correct interpretation.

However, to the phone company, such things as better cables, and improved switching and transmitting equipment, are also conceivable alternatives. For them, the channel is a much smaller portion of the over-all system, because there are fewer things which they are unable to change. The importance of the channel to the noise it introduces carries with it an obvious, but all too often overlooked lesson to anyone trying to design a system for separating signals from noise.

First lesson: Know thy channel

The first (perhaps most important) step is to determine the channel characteristics, i.e., the uncontrollable parameters of the system. These include a statistical description of those features that cannot be described deterministically (and then "calibrated out"). All too often, unfortunately, it has been fashionable, at least in the literature, to postulate those statistical distributions that most dramatically display the author's virtuosity at analytical manipulation, instead of determining noise statistics experimentally.

The matter is complicated when, as sometimes happens, the noise-contributing characteristics of a channel change from time to time, or, even while it's being used. (Examples are the sonar propagation conditions of the oceans under a traveling ship and the properties of the telephone lines for different service routings.) For some such situations, systems have been demonstrated which send prearranged test signals through the channel so that the receiver can compare them with its own models of what the test should look like. The comparison gives some information on the channel characteristics, and this information is then used to (automatically) alter the equipment outside the channel, so as to improve the over-all system performance.

But whether it's done automatically (as in some computer-telephone links) or manually (in a less controllable system), the first commandment for designers of signal extraction systems should be "Know Thy Channel!"

Given the best attainable description of the channel, the next step is to determine the optimum detection scheme. That is, one needs a method of distinguishing two noisy signals, a method which is insensitive to the characteristics of the channel or to the noises in it.

This raises an important dichotomy among signal-detection problems—the naturally produced signal (whose source is really part of the channel, since the experimenter has no control over it) vs. the artificially produced signal (which the experimenter can shape to his own purposes). For example, the radio astronomer receiving signals from remote galaxies clearly has no control over the signals he is trying to identify. On the other hand, a designer of tracking radar systems chooses the basic waveforms, or pulse trains, which he transmits; then, after they are reflected back at him with some noise added, he tries to interpret them. Obviously, he has an excellent idea of what the original signal looked like: He produced it himself.

These cases are actually near-extrema of a wide spectrum of signal-handling problems, of various channel lengths. Perusing that spectrum, one can readily see the importance of the experimenter's degree of control of the form of the signals produced.

Channels in point

Consider first the case of space telemetry, where we can control the shape of the signal, and where we know something of the channel statistics. (The channel's contribution to the

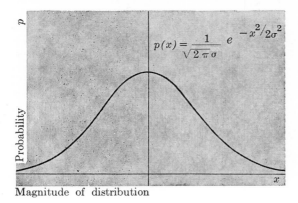

$$p(x) = \frac{1}{\sqrt{2\pi}\,\sigma}\, e^{-x^2/2\sigma^2}$$

Magnitude of distribution

Fig. 1-133. It's no accident that these "normal distributions" keep coming up in physical, economic, and even social science situations. The Central Limit Theorem of probability theory says that as more and more independent random phenomena, each having a probability distribution (with finite σ^2) are added, the result looks more and more Gaussian. So even when we "generalize" communication theory to detection situations unrelated to radio, the noise resulting from adding many small disturbances looks Gaussian.

variance =
$$\sigma^2 = \frac{\sum_{i=1}^{n} x_i^2}{n}$$

received signal is mostly receiver noise, rather than instabilities in the interplanetary medium.) The available evidence indicates the best way to describe the resulting effect is as "white Gaussian noise"—"white" because the noise is equally distributed over all frequencies of interest (but not *all* frequencies, because, strictly speaking, a constant energy level through *all* frequencies implies infinite total energy), and "Gaussian" because the probability, $p(x)\,dx$, of finding a disturbance within dx of magnitude x is described by the normal law (and is shown in Fig. 1-133).

For this important kind of noise, the optimum detector is one that compares the noisy incoming signal against descriptions of all the possible signals and selects the best fit. The proper method of comparison is correlation, where the noisy signal, $g(t) = f(t) + noise(t)$, is correlated (compared) for a time t against each possible $f(t)$, to find correlation coefficients, c_i as shown in the margin. When these expressions are normalized (so that a very loud $g(t)$ doesn't override all the others), the best fit gives the biggest c.

For the signals obscured with white Gaussian noise, it is now known that a set of waveforms like those in Fig. 1-134, are as un-alike as possible, that is, they have the least mutual correlation (which turns out to be a negative correlation of $-1/(n - 1)$, where n is the number of waveforms).

In Fig. 1-133, we see how a signal emerges more and more clearly from the noise as the integration time in the correlator increases. In such circumstances, where we know the

c_{ij} = correlation between any 2 of these = $\int_0^t f_i(t)f_j(t)\,dt = -\frac{1}{7}$, for $i \neq j$
$= +1$, for $i = j$

channel characteristics and can design the most appropriate signals, a few watts of transmitter power on a satellite can be heard and interpreted at interplanetary ranges.

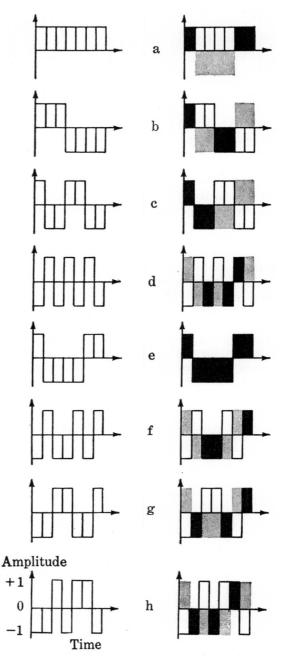

Amplitude
+1
0
−1

Time

Fig. 1-134. The optimum (in the sense that they are mutually distinguishable) choice of several normalized waveforms has mutual negative correlation. That is, if we compare any one of them (say, waveform e) against all the others), we find that it has more areas of disagreement (gray) than areas of agreement (black). In this simplex code of eight normalized waveforms, each mismatch has a correlation of $-1/(n - 1) = -\frac{1}{7}$; each waveform's correlation with itself is $+1$.

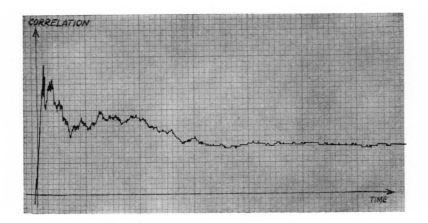

Another case we could consider is range radar. The round-trip distance to the target is, of course, equal to the velocity of the signal times the round-trip signal delay. The characteristics of the reflecting surface are part of the channel statistics, since they change the signal in a non-determined (an unpredictable) way.

An appropriate waveform is a modification of the code shown in Fig. 1-134. It is a binary simplex code composed of seven units of $+1$ and -1 (such binary codes are easily implemented with digital equipment) and has a negative correlation with each of its own shifted forms. Since the shifted waveforms are maximally distinguishable from one another, the delay of the round trip time (i.e., the range) can be extracted by correlation detection, even in the presence of considerable distortion. See Fig. 1-136.

The noise doesn't really have to be "white" or "Gaussian" for correlation detection to be optimum; but it is hard to find, in a mathematically rigorous way, the most general conditions under which it is optimum. The appropriateness of correlation detection is one of those really basic facts of life that transcends the hypotheses under which it is proved. Basically, comparing what comes in against the things it might have been is a darn good strategy, unless you have a really peculiar system. Generalizing somewhat, a good detector is a device that responds selectively to its "trigger signal" with a strong indication, while ignoring all spurious candidates.

In voice telephony, the communications engineer cannot decide what will be said, but he does have access to the voice before and after it is on the line. If he wishes, he may use "prechannel processing." In one clever example, the voice is broken up, by Fourier analysis, into its spectral components, like this:

$$a_0 + a_1 \cos t + b_1 \sin t + a_2 \cos t + b_2 \sin t + \ldots$$

Then, the first few Fourier coefficients are transmitted, and reassembled at the receiver to reproduce a fairly good replica of the original sound. Systems in this category (systems such as Bell Labs' Vocoder) require detailed knowledge of the bandwidth and other characteristics of speech and hearing, but do not necessarily require control of the vocal and auditory processes involved.

A more difficult problem is the discrimination of the seismic signals produced by nuclear explosions from other seismic disturbances. Although the engineer can't control the shape of the signals he is interested in detecting, he can, in principle, perform controlled experiments to

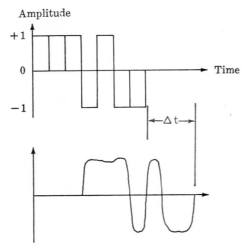

Fig. 1-136. This adaptation of the simplex code shown in Fig. 1-134 is ideal for range radar. Here, our signal is composed of seven units of plus ones and minus ones, and the signal has mutual negative correlation with each of its phase shifts. The phase shift between outgoing and incoming waveforms is proportional to range, so this system of correlation detection works well for ranging, even with considerable waveform distortion.

learn about their statistical character. (That is, it is technically feasible to perform such experiments, although the political feasibility changes from week to week.)

Then there's the poor radio astronomer; he has no control of the processes which produce his signals. As a result, his detection of weak signals is difficult, and the diagnosis of even relatively strong signals is subject to considerable error. Besides, there is very little that a radio astronomer can do to test the effect of the intergallactic medium on his signals—except for pious calculations. In his situation, the most that can be done is to improve his receiving equipment (it is already pushing the theoretical performance limits for sensitivity) and to construct working hypotheses about his source and other unavailable parts of his channel and derive various tests to confirm or refute them.

Some character and life in the channel

Our next example of a noisy channel is character recognition, particularly machine reception and recognition of messages sent by human communicators using various signal alphabets. The troublesome part of such a system is, of course, the encoder in the channel (i.e., the person in the channel).

The recognition of hand-printed block letters, cursive handwriting and speech are all difficult problems, and it is not surprising that the engineer assigned to them attempts to impose standardization on the human transmitter producing these signals. Certainly, the engineer's job is much easier if he can convert the problem from one of naturally produced signals to one of artificially produced signals, where he can choose the shape of the signals for optimum distinguishability. (An example of such stylization is the ERMA magnetic-ink system which has suddenly become common on bank checks.)

The biological sciences offer many problems of the detection of very specific small signals in random (and sometimes rather ambiguous) backgrounds. As a final example, consider the detection of a minute concentration of a specific organism. Several types of detectors may be appropriate. For example, a microbe may feed selectively on a particular nutrient, which can then be used as a signal amplifier. It was through the discovery and successful application of this principle of "biological amplification" that Joshua Lederberg received the Nobel Prize in 1958. This idea of getting a single particle of organism to grow, with the reliability of biological replication, into a macroscopically visible plaque on a nutrient medium has been successfully used to detect mutated forms of various organisms.

Another approach to organism-detection is to use the antibody-antigen reaction. That is, to diagnose a disease such as smallpox, we might test a sample of a suspected medium to see if it evokes a characteristic antibody response in a host tissue culture already immunized to the disease.

Problems of this sort can also be approached with sequences of tests on a sample of the signal. By listing the answers to the test questions, we can classify our specimen. In effect, this "catalog" routine is an elaborate switching network, which routes the sample from main trunks to sidings, and finally to its own pigeonhole. When we have a problem of classification (which letter of the alphabet is at hand?), it is a matter of finding the appropriate "matched filter," the device or procedure which exhibits very little response to any stimulus other than its "matched" signal. (Is it indeed the TB bacillus, or the "Start World War III" command coming through?!)

The strategy of ferreting these signals out of these noisy channels is quite different than for those we considered earlier. There, the problems primarily involved designing mutually distinguishable signals, so that, even after noise is added, it is relatively easy to distinguish them one from the other. (How *should* we design the letters of the alphabet so that, even at a distance, they are easy to tell apart?)

A little bit of significance

Now suppose we ask how noisy is any of the channels we considered. To answer this, we go back to our very elementary picture of a channel and consider what might happen to a very elementary piece of information—a yes or a no, a + or −, a 0 or 1—a *one-bit decision* between two equally likely outcomes. It's the amount of data needed to tell whether a perfect coin lands head or tails.

If the coin is crooked, and the probability, p, of it landing heads does not equal the probability, $q = 1 - p$, of it landing tails, there is less information involved. As Shannon showed, the answer to a $p:q$ question contains only $p \log_2 p^{-1} + q \log_2 q^{-1}$ bits, and this is less than 1 bit, unless $p = q = \frac{1}{2}$. The information which answers the p vs. q question, is written $H(p, q)$ and is variously called the entropy or the uncertainty.

When we ask our system the answer to a yes-or-no question, the noisy answer comes back in varying degrees of maybe. In other words, the 1 or 0 we should get from the experiment can only be believed with a probability of p. In this case, the minimum number of questions needed to resolve 2^n situations positively is some number $n/[1 - H(p, q)]$, which is more than n if p is not 1. That is, one must ask redundant

ERMA
NUMERALS

questions to combat the noise. The fraction of the bits that are in error is called the bit error rate, and appears as a noise specification for many data-handling systems.

However, there is a curious but important aside: This $n/[1 - H(p, q)]$ only applies if the "maybes" are independent. If the errors in the bits are somehow *related,* we have not lost quite as much information; therefore, it is not necessary to ask quite so many questions. Shannon pointed this out first—that the bit-error-rate is not the most appropriate performance criterion. He defines the *equivocation* as the minimum bit rate needed to correct all the errors using a parallel noiseless channel, connected like this:

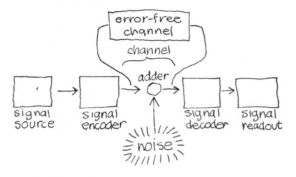

—and *this* is the right measure of the performance of a system.

My own favorite example is this: Suppose you know that a faulty switch has caused every second bit of a received message to be wrong, and you don't know whether it's the even bits or the odd ones. The bit-error criterion says that half the bits are right and half are wrong, and you don't know which are which, so there is no information coming through. (You could guess and be right half the time without any channel at all!) But the equivocation criterion says you only need one additional bit of information to specify whether the even bits or the odd bits should be reversed; so if the message was 10,000 bits long, the received information is 9999 bits!

The significance of significance

In this way, we arrive at a precise definition for the elusive and seeming metaphysical concept of relative significance of information bits. The significance of a bit of information at the source is proportional to the influence it exerts on the final processed data which reaches the signal designation.

Thus, if we know what data-reduction scheme will be used, we can apply straightforward, un-metaphysical, numerical analysis to settle the question of the relative significance of the component bits. Then we can use our insight into

the relative significance of the bits to "beat the system."

The dependence of bit significance on the data-reduction process at the end of the channel is dramatically demonstrated by biological data-reduction systems. For example, the intended destination of a TV picture is not a cathode-ray tube; it's somebody's head. The eyes pick it up; the brain processes it. So part of the problem is: What do the human perceptions do to the incoming visualization?

One process that certainly goes on is "local averaging." A checkerboard of small squares, alternately black and white, looks *gray* at a distance. The effect of this data-reduction process is that there are actually situations where the deliberate addition of noise improves the recognizability of the message.

Suppose a typical TV picture is sent over a channel which sends each dot in the scan as one of only four shades ranging from "black" to "white." The picture at the receiver will be a rather bleak silhouette. In 1961, L. G. Roberts of M.I.T. added some random noise at the transmitter end before quantizing some pictures to black, dark gray, light gray, and white. His transmissions, thus modified, generally resulted in *more* recognizable pictures, whether or not the channel adds in noise of its own!

To explain this paradox, we must first recognize that the result holds only for pictures with recognizable pattern and continuity. Such pictures are of course the rule for television, but the exception from the mathematical viewpoint that all possible juxtapositions of data should be equally likely. That is, pictures with recognizable patterns are statistically very special, and for *these signals* the quantization into black, dark gray, light gray, and white produces a stark silhouette effect.

So Roberts' stratagem in Fig. 1-137 is to put back enough stray dots to restore the *average* local intensities. We don't notice the detail that he's put them in the wrong places. We only observe a more natural, less silhouetted picture. You remember, I said that the *significance* of a bit of information at the source is proportional to the influence it exerts on the final processed data which reaches the signal destination.

The preliminary, deliberate addition of random noise is very effective for de-silhouettizing *these* pictures, but would have a *disastrous* effect on a picture consisting of four colors of dots to begin with, where these dots represented zeros, ones, twos, and threes of numerical data!

For sound or picture systems, part of the channel—that which you mustn't change—is the human brain (unless, of course, you're equipped for lobotomy). And since esthetic

Fig. 1-137. Sometimes, the channel includes the receiver and data processor. In the case of these TV pictures, the channel includes somebody's neural processes. The leftmost transmission was of a six-bit gray-scale. Reducing that to a two-bit scale of four shades (black, white, and two grays) gives the stark center picture. Noise introduced before quantizing the two-bit signal resulted in picture at right, which contains less information (in a digital-computer sense) than either of the others. But the neural process of local averaging of recognizable patterns results in the effect that you see. (Courtesy IRE, Information Theory Group and G. Roberts)

judgments, as well as fidelity judgments, of sound and pictures are the work of the very same cranial processor, some of the more fearless souls (e.g., J. R. Pierce of the Bell Labs) have even considered esthetic evaluations from the viewpoint of information theory.

To understand Roberts' phenomenon, we have to consider far more than the engineering fact of what he built, and how he processed his pictures. We have to consider the statistical nature of the class of "reasonable TV pictures," and even worry about the final data digestion in the brain.

As always, a proper understanding of the channel statistics (including the statistics of the "signals" which must be communicated) is irreplaceable. As I said before, "Know Thy Channel."

Further reading

Solomon W. Golomb suggested that those interested in this business go back to the basic sources to see what information theory really says. This, of course, means *Mathematical Theory of Communication* by Shannon and Weaver (U. of Illinois Press, 1949, $2.50), which starts with Shannon's classic dissertation and includes many further contributions. While you're digging into the basic references on getting signals out of noise, seek out N. Wiener's *Extrapolation, Interpolation and Smoothing of Stationary Time Series, With Engineering Applications* (Wiley, 1949, $4.50). Wiener was the first to apply the calculus of variations to the problem of finding the filter which will operate on a noisy signal (with known statistics) in such a way that the processed signal has the least infidelity, and today, every student learns optimum filters early in his career.

Shannon's most referenced first papers in information theory (and the ones that begin the book mentioned above) first appeared in the *Bell System Technical Journal* (in 1948), which today is still an important source of material on the subject, second, of course, to the *IRE Transactions on Information Theory*, which is published by the IRE's (now the IEEE's) Professional Group on Information Theory.

If, after all this heady source material, you'd rather start with a more popular orientation, you cannot do better than Pierce's *Symbols, Signals and Noise* (Harper, 1961, $6.50), which is delightful and informative reading and discusses information theory in everything from physics to art. Solomon W. Golomb is editor and co-author, with Baumert, Easterling, Stiffler, and Viterbi, of *Digital Communications* (Prentice-Hall, 1964).

THE ELECTRON PROBE

by Isidore Adler *

* Isidore Adler is project leader in x-ray spectroscopy at the Geological Survey, U.S. Department of the Interior, Washington, D.C.

IN BRIEF: *Wherever spatial distribution of elements in a sample is significant; wherever extreme precision in locating an elemental analysis is important; wherever truly nondestructive analysis in situ is indicated; and especially wherever the area of interest is down in the micron size range, the electron-probe x-ray* *microanalyzer has no peers among gadgets for doing the job. It can quantitatively determine all elements above sodium in atomic number in samples as small as a few cubic microns in volume—or on surfaces as little as 1 micron in diameter—with sensitivity that lies in the several hundred ppm range, and is accurate to within 1–2% of amount present in concentrations greater than a few percent. The probe uses the sample as target for a magnetically focused beam of highly accelerated electrons. Upon striking the sample, these excite the emission of x-rays whose wavelengths characterize the elements present, and whose intensities yield concentrations. Adaptation of the probe to scanning instead of point analysis offers a clear but qualitative map of element distribution over larger sample surfaces. Cost, of course, is high—$50–100,000.—S.T.*

■ Wilson's disease illustrates the well-known fact that inorganic elements play a vital role in metabolism and cell function. The disease upsets copper metabolism in human beings, and is frequently fatal. In studying disorders of this sort, a crucial first step is to map distribution of the misbehaving element in the body's vital organs. This has just been successfully accomplished, on the eyes of patients who had died of Wilson's disease, with the indispensable aid of an elegant new analytical tool called the electron-probe x-ray microanalyzer —or simply electron probe, for short.

Figure 1-138 shows how an electron probe traverse across corneal tissue located the elusive culprit, copper. The copper concentrates in a band just 5 microns wide, in Descemet's membrane, itself a thin layer only about 30 microns wide within the cornea. But locating the copper was just part of the problem. Its precise amount also had to be determined. This was easily done, conventionally, by comparing intensity of the copper peak in the membrane with intensities derived from separately prepared reference samples.

The electron probe, without which determinations of such exquisite delicacy would have remained impossible, offers unequaled power and flexibility in problems of chemical analysis.

It offers quantitative elemental determinations on sample surfaces as small as 1 micron in diameter, on volumes as little as a few cubic microns—in situ, nondestructively, with sensitivity in the several hundred ppm range, and accuracy within 1–2% of amount present, if concentration is over a few percent.

Remarkable spatial resolution is not the probe's only attractive feature. Take the recent development of the *scanning* electron probe, for example, in which—instead of point analyses, or linear traverses such as are shown in Fig. 1-138—analytical information for an entire sample surface is presented almost instantaneously on a cathode-ray screen, offering a precise map that shows distribution of elements of interest. A very pretty example of such an application is portrayed in Fig. 1-139.

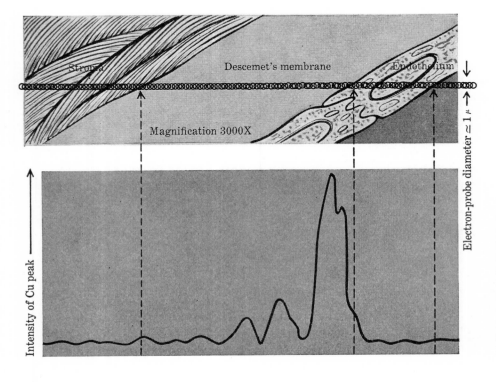

Fig. 1-138. Linear traverse with the electron probe across tissue taken from the cornea of patient who had died of Wilson's disease—an upset of the copper metabolism—produced this distribution, with unusual concentration of Cu in a band just 5 microns wide, within that part of cornea called Descemet's membrane.

Color Fig. 10. Drops of six different liquids (artificially colored) on a Teflon surface dramatize the importance of surface-free energy in adhesives. Surface-free energy of drops decreases from left to right. Only those liquids at far right have a low enough surface-free energy to spread on the low-energy Teflon surface as an adhesive should. See "Adhesives," in Chapter 2. (Courtesy Heka)

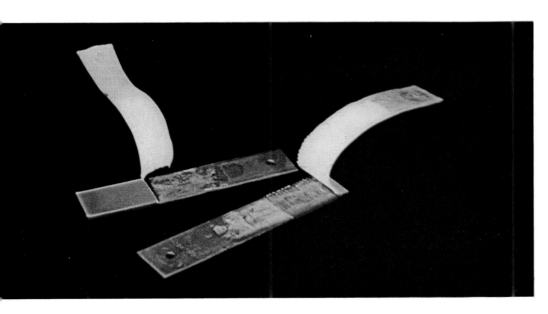

Color Fig. 11. Nearly any material can be made to stick without an adhesive — even one as slippery as polyethylene. Here, polyethylene, melted on a copper surface, forms such a strong joint that, in one case, the strip tore before the joint gave way and in the other, the strip peeled away, but left a thin frost of polyethylene behind. See "Adhesives," in Chapter 2. (Courtesy Heka)

Color Fig. 12. A ring of Y-shaped buttresses supports the dome of the Palazzetto dello Sport. The edge of the dome itself is scalloped to resist the bending moments that develop at the edge when the thin shell interacts with the relatively rigid supports. See "Modern Concrete Design," in Chapter 3. (Courtesy Richard Olmsted)

Color Fig. 13. In Toronto, Canada, a computer learns traffic patterns. Simulated traffic is never entirely valid. Test-track drivers (Fig. 3-4) complained everybody was too polite. This highly controversial Toronto experiment with computer control of real traffic is being carefully watched, for it is the first major attempt to let a digital computer try to optimize traffic flow by controlling signals for a thousand-intersection network. Each intersection has flux gate detectors in the connecting streets to sense the passage of vehicles. Telephone lines from existing signal boxes (top) connect the computer to detectors and signal controls.

At Toronto City Hall (center) Univac 1107 takes data on instantaneous traffic density from all intersections lit on map in background. TV screen and signal light display monitor below are aids for the computer operators during initial study phase during which various timings will be tried. Since digital computers will be able to correlate data on vehicle movements and the setting of the signals at each moment, it is expected to reveal ways to optimize the control of traffic in the network. Toronto experiment is drawing many visitors working in traffic field, including wary watchers who see too many variables just at a single intersection. Only time will tell whether heuristic programming — cut-and-try by computer—can optimize networks full of humans in cars. See "Traffic," in Chapter 3. (Courtesy W. Huffman, Univac Canada)

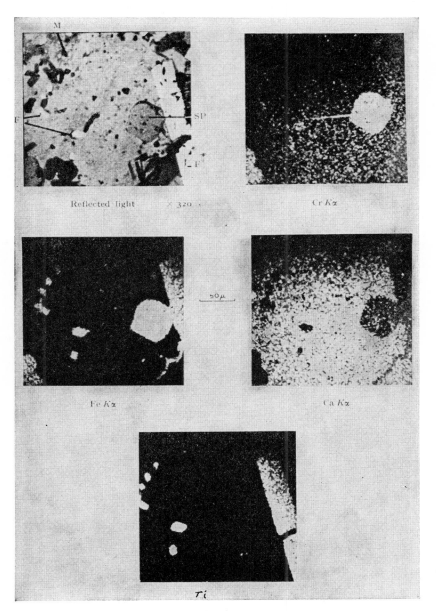

Fig. 1-139. Most recent adaptation of the spot electron probe uses electrons back-scattered from the sample surface to modulate intensity of the electron beam in a cathode-ray tube; yields almost instantaneous maps of an element's distribution over the surface, like those shown here. Method sweeps the sample surface with a finely focused electron beam, just like raster in television tube. At the same time, another electron beam traces output raster on the presentation tube. F-ferropseudobrookite; SP-spinel. (Courtesy Elsevier Publishers)

A tool to capture research imagination

Wherever spatial distribution of elements in a sample is significant; wherever extreme precision in location of an elemental analysis is important; wherever in situ analysis is to the point for any reason; wherever the sample of interest is down in the micron size range; and —as an added bonus—wherever it is important not to injure the sample, the electron probe has no peer.

In metallurgy the probe has been used to study diffusion across intermetallic boundaries; for study of segregation phases; for study of composition and thickness of superficial layers and thin films in corrosion and precipitation problems; and much more.

Electron probe microanalysis is being used in mineralogy and geochemistry to attack such problems as the composition of coexisting minerals, identification of new mineral species, and the nature of exsolution processes and of zoned crystals.

Geological and metallurgical uses are just part of the story, however. The probe can be used just as effectively on catalysts, glasses, ceramics, cements, and biological materials. And it is finding increasing use in semiconductor work, where detailed measurements of concentration profiles can yield diffusion constants in semiconductor-dopant interactions, and degree of solid solution in such systems as, for example, gallium and germanium.

One of the remarkable things about the electron probe is the way it captured the imagination of analysts in every field even during its gestation period—during 1957 and 1958—when there were fewer than a dozen homemade instruments in existence, and very few actual applications published.

Sensitive spot analysis, accurate and in situ

The reasons it captured research imaginations are not far to seek. The probe, to be sure, offers high accuracy and extreme sensitivity (quantitative determinations can be made on as little as 10^{-12} to 10^{-14} grams of an element). But the real research excitement was generated by the new accessibility of sample surfaces that could be as small as 1 micron in diameter, or sample volumes as little as a few cubic microns. And analytical capabilities depend not one whit on the element's state of chemical combination.

Besides all this, there's an important extra. Such minute sample volumes can be analyzed in situ—in their own naturally occurring matrices, among their own individual and unique natural surroundings. No costly and time-consuming separations are necessary. Indeed, in many applications it is precisely the spatial distribution of the elements which is all-important and which must be preserved. Yet most other analytical methods disrupt such spatial and matrix relationships, to one or another degree.

As for its adaptability to new applications, the probe can hold its own in any company. Aside from the scanning modification (early results of which were shown in Fig. 1-139, and which will be discussed in more detail later on) the probe also can be modified to obtain x-ray micrographs. And, with a variation of the principle upon which the scanning probe is based, good quality pictures can be obtained of the sample surface at high magnifications.

If your research imagination is excited by the probe's possibilities, you may be wondering by now what's the gimmick. Surely there must be some drawbacks, some difficulties. Of course, there are. Before tempering imagination with sober truth, however, we must know more about the probe itself and about the principles which underlie it.

A graduate thesis to fulfill dreams

The idea of using a focused electron beam for "in place" analysis was first conceived by Hillier in 1943, a result of his work on chemical analysis by means of energy losses suffered by electrons when traversing thin foils. The notion that the x-rays emitted by materials struck by electrons could also be used for chemical analysis even became the subject of a patent issued to him in 1947, but no practical use was ever made of this idea.

The original working electron probe, described by Castaing in a doctoral thesis under the guidance of Prof. André Guinier at the University of Paris, modified an electron microscope. This thesis could fulfill the dreams of any graduate student. It had great impact, as subsequent events have proved: Besides successfully designing a working instrument, it laid down the fundamental principles for doing quantitative spectroscopy with x-rays.

Following Castaing's work, a small number of instruments were built in Russia, England, and the United States. Whereas there were some 5 or 6 instruments in existence throughout the world in 1956, when we built ours at the Geological Survey, the number today is in the hundreds. The only probe commercially available at that time cost $140,000—a Castaing probe, purchased by the International Nickel Company. In contrast, the cash outlay for our instrument was only about $20,000. But it no longer pays to do it yourself, since electron probes are now available commercially here and in Europe, and prices are now lower, but not by much—they range from $50,000 to over $100,000 depending on degree of sophistication and number of attachments.

Commercial instruments vary from static probes, with conventional x-ray measuring techniques, to probes using electron-scanning systems with cathode-ray presentation. Another recent innovation that will soon reach the commercial market logically combines an electron microscope with the probe.

Regardless of variations and degree of sophistication in attachments, all probes achieve spot chemical anlaysis by exploiting the same basic principles—those underlying x-ray spectroscopy.

Something simple about x-ray spectroscopy

In the electron probe the sample serves as a target for a finely focused beam of electrons. These are accelerated under high potential, and when they strike the target the greatest part of their energy, of course, is dissipated as heat. But a small portion is converted into x-radiation and secondary electrons, both of which are emitted from the minute bombarded volume.

The back-scattered electrons can be used to gain information about element distribution over the entire surface of the sample, or to get magnified images. But it is the x-ray emission spectrum that concerns us now, because only this affords precise quantitative elemental analysis of discrete, small, sample volumes.

Figure 1-140 illustrates the nature of this x-ray spectrum: it consists of two distinctively different distributions of x-ray wavelengths and intensities. One is a continuous distribution that begins abruptly at some lower limit of wavelength, rises sharply in intensity, and then tails off in intensity as it extends over a broad range of wavelengths to higher and higher values.

This part of the spectrum, for our purpose, is a nuisance; it constitutes the background or noise out of which we must detect the signal that is important to us.

This signal consists of those sharp, narrow peaks in x-ray intensity that rise above the continuum. These peaks are not only restricted to a very narrow range in wavelength, they also occur at specific wavelengths which are exclusively a function of the element emitting the radiation. In other words, these peaks characterize the elements which yield them, and their intensity is proportional to the amount of element present in the sample; thus they are the heart of the electron-probe analytical method. But—such is life—it's impossible to excite them alone, without the troublesome continuous spectrum, when using electrons as the exciting radiation.

On this continuous spectrum, the low wavelength (or high-energy) limit at which the curves begin—known as the Duane-Hunt limit—depends entirely on the electrical potential accelerating the incident electrons. This limit obtains when all the energy of an incident electron goes into the making of a single x-ray photon, in a single collision with an atom of the sample. But much of the time the electrons lose their energy in a series of collisions—this leads to the longer-wavelength x-rays that comprise the continuum.

The over-all efficiency of such energy conversion, measurable by the area under curves such as Fig. 1-140, depends mostly on the atomic number of the target, and rises with increasing atomic number.

In order to generate the characteristic x-ray peaks, the electrons hitting the target must be accelerated with energy that exceeds the critical excitation energy of the various kinds of atoms present in the target. The concept of critical excitation energy can be best understood in terms of Bohr's classical picture of the atom, coupled with quite simple quantum-mechanical concepts.

How characteristic x-rays are generated

X-ray spectra are associated with energy transitions involving inner-shell electrons. This is in contrast to optical-emission and atomic-absorption spectra (see "Atomic Absorption Analysis," page 250) which arise from transitions involving the outer or valence electrons. There are several advantages to working with inner shell electrons. Due to the shielding effects of the outer electrons, the spectra obtained by avoiding them are relatively independent of the state of chemical combination of the atom, a fact of great importance in analysis. A second and perhaps even greater advantage is that the

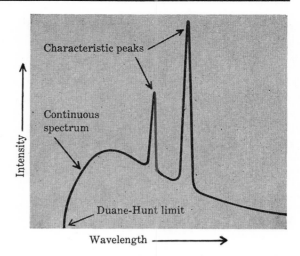

Fig. 1-140. X-ray emission spectrum, excited by bombarding an element with accelerated electrons whose energy exceeds the critical excitation energy for the element, consists of a continuous portion—the background or noise—and more intense peaks whose wavelengths characterize the element.

spectra are beautifully simple, and they show remarkable regularity in variation with atomic number ($\lambda \sim N^2$, where λ = wavelength and N = atomic number). Mosely clearly demonstrated this in 1914 for some 38 elements which were made to serve as targets of an x-ray tube. In two monumental papers he uncovered the structure of both the K- and L-shell spectra, and also clearly showed that atomic number was a more fundamental property than atomic weight. This not only provided undeniable support for the Bohr theory of atomic structure, it also established the basis for modern x-ray spectroscopy. Figure 1-141 demonstrates the simple relationship between atomic number and the wavelengths of characteristic x-rays.

Any process which removes an inner-shell electron from an atom causes emission of characteristic x-ray lines. The critical excitation energy—or energy needed to remove an inner-shell electron—equals the energy that binds the electron to the nucleus. Expressed as excitation voltages, the energy needed for producing characteristic x-rays ranges from 1 to over 100 kv, depending on the element. It rises, of course, with increasing atomic number. Figure 1-142 shows how it's done.

Kicking the electron out of the K-shell

When an inner electron is booted out of an atom by impact, its loss leaves the atom in what the quantum people call an excited state. And the atom only returns to the calm or ground state when the vacancy in the inner shell is filled by another electron from one of the shells further away from the nucleus.

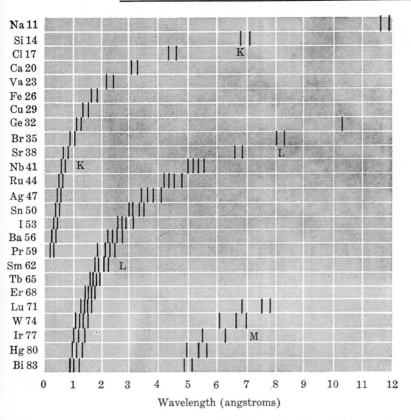

Na 11 · Si 14 · Cl 17 · Ca 20 · Va 23 · Fe 26 · Cu 29 · Ge 32 · Br 35 · Sr 38 · Nb 41 · Ru 44 · Ag 47 · Sn 50 · I 53 · Ba 56 · Pr 59 · Sm 62 · Tb 65 · Er 68 · Lu 71 · W 74 · Ir 77 · Hg 80 · Bi 83

0 1 2 3 4 5 6 7 8 9 10 11 12
Wavelength (angstroms)

Fig. 1-141. Simplicity of x-ray spectra is evident in plot of three major spectral series—K, L, and M—for various elements. Within any series, wavelengths at which lines characteristic of the element occur vary inversely as the square of atomic number. Since energy is the reciprocal of wavelength, it drops sharply below atomic number 11, making difficult detection of elements below sodium with most present equipment. But new more sensitive detectors are extending range.

To put some rather complex ideas qualitatively, the energy needed to hold an electron gained from shells further from the nucleus is less than that needed to retain the original inner electron. This difference in energy is emitted as characteristic x-radiation.

Precisely which outward electron shell donates an electron to keep peace in the family depends on certain selection rules that are un-

important here. But these selection rules do determine what kind of x-ray spectrum we get. The *K*-spectrum, for example, arises from transitions from outer shells to the *K*-shell when the exciting vacancy exists there; the *L*-spectrum arises from similar transitions to the *L*-shell, and so forth.

Figure 1-143 diagrams transitions responsible for some of the spectral peaks most useful in present-day x-ray spectroscopy. Obviously the *K*-spectrum is simplest of all since the allowed energy transitions all must be to the single *K*-energy level. The *L*-spectrum, on the other hand, is more complex because three *L*-energy levels are possible; and the *M*-electron shell—with no less than 5 energy levels permitted—has still more peaks in its spectrum.

As the number of peaks in a particular spectrum multiply, so does the probability that some peaks will overlap others. This, of course, makes x-ray spectra derived from outer shells approach optical spectra in complexity, and is one reason why the *K*-spectrum is most favored, whenever it can be used. Also, since the number of energy transitions allowed in the *K*-shell is less than in the others, the total energy that must be divided among such transitions is divided fewer ways, resulting in much the strongest intensities in *K*-spectra, and better quantitative results.

But as one deals with elements of increasing atomic number, the greater number of protons in the nucleus makes for greater binding energy holding *K*-electrons. This makes it difficult to obtain strong enough intensities of x-rays from the *K*-shell, except at exorbitant excitation voltages. Thus, for elements above an atomic number of approximately 50, the *L*-spectra must be used, in spite of the greater complexity in their interpretation.

Having produced characteristic x-rays, and having learned that wavelength is related in a simple and regular way to atomic number, we face a single remaining problem: how to detect and measure the intensity of the characteristic

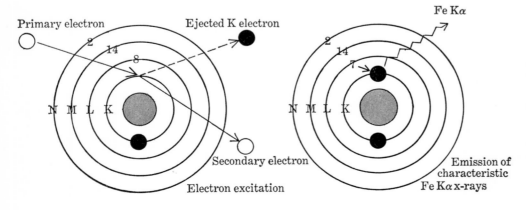

Fig. 1-142. Primary electrons that strike a K-shell electron with sufficient energy eject it out of atom, leaving atom in an excited quantum state. It returns to ground state when the vacancy in the K shell is filled by an electron from an outer shell. Difference in binding energies between original K electron and its replacement is emitted as characteristic x-rays. (Atom shown is Fe.)

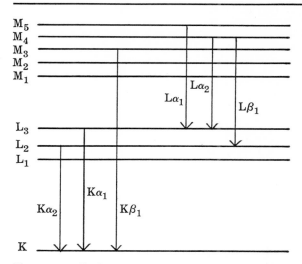

Fig. 1-143. *Single energy level permitted in the K-electron shell by quantum selection rules explains why K x-ray spectra are most simple. All transitions to K shell must be to this level. But possible sublevels in L shell number three, and M—with five—yields still more complex spectra.*

wavelengths. For this we can go back—very briefly—to the familiar work of Bragg, since Bragg's law is the basis for the x-ray spectrograph, and it, in turn, is a vital part of the electron probe.

Ignorance of the law is no excuse

The fundamental law of x-ray diffraction is given by Bragg's simple expression $n\lambda = 2d \sin \theta$, where λ is the wavelength, d is the spacing between atomic planes in the crystal from which diffraction occurs, and θ is the angle at which incident x-rays strike the atomic planes. The n represents the order or harmonic of x-ray reflection.

This expression shows that discrete x-ray wavelengths can be detected and identified simply by permitting them to reflect from a crystal whose interplanar spacing is known. Each wavelength incident upon such planes— as shown in the marginal sketch—will reflect at an angle θ that satisfies the Bragg equation. If a radiation detector then scans for characteristic wavelengths of reflected x-rays, it will detect them at the various appropriate angles. With d known and θ measured, determination of the wavelength follows routinely.

Intensity of x-radiation at any wavelength (or, now tantamount to saying the same thing, at any characteristic diffraction angle) is measured by either Geiger counters, proportional counters, or scintillation counters.

How, now, about the electron probe

Returning now to the working electron-probe analyzer, all existing microanalyzers—commer-

cial or home-made—contain the following basic components: an electron-beam forming system, a movable specimen stage capable of precise translation on a micron scale, a viewing system (optical or electronic or a combination of both), and one or more x-ray spectrographs. A schematic arrangement of components is shown in Fig. 1-144, and Fig. 1-145 shows our setup at the Geological Survey.

The x-ray spectrographs may be either scan-

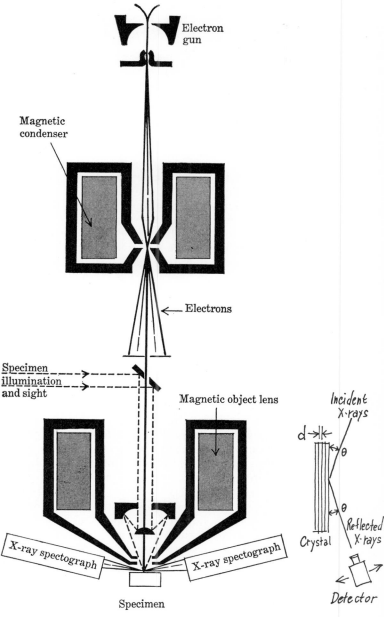

Fig. 1-144. *Heart of probe is stream of electrons coming from gun; it is magnetically focused in two stages to 1-μ spot size at specimen surface. Visual optics shown, and number of spectrographs, vary according to instrument and study desired.*

Fig. 1-145. The author's group built this probe, at the U.S. Geological Survey, for cash outlay of about $20,000 in 1956, when there were no more than six probes in the world and price of only probe commercially available was around $140,000. Commercial price now is $45–100,000, depending on extras. (Courtesy U.S. Geological Survey)

ners—used in assaying a sample whose elemental composition is completely unknown—or fixed-position spectrometers, whose detectors are preset in the diffracted θ position characteristic of the element of interest.

The source for electrons is a hot filament electron gun similar in every respect to the electron gun found in electron microscopes. The electron stream emitted by the incandescent filament is brought to a sharp focus at the specimen surface by use of two magnetic lenses, which reduce beam size in two stages. The two magic achievements sought by every electron prober are small spot size—1 μ or less—and high specimen currents, of the order of 0.1 to 1 μamp, although such large specimen currents are not always required. These parameters make for high resolution and greater sensitivity.

Chemical composition by pushing a button

More elaborate probes also contain scanning beam attachments, and cathode-ray tube presentation. The majority of electron probes featuring cathode-ray presentation have facilities for presentation of either x-ray or back-scattered electron effects. Most instruments rely on long persistence cathode-ray tubes for picture presentation, but at least one commercial instrument offers instantaneous presentation.

This scanning development is quite striking; recall Fig. 1-139.

Remember that when a sample is bombarded by electrons, both x-rays and secondary electrons are emitted, and each can tell us something about the composition of the sample. Thus, a focused electron beam is made to sweep continuously over a surface area of the sample of about 100 μ^2 (the rate of sweeping being under the control of the operator, and the mode of sweeping entirely analogous to the raster in a television tube). Simultaneously, an electron beam is made to trace a raster on the cathode-ray presentation tube. Either the characteristic x-rays or the secondary electrons emitted by the sample are used to modulate the intensity of the cathode-ray tube beam, yielding an almost instantaneous map of elemental distribution over the surface of the sample under investigation.

To work with an electron beam of small size and high intensity, we still must know exactly where the beam strikes the specimen. For this purpose a probe usually includes a high-quality microscope with resolutions of about a micron.

Initial positioning is accomplished by using substances that fluoresce under the electron beam, and the beam itself has a most obliging habit that confirms the location of an analysis. It causes a carbonaceous deposit to form as a contamination spot on the irradiated area, providing positive proof that the selected sample area has indeed been analyzed.

But if the beam can polymerize even pump oil vapor, what of the chemical changes it may induce in the specimen? And what of the other clouds in the silver lining I sketched so brightly at the outset?

Every silver lining has some clouds

It would be misleading to conclude with the idea that optimum results, particularly quantitative ones, can be obtained quite so simply. Several extra factors must be considered—sample preparation, development of appropriate standards, grain-size influences, and interaction of the sample with the electron beam are among the most important.

In order properly to relate observed x-ray intensities to concentration of an element, several corrections must be made. For instance, it is necessary to correct for absorption of x-rays as they emerge through the sample (which would result in spuriously low intensity readings), as well as for the possibility that the element being measured is being excited to inappropriately high intensities by secondary x-rays generated in the sample matrix. Correlation of such corrections with problems of standard preparation has received much attention in the literature, but improved theory, as well as practice, in this area could significantly increase quantitative accuracy of the method.

For ultraprecise quantitative work, optimum sample preparation also is a must. This means preparing highly polished surfaces, as nearly as possible free of relief. Additionally, the sample must be electrically conducting, since the surface is being bombarded by a carefully directed electron beam, and nonconductors would, of course, build up a surface charge, causing beam instability and wandering. While metal samples are conducting, mineral and biological samples generally are not. This presents very little problem, however; they can be made conducting by depositing a thin (100–1000 Å) conducting layer on them.

Last, but in many applications decidedly not least, the probe at present is limited to use with elements from sodium (11) on up in atomic number. This results from the fact, evident in Fig. 1-141, that for a given series of spectral lines the yield of x-rays drops off inversely as the square of atomic number; with present equipment this decreases sensitivities for the lighter elements below sodium to the vanishing point. Therefore, the important organochemical and biological elements—carbon, oxygen, and nitrogen, for example—generally lie beyond the probe's capabilities.

However, recent work in Japan, Great Britain, and even the US, using nondispersive x-ray focusing techniques, and new, more sensitive x-ray detectors (thin window and gas-filled, or even windowless—to cut down losses by absorption), seems to be bringing even these elements into the fold.

Further reading

For a look at that rare manuscript which author Adler refers to as "a thesis to fulfill a graduate student's dreams," see Castaing's doctoral effort at the U. of Paris (1951), also available as publication No. 55 of the French National Office of Aeronautical Research and Development (ONERA), entitled "Application des sondes électroniques à une méthode d'analyse ponctuelle chimique et cristallographique." If your French runs rusty after all this time, fear not, because there are two volumes—in English—that cover the ground completely. One is *Electron Probe Microanalysis* by L. S. Birks (Interscience, 1963), and the other is D. Wittry's chapter on x-ray microanalysis by means of electron probes in the *Treatise on Analytical Chemistry*, Kolthoff, Elving, and Sandell, eds. (Interscience, 1964). You can also find an excellent detailed review of the probe, including hardware matters, suppliers, and so on, in an article by Birks in *Analy. Chemistry*, Aug. 1960, p. 19A.

Other recent rundowns on the probe are Castaing's article "Electron Probe Microanalysis" in *Advances in Electronics and Electron Physics*, 13, p. 370 (Academic Press, 1960), and Duncomb's similar article in the *Brit. J. Appl. Phys.*, 11, 1960, 169.

Various fields of application in which the probe has created new opportunities for advance are reviewed in such publications as the recently issued *Symposium on Advances in Metallography and Electron Probe Microanalysis* (STP 317 of the ASTM, 1963), and the *Proceedings of the 2nd International Symposium on X-ray Microscopy and X-ray Microanalysis*, held in Stockholm in 1959 (Elsevier, 1960). An incisive brief look is taken at "The Use of Electron-Probe Microanalysis in Physical Metallurgy" by D. A. Medford, in the *J. of the Inst. of Metals*, 90, 217 (1962). If your x-ray spectroscopy needs refocusing, any one of the following should help: Parrish's series of articles on "X-ray Spectrochemical Analysis" in the *Norelco Reporter*, Vol. 3. No's. 2–5 (1956); H. Liebhafsky's "X-ray Absorption and Emission" in *Anal. Chem.*, 26, No. 1 (1954), or Birks and Brooks' "X-rays Lighten the Analytical Load," *Anal. Chem.*, 30, 19A (1958).

Chapter 2

Chemistry

THE CHEMICAL BOND†

by Louis P. Hammett and Sir Harrie Massey *

IN BRIEF: *The scientist's concept of the nature of the bond between atoms has changed many times over the course of years. Each new concept has been more or less useful in the continuing attempt to understand and predict the behavior of matter. The major currently accepted theories have been remarkably successful: Chemists have predicted most unlikely compounds following the rules laid down by quantum mechanics, and then have produced them—even while physicists feel that the mathematics is unmanageable for anything beyond H_2.*

In addition to the changes in theory with time, there seems to be a vast difference in one's concept of the "real" nature of the chemical bond depending on whether one is a chemist or a physicist. In this article a representative of each discipline discusses his respective viewpoint. They are Louis P. Hammett, recently retired as Mitchill Professor of Chemistry at Columbia University, and Sir Harrie Massey, Quain Professor of Physics at the University of London.

If you get the feeling, as you read the dialogue, that our present state of knowledge may someday represent the "classic" theory, of interest only as it can be modified or overthrown, it won't bother these men. They've watched it happen before.—H.W.M.

† Due to the complexity of the subject, we have departed from our usual narrative style in order to present this article in the form of the classic dialogue.—Ed.

* Louis P. Hammett is recently retired after forty years on the faculty of Columbia University in New York. He is currently revising his widely known book on physical organic chemistry. Sir Harrie Massey is Chairman of the British National Committee Space Research and Preparatory Commission, European Space Research Organization, and the author of several books on ionic and atomic collision and impact phenomena. Both authors are members of the editorial board of *International Science and Technology*.

CHEMIST HAMMETT: Perhaps the failure of chemists and physicists to understand each other goes back to a basic difference in their aims. To risk an exaggeration, the physicist searches for a unified field theory, the chemist for better ways of predicting and controlling the course of chemical reactions. With this aim, the chemist is much more prone than the physicist to accept approximate theories, provided they either seem to rationalize a useful empirical conclusion or to suggest interesting lines of experimental investigation.

PHYSICIST MASSEY: I would say this for the chemist: He has been able to create a maximum degree of order with a minimum of mathematics. The physicist, on the other hand, usually has been guided by the applicability of mathematical methods to simpler molecules.

Having said this, however, I think we must distinguish between different types of physicists. Those concerned, for example, with solid-state physics have an outlook which differs little from that of the chemist. Their aim, like the chemist's, is to make predictions, which must be largely qualitative.

The physicist working in high-energy physics, on the other hand, is seeking to examine the validity of existing laws and expects to discover new phenomena which cannot be interpreted within the existing framework. Thus, he always tries to deal with the simplest possible situation within his field, one shorn of complications arising from complexity.

FIG. 2-1. SOME EARLY STAGES IN THE DEVELOPMENT OF CHEMICAL-BOND THEORY

1806 Davey
1812 Berzelius } Electrostatic theory

In this theory, molecules were composed of certain numbers of atoms or radicals held together by electrostatic attraction between opposite charges. Davey thought charges developed when substances approached each other; Berzelius said they existed in isolation.

$$SO_3 + K_2O = SO_3 \cdot K_2O$$

1808 Dalton: Law of multiple proportions

Dalton and others showed that elements always combined in definite proportions, with small whole-number ratios, when they formed chemical compounds. This led to the concept of "combining powers" for each element, and numerical formulas for representing compounds.

$$1H + 1Cl = Muriatic\ Acid$$
$$2H + 1O = Water$$
$$3H + 1N = Ammonia\ Gas$$
$$4H + 1C = Marsh\ Gas$$

1834 Dumas: Monistic theory of valence

Dumas attempted to show that molecules must be regarded as entities by replacing hydrogen (positive) with chlorine (negative) in carbon compounds. He attributed to each element a certain combinatorial capacity—a valence—although he over-limited possible combining ratios. He also conceived the bar symbol between atoms in a molecule.

1855 Odling
1858 Kekulé and Couper } Tetravalence of carbon, carbon chains

Odling suggested that carbon was combined with four hydrogens in "marsh gas" implying tetravalence; Couper and Kekulé independently proposed carbon chain and ring formation in compounds such as benzene.

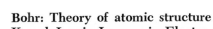

1870 Mendeleev: Periodic table

Mendeleev formulated his now-famous periodic table on the basis of similiarities in reactivity and combining power between elements, although he made no attempt to rationalize the reasons for the periodicity.

1862 Butlerov
1867 Kekulé
1874 van't Hoff and le Bel } Tetrahedral structure of carbon

Butlerov first proposed that the valences of carbon were arranged tetrahedrally to explain isomers of ethane, now known to be nonexistent. Kekulé used the concept to explain the links in acetylene and hydrogen cyanide. Working independently, van't Hoff and le Bel developed the concept into more general terms to explain optical phenomena and stereochemical aspects of organic compounds.

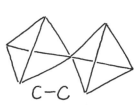

1913 Bohr: Theory of atomic structure
1916 Kossel, Lewis, Langmuir: Electron nature of chemical bond

Bohr theorized that electrons in an atom could only occupy specific orbits around the nucleus, with well-defined energy levels. Kossel, Lewis, and Langmuir proposed that the chemical bond was electronic in nature, and results from the coupling of lone electrons occupying the outer shells of linked atoms.

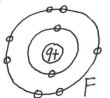

CHEMIST HAMMETT: The difference between the aims and methods of the chemist and physicist has a long history. Chemists had arrived empirically at effective working principles long before the theoretical key to all the problems of chemistry was embodied in the Schrödinger equation of wave mechanics. Even today, the amount of information which the chemist can derive directly from that equation is only a small part of what he knows. In physics, conversely, the invention of radio *followed* the formulation of Maxwell's equation, and grew out of it.

PHYSICIST MASSEY: Actually, the psychology of the two approaches is different. There are very few people who can be effective in both fields; the people who work with the various chemical approaches, and in fact the solid-state physics approach, are quite a different crowd from the people who work on field theory. Dirac, for example, would never have been interested in even as complicated a molecule as H_2. He would have thought it was not of use to his particular abilities at all.

CHEMIST HAMMETT: One of the interesting psychological aspects of the progress of chemistry is that for years the chemist has used with great success a model which is unrelated to the mass of physical theory. In the terms of this model, the atoms in a chemical molecule are held together by bonds. Each kind of atom can, and usually does, form a number of bonds which are characteristic of its kind. The direction in which these bonds form is also in a fixed relation to each other.

Since this model had remarkable success in predicting new carbon compounds and was successfully extended by Werner to inorganic complexes in the early years of this century, most chemists blandly ignored the fact that it was a poor model for the rest of chemistry.

In 1916, G. N. Lewis connected it with the rapidly developing electronic theory of atomic structure by what was still essentially an empirical observation. The inorganic compounds which did not fit the organic chemist's model were, according to Lewis, formed by transfer of electrons between atoms, and by spatially undirected attractions between oppositely-charged atoms.

Lewis proposed a concept of electron sharing for the spatially-directed bonds of organic compounds and inorganic complexes. These bonds he identified with a pair of electrons, held jointly between the bonded atoms.

His model, however, with its treatment of electrons as static point charges of electricity was completely inconsistent with the Bohr atom in which the electrons rotated about the nucleus in circular or elliptical orbits. I'm sure

Lewis knew about the Bohr model; he was the kind of chemist who would know things like that, as were many of those who enthusiastically accepted his model.

PHYSICIST MASSEY: At this stage both atomic physics and chemistry were in some respects in a similar situation to that of high-energy physics today. We did not know the laws which governed the behavior of atomic systems. Nevertheless, there was a remarkable background of ordered knowledge available, which is still of great importance. Without this background, quantum chemistry would still be a fairly backward branch of physics.

For example, going back to quite fundamental aspects, it is not obvious from quantum mechanics that it is a good approximation to think of molecules as primarily built up of atoms which preserve many of the characteristics which they possess when free. It is even more surprising that the ability of atoms to combine with other atoms can largely be expressed in terms of simple valency rules that apply irrespective of the detailed structure of the atoms involved.

Knowing from experiments, however, that these regularities do prevail, the quantum chemist can start from simple approximations that he knows to be reasonably reliable, without spending a long and largely fruitless time justifying them.

CHEMIST HAMMETT: In that line, your friend Dirac said in 1929, "The underlying physical laws necessary for the mathematical theory of a large part of physics and the whole of chemistry are now completely known." Fortunately for the chemist's psyche he didn't stop there, but went on to say ". . . the difficulty is only that the application of these laws leads to equations too complicated to solve." Approximations were the only way out.

MASSEY: Quite true. However, once the chemist made the approximations he could apply quantum mechanical principles to understand many exceptions to the older rules and to discern connecting relationships between different molecular properties.

HAMMETT: Actually, quantum theory wasn't very old before it began to demonstrate its usefulness for chemists. Heitler and London, working with the "electron cloud" concept of the atom structure (see Fig. 2-2) in 1927, were able to demonstrate theoretically that the two electrons in a hydrogen molecule have a high "probability density" *between* the two nuclei, which is responsible for the stability of the molecule. This demonstration gave considerable physical respectability to Lewis' idea of the shared electron bond.

Then Pauling showed in 1928 that the equations of quantum mechanics could be manipulated to show that a carbon atom can indeed form four equivalent bonds, each directed toward the vertices of a tetrahedron. The chemist's theory of the equivalence and spatial orientation of the carbon bond now had the same kind of respectability as his idea of the shared electron pair.

MASSEY: Perhaps the greatest revelation to come out of the introduction of quantum mechanics, of course, was insight into the actual nature of the forces binding the atoms in a molecule. We now know that the force responsible for *all* chemical phenomena is simply the long-known Coulomb force between charged particles—the electrical attraction between oppositely charged electrons and nuclei, and the repulsions between electrons and between nuclei. Once we'd gotten the right mechanics—wave, rather than classical Newtonian mechanics—we could show that electrical forces alone sufficed to explain atomic properties.

The new mechanics rose from a sequence of developments by physicists in the 1920's. First, de Broglie postulated that matter had to be represented by a wave. But the big breakthrough came in 1926 with Schrödinger, who reasoned that if matter behaved like waves, then there had to be a wave equation to govern the behavior of these waves. And so he sat down an equation similar in form to that which governs waves in the classical media of strings or water. It looks like this:

$$\nabla^2 \psi + \frac{8\pi^2\mu}{h^2} (E - V)\psi = 0$$

Once one had this equation, one could, in principle, determine the behavior of any particle of mass m in any potential-energy field V. This behavior, or as much of it as the uncertainty principle permits us to determine simultaneously, is contained in the wave function ψ, for $|\psi|^2$ gives the electron density (or equivalently, the probability of finding the electron) at any point in space, as shown in Fig. 2-2. Appropriate averages with $|\psi|^2$ as the weighting function tell us whatever can be known about the electron's behavior.

An interesting point of this equation is that the solutions ψ did not have to be wavelike. In fact, for electrons bound in atoms they are rather unlike waves, as we shall see. Perhaps the most important point to remember here is that the Schrödinger equation can be solved only for certain energy values (E) for an electron bound in an atom or molecule; thus, its solution simultaneously provides the permitted values of energy and the corresponding values of the wave function ψ for the electron. The lowest value of the energy corresponds to

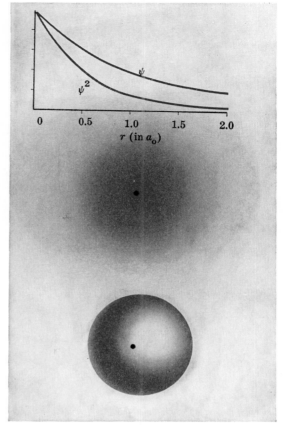

Fig. 2-2. You can visualize wave functions in several ways: plot ψ and ψ^2 against radius; cut a plane through a "charge cloud"; and draw a boundary surface to enclose bulk of cloud.

the most stable state of the electron, its ground state; the other energies represent states into which electrons can jump if properly excited.

There are two additional concepts about the electron to remember. One is spin—the mathematical property that is equivalent to its being capable of rotation about a polar axis in two opposite directions, at exactly the same speed—and the other is degeneracy. If more than one wave function is associated with one energy value, the state is said to be "degenerate." Degeneracy arises from the existence in the atom of symmetry of some kind, and leads to the possibility of a variety in the points at which a reaction may take place.

Getting down to specifics, we can look at the hydrogen atom, the great favorite of physicists. Here we have only one negative electron, moving in a potential field provided by the positively charged nucleus, which is sufficiently heavier that we can regard it as stationary. Now the solution of the Schrödinger equation provides us with a series of permitted energy values (energy levels) and corresponding wave functions. In the ground state, the lowest energy

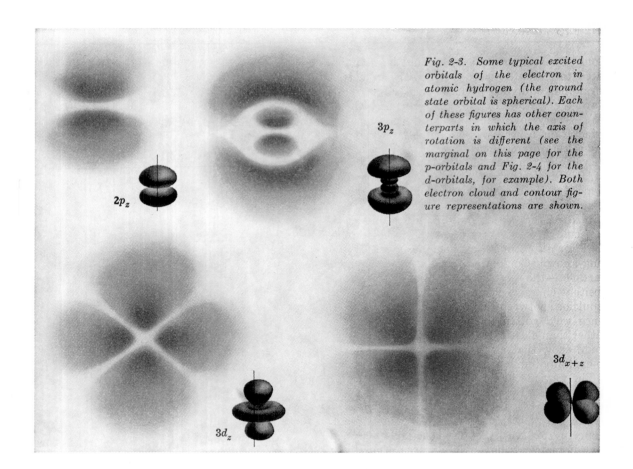

Fig. 2-3. Some typical excited orbitals of the electron in atomic hydrogen (the ground state orbital is spherical). Each of these figures has other counterparts in which the axis of rotation is different (see the marginal on this page for the p-orbitals and Fig. 2-4 for the d-orbitals, for example). Both electron cloud and contour figure representations are shown.

state in which the hydrogen atom is normally found, ψ is spherically symmetrical around the nucleus and behaves with distance from the nucleus as shown in Fig. 2-2.

The higher energy, excited states whose orbitals are shown in Fig. 2-3, would not be of interest to chemists except that they provide the prototypes of wave functions for the ground states of heavier atoms. These functions are usually characterized by three constants which fall out of the solution of the wave equation, and are allowed only certain values. These are the so-called quantum numbers n, l, and m, shown in the following table, of which only the first influences the energy.

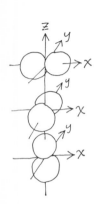

Quantum number	Allowed values	Corresponding orbital
n (principal)	1, 2, 3, etc.	1, 2, 3, etc.
l (azimuthal)	0, 1, 2, ... $n-1$	s, p, d, etc.
m (magnetic)	0, ± 1, ± 2 ... $\pm l$	—
spin	$\pm \frac{1}{2}$	—

In terms of this characterization, each orbital has its own type of symmetry properties. For example, there are three p-type orbitals, for which $l = 1$, shaped like dumbbells, and arranged along the three coordinate axes as shown in the margin; these three orbitals are entirely equivalent, except for their direction, and are linearly independent.

The five d-type orbitals, again all equivalent, possess considerably more complex geometry, but are symmetrical about different axes. They are shown in Fig. 2-4.

For a given value of n, and hence a given energy, there are n^2 orbitals, all of which are equivalent. Moreover, any linear combination of them is equally symmetrical. If a perturbation is applied, however, the equivalence of the orbitals will be wholly or partially removed. This means that certain orbital shapes are selected by the nature of the perturbation, and these are such that the total energy is minimized.

As an example of how this degeneracy arises, let's consider the simplest molecules, hydrogen (H_2) and the hydrogen molecule ion (H_2^+). (I remember when first lecturing on the new mechanics in 1929, and talking about the theory of chemical combination in terms of H_2^+, being asked by the chemistry professor whether a physicist ever thought of anything more complex than this ion-molecule.) In H_2^+, the nuclear force fields affecting the single electron are the same, so that at infinite separation of the nuclei it is immaterial from the point of view of the energy whether the electron is attached to one or the other nucleus. This twofold degeneracy is broken up as soon as the nuclei approach each other. The two states into which the single degenerate state splits can exhibit two types of symmetry. One tends to concentrate the electron density between the nuclei, where it acts as an attraction or a "cement," and so reduces the total energy contained in the molecule below that existing at infinite separation. The other has the opposite effect, leading to repulsion, as shown in the margin. This is the general pattern of the one-electron bond.

Suppose now we add a second electron to the system. As we saw before, it normally would go into the attractive orbital between the two nuclei. This state, however, is already occupied by one electron. From Pauli's exclusion principle, the second can only be admitted to the same attractive or "cementing" state if it possesses the opposite sense of spin, in which case it leads to further concentration of electron density between the nuclei. We thus get a stable H_2 molecule.

This is the simplest case of the two-electron bond, in which the essential factor is the pairing of two electrons with opposite spin.

HAMMETT: Actually, for chemical applications, the most important information to seek is the general shape of the wave function for the electrons in a compound whose existence is inferred from chemical evidence. This aspect determines how and where an atom will attach to another, and in what combination, and indeed almost all chemical phenomena.

MASSEY: A remarkable and most fortunate fact that the range of possible shapes for the electron wave function in other atoms and in molecules can be built up to a considerable degree from a knowledge of the wave functions for the electron in the hydrogen atom. This results primarily from the fact that the "shape," in particular the directionality, of the wave functions derives mostly from the l and m quantum numbers. These in turn reflect the quantized angular momentum of the electron.

The approach used to determine whether a specific group and number of atoms will form a compound, as well as what its properties will be, is straightforward: You first determine the minimum energy which atoms can take up, considered as a function of the nuclear configuration. Since the ratio of electron-to-nuclear mass is small, you usually deal with different nuclear configurations separately, calculating the electron energy for each as if the nuclei were at rest. If the minimum energy is obtained for a configuration in which all the nuclei are at finite separations, we have a stable compound which has the structure required by the configuration concerned.

The energy of a configuration arises from

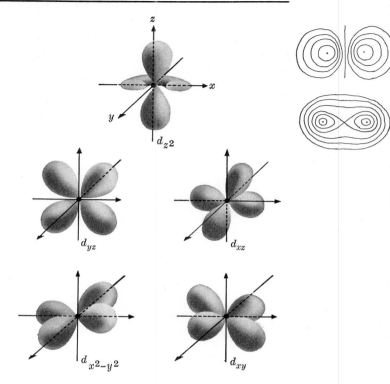

Fig. 2-4. *The five d-orbitals are equivalent. Because of their directionality, however, each is affected differently by the presence of combining atoms or complexing ligands.*

three sources—the electrostatic repulsion between nuclei, the kinetic energy of the electrons, and the potential energy of the electrons due to their interactions with the nuclei (attractive) and with each other (repulsive). To calculate the total energy of a proposed configuration, we average these three contributions over the probability density distribution for the electrons ($|\psi|^2$). If the total energy for the configuration is less than that of the total for the atoms at infinite separation, voilà, a stable molecule will exist.

HAMMETT: Unfortunately the actual calculations aren't usually as simple as your description of the process.

MASSEY: Well, obviously, the success of the calculations depends on an accurate knowledge of ψ; if this were known for each nuclear configuration there would be comparatively little difficulty in carrying out the calculations of energy. In practice, however, we do not know the ψ accurately for any case except that of H_2^+. Since the net energy of a system is very delicately balanced between the various repulsive and attractive contributions, quantitatively correct predictions are almost impossible unless a very good approximation indeed for ψ is available.

These ψs are terribly difficult to get starting

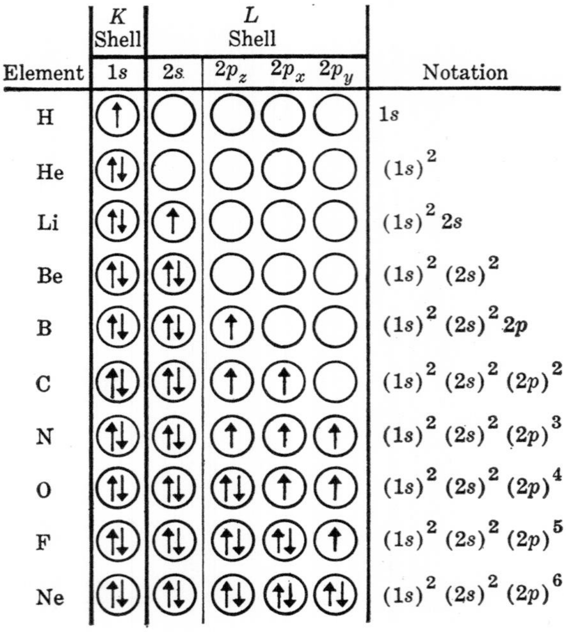

Element	K Shell	L Shell				Notation
	$1s$	$2s$	$2p_z$	$2p_x$	$2p_y$	
H	↑	○	○	○	○	$1s$
He	↑↓	○	○	○	○	$(1s)^2$
Li	↑↓	↑	○	○	○	$(1s)^2\,2s$
Be	↑↓	↑↓	○	○	○	$(1s)^2\,(2s)^2$
B	↑↓	↑↓	↑	○	○	$(1s)^2\,(2s)^2\,2p$
C	↑↓	↑↓	↑	↑	○	$(1s)^2\,(2s)^2\,(2p)^2$
N	↑↓	↑↓	↑	↑	↑	$(1s)^2\,(2s)^2\,(2p)^3$
O	↑↓	↑↓	↑↓	↑	↑	$(1s)^2\,(2s)^2\,(2p)^4$
F	↑↓	↑↓	↑↓	↑↓	↑	$(1s)^2\,(2s)^2\,(2p)^5$
Ne	↑↓	↑↓	↑↓	↑↓	↑↓	$(1s)^2\,(2s)^2\,(2p)^6$

Fig. 2-5. Available atomic orbitals of the elements are filled one electron at a time. The number of orbitals filled with unpaired electrons determines the effective valence to a great degree.

from scratch, but the chemical background available gives you clues to the general shapes that do exist. You can thus plug them in to get the approximate shapes of the wave functions. Fortunately, there is an encouraging qualification—if an energy is calculated for a system of atoms using an approximate wave function, then the correct energy will always be less than the approximate one, thus implying an even more stable compound.

At the point where we begin discussing molecules with more than two electrons, I suppose, the physicist begins to lose interest because of the need for gross approximations. But it is, of course, only the starting point for the chemist.

HAMMETT: Chemists have been living with approximations for generations. They even switch back and forth between approximations as each provides insight and information, and each shows its limitations.

Two of the major types of approximations used by the chemist these days are the **molecular-orbital** and the **valence-bond** theories. The valence-bond or electron-pair theory views the molecules as composed of atoms which preserve their identity, at least to a certain extent. Thus, it regards the formation of a molecule as the bringing together of complete atoms, which then interact.

MASSEY: To understand molecular orbitals, we should first understand atomic orbitals.

When an atom is visualized by the orbital method, it is "built up" by adding electrons into successive orbitals, as shown in Fig. 2-5. Hydrogen in the ground state has its single electron in the $1s$ orbital. The next element, helium, has two electrons; both are located in the $1s$ orbital, with their spins antiparallel as required by the Pauli principle. Lithium and beryllium add a third and fourth electron into the $2s$ orbital.

When you come to boron, you get the first existence of degenerate orbitals in the ground state, and this effects the order in which the electrons occupy the orbitals. Boron's fifth electron takes a $2p$ orbital, carbon's sixth should go into a *second* $2p$ orbital, and indeed, as far as the spectroscopist can tell from the ground state, it does in an isolated carbon atom.

HAMMETT: From the chemist's viewpoint, however, this is all wrong. According to our electro-pair idea, carbon should show a valence of two, but we know that it almost always displays a valence of four, implying four equivalent unpaired electrons in the outer shell. To achieve this state, the carbon atom must be excited out of its ground state, so that one of the $2s$ electrons is "promoted" into the unfilled $2p$ orbital, giving a state with four unpaired electrons. The increase in binding energy which this makes possible more than makes up for the energy required to produce the excited carbon state. Even this, however, would give us, according to our picture, three $2p$ orbitals and a spherical $2s$ orbital. However, the perturbation selects shapes which are combinations of $2s$ and $2p$ orbitals with maxima pointing towards the vertices of a tetrahedron. This tetrahedral configuration is the normal one for saturated carbon compounds. In chemical parlance the solution of combined s and p orbitals is known as hybridization.

HAMMETT: Another example of how the periodic table built up this way is helpful in determining effective valence is the oxygen atom. It has its eighth electron in one of the $2p$ orbitals, paired with another. This leaves only two unpaired electrons in the $2p$ orbitals. These two orbitals are equivalent to each other, although their directionality is perpendicular, and they are available for reaction with other atoms. The element thus normally exhibits a valence of two.

When two or more atoms come together to react, their electron distribution can be described by orbitals which may involve all the nuclei. These resulting molecular orbitals can be approximated by linear addition of the individual atomic orbitals.

The oxygen atom, for example, when confronted with two hydrogen atoms to produce a water molecule, "adds" orbitals in the manner shown in Fig. 2-6. The nitrogen atom, which possesses three lone $2p$ electrons, again all at 90° to each other, forms with hydrogen the ammonia molecule, also as shown.

MASSEY: Of course, in both of these molecules the actual valence angles determined by electron diffraction are larger than 90°—104° in H_2O and 107° in NH_3. Usually this is explained in terms of the repulsion between the hydrogen nuclei, but it points up the fact that the assumption that electrons are mutually independent of other nuclei and electrons in a molecule is far from strictly true, and that any accurate model must take into account *all* intramolecular "interactions."

HAMMETT: Chemists have long accepted carbon's tetrahedral configuration we mentioned in saturated compounds. However, reconciling the tetrahedral structure with the properties of the so-called unsaturated compounds could only be accomplished with considerable physical (and intellectual) strain. In ethylene (C_2H_4), for example, each carbon atom is bonded to the other carbon atom and to two hydrogen atoms. We know from electron diffraction, however, that the angles of these bonds lie in a plane at almost exactly 120° to each other, as shown in the margin, instead of the noncoplanar 109.5° required for tetrahedral distribution.

The hybrid orbital theory accounts for this by picturing a linear combination of two of the $2p$ orbitals and the $1s$ orbital, to form three wave functions whose maxima point toward the vertices of an equilateral triangle centered on the carbon atom. The three hybrid orbitals are available to form *two* bonds to hydrogen and *one* to the other carbon, which are not very different from the bonds in ethane. These bonds are called σ bonds.

The remaining $2p$ orbitals, one for each carbon, are only a little changed during this hybridization, and have their maximum concentration in the region above and below the plane of the triangle, somewhat as shown in Fig. 2-7. They then form another and weaker kind of bond called the π bond, in which the "electron cement" lies not between the two carbons but mainly in the regions just above and below a line joining them, as shown.

This concept of π bonds has been applied to the problem of the stability of the benzene ring (C_6H_6) with considerable success also. The six carbons in benzene lie in a plane, forming a regular hexagon; the six hydrogen atoms also lie in the same plane. For years, however, the actual bonding arrangement between carbon atoms has troubled scientists.

Kekulé postulated in 1865 that the structure

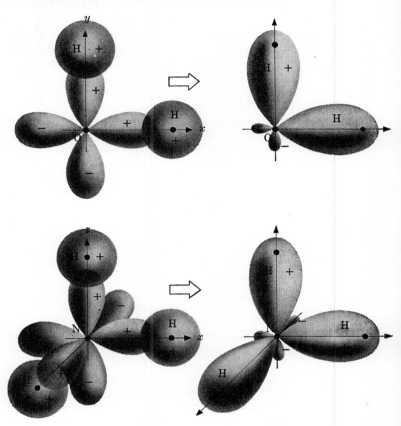

Fig. 2-6. *Top drawing shows two atoms of hydrogen (H), with spherical 1s orbital, approaching an atom of oxygen (O) with its 2p orbitals. The molecule H_2O shows the resulting "added" molecular orbitals. Similar situation for nitrogen (N) and hydrogen to produce ammonia is shown in the lower drawing.*

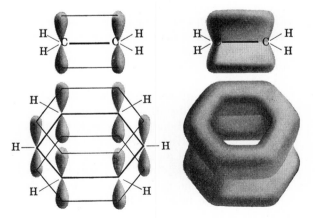

Fig. 2-7. *In ethylene, top, two 2p orbitals and 2s orbital combine to join carbon-carbon and carbon-hydrogens. This leaves one 2p orbital for each carbon to form an extra "cementing" π bond above and below the plane of the carbons. Analogous situation for benzene ring below is responsible for stability of compound.*

contained alternating double and single bonds. The big problem with this proposal was to explain the fact that benzene was far more stable and less reactive than compounds containing double bonds are expected to be. Also, the most strenuous efforts had failed to produce as many varieties as expected of substances in which other atoms or groups of atoms were substituted for the hydrogen. For instance, the Kekulé structure predicts that if two chlorine atoms replace the hydrogens on two adjacent carbons, two different compounds are possible (as shown in the margin). Instead, only a single disubstituted compound exists.

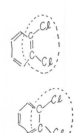

Most chemists met this problem by simply learning to live with it. Some thoughtful individuals rationalized the situation by saying that the actual structure might be intermediate between the structures represented. Others spoke of partial valences—carbon-carbon bonds which were each of the nature of a bond and a half.

Pauling's great contribution in this field was the recognition that whenever the electronic structure of a molecule is best represented as a "hybrid," the actual molecule is more stable than would be expected for any of the conventional structures, i.e., its total energy is less. Pauling called this difference in energy "resonance energy," and explained it in quantum mechanical terms of a linear combination of two or more wave functions which corresponded to a lower energy than any of the wave functions combined.

MASSEY: Another term for the concept of resonance is "mesomerism." This has the advantage of not implying that the compound actually "resonates" or alternates between two or more physical structures, but implies simply that the structure lies somewhere between those symbolized, and can only be represented by a weighted super-position of all of the various configurations.

HAMMETT: In contrast to the resonance-energy concept of benzene, the molecular-orbital concept ascribes the extra stability to the presence of the π bonds we mentioned in discussing ethylene. Hund, Mulliken, and Huckel proposed an orbital picture wherein each of the six carbon atoms is joined by σ orbitals to one hydrogen atom and to the adjacent two carbon atoms, with the bonds at 120° angles. The six electrons which are not employed in forming these σ bonds are distributed among a set of molecular orbitals which can be approximated as linear combinations of the six $2p$ orbitals, one for each carbon. The resulting π bonds, the regions of high electron density, lie in doughnut-shaped rings just above and below the hexagon

of the carbon atoms, in an analogous situation to that in ethylene.

Actually, the resonance idea had the essential virtue of a great theory for the chemist; it not only rationalized and improved the organization of what was already known, but it was also an extremely useful tool for predicting modes of chemical behavior that had not been previously recognized. Indeed, it would be difficult for anyone but Pauling (and perhaps even for him) to say whether he derived the idea more by inductive reasoning from his vast knowledge of the facts of chemistry or by deduction from his knowledge of quantum theory.

MASSEY: You've restricted yourself to discussing compounds containing a limited number of elements. There's a whole group of complex inorganic compounds to which quantum theory is now being applied in current discussions of bonding principles.

HAMMETT: You're speaking now of ligand field theory and especially of its application to compounds formed by the so-called transition elements, which include such elements as iron, chromium, and platinum. The chief unifying characteristic of these elements is that they all contain electrons in partly-filled d orbitals. Since there are five distinct d orbitals, the additional orbitals add considerably to the complexity of the geometry.

When these elements react, the concept of degeneracy arises again, and here is where ligand field theory enters.

In an isolated atom, all five d orbitals would have the same energy, and thus be degenerate or equivalent. When the atom is perturbed, however, for instance by surrounding ions or combining groups of atoms (which chemists call ligands from their ability to be *tied* to metal ions) this is no longer true. The *way* the degeneracy is split becomes of prime importance.

Although the subject is too complex to explore fully, one example may show how quantum-mechanical principles are applied. Let's assume a central atom with d orbitals as shown in Fig. 2-4, and four ligands which can be ions such as fluoride or cyanide, or polar compounds such as water or ammonia, placed on the x and y axes. All the ligands mentioned possess a negative charge or negative region of charge, and align themselves so that the charge is nearest the central atom. Thus, the electrostatic field will repel electrons from the directions of the x and y axes.

It is immediately apparent that in the $d_{x^2-y^2}$ orbital all four lobes are unfavorably placed—electrostatic repulsion is large. This adds energy to the molecule, and raises it considerably above the ground-state energy level, splitting the orbital from its previously equivalent brothers. The d_{xy} orbital is less affected, but still considerably so, while the remaining orbitals are relatively unaffected.

This splitting of the energy levels, as shown in the margin, gives rise to different types of complexes which can be formed by the various transition elements with different ligands. Thus we have compounds like $[Fe(CN)_6]K_4$; $[Fe(CN)_5NH_3]Na_3$; and $[Fe(NO_2)_6]K_2Ca$.

In retrospect, the whole development of quantum chemistry must seem to the admirer of elegance in science to represent the erection of an elaborate superstructure on an extremely shaky foundation. Wisely or not, most chemists go cheerfully about their business, using quantum theoretical ideas when they seem to help, and refusing to let the shakiness of the foundation bother them. Streitwieser, for example, has observed:

"For organic chemists, the importance of quantum mechanics lies not at all in exact calculations from first principles, but rather in providing heuristic concepts and insights in establishing qualitative and quantitative semi-empirical data and, especially, in facilitating the application of what has long been the organic chemist's most important tool: reasoning by analogy."

Further reading

For those wanting to get all bound up in a real study of chemical bonding, the basic books (that are still valid) are Slater's *Quantum Theory of Matter* (McGraw-Hill, 1953, $9), Pauling's *The Nature of the Chemical Bond and the Structure of Molecules and Crystals* (Cornell U. Press, 3rd Ed., 1960, $9), and Coulson's *Valence* (Oxford, 2nd Ed., 1961, $6). Two good elementary paperbacks develop the subject from a historical and developmental aspect, with some of the major interests of the authors showing through. They are *The Modern Theory of Molecular Structure* by Pullman, a French organic chemist (Dover, 1962, $1), and *Chemical Bonding and the Geometry of Molecules* by Ryschkewitsch, an inorganic chemist (Reinhold, 1963, $2). Also, almost any good elementary chemical textbook written in the last ten years will treat the subject from a quantum mechanical point of view.

Especially oriented toward teachers and those who use physical models to explain bonding concepts is a compilation of reprints from

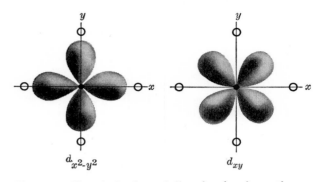

Fig. 2-8. Negatively-charged ligands placed on the x and y coordinates repulse d-orbitals to a varying amount, depending on their proximity. This in turn changes the energy levels of the otherwise equivalent states.

the *Journal of Chemical Education* called *Supplementary Readings for the Chemical Bond Approach*, compiled by Fitzgerel and Kieffer (Chemical Education Publishing Co., 1960, $3). Also perhaps more interesting than helpful is a paperback edited by Benfey called *Classics in the Theory of Chemical Combination* (Dover, 1963, $2), which reprints the original papers by early scientists like Wöhler, Liebig, and Kekulé.

Ligand field theory, one of the more recent theories of bonding in inorganic compounds, is well described in an article by L. E. Sutton, "Some Recent Developments in the Theory of Bonding in Complex Compounds of the Transition Metals" in the *Journal of Chemical Education*, **37**, No. 10 (1960). The theory is explained in a good deal more detail in Ballhausen's *Introduction to Ligand Field Theory* (McGraw-Hill, 1962, $12), but it's tough going.

The applications of the various quantum theories to specific fields are included in such volumes as *Quantum Biochemistry* by Pullman and Pullman (Interscience, 1963, $27.50), *Molecular Orbital Theory for Organic Chemists* by Streitwieser (Wiley, 1961, $13), *Chemical Applications of Group Theory* (Interscience, 1963, $12.50), and *Magnetism and the Chemical Bond* by Goodenough (Interscience, 1963, $12.50).

Finally, two good moderately technical reviews are C. A. Coulson's in *Reviews of Modern Physics*, **32**, 170 (1960), and Takayuki Fueno's "Electronic Structure and Reactivity of Large Organic Molecules," *Annual Review of Physical Chemistry*, **12**, 302 (1961).

NONEQUILIBRIUM THERMODYNAMICS

by Aharon Katchalsky *

IN BRIEF: *Classical thermodynamics dealt with closed systems in equilibrium, and it could not describe the irreversible transport processes of open systems. Modern insights about the components of entropy production and its relationship to time permit expressing the dissipation of a system's free energy as a function of forces and flows. A flow is seen to be drivable not only by the force to which it is conjugated—current by emf, for example—but also, through coupling, by the forces driving other kinds of simultaneous flows. Onsager's law reduces the coupling coefficients to the number necessary and sufficient to describe process behavior. Workers are still trying to give physical meaning to the coefficients of complicated systems involving many or rapid flows, but the understanding so far achieved of slow and simple systems has already explained old anomalies and predicated new data.—T.M.*

■ The verbal combination of "nonequilibrium" with "thermodynamics" sounds queer to the student of classical thermodynamics. He knows thermodynamics—or more precisely, thermostatics—as essentially a theory of equilibrium states (see Fig. 2-9). The powerful clarity of its laws and correlations, which has made them the ultimate criteria for the possibility or impossibility of processes, derives to a large extent from the fact that the systems it considers are in a well-defined state—that of equilibrium. One might well wonder whether the logical formalism of thermodynamics really can be extended to embrace the evanescent and transient phenomena of such irreversible processes as diffusional flow and the flow of heat through crystals.

Actually, the great masters who forged the fundamental concepts of the new science of thermodynamics during its first creative period, the nineteenth century, had no intention of limiting its scope to the dead ends of processes—to equilibrium states. They intended to work out a general formalism that would be able to describe real natural phenomena, nonequilibrium states, and irreversible processes. Indeed, the connotation of the fundamental concept "entropy" is evolution, and Clausius introduced

* Aharon Katchalsky is Head of the Polymer Research Department of the Weizmann Institute of Science, Rehovoth, Israel. He is also Professor of Physical Chemistry at Hebrew University in Jerusalem and President of the National Academy of Sciences and Humanities.

it precisely as a universal indicator for the developmental process in a state of irreversible flow.

In later years, many thermodynamicists were attracted by the crystalline clarity of thermostatics and built a consistent formal edifice that occupies, in present-day natural science, a place similar to that of logic in general thought. Still, the search for a thermodynamics of irreversible processes continued incessantly in the background.

It was clear that though balance sheets could be worked out at thermal or mechanical or chemical equilibrium, all real processes, whether of an engine or of a living organism, were nonequilibrium, irreversible processes. A suitable conceptual framework and mathematical apparatus had to be developed if a general thermodynamics of natural phenomena were to be an achievable goal.

For more than 80 years, many attempts were made which provided some valuable building blocks for the present-day structure but which did not combine into a consistent science until 1931. That year, Lars Onsager published the fundamental relationship that has underlain all subsequent developments. In 1945, H. B. G. Casimir removed some inconsistencies in Onsager's treatment and extended Onsager's relationships to cover polar phenomena. Since then, most notably in the postwar years, the new science has grown smoothly. The work of the Belgian and Dutch schools of physical chemistry led by Prigogine and deGroot, of such German physicists as Meixner and Meissner, and of the American Kirkwood has put the treatment of slow irreversible processes, at least, on a solid basis. In many cases—unfortunately not including turbulence—one may discern the beginning of an orderly, indeed "trivial," treatment of nonequilibrium phenomena.

Whether we like it or not, the ultimate goal of every science is to become trivial, to become a well-controlled apparatus for the solution of schoolbook exercises or for practical application in the construction of engines.

Now nonequilibrium thermodynamics has not yet reached this "classical" stage; its application still requires much ingenuity and profound study in many fields of science, such as the treatment of chemical kinetics and the description of biological phenomena. However, it can quickly become an operational tool that may be used with advantage by the nonspecialist.

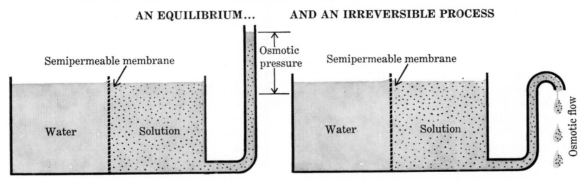

AN EQUILIBRIUM...   AND AN IRREVERSIBLE PROCESS

Fig. 2-9. The different kinds of systems treated by classical and modern thermodynamics can be created by rearranging the capillary of an osmometer in which a semipermeable membrane separates an aqueous solution from water. In one setup (left), a difference in hydrostatic pressure across the membrane is gradually built up as water molecules replace migrating solute ions, causing the solution level in the capillary to rise above the water level until a state of osmotic equilibrium is reached. The magnitude of the pressure head is derivable from solution properties by classical thermodynamics (thermostatics). If the capillary is bent (right) so that its opening is at the level of the water, the osmotic pressure difference causes an irreversible osmotic flow. Its magnitude is derivable—but only by using both membrane and solution properties and nonequilibrium thermodynamics.

The basic principles from which nonequilibrium thermodynamics starts its operations are known and generally accepted. They are the First Law (matter and energy are conserved) and the Second Law (entropy does not decrease) of thermodynamics.

The new trend appears first in the proposition that the laws can be applied locally to every element of a system and second in the assumption that the Second Law is valid also for nonequilibrium systems—if the irreversible changes they are undergoing are sufficiently slow.

The growth of inner entropy

Clausius found that if a system at temperature T exchanges an amount dQ of heat with its surroundings, then the change of entropy dS in the system is larger than or equal to dQ/T; that is

$$dS \geq \frac{dQ}{T} \qquad (1)$$

Clausius himself recognized that dQ/T is the entropy exchanged with the surroundings, or d_eS. So Eq. 1 implies that besides the entropy brought from the outside, there is an additional source of entropy created within the system, or d_iS. We may therefore rewrite Eq. 1 in the more explicit form

$$dS = d_eS + d_iS \qquad (2)$$

Now, d_eS, the entropy exchanged with the surroundings, may be either positive or negative; that is to say, the system may either obtain entropy from the external world or transfer entropy to external bodies. However, the peculiar property of d_iS is that it can never be negative; it is positive definite:

$$d_iS \geq 0 \qquad (3)$$

This inner entropy term is due to the dissipation of energy by nonequilibrium processes. Its positivity is another expression of the unidirectional properties, i.e., the irreversibility, of natural processes. The limit of very slow irreversible processes is an equilibrium process during which no energy is dissipated and $d_iS = 0$.

When we say that the entropy grows in natural processes, we imply the positive definite nature of d_iS; but we are also expressing another fundamental and striking property of this term: In contradistinction to mass and energy, entropy does not obey a law of conservation. It is a nonconservative quantity whose incessant production consitutes a singular indicator of the progress of natural processes.

This is the reason the thermodynamics of irreversible processes has chosen d_iS as the primary yardstick of all irreversible phenomena. However, an additional step is required to make d_iS a workable scientific tool—the explicit measurement of d_iS per unit of time.

Philosophers have been concerned with the directional properties of time for many years. Attempts to regard time as another coordinate of a four-dimensional world of events did not remove the mystery from the fact that one can move forwards and backwards in any space coordinate while regrettably one's movement in the time coordinate is restricted to a single direction.

In the flowery language of Eddington, there exists a pointed "arrow of time," and the direction of this arrow was early seen to be connected with the growth of inner entropy in cosmic irreversible processes. For physical purposes, however, we have to jump from general speculations to quantitative relations; we must connect time to inner entropy by a straightforward formula. This we do by writing the differential growth of d_iS with time t; namely, d_iS/dt. This differential is the rate of entropy production by irreversible processes; it is a basic operational parameter of nonequilibrium thermodynamics.

In isothermal systems, which are common both in mechanics and biology, it is often more convenient to consider not the production of entropy but a different though related function, the dissipation of free energy. This function is denoted by the Greek letter phi:

$$\Phi = T\frac{d_iS}{dt} \qquad (4)$$

This phi function was introduced by Lord Rayleigh at the end of the nineteenth century as an indicator for the degradation of the working capacity of mechanical systems due to dissipative frictional processes.

Thermodynamic forces and flows

When the fundamental assumptions of the thermodynamics of irreversible processes are put through the mathematical machine of differential equations, it is possible to obtain an explicit expression for the local entropy production or free-energy dissipation function.

It is found that Φ is the sum of terms contributed by every irreversible process proceeding in the system and that every term is the product of two members—a flow J_i and a force X_i, such that

$$\Phi = \Sigma J_i X_i \qquad (5)$$

where the summation is over the entropy-producing processes.

Generally, the flows J_i are perceived intuitively and have a simple physical meaning.

Thus, the flow of matter will be the vectorial transport of a number of moles or a number of grams of substance per unit area per unit time. Or the flow of heat, or of electricity, will be the transport of a corresponding quantity in a given direction per unit area and unit time.

Some of the flows have no direction in space and are merely scalar changes per unit time. An important flow of this type is the advancement of a chemical reaction or the extent of reaction per unit time.

Still other flows have to be specified by a more sophisticated dependence on space coordinates; they require treatment by tensors of second order. Such are the flows in anisotropic systems; e.g., the flow of heat in crystals.

Though the flows of thermodynamics are generally familiar, the forces are generally not the well-known mechanical forces of Newtonian mechanics. Thus the force conjugate to a diffusional flow of matter, the force which drives the transport of a given substance, is found to be the local drop in its chemical potential. The chemical potential itself, μ, is not an elementary concept. It depends in a rather complicated manner on pressure, temperature, concentration, and electrical potential, so that it is still a rather foreign concept to the practical worker despite its having been covered for many years in textbooks of physical chemistry.

A closer inspection, however, shows that the gradient of chemical potential is rather simple, for it is found to be a straightforward mechanical force per unit substance which drags the diffusing substance in solution.

Some other thermodynamic forces are more familiar. There is no surprise in observing that the force driving the flow of entropy is the fall in temperature, or that the force conjugated to the flow of electricity is the negative gradient of electrical potential.

Presumably the most difficult force to grasp is the force driving the advancement of a chemical reaction. This important force was first described by de Donder and denoted as the affinity of the reaction, A.

Consider a reaction of substance B and C giving rise to the reaction products F and G. If we assign each of the participants a chemical potential, say μ_B, μ_C, μ_F, and μ_G, then the affinity is $A = (\mu_B + \mu_C) - (\mu_F + \mu_G)$, or, more generally, it is the sum of the chemical potentials of the reactants, minus the sum of the chemical potentials of the reaction products. If A is larger than zero, the reaction is driven from left to right; if it is smaller than zero, the reaction proceeds in the opposite direction; but when $A = 0$, no reaction takes place and a state of equilibrium is attained.

Thermodynamic flows and forces have to be carefully assigned to the irreversible processes proceeding in the system; but then they can be fed into Eq. 5 and the dissipation function evaluated.

Dependence of flows on forces

The patient reader who has managed to read my article up to this point will surely stop and ask himself what we have achieved by our deliberation.

Apparently, after a lengthy analysis of flows and forces, the investigator will be able to combine them in a mathematical expression and

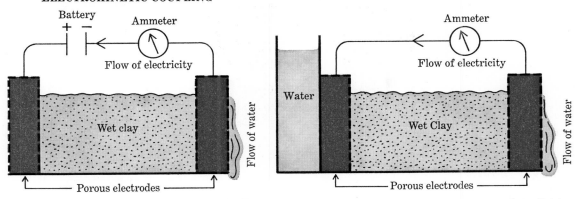

Fig. 2-10. The first coupled phenomenon was discovered by Rous in 1808 when (left) an electrical potential drove a flow of water as well as a flow of electricity through a wet clay conductor. In the reverse experiment (right), a pressure head drove not only a water flow but also an electric current. The electrokinetic coupling here is simply the fact that the water molecules are electrically charged.

have the satisfaction of knowing what the entropy production of his system is. But what does he gain by this knowledge? What new information, what clearer insight has he derived from this formal juggling with mathematical symbols?

The scientist or technologist will surely ask for a useful application and will not be satisfied with the mere possibility of adding a non-equilibrium label to the object of his interest.

In order to proceed, we have to supplement the dissipation function Φ with additional relationships, the most important being the dependence of the flows on the forces. The search for such dependences is almost as old as the study of energy conversions that underlies classical thermodynamics.

Already in 1811 Fourier observed that the flow of heat is linearly dependent on the gradient of temperature. Later, Fick noted that the diffusional flow of matter depends linearly on gradient of concentration, while Ohm found that the flow of electricity is linearly proportional to the electromotive force.

All of these cases demonstrated that in relatively slow processes, the rates of which are largely determined by frictional forces, the flow is a linear function of the force and may be written as

$$J_i = L_i X_i \qquad (6)$$

where the coefficient L_i is a proportionality factor, not necessarily constant but independent of both J_i and X_i.

But linear dependence is not the whole story. And, as is often the case in the history of science, the more complicated dependence was discovered several years before the simpler linear case.

In 1808, a pioneer colloid chemist in Russia named Rous studied the conductance of elec-

trical current by wet clay (Fig. 2-10). To his amazement, he observed that imposing an electrical potential difference across the clay led not only to the expected flow of electricity but also to a pronounced flow of water towards the cathode. Since, on *a priori* grounds, a flow of water should be driven by a pressure head, Rous made the converse experiment: he applied hydrostatic pressure to the piece of clay and obtained a flow of electricity.

Rous's ingenious electrokinetic experiments were the first to demonstrate the existence of coupled phenomena. They proved that a flow may not only be driven by its directly conjugated force but may also be coupled to other, nonconjugated forces. Thus the flow of electricity is evidently caused by an electromotive force, but it may be coupled to a hydrostatic pressure; and conversely, the volume flow of water may be coupled to an electrical force.

Some twenty years later, another group of coupled phenomena was found in the field of thermoelectricity (Fig. 2-11). Seebeck in Germany observed that if the ends of a bimetallic couple are heated to different temperatures, an electric potential difference is built up—across the conductor. Conversely, the French watchmaker Peltier observed upon passing an electrical current through the couple, that heat was transported from one junction to the other.

Onsager's principle of matrix symmetry

Neither Seebeck nor Peltier understood what they were doing; but their experiments, with that of Rous, made clear the importance of coupling. The idea that interrelationships between different flows may exist, and often occur in natural phenomena, matured slowly during the nineteenth century but did not find a consistent expression until 1931, in the "phenomenological" equations of Lars Onsager.

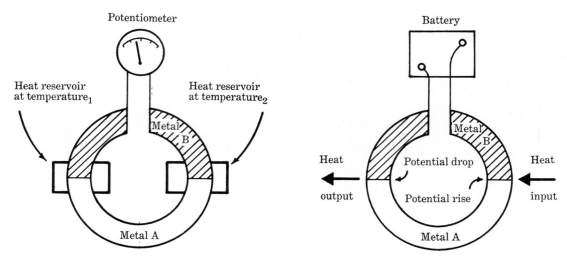

Fig. 2-11. A bimetallic thermocouple can be used to show two aspects of thermoelectric coupling. In the Seebeck effect (left), a temperature gradient between the junctions causes a flow of current as shown by a buildup of open-circuit e.m.f. The microscopic explanation of such thermoelectric coupling is that some metallic heat conduction is an energy transfer from hot electrons to cool electrons. In the Peltier effect (right), a weak flow causes vectorial heat transport from one junction to the other.

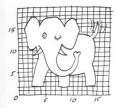

Onsager assumed that any flow is linearly dependent not only on its conjugate force but in principle on all other forces operative in the system.

For example, let us consider a system in which the flows J_1, J_2, and J_3 are driven by the forces X_1, X_2, and X_3. We shall now explicitly write the dependence of each of the flows on all three forces, as a generalization of Eq. 6:

$$J_1 = L_{11}X_1 + L_{12}X_2 + L_{13}X_3$$
$$J_2 = L_{21}X_1 + L_{22}X_2 + L_{23}X_3 \qquad (7)$$
$$J_3 = L_{31}X_1 + L_{32}X_2 + L_{33}X_3$$

What these equations state is that while, say, the second flow (J_2) is dependent on its conjugated force X_2 through the so-called straight coefficient L_{22}, J_2 also depends linearly on force X_1 and on force X_3 through the coupling coefficients L_{21} and L_{23}.

You'll note that the equations are linear; i.e., the flows are stated to depend only on the first power of the forces. This is by no means self-evident and is not always true; the flows may depend on some higher power of the forces or may exhibit still more complicated functional dependences.

It is rather lucky that in a great number of phenomena, at sufficiently low rates of flow (and it is here that we need the restriction of nonequilibrium thermodynamics to sufficiently slow flows), the linear relationships hold very well and nicely describe the observed behavior.

The real trouble with the phenomenological equations lies in the large number of coefficients required to master even the simplest cases. The determination of each coefficient requires a different experimental method, so that for the full description of a three-flow system we need nine independent experimental methods which may be neither available nor practicable.

I think it was Cauchy who said, "Give me five coefficients and I will plot an elephant; give me six coefficients and the elephant will wiggle its tail." Imagine what Cauchy could do with the nine coefficients imposed upon us in a simple three-flow case!

It is here that we are helped by the fundamental law of Onsager, which is rightly regarded as the cornerstone of nonequilibrium thermodynamics. The statement of the law is rather mathematical; it says, "The matrix of the coefficients is symmetrical" or

$$L_{ij} = L_{ji} \qquad (8)$$

For the three-flow system the requirement is that $L_{12} = L_{21}$, $L_{13} = L_{31}$, and $L_{23} = L_{32}$.

In words: those coupling coefficients are equal that are equidistant from the diagonal formed by the straight coefficients.

We shall soon see that this mathematical-looking statement does not merely reduce the number of coefficients required for the description of irreversible processes, it also leads to a series of very valuable and important physical relationships.

The proof of Onsager's law is based on a profound statistical-mechanical analysis. Actually there does not yet exist a sufficiently general and complete proof of its validity. However, many great scientific ideas have a range of importance and correctness wider than that originally envisaged by their creators. That this is also the case for Onsager's principle was shown recently by Donald Miller, who analyzed a large number of existing experiments and found that the principle holds in a variety of fields of physics and chemistry. You may therefore accept it as an empirically founded law of nature.

Now let us consider a few examples that will demonstrate how to use Onsager's law and what kind of predictions nonequilibrium thermodynamics makes.

Electrokinetics and membrane permeability

It seems fitting to take as the first example the first observation of coupled phenomena—the experiments of Rous (Fig. 2-10). The analysis is based on the work of Mazur and Overbeek, who pointed out that in this case we evidently have two thermodynamic flows—the flow of electricity I and the volume flow of water J_v. Then it is intuitively clear—but may be verified by constructing the dissipation function—that the driving force for the electric flow is the electromotive force E, while the force driving the flow of water is the hydrostatic pressure across the piece of wet clay Δp.

We may therefore write Onsager's equation in the form

$$I = L_{11}E + L_{12}\Delta p \qquad (9)$$

$$J_v = L_{21}E + L_{22}\Delta p$$

In Eq. 9, the coupling of Rous is brought to light clearly and definitely: we see that even if no electromotive force acts on the clay (that is, if $E = 0$), the existence of a pressure difference will produce an electric flow if the coupling coefficient is nonvanishing. Also expressed is the reverse coupling: when no pressure is applied ($\Delta p = 0$), the action of the electrical force will cause a volume flow of water.

Onsager's law now gives additional and quantitative information. Since by this law $L_{12} = L_{21}$, we deduce that the electrical flow per unit pressure, at $E = 0$, equals volume flow per unit e.m.g., at $\Delta p = 0$, or

$$(I/\Delta p)_{E=0} = L_{12} = (J_V/E)_{\Delta p=0} = L_{21} \quad (10)$$

Observe that Eq. 10 does not say how large is the flow either of electricity or of volume. Thermodynamics alone cannot say whether or not L_{12} is zero or, if not, what its magnitude is.

The other example I would like to consider is membrane permeability. Following the work

of Staverman, my friend Ora Kedem and I have devoted considerable time to the thermodynamic description of the permeability of nonelectrolytes and of electrolytes through simple or composite membranes. Here, I'll discuss only the very simplest case, of the transport of a single nonelectrolyte solute dissolved in water, through a homogenous synthetic membrane.

Let the membrane under consideration be separating two compartments containing two solutions of equal solute but of different concentrations. Let the resulting difference of osmotic pressure across the membranes be $\Delta\pi$.

Let us further assume that the hydrostatic pressure is unequal on the two sides of the membrane, so that there exists a pressure head Δp.

We now have two forces, $\Delta\pi$ and Δp, and our next task is to evaluate the conjugated flows. Consideration of the dissipation function Φ shows that, as expected, the flow conjugate to Δp is the flow of total solution volume across the membrane, or J_V. The other flow is more intriguing; it is the flow of solute relative to that of solvent: what we call the diffusional flow J_D.

With this information we can write

$$J_V = L_{11}\Delta p + L_{12}\Delta\pi \qquad (11)$$

$$J_D = L_{21}\Delta p + L_{22}\Delta\pi$$

Equation 11 immediately indicates several interesting phenomena. On *a priori* grounds we would imagine that volume flow would be driven only by hydrostatic pressure and that $J_V/\Delta p = L_{11}$ should be simply the filtration coefficient of the membrane. But Eq. 11 shows that even at $\Delta p = 0$, there may exist a volume flow driven by the coupled osmotic pressure. Such flows are indeed known; their magnitude depends on the coefficient of osmotic flow

$$L_{12} = (J_V/\Delta\pi)_{\Delta p=0}$$

A similar statement can be made about the diffusional flow J_D. Evidently, in order for a diffusional flow to exist, there should exist a difference in concentration expressed here as the osmotic difference $\Delta\pi$. But we see from Eq. 11 that even when $\Delta\pi = 0$, a diffusional flow may develop, through the action of the mechanical pressure

This remarkable behavior is real; it is well known to the colloid chemist as ultrafiltration. It depends on the capacity of the membrane to distinguish the solute from the solvent and to produce, under pressure, a relative or diffusional flow.

Again, Onsager's law leads to the conclusion

that the coefficient of osmotic flow has to be equal to the coefficient of ultrafiltration.

This is another case from which we recognize that Onsager's principle is not a mathematical statement but a law of nature, a statement about real relations between physical phenomena.

Before the advent of the thermodynamics of irreversible processes it was customary to describe membrane permeability by two coefficients—a coefficient of solute permeability (L_{22}) and a filtration coefficient (L_{11}). But Eq. 11 shows that three coefficients are necessary; and indeed, the previous neglect of the coupling coefficient L_{12} did lead to inconsistencies and misunderstanding.

A final observation will stress again the importance of the coupling coefficients. Let us consider from the point of view of nonequilibrium thermodynamics the classical measurement of osmotic pressure depicted in Fig. 2-9. In that experiment, a solution is separated by a semipermeable membrane from pure solvent, water in this instance. The solvent, driven by a difference in chemical potential, enters the solute compartment and a pressure Δp is built up. When the hydrostatic pressure Δp equals the osmotic pressure $\Delta \pi$, the volume flow stops ($J_V = 0$) and osmotic equilibrium is established.

At equilibrium, we put $\Delta p = \Delta \pi$ so that we can measure osmotic pressure by hydrostatic pressure. To our surprise, however, Eq. 12 shows that at $J_V = 0$, Δp is not equal to $\Delta \pi$ but rather $\Delta p = -(L_{12}/L_{11})\Delta \pi$! (Exclamation, not factorial.)

Our surprise diminishes if we consider that Δp should equal $\Delta \pi$ only for an ideally semipermeable membrane. In that case indeed $-L_{12}/L_{11} = 1$; but in real membranes, which are permeable to both solute and solvent, $-L_{12}/L_{11} < 1$ and the maximum pressure is smaller than the ideal.

Now we begin to recognize the importance of L_{12} as a measure of the selectivity of the membrane. We denote the ratio $\sigma = -L_{12}/L_{11}$ as the selectivity coefficient of the membrane. When $\sigma = 1$, the membrane is ideally semipermeable and distinguishes clearly between solute and solvent. When $\sigma < 1$, the distinction is less precise and solute may pass through the membrane. Finally, when $\sigma = 0$, there is no selectivity, and solute cannot be separated from solvent by a membrane process.

Almost needless to say, a quantitative measure of selectivity is of primary interest for the characterization of membranes. A clear grasp of this important parameter has been achieved only through the application of nonequilibrium thermodynamics.

Stationary states

Throughout our discussion we imposed no restriction on flows and forces. However, there are cases that deserve special consideration for their importance both in nature and in technology. Of these, the most important are the stationary states, which are attained whenever the forces applied are constant.

Consider for example a bar of metal to the ends of which we apply different but constant temperatures. The temperature difference will induce in the bar a flow of heat that will cause a change in all local temperatures. After a while, though, a constant distribution of temperature will be attained and the flow of heat will become steady.

The state of steady flow and of constant distribution of the parameters characterizing a system is the ultimate state of irreversible systems under constant forces. They play the same role in nonequilibrium thermodynamics as is played by states of equilibrium in classical thermostatics.

Steady states are typical of smoothly running engines, and, what is more intriguing, they are the stable states of living organisms. Indeed, most organisms, including man, undergo a process of rapid development in their youth, then reach a steady state at maturity—the well-known state of middle age. Living organisms have a special control system, the system of homeostasis, which corrects minor deviations from steady state, and, to be sure, modern engines are endowed with man-made homeostats that keep them producing at a constant rate.

Since all the parameters of a system are constant during a stationary state, the entropy is constant too, not changing with time. This means, in accord with our first equations, that the entropy created by steady flow is equal to the entropy given off to the surroundings.

Thus, only systems open to exchange of entropy with their environments can reach a steady state. A fully isolated adiabatic system can end up only in equilibrium or in explosion. This is the thermodynamic reason why all living beings are open systems, capable of stable existence in a stationary state.

Several years ago, Prigogine pointed out that steady nonequilibrium systems produce entropy at a minimal rate. This remarkable conclusion from Onsager's law sheds new light on "the wisdom of living organisms." Life is a constant struggle against the tendency to produce entropy by irreversible processes. The synthesis of large and information-rich macromolecules, the formation of intricately structured cells, the development of organization—

all these are powerful anti-entropic forces. But since there is no possibility of escaping the entropic doom imposed upon all natural phenomena under the Second Law of thermodynamics, living organisms choose the least evil—they produce entropy at a minimal rate by maintaining a steady state.

I hope that my brief introduction has disturbed you own steady state and will encourage you to dig deeper into the formalism, interpretation, and application of nonequilibrium thermodynamics.

Further reading

About as simple a serious primer as you could expect to find is Prigogine's excellent short book *Introduction to Thermodynamics of Irreversible Processes* (Interscience, 2nd ed. 1961, $5).

The standard book on the theory is available in two editions, of which the first is the easier: *Thermodynamics of Irreversible Processes* by deGroot (Interscience, 1952, $6). The second, fuller edition, is by deGroot and Mazur: *Non-Equilibrium Thermodynamics* (Interscience, 1962, $15.50). Another book, with the same title as the latter, by Fitts (McGraw-Hill, 1962, $7.95), represents a different school of thought

led by the late John G. Kirkwood; it is perhaps best assimilated by mathematicians.

Readers who would like to see how the theory deals with a real physical process important for technology should read Domenicali's painstaking "Thermodynamics of Thermoelectricity" either in *Rev. Mod. Phys.* **26,** No. 2 (April 1954) or as Paper 10 in *Selected Papers on New Techniques for Energy Conversion*, ed. by Levine (Dover, 1961, $2.85 paperback).

Spiegler, in *Trans. of the Faraday Society, 1958,* **54,** 1409, translated the phenomenological permeability coefficients of ion-exchange membranes into frictional and distribution coefficients amenable to physical interpretation.

Miller's review, referred to in the article, of empirical results establishing Onsager's reciprocal relation as an experimentally founded law of nature, appeared in *Chem. Rev.* **60,** 15 (February 1960).

"Thermodynamics of Flow Processes in Biological Systems" by Katchalsky and Kedem [*Biophys. J.* **2,** 53 (1962)] is a survey digestible by a reader equipped with the present article. A survey of the role of entropy in the living state, *Time's Arrow and Evolution* by Blum (Torchbooks, 1962, $1.65 paperback), relates the Second Law to life.

THE LIQUID STATE

by Henry Eyring, Joel Hildebrand, and Stuart Rice *

IN BRIEF: *An intriguing perversity of most researchers (and indeed, of man in general) is an almost universal penchant for mental challenges. These they not only accept, but seek out, pursue, and, when things get slow, even invent. Nature, it seems, is very obliging in this respect. So obliging, that within the range of common experience, at very ordinary pressures and temperatures and on a distinctly noncosmic scale, many such challenges still remain almost too challenging. The relationships within the liquid state pose such a problem.*

It's not that such problems have failed to attract study by able investigators. The liquid state has drawn the fascinated attention of great chemists and physicists from before the time of Röntgen to the present. The question is how to explain the macroscopic properties of liquids, their viscosities, melting and boiling characteristics, etc., in terms of the relationships among their component molecules—to

construct a model (or a mathematical description) of the liquid state. That subject is still rife with polemics.

Early liquids theorists had their choice of condensed-gas models and models which were overextensions of lattice theory, from solids (where it works beautifully) to liquids (there it works, almost). In this article, the leaders of three major schools of thought on the structure of liquids were brought together to outline, in the statements which follow, the views they represent. It seems that history offers little guidance (because the issues are far from resolved), that semantics can be quite a problem here too, and that alternative views are:

(1) If we removed about every eighth molecule from a solid and then placed the remainder in rapid motion, we would have a "gas" of roughly molecular-sized vacancies dissolved in the solid; that is, we'd have a liquid. (Eyring)

(2) Thermal agitation imposes on molecules in a liquid a state of maximum disorder; there is no trace of long-range order, except for that imposed by their density and by the rule that no two molecules can occupy the same place simultaneously. (Hildebrand)

* Henry Eyring is Dean of the Graduate School at the University of Utah in Salt Lake City. Joel Hildebrand is Professor Emeritus at the University of California at Berkeley. Stuart Rice is Professor of Chemistry and Director of The Institute for the Study of Metals at the University of Chicago.

(3) On the other (i.e., the third) hand, why adhere to any pictorial model at all? We could use approximations to represent the interactions among pairs and larger groups of molecules to calculate the all-important distribution function, i.e., the ratio of average molecular density some distance from any molecule to the bulk density of the liquid. From this, we could predict the macroscopic properties. (Rice)

Each of these ideas has met with considerable (but limited) success. An optimist would call that progress.—R.G.N.

EYRING'S FLUID VACANCY MODEL

The issue, of defining what a liquid is, centers around describing what the molecules are doing, in terms that lead to an explicit expression describing the macroscopic properties. Starting with the positions (here, q terms) and momenta (p terms) of the individual molecules, the essential, but very difficult, problem is to evaluate the integral in the equation for the (macroscopic) Helmholtz free energy, shown in the margin.

The integral, called the partition function, can be evaluated for gases, where configurations involving more than a few molecules can be neglected, and for solids, where crystallinity is assumed. In liquids with their lack of long-range order, the integrals involving many molecules cannot be neglected. Yet they are unmanageable. Faced with such difficulties one must either introduce mathematical approximations or develop a model for the liquid state. Using various approximations, the results for some properties are good, but there are always some properties for which the results are poor. It is clear that other approaches are needed.

When a simple substance (like argon) melts, it expands 12%. In spite of that expansion, x-ray diffraction indicates that nearest neighbors are at almost the same distance as in the solid. This would be consistent with removing every eighth molecule leaving ordinary vacancies. But the vacancies left are not ordinary vacancies. The molecules are in rapid motion jumping into the vacancies and smearing out the empty space enough so that light-scattering experiments fail to reveal the heterogeneity. This loosening leads to the disappearance of long-range order and to the appearance of mobile structures of less symmetry than crystals show. Hildebrand has argued against the presence, in liquids, of the essentially static, locked-in vacancies of the solid state. To this one must agree. The concept of mobile, fluid-

$$A = E - TS =$$
$$-kT\ln\frac{\int e^{-H/kT}dq_{3j}\ldots dp_{3N}}{h^{3N}N!}$$

A = Helmholtz free energy
N = no. of molecules
T = Temp.
S = entropy
k = Boltzmann's constant
h = Planck's constant
H = sum of kinetic + potential energies

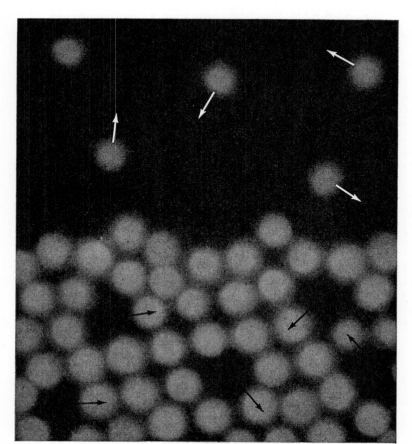

Fig. 2-12. A very successful model of the liquid state starts with a solid and, at random, removes molecules, forming vacancies. When the remaining molecules are placed in rapid and random thermal motion, the vacancies become fluidized; the solid melts and we have a liquid. The behavior of the fluidized vacancies mirrors the behavior that a gas comprised of the missing molecules would show. That is, the vacancies dart around, rotate, collide, and interact much as might the "real" molecules of a gas. But the vacancies can do other tricks: they can smear themselves out, in this model by Henry Eyring.

ized vacancies outlined here is something quite different.

Since liquids do supercool, it is clear that however solid-like the liquid may be, still there are no vestigial crystal nuclei large enough to act as centers of crystallization. Further, liquids superheat when they are heated in vessels clean enough that bubbles don't form on the walls. From this it is clear that pure liquids have no holes large enough to act as nuclei for bubble formation.

Bearing in mind these differences between a liquid and a solid containing static vacancies, it is still convenient to visualize the fleeting loose spots in the liquid as rapidly shifting vacancies. Melting is the introduction and fluidization of vacancies which enter the solid when there is enough expansion to loosen the structure and permit molecules to jump freely into the vacancies. As a result, vacancies travel in liquids with much the same ease that molecules show in gases.

Despite this smeared-out character of vacancies, it is reasonable to suppose that there is still a tendency for holes to approximate molecular size, because such size would cause the least disturbance to those molecules which, at any instant, are not directly engaged in the motion of a vacancy. Whenever it is clear from the context that these fleeting loosenesses are being referred, I simply call them vacancies. Whenever a more careful designation is needed, I speak of them as fluidized vacancies, to distinguish them from the comparatively static, sharply outlined vacancies which are found in solids.

Rectilinear diameters and the energy of a vacancy

One of the earliest applications of my model of fluidized vacancies was to explain the law of rectilinear diameters. This law says that the mean density of a liquid and its vapor is almost independent of temperature, decreasing linearly, slightly, as the temperature increases from the melting to the critical point.

If a molecule is removed from a liquid to the vapor (leaving a vacancy), all bonds to its neighbors are broken. In ordinary vaporization, although all bonds joining a molecule to its neighbor are broken, only half the energy of bonding should be charged against a molecule. (The other comes from the neighbors.) It follows that the energy needed to form a vacancy exactly equals the heat of vaporization and, insofar as the vacancy moves as freely as a vapor molecule, it has the same entropy associated with it. Consequently we expect the same concentration of vacancies in the liquid as of molecules in the vapor and the sum of the

two densities should be constant—except that lattice expansion causes the mean density of the liquid to decrease slightly with temperature. That is what, in fact, is observed.

Significant structure theory

The model just outlined provides the basis of a quantitative theory of liquids. We assume that the extra volume, to a sufficient approximation, arises from holes of molecular size, our fluid vacancies. In one mole of liquid there are $(V - V_s)/V$ moles of vacancies, where V and V_s are the volume of the liquid and of the solid at its melting point, respectively. If a vacancy is completely surrounded by molecules, it is presumably endowed with gas-like properties conferred on it by its neighbors jumping into it. On the other hand, a vacancy completely surrounded by other vacancies has no dynamic properties.

The proportion of positions adjacent to a vacancy which are filled is, in first approximation, V_s/V. The fraction V_s/V is then the probability that a vacancy has gas-like properties. Multiplying this chance, V_s/V, by the number of holes $(V - V_s)/V_s$ gives $(V - V_s)/V$ for the number of moles of vacancies endowed with gas-like properties. There must accordingly be $1 - [(V - V_s)/V] = V_s/V$ moles of effectively solid-like molecules.

Vacancies confer degeneracies on a solid-like molecule equal to the number of vacancies adjacent to it. If the total number of neighboring positions, both full and empty, is Z then the number of adjacent vacancies is $Z(V - V_s)/V$. For molecules to occupy these vacancies involves expending an energy

$$E = \frac{aE_s}{n_h} = \frac{aE_s V_s}{V - V_s}$$

which is inversely proportional to the number of vacancies n_h, and directly proportional to the energy of sublimation, E_s and to a characteristic dimensionless number for the liquid.

This quantity can be determined this way: In a solid, a vacancy next to a molecule is available for occupancy without pushing out encroaching neighbors. But this is not true in the liquid. In the process of melting, molecules gain kinetic energy of melting by spreading competitively into vacancies. According to the virial theorem, the kinetic energy is half the total energy of melting, E^m. Thus, at, or near, the melting point

$$\frac{aE_s V_s}{V - V_s} = \frac{n - 1}{Z} \cdot \frac{1}{2} E_m \simeq \frac{n - 1}{2Z} \frac{V - V_s}{V} E_s$$

Hence we have

$$a = \frac{n - 1}{2Z} \frac{V - V_s}{V} \frac{V - V_s}{V_s} = 0.0052$$

SOME OBSERVED PROPERTIES OF LIQUIDS

A challenge all physical theories eventually meet is the need to account for observed properties. Stuart A. Rice has outlined below some of those familiar macroscopic properties of simple liquids for which a successful theory of the liquid state must account—if it can.

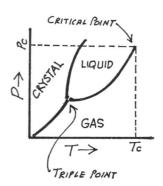

• As a rule, substances possess only one liquid modification. Exceptions are He^4 (with two liquid forms) and substances which can be isolated in pure quantum states (*ortho*- and *para*-hydrogen). In general, substances have one or more crystalline solid phases, some or all of which may coexist with the liquid phase. The liquid and solid phases can coexist along a continuous locus of temperature and pressure but the liquid, solid, and gaseous phases coexist at only one temperature and pressure. There is experimental evidence that equilibrium between a solid and liquid is possible at all temperatures so long as decomposition or ionization does not occur. In contrast, the equilibrium locus between the liquid and gaseous states terminates at a critical point, T_c. At each temperature below T_c, there exists a pressure (the vapor pressure) at which the (more dense) liquid phase and the (less dense) vapor phase coexist. Above T_c there is no distinction between gas and liquid; there is just a single fluid phase.

• Liquids vaporize discontinuously at that temperature for which the vapor pressure equals the external pressure. The vaporization requires the absorption of a quantity of heat per unit mass, L_v, the latent heat of vaporization. The transition from the liquid to a crystalline phase occurs at a fixed temperature, determined by the external pressure, and the transformation releases a quantity of heat per unit mass, L_f, the latent heat of fusion. Both these transformations are described by the Clapeyron equation, $dp/dT = L/T\Delta V$, which relates the external pressure, p, to the temperature of the transition, T, the latent heat of transition, L, and the volume change in the transition ΔV.

• In vaporization, $\Delta V > 0$ for all substances, and therefore the boiling point always increases if the external pressure is increased. In fusion, ΔV is usually positive, but exceptions occur. The most notable exception is water, for which there is a range of temperatures where increasing the external pressure decreases the freezing temperature. Bi, Ge, and Sb also show this property. In contrast to this discontinuous behavior of crystalline phases, non-crystalline solids generally do not have definite transitions, but soften gradually to a liquid phase with increasing temperature.

• Still, there is no simple relationship connecting the pressure, volume, and temperature of a liquid over the entire fluid range. For small changes from some fixed p_0, V_0, T_0 a simple power series expansion is useful,

$$V = V_0 \left[1 + \frac{1}{V_0} \left(\frac{V}{T} \right)_{p_0} (T - T_0) - \frac{1}{V_0} \left(\frac{V}{p} \right)_{T_0} (p - p_0) \right]$$

but this equation of state usually fails if $(p - p_0) > 100$ atm and $(T - T_0) > 10°C$.

• The electrical properties of liquids are determined by the density of charge carriers. Except for liquid metals, molten salts, and solutions of salts in ionizing solvents, the electrical conductivities of liquids are small. In molten salts and solutions of salts, current is carried by ions of the salt; in liquid metals electrons carry the current. Even when the density of charge carriers is zero, a liquid may still react to an impressed electric field by the microscopic rotation of permanent molecular dipoles.

• The dielectric constants of nonpolar liquids (which have no molecular dipole moment) are generally between 1 and 3. Polar liquids can store field energy by partial alignment of their molecular dipoles. As a result, their dielectric constants are much larger, of the order of 10–100 times larger, than those of nonpolar liquids. In general, except for liquid crystalline phases, the electrical properties of liquids are isotropic. In nonpolar liquids, refractive indices in the visible spectrum generally follow the square root of the low-frequency dielectric constant; polar liquids have refractive indices in the visible spectrum, which are of the same magnitude as are nonpolar liquids.

• The absorption spectra of liquids cover the entire electromagnetic spectrum. Dispersion at radiofrequencies arises from dipolar orientation and depends primarily upon the interaction between molecules. Dispersion at higher frequencies arises primarily from absorption within one molecule, but, because of the perturbing influence of intermolecular forces, changes in frequency and intensity (and the broadening of vapors spectral lines) are observed.

$$f=\left[\frac{e^{E_s/RT}}{(1-e^{-\theta_c/T})^3}\left(1+n\frac{V-V_s}{V_s}e^{-aE_sV_s/(V-V_s)RT}\right)\right]^{NV_s/V}\left[\frac{(2\pi mkT)^{3/2}}{h^3}\frac{eV}{N}\right]^{N(V-V_s)/V}$$

Constants used: $n=10.80$ $a=0.00534$ $E_s=1888.6$ cal/mole $V_s=24.98$ cm^3 $\theta_c=60.0°$K

	Melting Point			Boiling Point			Critical Point		
	V_m	S_m	P_m	V_b	S_b	T_b	T_c	V_c	P_c
Calc. →	28.90	3.263	0.732	29.33	19.04	87.29	149.7	83.68	52.93
Expmt. →	28.03	3.35	0.674	28.69	17.85	87.29	150.66	75.26	48.00
Δ (%) →	+3.11	−2.61	+8.55	+2.22	+6.68	0	−0.63	+11.2	+10.3

Column Symbols: **V**=molal volume, cm^3 **S**=entropy, calories/mole°K   **P**=pressure, atm.   **T**=temp.°K

Fig. 2-13. The partition function in quantum-mechanical form is written here as the product of a "solid-like" function (left) and a "gas-like" function. Starting with molecular conditions, it can predict macroscopic properties like these, in close agreement with experiment. Predictions for other liquids are about as good as those for argon.

An a of 0.00534 is required to fit experimental data. The fraction ½ results from the fact that a molecule expanding into one of its Z neighboring positions acquires ½ of its kinetic energy of melting. The factor $(n-1)$ comes from the fact that there are only $(n-1)$ nearest neighbors competing for a vacancy in addition to the neighbor in question. Our model thus fixes all the parameters of liquid theory except those fixed by the properties of the solid.

From that expression for the energy expended for a molecule to occupy a vacancy, we can obtain the all-important partition function I mentioned earlier, that is, we can relate the microscopic molecular behavior to the macroscopic properties of liquids. For argon-like liquids, the partition function is obtained in the quantum mechanical form shown in Fig. 2-13.

Matching the model to experiment

Molecules in the molten state approximate close packing, for which $Z=12$. Since argon expands 12% on melting, we have $V_s/V=0.88$ which gives $n=ZV_s/V=10.7$. When n is chosen to best fit experimental data, the best value is $n=10.8$. This value (10.8) is also about what x-rays give for the number of nearest neighbors.

Substituting the partition function of Fig. 2-13 into the equation for Helmholtz free energy, we can calculate all the thermodynamic properties of, say, argon. We get the table in Fig. 2-13. E_s, V_s and θ are obtained from the properties of the solid; n is predicted by the model, while a has about the expected value.

At my lab, we've used this theory to calculate the thermodynamic and transport prop-

erties of ordinary liquids, of molten salts, and of liquid metals. The agreement is about as good as it is for argon.

At very high temperatures, the molecules act like hard spheres, with a van der Waals volume, whenever their vibrational energy exceeds the heat of sublimation. These corrections, which are natural consequences of the model, extend the useful range of the theory to very high pressures and temperatures with highly satisfactory results.

In calculating the properties of simple molten salts, such as NaCl, one must remember that each ion of one sign is surrounded by six positions for ions of the opposite sign. Thus the coordination number, Z, is taken equal to six instead of twelve. Further, since NaCl molecules, rather than individual ions, occur in the vapor, we expect pairing of Na$^+$ vacancies with Cl$^-$ vacancies in the liquid. The paired vacancies dart around and rotate much as do the molecules in the vapor.

When these ideas are incorporated into the partition function, the same agreement is obtained for NaCl as for simple (i.e., the nonpolar and spherical) liquids. In particular, the new Z leads to a prediction of about twice the expansion upon melting as simple liquids exhibit; experiment confirms the prediction.

Liquid metals pose an added complication. Since the conducting (the outer) electrons are spread out over the positive ions, only vacancies for positive ions appear in the liquid. But positive ions are only about a third the volume of atoms, so the vacancies are about a third as large and the calculated expansion upon melting is about 4% instead of 12%, agreeing with experiment. In metals, paired fluid vacancies as well as single vacancies are assumed in writing the partition function, again, with good results.

To calculate surface free energy, we must only correct the energy of sublimation of a particular layer for the excess or deficiency of molecules in adjacent layers. The corrected E_s is then used in the partition function to calculate the change in the Gibbs free energy of that particular layer.

Adding the change in free energy for the layers in and near the surface, gives the total surface energy for the liquid in good agreement with experiment over the whole liquid range. The calculation of surface tension achieves this notable success by requiring self consistency in initial and calculated densities, and it does so without introducing any adjustable parameters.

Viscosity: interpretations *and* deviations

Even when both liquid and solid phases have the same free energy and the same temperature as, for example, they do at the melting point, their viscosities differ, i.e., different shear stresses are needed to maintain unit velocity gradient in the two phases. This difference in viscosity must arise from the change in structure. Simple liquids, although they melt at very different temperatures, normally have the same viscosity (about two centipoises) at their T_m's. Batschinski noted long ago that the reciprocal of the viscosity, the fluidity, is a proportional to the volume of the liquid minus a volume very close to that of the solid.

These viscosity findings are natural consequences of our model, if we consider the shear surface between two layers of molecules. Shearing occurs as molecules on either side of the shear plane move into whatever vacancy will relieve the accumulated stress. This motion can only occur during the time a vacancy is available for occupancy. The probability of such a vacancy being at a particular point will be proportional to the number of vacancies present, i.e., to $V - V_s$. Thus the rate of shear, i.e., the fluidity, is proportional to this excess volume. This explains Batschinski's findings.

Besides, there is ordinarily about the same concentration of vacancies in different liquids at their melting points. The rate of jumping is the same for every simple liquid at its T_m. Accordingly, we expect single liquids to have the same viscosity at their very different T_m's. They do.

Since viscosity is such an intimate reflection of structure, it has been interesting to interpret the deviations from the two centipoises of normal liquids in terms of liquid structure. For example, long linear polymers flow by the jumping of individual segments; this occurs only when adjacent segments are in appropriate positions. Flow is further complicated by tangling but it is possible and interesting to sort out quantitatively these effects in terms of one model.

Bulk viscosity and the broad picture

As pressure is applied to a liquid, there is loss of energy from the pressure wave either (1) by the heat generated as translational degrees of freedom flow into internal degrees of freedom or (2) by the collapse of liquid structure. These relaxation processes yield energy losses analogous to viscous shear, and are lumped together as bulk viscosity. All this is understandable if we interpret the relaxation process, as pressure is applied, as the transformation of the fluidized vacancies into phonons which then travel to the outside with the velocity of sound. During expansion, phonons start at the surface and are reabsorbed at some point as fluidized vacancies. The current treatment postulates holes smaller than molecules. Only a reinterpretation of parameters would be involved in treating the structures as fluidized vacancies.

The calculation of the properties of liquids from a liquid model is analogous to the procedure used in x-ray analysis. There, one assumes a model structure for which a diffraction pattern is calculated. This is compared with the observed pattern. In both liquid theory and x-ray analysis the model can be refined until it agrees with experimental results.

Besides the interpretation of liquid structure already achieved, a more challenging aspect of the significant structure approach to liquid structure is the insight that it gives into all sorts of complicated structure problems. The alternative is to calculate the density distribution directly from the x-ray diffraction pattern and so deduce the structure. Analogously, in liquid theory one can bypass all models and try to calculate the partition function directly. With such difficult problems, both types of approach are appropriate. [This alternative approach, formidable as it is, has been made using statistical mechanics, as described by Stuart A. Rice.]

HILDEBRAND'S EVIDENCE FOR MAXIMUM RANDOMNESS

In the course of many years of study of solutions of components whose molecules are nonpolar, it has been necessary to give constant thought to the nature and structure of the liquid state. In order to formulate the thermodynamic properties of a liquid solution in terms of the properties of its components it is necessary to have at least an approximately valid concept of the structure of both the solution and its pure components. Formulations that have by now passed severe tests are based upon models in which the molecular array possesses maximum randomness, with no trace of the long-range order characteristic of crystal lattices, in other words, upon a model of the liquid state for which the radial distribution function is so rapidly damped as to become unity within a very few diameters. The subject was dealt with at some lengths in a recent book by R. L. Scott and myself. We asserted in the final summary and critique: "A pure liquid, if composed of nonpolar, symmetrical, compact molecules, has a structure of maximum randomness, as represented by the radial distribution function. There is no quasi-crystalline or lattice structure; there are no 'holes' of definite size or shape, no discrete molecular frequencies or velocities, and no distinguishable 'gas-like' and 'solid-like' molecules."

I have a wealth of evidence to support the above statement.

The evidence against solid-like models

1. When x-rays are scattered by simple liquids they give no trace of the line structure given by crystals. I have x-ray photographs of liquid and solid gallium at nearly the same temperature. The solid gives lines; the liquid does not.

Morrell and I in 1934 constructed a model of a liquid consisting of gelatin balls in a gelatin solution that had been previously boiled to prevent forming a jelly. Because the balls and the solution had almost equal density and refractive index, the balls were nearly invisible except for a few that had been colored. The mixture was vigorously shaken in a cubical plate-glass vessel.

The shaking was suddenly stopped and a photograph showing two faces at once taken at right angles with a mirror and illuminated by an electric spark. The coordinates of the colored balls were measured and the radial distances between pairs calculated. A plot of the frequencies of these distances gave a "distribution function" quite like the function for mercury obtained from x-ray scattering. Since the gelatin balls are arrayed in maximum disorder, the same is true of the molecules in the liquid mercury.

2. White phosphorus melts at 44°C but we have cooled liquid drops to minus 70°. If the liquid contained any incipient crystal lattice structures it seems inconceivable that they would not grow when subjected to such drastic undercooling.

3. Eyring has assumed the existence of holes in liquids whose size is related to the size of its molecules, as in crystals. If that were the case, one should be able to insert small molecules of another substance more easily into a liquid composed of larger molecules than into one whose molecules are smaller, just as one could insert plums into a box of grapefruit without expanding but not into a box of small oranges. Well, what are the facts? The molecules of a certain silicone, $(CH_3)_8Si_4O_4$, are three times as large as those of CCL_4 and five times the volume of iodine molecules. When iodine is added to these liquids, however, both expand to the same extent; the iodine finds no larger "holes" in the silicone.

4. Eyring claims that molecules in liquids are in one or another of two distinct states "gas-like" and "solid-like." Archer and I pointed out that *meta*-xylene and *para*-xylene have nearly identical boiling points and specific volumes down to the freezing point of the *para*- at 13.2°C. The *meta*- does not freeze till minus 47°. One would suppose therefore that if "solid-like" means what it says there should be many more solid-like molecules of the *para*- than of the *meta*- at say 15°, and since the solid is much denser than the liquid the specific volumes of the liquids would be rather different just above the freezing point of the *para*- but that is not the case. The same is true of their specific heats.

5. Viscosity is even more sensitive than density to possible differences in structure. E. B. Smith and I determined the viscosity of *meta*- and *para*-xylenes. The viscosity of the *para*-xylene is only slightly different from that of *meta*-xylene even in its supercooled region. Both molal volumes and viscosities of these two isomers show clearly that crystallization and melting are completely discontinuous processes.

6. The thermodynamic function that gives information about structure is entropy. I and my co-workers have adduced a wealth of evidence to show that the entropy of mixing is not sensibly affected by disparity in molecular volumes.

The theory of regular solutions, based upon random mixing, a theory without "holes" in it, successfully accounts for the violet, regular solutions of iodine in which its mole fraction ranges from 6.25 mole percent in $CHBr_3$ to 0.0180 mole percent in C_7F_{16}. No advocate of "cells," "lattices," or "solid-like" molecules has even begun to find a correlation like this. Indeed, all such approaches fail utterly to deal with mixtures of molecules that differ appreciably in size.

Mix-crystals cannot be formed, in the absence of chemical effects, from molecular species that differ more than a very little in size. Two "liquid lattices" would similarly have to possess nearly equal dimensions in order to mix without breaking up the lattice structure, which would be accompanied by a large excess entropy of mixing.

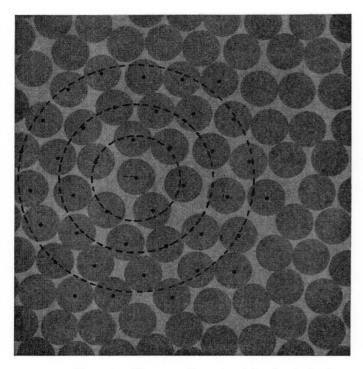

Fig. 2-14. The two dimensional "molecules," above are located at random with one reservation: No two overlap. A plot of probable circle density vs. distance gives a liquid-like distribution function, as is shown below.

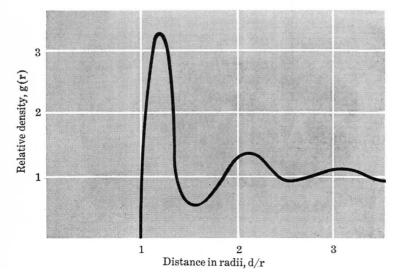

7. According to the "hole theory," diffusion takes place by jumps in lengths of the molecular diameter from a lattice site into a hole, with an "energy of activation" required to surmount a barrier. We have determined the temperature coefficient of diffusion at constant volume, where the number of "holes" would have to be constant; we found that it depends simply upon the kinetic energy of the molecules. All the molecules are participating in a "random walk" in steps much smaller than the molecular diameter.

8. B. J. Alder, who studied liquids by a "molecular dynamics" computer method, says of the breakdown of crystal structure upon melting, "once this has happened, the whole region becomes disorganized, and subsequently no discernible order is present, and no holes can be observed."

Quasi-lattice structures have not accounted for such facts nor for phenomena of crystallization, extreme supercooling, partial molal volumes, diffusion, and x-ray scattering. Furthermore, I don't think the "lattice" models can reasonably be brought into accord with these facts.

RICE'S FORMAL APPROACH

One of the major unsolved problems of contemporary physics and chemistry is the development of a practical description of the liquid state in terms of the, presumed known, intermolecular forces and intermolecular geometry. I emphasize the word practical because it is easy to write down a formal and exact theory so general and magnificent that no predictions can be made. It is also easy to construct a wide variety of simple models of the liquid which, by the use of adjustable parameters (often poorly defined) can be made to fit the observed properties.

These models represent particular parameterizations of the problem. However, a parameterization must be accurate if it is to be valid and useful, and for that reason most simple models proposed to date must be considered unsatisfactory. In this section, I will describe the general theory of liquids, and how it relates macroscopic properties to microscopic structure.

Balance of forces, molecular scale

Structure on the molecular scale is determined by the balance between the ordering imposed by intermolecular forces and the disorder of thermal motion. At low temperatures, the intermolecular forces predominate to give the completely ordered structure characteristic

Color Fig. 14. Bumper to bumper traffic in the sky is an invisible problem. The airborne view (above) of the New York terminal area approached from the northern New Jersey coast is one the pilot must imagine, but never sees. What he does have is the latest chart, a two-dimensional guide through this metroplex of multiple airports. It shows few changes since the model above was built five years ago to help envision and improve the many arrival and departure routes. Controllers must be aware of which routes are in use, for they change with traffic, wind, and weather.

It was hazy with occasional rain June 7, 1963 when controllers at the New York center (right) were saturated for 14 hours straight by 3700 flights in this area. Between 4 and 6 P.M., for example, there were 32 flights simply holding over Colts Neck, N.J. (encircled in Fig. 3-10), and 32 arrivals, 23 departures, 40 overflights moving through another sector to the north. During that time, each of the two controllers for this sector handled 27 aircraft per hour, almost twice the average of 15 per hour set as a capability limit by the FAA. (The Air Traffic Controllers Association says 5 aircraft at any moment is a safe limit, though in complex situations a controller can be saturated by just 3 flights at once.)

The tense situation and 2-hr delays of June 7th will be repeated, for Idlewild Airport is now saturated—runways and controllers handling their traffic limit—for 4 hours every day. By 1968, all airports in the New York area will be turning traffic away every day in the week. See "Air Traffic Control," in Chapter 3. (Courtesy W. Osmun (top) and S. Falk)

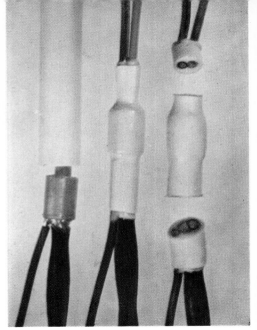

Color Fig. 15. Accelerator installation requires labyrinth to protect against stray radiation. Accelerator snout can be seen reflected in second of two mirrors in above view from
head end of conveyor line that carries polyethylene slabs. At right, heat-shrinkable
polyethylene tubing, a product of irradiation, seals solidly onto a wire splice. Tubing
slips easily over splice; relatively gentle heating is all that is required to form tight seal.
See "Radiation Processing," in Chapter 3. (Courtesy High Voltage Engineering Corp.,
Burlington, Mass., and Raychem Corp., Redwood City, Calif.)

Color Fig. 16. Radiation and food. Below, design for a cobalt-60 irradiator to disinfest
wheat—insects destroy 5% of world's grain harvest. Right, 1.3-megacurie source at U.S.
Army Natick Laboratories, world's largest, used for experiments on food preservation.
Bottom right, irradiated strawberries resist mold. See "Radiation Processing," in Chap-
ter 3. (Courtesy U.S. Army Natick Laboratories; Isotopes Development Division, U.S.
Atomic Energy Commission; Prof. E. Maxie, University of California at Davis)

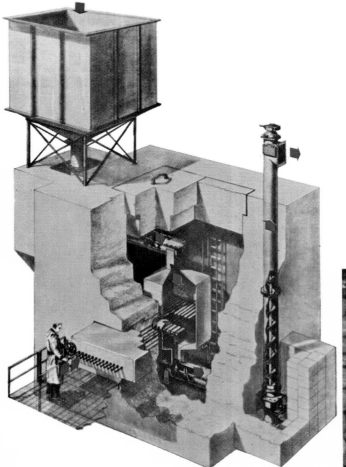

of the crystalline lattice. At high temperatures, thermal motion predominates to give the random and featureless structure of a gas. The structure of liquids corresponds to a degree of order intermediate between that of the crystalline solid which can be described by the theory of space lattices (cell theory) and the featureless structure of a gas.

When a crystalline solid melts, the long-range order of the crystal is destroyed. However, a residue of local order persists in the liquid state with a range such that the vestigial order becomes imperceptible at distances more than several molecular diameters. The local order of the liquid state is described by a pair correlation function $g(r)$, i.e., the radial distribution function. Of course, all interactions among molecules (and the resulting properties) are critically dependent on their relative whereabouts, i.e., on $g(r)$.

When $g(r)$ is unity everywhere, the fluid is completely disordered, a characteristic of dilute gases. Departures of $g(r)$ from unity measure the local order established by a molecule in the arrangement of its neighbors (see Fig. 2-12). The position of the maxima roughly corresponds to the first few coordination shells of the crystal lattice of the parent solid. The minima roughly correspond to distances intermediate between the shells of neighbors.

The function $g(r)$ specifies only average local density; significant statistical fluctuations from it must occur as molecules exchange neighbors with other molecules in the course of thermal motion. Other observable effects of the statistical fluctuations are the diffuse peaks of $g(r)$ (compared to the precise order of a crystal) and the rapid approach of $g(r)$ to unity beyond a few molecular diameters.

Experimentally $g(r)$ is determined by the coherence of waves scattered from different points in the liquid. Since $g(r)$ differs from unity for small r only, coherence requires wavelengths shorter than the molecular scale, such as x-rays and thermal neutrons.

Distributions and interactions

If the molecules of the liquid interact with a potential energy of interaction, $U(r)$,

$$pV = RT - \frac{2\pi N\rho_0}{3} \int_0^\infty r^3 \frac{dU}{dr} g(r)\, dr$$

$$L = \frac{3RT}{2} + 2\pi N\rho_0 \int_0^\infty r^2\, U(r)\, g(r)\, dr$$

Clearly, a theory of liquids that hopes to relate pressure, volume, temperature, and latent heat to molecular interactions requires an interpretation and calculation of $g(r)$.

A simple interpretation of these equations illustrates the importance of knowing the distribution of molecules in space: If the molecules are completely uncorrelated, then $\rho(r) = \rho_0$ and the probability density of finding a pair of molecules at points r_1, and r_2 is simply ρ_0^2. Now $g(r)$ represents the excess probability density of finding a molecule at a distance $r = r_2 - r_1$ from a molecule at r_1.

If molecules interact in pairs, the average energy of the liquid equals the average energy of a pair multiplied by the number of pairs of molecules in the system. The kinetic energy of the molecules gives rise to an RT term (the same as in a gas). The average interaction energy between molecules is determined by the energy at r, multiplied by the probability density of them being r away, integrated over all distances between them. Taking into account the N molecules in the liquid, gives the above equations.

Quasi-crystalline models of local liquid structure can be used advantageously to interpret $g(r)$. There it is recognized that long-range crystalline order is absent, the local arrangement of the neighbors of each molecule is regarded as a blurred replica of the first several coordination shells of a single crystal lattice, or a superposition of different lattices.

In general, quasi-crystalline models are most useful when correlation between molecules is very strong because of a specific orientation dependent force (such as a hydrogen bond). But for simple monoatomic fluids, these models are often misleading because they inherently overestimate the molecular order.

Unfettered and unaided by preconceptions

A much more promising approach is direct calculation of $g(r)$ without any appeal to special models. The principal difficulty centers around deriving a closed equation for $g(r)$. Because a pair of molecules interacting with a third requires the specification of the molecular density of triplets of molecules (i.e., the probability density of finding three molecules at r_1, r_2, r_3), all rigorous equations for $g(r)$ depend upon knowing the three molecule correlation functions. Approximations are needed.

The approximations take one of two forms: Either the three-body correlation is expressed in terms of two-body correlations (Kirkwood's method), or an attempt is made to compute certain classes of contributions (by no means all contributions) to $g(r)$ representing simple ways in which a third molecule interacts with a pair of molecules. These contributions can usually be written as a formal series, in principle exact, if all terms are evaluated.

Calculations have been carried furthest with the first alternative. A comparison of the theo-

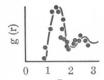

retical and experimental $g(r)$ is given in the margin for liquid argon at 91.8°K and 1.8 atm. In general, the theory predicts too large a compressibility. Probably the major source of error is the assumed relationship between the densities of molecular pairs and triplets.

The general theory based on the calculation of $g(r)$ can also describe the phase transition between liquid and crystal. In addition, the phase boundary between liquid and gas calculated from the theory reproduces very well the qualitative aspects of experimental fluid isotherms.

In summary, a theory of the equilibrium properties of liquids, including phase transitions, can be constructed from a detailed study of the distribution of molecules in space. Because of approximations made in the calculation of $g(r)$ under varying conditions, the currently available theory is only in semiquantitative agreement with experiment. However, the theory has no adjustable parameters, and all macroscopic properties are related directly to the (presumed known) properties of the molecules. Moreover, the theory is internally consistent. In my opinion, the distribution function method is the most satisfactory approach now available to a real theory of liquids.

Dissipation and nonequilibrium

Dissipative processes arise from the transport of mass, momentum, and energy. In each case there exists a phenomenological relationship between a flux and the force which is responsible for the flux. Dissipation also accompanies relaxation processes. In some cases, the relaxation time for reorientation is (approximately) proportional to the viscosity of the liquid.

In a dilute gas, the transport of mass, momentum, and energy occurs by the actual movement of individual molecules from one place to another. In a crystalline solid the transfer of energy is effected by lattice vibrations without requiring, on the average, the displacement of any molecules. Also, in a gas, a molecule may move freely until it collides with another, but in a solid, displacement from one to another lattice site requires imperfections—vacancies or dislocations—before molecular motion is possible. In a liquid, the motions are very complex, with characteristics between those in a gas and a crystalline solid.

A major difficulty faced in constructing any theory of nonequilibrium processes based on molecular motion is reconciling the time reversibility of mechanics with the time irreversibility of dissipative phenomena. In the theory of dilute gases, irreversibility is introduced with the assumption of molecular chaos, i.e.,

the molecules are uncorrelated before each collision and so collisions are uncorrelated. Some liquid theories dodge this fundamental question and assume irreversibility by fiat.

The only method available for the study of irreversible processes in strongly interacting systems is the time-smoothing method of Kirkwood. The basic idea is that there exists a time, τ, during which some (possibly complex) dynamical event occurs, and of such length that an event in one interval τ is independent of a similar event in the succeeding τ. For dilute gases, the assumption of molecular chaos means choosing τ long compared to the duration of a collision but short compared to the time between collisions. Molecular dynamics is then reduced to the description of isolated two-body encounters.

It's all a matter of tau

A description of molecular dynamics based on binary collisions is obviously of no use in a dense liquid. In a liquid, any molecule is in continuous interaction with all its near neighbors. To visualize a typical dynamic event, a pair of molecules may be imagined to have a near encounter during which strong repulsive forces act. After this repulsion separates the pair, the individual molecules move erratically in the rapidly fluctuating force field generated by the neighboring molecules. The motion of a molecule in a liquid resembles, in some ways, the motion of a massive Brownian particle.

In this description of the liquid, the dynamic properties of a molecule are described by a friction constant, $\zeta = kT/D$, which is uniquely defined in terms of the intermolecular potential. Indeed, ζ depends on the correlation between the force acting on a molecule at time t and the force acting on that molecule at $t + s$. This idea, embodied in the dynamical description, leads to a theoretical heat current, stress, tensor, etc., which can be identified with the coefficients of thermal conductivity, viscosity, etc. For example, I have shown that diffusion coefficient has the form in the margin. This theory is best tested with liquids Ar, Kr and Xe. See margin for typical results.

Similarly, Davis Meyer and I investigated the mobility of ions in liquid Ar and like fluids. In this case, g is changed from its value around a neutral molecule by electrostriction. The theory is developed from the same principles I outlined above, with the addition of a polarization potential to the intermolecular potential.

Equations similar in structure to the one in the margin can be obtained for the coefficients of viscosity, but these have not yet been subjected to extensive experimental verification.

$$\zeta = \frac{kT}{D} = (4\pi_m{}^2 C_0{}^3 P_0)^{-1} \left[\frac{Nm}{3V} \int \nabla^2 U(r) g(r) d^3 r \right]^2$$

SELF-DIFFUSION (Ar)

T (°K)	$D_{exp.}$ ×10⁻⁵ cm²/sec	D_{theory} cm²/sec
90	2.35	2.22
100	3.45	3.22

If we include the effect that the motion of a molecule forces a modification of the local structure of the liquid away from the equilibrium structure, then the predictions of the theory improve. But the calculation of the resulting nonequilibrium pair correlation functions is extremely difficult. The nonequilibrium pair correlation function also appears in the analysis of the inelastic scattering of neutrons.

A simple picture of the motion of a molecule in the liquid coupled with the distribution function approach to the theory of liquids can yield quite good agreement with experiment. Moreover, this agreement is obtained without the use of any arbitrary adjustable parameters and is consistent with an irreversible approach to equilibrium based on reversible molecular dynamics.

The exact formal relationships for the various transport coefficients of a liquid can be expressed in terms of an equilibrium average of the autocorrelation functions for certain dynamic variables. Because the relationships are exact, important advances in our understanding of the liquid state will probably come from implementation of suitable approximations within the exact formalism. It is likely that this will be one of the most promising avenues for future investigation.

Further reading

Theories of the liquid state have been evolving over the pages of *J. Chem. Phys., Phys. Rev., J. Appl. Phys.*, and in the learned journals elsewhere, particularly *Proc. Roy. Soc.* and *Disc. Faraday Soc.* The British journal *Nature* has had, in recent years, several good discussions of this subject; worth special note is J. D. Bernal's paper in Vol. **183**, 1959, which describes some consequences of structure. Another important journal has been *Proc. Nat. Acad. Sci.*, which, especially since 1958, has carried many articles on liquid structure. Of these, Vols. **46** and **47** (1960, 1961) are noteworthy for Eyring's demonstrations of the calculation of thermodynamic and transport properties of ordinary liquids, molten salts, and liquid metals.

Three times, in recent years, Hildebrand has published summaries of the evidence supporting his concept of maximum randomness in opposition to lattice concepts. He touched upon the subject in his Spiers Memorial Lecture, published in *Disc. Faraday Soc.*, **15** (1953). Hildebrand's contribution on liquid structure was published in *Growth and Perfection of Crystals*, edited by Doremus (Wiley, 1958, $12.50), and, with Archer, "Evidence Concerning Liquid Structure" in *Proc. Nat. Acad. Sci.*, **47**, 1961. Another relevant book by Hildebrand is his *Regular Solutions* (Prentice-Hall, 1962, $7.50).

Few serious students go very deeply into liquids before they encounter Rice's recommendation for further reading: *Molecular Theory of Gases and Liquids* by Hirschfelder, Curtiss and Bird (Wiley, 1954, $22.50); it is dense, but classic.

SILICON CHEMISTRY

by John L. Speier and Melvin J. Hunter *

IN BRIEF: *Silicon is the archetypical inorganic element: the earth's crust, to a depth of 10 miles, is one-fourth silicon (by weight). It is chemically similar to the organic element, carbon, in tetravalency, crystalline structure, and other properties. However, the similarity is not great enough to allow a silicaceous "organic chemistry" to exist. The larger size of the silicon atom, and the consequent difference in its chemical bonding—for instance, silicon does not form double bonds—prohibit making silicon analogs of many carbon compounds. But it has proven possible to make a growing line of organosilicon compounds, the essence of which is a carbon-silicon bond. Of these compounds, the silicones are the best known, but others are being explored, particularly those with organic functional groups like the amines and alcohols as sidechains. The hope is to unite the virtues of inorganic and organic chemistry.—T.M.*

* Both authors are with Dow Corning Corp. in Midland, Michigan; John L. Speier is Supervisor of the Organofunctional Research Laboratory, and Melvin J. Hunter is Vice President and Director of Research.

■ When Mendeleev arranged his Periodic Table of the elements, he placed silicon directly beneath carbon. Their closeness raised an expectation that silicon would be valuable not for its unique virtues but for those it shares with its more famous congener.

The expectation was false; silicon is not a poor man's carbon, it is valuable in its own right. Still, the old idea dies hard.

Don't blame Mendeleev for the misconception. As Fig. 2-16 shows, he had every reason to list silicon as the next entry after carbon in Group IV, the keystone column of his Table. The real cause of the misconception lay in the mental attitudes of his contemporaries.

Fig. 2-15. Stable O-Si-O and C-Si-C bonds in silicone rubber (right) made it resist 10 years in outdoors better than organic rubber (left) resisted 2 years in same weather. (Courtesy Dow Corning Corp.)

It was the nineteenth century. Many of the best chemical minds were absorbed by the great variety and obvious importance of carbon compounds. It's not strange that their imaginations should envision a silicon-based "organic chemistry."

Yet little work was done to explore the possibility. No metabolism on earth depends on silicon, even though it is exceeded in abundance on earth only by oxygen. So the chemists of a century ago had no natural Si "organic" compounds to invoke their powerful desire to duplicate by synthesis. Maybe more important, silicon is difficult to obtain as a free element;

	Atomic number	Atomic weight	Specific gravity (at 20° C)	Melting point	Boiling point	Valence
Si	14	28.09	2.42	1420°C	2355°C	4,6
C	6	12.011	amorphous 1.88 graphite 2.25 diamond 3.51	3550°C	4200°C	2,3,4

Fig. 2-16. First two elements in Group IV of the Periodic Table have several similar properties.

	Si	C	H	N	O	F	Cl	Br	I
Si	81.3-85	−89	94	77	108	135	106	74	56
C	86-89	85	90-98	72.8	85.5	116	81	68	51

Fig. 2-17. Almost all of silicon's bonds to other elements are stronger than carbon's, as measured by the thermal energy required to break them. However, high bond energies don't necessarily imply lack of reactivity, as bonds can dissociate as a result of other forces than heat.

that is, it was difficult a century ago. The difficulty was certainly not a matter of supply: to a depth of ten miles one fourth of the weight of the earth is silicon. The trouble is that silicon is so reactive that in the earth's crust, every atom of silicon is bound to oxygen, as quartz sand or silicate rock.

Let no man put asunder

Indeed silicon has a great affinity for oxygen. Even at room temperatures, it will displace hydrogen from water, needing only the presence of an alkaline catalyst:

$$Si + 2H_2O \xrightarrow{catalyst} SiO_2 + 2H_2$$

Note that the formula for silicon dioxide, or silica, is SiO_2. All forms of silicon dioxide are composed of tetrahedra, with four oxygen atoms at the corners and a silicon atom at the center. This arrangement would seem to make the formula SiO_4, but each atom of oxygen is shared with another atom of silicon (see Fig. 2-18). This sharing makes a quartz crystal one giant molecule with the average composition SiO_2.

Now the Si-O bond is intrinsically a strong one. It takes a relatively large amount of thermal energy to dissociate the silicon and oxygen—a larger amount, for example, than it takes to break the analogous carbon-oxygen bond. The exact values of these and other comparable bonds of carbon and silicon to the same elements are tabulated in Fig. 2-17. You can see that, in general, bonds to silicon are stronger than the same bonds to carbon. This high

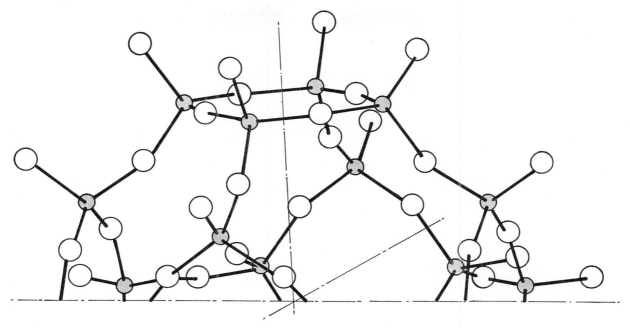

Fig. 2-18. Basic unit of all silicate structures is a tetrahedron with four oxygen atoms as its corners and one silicon atom at its center. In quartz and the other forms of silica, each tetrahedron shares all of its corners with other tetrahedra in a three-dimensional network (above) that has a silicon:oxygen ratio of 1:2.

bonding strength does not necessarily imply low reactivity because strong bonds can be dissociated by other than thermal forces, as in redistribution reactions described below.

However, thermal dissociation is the method used today to prepare many tons of silicon each year, by heating sand and coke in an electric arc furnace at a temperature of 1700°C:

$$SiO_2 + 2C \xrightarrow{heat} Si + 2CO$$

Silicon obtained by this process is used to make alloys with iron or aluminum. Being transparent to infrared radiation, silicon lends itself for use in infrared optics. And, in ultrapure form, silicon is used for semiconductors and rectifiers.

In our opinion, however, the most important use of silicon is as an element in chemical compounds.

Poor man's carbon

We said earlier that, in the years when organic chemistry reigned supreme, little work was done to explore the chemistry of silicon, and what little there was had as its incentive the hope of finding silicon analogs of organic compounds.

For example, early in this century the silicon hydride analogs of such common hydrocarbons as methane (CH_4) and ethane (C_2H_6) were prepared, in order to compare the two systems (see margin sketch). They were not at all like their hydrocarbon analogs. For instance, silicon hydrides were so highly reactive that they would explode spontaneously on contact with

air. Silane would also reduce water at room temperature, especially if a basic catalyst were present, according to the reaction:

$$SiH_4 + 2H_2O \xrightarrow{catalyst} SiO_2 + 4H_2$$

A hydrocarbon does this only at bright red heats.

Gradually, evidence accumulated that silicon did not behave enough like its cousin, carbon, to permit predicting the chemical properties of silicon analogs of organic chemicals. Trisilylamine, in which silicon replaced the carbon in $(CH_3)_3N$, was scarcely basic, while the original trimethylamine was a strong base. Siloxanes, compounds with Si-O-Si linkages analogous to C-O-C ether linkages, did not behave like ethers. And so forth, until at least to chemists it was clear that silicon was not a poor man's carbon. But *why* wasn't it?

Male and female made He them

Compare an atom of carbon with one of silicon (see margin sketch). Carbon is the smaller atom, having only six orbiting electrons in two shells, while silicon has fourteen, in three shells. Both have four of their orbiting electrons in their outer, valence shell. But carbon's valence shell is only a second orbital shell, and so can accept only four additional electrons to form covalent chemical bonds. Silicon's valence shell, however, being a third orbital shell, can accept not just four but up to fourteen more electrons.

In both silicon and carbon, the valence elec-

Methane
H
|
H–C–H
|
H

Silane
H
|
H–Si–H
|
H

Silicon
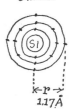
k–r–›
1.17Å

Carbon

›|r|k
0.77Å

trons form chemical bonds with four other atoms so that these atoms are arranged symmetrically in space about the central atom. The valence electrons in carbon compounds tend to hold other atoms rather rigidly in their position in space. In silicon compounds, the valence electrons are farther from the silicon nucleus, and shielded from its positive charge by the two inner shells of electrons. As a result, atoms attached to silicon seem to be held much less rigidly.

If an atom or group bonded to silicon has a pair of unshared electrons, it may easily leave the first silicon atom and link to a different silicon atom, driven by nature's urge to maximize randomness. A redistribution of the atoms may result, so that they become arranged around the silicon atoms in all possible combinations. No such redistribution reactions occur in the analogous carbon compounds.

As a result of these differences in their valence situations, silicon and carbon are not as readily interchangeable as their proximity in Group IV once seemed to suggest. The silane that it was thought might be similar to methane is not really so, because silicon forms a bond with hydrogen that is polarized in the sense of Si^+H^-, and this behaves chemically quite unlike a carbon-hydrogen bond, which is polarized C^-H^+. As a result, silicon hydrides behave not like the paraffin series of hydrocarbons but like metal hydrides, as good reducing agents. An oxygen atom links with a silicon atom without the SiH having to dissociate, unlike the analogous C-H bond, which needs to be broken as by flames before the carbon will oxidize.

Or take the trisilylamine that was expected to resemble trimethylamine. Where the organic compound had the three methyl groups and the extra unshared pair of valence electrons arranged almost symmetrically in space about the nitrogen to form a tetrahedron (see margin sketch), the silicon analog has a planar, neutral molecule, in which all of the silicons are equivalent from a valence point of view. This means that the unshared pair of valence electrons from the nitrogen have disappeared simultaneously into all of the orbitals of the silicon atoms, so that on the average each silicon-nitrogen bond has a certain amount of double-bond character, without being a true double bond. Wherever these electrons are, their unavailability for valence bonding accounts for the difference in chemical behavior between the two amines.

At this stage in the discussion, you won't be surprised to learn that the siloxane linkage Si-O-Si differs from the ether linkage C-O-C not only in forming a more obtuse angle—as

Trimethylamine

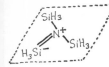

Trisilylamine

much as 150° versus 110°—but also in having a certain amount, about 25%, of double-bond character. This means that, on the average, there is a 25% higher concentration of electrons between the nuclei of silicon and oxygen than is needed for a covalent bond. The effect of this situation is a straightening of the bond angle, a shortening of the bond length, and an increase in the bond strength, all of which helps to make quite a difference in properties between the anesthetic diethyl ether and its siloxane analog.

After describing the importance of partial double bonds to silicon, we should point out that no full double bond to silicon is known—one in which four rather than two valence electrons are concentrated in the region between the atomic nuclei. Perhaps in an electric arc, Si=O has been seen spectroscopically, but under ordinary circumstances no one yet has made a compound with a double bond to silicon.

No Neptunese sandmen

The difficulty or impossibility of making double bonds to silicon keeps silicon from making analogs comparable to very important classes of organic chemicals. No aromatic structures such as benzene (see margin sketch) are known for silicon. No silicon compounds analogous to carboxylic acids, esters, amides, anhydrides, aldehydes or ketones, nitriles, olefins, or acetylenes have been made, nor do any of these seem likely at the present time. Most of the structural units of vital importance to biochemistry have no formal counterparts among silicon compounds.

If there can be no silicon analogs of the most vital biochemicals, then the science fiction stories of organisms on other worlds, where life processes are dominated by silicon as ours are by carbon, must almost certainly remain fiction (see Fig. 2-19).

Here on earth, despite the vast abundance of silicon compounds, living organisms seem to have little or no use for any of them. Nitrogen, oxygen, sulfur, and phosphorus, together with at least twelve other common elements, have been thoroughly incorporated into the metabolism of animal and plant life. But silicon has not. This is undoubtedly due to the great chemical resistance of the silicates.

If you can't lick 'em, join 'em

The tenacity of the siloxane linkage discouraged not only the evolution of sand-eating organisms but also the development of inorganic silicon chemistry. While early experimenters found silicon to be more than reactive enough, combining directly when heated with many common elements like the halogens to form compounds not found in nature, all of

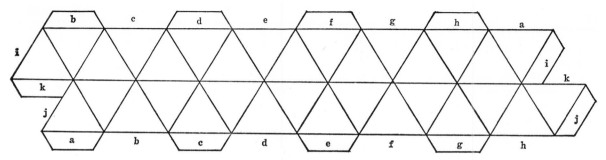

Fig. 2-19. This plan—cut out, folded on lines, and with tabs pasted to matching edges in the order shown—forms a ring of tetrahedra so flexible it rotates as sketched on page 214. Similarity to silicone rings linked at one corner inspires science fiction thoughts of siliconches on other worlds, silicontorting such cell-shells for torque or warmth.

these new compounds had an impressive tendency to return rapidly to silica by reaction with water.

It seemed for a long time that silicon compounds always had to return to the silica from which the silicon came, no matter what the other element in the compound, be it halogen or hydrogen or whatever. Until someone thought of linking silicon to—carbon.

SiC, SiC, SiC

Just as no free silicon has been found on earth, no carbon-silicon bonds from terrestrial sources have been found. The carbon-silicon bond, as known today, comes only by man-directed routes:

$$SiO_2 + 3C \longrightarrow -Si-C-$$

Bonding silicon to carbon was the breakthrough that foretold the feasibility of our modern-day silicone industry. The Si-C bond is not very reactive. It does not break easily or return to silica as the almost inevitable end of every experiment.

The Si-C bond seems to be similar to the C-C bond of organic chemicals. To stress this similarity, only compounds having a Si-C bond are referred to as "organo-silicon" compounds.

As long as the silicon-carbon bond is present, reversion of a silicon compound to silica is very difficult. Still more important, the desirable properties of hydrocarbon side chains can be added to those of inorganic backbones when each silicon atom is linked to carbon atoms in one dimension and to oxygen atoms in another. Such a structure is the all-important unit in the organo-silicon compounds known as "silicones."

The origin of silicones

The first concerted effort to understand the chemistry of silicon in an environment of attached hydrocarbon radicals was begun a century ago. Fifty years later, researchers produced a wide variety of organo-silicon

intermediates. By hydrolyzing dichlorosilane, $(CH_3)_2SiCl$, they expected to prepare $(CH_3)_2Si=O$ with a silicon double bond to oxygen similar to the carbonyl $C=O$ group in acetone, $(CH_3)_2C=O$. One researcher intended to call these compounds silico-acetones, or "silicones."

But no $Si=O$ compounds were found. (No double bonds to silicon!) As expected, the products analyzed for one atom of silicon and one of oxygen, but the compounds were eventually seen to be low polymers of silicon and oxygen with two hydrocarbon groups on each silicon—that is, dimethylsiloxane:

$$\begin{array}{c} H \\ | \\ H-C-H \\ | \\ -O-Si-O- \\ | \\ H-C-H \\ | \\ H \end{array}$$

The complex polymeric substances which were obtained were largely ignored for 30 years.

Silicone research in America

In 1929 the scene shifted from Europe to the United States, where, at the Corning Glass Works, these new polymers were used as varnishes for fiberglas electrical insulation. The new varnishes were stable at more than 100°C higher than conventional organic varnishes. The first industrial application for organosilicon polymers was born.

Simultaneously, fluid polymers were being investigated at Mellon Institute, where it was found that dimethylsiloxane polymers could be made with many unusual physical properties, which will be described below. Between 1942 and 1946 four hundred seventy tons of organosiloxane polymer products were prepared to supply ignition-sealing compounds for high-flying aircraft. The silicones prevented corona discharges that, as static, could be detected by enemy radio-direction finders. Thus silicones helped accelerate the adoption of radar by our enemies.

After the war, silicones became established as a marked advance over organic polymers and plastics for resistance both to weather (see Fig. 2-15) and heat (see Fig. 2-20). However, the military was not content with these advances and an intense search for even more heat-resistant polymeric substances was put in motion. Although marked progress has been made, no other combinations of elements have surpassed those obtained from the carbon-bonded silicon system.

State of the silicone art

Chemists now know how to prepare a wide range of silicone compounds. Volatile fluids, viscous fluids, rubbers, soft resins, and hard resins can all be obtained by proper manipulation and selection of the intermediates. The technology is a well-developed art. It deals

$$\text{primarily with} \quad \left[\begin{array}{c} CH_3 \\ | \\ -Si-O \\ | \\ CH_3 \end{array} \right] \quad \text{or methyl silicones,}$$

in which the number of methyl (or phenyl) groups and their positions in the molecules are controlled to determine the properties of the finished silicone.

If only *one* organic group is attached to silicon, cross-linked, three-dimensional polymers result.

If *two* organic groups are attached to silicon, cyclic or chain compounds can be made.

If *three* organic groups are attached to silicon, a fluid is made.

A typical silicone fluid will have a polymeric structure like that of the chain shown here:

$$(CH_3)_3SiOSi \begin{array}{c} CH_3 \\ | \\ -O-Si-O \\ | \\ CH_3 \end{array} \begin{array}{c} CH_3 \\ | \\ -Si-O \\ | \\ CH_3 \end{array} \begin{array}{c} CH_3 \\ | \\ --Si(CH_3)_3 \\ | \\ CH_3 \end{array}$$

The length of such a chain can be controlled to make volatile fluids or viscous gums. In any case, it contains no weak linkages. We have here a very stable fluid with a structure unlike any polymer in organic chemistry.

The Si-O-Si linkages which make up the polymer backbone permit each dimethylsilyl group to rotate freely about the Si-O bonds as though these were well-lubricated ball-and-socket joints. Meanwhile the polymer backbone is also flexing in three dimensions. So the structural units in the polymer move with a strange freedom, sweeping out volumes of space so that two such molecules cannot approach each other closely.

As a result, silicone molecules have intermolecular attractive forces that are very low not only for each other but also between themselves and other compounds. This is reflected in low surface tensions, low densities, and low heats of fusion. Conversely, the fluids are compressible—we call them "liquid springs"—have large molar volumes, and freeze at very low temperatures. The fluids change viscosity with temperature less than any other kind of polymeric fluid that is available.

These properties, and the molecular situation expressed by them, lead naturally to particular applications. The random motions of the backbone sections and of the side groups help to make silicone fluids incompatible with solvents, including water: alien molecules can't

Fig. 2-20. Silicone rubbers not only resist temperatures up to 315°C, as shown by use as molds for molten type metal, but also keep resilience down to −90°C, permitting use as seals for high-altitude aircraft windows. (Courtesy Dow Corning Corp.)

Fig. 2-21. A finish 0.0001 in. thick of an organofunctional silicon compound kept treated part of steel gear from corroding during 12 hr. in 85% rel. humidity. (Courtesy Linde Co.)

come close, and even if they could, the Si-O bond does not have the lone pair of electrons necessary to form the kind of weak bonds found between solvent and solute molecules. This incompatibility makes silicones good release agents in the molding of rubber, makes them good water repellents, and, with the lack of toxicity that stems from their inertness, good fillers and vehicles for cosmetics and lotions. Their low surface tension makes them good defoaming agents. And their fairly constant viscosity over a wide range of temperatures means that their vibration damping is constant, so they make good dampers.

Rubbers and resins

Very long dimethylsilyl chains have been made with molecular weights that exceed one million. By establishing a few cross-links in such a high polymer, a vulcanized rubber results. The free rotation discussed for the fluid is still present in the rubber, so that rubbery properties persist even at −90°C or at above 200°C. This is an exceedingly wide temperature range for rubbery properties, matched by no other commercial material available in all the fabricated forms in which a rubber can be used.

An impressive application for these rubbers is becoming important to surgeons. They have found that silicone rubbers cause no response or reaction when implanted in human tissues. Also, in such a situation, the silicone is ageless, changing in no way with time. So silicone tubing is being used to replace damaged arteries, and silicone film the membrane which covers the human brain; silicone tubing and membrane are also used in some heart-lung machines.

Organosilicons forever

While no serious student of the subject expects to develop a complete "organic" chemistry based on silicon, it would be possible to replace a carbon atom with a silicon atom or add a silane grouping to any one of at least 100,000 well-known organic chemicals. Cause for doing this or usefulness of the products thus obtained still lies mostly in the future.

In certain areas, however, silicon chemists are already making progress. Before the Second World War, for example, no attractive method was known to make organosilicon compounds containing functional groups, such as amines, ketones, aldehydes, phenols, etc., in the organic substituents on the silicon. Such compounds may be called organofunctional silicon compounds. Today, several thousand of these are known (see Fig. 2-21).

The presence of functional organic groups in silicones may lead to biologically active products useful as drugs, insecticides, bacteriocides,

herbicides, etc. The development of this field is in its infancy, but the large numbers of patents and scientific publications in recent years indicate vigorous growth.

A final long look at organosilicon perspectives calls forth this prophecy: The chemistry of silicon harnessed to carbon will continue to play an increasingly greater role in academic and industrial lives.

At the present time, data on 5000 organofunctional silicon compounds of proven structure are on file in the authors' office. Few of these have been known for more than 15 years; but most of them have been known for as long as five years—which shows what a time-lag there unfortunately is between scientific research and technological development. Only about a dozen of these 5000 have been made commercially available; one that has is the fluorosilicone described in "Fluorine Chemistry," page 218.

Additional new chemical structures defying enumeration are entirely feasible, and the attention these are now beginning to receive makes us confidently predict rapid expansion for silicones both in kind and volume for years to come.

Further reading

A brief but good description of the basic chemistry of silicon compounds and their uses will be found in *Silicones*, by Meals and Lewis (Reinhold, 1959, $5.95).

The book which best covers the entire field of organosilicon chemistry is Eaborn's *Organosilicon Compounds* (Academic Press, 1959, $15). This volume is an excellent statement of the position of the science, but merely touches upon its industrial technology.

A book that is largely devoted to industrial applications of silicones is McGregor's *Silicones and Their Uses* (McGraw-Hill, 1954, $6.75), but it has an introductory chapter on the history of silicon chemistry that is very well done.

Only one review has been written about organofunctional silicon compounds. This is an excellent article by George, Prober, and Elliott in *Chem. Rev.*, 1065–1219 (1956), which has more than 600 references to the original literature.

The possibility of alien life based on compounds of silicon in place of carbon compounds is discussed in the second half of *Life in the Universe*, by Jackson and Moore (W. W. Norton & Co., 1962, $3.95).

Full directions for constructing rotating rings of tetrahedra from one sheet of paper are given on pp. 153–154 and 215–217 of *Mathematical Recreations and Essays* by Ball, revised by Coxeter (Macmillan, 1960, $3.95).

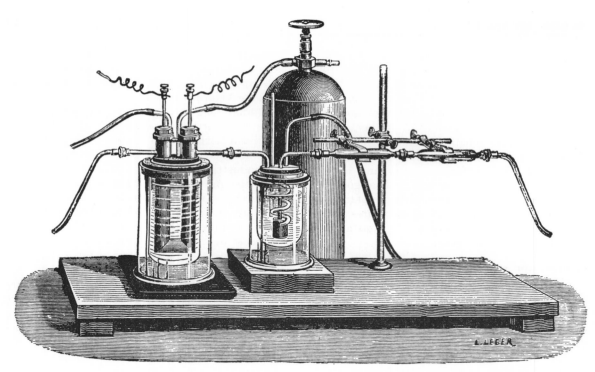

Fig. 2-22. Current fluorine production processes are direct descendants of Moissan's. "Nous avions pensé au début de ces recherches que, sous l'action du courant, le fluorure de potassium en solution dans l'acide fluorhydrique se déboublait en donnant, au pôle positif du fluor gazeux, et au pôle négatif du potassium. KF = K + F." Here, the electrolytically produced fluorine is passed through a cold trap and filters to trap entrained HF and other impurities. (From Le Fluor et ses Composés, *by H. Moissan, courtesy S. A. Edelstein collection)*

FLUORINE CHEMISTRY

by Ogden R. Pierce *

IN BRIEF: *Like the proverbial lady riding a tiger, the chemist who is handling the most chemically active element of all is dealing with a powerful critter, and his skill in controlling it is of the essence of his success. So it is no wonder that fluorine is old yet most fluorine uses are new. It is mineralogically quite abundant, and now that fluorine is commercially handled in large amounts, this volatile oxidizer can look forward to a very bright future indeed.*

But not only can it power rockets, etch glass, and burn off old concrete and asbestos; fluorine substituted for hydrogen in organic molecules is the basis of new families of inert resins, elastomers, aerosols, and lubricants, some of which are stable at temperatures once considered the exclusive province of inorganics. The attractive features of all these materials stem from the tenacity of the fluorocarbon bond and from the compactness of the structures formed by an element with small atomic radius.

However, high bond dissociation energy is no panacea, and therein lie the major troubles: the rigidity of the C-F bond must be relieved with molecular "hinges" to avoid brittleness; fluorination processes are hard to control; costs tend to soar like reaction rates. Now some balms to these banes are in the offing.—R.G.N.

■ June 26, 1886 marks one of the momentous days in the history of chemistry. On that day, Professor Henri Moissan of the École de Pharmacie in Paris achieved the first successful preparation of elemental fluorine. After nearly seventy-five years of vain effort by many chemists, Moissan found that electrolysis of a molten mixture of potassium fluoride and hydrogen fluoride in the absence of water produced fluorine readily and in an easily purifiable form. A new field of chemistry had been opened. However, as is true of many great discoveries, the real significance of this event would not become apparent until the urgency of World War II brought about development of Moissan's work for use in the preparation of uranium hexafluoride as a key intermediate in the manufacture of the first atomic bomb.

Separation of the active ^{235}U (here I use the notation favored by chemists for the uranium

* Ogden R. Pierce is Research Supervisor of the Fluorine Research Laboratories at Dow Corning Corp., in Midland, Michigan.

isotope of atomic weight 235) isotope from the more abundant but less desirable ^{238}U was based on a vapor diffusion process using uranium hexafluoride, UF_6. This compound was obtained from the reaction of UO_2 with HF to produce UF_4, "green salt," which was then treated with fluorine to produce UF_6. Handling of UF_6 proved extremely difficult, due to its great chemical reactivity, especially with organic oils and greases. The need for stable substitutes for these materials gave impetus to the technology which ultimately produced the fluorocarbon family of organic compounds, the basis of the modern fluorochemical industry.

From fluorspar, fluorine

The ninth element on the periodic chart is estimated to be thirteenth in abundance. (It's more abundant than chlorine, if you ignore the oceans.) Its principal mineral sources are cryolite (Na_3AlF_6), fluorite (CaF_2), apatite ($CaF_2 \cdot 3Ca_3(PO_4)_2$), and a miscellaneous group with low fluorine content including lipidalite, amblygonite, and topaz. Of these, fluorite, also termed fluorospar, is by far the most important source for commercial applications. It occurs on every continent of the world and is found in the United States in the Illinois-Kentucky area. The present world production of fluorspar is estimated at nearly two million tons a year, with total reserves of nearly seventy-five million tons. Of this, nearly half is on the North American continent.

The present-day preparation of fluorine is much the same as that described by Moissan. The mineral fluorite is converted to hydrogen fluoride:

$$CaF_2 + H_2SO_4 \rightarrow 2HF + CaSO_4$$

The hydrogen fluoride is mixed with potassium fluoride and the molten mixture is electrolyzed. However, instead of the platinum electrodes and platinum or copper cell body employed by early workers (of which six grams of platinum were consumed for every gram of fluorine produced), the modern cell uses carbon anodes and uses steel for both the cathodes and cell body. This way, continuous operation, using currents of several thousand amperes, can produce fluorine at less than \$1/lb. While this cost is high compared with the 3¢/lb cost of chlorine, it is comparable with the cost of either of the other two halogens, bromine and iodine.

Fluorine coming from the cell is purified by passing it over sodium fluoride pellets to remove entrained HF; then it is compressed for storage in cylinders. Corrosion of materials of construction for use with fluorine has been of concern in the past and such metals as nickel and copper were recommended even under mild conditions. (When water is present, HF and a complex of fluorine oxides form immediately, and these aggravate the corrosion picture considerably.) However, dry gaseous F_2 at room temperature can be handled safely in steel and is shipped in steel containers. A recent innovation in shipping is the development of a large container holding 5000 pounds of liquid fluorine which can be transported by truck safely to any spot in the United States.

How fluorine behaves

Fluorine exists at room temperature as a pale yellow gas which condenses to a yellow liquid at $-188.2°C$ and freezes at $-218°C$. The density of the gas is 1.319 relative to air and the specific gravity of the liquid at its boiling point is 1.11. Of more practical interest is the fact that its critical temperature is $-129°C$ and the critical pressure is 55 atm.; this creates some problems in compressing and storing the material.

Perhaps the single most important thermodynamic property of fluorine is its bond dissociation energy, that is, the 37 kcal/mole required to split the F_2 molecule. This value is subject to some criticism and is more comparable to the value for iodine than to the higher value for chlorine. However, in view of the great reactivity of fluorine, 37 kcal/mole appears to be logical and is used by many researchers in discussing the thermochemistry of organic fluorine compounds.

Fluorine is the most reactive of the elements. This can be spectacularly demonstrated by burning materials such as glass or metals or even concrete in a stream of fluorine. Boron and silicon burn to form boron trifluoride and silicon tetrafluoride. Amorphous carbon gives carbon tetrafluoride but graphite forms an interstitial fluoride that results in swelling of the carbon to nearly double its original volume. When fluorine is reacted with hydrogen, a tremendous energy release is obtained.

With a low molecular weight for reactants and products, this last reaction offers interesting possibilities as a propellant system for rockets. The specific impulse of the $H_2 + F_2 \rightarrow 2HF$ reaction is around 400 sec. The design and study of hydrogen-fluorine motors is presently under way both at Textron's Bell Aerosystems Co. and at Rocketdyne.

In view of this great reactivity, elemental fluorine has found only limited application in chemical processes other than those connected with the AEC. However, indirect methods of fluorination, beginning with the work of F. Swarts early this century, have created a new chemical industry based upon the organic compounds of fluorine. The success of these

Fig. 2-23. Rocket fuels like hydrogen and hydrazine ignite on contact with a fluorine oxidizer. Such hypergolic combinations simplify multiple starting procedures in flight. Besides, liquid fluorine in propellant combinations can deliver specific impulses over 400 seconds. Other promising liquid oxidizers for rocketry include storable chlorine trifluoride. (Courtesy Dow Corning Corp.)

materials lies in the unique properties which substitution of fluorine for hydrogen imparts to an organic molecule. For a better understanding of this, a consideration of the nature of the fluorine atom and the carbon-fluorine bond is in order.

What makes fluorocarbons different?

Many of the unusual physical properties of the highly fluorinated organic compounds known as the fluorocarbons can be directly related to the nature of the C-F bond and its differences from other halogen-carbon bonds. Start with the properties of the fluorine atom: Fluorine is univalent, exists as a single isotopic species and has the electronic configuration $(1s)^2(2s)^2(2p)^5$. In this respect it differs from the other halogens which have electrons in higher energy orbitals capable of entering into additional bonding.

Of general importance are several concepts by which atomic properties can be described. The first is electron affinity or the energy released when a fluorine atom receives an electron to form a chemical bond. This, together with its ionization potential, constitutes an element's electronegativity, its ability to attract electrons and form a chemical bond. In both respects, fluorine has the largest values and therefore it has the greatest ability of all the halogens to form a stable bond. Even the rare gases, xenon and krypton, formerly thought to

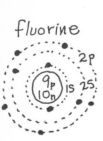

be chemically inert, have been recently shown to react with fluorine to form the compounds XeF_4, XeF_6, KrF_2, and the like. Fluorine compounds with the rare gas, xenon, have been announced by researchers at Argonne Labs.

Another important property is atomic radius or, essentially, the size of the atoms when chemically combined. Again, the fluorine atom is unique in that it is the smallest of the halogens and can form a much more compact structure when chemically combined in molecules. The real significance of this property will be illustrated a little later.

A third property of interest here is the polarizability of the atom, or the degree of tightness with which the electrons are held in a given configuration. In this respect, fluorine is again different from the other halogens in that, under various stresses, it retains its electronic shape in a chemical bond to a much greater degree.

From this, a simple model of the C-F bond can be constructed in which one can visualize a compact shell of fluorine valence electrons that are hard to distort from their ground state configuration. When considered together with the small atomic radius of the fluorine atom, the relatively short distance between F and C in the bond, and the very high bond dissociation energy, the picture emerges of a stable "substructure" which, when multiplied many times over in a highly fluorinated compound, gives rise to the many desirable properties of fluorocarbons. The multiplication of the C-F substructure has one other effect: It creates molecules with weak intermolecular forces or a low "internal pressure." Boiling points are below those of other halogen derivatives; many fluorocarbons boil in the same temperature range as the corresponding hydrocarbons. The result of all this is a rather dramatic effect on the various physical properties of fluorocarbons.

The refractive index reflects the small atomic refraction which in turn is due to the low polarizability. In fact, refractive indices of fluorocarbons are less than those of any other class of compounds.

The solubility of the fluorocarbons is among their more interesting properties. Most of the common organic solvents fail to dissolve them, because of the weak intermolecular forces in the liquids. For example, a typical fluorocarbon, perfluoromethylcyclohexane (C_7F_{14}), is insoluble in methanol and only slightly soluble in solvents like benzene and ethyl acetate (3 and 15% by weight, respectively). This property is quite useful in polymers, they can be made solvent resistant by fluorine substitution.

Another characteristic is low surface tension (in the range of 10–20 dynes/cm), again a result of low intermolecular forces. When fluorocarbons are introduced into either an aqueous or organic system, the surface tension of the entire system is drastically reduced. This also shows up in observations on the wettability of solid surfaces. A surface composed of closely packed CF_3 groups has a very low surface energy (6 dynes/cm) and will not be wet by most organic oils. Similar effects are shown by most highly fluorinated bulk polymer surfaces, though the presence of substituents other than fluorine can raise the surface energy and so increase wettability. Using this principle, a commercial textile finish (3M's "Scotchgard") has been developed. It imparts oil and water repellency to cloth. The active ingredient contains a long fluorinated alkyl chain.

The very high dissociation energy of the C-F bond (110–120 kcal/mole) imparts great thermal stability to highly fluorinated molecules. This, together with their inherent resistance to oxidation (they're already highly "oxidized" by the fluorine in them), offers the potential of organic materials stable at temperatures usually considered only for the inorganics. As examples, both hexafluorobenzene, C_6F_6, and perfluorocyclobutane, C_4F_8, are stable in the range of 1200–1400°F. One can foresee polymers, with these as building blocks, in use at temperatures more than twice those of presently available materials.

It would seem from this that fluorine does nothing but enhance the value of a molecule in which it is substituted. In most instances this is true. However, one adverse effect arises from the rigidity of the C-F bond; this is often referred to as chain "stiffening." A high degree of fluorine substitution in a carbon chain results in a molecule that repels its neighbors, and consequently such molecules don't enter into con-

Fig. 2-24. One trick to safely transporting large quantities of elemental fluorine involves cryogenically cooled tank trucks. An inner vessel of liquid fluorine is kept below fluorine's boiling point (−306°F) by supporting it in a bath of liquid nitrogen. An outer double-walled shell is used as a large dewar flask to retain the liquid nitrogen. With this type of vehicle, up to 5000 pounds of liquid fluorine can be trucked safely. (Courtesy Allied Chemical Corp.)

figurations in which they entwine themselves around each other as many hydrocarbons do. One result of this is a rapid change of viscosity with temperature in liquids and a relatively high stiffening temperature in fluorocarbon elastomers. While this is not particularly desirable, it can be reduced by the introduction of hinge points of oxygen or nitrogen in the backbone of the polymer chain.

The flourishing fluorocarbon family

A simple visualization of a fluorine-containing organic molecule is a multiplicity of rigid C-F bonds presenting a surface of fluorine atoms which act much like armor plating to shield the other more vulnerable bonds in the molecule from attack. In so doing, the fluorocarbon prefers to remain a distinct moiety and thereby exhibits its unusual properties.

The fluorocarbons, as a class, exhibit chemical inertness, low toxicity, low flammability, high thermal stability, and low solubility in common organic solvents. These properties have resulted in many applications, the largest of which are as aerosols and refrigerants. The production of chlorofluoromethanes, -ethanes, and -ethylenes amounts to about 300 million pounds a year in this country and is increasing. These materials are made as follows:

$$SbCl_5 + 3HF \rightarrow SbF_3Cl_2 + 3HCl$$

$$CCl_4 + SbF_3Cl_2 \rightarrow CCl_2F_2 + SbFCl_4$$

$$SbFCl_4 + 2HF \rightarrow SbF_3Cl_2 + 2HCl$$

(CCl_2F_2 is familiar under the trade name, Freon.) The process is adaptable to continuous operation and is employed in many commercial fluorination reactions.

The aerosols were first used in the "bug bombs" of World War II, and, due to the popularity of the principle, now find use as propellents in a wide variety of products for household and personal application. Recently a new fluorocarbon, octafluorocyclobutane (see margin sketch), was approved for use as a food aerosol. That illustrates the tremendous chemical stability of these materials.

The average home refrigerator contains 1 or 2 pounds of a fluorocarbon gas, such as CCl_2F_2, which has entirely replaced the older materials, sulfur dioxide or ammonia. In the past few years the rapid increase in home air conditioning has created even larger markets for fluorocarbon refrigerants.

Another class of fluorocarbon products, resins, has been developed over the past twenty years. These materials are thermally stable, resistant to chemical and oxidative attack, and excellent dielectrics. The two most important commercial resins are based on polymers of tetrafluoro-

ethylene (duPont's Teflon) and chlorotrifluoroethylene (3M's Kel-F and others) and find use as gasketing material, packings, tubings, wire and cable coatings, and pipe linings. The estimated yearly production of fluorocarbon resins is 8–10 million pounds having a market value of $60–70 million.

Flexibility, fluidity, and fluorosilicones

Low solubility in organic media, oxidative stability, and thermal stability can extend the usefulness of a rubbery polymer considerably. With this stimulus, research in recent years has produced several fluorocarbon elastomers, three of which are now commercial products.

The first rubbers to be considered, duPont's Viton and 3M's Fluorel, are carbon chain polymers prepared by copolymerization of vinylidene fluoride ($CH_2 = CF_2$) with hexafluoropropene ($CF_3CF = CF_2$). In such a chain, the two monomers probably combine in a ratio of approximately 80:20. The resultant polymer is a tough, rubbery material with tensile strength exceeding 2000 psi and elongation in the range of 100–400%. It is serviceable up to 600°F for short periods, but its more practical temperature limit is around 500°F.

Perhaps the most striking property is its resistance to swelling in organic media. It is only slightly affected by gasoline, jet fuel, hydraulic oils, and the many aromatic and chlorinated hydrocarbons used industrially. However, due to the "stiffening" effect of the C-F bond, the rubber becomes brittle and generally unusable at temperatures not much below 0°F, depending on the thickness of the sample.

A third elastomer, Dow Corning's Silastic LS-53, uses a different structural approach to achieve essentially the same end result, a solvent-resistant rubber. This polymer is composed of the units $(CF_3CH_2CH_2SiCH_3O)_n$, where $n = 5000$–6000; it is a member of the silicone family. It has a tensile strength of approximately 1000 psi, elongation in the range 100–300%, and is serviceable to 500°F. It too is only slightly affected by organic solvents and finds application where resistance to jet fuel, hydraulic oils, and the like is necessary. Because the polymer chain consists of repeating SiO units and the fluorine substitution is only on the side chain, the inherent flexibility of the silicone structure is retained. Consequently, the polymer is flexible at low temperature and is useful to as low as −90°F. Research is continuing in the area of fluororubbers containing heteroatomic chains.

Fluorine substitution has been known for some time to impart lubricity to an organic molecule and lubricants based on polymers of chlorotrifluoroethylene were evolved in the

Octafluoro-cyclobutane

nineteen-forties. These materials have good lubricity, chemical inertness, and a high density important to gyro flotation applications. However, the structure suffers from the stiffening effect mentioned previously, and, as a result, the change of viscosity with temperature is rather large. This limits application of these polymers. Such important areas of use as hydraulic fluids and jet engine lubrication require a much more rigid control of viscosity than is possible with structures of this type.

A second class of compounds which has been evaluated comprises the fluoroesters, in particular the fluoroalcohol esters of dibasic acids where $H(CF_2)CH_2$ replaces the terminal H's.

These substances are equal to non-fluorine esters in lubricity, which is quite good, and are very stable to oxidation. Unfortunately, their relatively high pour points and large changes of viscosity with temperature place restrictions on their usefulness.

Most recently, fluorosilicone fluids (Dow Corning's FS-1265) have become commercially available and may offer a solution to the problem of the large viscosity-temperature coefficient associated with fluorolubricants. These fluids are polymers with the structure

$$(CH_3)_3SiO(CF_3CH_2CH_2SiCH_3O)_nSi(CH_3)_3$$

where $n = 10$–200. Their lubricity is comparable to a good mineral oil lubricant and they have excellent viscosity-temperature relationships. Again the use of a heteroatomic polymer chain has overcome the effect of fluorine substitution on chain flexibility.

These properties, together with thermal and oxidative stability, encourage application in areas not presently adaptable to use with other fluorine-containing lubricants. One other interesting property of these fluids is their ability to defoam organic solvents such as perchloroethylene, a function of the low surface tension of the fluorosilicones. (The low surface tension makes large bubbles mechanically unstable and it is impossible to form foams.)

Research strategy for fluorocarbons

There are two principal goals (which tend to be mutually antagonistic) at present in fluorocarbon polymer research. One is to create materials of great thermal stability and the other is to improve low temperature properties. Stability is being sought by employing stable fluorocarbon units such as perfluorobenzene (C_6F_6) or perfluorocyclohexane (C_6F_{12}), as building blocks for the polymer. Either direct combination of the groups as:

which has been accomplished where $n = 9$ or less, or using a "hinge" in the chain as:

should provide much more chain flexibility. Work is progressing along these lines and shows promise of early positive results.

Fig. 2-25. In this Fisher-Hirschfelder model of a fluoro-silicone molecule, fluorine atoms (small white spheres) form a protective "armor plating" around the other constituent atoms of carbon (black) silicon (large light grey) and oxygen (small grey). (Courtesy Bell Aerosystems Div. of Textron Corp.)

A second route to thermally stable fluoro-carbon polymers is being taken by using nitrogen atoms to bridge the fluorocarbon segments. In this case, the polymer system is composed of perfluoroalkyl triazine rings

Polymers of this structure have been shown to be stable above 700°F and have excellent chemical and radiation resistance.

In an effort to obtain both maximum solvent resistance and low temperature applicability, studies are under way of the copolymer system of CF_3NO and $CF_2 = CF_2$ to give a structure as:

This material has good resistance to chemical attack and a brittle point of $-70°F$, but lacks thermal stability. However, it is expected that improvement in cross-linking reactions will increase its heat stability.

A recent fluorocarbon polymer, polyhexa-fluoropropylene,

has been described which offers properties similar to other fluorocarbon resins but, due to its lower softening point, is more easily molded. This material is prepared by reaction of $CF_3CF = CF_2$ with a peroxide catalyst at 200°C and 45,000 psi reaction pressure (illustrating that it's not easy). The plastic product is chemically inert, solvent resistant, and has excellent electrical properties.

These are only a few of the possibilities in the polymer chemistry of fluorine compounds. The future of this field is bright.

Problem: getting fluorine into polymers

If there is any cloud on the horizon of fluorine chemistry, it lies in the area of methods of fluorination. Perhaps the principal drawback to the use of fluorine compounds, particularly polymers, is the high cost of producing monomers. Even after many years of research and development, most of the polymers range from $6–10/lb with a few of the newer ones costing up to $16/lb. (Most organic polymers cost less than $1/lb.) This is due mainly to the lack of a good, inexpensive method of introducing many fluorine atoms into an organic molecule without resorting to indirect (oftentimes cumbersome) techniques.

There are three principal ways to fluorinate:

$$(a) —\overset{|}{\underset{|}{C}}Cl + HF \text{ or metal fluoride} \rightarrow —\overset{|}{\underset{|}{C}}F$$

$$(b) —\overset{|}{\underset{|}{C}}H + F_2 \text{ or metal fluoride} \rightarrow —\overset{|}{\underset{|}{C}}F$$

$$(c) \quad \overset{|}{C} = \overset{|}{C} + HF \text{ or } F_2 \rightarrow F\overset{|}{\underset{|}{C}}-\overset{|}{\underset{|}{C}}H \text{ or } F\overset{|}{\underset{|}{C}}-\overset{|}{\underset{|}{C}}F$$

Method (a) has found wide application, but is limited by its inability to form a large number of C-F bonds as well as by the availability of the starting chlorocarbon. Only compounds containing one or two carbons can be considered practical at this time. Method (b) does enable one to obtain a high degree of fluorination, but control of the reaction is extremely difficult due to large reaction heats and consequent rupture of the carbon chain. Any functionally reactive groups in the starting molecule are usually destroyed during the reaction. Method (c) is useful, but can furnish only a few C-F bonds per molecule, depending on the number of unsaturated linkages present. However, it does constitute a method of commercial interest today, particularly for the preparation of vinyl fluoride.

It would appear that research efforts should be directed to the ultimate goal of forming a C-F bond from a CH or CX (X = halogen) bond, as few or as many as desired, using a simple, inexpensive fluorination agent. As is true in most difficult problems, the final solution will be reached only after a series of steps, each often seeming insignificant. Several of these steps are under investigation now, with three recent developments of most significance.

The first is the discovery that sulfur tetrafluoride will replace oxygen in a carbon-oxygen bond with fluorine. The second is the recognition that a fluoride ion in a polar solvent is a strong nucleophilic agent; it has an affinity for positive sites which makes it capable of displacement reactions on a carbon atom. The third is the finding that nitrosyl fluoride (NOF) can introduce fluorine by exchange with another halogen atom. While these alone do not achieve the research goal outlined, they indicate the many possibilities heretofore unsuspected in fluorination methods and agents.

Further reading

Although this article is about compounds of fluorine, rather than the element, readers seeking the most complete discussion of the occurrence, preparation, and physical and chemical properties of elemental fluorine will find it (written in German) in *Fluor: Gmelins Handbuch der anorganischen Chemie*, No. 5 (Verlag Chemie).

In early 1962, three selective bibliographies became available from OTS (U.S. Department of Commerce, Washington 25, D.C.) for 10¢ each: *Fluorine and Fluorine Compounds* (SB 491), *Fluorides* (SB 492), and *Fluorocarbons* (SB 493). These list U.S. government research reports, translations, and other technical documents.

Manhattan Project work on fluorine chemistry was compiled in *Preparation, Properties, and Technology of Fluorine and Organic-Fluoro Compounds*, ed. by Slesser and Schram (McGraw-Hill, 1951, $11.50). It's not too difficult technically and gives a good sense of history, but is now outdated.

An up-to-date review of preparative fluorine chemistry by Pierce and Lovelace, called "New and Varied Paths for Fluorine Chemistry," appeared in the July 9, 1962 issue of *Chemical & Engineering News*. You can get a reprint for 50¢ from Reprint Dept., ACS Applied Publications, 1155 16th Street, N.W., Washington 6, D.C.

A quick bird's-eye view of the organic field is given in *Fluorine And Its Compounds*, by Haszeldine and Sharpe (Wiley, 1951, $2).

Somewhat more difficult is Hudlicky's *Chemistry of Organic Fluorine Compounds* (Pergamon Press, 1961, $9.50).

A bit outdated, but quite detailed, are the two volumes of *Fluorine Chemistry*, ed. by Simons (Academic Press, 1954 and 1958, $15 each). Three more volumes are in preparation.

Most recent, and very detailed indeed, are the two volumes of *Advances in Fluorine Chemistry*, ed. by Stacey, Tatlow, and Sharpe (Butterworths, 1960 and 1961, $8 each).

More a reference book and review than a discussion, being essentially a compilation of valuable tables, is *Aliphatic Fluorine Compounds* by Lovelace, Rausch, and Postelnek (Reinhold, 1958, $12.50).

Also worthwhile is D. Osteroth, *Chemie und Technologie Aliphatischer Fluoroganischer Verbindungen* (F. Enke, Verlag, Stuttgart, Germany, $15.00).

TOOLS FOR ANALYTICAL CHEMISTRY

by Theodore Melnechuk *

IN BRIEF: *Since about 1940, analytical chemistry has adopted three new kinds of instruments. Classical wet methods have in part been made automatic. Much faster, more sensitive instrumental methods that employ physical rather than chemical effects have come into widespread and increasing use. And the signals from both approaches are now automatically recorded in graphic or digital form. The resulting freedom from much previous routine, separations hundreds of times faster than traditional distillation, and methods sensitive to more subtle atomic events have enabled analytical chemists to tackle more difficult analyses than feasible heretofore. Increased speed permits many more analyses per day and prompt feedback of results for controlling product streams.*

But wet chemistry remains the method of choice in some situations and is in many others inextricably entwined with instrumental methods. Both approaches seem likely to make use of effects with weaker energies and shorter times as bases for future techniques.—T.M.

■ Up till twenty years ago, the analytical chemist relied almost entirely on chemical reactions as his means for determining the composition of materials. After tediously preparing a sample and checking its physical properties, he would react it with reagents and, from the kind and magnitude of the changes that followed, he could tell, after some hours or days, what substances and how much of each it contained.

Nowadays, a large share of all chemical analyses are made in minutes, with the use of instruments that are based not on chemical but on physical interactions. And the list of such instruments is ever growing.

Is physics devouring chemistry? Are wet chemical methods really on the way out?

Not to keep you in suspense, the answer is no. At least not altogether and not right away. The analytical tool kit keeps getting bigger, but the new tools don't replace the old tools.

* Theodore Melnechuk, now Director of Communications for MIT's Neurosciences Research Program, Brookline, Massachusetts, was formerly Associate Editor of *International Science and Technology*.

Actually, three kinds of instruments have enriched modern chemical analysis. (1) Devices have been developed that mechanize much of the routine of classical techniques. (2) The recording of data has also been mechanized, being read out now in graphic or digital form. (3) Most revolutionary, however, are the new analytical instruments based on physical rather than chemical effects.

Some of these instruments are new only to analytical chemists, having long been familiar in other scientific fields. Crystallographers have long used x-ray diffraction, for instance, and astronomers have been using spectrometry even longer (see Color Fig. 4).

But most of the new instruments are altogether new. In 1940, only a handful of infrared and ultraviolet spectrophotometers existed, none of them recording, and there was no equipment at all for x-ray fluorescence, gas chromatography, mass spectrometry, electron miscroscopy, nuclear magnetic or electron spin resonance, and—remember?—no readily available sources for radioactive isotopes, deuterium, or compounds tagged with C^{14}.

The new tools are invariably faster and often more sensitive than the old. They approach in sensitivity man's most exquisitely sensitive analytical tool—his nose.

Wet chemistry

A typical wet analysis can be time-consuming. First, as in all chemical analyses instrumental as well as wet, a representative sample must be obtained—a task not necessarily easy when the unknown is not a gas. Second, it must be prepared for analysis, perhaps by removing components that are apt to interfere, perhaps by changing its chemical state, or by dissolving it in water or some other solvent. Then, usually, the analyst must determine its composition. This can mean any or all of a number of things. It can mean no more than separating the various constituents. It usually means at least identifying the isolated constituents. The latter is qualitative analysis.

But even a "qual" report should give some quantitative information. A sample shown to contain sulfur, iron, tin, zinc, and copper may still be any one of many things—an impure sulfide, say—until the fact that the sulfur and iron are traces (less than 0.1%), the tin a minor (0.1–5%) and the zinc and copper major (more than 5%) constituents proves it to be brass.

Quantitative analysis can be elemental, measuring the amount of elements, as in most inorganic analyses, or it can be functional, measuring the amounts of compounds, radicals,

side chains, and other functional groups, as in most organic analyses.

In an analysis of a mixture of isomers, functional analysis shades into structural analysis, which looks into the spatial configuration of constituents, and thus can distinguish between right-hand and left-hand forms of the same chemical.

Each kind of analysis has its own routine strategies. In running a typical "qual," you first do a series of preliminary tests for physical properties. Then, typically, after grinding and dissolving the sample, you classify by group, then narrow down to a distinct class, then pinpoint each chemical—a long drawn-out affair of applying tests that are progressively more selective until you reach the one that is specific.

Here wet quantitative analysis begins. If volumetric, it measures the amount of a substance by determining the amount of a standardized reagent, called the titrant, required to react with all of the unknown, according to the appropriate reaction formula.

The trick is to tell when all the constituent of interest has reacted. This end point is often signaled by a change of color on the part of some added indicator chemical. Then the volume of titrant needed to combine completely is measured and the amount of the investigated constituent calculated.

In gravimetric analysis, a standardized reagent is added to a solution of the sample to form some reaction product which is then isolated, purified, and weighed.

Thus the classical tools for wet chemical analysis are the volumetric flask for diluting a sample to a known concentration; a calibrated buret for measuring and dispensing the reagent; a pipet for transferring exact amounts of liquid; a reaction flask, a stirring rod, and an accurate balance. Filters, crucibles, and furnaces for igniting precipitates are accessory tools. They also include the standard reagents and indicators—and the hand and eye of the analyst.

These are potent tools. With them, beginning in 1883, Emil Fischer determined the empirical and structural formulae of the sixteen sugar isomers by wet chemical methods alone, despite the complexity of these carbohydrates, their hard-to-handle syrupy state, and their complicated molecular shapes.

But it took him twenty years.

Of chemicals, by chemicals

Of course, Fischer had little alternative. Few prototypes of contemporary instruments were available to him. Those that were—the spectrograph, say—he probably never considered for analytical use.

As the name of their profession indicates, analytical chemists consider themselves chemists first, analysts second. To this day, a synthetic chemist somehow obliged to analyze the course of his own new reaction or the composition of its products will first think of turning to a wet method, because reactions are familiar to him.

The rise of instruments

Today each step of a classical titration can be made automatic, even to the detection of the end point. A large part of the recent revolution in analytical instrumentation has been just such mechanization. Manufacturer's catalogs list many such devices for freeing the determinator from the drudgery of measuring and pouring and stirring and watching. There even exist all-in-one outfits, such as the so-called benchtop and robot analyzers and titrimeters, that do every step of the job.

You might think that this mechanization was the route whereby the nonclassical instruments entered analysis. Not at all. Automatic titration came along rather recently, only about five years ago—well after the influx of instruments not classically chemical.

If automatic titrators didn't lead the parade, was it the already existent instrumentation that was the first to be accepted? Oddly enough, the instrumental method that led the invasion of analysis was not one of the familiars, but a comparatively new invention—polarography. Introduced to America in 1932 by its Czechoslovakian inventor Jaroslav Heyrovsky, it did not really catch on until the spring of 1939, when its virtues were urged in a review by I. M. Kolthoff. (In 1959, Heyrovsky received the Nobel prize for his 1922 invention.)

Polarographic instruments are electroanalytical; each contains an electrolyte in which an electrolyzable sample is dissolved. As the applied voltage varies in a known way, the instrument plots a sigmoidal curve of the current that passes through the solution, between a reference electrode and a polarizable electrode formed by a series of mercury drops. The inflection point of the curve is fairly characteristic of a given constituent but the limit of the curve is quite directly related to the concentration. So while it is only a poor qualitative tool, it is an excellent quantitative tool—at least for traces of elements that are electrically oxidizable or reducible.

After polarography came the deluge: emission spectroscopy and absorption spectrophotometry, which had been available but little called upon, were swept up in the instrumental fad, to be followed by mass spectrometry, x-ray diffraction, gas chromatography, and magnetic resonance—to list but a few of the major methods in the approximate order of their coming.

The impact on science and industry

In two decades, a revolution occurred, and today analytical chemistry is the richer in scope and depth because it now has at its disposal an enlarged kit of tools.

The first benefit conferred by the instrumental influx has been increased speed of analysis. Speed has been achieved both by speeding up separation, as in gas chromatography, or—as in infrared absorption "as is" analysis—by eliminating it altogether. Most instrumental determinations are far faster than classical tests. In twenty minutes, a gas chromatograph recently separated a cut of crude oil into 52 components that a group of petroleum chemists had taken twenty *years* to separate by distillation. A gravimetric determination of tinplate on steel that required several hours is now done by continuous x-ray fluorescence in a few seconds.

Manpower has also been saved by such instruments as automatic amino acid analyzers. Samples still take 1 to $1\frac{1}{2}$ days to go through but no one has to sit there and watch anymore.

Of course the new instruments have several requirements for calibration. All they really yield are indefinitive curves or figures that must be compared with the curves or figures of precise determinations of pure standards. The invaluable helps in this area are the more than 600 different standard materials available from the National Bureau of Standards—mostly chemicals, ceramics, metals, ores, and radioactive nuclides. The NBS sells more than 60,000 samples of these standard materials a year to other laboratories for maintaining the accuracy of apparatus and equipment, and controlling chemical processes. All of them are certified either for chemical composition or with respect to specific chemical or physical properties.

A peek at principles

All analytical methods, wet and instrumental, measure some unique effect caused in a substance by its interaction with one or more forms of energy.

These effects occur at different levels of structure. Some, such as melting and freezing, involve forces between the molecules of substances. Others, like thermal conductivity and the emission of infrared spectra, occur at the molecular level, as the molecules rotate and vibrate. Going still deeper, chemical reactions involve valence electrons, while the emission of x-rays comes from jumps between inner orbitals. Then there are nuclear effects, such as magnetic resonance, and finally intranucleonic effects, exploited in radiochemical analysis.

One way to index analytical methods would be in terms of those structural levels, but I will classify the methods by the several kinds of interacting energy that cause the various effects. For one thing, it keeps the chemical methods together as a group; for another, it corresponds to real subdivisions within the profession—electroanalysts, spectroscopists, resonance specialists, and so forth.

Postponing comparison of the methods, here are brief descriptions of the major methods in each group.

Thermoanalysis

Substances change as their temperatures change, and in characteristic ways. Thermal methods monitor these changes.

Thermogravimetry measures the decreasing weight of a substance in a vacuum, or in an atmosphere either inert or its own, as it is heated to high temperatures in an automatic-recording thermobalance. Plotting Δw versus T gives a curve that profiles the characteristic ranges and rates of physico-chemical changes that cause a loss of weight.

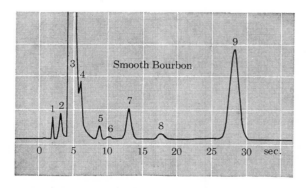

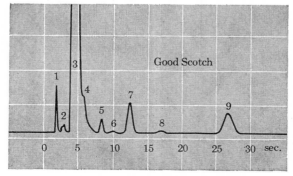

Fig. 2-26. Whiskey chromatograms ("C-grams"?) show resolution of 9 fractions in 30 minutes. Areas under peaks measure amounts. Peak 1 is acetaldehyde (CH_3CHO), 9 is fusel oil ($C_5H_{12}O$)—cause of flavor and hangover; 3 is ethanol ($H_2OOC_4H_{10}$). (Courtesy Wilkens Instrument and Research, Inc.)

In differential thermal analysis, thermocouples or thermistors connected in series but in opposition measure the differences in temperature between the sample and a reference compound as they are heated at a common rate. Processes that evolve or absorb heat in one but not the other substance show up as peaks or troughs on the DTA curve, which thus establishes how the substances differ or are identical. This technique is being widely used in polymer studies.

Cryometry, for all the cold implicit in its name, is also an important thermal method. It plots the freezing curve of a sample, in particular the freezing point, and so is a good method for testing the purity of a substance whose identity you know.

The methods above measure amounts of heat or transition temperatures. The thermal conductivity of a substance has also been made the basis for a quantitative analytical method—the famous gas chromatography.

A gas chromatograph isolates and measures the volatile fractions of a mixture of elements or of compounds. Only the quantitative function is based on thermal conductivity, the detection devices being heated wires or thermistors that signal the amount and duration of the cooling effect upon them of each substance that streams by.

The source of these substances is the chromatograph column, which is packed with a sorbent. A vaporized sample is injected at the column inlet into a stream of carrier gas, which moves it toward the detector. As the sample moves through the column, its constituents travel at different and characteristic rates, determined by their vapor pressure, solution interaction, and diffusion. So a sample that goes into the column as a plug of vapor emerges as a series of separated bands, which can be measured and collected.

As they emerge, their concentration is measured as a function of time as previously described and, if recorded, describes a curve called a chromatogram (see Fig. 2-26). Each peak on a chromatogram signifies the passage of an isolated fraction of the sample. Therefore, from its time of emergence, height, width, and area, qualitative and quantitative data can be determined and related to the original sample.

The time of arrival and passage is usually a matter of minutes and sometimes of seconds, even when half a dozen components are being resolved. This is a far cry from the matter of hours that so much of wet chemistry is. And that's without counting in the additional time required by classical methods to isolate the components.

No wonder, then, that gas chromatography is

often hailed as the most important analytical advance in recent years; in fact, it was only 1952 when A. J. P. Martin and T. James published their work on the earliest form of it. Since then, about 10,000 GC's have come into use. Some of these are home-made setups, but the current market for commercial models is close to $4 million, and is being supplied by more than 20 manufacturers.

However, gas chromatography can't do everything. It works only for samples vaporizable up to about 500°C without decomposition. It's rapid, but needs time-consuming calibration and interpretation.

Wet and electroanalysis

Earlier I described the classical titrimetric methods, and then how they are benefiting from labor-saving devices (did I mention the new bottle washers?). Many of the new instruments do little else than signal the end-point of classical (if automatic) titrations in a non-chemical way. Some photometrically perceive the traditional color change; others use electrical effects as indicators. Amperometric titrations, as the name suggests, measure the change in current proportional to the change in concentration of reactants and products. In potentiometric and conductometric titrations, voltage and resistance changes are correspondingly monitored. Perhaps the widest industrial application of potentiometry is in electronic pH meters, which can measure acidity with great accuracy.

Electrical energy also gets involved with chemical reactions in the methods of coulometry and electrodeposition, in which electrons are used as a reagent for titration and separation, respectively. They apply Faraday's laws of electrolysis, which state that—independent of temperature, solvent, and electrolyte concentration—the number of chemical equivalent weights of a substance produced at an electrode is proportional to the quantity of electricity passed through the solution. In coulometry, the current is measured; in electrodeposition, the reaction product is weighed.

The most important electrochemical method, polarography, has already been described. It has a few relatives that are classed with polarography under the general term "voltammetry," since all of them monitor current-time-potential relationships at electrodes immersed in electrolytic solutions. Their interrelationship is illustrated in Fig. 2-27.

Casting light on the subject

The largest single class of new analytical instruments contains those that employ electromagnetic radiation to interact with the sample.

As a group they are called optical, even though visible radiation is a narrow band indeed in the spectrum of wavelengths used, which runs from the short wavelengths of gamma and x-rays to the longer wavelengths of microwaves.

Now the energy of electromagnetic radiation varies inversely with wavelength: the shortest wavelengths have the highest energy. So you can select radiation frequencies to interact with different levels of electron energy, to yield qualitative, elemental, functional, and structural data.

For instance, microwaves and infrared radiation interact with molecular vibrations or rotations and with weak interatomic bonds; uv and visible radiations interact with strong interatomic bonds and valence electrons; x-rays interact with inner-shell electrons; and gamma rays interact with atomic nuclei.

These waves can interact with matter in six ways; the matter can emit, absorb, reflect, diffract, refract, or polarize them.

The measurement of emission and absorption spectra is called spectrometry. Important spectrometric principles and methods are illus-

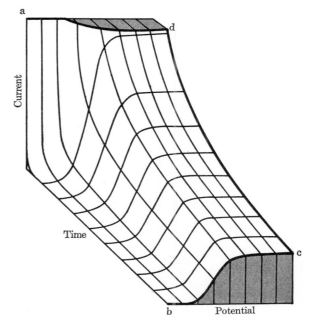

Fig. 2-27. All methods of voltammetric analysis employ a series of hanging mercury drops as microelectrodes. Each method holds constant a different one of the three parameters current, potential, and time. Therefore the various methods can be represented by intersections of planes with the current-time-potential surface given by the general equation for micro-electrodes systems. Curve bc is a conventional polarographic wave. Curve dc typifies outputs of constant-potential voltammetry. Curve ad is a graph from chronopotentiometry. (Courtesy W. H. Reinmuth, Columbia University)

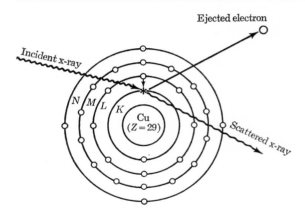

Fig. 2-28. X-rays bombarding an atom (here, copper) eject one or more inner electrons. As outer electrons move in to replace them, the atom releases fluorescent x-radiation of a wavelength peculiar to the element and orbits involved.

trated in Color Figs. 4, 5, and 7.

When emission spectra are being measured, the method is called spectroscopy. (A spectrograph is a spectroscope that photographs the spectra.) One new spectroscopic method is x-ray fluorescence, whose principle is illustrated in Fig. 2-28.

The measurement of absorption spectra is called spectrophotometry. It is especially important in organic analysis where, especially in the infrared region, absorption analysis has proven a powerful tool for identifying functional groups. The infrared spectra are extraordinarily informative, as illustrated in Fig. 2-29. R. B. Woodward, Loeb Professor of Chemistry at Harvard, who uses infrared

spectra in elucidating the structure of biochemicals, has said that "no single tool has had a more dramatic impact upon organic chemistry than infrared measurements."

A new optical method called spectropolarimetry depends upon the Cotton effect—the combined phenomena of unequal absorption and unequal velocity of transmission of polarized light of different wavelengths, in optically active substances. The effect can be correlated with the structural and stereochemical features of organic compounds, as illustrated in Fig. 2-30.

Magnetic methods

You can get information about a sample's composition and structure from interactions of the nuclei and electrons in its constituent atoms with a magnetic field.

The mass spectrometer (see Color Fig. 9) ionizes a sample, then sends the ions at uniform speed through a uniform magnetic field and a perpendicular electrostatic field. Their combined action makes each ion travel in a cycloidal trajectory; its exact radius of curvature—usually somewhere in the 10–15 cm range—is determined by the ion's mass, velocity, and charge. So all ions of identical mass-to-charge ratio are focused into one beam. The various beams form a mass spectrum. Resolution can be so fine as to distinguish between the close lines of two compounds with the same mass number, say $C_2{}^{12}H_5{}^1$ and $C^{12}C^{13}H_4{}^1$, whose masses differ by only 1 part in 75,000. Like the gas chromatograph, mass spectrometry is much used in the petroleum industry.

Resonance methods—*nuclear magnetic and*

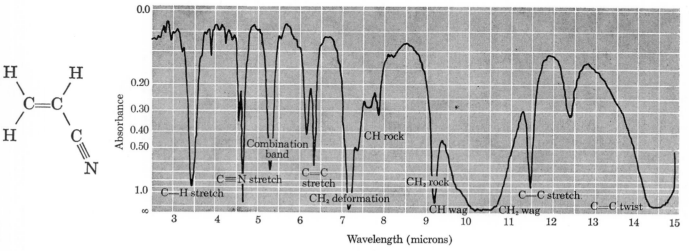

Fig. 2-29. For qualitative analysis of organic chemicals, their infrared absorption spectra are checked for bands that reveal functional groups like =CH$_2$ and —CN. Spectrum above shows strong absorption bands at wavelengths where frequencies of ir radiation match those of labeled motions of such groups in acrylonitrile molecule sketched in margin. (Courtesy Perkin-Elmer Corp.)

electron *spin,* whence cometh the acronyms NMR and ESR—detect the absorption of rf and microwave radiation respectively by nuclei with magnetic moments not equal to zero and unpaired electrons, which are precessing at a resonant frequency determined by the strength of an applied magnetic field. NMR will reveal not only the presence of a magnetic nucleus, such as hydrogen's, but also its interaction with nearby nuclei. It is therefore a potent method for determining molecular structure. In ESR, too, the frequency at which the electron absorbs radiation is affected by nearby atoms and nuclei. So its resonance signal can give you information about the structure of paramagnetic materials or free radicals, which contain unpaired electrons.

Radioactivity for analysis

All radioactive substances share two properties important for analysis. First, a radioisotope's rate of disintegration rarely affects and is never affected by its chemical environment. That means you can replace a normal atom by—or convert it into—a radioactive one, to trace its fate during a chemical reaction. The conversion would be done by fast-particle bombardment; the detection and measurement of the tracer element would be done by beta-ray or gamma-ray spectroscopy.

The other analytically important property of radioisotopes is that the intensity of a substance's characteristic decay is directly proportional to the number of hot atoms in it. You can identify and measure a radioactive element by measuring its rate of decay and the wavelength of its emitted energy even when its mass is as small as 10^{-10} g in the case of compounds or 10^{-12} g in the case of elements. This makes radioactive tracer analysis orders of magnitude more sensitive than any other analytical method for those elements—unlike nitrogen and oxygen—that have suitable radioisotopes.

The main hitch is the high price of equipment for measuring radiation.

Comparing the various instruments

Since sales of analytical instruments have increased by a factor of 10 in the last 20 years, it is clear that the technical community has found that it pays to go instrumental, at least in some cases. In 1960, Esso published the total capital cost of all its analytical instrumentation. The figure was $1,090,000.

The comparison table on pages 232 and 233 attempts to give you a general idea of how some important analytical methods compare. Its headings are the questions that an analytical chemist would ask of any new method. The rat-

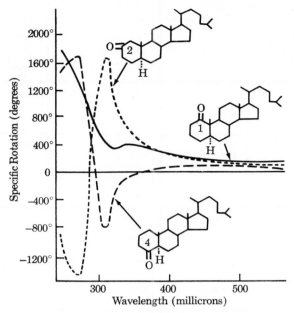

Fig. 2-30. Automatic recording spectropolarimeters are used to study the molecular configuration of optically active organic chemicals. The instrument plots the optical rotatory dispersion (ORD) of functional groups in uv radiation. The typical ORD curves shown were used to distinguish three cholestanone isomers that differ only in the position of the attached carbonyl group. (Courtesy C. Djerassi, Chemistry Dept., Stanford University)

ings given are only generally true; specific instances might belie a given rating.

You can see from the table that there are preferred methods for dealing with different situations—freezing-point assays for high-purity substances, emission spectroscopy for identifying traces of elements. But it is also clear that no one method can stand alone.

Granting the need for general analysis to maintain a battery of methods, you might ask whether there weren't some half-dozen workhorses that would do for most situations—some hard core of analytical methods whether wet or instrumental.

Forced to pick six methods, most analysts would probably agree on these: for inorganic analyses, emission spectroscopy; for organic analyses, gas chromatography, mass spectrometry, and infrared absorption spectrophotometry; and, for both inorganic and organic analyses—wet chemistry.

You already know the virtues of the five named instrumental methods. But what of the wet? Why is it still used if it is so slow?

Well, for some situations it is still the method of economic choice, especially in routine tests for one element, but also in the development of new reactions. In the latter, samples are never the same, so it doesn't pay to obtain reference

THE METHODS		SAMPLE	TIME	SPECIFICITY	QUALITATIVE ANALYSIS	
What form of energy does it use?	Name	Are there any limits on the sample?	Total time for an analysis (Long > 2 hrs, short < ½ hr)	How is it for determining a substance despite the presence of other substances?	What is measured?	How good is it for this use?
Thermal	Cryoscopy	sample must be crystallizable	fair	poor	freezing point	excellent for proof of purity but poor for identification
	Gas chromatography	sample must be volatile within operating limits of the instrument; is retrievable only as fractions	short	good	relative solubility in selected solvent	fair to good
Chemical	Wet methods (elemental inorganic)	none, but is not retrievable	generally long	excellent for elements, poor for compounds	specific chemical reaction	good
	Wet methods (elemental organic)	sample must be combustible, and is not retrievable	fair to excellent	excellent for elements, poor for compounds	specific chemical reaction	good
	Wet methods (functional organic)	sample must be soluble, and is not retrievable	generally long	generally good	specific chemical reaction	poor to fair
Electrical	Polarography	component must be electrically oxidizable or reducible; sample is not retrievable	fair to good	poor to fair	applied potential	poor
Optical (Electromagnetic)	Emission spectrometry	none, but sample is not retrievable	after calibration, shorter than wet methods	excellent	wavelength of emitted light	excellent
	X-ray fluorescence	none	shorter than wet methods	excellent	wavelength of emitted x-radiation	excellent
	Ultraviolet absorption	component must absorb uv radiation	good	poor to fair	wavelength distribution	poor to fair
	Visible absorption	component must absorb visible radiation	poor to good, depending on method	poor to fair	wavelength distribution	poor
	Infrared absorption	component must absorb ir radiation	good	fair to good	wavelength distribution	good
	X-ray diffraction	components must be crystalline	good	excellent	x-ray diffraction patterns and angles	excellent
Magnetic	Mass spectrometry	components must be sufficiently volatile within operating limits and sample is not retrievable	fair, once equipment is operating and calibrated	good	mass distribution	good
	Nuclear magnetic resonance	sample must have magnetic nuclei	depends upon instrumentation	fair to good	radio frequency at which nuclei precess	excellent
Radioactive	Activation analysis	elements must have suitable radioactive isotopes	short, after activation	excellent for all elements that can be activated	energy and decay rate of induced radioactivity	excellent

Adapted from S. Siggia, Olin Research Center.

A COMPARISON OF FIFTEEN IMPORTANT METHODS

QUANTITATIVE ANALYSIS		SENSITIVITY			PRECISION	PRICE
What is measured?	How good is it for this use?	How accurately does it detect a substance in the concentration ranges of ...			How reproducible are its results?	How much does instrumentation cost? (High > $20,000, low < $10,000)
		Trace quantity (0.1% and below)	Medium concentration	High purity (98-100%)		
freezing curve	excellent for high purity but poor in other ranges	poor	poor	excellent	excellent in high purity, poor in the other ranges	low
thermal conductivity	excellent	excellent	excellent	fair	good	low
magnitude of physical change or amount of reactant	good for elements	generally poor	good	good	good	low
magnitude of physical change or amount of reactant	good for elements, poor for compounds	generally poor, good for some elements	good	good	good	low
magnitude of physical change or amount of reactant	poor to excellent, depending on ranges	poor to fair	excellent	fair	poor to excellent, depending on ranges	low
amount of current flowing	excellent in trace range, poor to fair in other ranges	excellent	fair	poor	poor to fair	low
amount of emitted light	good in trace ranges, fair in higher ranges	excellent	fair	poor	good in trace ranges, fair in other ranges	high
amount of emitted x-radiation	poor to good, depending on range	poor	good (1-10%), fair (> 10%)	poor	poor to good, depending on range	medium
amount of radiation transmitted	excellent in trace ranges, poor to fair in other ranges	excellent	fair	poor	poor to excellent, depending on range	low to medium
amount of light transmitted	good in lower, poor in higher ranges	good	good	poor to fair	good	low to medium
amount of radiation transmitted	good, except in trace and high purity ranges	poor	excellent	fair	good	low to medium
amount of radiation reflected	fair to poor	poor	good	good	poor for quantitative use	medium
amount of ion current	good, except at extreme ranges	fair	good	poor to fair	good, except at extreme ranges	medium to high
amount of radio frequency energy received in detector coil	fair to good	poor	good	poor	fair to good	high
amount of induced radioactivity	excellent in trace range	excellent	fair	poor	excellent in trace range	high

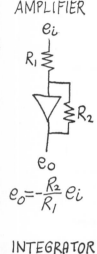

Fig. 2-31. If this mixture were analyzed in a mass spectrometer, which would split the triple bonds, the functional groups shown paired would be confused. But if it were first separated into its three fractions in a gas chromatograph, the mass spectrometer would measure each fraction correctly.

AMPLIFIER

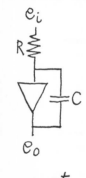

$$e_o = -\frac{R_2}{R_1} e_i$$

INTEGRATOR

$$e_o = -\frac{1}{RC} \int_0^t e_i \, dt$$

DIFFERENTIATOR

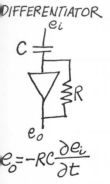

$$e_o = -RC \frac{\partial e_i}{\partial t}$$

standards whose properties would have to be known in order to calibrate an infrared absorption spectrophotometer or other instrument and standardize a procedure.

In other situations, instruments do not yet yield sufficiently precise—i.e., reproducible—results. Take the aldehydes. For some obscure reason, they don't always absorb infrared at the same wavelengths or at the same intensities. So wet methods must be used to determine them—methods related not to their quantum mechanics but to their chemistry.

Sometimes the instrument isn't specific enough. Infrared absorption analysis can't always distinguish —OH— from —NH— absorption bands, for example. In this case, a chemical test—sodium fusion—will establish the presence or absence of nitrogen.

The interdependence suggested by the last example often happens on a grand scale, with both wet and instrumental methods being shot at a problem like left jabs and right crosses. An analytical system devised by Sidney Siggia, director of analysis at the Olin Research Center, to monitor the oxidation of anthracene to anthraquinone, used ultraviolet absorption for the anthracene, polarography for the anthraquinone, and chemical methods for the numerous impurities and byproducts.

At the least, wet chemistry will often be used to make a sample susceptible to instrumental analysis. As Dr. Siggia said while chairing last year's Gordon Conference on Analysis, "The sample isn't sacred," and adroit chemical alteration of a sample will extend the range of an instrument. In the anthracene reaction cited shortly above, polarography could not determine the anthraquinone sample in the presence of anhydride side products. By adding lithium hydroxide, the anhydrides were converted to salts that did not interfere.

Sometimes, of course, several instrumental methods can be used in series. In a sense, the gas chromatograph is already a tandem instrument that combines a packed column for separating and a detector for quantitative analysis. To identify its measured pure unknowns, it is very often hitched to instruments for infrared absorption or mass spectrometry.

In such tandems, the order of use can be critical, as in the case illustrated in Fig. 2-31.

Trends in analysis

The teaming up of instruments into combinations is a trend that all agree will increase. At the same time, some analysts agree with William H. Reinmuth of Columbia University that the yen to innovate will drive some lab managers into building "do-it-yourself" arrangements, like hi-fi radio sets, assembled at least at the automatic recording end from cheap and versatile electronic components. Prof. Reinmuth points out that a comparatively inexpensive operational amplifier originally developed for analog computers can be used not only to amplify analytical signals from a transducer but, with the simple changes in its associated circuitry sketched in the margin, as the kind of integrator used to compute the area under a chromatogram peak or as the kind of differentiator often needed in electroanalysis when you want to make a slight increase be more graphically indicated as a peak.

Pondering the optical methods in his capacity an adviser to the president of Fisher Scientific Co., George L. Buc has gone on record as predicting eventual filling of the application gaps in the electromagnetic spectrum—perhaps with the use of lasers as exciters of emission; increased speed in the obtaining of spectra; and increasing use of computers to convert the multitude of raw spectral data into quantity units.

A trend toward smallness is evident throughout all chemical analysis. Average sample size is certainly decreasing, and so are determination time and the energy of the determining interaction. The energies involved in the latest instrumental method, NMR, are very small compared to those of chemical reactions, while the time scale of a radioactive event is measured in 10^{-17} seconds. One looks forward to seeing what subtle effects will be exploited in the next generation of analytical instruments.

The subtlest, most powerful tool

The tool alluded to is, of course, the mind of the analyst; the robot knows nothing. Experimental tools and techniques presume a capacity in the analyst to understand the nature of the problem prompting the analysis, to select the best means for attaining the goal, to evaluate the analytical data, and to correlate it into a conclusion that elucidates the chemistry of the problem—in addition to a mastery of the instrument.

All this requires not only an analytical turn of mind but also a firm grounding in the theory of errors and chemistry. Without a knowledge of chemistry, the analyst dwindles to a mere determinator.

Many an analytical chemist is anxious lest the obvious simplicity of much instrumental analysis downgrade his status in managerial eyes. To run an analysis, to get a number, you no longer have to know any chemistry; you plug in and turn on a machine and out comes a piece of paper. But in the recent words of Lawrence T. Hallett, editor of *Analytical Chemistry,* "If he remains the master and not the slave of the tools that he uses in his work, and if he keeps clear the distinction between an analytical scientist and the analytical technician tied to his instrument, his future need hold no fears."

Further reading

For a less sanguine opinion as to the future role of wet chemistry in analysis, read Liebhafsky's "Modern Analytical Chemistry: A Subjective View" in the June '62 *Analytical Chemistry.* Two other general surveys analysts urge reading are Chernside's "The Enlargement of Horizons in Analytical Chemistry" in *Analyst* **86,** 314 (1961) and "The Coordination of Analytical Techniques in Industrial Research" in *Svensk. Kem. Tidskr.* **73,** 255 (1961).

Old one-volume standbys are Hillebrand & Lundell's *Applied Inorganic Analysis* (Wiley, 1953, 2nd ed., $18.50) and Siggia & Stolten's *An Introduction to Modern Organic Analysis* (Interscience, 1956, $5.50). Neither of the two books covers all of the techniques now available, of course, but are considered classics for what they do cover.

A systematic approach to the science and technology of instrumental analysis is Strobel's *Chemical Instrumentation* (Addison-Wesley, 1960, $9.75), while Bair's *Introduction to Chemical Instrumentation* (McGraw-Hill, 1962, $10.75) outlines the principles of the chemical signal sources and the electronics that handles them. *Instrumental Analysis,* Vol. III of *Standard Methods of Chemical Analysis,* edited by Welcher (Van Nostrand, in press), will cumulate the recent series of articles by Lewin in *Journal of Chemical Education.*

"Gas Chromatography" by Safranski, Nogare, and the staff of *Chem. & Engineering News* is an excellent survey of principles, uses, and commercial instruments, published in the June 2 and July 3, 1961, issues: a copy costs $1 from Reprint Dept., ACS Applied Publications, 1155 16th St., NW, Washington 6, D.C. A film with the same title, and one on "Infrared Spectroscopy," can be borrowed free from Modern Talking Picture Service, Inc., 3 East 54th St., New York 22, N.Y. *X-ray Absorption and Emission in Analytical Chemistry,* by Liebhafsky, Pfeiffer, Winslow, and Zemany, is the classic book on this optical method (Wiley, 1960, $13.50). Activation analysis can be studied at nominal cost in an outsiders' participant program at General Atomics, San Diego, Calif. (call V. Guinn, GL 9-2310). *Basic Principles of the Tracer Methods,* by Sheppard, tells in detail what can be done with the results (Wiley, 1962, $8).

As for standards, the 600-odd available from NBS are catalogued in Misc. Pub. 241: *Standard Materials* (D.C.: National Bureau of Standards, Washington 25, 30¢). Information on the new ASTM standards is available from American Society for Testing and Materials, 1916 Race St., Philadelphia 3, Pa. The catalogue of approved American Standards is available free from American Standards Association, 10 E. 40th St., New York 16, N.Y.

The many analytical instruments and their manufacturers are listed in the April 1962 *Analytical Chemistry,* which also contains the latest biennial survey of fundamental analytical literature. The May 1962 issue of that magazine contains a historical report, "Impact of Instrumental Analysis on American Industry," based on reports by men in the chemicals, aluminum, communications, petroleum, photographic, and pharmaceutical industries. It also predicts trends in each industry. Analytical control of product stream is covered in *Continuous Analysis of Chemical Process Systems* by Siggia (Wiley, 1959, $9.25).

TAILOR-MAKING PLASTICS

by Herman F. Mark *

IN BRIEF: *Now there's a new approach to organizing the search for desirable properties in organic polymer plastics. It uses the points of a triangle to epitomize the principles of crystallization, crosslinking, and rigidity of backbone. Processes based on the first two principles have been used for years to achieve better properties in classical materials such as polyethylene and*

* Herman F. Mark recently retired as Director of the Polymer Research Institute at the Polytechnic Institute of Brooklyn. He is the author of a dozen books on polymers and over 400 journal articles.

Bakelite. The third point, rigid backbone, is now being investigated. From these studies, a new class of materials has come. Even more important, arranging the principles in a triangle suggests how you can attempt combinations of specific pairs of principles and move along the sides of the triangle. Still more interesting for the future is the possibility of making materials out in the middle of the triangle, thus using all three principles to come up with property combinations yet unknown.—H.M.

■ The first plastic materials were discovered by chance—serendipity if you will—when one investigator saw possibilities in the gooey mess his predecessors would have consigned to the "gunk barrel." This is the way the world first received Bakelite in 1909 and nylon in the early 1930's. As the possibilities and limitations of the increasing number of polymeric materials became better known, however, more serious work was begun to discover the structural details which made polymers desirable, and to exploit these by specific synthesis.

This work has helped formulate the principles describing the relationships between structure and properties in polymers, at least in an empirical and generalized way. Polymer chemists and engineers now have working hypotheses for designing new molecules with predetermined properties to fulfill specific functions. Although the hypotheses are rough and general, they have been very successful in use, proving once again that a poor theory is better than no theory at all.

Now, a new class of polymers is emerging. By themselves, these show promise of providing better physical and chemical properties than many presently used materials. Perhaps even more important, however, they help point the way to improved modifications of other basic types of polymers, to allow an almost unlimited gradation in properties for tailor-made materials. This new class is the so-called rigid backbone polymers. Conventional polymers have a long backbone chain of carbon, oxygen, or nitrogen atoms hooked to each other by single bonds of the C-C, C-O, and C-N type; or they have shorter chains rigidly attached to one another in a network of "crosslinked" grids. The new polymers are different.

Before examining these materials in detail, let's look at the properties which make polymers, or indeed any material, useful and the combinations of properties needed for a given application.

Only in rare cases is successful practical application of organic polymers made possible by increasing a single property to an extravagantly high value. In most instances it is some combination of several properties which makes a material valuable and attractive. For example, use of polymers as fibers, films, coatings, and adhesives requires a combination of properties which, although it varies for a specific application, remains essentially the same for the entire field. It is a combination of: (a) High modulus of rigidity; if possible, higher than 500,000 psi. (b) High softening or melting point; if possible, higher than 300°C. (c) High tensile strength; if possible, higher than 100,000 psi. (d) High elongation to break; if possible, above 15%. (e) High resistance to solvents and swelling agents, even at elevated temperatures. (f) High resistance to deterioration through heat, radiation, and aggressive chemical reagents. Favorable values of (c) and (d) mean a large input of energy to break or tear off a piece of the material. This, in practical terms, manifests itself as impact strength and abrasion resistance.

Any material that incorporates a reasonably favorable combination of these properties will be useful in the fields mentioned. It will be especially useful if you can combine these properties with the inherent low density and low cost of organic polymers.

In a general and simplified sense, there are three main principles for achieving such combinations; two of these have been useful in the past, and the third should be of help in developing working hypotheses for future efforts. They are: crystallization, crosslinking, and inflexible chain molecules.

Crystallization very useful

Crystallization has long been known to be a very valuable property of linear, flexible macromolecules, whenever one wants good thermal and mechanical properties. Crystallization in polymers obviously means something quite different from crystallization in metals, salts, or small organic molecules. It describes the formation of domains or regions of high lateral order in an otherwise amorphous material, domains where the spaghetti-like, tangled molecules line up with each other for a discrete distance and pack close together like match sticks in a bundle as shown in Fig. 2-32. These domains, when scattered through the amorphous matrix, add to the strength of the polymer in much the same way that precipitation hardening does in metals.

For example, linear polyethylene, a completely nonpolar material with weak interchain bonding, is rigid, high-melting (130°C), strong, tough, abrasion-resistant, and insoluble in anything at room temperature only because it possesses a strong tendency to crystallize. The same is true for isotactic polypropylene (melting point 170°C) and for isotactic polystyrene (melting point 230°C). "Isotactic" implies that all the substituent groups are arranged along the polymer chain in a regular order, as shown in the margin, allowing better "packing" of the molecules than when they are arranged in a random fashion.

If the macromolecules contain polar groups —"polar" groups or molecules are those which exhibit a dipole moment, those in which a permanent separation exists between positive and negative charges—and are of regular architecture, even better combinations of mechanical and thermal properties result; examples include polyvinyl alcohol (Elvanol), polyvinylidene chloride (Saran), polyformaldehyde (Delrin), and many aliphatic polyesters and polyamides such as polycaprolactam (Perlon) and 66 or 610 nylon. (Trade names listed here and later are typical and not inclusive.)

In all these cases, the intrinsically flexible chain molecules of regular architecture have a distinct tendency to crystallize; inside the crystalline domains a systematic accumulation of interchain forces adds rigidity, reinforcing the entire structure till the system becomes hard and insoluble with a high softening temperature.

The behavior of natural rubber illustrates the influence of crystallization. In the unstretched state, it is very soft (modulus around 20 psi), melts at low temperatures, and dissolves easily in toluene or acetone. As samples are stretched, their chain molecules straighten and become parallel, as if a zipper were run along their length to establish a firm lateral bonding. On further stretching, additional lateral order is established, until at 600 or 700% elongation the extended ribbon or filament has a modulus of 20,000 psi. At this stage, the polymer swells only moderately in organic solvents, and sof-

tens only at high temperatures. Elongation of rubber, and incidentally of many synthetic elastomers with regular chain structures, evidently confers rigidity by forming elastomer crystals, which act as a natural reinforcing filler. This also occurs when polyethylene (Alathon), polyformaldehyde (Delrin), and the nylons are drawn.

Since these crystalline domains are relatively ordered, when compared with their amorphous matrix, they will melt at rather well-defined temperatures, depending on the material. When the melting point of the crystalline domains is *below* the ambient temperature, elongated samples of the polymer will have a tendency to contract; as a consequence, the material will be an elastomer. If, however, their melting point is substantially *above* this temperature level, they will have the character of strong, rigid fibers. Thus polycisbutadiene and polycisisoprene are rubbers (their elongated samples contract) because the melting point of their crystalline domains is around 20°C, whereas 66 nylon is a fiber (crystalline melting point around 260°C).

Crystallization of linear flexible macromolecules is thus a phenomenon which has numerous practical applications. It has also stimulated a profound statistical analysis of the thermodynamics of macromolecular systems that has provided a firm and dependable mathematical foundation. The concept has helped to rationalize observations such as the reduced contractibility of many rubbers at low temperatures and the shrinkage of many fibers at elevated temperatures and/or in the molten state.

Crosslinking works well too

We have long known that favorable combinations of the properties mentioned earlier

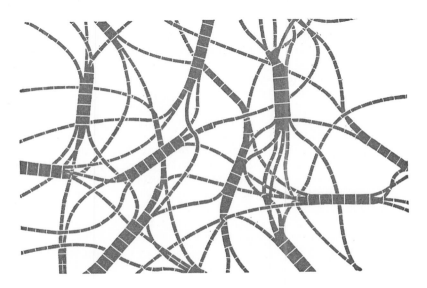

Fig. 2-32. Crystallization in polymers denotes areas where polymer chains line up for discrete distances, adding strength to matrix.

— X — X — X — X — X — X — X— Natural rubber

— X — X — X — X — X —
— X — X — X — X — X —
— X — X — X — X — X
— X — X — X — X — X —   Vulcanized soft rubber

— X — X — X — X — X — X —
— X — X — X — X —
— X — X — X — X — X —
— X — X — X — X — X —   Vulcanized hard rubber
— X — X — X — X — X —

$$X= (-CH_2 - \underset{\underset{CH_3}{|}}{C} = CH - CH_2 -)$$ Isoprene unit

Fig. 2-33. As more and more crosslinks are established in natural rubber, product grows rigid.

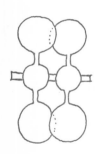

can also be obtained entirely apart from the phenomenon of crystallization by the *chemical crosslinking* of long, flexible chain molecules. Rubber can again serve for a convenient example. As we reduce the original segmental mobility of the individual chains by establishing strong, localized carbon-sulfur and sulfur-sulfur crosslinks, the material becomes more rigid, higher softening, and less soluble. As we continue to introduce more and more cross-links, as shown in Fig. 2-33, the average distance between them along the flexible chains decreases and the system becomes progressively "stiffer." We finally wind up with hard rubber or Ebonite, a very rigid material with an extremely high softening range, which neither dissolves nor swells in solvents.

At first glance, the effect of such crosslinking is very similar to that of crystallization; however, there are several important differences:

(a) In a crystalline system the rigidity is a result of *many* regularly spaced lateral bonds between the oriented chains; each of these bonds is *weak*—the ultimate effect comes from their large number and regularity. In a cross-linked system the bonds between the flexible chains are *strong* and *strictly localized;* in their entirety they are randomly arranged in the system. As a result, crystallization is a reversible phenomenon, crosslinking is irreversible.

(b) Crystallization is a *physical* effect that takes place at all temperatures, and is strongly influenced by physical processes such as orientation and swelling. Crosslinking, on the other

hand, is a *chemical* phenomenon that requires certain special reagents; it is accelerated by elevated temperatures but not much influenced by orientation or swelling.

Most thermosetting resins—hard, infusible, insoluble products—are the result of the cross-linking process; these include all hard rubbers, urea-, melamine-, and phenol-formaldehyde condensation products, polyesters that use glycerol, trimethylol propane or pentaerythritrol as components, and resins that are hardened by grafting styrene on a polyester backbone that contains aliphatic double bonds (Selectron, Perspe).

Now, a new approach

Crystallization and crosslinking produce stiffness, high softening, and low solubility by establishing firm lateral connections between *intrinsically flexible* chains; it now appears that one more independent avenue is open that leads to the same results. This approach uses the principle of building stiffness into the individual chains, by constructing them so that their segmental motion is restricted. For example, the hardening effect of adding bulky substituents to the polymer chain, as shown in the margin, is apparent in polystyrene, which is basically a chain of carbon atoms with a benzene ring appended to alternate carbon atoms. Although the polymer is amorphous and has no crosslinks, it is still a hard, relatively high-softening material (90°C). The absence of crystallinity results in complete transparency, while the absence of crosslinking produces thermoplasticity (reverse moldability) and easy flow characteristics. Similar characteristics exist in polymethyl methacrylate (Lucite). Here the intrinsically flexible, linear backbone chains are stiffened by two substituent groups—methyl (CH₃) and carboxy methyl (COOCH₃) at alternate carbon atoms, as shown in the margin; the resulting amorphous, thermoplastic polymer is hard, brilliantly transparent, and relatively high-softening (95°C).

The only weakness of either polymer is their low resistance to swelling and dissolution; apparently the bulky and eventually polar substituents produce favorable mechanical and thermal effects by altering the over-all mobility and flexibility of the chain segments, but cannot offer sufficient resistance to the penetration of the systems by solvent or swelling agents. The latter process is a strictly localized phenomenon, and depends on the affinity of the substituent groups for the particular solvent molecules.

The hardening influence on the polymer of the appropriate substituents is even more noticeable in polyvinyl naphthalene, polyvinyl carbazole, and polydichlorostyrene (the substituents involved are shown in Fig. 2-34). All these materials are amorphous and uncrosslinked, with excellent transparency, high rigidity, high-softening ranges, and even considerable resistance to dissolution and swelling. They are all reversibly softening, soluble thermoplastic resins.

Early efforts disclosed qualitatively that similar effects could be produced either by making the backbone chains themselves rigid instead of flexible, or by adding substituents to flexible backbones so that crystallization was prevented. Classical examples of the latter are cellulose acetate and nitrate, both widely used for years. Here the backbone chains, as shown in Fig. 2-35, are composed of glucoside units, and represent considerable intrinsic stiffness. Also, during processing, the acetyl and nitrate groups attach themselves irregularly and incompletely, thus preventing the formation of crystalline order. Both materials are thermoplastic resins—hard, transparent, high melting, and amorphous.

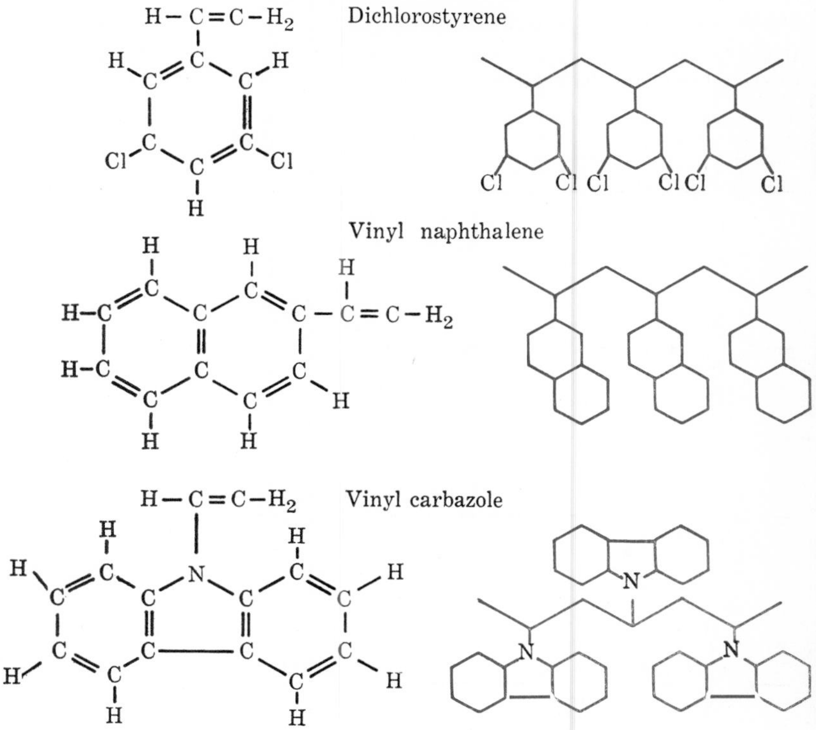

New backbones for old

Recently, investigators have studied the principle of using intrinsically rigid chains more systematically, and have found several new and interesting embodiments. Some of the rigid monomeric units investigated include those shown in Fig. 2-36, and from them a series of polymers has been synthesized. These materials, although substantially amorphous and uncrosslinked, are hard, high-softening, and solvent-resistant. The first examples of this group were the polycarbonates, such as GE's Lexan and the various linear epoxy resins; both types are based on bisphenol. More recent representatives are the polybenzimidazoles, polyimides, and polyphenyl oxazoles, which exhibit unusually high resistance against softening, swelling, and decomposition.

One group of polyimides being developed by Du Pont, for example, shows a lifetime (as an electrical varnish insulation) of over 1000 hours at 300°C (100,000 hours at 205°C) and is almost unaffected by most common solvents, oils, and fluorinated refrigerants. Fibers and papers made of the same material are claimed to retain half

Fig. 2-34. *Bulky substituents added to inherently flexible chain reduce its mobility by interfering with free rotation, thus add stiffness.*

their strength at 275°C, will not melt, and can be ignited only with difficulty at 300°C (they are self-extinguishing when the flame is removed).

Transparent films can even be made from the material; they possess similar resistance to heat, solvents, and abrasion. Du Pont calls them "H" films."

A lot, but never enough

Chemists seldom find themselves in the position of having three different approaches to a favorable combination of valuable properties, so this situation represents almost an embarrassment of riches. But scientists are never satisfied, so they're now exploring various *combinations* of these principles to see if they can be exploited to produce even better results. As a convenient aid in analyzing the combinations, we can construct a triangle, as in Fig. 2-37, in

Fig. 2-35. *Cellulose triacetate uses natural rigid backbone, modified with acetyl groups (OAc in drawing) to provide better properties than natural cellulose.*

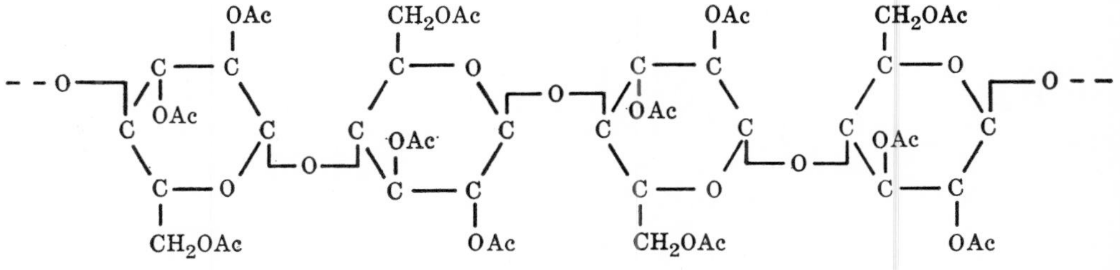

HOW TO STIFFEN THE SPINE

Usual "condensation" polymers are made by reacting two chains bearing reactive groups.

Typical condensation reaction gives straight, open chain (i.e., nylon)

$$
\mathrm{-NH + HO-C- \longrightarrow -N-C- + H_2O}
$$

For rigid backbone (no open chain) want ring formation

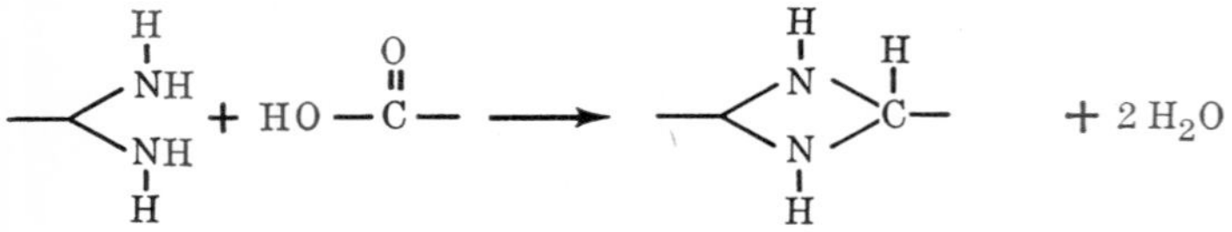

$$
\mathrm{+ HO-C- \longrightarrow + 2\,H_2O}
$$

or

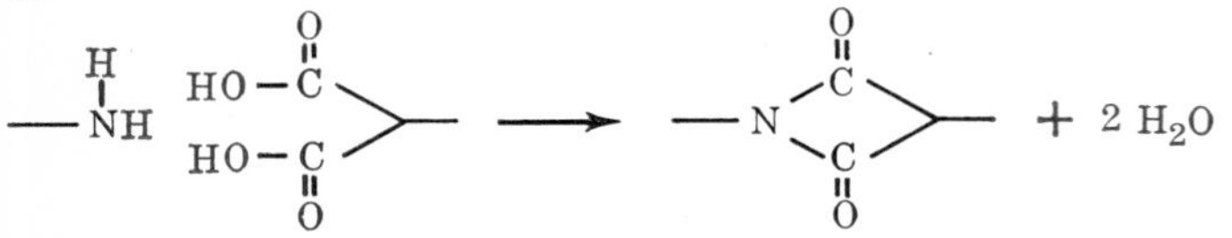

$$
\mathrm{-NH + HO-C \longrightarrow -N \cdots + 2\,H_2O}
$$

or even better

$$
\mathrm{+ HO-C \longrightarrow + 2\,H_2O}
$$

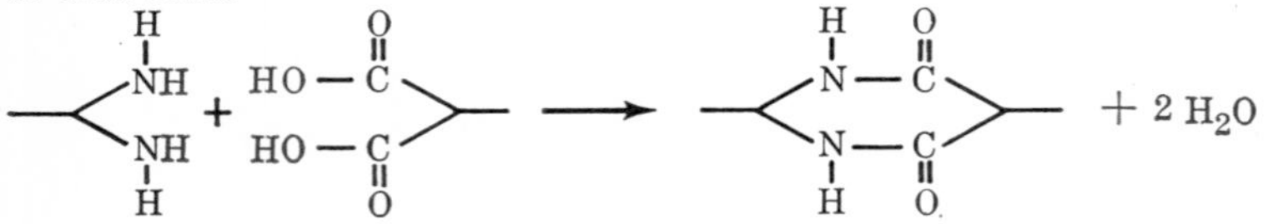

Useful monomers for rigid-backbone polymers:

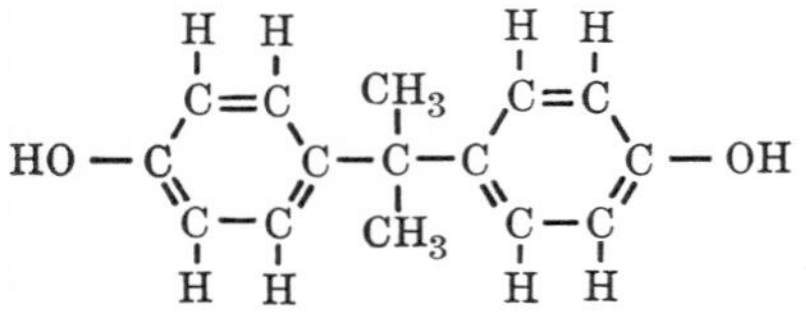

Bisphenol

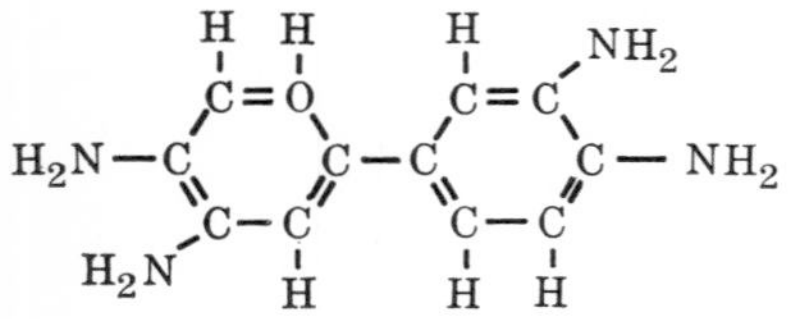

Tetramino diphenyl

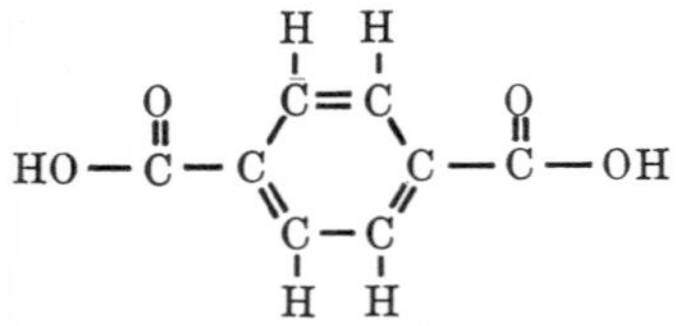

Terephthallic acid

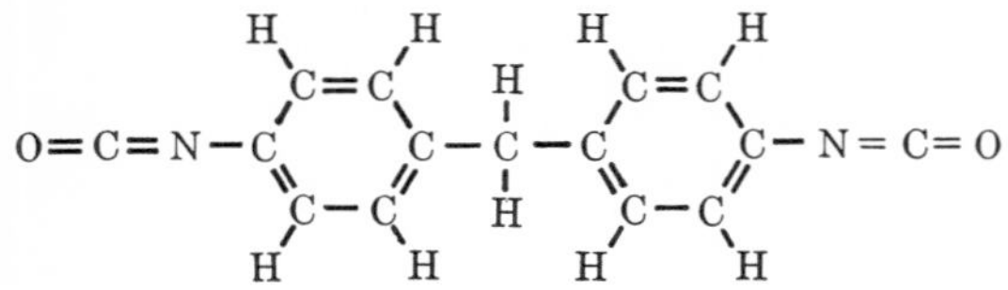

Methylene bisphenylisocyanate

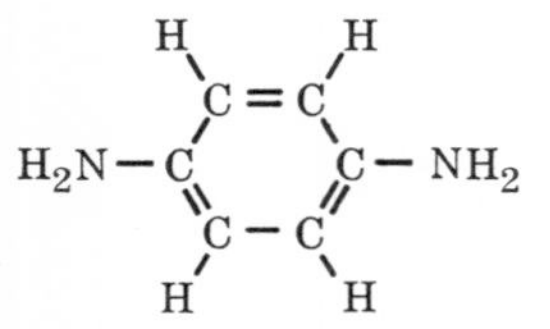

p-Phenylene diamine

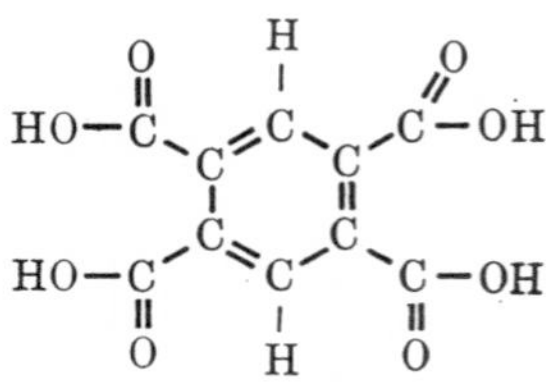

Pyromellitic acid

Fig. 2-36. New monomers provide "condensation polymers" with unusually rigid backbones.

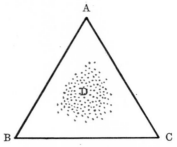

A represents *crystallization* of systems with *flexible* chains

B represents *crosslinking* of systems with *flexible* chains

C represents systems with *stiff* chains

D represents possible combinations of A, B, and C

Fig. 2-37. Triangular arrangement of principles of polymer morphology aids in visualizing new approach to tailor-making plastics.

which the three principles are represented by the three corners.

Corner *A* is populated by a large number of crystallizable polymers with flexible chains which have proved particularly successful as fiber and film formers. In general, they are thermoplastic, relatively soluble, and range from translucent to opaque.

In corner *B* are located the typical thermosetting, highly crosslinked systems. These are typically insoluble, nonswelling, heat-insensitive, hard, and sometimes brittle materials.

Finally, corner *C* represents those amorphous thermoplastic resins with inflexible backbones which we have just described. These typically exhibit relatively high rigidity and softening ranges.

Two points are better than one

One can now ask whether a combination of two principles would help in arriving at products with even more attractive and valuable properties, thus leading to exploration of the *sides* of the triangle, rather than the corners only.

As a matter of fact, the line from *A* to *C* accommodates several known, interesting fiber and film formers. One of them is polyethylene glycol terephthalate (Terelene, Dacron), in which the para-phenylenic units of the terephthalic acid introduce enough chain stiffening into the polymer to bring its melting point up to about 260°C. This is as high as that of 66 nylon, even though the polyester has none of the lateral hydrogen bonding available to stiffen its solid crystalline phase which nylon does. In this case, then, chain stiffening cooperates with crystallization to produce attractive properties, even though neither principle approaches very high values.

Cellulose, as we have mentioned, is another case (albeit not a man-made example) in which excellent fiber and film-forming properties are built up by a combination of chain stiffening, C, and crystallinity, A; these two effects together produce a polymer which is extremely rigid, does not melt at all, and is soluble only in a very small number of particularly potent liquid systems. The presence of substantially rigid chains has the favorable consequence that high tensile strength and high-softening characteristics become apparent even at relatively low degrees of crystallinity. This places cellulose somewhere in the middle of the line connecting A and C. Many of the recent spectacular improvements in cellulosic filaments capitalize on the dual origin of its fiber-forming potential.

Another example of a beneficial combination of A and C is cellulose triacetate (Arnel), in which the capacity to crystallize superimposes several favorable properties on the normal cellulose acetate. This includes, particularly, insolubility in many organic liquids and thermosetting properties through additional crystallization.

The AB side of the triangle includes materials whose backbone molecules are flexible and crystallizable, but which are also crosslinked slightly or moderately. This group includes natural rubber, butyl rubber, neoprene, and the so-called stereo rubbers—polycisisoprene and polycisbutadiene. In these last two materials, the double bonds which are located in the backbone chains have all the same configuration, "cis," in contrast to the older types of polybutadiene and polyisoprene where a random mixture of cis and trans double bonds exists. Because of the regularity in the new materials, they crystallize to a greater extent than randomly structured molecules and thus behave like natural rubber and other linear regular chain polymers. Since the cis double bonds are active crosslinking groups, these molecules can be hardened by crosslinking. Depending on the degree of such crosslinking, compounds of this type lie closer to or further from point B.

Until now we have only considered systems of one component—a single specific polymer or copolymer; elastomer technologists, however, usually produce additional stiffening and temperature resistance by adding a filler such as carbon black, silica, or alumina to their compounds. The fine, hard crystalline or pseudo-crystalline powder reinforces the system by restricting the segmental mobility of the flexible chains of the original polymeric matrix.

This restriction arises because the chains attach themselves to the surface of the small, hard filler particles by strong adsorptive forces. Thus, the presence of a reinforcing filler simulates normal crystallization of the backbone chains, and brings the system closer to point A.

The line from B to C is now being populated with useful polymers in an attempt to increase the rigidity, softening temperatures, and insolubility of stiff chain systems through additional crosslinking. Examples are the raising of the heat distortion of acrylic and methacrylic polymers by incorporating reactive units like allylmethacrylate (Selectron) or ethylene glycol dimethacrylate, and "curing" epoxy resins that are based on stiff chain elements such as bisphenol and cyclic acetals of pentaerythritol. Interesting attempts are now underway to improve the properties of the more recent amorphous systems with intrinsically stiff chains by cautious crosslinking. This would move these materials from point C along the side of the triangle toward B. The main reason for these efforts is to improve the resistance of such systems to swelling and dissolution at elevated temperatures.

Since we have been able to combine the various *pairs* of principles, a natural (and greedy) question is whether a proper combination of all three wouldn't lead to still further improvements in property combinations. Much exploratory work is presently being done to attempt to find answers to this question, and certain interesting results have already been obtained. One successful incorporation of all three principles has been made in cellulose, whose rigid chains can be brought to a moderate degree of crystallinity in cotton, by aftertreatment, or in rayon, by appropriate spinning; fibers result which possess satisfactory strength, elongation, hand, and dyeing characteristics, but insufficient "recovery" power. If, in addition, a cautiously controlled system of crosslinks is introduced through the use of bifunctional reagents, the original good properties are unchanged, while recovery power and wrinkle resistance are substantially improved. Interesting combinations of hardness, toughness, high-heat resistance, and insolubility have also been obtained with mildly reticulated, amorphous, stiff-chain systems of the epoxy and urethane type by simulating normal crystallization by reinforcing filler.

Combinations of all three principles would be situated somewhere in the center of the triangle, which still represents a veritable terra incognito. However, scientists in many laboratories are directing their efforts to the synthesis and production of polymers in the area, and it appears only a matter of time (and some luck) before we have at our disposal organic polymers and copolymers with combinations of properties far superior to those at our disposal today.

Further reading

There are many books on the general subject of plastics and the structure of polymers. With the rapid growth in numbers of monomers, however, it is wise to stick to the more recent editions. One good general book is Billmeyer's *Textbook of Polymer Chemistry* (Interscience, 1957, $13). The structure of materials is dealt with more extensively in *Properties and Structure of Polymers* by Tobolsky (Wiley, 1960, $14.50). For more information on the use of plastics, see *Engineering Properties and Applications of Plastics* by Kinney (Wiley, 1957, $7). Also, Interscience has published a volume called *Morphology of Polymers*, part of a symposium held at Los Angeles by the American Chemical Society in April 1963, that is a good rundown on the state of the art in morphology, structure, etc. ($7). Anyone really interested in polymers should know the *High Polymer Series* put out by Interscience, now 15 volumes long.

The group of rigid backbone polymers is too new to be covered extensively in the above books, but if you're interested, you might look at a number of recent papers by C. S. Marvel in the *Journal of Polymer Science*.

CORROSION

by T. P. Hoar *

IN BRIEF: *Corrosion is a destructive process that is not yet completely understood despite the enormous amount of research on it over the last 50 years. This is because its mechanisms are complex and vary from metal to metal and environment to environment. Basically, corrosion involves the movement of metal positive ions from positions of stability with electrons in the metal lattice to other positions of stability in the environment where they are stabilized by negative anions.*

To prevent these electromechanical reactions from occurring, several steps can be taken: corrosion-resistant alloys may be chosen; less resistant metals may be isolated from the environment by inert coatings; the potential driving the corrosion process can be lowered (cathodic protection); or the surface potential can be held at a level where the metal is essentially passive (anodic protection).

Significant developments are taking place in all these areas. Furthermore, new and sensitive electronic instrumentation is yielding insights to the more intractable problems—such as very slow corrosion and stress-corrosion cracking. As more of corrosion's secrets are learned, the damage problem is sure to ease. Beyond this, technologies that benefit from corrosion—machining, metal refining, engraving, battery design—are bound to flourish.—F.P.

■ Corrosion used to be a dirty subject. The very words—rust, tarnish, dissolution—have indeed an ill-omened ring that has been apt to put off the scientific seeker for pure knowledge, and to make designers and engineers push all thoughts of the matter into the depths of the subconscious. Even the jargon on the positive side contains too many words of dubious connotation in other fields—protection, inhibition, passivity, restrainer—and there is no felicitous translation of the French "anticorrosion."

Our medical friends here in England have had better luck with the language: soon after the formation in the U.S. of the National Association of Corrosion Engineers, *they* became part of the National *Health* Service in the U.K. They did not have to be called the National Association of Sickness Engineers.

The semantic situation is of real importance in the development and deployment of knowledge in any scientific or technological field: budding scientists are as incurably romantic as the rest of humanity, and they are attracted to a particular field of study as much by its potential poetry as by its prosaic rewards.

Today, the corrosion specialist occupies a respected if modest place in the hierarchies of pure science and of engineering: he has risen above his own nomenclature. Ulick R. Evans quotes with pleasure the reply of a distinguished scientist to his lament not long ago that "corrosion" was still regarded as rather disreputable: "But *you* have made it respectable."

In the present article, I hope to show, from a few examples with which I happen to be familiar, that research and practice in the field of metallic corrosion and its prevention or alleviation is rather more than a "respectable" pursuit; that indeed it requires as elegant experimentation and as great clarity of thought as any other part of physical chemistry and metallurgy; and that it can from time to time produce those moments of pure beauty for the researcher, and of satisfaction that "it works"

* T. P. Hoar is on the staff of the Department of Metallurgy, Cambridge University, Cambridge, England.

for the engineer, that are so important in making science the romantic occupation that it is.

The inert barrier approach

Corrosion is the chemical interaction of a metal or alloy with its environment. The majority of useful metals have a thermodynamic tendency to react with most natural environments, and all metals react with some environments. We usually require a metal as a material of construction to withstand particular environments—the atmosphere, the sea, sulfuric acid, beer—and the most obvious way to prevent corrosion is to interpose, between the metal and the environment, a third phase that is chemically inert to both metal and environment and that adheres tenaciously to the metal as an impervious, though very thin film—in fact, the perfect paint.

Paints and other organic coatings have always been high in importance in the corrosion prevention field, and have recently been improved greatly through the advent of the newer plastic materials. Thirty years ago, there was no better protective for structural steel than a red-lead—linseed-oil "inhibitive" primer followed by red-oxide—linseed-tung-oil "water-excluding" top coats. We know now that red-lead primers are under some conditions poorly inhibitive and that red-oxide top coats are far from water-excluding.

However, many other inhibitive pigments are now available. They include lead compounds and the powdered metal itself, as well as a wide range of sparingly soluble zinc chromates. Furthermore, progress in water-excluding coatings has been considerable. Whereas water and oxygen can pass through the classical paint coatings much more rapidly than they are required for the corrosion reactions on bare steel, they are well held up by some of the improved modern coatings based on bitumen.

Still greater all-round improvements have come through the introduction into paints of vinyl-, epoxy-, and polyurethane-based media, and through the development of thick coatings of polyethylene, polypropylene, and nylon applied by spraying or by powder-dipping. One or more of these newer organic coatings is often suitable for a particular difficult problem of protection, up to moderate temperatures; while for high-temperature protection, advances in inorganic coatings or refractory ceramics have been steady, if less spectacular. For intermediate temperatures, glass and vitreous enamel coatings have maintained a steady advance.

But—and it is a big "but"—protection of a metal from reaction with its environment by means of an intervening inert phase suffers from one great drawback in practice: however carefully applied, coatings may have gaps and, however tenderly used, they will in time develop further gaps. If metal and environment react at these gaps, undermining of the coating will in time render it inefficient or useless.

Inert coatings have, of course, other obvious disadvantages in many situations, but it is their inability to take care of more than minimal amounts of bare or bared metal surface that is the main factor limiting their usefulness. This has stimulated innumerable researches into corrosion mechanism and rate, and has caused some engineers to abandon painted structural steel for bridges in favor of reinforced prestressed concrete (see "Modern Concrete Design," page 371) in which, it is to be hoped, the steel rests in a non-corrosive environment.

Let us look, then, at some of the basic ideas about corrosion, and see how they are being applied in practice for its control.

The fundamental reaction in corrosion is the removal of metal positive ions from their positions in the *metal crystal lattice*, where they are stabilized electrically by the metal negative electrons, to positions in the *environment* where they are stabilized by negative anions. This is an *anodic reaction*, and must be accompanied by a corresponding *cathodic reaction* in which the metal electrons thus freed either remove cations from the environment, or create anions. Thus for iron corroding in an aqueous acid, we have

$$Fe_{lattice} - 2e \rightarrow Fe^{2+}{}_{aq}$$

as the fundamental anodic reaction, and

$$2H^+{}_{aq} + 2e \rightarrow H_2$$

as the equivalent cathodic reaction. More commonly in most natural aqueous environments, where the concentration of protons is fortunately low, the equivalent cathodic reaction is the reduction of dissolved oxygen,

$$\tfrac{1}{2}O_{2aq} + H_2O + 2e \rightarrow 2OH^-{}_{aq}$$

and at high temperatures, as in oxide scale formation, it is

$$\tfrac{1}{2}O_{2gas} + 2e \rightarrow O^{2-}{}_{scale}$$

The anodic and cathodic reactions are always equivalent electrically. They may occur very close together; alternatively, owing to the great mobility of electrons within the metal, they may take place at great distances from one another on the metal surface undergoing attack.

When iron dissolves in an acid, for example,

the sites of anodic reaction are the edges, corners, and kinks of the surface layers of atoms, with cathodic reduction of protons occurring at adjacent atom sites, say 2–3 angstroms (10^{-8} cm) away:

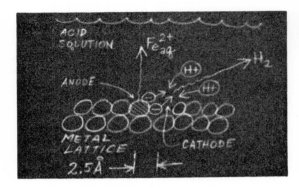

When a steel pipeline corrodes in the soil, the anode may be a bare patch in the coating a mile away from another bare patch that happens to be well oxygenated and therefore able to serve as a cathode:

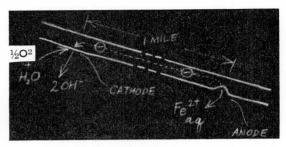

And when iron forms mill-scale, the metal/scale interface is the anode and the scale/air interface the cathode, the scale itself forming both electronic and electrolytic connection between anode and cathode:

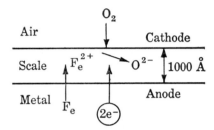

Fig. 2-38. These two bridges, each needing protection against a wee Scots mist, provide an interesting contrast in corrosion prevention methods old and new. In the background is the famous Forth Rail Bridge built over 60 years ago across the Firth of Forth near Edinburgh, Scotland. The sea-mist environment there is so severe that its classical paint protection has been renewed continuously since its erection—each renewal taking 30 months. In the foreground is the new Forth Road Bridge as it looked under construction. Its two middle suspension towers are prefabricated from welded boxes each $30 \times 9 \times 6$ ft and erected by bolting. Before erection, each box was grit-blasted, then sprayed with a zinc coating and etch primer; this was followed by an undercoat of zinc chromate in a phenolic medium, plus two coats of phenolic paint containing over 60% of micaceous iron oxide. It is hoped that this novel scheme will give at least 15 years' protection before recoating is needed. (Courtesy Wide World)

Problems of corrosion thus nearly always pose the following questions: (1) What are the anodic and cathodic reactions? Can they be studied separately? (2) Where do they take place? (3) How fast can they proceed? Can their rates be altered? And most importantly, (4) do the anodic and cathodic products, either of themselves or when and if they mix, form any kind of "inert" barrier tending to hinder either reaction?

Early work at Cambridge and elsewhere gave partial answers to all of these questions for particular cases. As an example, we investigated the corrosion of iron and steel plates partly immersed in stagnant saline solutions—a common marine situation. The corrosion distribution was found to be as sketched in the margin: attack began at the edges, spread inwards, and then ceased to spread, while alkali was formed at and near the waterline. Now, by cutting one of the plates along the zone of demarcation as shown in the lower sketch, and joining the pieces through a milliammeter, we were able to show that current flowed equivalent to the amount of metal dissolved at the anode. That is to say, this corrosion is definitely electrochemical in nature and obeys Faraday's law quite closely.

The same approach was used in the U.S. to show the existence of corrosion current between pits (anodes) on the surface of aluminum and the unpitted surface. Analogous with the iron in salt water case cited above, two pre-pitted plates were used in this experiment, as sketched in the margin. On one plate, the pits were waxed over; on the other, the unpitted surface was so protected. Connecting a milliammeter between them and immersing them in salt water revealed again the current flow between corrosion sites and the as yet unattacked adjacent metal.

In a more sophisticated experiment, we measured the electrode potential at the anodic and cathodic zones on corroding iron by means of capillaries leading to a standard half cell. We then determined the current corresponding to any particular potential by applying a variable external emf source between *separated* anodes and cathodes. The resulting "polarization curves" (see sketch) allowed subsequent potential measurements to be used for estimating corrosion currents on metal carrying both anode and cathode (unseparated), and we could deduce the corrosion rate therefrom.

In this same way, we recently estimated the currents flowing down minute cracks in a stainless steel specimen undergoing stress-corrosion cracking: the cathode polarization curve of a noncracking piece of metal was first determined, then the potential of an isolated piece undergoing cracking; this allowed us to estimate the current leaving the cathodic surface of the metal and thus entering the anodic cracks.

The newer instrumentation

The relatively simple electrochemical methods outlined above are today supplemented by many more complicated techniques. Thus measurements of changes of electrode impedance by ac-bridge and dc-pulse methods are throwing light on both the electrolytic double layer and, particularly, on the thickness and properties of films deliberately produced, as on aluminum and other metals, as corrosion preventatives.

The electrolytic double layer is a region at a metal/solution interface where there is a separation of electrical charge over a very small distance. Positive (or negative) ions may be preferentially adsorbed from the solution onto the metal surface; this charge and its image in the metal form a layer that has some of the characteristics of a capacitor. If we know more about the nature of this layer, we can gain greater insights into the electrochemical reactions that occur at the metal surface.

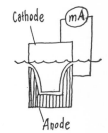

Corrosion preventative films are also being studied by ellipsometry. In this optical technique, the measurement of the change of the ellipticity of polarized light after reflection from the surface gives information about films too thin to be visible. The theory of this method was worked out nearly a century ago, but commercial instruments have become available only within the last decade.

However, perhaps the most important recent instrumental aid to corrosion research is the potentiostat, by which a metal surface may be maintained at constant potential over long periods. By this means, a metal's long-term corrosion behavior may be observed and, most importantly, any external current flowing may be measured as a function of time.

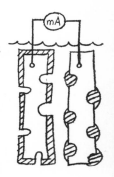

The potentiostat and its uses

This device (see Fig. 2-39) was introduced around 1940, for the study of single electrode reactions, and adapted about 1950 for the direct study of corroding metals on which both anodic and cathodic reactions are occurring simultaneously. Potentiostatic investigation has since been much used for the study of anomalous corrosion behavior, especially that of relatively resistant metals and alloys that occasionally show catastrophic breakdown.

For example, when 18%-chromium-8%-nickel stainless steel is in contact with dilute sulfuric acid with access of air, it may resist attack for a considerable time. Then it may quite suddenly start to corrode vigorously, and may equally suddenly stop: in fact, the conditions giving

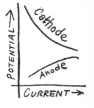

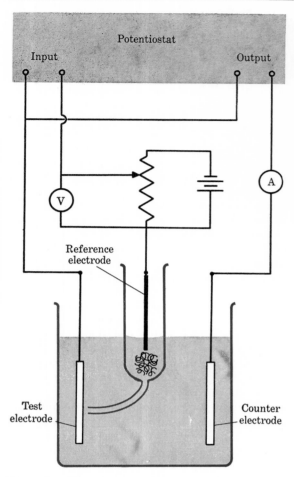

Fig. 2-39. The potentiostat, as used in corrosion studies, works like this: to hold constant the potential difference between the test electrode and the solution (its electrode potential) and a known reference electrode, we connect the cell formed by the test and reference electrodes in series with a potentiometer circuit. We then adjust this to give the required emf (equal and opposite to the desired test-electrode—reference-electrode emf) by means of the voltmeter V (or a calibrated rheostat). The circuit is then completed to the input of the potentiostat. The output then provides, through an ammeter A and a counter-electrode, a measured or recorded current to the test electrode appropriate to its electrode potential. If this varies, and so alters the emf of the original cell, the voltage received at the input is not zero. This "error signal" operates the electronic servo to give an output that restores the desired electrode potential.

"active dissolution" and "passivity" at any anodic zones are very finely balanced. A closer look at the results of a potentiostatic study will show this.

If a specimen of such steel is polarized potentiostatically as anode, under conditions of slowly increased polarization (with an externally applied emf), the current flow may be recorded, giving a curve that looks like this:

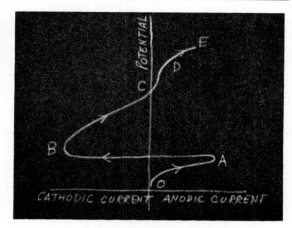

Here, the OA part of the curve sketched represents increasing anode dissolution in the active condition; AB is the onset of anodic passivity caused by the growth of an invisible oxide film on the anode surface; BC shows a *cathodic* current developing caused by the oxygen-reduction reaction on the now oxide-filmed surface. Then CDE occurs, a new anodic reaction supervenes—either the evolution of oxygen at high potentials or the *transpassive* dissolution of the passivating film by oxidation dissolution, as of Cr_2O_3 to soluble CrO_3.

The situation is made much clearer if the anodic and cathodic reactions are studied separately. This can be done for the anodic reaction in our example if the acid is rigorously de-aerated, so that no cathodic reduction of oxygen can occur. Then, the slow "potential sweep" on the instrument leads to the following solid curve:

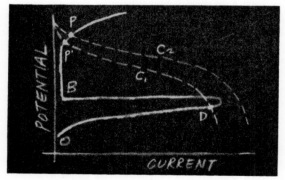

At passivation, the measured current (now equal to the anode current) falls to a very low value—in favorable cases to around 10^{-9} amp/cm^2.

Now, if such a passivated surface is tested in the same solution but with oxygen present, a downward potential sweep leads to *cathodic* curves such as C_1 or C_2, the latter being for the higher oxygen content. The cathode current (dashed lines) is here plotted on the same side of the potential axis as the anode current. This emphasizes that a quite small variation of cathodic oxygen-reduction rate can lead to the setting up either of *fast-dissolving* conditions, represented by the intersection of C_1 and the anode curve at D, or *passive* conditions, represented by the intersection of C_2 and the anode curve at P. (When anodic and cathodic reactions are taking place on the same piece of metal, close together, they polarize each other to nearly the same potential—that of the intersection of the two potential/current polarization curves in the sketch above.)

It is true that the smaller cathodic reduction rate can *maintain* passivity at P'. But in the event of mechanical damage to the passivating film, cathode C_1 cannot give enough current to the anode to re-passivate it by repairing the film, whereas C_2 can—by bringing the cathode current past the "nose" of the anode curve. Thus quite small fluctuations in the degree of aeration of the solution may give conditions under which 18-8 stainless steel is rapidly attacked and made useless, or on the other hand is passive, maintained so and kept self-passivating, being thus a valuable material of construction.

Anodic protection

Potential *control* is a practical use of the potentiostat. Here, the potential of a corrosion resistant material is maintained in the region of BP of the preceding sketch by means of a counter electrode and an external source of emf. Under such conditions the metal remains passive indefinitely, with dissolution that can often be negligible, and "anodic protection" is obtained.

It is not necessary to use a refined electronic potentiostat for this kind of control: all that is needed is a power source that can (1) furnish the passivating current (just greater than OD) for a short time should the passivity fail momentarily through mechanical damage of the film and (2) maintain the potential in the passive range BP, along with the very small current there required, indefinitely.

In work now in progress at Cambridge, we are using the potentiostatic principle in a rather different way. There are a number of metals and alloys used in practice for surgical implants, for which the prime requirements are adequate strength and very high corrosion resistance. Certain alloys, although passive in body fluids to such a degree that their corrosion is visually undetectable after many months, do nonetheless dissolve very slowly, giving metallic ions that may be harmful to tissue.

The problem is to estimate this very small production of corrosion products. The method followed is simple in principle: we first measure the natural potential of the alloy over a protracted period while it is exposed to a fluid simulating body fluids. We then take a specimen of the alloy and expose it to the same fluid, but with possible cathodic reactants such as oxygen completely removed, and with the metal potential controlled by the potentiostat to the natural potential previously measured. The very small anode current flowing is then a measure of the very small corrosion rate under natural conditions, and we can if desired follow it for months. Of course, there are experimental difficulties, but we think we can surmount them.

Stress-corrosion cracking

During the last 20 years, many practical problems of alloy fracture under the conjoint influence of tensile or torsional stress and a corrosive environment have come to light, and this so-called "stress-corrosion cracking" has been intensively studied. Fracture takes place only when stress—either applied or locked-up—and the corrosive environment are simultaneously present. It may be either *intergranular,* as in the case of stressed brass exposed to ammoniacal liquors and of stressed high-strength aluminum alloys exposed to chloride solutions; or it can be *transgranular,* as in the case of chromium-nickel stainless steels exposed to chloride solutions (Fig. 2-40).

The fractures look rather like brittle cracks and are indeed still regarded as a type of brittle failure by some; but a while ago we suggested that the propagation of many stress-corrosion cracks is not by brittle fracture but rather by the rapid anodic dissolution of metal at the advancing edge of the crack.

Several pieces of evidence in particular tend, in our view, to make the brittle fracture hypothesis untenable in many cases. First, alloys that show stress-corrosion cracking phenomena are inherently ductile: in the strong aluminum alloys, for example, the cracks follow the ductile material at the grain boundaries rather than cross the very much less ductile grains. Second, the cracks usually propagate much more slowly than brittle cracks, which go at sonic speeds. Furthermore, cracks can be stopped indefinitely by the application of cathodic protection—the lowering of the metal electrode potential by externally applied emf to values at which any anodic process is negligible. This shows the necessity of having anodic action for the crack to progress.

To settle the problem, we have made potentiostatic measurements on wires of 18-8 stainless steel held at the potential at which it undergoes stress-corrosion cracking in hot magnesium chloride solution. This potential pro-

Fig. 2-40. *Stress-corrosion cracking is a special form of corrosion that occurs only when a susceptible metal is simultaneously stressed and exposed to a corrosive environment. It looks like a brittle fracture, but may be mechanochemical in nature. That is, local yielding at the crack's advancing edge promotes corrosion currents high enough to allow corrosion to proceed at about the rate observed for stress-corrosion crack propagation. Intergranular crack at right is in stressed brass exposed to ammonium sulfate-copper sulfate solution; transgranular crack at left is in Cr-Ni stainless steel exposed under stress to magnesium chloride solution. Magnification: ×150; stress is vertical. (Courtesy T. P. Hoar, University of Cambridge)*

duces an anodic current density of some 10^{-5} amp/cm² on the alloy; it is not truly passive, but it dissolves extremely slowly.

The wire is then stretched at some 100% per minute—about the rate at which the metal at the advancing edge of a crack may be calculated to yield. The yielding thus generated produces a dramatic rise of anode current density to over 0.1 amp/cm². Such current densities are sufficient to account for the observed rates of crack propagation in metal loaded to about the 0.1% proof stress—a common design stress level (see margin). At this level, however, it is only the even more heavily stressed metal at the crack tip that is rapidly yielding.

Other alloys prone to similar stress-corrosion cracking, such as iron-nickel alloys with 5–15% nickel, show a similar "mechanochemical" effect under conditions of over-all rapid yielding. The higher nickel alloys in the same system, however, do not stress-corrosion crack and do not show the mechanochemical effect.

The question remains: why should yielding of an alloy produce such a very large increase—more than 10^4 times—in the anodic reactivity of the surface? There appears to be some correlation between the submicroscopic dislocation structure of an alloy and its susceptibility to stress-corrosion cracking; we are now seeking a similar correlation between structure and mechanochemical reactivity.

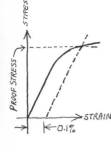

Meanwhile, it seems fairly certain that for stress-corrosion cracking to occur, there must be present a rather specialized alloy structure (one showing considerable ductility by restricted slip), a high rate of supply of anodic reactants (often chlorides) in solution, and a specifically high rate of anodic reaction between the disarrayed alloy surface and the solution. Stress-corrosion cracking can be *avoided* when one or another of these conditions is absent; and it can be *prevented* by cathodic protection. We need more general knowledge of its mechanism before we can design alloys in which we can count on its absence under all conditions, without recourse to specialized preventive measures.

The ad hoc approach today

Some of the research techniques described above—simple in principle, but often requiring complex instrumentation and very careful interpretation—are already yielding results of the highest value in the practice of corrosion control. It should not be thought, however, that the day of the simple common-sense experiment is over.

An example is our recent discovery of the interesting properties of some of the zinc-aluminum alloys as protective coatings for structural steel. Zinc and aluminum have long been used separately for this purpose. In Europe and especially the U.K., coatings of either metal applied by spraying have been very popular protective measures for structural steel, either as-applied or as a basis for a subsequent paint system. Thus the new Forth Road Bridge across the Firth of Forth near Edinburgh, now nearing completion, has suspension towers that were zinc-sprayed and painted before erection. We hope that this novel scheme will give at least 15 years' protection against the sea-mist atmosphere that prevails, in contrast to the classical paint on the nearby Forth Rail Bridge, which has been continuously repainted from end to end (it takes 2½ years) since its erection 70 years ago.

Some years ago we initiated, at Cambridge, atmospheric tests on steel specimens sprayed with zinc powder, aluminum powder, mixed zinc and aluminum powder, and a series of zinc-aluminum alloy powders. These tests have shown that some of the mixed powders and alloy powders give rather better results under some atmospheric conditions than do either of the separate metals. The differences are not dramatic, but sufficient to justify the recommendation, for conditions in which it is difficult to decide between straight zinc or aluminum, of a 50–50 alloy powder as the choice likely to give somewhat superior results.

Now it seemed to us interesting to find out whether any of the alloys or mixtures left over from the above research showed resistance to the stagnant saline conditions obtaining on steel structures immersed in water—conditions known to be inimical to both zinc and aluminum. Such conditions can lead to the development of anodic acidity and consequent hydrogen evolution, with altogether too severe "sacrificial" corrosion of the protective coatings.

Very simple "beaker" tests were conducted, and it turned out that zinc alloyed with some 25–35% of aluminum corrodes much more slowly than either separate metal in stagnant salt water. The slower corrosion is caused by the much firmer and more adherent nature of the corrosion products, which form a compact hard layer on the alloys in contrast to the fluffy material formed on either separate metal. We are investigating the nature of the firm coating by various sophisticated methods including potentiostatic control, x-rays, and electron-probe microanalysis (see "The Electron Probe," page 175). Meanwhile, there is little doubt that the practical application of sprayed zinc and aluminum will be extended by the use of Zn-Al-alloy powders sprayed on for stagnant salt-water conditions.

It is important to note that the firm coating discussed above is an instance where a corrosion product *itself* forms a rather inert bar-

Fig. 2-41. The ubiquity of stress-corrosion cracking is well illustrated by the cracks in the base of this brass fire hydrant. Corrosive environment here was probably brass cleaner and other ammoniacal solutions indigenous to large urban areas. (Courtesy Heka)

rier between the metal and its environment and, moreover, a barrier that heals itself if it becomes broken. This is an advantage over nonhealing barriers such as paint and enamel. When a sprayed metal is followed by a paint coat, this firm compact corrosion product has other advantages: it tends to fill and block the pores in the sprayed metal layer, and may even block the pore or crack in the paint that let in the salt water that caused the corrosion. Loose, fluffy corrosion products do not block pores in metal-sprayed coatings and may disastrously undermine and remove paint.

Benign corrosion

The malignancy of corrosive attack has been so often emphasized—at least one monograph represents the process fancifully as a revolting-looking evil spirit—that it may be interesting to conclude with a few examples where corrosion plays a beneficent role.

A familiar instance is the production of the "patina" on copper roofing by slow atmospheric attack; besides forming a self-healing inert barrier that slows down the corrosion with time, the layer of basic copper sulfate is prized by many for its pleasant green color. Much more important, but often overlooked because invisible, are the very thin air-formed oxide films produced by "dry" corrosion on fresh surfaces of stainless steels, titanium, and even aluminum: without these almost impermeable inert barriers, these metals, which are normally reactive, would be unusable.

In other fields, a corrosion process can be beneficial when, far from producing products that quickly stifle it, the attack proceeds rapidly. Gold is extracted readily from the large quantities of quartz with which it occurs by corroding it out with cyanide, water, and oxygen. The use of metals as anodes in primary batteries is merely a utilization of their chemical energy to produce electrical energy, and is unquestionably another case of benign anodic corrosion.

The processes of electropolishing, electrodeburring, and electromachining (see "Nontraditional Machining," page 397) are all cases of anodic corrosion controlled electrically to produce desired effects. In pickling, etching, and chemical polishing, straight corrosion processes, not controlled electrically, are used to produce results ranging from metal preparation (large-scale and for microscopy) to photographic engravings.

It seems to me odd that this wide range of benign corrosion processes has been relatively little investigated as compared with the intensive research into malignant corrosion conducted during the last half-century. Most of these processes will probably be much improved, to the technical and economic advantage of those who use them and live by them, when research commensurate with their importance is conducted on them.

When corrosion becomes art

The beneficent influence of corrosion has been felt in the field of sculpture, even though "bronze disease," a penetrating type of corrosion found in old bronze articles, is a source of worry to antiquaries. However, at least one modern abstract sculptor, whose work I saw recently in New York, has hit upon a better interaction of bronze with its environment. He starts with a splash of bronze that looks, to a metallurgist like myself, as if it might have been accidentally spilled on the foundry floor. This rather dull piece of metal, however, has

been corroded in parts to a splendid green patina by means of, evidently, a slightly ammoniacal solution on the origin of which it may be unwise to speculate; and it has been given here and there a gay brick-red hue, toning off to purple and blue, by oxidation—perhaps by being petulantly flung into the furnace for a few moments. Whatever the technique, the result and others like it sell at around $5000: so that the creator should certainly regard *his* corrosion as benign.

Further reading

For further insight into corrosion and protection matters, we suggest *The Corrosion and Oxidation of Metals* by U. R. Evans (Arnold, London, 1960) and the same author's *Introduction to Metallic Corrosion* (Arnold, 1963). A classical American work is *Corrosion: Causes and Prevention* by F. N. Speller (McGraw-Hill, 3rd Ed., 1961); and the *Corrosion Handbook* by H. H. Uhlig (Wiley, 1948) contains authoritative articles on many aspects. Professor Uhlig's recent *Corrosion and Corrosion Control* (Wiley, 1963) is an excellent introductory treatise. *Corrosion Handbook* is also the title of a newer, British reference work by L. L. Shreir (Wiley, 1963). For a single, short, handy reference, get "The Nature and Control of Corrosion," one of *Electro-Technology's* Science & Engineering Series (Sept., 1960, 205 E. 42 St., N.Y.). In "The Anodic Behavior of Metals," a long chapter in *Modern Aspects of Electrochemistry, No. 2*, edited by J. O'M. Bockris (Butterworth, 1959), our author reviews and discusses some 350 of the more important recent fundamental papers about metal anodes. A short document that focuses on the electrochemical processes in corrosion is "Corrosion in Action." This study is essentially the narrative of an Inco film bearing the same name. To obtain a copy, write to W. D. Mogerman, editor of the Inco *Corrosion Reporter* (an interesting, informative, and entertaining periodical to receive, incidentally), The International Nickel Co., 67 Wall St., N.Y. Reservations for the one-hour, 16-mm. color film mentioned above may be made through Rothacker, Inc., Time and Life Building, N.Y.

ATOMIC ABSORPTION ANALYSIS

by Herbert L. Kahn and Walter Slavin [*]

IN BRIEF: *Atomic absorption spectroscopy is a relatively new method for determining the presence and amount of an element in a sample*

*Herbert L. Kahn, an electronics engineer, and Walter Slavin, a physicist, collaborate, at the Perkin-Elmer Corp., Norwalk, Connecticut, in developing ultraviolet and infrared spectrophotometers.

of unknown composition. It superficially resembles flame photometry in that the material to be analyzed is vaporized in a flame. But in flame photometry, it is the light emitted by the flame that is analyzed spectrally. In the new technique, one measures the absorption in the flame of light from yet another light source.

The vaporized sample is irradiated by a lamp having a cathode made of the element being sought. The ground-state atoms absorb the resonance line emitted by the lamp, thus diminishing the intensity of its light. The percent absorption, as noted by a photodetector, is a measure of the element's concentration which, depending upon the element, can be detected in concentrations ranging down to 0.005 ppm. Advantages of the method are two: it provides a notable increase in sensitivity since it detects atoms in the ground state; it is highly specific and eliminates optical interference since it operates on the very narrow resonance lines of the element sought. Future development is focusing on three features: lamp design, flames and other vaporization methods, and elimination of specific chemical interferences.—F.P.

■ Nearly every college science student is faced, one black day, with a problem in "qualitative analysis." A beaker full of mixed liquids is thrust into his hands, and he is besought to determine which metals it contains, and possibly how much of each. The external clues are few. If the liquid is blue, there may be copper in it. If, when flung into a Bunsen burner, it burns bright yellow, it almost certainly contains sodium. Unless the student plans to specialize in chemistry, the ensuing malodorous months in the laboratory are almost certain to leave a scar.

At least one former student, entering the service of an instrument company five years after graduation, was still moved to ask the indigenous scientists whether there existed any instrument which might have helped him in his quest. The savants mumbled apologetically. A flame photometer, in some instances, they said. And, of course, there's emission spectroscopy. . . . In the main, however, the student would have to go it alone.

The recent revival of atomic absorption spectrophotometry now promises to alter the balance in favor of the student, and at the same time aid agricultural chemists, medical analysts, metallurgists, and many others who are interested in measuring the concentration of metals in compounds. Although this technique is an excellent tool for qualitative analysis, its real beauty lies in its capacity to give accurate quantitative results at concentrations of a few parts-per-million (see Table 1).

In order to obtain an understanding of this technique, it is probably best to review flame photometry, which is based loosely on the fact that a sodium flame burns yellow. The reason is that sodium atoms, when excited, emit radiation at a wavelength of 5896 angstroms, which is in the visible, yellow portion of the spectrum. When it is desired to measure the amount of sodium present in a sample, it is therefore necessary only to burn the sample in a flame, and pass the resultant light radiation through a monochromator which transmits only the desired wavelengths around 5896 Å. The output from the monochromator is converted to electrical energy by a photodetector, and is eventually read out on a meter. The meter reading is proportional to the concentration of sodium in the sample.

This technique works very well for sodium, and also for certain other elements which are easily excited, and whose emission lines are reasonably distant from those of other elements. When you come to a metal like magnesium, however, two new factors complicate the situation. First, the emission lines of magnesium lie right in the thick of the emission lines of other metals that may be present in the sample, requiring a very fine monochromator to separate the magnesium lines from the rest. Second, at presently obtainable flame temperatures, for every magnesium atom that becomes excited, hundreds remain in their unexcited, or "ground" state. Obviously, if it were possible to detect the unexcited atoms, sensitivity could be greatly increased.

Needed: an atomic Sherlock Holmes

This detection is accomplished by using the energy absorption characteristics of the unexcited atoms in the sample. In essence, light energy is radiated from an emitter made of the *same metal* whose presence and amount in the sample we are trying to determine. These light waves are allowed to impinge upon atoms of the sample metal, made accessible for such impingement by its introduction, in solution form, into a flame. (The flame is merely a convenient way to vaporize the sample, whereas in flame photometry it is the source of emission.) Some of the emitted photons impinge and are absorbed, thus diminishing the intensity of the original light beam. The amount of diminution (or atomic absorption) depends upon the concentration present of the metal under study. Thus, by measuring the percent absorption, we can deduce the amount of metal present.

This interaction between radiation emitted and absorbed by the same metal is the basis of the atomic absorption method and the source of its name. With the unexcited atoms in the sample now detected and brought into play, we begin to see how increased sensitivity over straight flame photometry comes about. We must look deeper into the absorption process, however, to see precisely how this occurs. This will also tell us more about how the process separates out the presence of a particular metal amid the conflicting radiations of other metals in the vaporized sample.

Table 1.
ATOMIC ABSORPTION DETECTION LIMITS FOR VARIOUS ELEMENTS

Aluminum	0.02	Mercury	0.5
Antimony	0.2	Molybdenum	0.2
Barium	1.	Nickel	0.05
Beryllium	0.05	Palladium	0.3
Bismuth	0.2	Platinum	0.5
Cadmium	0.01	Potassium	0.005
Calcium	0.01	Rhodium	0.3
Cesium	0.05	Rubidium	0.02
Chromium	0.01	Selenium	1.
Cobalt	0.2	Silver	0.02
Copper	0.01	Sodium	0.005
Gallium	1.	Strontium	0.02
Gold	0.1	Tellurium	0.5
Indium	0.2	Thallium	0.2
Iron	0.05	Tin	2.
Lead	0.1	Titanium	1.
Lithium	0.005	Vanadium	0.5
Magnesium	0.003	Zinc	0.005
Manganese	0.01		

Now, quantum mechanics teaches us that atoms of a particular element can absorb energy *only* at certain discrete wavelengths, which correspond to the energies required for electrons to make the jump from one permitted level to another. These wavelengths can generally be grouped into two kinds: "resonance" wavelengths, which represent jumps from the unexcited, "ground" level to an excited one, and the others, which occur when electrons go from one excited level to a higher level of energy.

Our sample, even after being vaporized in the flame, is at such a temperature that most of the atoms are in their ground state. Here is where the element of discrimination comes in, for the metal we are seeking (if it is in the sample at all) will only absorb radiation at wavelengths corresponding to one of its own excited states. Thus, by irradiating the sample with an emitter made from the element we seek, any interaction at all gives away the presence of the element, and the degree of the interaction gives us the amount present.

Now, let us consider sensitivity. When the flame is irradiated by our emitter—a source of discrete wavelengths, all of them characteristic of the metal we seek—the resonance lines will be absorbed much more strongly than any of the others. Since the ground state electrons may be kicked into one or more permissible energy states, a given element may exhibit more than one resonance line. However, for each element there is one line where the degree of absorption for a given concentration is highest. This is referred to as the "best" resonance line for that element. Table 1 tabulates the detection limits corresponding to 1% absorption at the "best" resonance wavelength for a number of elements.

To get these optimum sensitivities, the photodetector must see only the best resonance line, which is determined experimentally for each element.

Let there be light

Clearly, the key to the atomic absorption technique is the source of the emission lines of the metal we are seeking. Such sources are available in a variety of styles. A simple way to get the desired lines is to burn large quantities of the proper element in a flame. Arc lamps, filled with a vapor of the proper material, are frequently used. At present, the most popular and effective source for most metals is the so-called "hollow cathode" lamp, which is merely a gas-filled tube whose cathode is made of the desired material. The hollow-cathode lamp emits very narrow spectral lines whose intensity is very stable. Since such lamps have been used for years in such specialized tasks as wavelength calibration, the know-how of making them is well advanced. In Fig. 2-42, the cathode is the hollow cup, while the thick wire nearby is the anode. When a current is passed through the lamp, the interior of the cup glows, showing that it is emitting the spectral lines of its metal in large and powerful quantities.

The power of the atomic absorption principle can be demonstrated by a very simple, but dramatic experiment. The room is darkened, and the radiation from a mercury lamp (whose envelope is transparent to ultraviolet but opaque to visible light) is permitted to illuminate a fluorescent screen. The vapor from an open flask of mercury at room temperature is then passed between the lamp and the screen. Very black shadows appear, revealing the mercury vapor trails. That is, the few atoms that escape from the surface of the mercury are enough to cause total absorption of the resonance line emitted by the lamp.

Fig. 2-42. Emitter for atomic absorption analysis is this hollow-cathode lamp. Cup is made from metal sought so that lamp will emit spectral lines of this metal for absorption by its atoms in the sample.

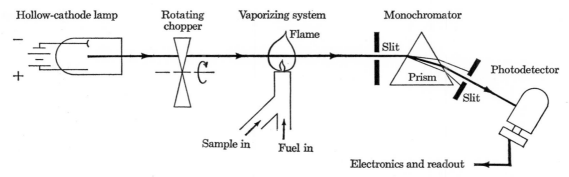

Fig. 2-43. *Atomic absorption system shows many components that have counterparts in flame photometry: vaporizing system, monochromator, photodetector, and electronics-read-out unit. In atomic absorption, however, measuring absorption in the flame of light from the emitter (at far left) replaces spectral analysis of light from flame. Photodetector sees two signals: a chopped light beam from the emitter, and a steady, unvarying beam from the flame. Detector electronics is easily made insensitive to the latter, eliminating from the reading emission from the flame and the excited atoms within it.*

A simple atomic absorption instrument appears schematically in Fig. 2-43. The light from the hollow-cathode lamp passes through a flame, in which the sample is being converted to an atomic vapor. The light then passes through a monochromator, and is detected and converted to a meter reading. Figure 2-44 shows a typical emission spectrum from a hollow-cathode lamp, together with an absorption line of the sample and how the two combine to create a signal for the detector. This shows why the monochromator for atomic absorption may be much simpler than its counterpart in any versatile flame photometer: its only function is to eliminate the nonresonance lines emitted by the lamp. We see, also, the value of using a source of discrete emission lines, characteristic only of the metal being sought, rather than a continuous source like a light bulb. A light bulb would radiate at all wavelengths, so that the indicated absorption would depend not only on the sample concentration, but on how efficiently the monochromator would screen out the wavelengths that the sample cannot absorb.

Origins and applications

The principles of atomic absorption have been known for a long time. We have seen it completely described in a book published in 1872 (see the additional reading following this article). In that period, the great Kirchhoff and others suggested that the technique might become important in chemical analysis. However, chemists did not take it up, though some physical measurements were made with the use of this system. It was not until 1955 that the Australian physicist Alan Walsh rediscovered its analytical importance, and brought together the components and information to produce a useful instrument. A remarkable group in Australia and New Zealand rapidly made excellent ap-

plications studies, quickly entrenching the technique in those countries. From there, under the energetic guidance of Walsh, the technique spread to South Africa, England, and eventually to Russia. American interest has been much slower to develop, lagging to such an appalling degree as to move Walsh recently to refer to the U.S. as an underdeveloped nation. (This is nothing, of course, that could not be corrected with the aid of a large Australian loan.)

In thinking about applications for atomic absorption, it is well to keep in mind how it differs from spectroscopy. In spectroscopy, we often say: *Here is an unknown sample, let's see what is in it.* In atomic absorption, we are looking for a specific metal, so we say: *Here is an unknown sample, let us see how much calcium is in it.* To indicate the large variety of applications that already exist, we will cite some of the more interesting ones:

(1) Atomic absorption is routinely being used to study low-level impurities in metals and alloys, and on their surfaces. Zinc, another metal very easy to find by atomic absorption and very difficult by other means, is being determined in copper and aluminum alloys. Atomic absorpton is replacing other methods for finding lead in copper alloys and steels. The complete determination takes only 20 minutes.

(2) In medicine, atomic absorption is finding favor as a means for measuring calcium and magnesium in blood. Calcium can be determined, though with difficulty, by flame photometry, while magnesium is extremely difficult except by atomic absorption. Atomic absorption is also being applied to the detection of heavy metals in biological fluids.

(3) Agricultural chemists employ atomic absorption to detect the presence of at least thirteen metals in soils and plants. In one experiment, trace quantities of strontium are being artificially introduced into plant systems, after

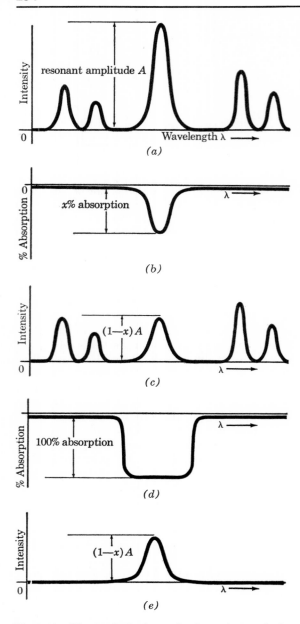

Fig. 2-44. The method of atomic absorption analysis: (a) hollow-cathode lamp emits this spectrum; (b) sample absorbs only at the resonance line; (c) spectrum emitted from lamp looks like this after resonant absorption in the sample; (d) monochromator blocks out all but a band of wavelengths around the best resonance line; (e) this diminished resonance line, which goes to the photodector, is the result.

which the distribution of the strontium is studied. From this, it is possible to predict the effect of radioactive strontium-90 on the food supply. Since strontium-90 may yet kill us all, atomic absorption will help us understand better the mechanics of our passing.

(4) For decades, petroleum chemists have been having a hard job checking on just how much lead was being put into their gasoline.

At least one gasoline producer is now determining the concentration routinely by atomic absorption; another is measuring nickel, copper, iron, and sodium in crude oils and catalysts.

And here is a really "blue-sky" possibility: It has been suggested that one of the first packages to land on the moon contain a simple atomic absorption apparatus, together with an arm that would scoop up handfuls of dirt and throw them into the instrument. However, there are other techniques (see "Tools for Analytical Chemistry," page 225) that seem more suitable for this purpose.

This list could easily be lengthened, for the number of articles published on the technique has been expanding at a geometric rate.

All that glitters is not gold

So far, the impression may have been given that the atomic absorption method is extremely simple to use, and that one need do no more than throw the sample into the flame and read off the answer. While the use of the technique is even now simple, and will no doubt become more so, a few caveats must nevertheless be mentioned. These fall into three classes: limitations, interferences, and inconveniences.

As far as limitations are concerned, several desirable metals are still beyond the reach of atomic absorption, for two different reasons. Until recently, it has been difficult to detect aluminum, for example, because as soon as it is vaporized, it forms a refractory oxide in the flame. On the other hand, at present flame temperatures, it is very difficult to vaporize such metals as tungsten at all. Certain techniques of raising flame temperatures might be used in such cases, but would add to instrument complexity.

Interferences, which can be defined as any physical, chemical, or instrumental factors tending to defeat an analysis, form a large and complex group. At the outset, let it be said that interferences are by no means peculiar to atomic absorption, but are found also in flame photometry and emission spectroscopy, its two most important rivals. Indeed, atomic absorption is free of the optical interference that sometimes plagues the other techniques. Since atomic absorption depends upon the very narrow and specific absorption by the sample of a very narrow emission line from the source, the spurious contribution by one metal to apparent absorption by another for optical reasons is essentially impossible, even if the absorption lines of the two metals are close together by ordinary standards.

However, there are sufficient *chemical* interferences to keep research men alert. For example, unless preventive measures are taken, the presence of silicon will depress the absorption in an analysis for strontium, which could be pretty embarrassing if one is checking the presence of trace quantities of strontium in soils. The reason for the interference is that strontium silicate is a highly refractory compound. The commonly used expedient is to add to the sample large quantities of a metal similar to strontium, such as magnesium or calcium. This keeps the silicon occupied in forming silicates with the more plentiful metal. A list of a whole series of specific analyses will be found in the references following the article.

Another common form of chemical interference is known as "enhancement." In order to understand this, one must know that the generally accepted standard for the spectral absorption of a metal is found by testing a simple inorganic compound of the metal in *water* solution. Table 1, for example, is based on samples in water solution. The sample, thus dissolved, is atomized, and then mixed with the fuel in the flame and burned. Now sometimes *organic* rather than aqueous solutions must be used—when analyzing oils, for example. It turns out that in *organic* solutions the absorption for a given concentration of a metal can rise quite sharply. From this we say that the organic solution "enhances" the absorption of the metal. The reason may be that the lower surface tension of the organic solution permits the atomizer to form it into smaller droplets, atomizing the solution more completely, and thus enabling the flame to vaporize more of it.

These complexities lead inevitably to two approaches to any given problem: the "cookbook" and the "working curve." Many of the articles published on atomic absorption describe specific analyses—showing how to eliminate known interferences, what fuel to use, how

high a flame, and so on. The routine analyst is then able to use the appropriate article as a cookbook for his own work. The working curve approach stems from another question: If one is testing for, say, magnesium and the indicated absorbance is 0.5, what does that tell about the actual concentration of magnesium in the sample? To find the answer, the analyst makes up a number of solutions containing various known quantities of the metal he seeks in his sample. By running these in his instrument, he comes up with a curve of concentration versus absorbance, which might look like Fig. 2-45. This is his working curve—essential to any atomic absorption analysis.

The various inconveniences associated with it represent another drawback of atomic absorption at the present time. As in the case of interferences, these inconveniences are in most cases less than those encountered when using alternate techniques. Possibly the most important inconvenience is that the sample must be converted into a solution before it can be atomized into the flame. While it is usually possible to do this, the procedure in such specialties as steel analysis is sometimes so cumbersome that analysts prefer to use a technique like emission spectroscopy, where the solid sample is simply vaporized in an arc.

A second (though minor) inconvenience is that it is necessary to change the hollow-cathode lamp, and to reset various instrument parameters, each time we want to test for a different metal. Multiple-element hollow-cathode lamps have often been unsuccessful, because, when such lamps are excited, one element tends to dominate the radiation, to the exclusion of the others. Some ingenious schemes have been propounded, and it may be considered a safe bet that this problem will be solved

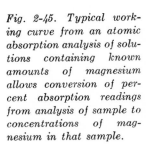

Fig. 2-45. Typical working curve from an atomic absorption analysis of solutions containing known amounts of magnesium allows conversion of percent absorption readings from analysis of sample to concentrations of magnesium in that sample.

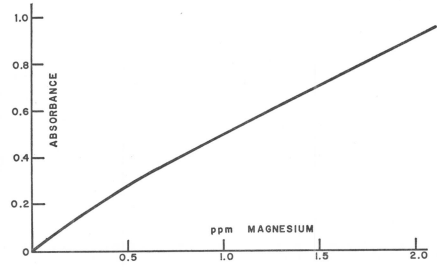

before much time passes. The resetting of the instrument parameters (wavelength, electronic gain, lamp current, monochromator dispersion) can be automated at considerable expense. However, the inherent instrument principle is so simple, and so little difficulty is involved in making the adjustments manually, that present instrument concepts tend to rely on the operator to set up the analysis.

Finally, one further drawback of a so-called single-beam instrument, such as that shown in Fig. 2-43, is the fact that lamp emission and photodetector sensitivity are directly involved in absorption measurement. This involves the use of somewhat complex electronics to regulate these two quantities, plus fairly frequent checking of operating conditions. Many specialists consider the inconvenience of single-beam work of little importance, and prefer the simplicity of the single-beam approach. The authors prefer to avoid this problem by using another approach—the double-beam principle illustrated in Fig. 2-46. The advantage of this system is that variations in source intensity, detector sensitivity, and optical transmission are cancelled out and do not appear as factors in the final measurement.

Dat ole debbil, flame

It may have struck the reader that the nature of the flame is at the root of most of the limitations, interferences, and inconveniences. This is true. The flame and atomization system is sometimes nonlinear and always mysterious, while everything else is linear and understood; the flame uses oxygen, which complicates many analyses; and often the flame is simply not hot enough. Much present and future research, therefore, must obviously have as its aim a means of getting rid of the flame.

At present the flame is the most accessible, economical, and reliable source of heat, but,

nevertheless, encouraging progress in its elimination is being made. A Russian, L'vov, reports a sampling system built around a directly heated carbon furnace, whereby he is able to obtain remarkable sensitivities for metals that are not readily dissociated in a flame. Our laboratory is experimenting with flash lamps, first proposed by L. S. Nelson of Bell Labs for a different application. A gas-filled helical tube is placed around an airtight enclosure containing a small sample. The sample is then vaporized by passing a brief, intense electrical flash through the helix. This produces temperatures which equal or exceed that of the flame, without the presence of oxygen. Meanwhile, in Australia, Walsh is testing what he calls a sputtering chamber—essentially a second, demountable hollow-cathode lamp in which his sample is the cathode.

If a flameless sampling scheme does become practical, the advantages will be numerous. It will be possible to analyze solid samples without the trouble of dissolving them. The questions of enhancement, oxidation, and atomization will simply be bypassed. Perhaps most important, it will be possible to test for elements such as phosphorus and iodine, whose resonance lines lie in the region below 1950 Å, where the mere presence of oxygen causes the absorption of most of the light, and where the entire optical path must be purged with nitrogen or helium in order to achieve results. Finally, it may prove possible to penetrate to even lower wavelengths, into the "vacuum ultraviolet," where molecules and non-metallic elements have their resonance lines, and to apply atomic absorption to the determination of oxygen, hydrogen, and similar elements.

No matter whether these predictions come true, or whether future breakthroughs guide research into entirely different paths, it seems

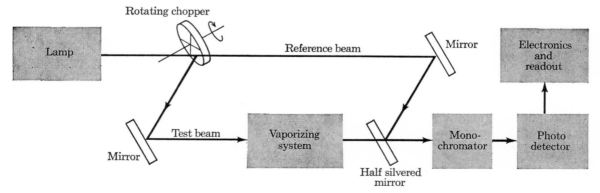

Fig. 2-46. In double-beam atomic absorption spectrophotometer, light emitted from lamp is split. Half passes through the flame and is partially absorbed depending on concentration of metal in sample. Other half travels, unattenuated, as a reference beam to the monochromator. Absorption is measured by the ratio of intensities of the two beams.

certain that the coming years will produce important advances in this very young, already very powerful technique.

Further reading

The original concept of atomic absorption analysis will be found in a fascinating old book, Schellen's *Spectrum Analysis* (Appleton, 1872). This book, if it can be found by your librarian or your rare-book dealer, reviews the work of Kirchhoff and his contemporaries in this field. Walsh's original article outlining the basis of modern atomic absorption technique was "The Application of Atomic Absorption Spectra to Chemical Analysis," and it appeared in *Spectrochim. Acta*, **7**, p. 108 (1955). Walsh's chapter on the subject in *Advances in Spectroscopy* (Interscience, 1961, Vol. 1, $12.50), is the best discussion of the theoretical foundation of atomic absorption. A more general recent review is that of J. B. Willis, "Analysis of Biological Materials by Atomic Absorption Spectroscopy," in *Methods of Biochemical Analysis*, D. Glick, ed. (Interscience, 1963). The only single book on the subject is a thin one, *Atomic Absorption Spectrophotometry* (Pergamon, 1962, $5), by Elwell and Gidley, who have applied the method to metallurgical problems at Imperial Chemical Industries in Great Britain. A broad overview of the new physical instrumentation that is crowding out the slower chemical methods of analysis can be found in "Tools for Analytical Chemistry," page 225. This article also contains an excellent bibliography. A comprehensive bibliography on atomic absorption analysis itself, containing many items on specific applications, will be found in a series of newsletters being published on the subject by the Perkin-Elmer Corp., Norwalk, Conn. This series may be obtained without charge by writing to the authors of this article at this firm.

MOLTEN SALTS

by Benson R. Sundheim [*]

IN BRIEF: *Salts fused into the molten state are an important class of liquid electrolytes. In some respects they resemble very concentrated aqueous solutions of the same salts, generally having thermal conductivities, diffusion coefficients, viscosities, and surface tensions like those of water, sometimes even at room temperature. But, lacking solvent molecules, and being ionic liquids, they conduct electricity a million times better than water. This conductivity, plus the different stabilities of metal ions when dissolved in fused salts rather than water, has long been exploited in the electrolytic preparation of several metals. Other curious solvent properties hint at possible technological advances in chemical synthesis. Since ionic liquids can become vitreous when cooled, new types of glasses and ceramics have been made with them. And, already used in heat treating, molten salts seem likely to be used for heat transfer and in power generation by nuclear reactors, fuel cells, and thermoelectric cells.—T.M.*

■ Until very recently, chemists tended to concentrate their attention on chemical reactions taking place near room temperature and, by and large, in aqueous solutions. This is doubtless a reflection of the fact that the experimenter, viewed as a chemical system, is himself an aqueous system thermostated at 37°C and at a constant pressure of one atmosphere.

* Benson R. Sundheim is Professor of Chemistry at New York University in New York.

Since recent advances in technology began to push the limits of accessible temperatures and pressures into very high and very low regions, whole new areas of chemistry and physics have been rapidly developing. The field of molten salts is a case in point.

For example, molten-salt research has already led to important and exciting means of processing atomic fuels in a continuously operating liquid reactor. It has led to thermoelectric materials usable over a span of as much as 1000°C, as well as to airborne fuel cells that produce electricity directly from the combination of hydrogen and oxygen, and other important technological advances.

In addition to results already obtained, one can more or less clearly foresee other equally important products still in the developmental stage. Furthermore, research at elevated temperatures has proved to be a tough testing ground for many current theories of liquids and of electrolytes.

So, because of their intrinsic interest and because of their possible and actual technological uses, molten salts have been the subject of intensive study in recent years.

Salts in the liquid state

The term "molten salt" encompasses a number of kinds of chemical systems. Originally it merely denoted the liquid formed by fusing a crystalline salt, which is defined simply as the product of a reaction between an acid and a

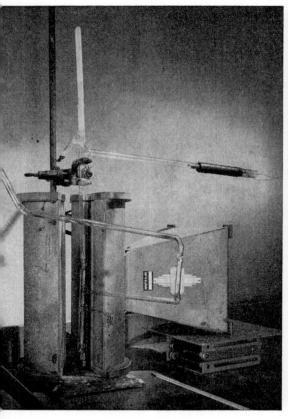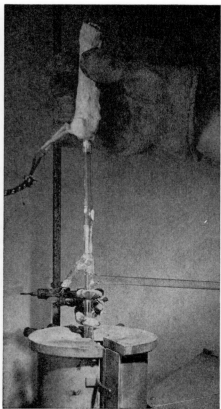

Fig. 2-47. Setup (left) for a recent pilot experiment in dissolving lithium in its molten chloride used a glass cell blown by one of the author's graduate students. A lithium chloride-potassium chloride eutectic in the top of the evacuated cell was heated (center) until the fused salts trickled down, past a previously broken seal, into the bottom. (KCl was in the mix to lower its m.p. below that of glass.) Then the bottom was sealed off (right) while applied heat kept the salts molten. (Courtesy Scott Hyde)

base. The similarity in behavior of other liquid systems to, say, fused sodium chloride, has led to the common practice of using the terms "molten salt," "fused salt," and "liquid electrolyte" more or less interchangeably. That is, if a system is composed at least in substantial part of ions (as evidenced by its ability to conduct electricity) and if its study requires temperatures well above room temperature, it is called a molten salt. Thus, liquid NaOH (m.p. 318.4°C) is a fused salt, whereas liquid HCl (a nonconductor, m.p. −112°C) is not.

Ordinary table salt is perhaps the most familiar solid salt. When pure crystalline sodium chloride is heated above 805°C, it melts sharply to a clear, colorless, mobile liquid, looking rather like water.

As a matter of fact, many fused salts look more or less like liquid water. To be sure, systems which may be called fused salts span a very wide range of physical properties, as tabulated in Fig. 2-50. For example, gallium tetrachlorogallate ($Ga^+GaCl_4^-$) is a liquid at room temperature, whereas many salts do not melt until they are raised to several thousand degrees centigrade. Some materials such as the silicates and borates have viscosities that

are high and very strongly dependent upon temperature, whereas others such as the alkali halides have viscosities near that of water and are only slightly temperature-dependent.

Many liquid electrolytes are clear and colorless, but some are quite dark; e.g., salts of transition-metal ions are intensely colored. Nevertheless, the refractive index usually falls in the range 1.4–2.4, the surface tension near one millipoise. So it is approximately correct to say that most fused salts are liquids with viscosities, thermal conductivities, diffusion coefficients, and surface tensions which are in the same range as that of water.

From one point of view, water itself can be considered as a molten salt because it is a liquid electrolyte, albeit a very weak one. However, water lacks the corrosiveness, the electrical conductivity, and the high melting point of the "main sequence" of molten salts.

In passing, we may note that a long liquid range between melting and boiling points is characteristic of liquid electrolytes. Water obviously lacks this characteristic spread.

The property of remaining liquid at elevated temperatures has led to a number of technological applications of molten salts. For example,

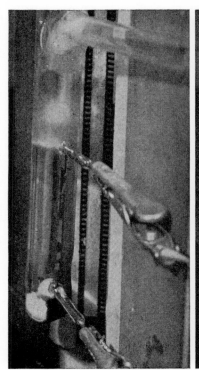

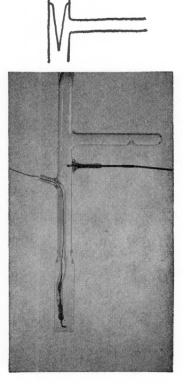

Fig. 2-48. As current flowed through the melt (left), chlorine was liberated at the anode as expected. But the cathode zone did not signal liberation of metallic lithium by turning blue. Instead (right) a dark color indicated that the tungsten electrodes had unexpectedly served as a solvent for the lithium. Thus the pilot experiment showed a need for the design modification now in progress. (Courtesy Scott Hyde)

Fig. 2-49. "Breakseal" (above) is all-glass valve easily broken to open ampule of salts. Commercial glass cell (below) has optical flats for spectroscopic analysis of melts. (Courtesy Scott Hyde)

so-called acid-core soldering flux, used in structural soldering (but not in electrical soldering, lest corrosion open the circuits) is zinc chloride, a fused salt.

High temperature liquids

For many years, industry has made use of molten salt baths for heat-treating purposes. In a number of special applications, nickel-chromium alloys are descaled by use of a fused salt which loosens oxide scales. In the hot-dip process for aluminum coating, fused-salt mixtures usually based on cryolite are used as a flux to protect the aluminum from being oxidized. The fused salt also serves as a preheating bath while protecting the metal from oxidation, and since it coats the metal as it is removed from the bath, it helps to prevent oxidation while the metal is cooling.

As might be expected, heat-transfer applications are now becoming progressively more important. For instance, temperatures can be maintained within fluidized catalyst beds for petroleum cracking by circulating a thermostated fused salt through pipes embedded in the reactor. It is also possible to control the temperature of gases by bubbling them directly through the fused salt.

Liquid electrolytes

As indicated previously, molten salts conduct electricity better than does water. In most salts the specific electrical conductivity is of the order of several reciprocal ohm-centimeters, which is about a million times higher than that of water.

Accordingly, the dielectric constant for liquid electrolytes is not well defined since the dielectric loss is so high. That is, most molten salts conduct electricity so well that it's difficult to measure the capacitance of condensers that contain them.

A direct consequence of these properties is the fact that a very considerable amount of effort has been devoted to the development of molten-salt fuel cells. Under certain circumstances, high-temperature operation is acceptable, which means that molten-salt electrolytes may be used. For example, a fuel cell that burns carbon monoxide, methane, or other carbonace-

PROPERTIES OF LIQUID ELECTROLYTES

FORMULA	LIQUID	MELTING POINT (°C)	BOILING POINT (°C)	DENSITY AT T (g/cc)	ELECTRICAL CONDUCTIVITY AT T (ohm^{-1} cm^{-1})	VISCOSITY AT T (centipoise)	TEMP. (°C)
H_2O	Water	0	100	0.9986	4×10^{-8}	1.0559	18
Hg	Mercury	−38.87	356.58	13.546	1.1×10^4	1.554	20
$CdCl_2$	Cadmium Chloride	568	960	3.366	1.939	2.31	600
CsCl	Cesium Chloride	646	1290	2.733	1.273	· · ·	700
$PbBr_2$	Lead Bromide	373	916	5.265	· · ·	2.98	550
$PbCl_2$	Lead Chloride	501	950	4.802	· · ·	2.75	600
LiCl	Lithium Chloride	613	1353	1.4630	6.1717	· · ·	700
KCl	Potassium Chloride	776	1500	1.2073	1.7349	· · ·	800
KI	Potassium Iodide	723	1420 (1330)	2.3339	1.5188	· · ·	800
AgBr	Silver Bromide	434	700	5.402	· · ·	2.27	600
NaCl	Sodium Chloride	801	1413	1.5024	3.8815	· · ·	900
NaI	Sodium Iodide	651	1300	2.0254	3.3134	· · ·	900
$NaNO_3$	Sodium Nitrate	306	380 decomp	1.888	1.068	· · ·	350

Fig. 2-50. The first two entries in this list of liquid electrolytes are there for purposes of comparison, to help "place" the values given for the properties of the molten salts that make up the remainder of the list. Most of the molten salts cited are halides because halides have been studied the most.

ous gases, and utilizes molten carbonates as the electrolyte has been developed by the Leesona-Moos Corporation in the United States and the Sonde's Place Laboratories in Great Britain.

Ionic liquids

While molten salts conduct electricity a million times better than water, they are about a thousand times poorer than mercury at room temperature.

Clearly, a molten salt must conduct elec-

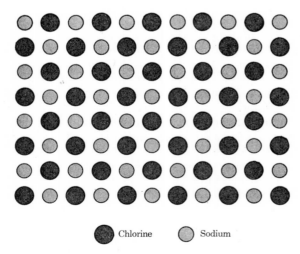

Chlorine   Sodium

Fig. 2-51. Solid NaCl at low temperature is a nearly perfect crystal in which cations and anions alternate in a regular array, shown here in two dimensions. Heat knocks ions out of the lattice, causing structural defects.

tricity by a mechanism different from that of electrical conduction in metals, which is electronic. On the basis of its physical and chemical properties, a molten salt is considered to be a fluid composed of positive and negative ions that move freely throughout the melt. To understand such a liquid electrolyte, it is helpful to consider the conditions that lead to the existence of the liquid state.

The state of organization of matter is controlled in part by two important opposing principles: the drive towards minimum potential energy and the drive towards maximum randomness. The first of these is described in terms of the internal energy and the second in terms of the entropy, and the relationship between these two is the central problem that faces the science of thermodynamics.

At any temperature, a chemical system achieves some compromise between these two forces, even as each of us in our private lives compromises between the drives for maximum security and maximum freedom.

Thus, at very low temperatures, an aggregate of positive and negative ions will be organized as the kind of perfect ionic crystal shown in Fig. 2-51, because only in such a three-dimensional array is the potential energy of the system as a whole at a minimum.

Heat degrades the lattice

As the temperature of such a system is raised, the thermal kinetic energy tends to disrupt the perfect crystalline structure, causing lattice defects to appear. That is, a few lattice sites may become vacant, some ions may move into interstitial positions or more complicated disarrays involving more ions may occur.

In any event, the net result is to introduce a slight disarray so that the long-range regularity is still perfectly evident but contains a number of minor errors in detail.

The degree of randomization can be measured numerically in terms of the entropy S, while the balance between the internal energy E and the thermal disorganizing force is written as the free energy, $F = E - TS$. At equilibrium, $\Delta E = \Delta(TS)$, so that the drive towards minimum potential energy is balanced by the drive towards maximum randomness.

The fusing of the salt

Note that the entropy term occurs with the factor T. Its relative importance increases steadily with temperature.

Thus, when a perfect ionic crystal is heated, the number of defects present at equilibrium increases rapidly with the temperature, because of the increase in the term TS. At some point this increase becomes catastrophic, so that a major change in the organization of the crystal occurs, with a large increase in the randomness and hence in the entropy of the system. This increase in randomness takes place at the expense of an increase in potential energy—a decrease in stability—which is equal to the heat of fusion.

The liquid state that results from this reorganization is characterized by a new compromise between the potential energy and thermal disorganization. In general, one may expect that a positive ion is still principally surrounded by negative ions, since the close approach of two ions of the same sign would entail a very large contribution to the potential energy. On the other hand, all semblance of long-range order disappears, since a great deal of disorganization can be accomplished in this way at the expenditure of relatively little potential energy.

Thus, as shown in Fig. 2-52, we believe that a typical liquid electrolyte such as fused sodium chloride is characterized by a sort of quasi-crystal structure, in which the immediate environment of any single ion roughly resembles the state in the crystal. However, the long-range order has been almost completely destroyed as a consequence of a structure that is highly defective (in the solid-state sense).

This fact produces another difference between a crystal and a fused salt in that the mobility of the ions is a great deal higher in the fused salt than in the corresponding crystal.

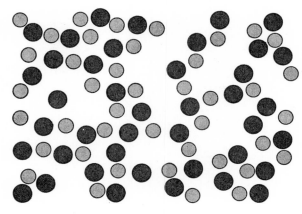

Fig. 2-52. Molten NaCl is a liquid through which cations and anions can move freely. At short range, ions still have a quasi-crystalline environment but the long-range regularity is gone.

For the same reason, the viscosity approaches that of water, since shearing motion is easy. In general, the exceptions reflect either the presence of special structural features, such as the possibility of oxygen bridges, which lead to the formation of glasses, or the occurrence of covalent bonds that are not dissociated, so that the material scarcely conducts electricity, as in the cases of Hg_2Cl_2 and $AlCl_3$.

Measuring the distribution of the ions

This mental picture of ionic liquid structure as resembling a disordered crystal can be compared with experiment. It is quite possible to get a rough picture of the arrangement of ions in a liquid electrolyte by direct measurement.

Of course, since the particles are in ceaseless motion and since the structure is disordered, it is not possible to state definitely how the environment of a given particle is organized. Rather we must deal with averages.

The quantity that contains this sort of information is called the radial distribution function. It may be determined with the aid of x-ray and neutron diffraction measurements, which is essentially the same method used to locate the position of atoms in crystals. The radial distribution function obtained in this way is defined as the probability of finding particles in a given volume element at a distance from a central particle.

An interesting technical problem arises here in the case of molten salts, since there must be three types of distribution functions involved: (1) the distribution of positive ions around a positive ion; (2) the distribution of negative ions around a positive ion, which may also be used to give the distribution of the negative ions around a positive ion; and (3) the distribution of negative ions around a negative ion.

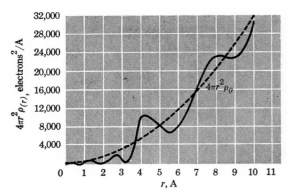

Fig. 2-53. Radial distribution function of ions in a liquid salt—here Li^7Br—is startlingly similar to that of a crystal. There is a parabolic increase in probability of finding another ion as you go farther from any particular ion; this simply expresses increase in volume of space and is shown by the dotted curve. More significant are the probability peaks at distances of 2.68 and 4.12 A: In a crystal these would occur at 2.85 and 4.03 A. The size of the peaks are also about the same. (Mysterious-looking units in which curve is plotted arise from the x-ray diffraction observations it is based on.) (Adapted from N.Y. Acad. of Sci. Annals, Vol. 79, p. 771)

The problem of disentangling these three distribution functions has not yet been completely solved, but some general conclusions can be definitely drawn. Each of the radial distribution functions starts at zero (see Fig. 2-53), indicating that the center of a neighboring ion cannot be closer than a minimum distance from the central ion. Then it rises to a maximum that gives the most probable distance to the nearest neighbor.

In a number of simple molten salts, the experimental distribution functions indicate that the nearest neighbors have moved even closer to a central atom than they are in the crystal. At the same time, the volume has increased by about 15% upon melting!

These two facts can be reconciled by assuming that the average coordination number, or number of nearest neighbors, has been reduced from six in the case of crystalline sodium chloride to approximately five in the melt, but that these five are packed more closely around the central ion. The volume increase implies that there must be interstices (sometimes called holes, vacancies, or defects) of various sizes scattered throughout the liquid. Considerations such as these determine many of the properties whose use will be discussed below.

Novel glasses

Some ionic structures are capable of forming large, chemically bonded aggregates that are disordered. For example, mixtures of silica

with sodium oxide lead to highly viscous melts, which tend to give glasses on cooling. The high viscosity is associated with complex structures such as chains, rings, and more complicated three-dimensional arrangements (see Fig. 2-54).

Upon cooling such a system, the high viscosity tends to prevent the movements necessary to reach the equilibrium crystalline state, and so the liquid-type organization persists. That is, the short-range order in the aggregate remains, but there is no long-range order.

On this basis, glasses are formed from a variety of fused-salt mixtures containing such oxides as those of boron, silicon, and phosphorus. And, with the increase in our understanding both of the structure of the liquid and the kinetics of reorganization upon cooling, it has become possible to design new classes of glasses and ceramics (see "Modern Glass," page 266).

Examples include the Corning product "Pyroceram," which has unusual resistance to mechanical and thermal shock, and is used for nose cones and cooking utensils; highly selective membranes made by the Beckman Instrument Company and based on lithium aluminum silicate glasses that permit ions of one size to pass through the glass, but not ions of another size; glasses that conduct electricity, glasses that are photosensitive, and many others with special properties.

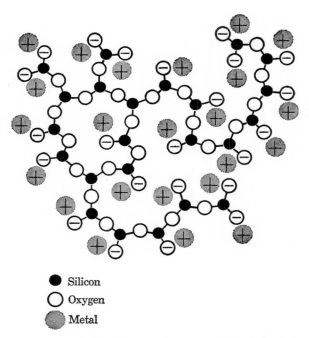

● Silicon
○ Oxygen
◉ Metal

Fig. 2-54. Sodium-oxide silicate glass has an aperiodic structure of silicon, oxygen, and sodium ions, drawn in two dimensions. The geometry of the negatively-charged network varies with composition. Other fused oxides form similar glasses.

Fused salts as solvents

Molten salts are good solvents. The many possibilities inherent in this property are only beginning to be explored, but a number of facts are known:

Many molten salts are solvents for the metals corresponding to their cations; thus, at sufficiently high temperatures, sodium is miscible in all proportions with the molten sodium chloride. These solutions are intensely corrosive and their careful study by Max Bredig and co-workers at Oak Ridge National Laboratory represents a real experimental tour de force. They have the unusual property of simultaneously developing electronic and ionic conductivity. For, as the composition of such a solution is varied, we proceed gradually from a purely ionic conductor, the salt, to a purely electronic conductor, the metal.

On the salt-rich side, the metal atom, which may be thought of as an ion plus an electron, behaves like a salt in that it lowers the freezing point, perhaps enters into complex ionic structures, etc. As more and more metal is added to the solution, the electron orbitals apparently begin to overlap. The electronic conductivity rises rapidly as the electrons are able to slip from one orbital to another. As the overlapping of neighboring electrons becomes more complete, the system becomes progressively more like a liquid metal.

It is particularly interesting that none of the physical properties changes discontinuously. Intermediate compositions must correspond to states in which both electronic and ionic conductivity occur together. We may expect a study of such systems to provide considerable insight into the nature of metals and semiconductor systems (see Figs. 2-47, 2-48, and 2-49).

Fused salts tend to be soluble in each other as long as both are liquid, but some exceptions to this have been noted. In fact, a great deal of the early research in this field was devoted to the determination of phase diagrams for a number of systems.

Furthermore, there are a number of curious solvent properties possessed by fused-salt systems which have not yet been thoroughly exploited. For example, the halides are quite soluble in their corresponding alkali halides, presumably giving rise to the trihalide ion. This kind of solution might be expected to have remarkable oxidizing power in high-temperature systems. As another example, sulfur dissolves readily and reversibly in molten KCl to give a blue solution. Such solutions may provide new routes to the synthesis of a number of metal sulfides.

The solvent power of molten salts suggests that one very important use for molten salts will be in a role traditionally played by water —that is, as a reaction medium for chemical syntheses both inorganic and organic.

In the laboratories of Prof. O. Glemmser at the Anorganisch-Chemisches Institut of Göttingen, hydrides, cyanides, cyanates, thiocyanates, and fluorine-containing compounds have been prepared from various reactants through reactions with appropriate salts dissolved in molten salts. This technique has been extended to such organic syntheses as that of olefins from alcohols and in the chlorination of benzene shown in this equation:

$$C_6H_6 \xrightarrow[\substack{(AlCl_3-NaCl-KCl \\ melt\ at\ 100°C)}]{(Cl_2)} C_6H_5Cl \ (80\% \text{ yield})$$

In this melt, the di-, tri-, and tetra-chlorobenzenes can be prepared by raising the temperature to 200°C.

Such promising results should motivate increased exploration of this little-known area of high-temperature chemistry. As high-temperature laboratories increase in number, I expect that important contributions will be made to chemical theory and to techniques of synthetic chemistry.

Electrometallurgy in molten salts

As suggested by its use as a reaction medium, for many purposes a molten salt may be treated as if it were a very concentrated solution in water of the corresponding salt.

However, the fact that ions in fused-salt solutions are essentially surrounded by the ions of the opposite charge and that solvent molecules are absent, leads to a chemistry which is roughly similar to, but different in detail from, that encountered in aqueous solutions and other solvents.

For example, the oxidation potential of metal ions with respect to their metal electrodes is frequently very different. Thus, in fused KCl the univalent cuprous ion is more stable than the bivalent cupric, whereas the reverse is true in aqueous systems. And, in the molten eutectic of LiCl with KCl, it is possible to obtain, under proper circumstances, three oxidation states of titanium: 2+, 3+, 4+, and of uranium: 4+, 5+, 6+; whereas many of these ions do not occur as such in other solvents.

These modifications in the sequence of stabilities, together with the fact that the fused salts are generally good conductors of electricity, may be used to advantage in the electrolytic preparation of various metals. Such applications of molten salts to the chemical problem of isolating metals from their salts are not new. Indeed, the first reported example of electrometallurgy at high temperatures was the preparation of sodium metal by electrolysis of molten NaCl reported by Sir Humphrey Davy in 1807.

In the modern version of Davy's experiment, NaCl is mixed with $CaCl_2$ to reduce the melting point of the electrolyte to about 580° and then is electrolyzed in a Downes cell. (A line of cells used for this purpose is shown in Fig. 2-55.) Similarly, the Hall process (which dates back to 1886) prepares aluminum by electrolysis of Al_2O_3 dissolved in fused cryolite (sodium-aluminum fluoride). Along the same lines, the Dow process for the production of magnesium is based on the electrolysis of a fused mixture of $MgCl_2$, NaCl, and $CaCl_2$ near 700°C.

A number of the less common metals such as zirconium, tantalum, niobium, and titanium have been prepared by reducing their fused halides with Mg, Na, or Ca, which in turn are made by electrolysis of the fused electrolyte. In certain cases, an impure sample of metal made by some other process is refined electrolytically by using it as the anode in fused-salt electrolysis. The purified metal plates out at the cathode.

An interesting variation of this technique has been reported by the Norton Company,

Fig. 2-55. Molten NaCl is electrolyzed in Downes cells like these to produce more than 100,000 tons of metallic sodium annually in the U.S. (Courtesy U.S. Industrial Chemicals Co.)

which has made high-quality titanium by the electrolysis of titanium carbide anode in a fused salt.

There is no doubt that the next few years will see the large-scale preparation of many other metals such as beryllium, tantalum, and tungsten by electrolysis of liquid electrolytes.

Finally, the separation of isotopes of a number of materials by fused-salt electrolysis has been the subject of intensive study by a number of laboratories. Successful separations of a number of isotopes have been reported. For example, it is possible by this means to isolate the isotope of Li^6, which is used in thermonuclear devices.

Thermoelectric generation

If a temperature gradient is imposed across a fused-salt cell that is fitted with a pair of electrodes reversible to one of the ions in the salt, a thermocell is formed that is capable of producing electrical power. The thermoelectric power produced by such a device may be 5 to 10 times that from a metallic thermocouple and may be constant over temperature ranges of as much as 1000°C. Such a thermocell may have a figure of merit as high as several times 10^{-3}, which compares favorably with semiconductors; and it is cheap, sturdy, and easy to fabricate.

In my opinion, there will be increasing use of the thermoelectric converters based on this principle. Perhaps also they will be combined with reactors. That is, a chemical or nuclear reactor employing a fused salt as the reaction medium will be the high-temperature source of the thermoelectric device, with the fused salt also serving as the thermocouple for converting the heat to electricity.

How molten salts changed one technology

Nucleonics is a prime example of a technology that has already been shaped by straightforward utilization of the properties of molten salts.

First, fused-salt systems have played an important role in the preparation of reactor materials such as uranium and zirconium. Very early, a group at Westinghouse headed by John Marden developed a process for the preparation of reactor-grade uranium by the electrolysis of fused potassium uranium fluoride. More recently, the General Electric Knolls Atomic Power Laboratory explored a continuous-feed method whereby uranium oxide is introduced into a cell which contains a fused mixture of uranium fluoride. As the uranium metal is formed it collects in a liquid pool about the cathode at the bottom of the cell. Horizons, Inc., has prepared thorium metal by electrolysis of molten sodium-thorium chloride. And high-purity cerium metal has been made at the Bureau of Mines by electrolysis of fused cerium oxychloride.

Next, molten salts are used as fuel solvents for liquid-fueled nuclear reactors, a reactor concept that has attracted considerable interest. It is based on dispersion of the fuel (uranium or thorium) in a circulating liquid.

The advantages of such liquid reactors include: the flexibility with which the fuel concentration can be adjusted; the wide choice of operating temperatures; the mechanical stability to radiation damage, since solid reactors encounter difficult problems of containing the fuel in supporting cartridges; and, most important, the possibility of operating a continuous process for the removal of fission products.

Solvents which have been seriously considered for this purpose include water, liquid metals, and fused salts. The principal technical problem has to do with finding structural materials that resist corrosion.

The exploration of fused-salt reactors has been carried out for some years at the Oak Ridge National Laboratories. In the 1954 Aircraft Reactor Experiment (ARE), it was shown that a mixture of molten sodium and zirconium fluorides containing uranium fluoride could be used.

Another mixture of molten fluorides is currently being studied in a fast-neutron reactor. In this sort of design, combined breeding of new nuclear fuel and production of electric power seems feasible.

Third, molten-salt reactors have been important in the treatment of spent fuels from reactors of other sorts. For example, the liquid metal fuel reactor (LMFR), which was studied in detail at Brookhaven National Laboratories, extracted fission products from the liquid uranium-bismuth fuel by a liquid mixture of magnesium, sodium, and potassium chlorides. It is possible to adjust the oxidation potential of the fused-salt system so as to oxidize the lanthanide elements with the $MgCl_2$ while not affecting the uranium. The oxidized fission products are then carried away with the fused-salt phase and the metal phase returned to the reactor loop.

Finally, another application of fused salts to nuclear reactors is as heat-transfer agents —either as the primary coolant or to transfer heat from the primary coolant.

These varied applications of molten salts to reactor technology are partly the result of necessity, conventional methods being unsuitable, and partly the result of an adventurous approach to the solution of chemical and engineering problems.

In the near future

Molten-salt technology is expanding rapidly. We may expect further advances in electrometallurgy, chemical reactors, nuclear reactors and thermoelectric devices in which fused-salt systems figure importantly. The pace of academic research in liquid electrolytes is rapidly quickening and I expect to see significant contributions to an understanding of the effect of long-range forces and of the liquid state.

Further reading

For a general orientation with a stress on industrial applications, read Ellis's article, "Fused Salts," in the Oct. 10, 1960 issue of *Chemical & Engineering News*.

The basic literature of the subject is very extensive and appears mainly in scientific journals. An exhaustive and critical review of the literature is given in an article by Blomgren and Van Artsdalen in *Ann. Rev. Phys. Chem.* (1960). Another review, and one that contains the tables of physical and chemical properties upon which this article's Fig. 2-50 was based, is "Molten Electrolytes," by Bloom and Bockris, a chapter in *Modern Aspects of Electrochemistry, No. 2*, ed. by Bockris (Academic Press, 1959, $13.00).

Two dozen papers resulting from a conference held and supported by the N.Y. Academy of Sciences in 1959 have been published in their *Annals*, **79**, pp. 761–1098. Covering only recent research, the papers give a good picture of the degree of sophistication then current.

Still more sophisticated is the series published by The Faraday Society (No. 32, 1961) as "The Structure and Properties of Ionic Melts."

A fairly complete and comprehensive survey of Russian and non-Russian work on the electrochemistry of molten salts, and one with a nice balance between theory, experiment, and examples, is *Electrochemistry of Fused Salts*, by Delimarskii and Markov, tr. by Peiperl, ed. by Wood (Sigma Press, 1962, $12.50).

Finally, a collection of extensive reviews of academic research will be found in the book *Fused Salts*, ed. by Sundheim (McGraw-Hill, 1964).

MODERN GLASS

*by S. Donald Stookey ***

IN BRIEF: *Today's glass is the product of centuries of glass-making art—leavened by modern science. Its precise molecular structure is still a matter of conjecture and controversy, but this perplexing material is slowly yielding its secrets as modern analytical tools focus upon it.*

Much of this new knowledge is leading to new and different glass forms: Glass that can be machined chemically after sensitizing the area to be machined by exposure to light and heat; glass that converts from an amorphous structure to a strong, crystalline, ceramic-like material resistant to thermal shock; and glass that appears to be electronically conductive.

Developments in modern glass are benefiting other sciences too: For example, controlled nucleation in glass-ceramics may reveal just how phase changes occur in other materials; and study of ion exchange mechanisms in glass electrodes can possibly tell us how certain basic processes of human metabolism take place. —F.P.

■ A new world is suddenly unfolding to the startled glass technologist as he gazes into his six-thousand-year-old crystal ball. As his eyes gradually adjust to seeing in molecular detail, the familiar transparent solid turns out to hold a frozen mass of hidden fairy-tale princesses, powerful sleeping giants, and unknown creatures of all kinds, condensed to molecular size and trapped in an unexplored labyrinth; each waiting to be brought to life by the proper magic word.

In more practical language, we are learning that glass consists literally of chemical species in a frozen state of suspended animation, somewhat as free radicals are trapped by freezing them. By using the proper catalyst—which may be high-energy radiation or internally precipitated colloids or heat, or a combination of these —a really astonishing variety of electronic, chemical, and physical changes can be initiated and controlled, resulting in a multitude of new materials. Some of the current discoveries are completely reversing traditional concepts. For example:

Glass strengthening techniques now in the laboratory may soon change our traditional concept of glass as a material that is fragile and brittle to one that is strong and flexible.

Long known as an electrical insulator, glass

*S. Donald Stookey is Director of Fundamental Chemical Research at Corning Glass Works, Corning, New York.

in some of its new forms becomes an electronic conductor.

Distinguished from most other solids by its noncrystalline amorphous structure, glass now is found to be a perfect medium for *controlled* crystallization, and has become the spawning ground for a growing number of unique new crystalline materials—as shown in Fig. 2-56, for example.

Famous for its impermeability to liquids and gases, high silica glass has been found to be selectively permeable to the smallest gas molecules such as helium, neon, and hydrogen; it can be used as a molecular sieve.

Although it is a completely rigid nonreactive material below its annealing temperature of five to six hundred degrees, yet glass permits rapid diffusion and exchange of certain monovalent ions such as those of silver, copper, sodium, lithium, and potassium, well below the annealing temperature.

The nature of glass

Let's start our more detailed description of the newly evolving technology of glass by discussing our present concepts of its chemical and physical nature. Immediately it becomes necessary to say that no two experts agree on the subject of the molecular structure of glass. For example, the proceedings of the most recent All-Russia Glass Congress report that the main emphasis of Russian glass research for the preceding five years was on glass structure. So what you read here should not be taken as a consensus of all glass scientists, or even two of us.

Molten silica is an extremely viscous liquid. It can be visualized as a three-dimensional polymer whose basic structure is a network of tetrahedral silicon dioxide molecules, Fig. 2-57, joined to one another by oxygen bonds at the corners in random manner. Figure 2-58 shows this random network in two dimensions; in the molten state, the chemical bonds are continually breaking and re-forming. This molten glass is a universal solvent, capable of incorporating almost every chemical element in its structure. Some elements can replace silica and become part of the network; but most (for example, sodium and calcium) become an ionic plasma moving through holes in the polymer network, loosely bonded to the silica through oxygen bonds, as shown in Fig. 2-59. We can picture the sodium ions as high-temperature fish swimming through a three-dimensional net whose meshes become gradually more rigid and

Fig. 2-56. One of the new glasses that can be changed to crystallized glass-ceramic. Here it's shaped into a missile nose cone. In its transparent glassy state, undergoing inspection at right, it is ready for heat treatment to form millions of tiny nuclei and cause crystals to grow on these centers. The matured glass-ceramic has great resistance to erosion and thermal stress. (Courtesy Corning Glass Works)

smaller in size as the material cools. Such "network modifiers" greatly increase the high-temperature fluidity by breaking some of the silicon-oxygen bonds.

As the molten glass cools, the network be-comes more and more rigid until, usually at 400° to 600°C, it is completely solid. The plasma, however, usually does not "freeze" at such a high temperature as the network, so that at temperatures where the glass is completely rigid, diffusion and chemical reaction can still occur among the modifier ions. At still lower temperatures, but still above room temperature, the plasma also freezes so that no translational motion of molecules or ions can occur. At room temperature, high-energy ionizing radiation can produce electronic transitions, but not molecular rearrangements.

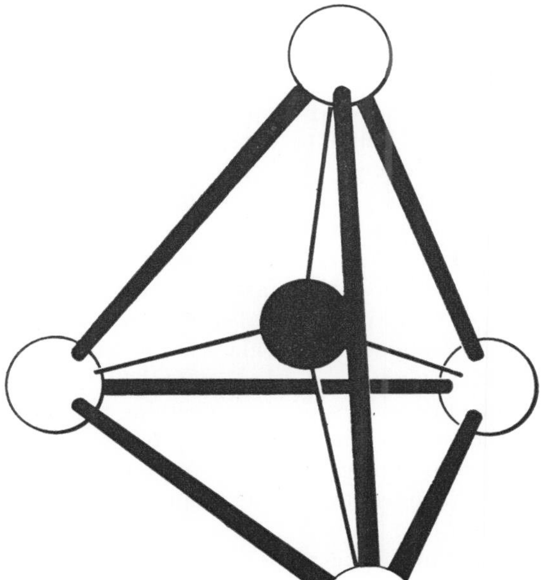

Fig. 2-57. The silica tetrahedron, basic ingredient in glass, has four ions of oxygen, one of silicon (Courtesy Corning Glass Works)

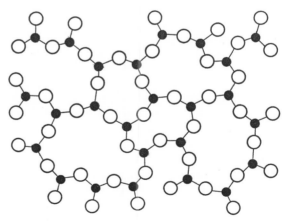

Fig. 2-58. The simplest glass can be thought of as a network of silica tetrahedrons linked together at their corner oxygen ions—as shown in the two-dimensional representation above. (Courtesy Corning Glass Works)

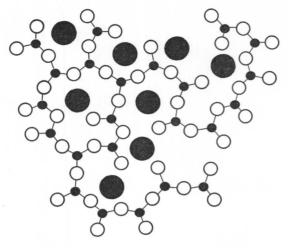

Fig. 2-59. A more complex glass, like the sodium-silicate type sketched two-dimensionally here, has secondary metal ions that modify the network, breaking some of the oxygen-silicon bonds and making the glass more fluid when molten. (Courtesy Corning Glass Works)

We can see then that the simplest glasses, except for one-component glasses like plain fused silica, are molecular two-phase systems although they are amorphous by any macroscopic or microscopic observation. In more complex glasses such as the alkali borosilicates, two interpenetrating polymer networks can be present, one containing mostly silica, the other mostly boric oxide. At low temperatures these two networks tend to separate into really discrete phases, so that submicroscopic channels or droplets of alkali borate glass are present in a silica matrix. This behavior is the basis of high-silica glass, which is made by heat treating a special alkali borosilicate glass to induce this channel-type phase separation, leaching out the alkali borate with acid, then heating the porous silica skeleton until it shrinks and consolidates as reconstructed 96% silica glass.

Such structural complexity is compounded by constituents that may interact in oxidation-reduction pairs or precipitate from solution as crystals. Small wonder that scientists disagree on "a" glass structure, and that few scientists are rash enough to explore this untidy jungle—neither truly liquid nor truly crystalline, but related to both.

Having been one of the foolhardy explorers into this wilderness, and having been invited by the editors of this journal to elucidate recent developments in glass from a personal point of view, I will take the liberty of emulating Sinbad the Sailor and tell you some of the discoveries in which I have taken part and how they came about.

Glasses that respond to light

A good starting point is an early foray of mine into glass research, the purpose of which was to investigate and improve upon the "opal" glasses. These did not turn out to be melted gem stones, as I had first guessed, but opaque or translucent white glasses containing colloidal inclusions, usually crystalline, that scatter light.

Literature survey disclosed, among other things, the recipe of an early German glassmaker calling for ground deer bones to make "bone-ash" opal. Such romantic findings are part of the fascination of research in a medium that has thousands of years of history. (Bone-ash opals, in which calcium phosphate is the insoluble phase, are still manufactured.)

I was soon struck by the apparent similarity between the behavior of certain opal glasses containing sodium fluoride, and that reported for the rare and beautiful gold and copper ruby glasses. All of these glasses remain clear when they are first cooled, but develop opacity or color by precipitating colloidal particles when they are reheated. Meanwhile, R. H. Dalton of our laboratory had recently discovered that a copper ruby glass, irradiated with ultraviolet light while in its colorless state, developed a darker red color after reheating.

Jumping to the erroneous conclusion that, therefore, similar exposure of a sodium fluoride glass would result in a photosensitive opal, I found that ultraviolet light had no effect whatsoever on this glass.

The answer to this puzzle proved to be that the sodium fluoride precipitation results from a simple supersaturation, with crystal nuclei forming at such low temperatures that the glass must be reheated in order that crystals can grow. The gold and copper rubies, on the other hand, were found to develop their color in a complex sequence of chemical oxidation-reduction reactions, of a temperature-sensitive type perhaps unique to glass. The metal dissolves as an oxide in the melt, is frozen in an unstable oxidized state as the glass cools, then is slowly reduced to insoluble metal colloid by polyvalent ions in the glass as the glass is reheated at low red heat. Some of the polyvalent reducing agents are oxides of tin, selenium, antimony, and arsenic. Ultraviolet light promotes the reduction of copper, by producing photoelectrons which then combine with copper ions in the glass.

This knowledge made it possible to develop photosensitive copper ruby and gold ruby glasses, which remained colorless even on reheating, except in the areas exposed to ultraviolet light through a photographic negative.

Then it occurred to me that these photographically produced metal crystals, if they were precipitated in a glass supersaturated with sodium fluoride, might trigger the growth of sodium fluoride crystals and give me the photosensitive opal glass I had failed to produce before. This proved to be true; not only could sodium fluoride, but several other kinds of crystals be *nucleated* in three-dimensional photographic patterns. The translucent windows in the north wall of the United Nations Assembly Building are made of photosensitive opal glass with a marble pattern produced in this manner.

A year or so later, in the early days of television, we were confronted with a different practical problem: how to drill a quarter-million small, precise holes through a glass plate, to make an aperture mask? On a long-shot chance, I tested all of the photosensitive opal glasses and discovered that the crystallized photographic pattern in one of them, a lithium silicate glass that had been shelved as useless, was much more readily dissolved in hydrofluoric acid than was the surrounding clear glass. Before long we had a plate of glass with a hexagonal array of small holes; and this led to the development of chemically machineable glass. This glass is finding increasing use in the electronics industry because of its capability of being mass-produced in precise complex shapes like those shown in the panels illustrated in Fig. 2-60.

An accident leads to glass-ceramics

Chance, in the form of a runaway furnace, now took a hand. A plate of photosensitive glass that had been irradiated was accidentally heated to several hundred degrees higher than its usual developing temperature. The plate, which we had expected would melt to a pool of glass, altered instead to a hard strong crystalline ceramic—the first member of a now rapidly growing family of crystalline ceramics made from glass, the Pyrocerams. This was not an isolated case; my colleagues and I soon found that the principle of nucleation-controlled crystallization of glass can be very broadly applied. Figure 2-61 shows three stages in the process of nucleation and crystallization in a glass-ceramic.

Meanwhile, a search for materials suitable as radomes for supersonic missiles made for the Navy by the Johns Hopkins Applied Physics Laboratory, singled out some of the new glass-ceramics as being almost unique in meeting the requirements of strength, resistance to supersonic rain erosion and thermal shock, and radar-transmitting properties. This led to pilot production and testing of radomes for the Terrier and Tartar missiles now standard on the

Fig. 2-60. In a photosensitive glass, detailed patterns can be reproduced on exposure to light and heat treatment. Exposed areas dissolve in acid more easily than clear glass, so that pattern—here ports, chambers, and channels for fluid amplifier circuits—can be etched. Lower panel is cerammed for greater strength. (Courtesy Corning Glass Works)

missile ships of the Navy. Use of new glass manufacturing methods, developed in continuous-tank production of optical glass, resulted in radomes that can be mass-produced uniformly and not individually tailored to meet the boresight tolerances required for accurate aiming of the missile. One of these is illustrated in Fig. 2-58. More and more varieties of radomes, ultrahigh-frequency windows, and antennas are being made of glass-ceramics.

The strength, chemical resistance, and thermal shock resistance of some of the low-expansion glass-ceramics suggested that they could be valuable for domestic use as well as for defense; and we developed the now-popular heat-resistant ceramic utensils for cooking and serving food. A new high-strength glass-ceramic tableware will soon be commercial.

Still newer glass-ceramics are now in the development stage, each tailor-made for a special area of use. One, having exceptionally high dielectric constant, is being developed for capacitors; another, containing crystals of an electronic semiconducting oxide, will be used for high-temperature resistors. And a third variety of glass-ceramics, highly crystalline, contains crystals so small that they do not scatter light, and this glass-ceramic is as transparent as glass. The crystals are beta-eucryptite, a strange mineral which shrinks, instead of

Fig. 2-61. Electron micrographs show conversion of amorphous glass to crystalline glass-ceramic. At top is a flake of essentially amorphous glass containing dissolved nucleating agents. Heat treatment produces nuclei which initiate growth of crystals—the small dark spots (100 angstroms across) in center photo. At bottom, crystallization is almost complete, with crystals now grown to 600 angstroms across. Further treatment coalesces crystals into larger ones. Magnification: 165,000×. (Courtesy Corning Glass Works)

expanding as do most crystals, when heated. The resultant glass-ceramic has a negative coefficient of expansion.

Stronger glasses with crystalline armor

The latest chapter in this story can be found in a paper presented in July 1962 by my colleagues and myself at the International Glass Congress in Washington, D.C. This paper describes two methods, still in laboratory stage, of producing glass armored by a transparent skin of the negative-expansion eucryptic glass-ceramic. This armored glass has a bending strength of 100,000 psi, compared to less than 10,000 psi for commercial annealed glass, and maintains most of its strength after abrasion. We believe that these glasses can belie the reputation for fragility and brittleness that now is deserved by glass.

Since lack of strength has been the Achilles' heel of glass, it is worth examining the reasons for it to help us understand the new cures. The key to both the strength and the weakness of glass is in its amorphous structure. We can regard any piece of glass as a single molecule, a three-dimensional polymer whose strength is equal to the interatomic bond strengths. Therefore, as long as the surface is free from flaws, glass is fantastically strong. Fibers have been measured at one million psi, quarter-inch diameter rods at 400,000 psi in tension. By contrast, the strongest steel alloys have tensile strengths in the 200,000 to 400,000 psi range. Compressive strength of glass is also of the order of hundreds of thousands of pounds per square inch.

Why then is glass so weak? Unfortunately, any contact with solid surfaces produces surface scratches. These become sites of highly concentrated stress when the surface is put into tension; and since the glass does not flow to relieve the local stress, a relatively low over-all tension is sufficient to extend a scratch into a catastrophic crack.

An obvious way to maintain high strength is to protect the surface from abrasion, by coating with rubbery plastics or with slippery silicones before it has become scratched. These methods are in fact being employed for some types of glass containers, and for "armored" industrial pipe. Such plastic coatings serve another useful purpose, in preventing loss of the contents if the glass breaks.

A most promising principle for strengthening glass has been known for many years, and is practiced in the form of "chill tempered" glass. The principle, stated simply, is that tensile strength increases proportionally with the previously induced compressive stress in the surface layer of glass.

In chill tempering, an object is cooled rapidly

from just below its softening point. Since the inner portion cools more slowly than the surface, it continues to contract after the surface is essentially rigid. Thus, compressive stresses develop in the surface layer with compensating tensile stresses in the interior.

Chill-tempering is capable of inducing compressive stresses up to about 20,000 psi under favorable circumstances, but is limited to relatively thick glass and simple shapes because of heat-flow problems, and its strengthening effect is permanently lost if the glass is reheated above 400°C.

New methods of inducing stress are free from these limitations, and in addition can induce much higher compressive stress, well over 100,-000 psi. The two methods of chemical tempering or armoring mentioned earlier both involve forming transparent polycrystalline layers within the surface of glasses of appropriate chemical composition. The crystallized skin, which is grown at a high temperature, has a negative thermal expansion and thus expands as it cools. The shrinking of the internal glass induces an extremely high compression of the skin, resulting in high strength. Figure 2-62 shows how this technique compares with chill-tempering.

One of the new methods employs surface-nucleated crystallization of a lithia-alumina-silica glass. The other, more complex, begins with a soda-alumina-titania-silica glass, replaces the sodium ions in the surface by lithium ions at high temperature—by immersion in a molten lithium sulfate bath, and ends with titania-nucleated crystallization of eucryptite crystals at the surface of the glass.

Other uses for ion exchange

The application of ion exchange in strengthening glass is only one of many examples of ionic and molecular diffusion and exchange, unfamiliar to most of us, that play significant parts in the manufacture and uses of glass.

The modern glass manufacturer immerses carbon electrodes into his continuous tank of molten glass and helps to heat it more uniformly by using the glass melt as a resistance; and he heats and seals glass parts by taking advantage of the ionic conductivity of glass at elevated temperatures.

The familiar red-stained chemical glassware and the yellow fog lenses of auto headlights are colored by reactions in which copper or silver ions replace an equal number of sodium ions in the glass surface at high temperature and are then reduced to colloidal metal by hydrogen or other reducing gases.

Even at room temperature, the performance of glass electrode pH meters depends on ion

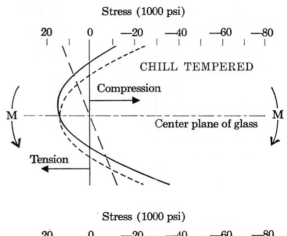

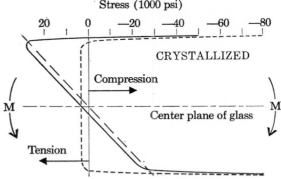

Fig. 2-62. Two ways to strengthen glass both depend on canceling tensile stress on surface by pre-stressing in compression. In diagram, dotted line is the pre-stress. Dashed line is stress created by external bending load M. Solid line shows net stress. Note that surface stress in crystallized glass stays much farther into compression range than in chill-tempered glass. (Courtesy Corning Glass Works)

exchange between hydrogen ion in the solution being tested and cations in the glass electrode immersed in it. New glass electrodes have recently appeared on the market which also measure sodium and potassium ion concentrations, and even calcium concentration determinations have been reported. One of the researchers in this field is George Eisenman, a medical doctor who is learning to interpret the structure of glass from glass electrode potentials in solutions of various cations. He hopes that glass electrodes can be used to understand the way in which cations such as sodium and potassium move through living tissues, since such movement is crucial to many metabolic processes.

New insight into nucleation

The discoveries in the photochemistry and crystallization of glass described earlier have aroused the interest of a number of scientists researching the fundamental mechanisms involved in the earliest stages of a photochemical reaction or of crystallization.

An example is the finding by R. D. Maurer of Corning that the smallest stable gold particle capable of growing into a gold crystal consists of 3 or 4 atoms; and that the smallest silver particle capable of nucleating the growth of a lithium silicate crystal is 80 angstroms in size. Such information can be valuable in testing theories as diverse as the theory of the photographic latent image, or the quantitative theory of nucleus formation in phase changes such as condensation of vapor or crystallization. Perhaps it is coincidence, perhaps not, that other investigators had previously found the "critical nucleus size" of supercooled water vapor—the smallest-size stable droplet capable of growing—to be also about 80 angstroms.

Considering the fact that every change in state of matter—condensation of vapor to a liquid or a solid, crystallization or evaporation of a liquid, formation of a new crystal from an old one, every chemical reaction— must be initiated by formation of nuclei of the new phase, it is amazing that so little fundamental research has been done on the subject of nucleation. One reason for the dearth of experimental research may be the difficulty of holding the submicroscopic nucleus still and preventing its instant alteration to a larger particle before its properties can be studied. If this is so, the new glass-ceramics may become a useful medium for this important research because the crystallization process can be initiated, controlled, or halted at will simply by cooling the glass (see Fig. 2-61).

Fig. 2-63. Lightweight mirrors for airborne and satellite-borne telescopes are constructed from fused silica because of its negligible dimensional change with varying temperature. (Courtesy Corning Glass Works)

By being able to thus examine the nuclei in situ, it becomes possible to make measurements of their number and size—a difficult procedure by condensation methods. This will permit a comparison between various theories of nucleation kinetics, since all such theories include the critical nucleus size and nucleation frequency as fundamental parameters. This is true even of Willard Gibbs' early formulation relating the thermodynamic work required to form the smallest (critical) stable particle of a new phase.

Can glass be electronically conductive?

All of the electrical charge carriers in glass have traditionally been believed to be metal ions. One disadvantage of ionic conduction in glass is that movement of ions through the glass by diffusion alters the glass composition. This means the electrical characteristics of the glass can constantly vary with time. For example, glass conducting direct current by ion exchange can become "polarized" so that the conduction process becomes blocked.

Much research is being directed toward overcoming such problems. Researchers in England (J. E. Stanworth), Holland (H. J. I. Trap and J. M. Stevels), and in the U.S. (A. David Pearson et al. of Bell Telephone Laboratories) are currently reporting electronic conductivity in a variety of glasses. Some of these contain high concentrations of vanadium pentoxide; others contain a single element additive in two or more valency states; and still others are low-melting, nonoxide glasses combining arsenic, tellurium, and iodine.

Undoubtedly there will be controversy as to whether these are truly amorphous glasses or whether the electrons originate in a crystalline component. Here again, the thorny question of molecular structure arises. It may be that an intermediate structure exists that permits electronic conductivity—a structure in which the molecules are more nearly ordered, as they are in crystals.

Strong glass is flexible

We all think of glass as being rigid and brittle. In reality it is more elastic and flexible than spring steel. The reason that we have not been able to use this valuable property, except in glass fiber, is again the low strength. When we have mastered the strength problem, we have automatically gained the important bonus of flexibility and elasticity. Glass springs, flexible windows, and other manifestations of these properties, are within sight. Already, tempered glass springs have been flexed for millions of cycles without the work-hardening or fatigue that occurs in metals.

While glass is elastic, it is completely non-malleable and nonductile except at high temperatures. Ductility implies an irreversible yield or flow under stress, lead metal being a good example of ductile material. If we could give glass a little ductility, it would help a great deal in decreasing the complete, "catastrophic" nature of the break, as well as preventing very high local stresses from building up without relief by flow.

So far, there seems to be no practical solution to this problem. It may be that current work by J. A. Pask at the University of California and others on the ductility of single crystals of the alkali halides and magnesium oxide will shed some light on this problem, particularly with respect to the glass ceramics. However, the step from single crystals to polycrystalline materials is sure to be great.

Oldest glass gets new research

Fused silica is a one-component glass, simply silicon dioxide, and as such is one of the simplest and oldest glasses in existence. Traditionally, it has been made by melting quartz sand, but many modern applications for this material require a purity and homogeneity beyond that provided by this simple method.

High-purity silica can now be made by high-temperature hydrolysis of silicon tetrachloride. The products of this reaction are pure silicon dioxide and hydrochloride acid. The silica condenses out continuously as a growing disk of optical-quality, amorphous glass. The HCl passes off as vapor.

Where is this improved material utilized? Recent research has shown that the small gas molecules of helium and hydrogen, normally blocked by glass, diffuse readily through high silica glass. Hence, serious thought is being given to use of such glass as molecular sieves for separation of helium from natural gas. Hydrogen diffuses more slowly than its molecular size would suggest, the reason being that it reacts chemically with the glass.

High-purity silica crucibles are employed in manufacture of pure single-crystal silicon for transistors. The same high-purity material is the heat of acoustical delay lines used in computers, because its attenuation of sound waves is uniquely low. Thus, an electrical signal can start a sound wave bounding around inside a specially shaped piece of silica until the acoustic energy is needed to generate a second signal. This high-purity silica glass is also transparent to the whole optical spectrum from the vacuum ultraviolet (185 millimicrons) to the near infrared, and is not discolored—as many glasses are, including less pure silica—by exposure to high-energy radiation, so that it is useful in special optical instruments employing light in the uv range.

Further reading

If your knowledge of the subject is, like most glass, amorphous and not crystallized, it might make sense to start your study by going to the movies. Corning has prepared a color 16-mm film, "The Nature of Glass," for technical audiences, that runs 37 minutes, and can be obtained on loan free from Association Films Inc., 347 Madison Ave., New York. For an introduction to the history of glass, you might see Freda Diamond's *The Story of Glass* (Harcourt, 1953, $3.75). For detailed information on this aspect, consult the very complete library at the Corning Museum of Glass, Corning, New York.

Useful data on many glass formulations will be found in two basic references: *Properties of Glass* by Morey (Reinhold, 1954, $16.50) and *Glass Engineering Handbook* by Shand (McGraw-Hill, 1958, $10). A most detailed treatment of glass structure appears in a sequence of four papers by Condon under the general title "Physics of the Glassy State" in *Am. J. Phys.*, **22** (1954), as follows: (I) Constitution and Structure; (II) The Transformation Range; (III) Strength of Glass; and (IV) Radiation-Sensitive Glasses. A complete summary on glass-ceramics is the chapter by Stookey and Maurer, "Catalyzed Crystallization of Glass," in *Progress in Ceramic Science*, Vol. 1, edited by Burke (Pergamon, 1961, $10). For a basic book on crystal formation, see *Crystallization—Theory and Practice* by Van Hook (Reinhold, 1961, $12.50).

For the most recent developments in glass, you should get the proceedings of the 6th International Glass Congress (held in Washington, July 1962): *Advances in Glass Technology*, edited by Pearce and available now (Plenum, 1962, $21). Proceedings of the 5th Glass Congress in 1959 may be obtained by writing to Dr. H. Trier, Secretary, Verlag der Deutschen Glastechnischen Gesellschaft, Frankfurt-am-Main ($18). On glass-ceramics, valuable recent papers will be found in the proceedings of the April 1961 Symposium on Nucleation and Crystallization, published by the American Ceramic Society, Columbus, Ohio.

STARCH

by Sheldon A. Buckler and Felix J. Germino *

IN BRIEF: *Every so often, industry's haste in adopting the revolutionary new materials coming out of chemical and metallurgical laboratories makes waste—it throws out highly useful natural materials. Such seems to be the case with starch. Recently, however, new appreciation of good basic properties, new chemical modifications, and new genetic approaches have brought starch to renewed usefulness. For example, dialdehyde starch is moving strongly into paper treating, replacing melamine-formaldehyde resins. Combined with ethylene glycol, starch makes the backbone of an interesting rigid urethane foam. Amylose, one of the two fractions of natural starch, makes a transparent film for packaging which could displace cellophane in some of its major applications. Coupled with edibility, price advantages, and a wealth of handling experience, the future for starch could well come up smelling like fresh bread.— H.W.M.*

■ Starch, one of nature's universal building blocks, has been used for centuries as an industrial polymer. Its organic, long-chain molecules are still almost unrivaled in their symmetry, even by the latest developments of the plastics industry. With the traditional contempt bred by familiarity, however, it has suffered neglect over recent years, as newer, more glamorous synthetics come forth in continuing succession. Still, there has been enough appreciation of the unique position of starch in some industries to keep it from being completely engulfed, and now competitive pressures and a new awareness of the possibilities available through chemical modification have aroused a new interest in this age-old material.

Although starch occurs in the seeds, roots, and tubers of plants grown in almost all parts of the world, its chemical structure varies little from source to source. There is variation in the size of the granules, from 5 μ average diameter in rice starch up to as high as 100 μ in potato starch. Corn, the favored source of starch in the U.S., has granules which average 15 μ in diameter. Chemically, starch is composed of a mixture of two polymers, amylose and amylopectin. Each is based on closed-ring anhydroglucose

* Sheldon A. Buckler and Felix J. Germino worked together in the equipment and processes side of starch research at the American Machine and Foundry Co. laboratories in Springdale, Connecticut. Since preparing this article, Buckler has moved to the Polaroid Corp., Cambridge, Massachusetts.

units, similar to those in ordinary sugar molecules, "condensed" into long chains as shown in Fig. 2-64. The variations in properties of these two polymers result from differences in the way these units are arranged in space— amylose is a long, linear chain of anhydroglucose units, while amylopectin is branched, its structural model in the figure looks like a bush. In ordinary corn, these polymers are present in a three-to-one ratio of amylopectin to amylose.

The molecular weight of the polymers in starch also varies from botanical source to source. In corn, amylose runs from about 40,000 to over 3 million, while the amylopectin goes up from 1 million to perhaps as high as 80 million, although there is no general agreement on the actual value. In potato starch, the amylose has a substantially higher molecular weight, but that of the amylopectin is in about the same range.

One of the most obvious advantages enjoyed by starch is its price—about 5¢ per pound, less than half that of the cheapest synthetic polymer. This results partly from its agricultural source, partly from the efficiency of the wet-milling process by which it is extracted, and partly from the tremendous volume produced. Of the 5½ billion pounds of starch produced in this country last year, more than a third went into industrial applications in the paper and textile fields, and in areas in the food field where its edibility is helpful but not an important nutritional factor. This volume is actually more than that of the polyethylene produced annually. The balance goes into food uses, with conversion to sugar (dextrose) and syrup leading, and into food-related areas.

Paper a big customer

In the industrial field, the paper industry uses starch to the tune of one billion pounds per year. The traditional application is as size, to fill the pores in the paper and make it hold together better, imparting better strength and surface properties at minimum cost. The starch is added at the "wet end" of the paper machine, while the pulp is in very dilute form. Actually, most of the natural starch added this way goes right on past the paper fibers, and out into the waste water, complicating the disposal problem. (As the starch breaks down in the stream or pond, it takes up oxygen from the water, suffocating any fish or vegetation present.) Two approaches are now being investi-

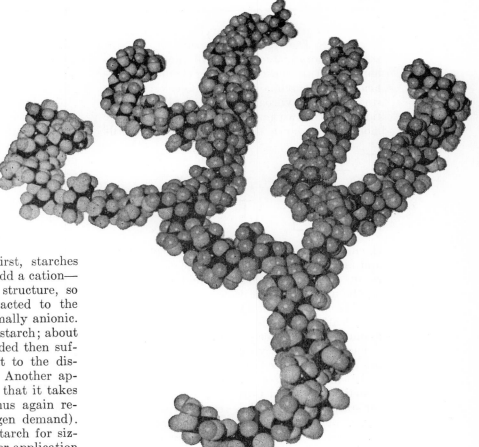

gated to solve this problem: First, starches are being chemically modified to add a cation—positively charged ion—to their structure, so they will be more strongly attracted to the fibers of the paper, which are normally anionic. This increases the retention of the starch; about one third of the usual amount added then suffices, and the amount flushed out to the disposal area is drastically reduced. Another approach is to modify the starch so that it takes up less oxygen as it degrades, thus again reducing the BOD (biological oxygen demand).

Nothing really competes with starch for sizing paper; however, there is another application in the paper industry where a modified starch is now displacing some of the synthetic resins used for adding wet strength. Traditionally these have been urea-formaldehyde or melamine-formaldehyde resins. One of their disadvantages has been that they are *too* good; papers treated with these materials keep much of their strength even when soaked in water for long periods, making it almost impossible to salvage or dispose of them simply.

In paper mills, for example, cuttings, waste, and off-specification products, called "broke," are normally dumped back into the pulping tank to be re-pulped, to recoup some of the processing expense. Wet-strength papers cannot be so treated, and must be disposed of in other ways. Also, wet-strength treated face and bathroom tissues don't disperse when disposed of, leading to serious problems in sewage disposal plants.

Now, so-called dialdehyde starch is being used increasingly for wet-strength treatment. It provides good strength under short-time water exposure, but breaks down rapidly under prolonged immersion. This results from the difference in the "crosslinking" bonds in dialdehyde starch and, say, melamine-formaldehyde resin (see "Tailor-Making Plastics," page 235). In melamine-formaldehyde, the crosslinks are strong, covalent bonds which are stable in

Fig. 2-64. Chemically, starch is made up of anhydroglucose units (drawing) hooked together in chains. In amylose, the chains are long and straight; in amylopectin, they look more like the bushy molecular model above, built under G. V. Caesar's direction. (Courtesy Fisher Scientific Co.)

water. In dialdehyde starch, the chemical bonds are termed "hemiacetal," and are more susceptible to water attack. In time, they tend to revert to the free aldehyde starch plus paper.

An additional possible "fringe benefit" of using dialdehyde starch as a wet-strength agent is its softer "hand" over melamine-formaldehyde in wet-strength paper towels. The starch seems to produce less roughness than the conventional crosslinked wet strength agents. Where water *resistance* is required in a paper in addition to wet strength melamine-formaldehyde is still without competitor.

Economical production of dialdehyde starch

resulted from a ten-year development program at the U.S. Department of Agriculture's Utilization Laboratory in Peoria, Ill., and it is perhaps one of the most interesting chemical modifications of starch now running. Cleavage of the ring in the anhydroglucose unit, and its oxidation to form two reactive groups on the same molecule as shown below, provides a versatile

$$\left[\begin{array}{c} CH_2OH \\ C-O \\ H \quad OH \quad H \\ C \quad C-O- \\ H \quad OH \end{array} \right]_x +HIO_4 \rightarrow \left[\begin{array}{c} CH_2OH \\ C-O \\ H \quad H \\ C \quad C-O- \\ O \quad O \end{array} \right]_x +HIO_3+H_2O$$

chemical compound from a cheap precursor, and many other interesting applications should result. For example, its crosslinking properties can be used to harden protein glues and photographic emulsions; it can also be used for tanning leather, and as a wet-strength agent in manufactured tobacco sheet.

During the past year the Peoria laboratory has also announced a new chemical process which may prove a major boon for the construction field, and provide a high volume use for starch. Here, starch is reacted with ethylene glycol or other polyalcohols, to provide the backbone for rigid polyurethane foams. Foams made from these materials and propylene oxide

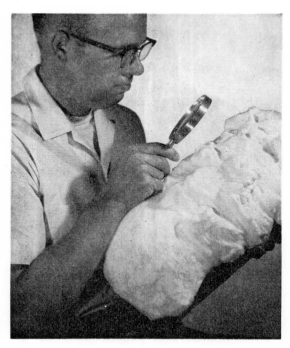

Fig. 2-65. Foams made from starch compare with commercial foams in density and crush resistance. They were developed by USDA's F. H. Otey (above), Bonnie Zagoren, and C. L. Mehltretter. (Courtesy USDA Northern Utilization Research Lab)

can then be used in insulation or construction applications. Successful development of this process would make an interesting marriage between starch, the traditional material, and the synthetic alcohols, oxides, and isocyanates.

Another application of starch which bears watching is its use in forming microporous plastic materials—materials which will hold back liquids but transmit vapors. Here, starch granules are mixed into a hot plastic mass such as nylon, polypropylene, or polystyrene; the plastic is then milled and sheeted out normally. Once cooled, the sheet with its entrapped starch is soaked in boiling water to make the granules swell. Then they are leached out completely with sulfuric acid, leaving voids in the plastic.

The presence of these micropores endows the sheet goods with the special transmission properties, and could solve problems like the plastic raincoats which now leave you wet from condensed perspiration while protecting you from the rain outside. Microporous plastic can also be used as a filter material or dielectric membrane.

Let's break it down

So far we've talked only about starch as an entity, however modified. Let's now take a look at the two constituents separately, to see whether there isn't promise of their use independent of each other. The presence of two fractions has been recognized since the turn of the century, but it wasn't until the early 1940's that T. J. Schock of Corn Products Co. first separated the linear, chain-like amylose from its compatriot, branched, bush-shaped amylopectin. His laboratory technique called for heating the starch to about 90°C to dissolve it completely, then adding butyl alcohol. This formed an insoluble complex with amylose, leaving the amylopectin in solution. While this process was too expensive for commercial use, it did provide laboratory quantities for investigation. As might be expected from its geometry, amylose proved to have substantially different properties from the mixture contained in starch. It is much less sensitive to water, for example, to the point where it is insoluble under ordinary conditions. It also possesses far superior film-forming properties.

Before significant industrial interest could be aroused, however, a practical source of amylose had to be developed. Two approaches—one through chemistry, the other based on genetics—have now borne fruit. A practical process for separating amylose from potato starches has been developed by Muetgeert, Bus, and Hiemstra of the Netherlands Organization for Applied Scientific Research (TNO) in Delft, Holland. Also, Etheridge, Lippincott, Mac-

Donald, and Wagoner of the A. E. Staley Manufacturing Co., Decatur, Ill., have a process that accomplishes the same thing with cornstarch. The Dutch method involves a "salting out" process, in which the amylose fraction is selectively precipitated from hot aqueous starch solutions by adding inorganic salts such as magnesium sulfate. This operates on somewhat the same basis as the freshman chemistry experiment for decreasing the solubility of table salt in water by adding alcohol, causing the salt to precipitate out.

In the Staley process, starch is held at elevated temperatures with a carefully controlled time-temperature cycle until the amylose molecules congeal into large clumps. These then precipitate out, leaving the nonagglomerated amylopectin behind in solution. Pilot plants in both countries are now producing amylose in large quantities.

Quo vadis residue?

One of the big problems in both processes, or indeed in any process based on extracting 25% amylose from 75% amylopectin, is what to do with the residue. This problem has not yet been solved. Amylopectin can, of course, be used as a precursor for sweeteners, just like starch, but for this end use it can command only the 5¢ price paid for natural starch. Under these conditions, the entire cost of processing must be borne by the amylose. If a profitable use for refined amylopectin could be found, it would help reduce the cost of the amylose. So far, few are known.

Corn breeders have attempted to solve the problem genetically with considerable success. Their goal: hybrid corn containing 100% amylose starch. First hybridization attempts produced a corn whose starch was 50–60% amylose. A substantial crop of this hybrid was grown in the U.S. in 1962 under the name of amylomaize, and its high-amylose starch found a ready market as a size for glass fibers. Some changes in the wet-milling process were needed to handle the corn, because of the lower solubility of the starch. More recently, a hybrid containing nearly 80% amylose has been developed; at the moment this appears to be the upper limit breeders can attain with available genetic material. However, even at this level, too much amylopectin remains for some end uses. In addition, the molecular weight of the amylose in these hybrids is somewhat reduced compared with that extracted from ordinary corn, and this reduction affects some of the desirable attributes of the amylose polymer. Oddly enough, a 100% amylopectin cornstarch has existed for some years; it comes from a strain called "waxy maize"; both "Maizey's"

look alike, to the point where strict segregation must be practiced from seed to mill, to keep the crops isolated and identifiable.

Even if you assume that no more profitable outlet for amylopectin will be found, however, it seems reasonable to expect that amylose will ultimately be available at prices around 15¢ per pound. While this is three times the price of ordinary starch, it is still in the lower cost range of the synthetic organic polymers with which it will compete. Where then do the attractive possibilities lie?

What'll we do with it?

As might be expected, starch producers are actively investigating amylose in applications where starch itself has experienced competitive pressures in performance and cost, especially from polyvinyl alcohol and carboxymethylcellulose. These include permanent textile finishes and paper coatings. However, they are directing a major part of their effort at a totally new use, that of packaging film.

Amylose can be formed into clear, tough, edible films that have very good "barrier" properties towards oxygen, grease, and various flavors and aromas. These features combine with good low-temperature physical properties such as toughness and strength. Amylose film is thus an attractive candidate for freezer wrap, for use in food packaging where protection from atmospheric oxygen is important, or in the development of edible convenience food packets. Amylose-wrapped frozen vegetables, for example, can be dropped into boiling water, package and all; the package dissolves, adding only a little edible starch to the recipe. Bakeries can prepackage their nutrient additives in amylose packets and drop the whole thing in at mixing time.

Amylose film, like cellophane (derived from its chemical cousin cellulose), has the disadvantages of high moisture permeability and a tendency to get brittle when exposed to arid conditions. However, these defects can be remedied, at least in part, by using moisture-proof coatings like nitrocellulose and suitable plasticizers such as glycerine, both now used with cellophane films.

Also being investigated is the use of amylose coatings for edible encapsulation of foods which are friable or which would benefit from atmospheric protection. In Japan, for instance, candy gum drops are being coated to reduce their stickiness.

You name it, you make it

All three basic processes of the film-making art—casting, extrusion, and regeneration—have been investigated with amylose at the laboratory stage and beyond. At the moment, casting and extrusion show the greatest promise. In contrast, cellophane manufacture from cellulose requires regeneration involving the use of expensive chemical solubilization as its film-forming process, since cellophane lacks the necessary solubility or thermoplastic properties for other film-forming methods. Amylose possesses adequate solubility and thermoplasticity to permit the use of the cheaper casting and extrusion processes.

Lest the last statement sound too simple, let's admit quickly that amylose cannot be melted. How then can it be cast or extruded? The answer—add water or plasticizers. Although amylose is insoluble in water up to the boiling point at atmospheric pressure, it forms concentrated solutions readily at 140°C and higher under pressure. These solutions remain stable for long periods of time when the pressure is relieved, if the solution temperature is maintained at 80°C or so, providing the basis for the casting process. Amylose film can thus be prepared continuously by pumping an amylose-water slurry into a heated pressure zone, followed by casting onto a moving belt and drying.

When combined with plasticizers such as glycerine or sorbitol, amylose becomes thermoplastic enough to extrude as a film or in other shapes. Best results have been obtained when substantial amounts of water are added as a

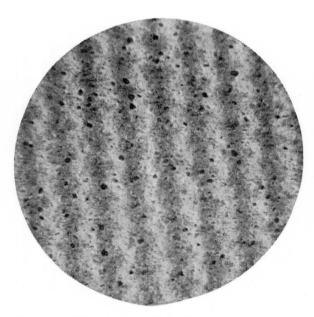

Fig. 2-66. Water-proof plastic film contains micropores that allow water vapor to pass, stop liquid phase. Microphotograph shows surface of film, made by Reeves Bros., magnified 50X. (Courtesy Reeves Bros.)

coplasticizer; the water must be removed by subsequent drying on heated drums or by other means. Figure 2-66 shows a container made of extruded film by this process at the Midwest Research Institute in Kansas City, Mo., who developed it for the corn-growing state of Nebraska. One disadvantage associated with extrusion is the increase in gas permeability of the film resulting from the relatively large amounts of plasticizer required. Nevertheless, the process is promising enough to warrant building a pilot plant.

The physical chemistry of amylose in solution and in the gel and solid states is still largely a mystery, although it is a subject of great fundamental and industrial importance. There is no clear picture of the state of amylose in solution; different kinds of evidence from light scattering and intrinsic viscosity measurements point to structures such as a rigid rod, random coil, or a more ordered helical coil. In any case, solutions of amylose tend to undergo the process of retrogradation or precipitation, familiar to all who have watched gravy or wallpaper paste set up, resulting from intramolecular association of the polymer molecules. The initial grouping takes place through hydrogen bonding between the hydroxyl groups; if they are "blocked" by chemical modification, agglomeration can be delayed or prevented. This agglomeration otherwise leads to a more ordered gel stage, which then can be dried to a solid crystalline state.

Solid amylose exists in at least two crystalline modifications, as well as an amorphous form. The more stable crystal is called the B state; its structure corresponds to a collapsed helix or an extended linear chain, as shown in Fig. 2-67. Slurries of this crystalline form must be heated in an autoclave to produce a water solution. The second crystalline state corresponds to a full helical coil form; it is called the V state, from the German Verkleisterung, or "pasted." Again appealing to freshman chemistry, this form of amylose is responsible for the blue color produced in the starch test for iodine. The colored product is an inclusion complex of iodine molecules in the lumen, or hole, of the helical V amylose molecule. This physical state bears a striking similarity to the helical configurations of the chemically unrelated proteins; it results from similar stabilizing hydrogen-bond interactions at each turn of the coil. This helical form of amylose is soluble in cold or hot water when freshly prepared, but crystals stored under moist conditions tend to revert to the B condition.

Chemical modification of amylose to produce derivatives which will both dissolve in cold

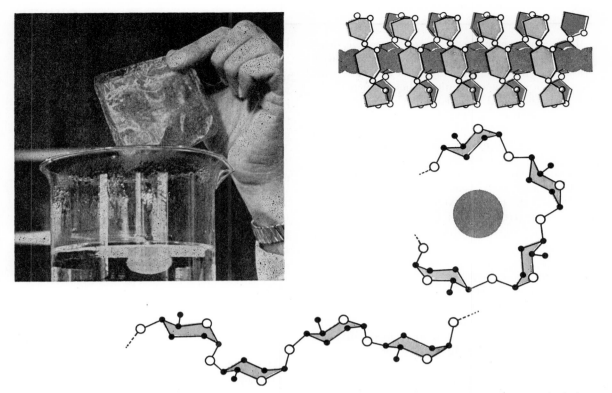

Fig. 2-67. *Amylose V molecule takes form of helix (top). As helix forms it entraps inclusions such as iodine (as in starch test for iodine). Middle drawing is molecule "end-on" with inclusion compound. In amylose B (bottom), helix is stretched out. Photo shows edible-film food package made from amylose being dropped into boiling water. (Courtesy Midwest Research Institute)*

water and then gel has been unsuccessful. Recently, however, an amorphous physical form was produced by drying amylose very rapidly. This amorphous material is readily water-soluble at all temperatures. The solutions obtained gel as rapidly as solutions formed by crystalline amylose or starch and are, therefore, useful in formulating instant puddings, or possibly water-dispersible packaging films.

Complexes on a molecular scale

In recent years, physical chemists in both academic and food fields have looked with interest at complexes produced by adding organic compounds to amylose solutions. They have found that as amylose forms into a helix in a solution, the size of the lumen will vary to accommodate molecules of different sizes, unlike the lumen of other inclusion hosts such as clathrates. *V* complexes with a wide range of organic molecules, including aliphatic and aromatic hydrocarbons, halocarbons, alcohols, aldehydes, ketones, and carboxylic acids have been prepared and studied.

As far back as 1903, the German chemist and bacteriologist Franz Schardinger treated starch with an extract of *Bacillus macerans*, one of the organisms responsible for food spoilage. From the brew he isolated com-

pounds possessing a puzzling combination of properties and composition. In time, the structures of these compounds were worked out and they proved, to the delight of organic chemists, to be large rings of anhydroglucose units joined end to end. The smallest of these compounds, the α-Schardinger dextrin or cyclic dextrin, contains six glucose units as shown in Fig. 2-68. The β and γ dextrins contain seven and eight glucose units respectively.

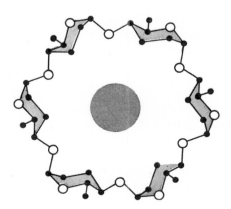

Fig. 2-68. *When amylose helix breaks, coils rejoin to form cyclic dextrins with six, seven, or eight anhydroglucose units. Dextrins can then be used to "trap" compounds.*

Like amylose in the V state, the cyclic dextrins form inclusion complexes, but of greater stability. Since inclusion by the cyclic dextrins is possible with a molecule rather than a crystal, as is the usual case, complex formation can occur in solution as well as in the solid state. This has led to investigations of the catalytic properties of the cyclic dextrins viewed as the binding site of a model enzyme system. The range of organic and inorganic compounds, including gases, which can be complexed by one or more of the cyclic dextrins is very extensive, but each dextrin takes in a narrower spectrum of sizes and shapes, as determined by the size of its own lumen.

On the practical side, recently issued patents point to an interest in using these picturesque starch derivatives for entrapping and retaining delicate flavor and aroma bodies in processed foods, tobacco products, and even chewing gum. There is also some possibility of using cyclic dextrins in separation processes much like those based on molecular sieves. The dextrins would be used in filter beds, much as the Zeolite molecular sieves are now used. Recovery of the entrapped body is simple: hot water releases it almost instantly.

The cyclic dextrins and amylose V are related in a definite sense. We can imagine that the enzyme from *B. macerans* cut the amylose helix at each turn, and rejoined the ends to give ring compounds with the same repeating glucose unit as the parent. This can be termed a "trans-glycosylation" reaction. Although we know of no way to do this with simple chemicals, the enzymatic process has been developed as a practical source of the cyclic dextrins in at least three major laboratories.

All told, starch still retains a number of interesting challenges and is showing remarkable vitality for an old timer. Given enough time, it may yet become as widespread in the worlds of science, technology, and commerce as it is in the kingdom of nature.

Further reading

There are two good reviews on the fundamental chemistry and technology of starch, as well as its traditional applications, but they are both out of print: *Starch and Its Derivatives* by Radley (3rd Ed., Wiley, 1954) and *Chemistry and Industry of Starch* by Kerr (2nd Ed., Academic Press, 1950).

There is really no comparable work in print now, but Whistler of Purdue is preparing a three-volume work for publication in 1965. There is a good section on starch in *Water-Soluble Resins*, edited by Davidson and Sittig (Reinhold, 1962, $7.50), and you'll also find out a good deal about some of its competitors such as polyvinyl alcohol, carboxymethylcellulose, and polyvinylpyrrolidone. *Industrial Gums (Polysaccharides and Their Derivatives)*, edited by Whistler (Academic Press, 1959, $25), puts starch in another context, with other natural products like gum ghatti, locust bean gum, and "lesser known seaweed extracts."

If you're specifically interested in fractionation, there is a good run-down in the 1961 *Advances in Carbohydrate Chemistry* (Academic Press, Vol. 16, $14.50). Wolfrom edits these annual volumes; Vol. 12 (1957, $14) includes the first paper on the cyclic dextrins. Amylose V complexes were first described by French, Pulley, and Whelan in *Die Stärke* **15**, No. 10, dialdehyde starch first by Dronch and Mehltretter in the *Journal of the American Chemical Society* **74**, 552 (1952).

Interest in the field of natural polymers has now grown to the point where a brand new bimonthly professional journal has been established, called *Biopolymers* and edited by Murray Goodman of Brooklyn Poly (Interscience, $36/yr.).

For those who like to go to annual meetings, there are two of interest: the Starch Roundtable, sponsored by the Corn Industries Research Foundation (1001 Connecticut Ave., N.W., Washington, D.C.) and the Gordon Research Conference on Carbohydrate Chemistry.

ADHESIVES

by Louis H. Sharpe, Harold Schonhorn, and Charles J. Lynch*

IN BRIEF: *Although no one knows for sure yet, it's beginning to appear that adhesives stick for a ridiculously simple reason: intimate molecular contact. It comes to this: Put any two materials close enough together and they will*

* Louis H. Sharpe and Harold Schonhorn work with adhesives at Bell Telephone Laboratories, Murray Hill, New Jersey, where Sharpe is Supervisor of the adhesives group. Charles J. Lynch is Associate Editor of *International Science and Technology*.

adhere. Adhesion needs no chemical bond, no electrostatic force, no mechanical dovetailing. Recently, this simple theory has drawn strong support from a series of experiments demonstrating that there is a natural adhesive force between any two materials—even materials no stickier than polyethylene or Teflon. The trick is in knowing how to take advantage of that natural force.

This theory leads logically to a somewhat

surprising result. Because the forces between molecules are universal, it turns out that the forces of adhesion between two materials will always be stronger than the forces of cohesion in one or the other of them. Therefore, a properly made adhesive joint never fails "in adhesion," it always fails in the bulk of the adhesive or the bulk of the material it is adhering to.

During the time this theory has been maturing, the technology of adhesives has come a long way, principally through the development of synthetic polymer adhesives. Modern polymer adhesives can bond most materials, often more strongly than with rivets or bolts.—C.J.L.

■ If you or I had invented the world, chances are we would have botched the job. For eventually we would get around to inventing a way to hold the solid stuff of our world together. This is too all-encompassing a job to entrust to the selective interactions of chemical bonds. So it is likely that we would cook up some kind of "universal intermolecular force" and let it go at that. But in our haste to keep the world from falling apart, we would no doubt forget to invent some means, at the same time, to keep these universal forces of adhesion in check. That would be disastrous: Before our homemade world was ten seconds old, all its moving parts would lock solid, stuck fast with the universal glue of our own inventiveness.

Now nature has been somewhat less reckless than we would have been, and somewhat more cunning too. She did invent a "universal intermolecular force" to keep the solid matter of her world together, but she made it an exquisitely refined and well-controlled force. Not that it's a weak one; it is, after all, the force that holds the atoms of a steel building together at the places where they are not held together by covalent, metallic, or other chemical bonds, and it often accounts for more than 80% of the binding forces in solids.

But, somehow, it doesn't jam things up. Even though it acts between any two molecules or atoms when they are close together, and even though it is never turned off, still the railroad wheels of the world do not weld to their rails and the hockey pucks of the world do not freeze to the rink. Nor, more to the point, can the broken coffee cups of the world be mended by simply pushing the ragged edges of the two mating pieces together, even when they are pushed together so tightly that the line of fracture is all but invisible; not the slightest vestige of a healing force is apparent. The intermolecular forces are still there, but all the pushing in the world (King's horses and King's men included) apparently does not make the parts stick.

In fact, the self-adhesive force between two solid pieces of most materials is so small that we usually have to use an intervening material —an adhesive—when we want two solid materials to stick. Now the paradox in all this is that the thing that makes the adhesive work is apparently the very same force that held the coffee cup together before it was broken: its cohesive intermolecular force.

How does nature get by with such an on-again/off-again force? That question has been puzzling adhesive chemists for a long time. No one yet knows precisely why some materials stick together while others don't. We (meaning the two of us at Bell Labs) are beginning to believe that the key to it all lies in a statement made in the last paragraph: that "the thing that makes the adhesive work is *apparently* the same force . . . [as the] cohesive force." This statement derives from a theory of adhesion—called the adsorption theory—which is steadily gaining favor today. Because we are confident that this theory represents the broadest view of the adhesion phenomenon—a confidence supported by our recent experiments—it is the theory we will discuss at length here.

Glue by any other name . . .

Trying to understand why things stick has importance far beyond the adhesive industry. Adhesion is what keeps the paint from falling off your house. It is ultimately the reason why things get dirty, and it also accounts for the invention of the aircraft deicer. Adhesion is one of the sources of friction (or "sticktion" if you like), yet it is also what causes a friction-cheating film of lubricant to cling to bearing surfaces.

Today adhesives themselves are doing things they have never done before. Within the last few years metal-to-metal adhesives have been developed to the point where they are replacing rivets, bolts, and other forms of fasteners in even the most demanding applications. There are few materials that cannot be bonded today.

Suppose we return to that broken coffee cup. If a man had set about mending that cup five or ten years ago, undoubtedly he would have reached for a tube of cellulose household cement or, if he were feeling more ambitious, might have mixed up a batch of some kind of animal glue suitable for crockery. (We called one "cement" and the other "glue." Strictly speaking, cements are materials made when rubbers or thermoplastic resins are dispersed in a volatile solvent, while glue is the stuff made from horses' hoofs and other such natural proteins. "Paste" and "mucilage" are other labels that refer to particular kinds of stickum. They're all adhesives.)

Today, our coffee-cup mender might very

well choose one of the two-part epoxy adhesives in place of a more traditional material. If he did, he would probably do so with the idea that the epoxy would form a stronger joint than the other types. And, if he felt obliged to explain such things to himself, he would probably tell himself that the joint is stronger because the epoxy "sticks better" to the coffee-cup edges.

The epoxy may, in fact, "stick better," but the interpretation of this will depend on which theory of adhesion you choose. One theory, for example, will tell you that adhesion occurs because of a chemical bond between the adhesive and the material it's sticking to. Another will say that there is an electrostatic attraction between the two, or that there is a chemical similarity and a diffusion of one material into the other. Still another theory will explain that the adhesive penetrates re-entrant crevices and cavities in the surface and therefore clings by means of a strictly mechanical interlock.

It is our view that any or all of these effects may occur in specific instances but that none of the theories is sufficiently universal to explain all cases of adhesion. Adhesion, it seems to us and probably to a majority of today's adhesive scientists, is in the broad sense a matter of physical adsorption—an attraction mechanism inherent in any surface. Physical adsorption is the mechanism that holds molecules of gas to such unreactive materials as gold or Teflon. Indeed, it is probably physical adsorption that first draws molecules of gas to more active surfaces, although this may be followed by chemical adsorption. (See Color Fig. 10 for surface free energy comparisons.)

Forces—at close range

In physical adsorption, molecules are drawn together by the so-called van der Waals forces. These are a collection of secondary valence forces, some of which depend on the chemical species of the two adhering molecules. There is, however, a universal component of the van der Waals forces, a force that acts between molecules regardless of their chemistry. This is the London dispersion force—nature's equivalent of that "universal intermolecular force" we invented at the beginning of this article— first recognized by Fritz London in the mid-1930's.

Dispersion forces arise because the instantaneous distribution of electrons around an atom is never evenly balanced but is always distorted, causing the atom to have a net polarity. Because of this, all atoms have, in effect, a north and a south pole, and they are drawn together through the mutual attraction of their opposite poles. The atoms must be very close; it is calculated that the force field diminishes as the seventh power of the distance between atoms.

Dispersion forces are weak, as interatomic forces go; on the average, they may have an energy of about 1 kcal/mole while the average chemical bond has an energy of around 100 kcal/mole. Still, they are sufficient to explain the strength of adhesive joints.

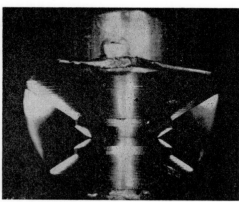

Fig. 2-69. Even two solid surfaces will adhere if they can get close enough together. This copper specimen, fractured in a vacuum, was rejoined by simply pressing the broken faces back together. The experiments, part of a program to study cold welding in outer space, were performed by J. L. Ham of National Research Corp. (Courtesy National Research Corp.)

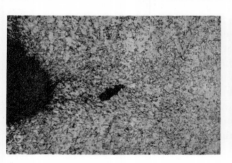
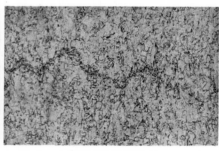
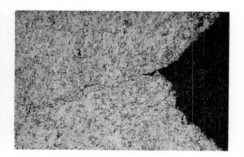

The evidence of that is that they are also the forces of cohesion. In a long-chain polymer, strong chemical bonds hold the links of the chain together, but dispersion forces hold the chains to each other. In a steel rod, strong metallic bonds link many atoms of the metal, but dispersion forces hold the rod together along crystal boundaries and at faults in the crystals. Dispersion forces are the weakest links in any solid material—and are therefore the forces we pull against when we try to pull the stuff apart.

This suggests something important about adhesive joints: the adhesive attraction between a cohesively strong material and a cohesively weak material will always be stronger than the weak material. If we could somehow make a piece of copper adhere to a piece of steel, the dispersion bonds between the copper atoms would always break before the bonds between the copper and the steel. This appears reasonable when one reflects that the strength of the bond between molecules of material *A* and molecules of material *B* might well be the geometric mean of the strengths of the *A-A* and the *B-B* bonds. And more rigorous theory supports this simple intuition. Theoretically, it appears, the weaker material will always fail before the bond between the materials fails. (Color Fig. 11 shows such a joint between polyethylene and copper.)

The world is an adhesive

It does sound as if this principle violates experience. Suppose we press a piece of steel against a piece of glass and then pull them apart. We seem to be insisting that the two materials will not separate, once they have been in contact, or that if they do separate we will either leave a film of glass on the steel or a film of steel on the glass.

Of course the catch is that the steel and the glass may never have been in contact—for any of several reasons. In the first place, the steel may be covered with a coating of oil or a layer of oxide. When the two solids are brought together, the contaminating layers rather than the steel touch the glass. They adhere, of course, as will any material, but they are weak and they fail in cohesion—leaving a bit of the contaminant stuck to the glass. Strictly speaking, this is not poor adhesion, it is the failure of a layer of weak material between the two stronger materials.

Now another reason the glass does not stick to the steel might be that the surfaces are not smooth. Although a piece of fire-polished soft glass seems to have a very smooth surface, electron micrographs show a roughness of about 400 Å, peak to peak. The actual area of contact, and of adhesion, is tiny.

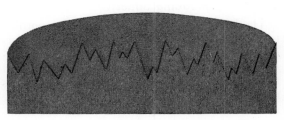

Fig. 2-70. *Unless an adhesive spreads, roughness present on any real surface may prevent the extensive and intimate intermolecular contact necessary for a strong adhesive joint.*

As long as we're exploding popular myths, we may as well point out that the adsorption theory of adhesion completely destroys the popular notion that adhesives are necessarily sticky, clinging, tacky substances. Any material is, at least potentially, an adhesive; some are just better than others. Water, for example, is a fine adhesive; it flows nicely and therefore achieves a close molecular contact with the substrate. Unfortunately, its shear strength is too low when it is liquid and its ductility is too

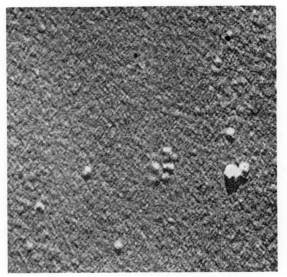

Fig. 2-71. *Even an apparently smooth surface is rough. This is an electron micrograph of a fire-polished soft glass surface. The small-scale roughness is on the order of 300 to 400 Å. (Courtesy Bell Telephone Laboratories)*

low when it is frozen. Besides, it evaporates. Copper is also an adhesive, but it is limited to joining materials that can stand copper's high melting temperature; the process is known as brazing.

Even polyethylene, a most vexatious and slippery material, is an adhesive. In fact, it is potentially a very good adhesive if it is handled properly. We have formed many joints using polyethylene as an adhesive, as we will describe further on (Color Fig. 8).

Under the spreading adhesive

The key to strong adhesive joints, according to this theory, is extensive and intimate intermolecular contact. Recalling that the dispersion force diminishes as the seventh power of the distance, it is clear that the two materials must approach within a few angstroms if they are to adhere. Although we have ignored it until now, the only way to achieve this extensive and intimate contact is to make one of the materials fluid during some phase of the bonding process.

For best joint strength, however, the adhesive must be more than fluid; it must also spread. Water, for example, is fluid, but it will not spread on polyethylene. An adhesive that does not spread will not flow into the surface crevices very easily, will simply bridge across the tops of the surface mountains, and will consequently form a weak joint.

The matter of spreading has been studied and discussed for many years. It turns out that it is possible to predict whether a liquid will spread spontaneously on a solid. It comes down to the old matter of adhesion and cohesion: If the molecules of the liquid stick to the solid better than they do to themselves, the liquid will spread. Or, more precisely, if the work of adhesion exceeds the work of cohesion, the liquid will spread.

Dupré was the first (1867) to show that this can be expressed in terms of the surface free energies to the two materials in the following manner: The thermodynamic work of adhesion is equal to the surface free energy of the solid in a vacuum, F_S, plus the surface free energy of the liquid in contact with its vapor, F_{LV}, minus the free energy of the newly formed interface between the liquid and the solid, F_{SL}. Hence:

$$W_{adh} = F_S + F_{LV} - F_{SL}$$

The work of cohesion comes out of this same equation. It is the work of adhesion of a liquid spreading on itself

$$W_{coh} = 2F_{LV}$$

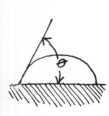

Therefore, a liquid will spread on a solid if the spreading coefficient Sp, as defined by the following equation, is greater than zero.

$$W_{adh} - W_{coh} = F_S - F_{LV} - F_{SL} = Sp$$

or if

$$F_S > F_{LV} + F_{SL}$$

For those readers unfamiliar with the language of physical chemistry, the term "surface free energy" may seem a bit puzzling. How does a surface come to have an energy in the first place? Strictly speaking, surface free energy is the energy difference between an atom in the bulk and an atom on the surface. The atom on the surface has a higher energy because of the unbalanced forces there. In the case of a liquid, the surface free energy reduces to the surface tension. This is easily measured with a DuNouy tensiometer or similar instrument.

Not so with solids. Their surface free energies are more difficult to relate to common-material properties and are almost impossible to measure directly. In fact, a meaningful value for an equilibrium surface free energy may not exist because solid surfaces are generally under stress created during solidification and are consequently not equilibrium surfaces. In one interesting attempt to measure solid surface free energies directly, a series of thin copper wires, each held at a different tensile stress, was heated slowly in a furnace. When the wires approached their melting point, those with a tensile stress greater than their surface tension began to stretch, while those with surface tension greater than tensile stress began to shrink. The stress in the wire that neither shrunk nor stretched indicated the magnitude of the solid's surface tension.

There are several indirect methods for determining the surface free energy of solids. One of the most popular compares the surface free energy of the solid with that of a liquid having a known surface free energy. The two are compared by placing a drop of the liquid on the solid and then measuring the equilibrium contact angle between the surface of the solid and a line tangent to the surface of the liquid at the point of contact (see margin). For liquids with surface free energy greater than that of the solid, the contact angle will have a positive value. Knowing the contact angles and surface free energies for several liquids on the same unknown solid, it is possible to compute the surface free energy of a liquid that would *just spread* on the solid.

This is not, however, the true surface free energy of the solid. W. A. Zisman, of the Naval

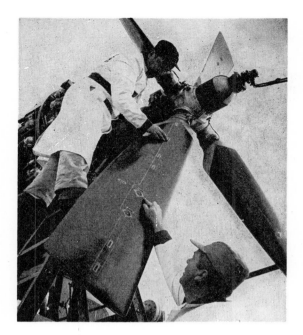

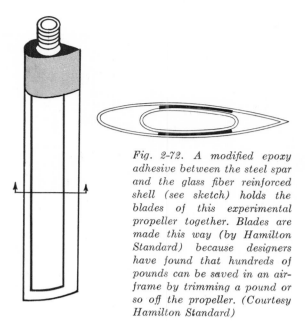

Fig. 2-72. A modified epoxy adhesive between the steel spar and the glass fiber reinforced shell (see sketch) holds the blades of this experimental propeller together. Blades are made this way (by Hamilton Standard) because designers have found that hundreds of pounds can be saved in an airframe by trimming a pound or so off the propeller. (Courtesy Hamilton Standard)

Research Laboratory, who was the first to present this work, calls this the critical surface tension of wetting for the solid. Unfortunately, the values obtained this way vary depending on the series of liquids used to determine the contact angles. F. M. Fowkes at Sprague Electric Co. has shown that surface tension is the sum of many intermolecular forces and that some of these may not interact with certain solids. Water, for example, will not spread on mercury even though the surface tension of mercury is around 500 dyne/cm while that of water is 72 dyne/cm. This is because there is a large component of mercury's surface tension that does not interact with the water.

The method has a further disadvantage. It is useful only for solids with low surface free energies since it depends on the availability of several liquids having a surface free energy higher than that of the solid, and there are not many liquids with a high surface free energy. But this is not a serious disadvantage in the study of adhesives since it is the solids with low surface free energy that pose the most difficult bonding problems; most liquids spread easily on metals and other solids with high surface free energy.

Despite its disadvantages, the concept of critical surface tension of wetting for solids provides a useful working relationship between the surface free energies of solids and liquids. Surface tensions of a number of liquids and critical surface tensions of wetting for a number of solids are shown in the table in the next column.

Forth, but not back

Notice that the equation that sets out the conditions for spreading is not an equation at all; it is an inequality. This fact has very im-

SURFACE FREE ENERGIES OF SOME COMMON MATERIALS

Material	F (dyne/cm)
Teflon	18.5*
Polyethylene	31*
Polystyrene	33*
Polyvinyl chloride	40*
Nylon	46
Epoxy	47
Water	73
Aluminum	~500†
Tin-lead solder	~500†
Mercury	~500
Silver	~900†
Copper	~1100†

* Critical surface tension for wetting
† Near melting point

Fig. 2-73. There is nearly 3300 ft² of bonded honeycomb sandwich paneling in the supersonic B-58 Hustler, enough to consume over 900 lb of epoxy-phenolic and nitrile-rubber-phenolic adhesives. The wing skin is attached solely by these adhesives and skin loads are transmitted across this bonded joint despite temperatures from −65°F to 260°F. (Courtesy General Dynamics, Fort Worth)

portant consequences in making adhesive joints. The "greater than" sign means that if A spreads on B, B will positively not spread on A. In terms

Fig. 2-74. A solvent-dispersed epoxy adhesive replaces eight rivets in bonding the laminates of this motor stator. Notice that bonded assembly behaves like one piece during final machining. (Courtesy Pittsburgh Plate Glass Co.)

of adhesive joints, we can go further and say that if A forms a strong joint when used as an adhesive between two pieces of B (A being the liquid), then B will not, in general, form a strong joint when used as an adhesive between two pieces of A (where B is now the liquid).

That last statement needs some qualification. When we say "B will not form a strong joint with A," it does not mean that thermodynamics forbids the adhesion of B to A. It only means that thermodynamics discourages the spreading of B on A to the extent that the two will not

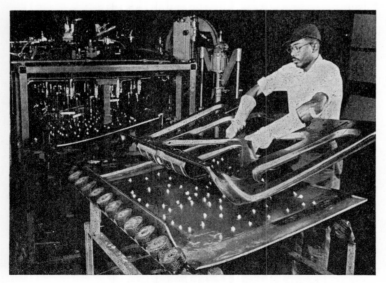

Fig. 2-75. The hood assembly on Ford cars is held together with 96 "Hershey drops" of adhesive applied with an automatic machine (background). After hood is painted, the assembly passes through a paint-bake oven that cures paint and adhesive in one step. The adhesive bonds securely, even when applied over oily metal. (Courtesy Minnesota Mining and Manufacturing Co.)

form a strong joint, given a reasonable amount of time. Nor does it mean that thermodynamics forbids B from coming into contact with A, for the two materials can easily be made to achieve extensive contact by reversing their roles. When the two materials are in complete interfacial contact, thermodynamics cares not a whit whether you got there by spreading A on B or by spreading B on A; it's of historical interest only.

The spreading rule must be applied with some caution. If the liquid is a solvent for the solid, for example, then all bets based on surface energetics are off. The resulting contact angles are universally lower than those that would be anticipated on the basis of energetics alone.

A slippery stickum? Surely not

One of the remarkable things about the spreading relationship was the failure by most investigators to recognize the significance of the "greater than" sign to the matter of practical adhesion. Until recently, the sign has been interpreted to mean only that liquids with a high surface free energy would not spread on solids with a low surface free energy. But there is another side to the matter. Suppose we reverse things. If the high-energy liquid won't spread, suppose we solidify it and melt the low-energy stuff on it. Under those conditions the two materials should establish the necessary extensive and intimate interfacial contact more easily.

That is exactly what we did in a series of experiments performed about a year and a half ago. Polyethylene is a notoriously uncooperative material when attempts are made to bond it to another material with an adhesive. The spreading relationship shows why. Polyethylene has a critical surface tension of wetting of 31 dyne/cm and there are very few conventional adhesives (if any) with a surface free energy lower than that. Attempts to bond polyethylene structurally with a conventional epoxy adhesive are doomed to failure because a typical epoxy has a surface free energy of about 47 dyne/cm and will not spread on the waxy plastic. In the past, the solution has been to oxidize the polyethylene surface, boosting its surface free energy and making it acceptable to a variety of adhesives with a high surface free energy.

Reversing the roles of the two materials, we melted the polyethylene on the surface of a cured epoxy. The polyethylene spread as predicted. To test the joint, we made up specimens each consisting of a sandwich of aluminum, epoxy, polyethylene, epoxy, aluminum. Epoxy forms a strong joint with aluminum and is, in fact, one of the better adhesives for aluminum. Joints formed in this manner showed a tensile-

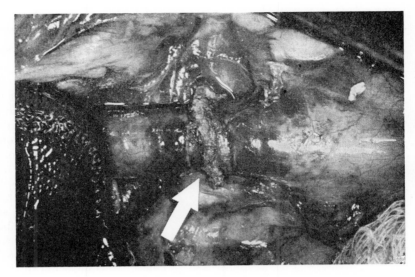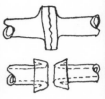

Fig. 2-76. "Sponge." "Sponge." "Forceps." "Forceps." "Glue." "Glue." Sounds out of place in an operating room but adhesives have closed a variety of surgical incisions (veins, arteries, intestines) in experimental operations on animals. At left, a large blood vessel was joined with a cyanoacrylate adhesive (see sketch) by surgeon J. E. Healey and associates at the University of Texas. (Courtesy J. E. Healey, Jr.)

shear strength (strength of a lap joint stressed in axial shear) of 2300 psi.

When we first announced our results, many people found it difficult to believe that a joint could be formed that way; indeed, there are still those who find it hard to accept, particularly in view of our statement that there is nothing special about the polyethylene except to be certain to select a material which does not contain waxes that would produce a weak boundary layer. There are no tricks.

One reason for the reluctance to accept our result is that it upsets the longstanding (since 1939) deBruyne rule of adhesion, which, truth to tell, was probably losing favor anyway. The deBruyne rule is a compatibility rule for adhesives that develops from the observation that all materials (solids, liquids, adhesives, everything) can be divided into two classes: polar materials—those whose molecules have separated centers of electrical charge—and nonpolar materials. The deBruyne rule says that an ad-

Fig. 2-77. Polyethylene will not normally form a strong joint with epoxy because liquid epoxy will not spread on polyethylene. The two are joined firmly in the photo above by reversing their roles and melting the polyethylene on the solid epoxy. (Courtesy Bell Telephone Laboratories)

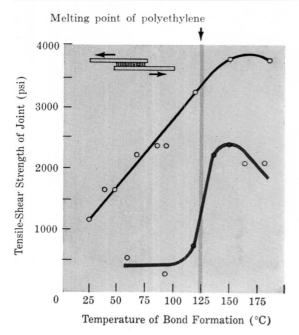

Melting point of polyethylene

Tensile-Shear Strength of Joint (psi)

4000

3000

2000

1000

0   25   50   75   100   125   150   175

Temperature of Bond Formation (°C)

Fig. 2-78. Strength of aluminum-epoxy-polyethylene-epoxy-aluminum joint (color curve) increases sharply when liquid epoxy is cured at temperatures above polyethylene's melting point, although it never reaches the strength of an aluminum-epoxy-aluminum joint (black curve).

hesive must match the material to which it is to adhere; a polar solid requires a polar adhesive and a nonpolar solid requires a nonpolar adhesive. Now assuming you can identify polar and nonpolar materials (and that's not always easy), the deBruyne rule says that epoxy may form a strong joint with metal (polar to polar) but epoxy will not form a strong joint with Teflon (polar adhesive to nonpolar solid).

The polyethylene-epoxy experiments showed that at least part of the deBruyne rule is not valid, for here is a nonpolar adhesive (polyethylene) forming a strong joint with a polar solid (epoxy). There are still those who stand by the rule even though deBruyne himself has recently stated that he believes the nonpolar-to-polar portion of the rule to be incorrect.

The polyethylene experiments also emphasize the role of viscosity in making adhesive joints. At first glance, one would assume that a thin, watery fluid would wet a surface much more easily than a thick syrupy one. In this case, however, the molten polyethylene spreads on the epoxy even though its viscosity is many times greater than that of the uncured epoxy (10^6 centipoise vs. 10^3 centipoise). Low viscosity may help to speed spreading, but if the surface energetics aren't right, even a thin adhesive will just sit there.

Well and truly stoppered

From the arguments and the experimental evidence just presented, it would be tempting to conclude that the world could easily survive on just one kind of adhesive—a liquid having an extremely low surface free energy, which solidifies to a tough solid when spread on the surfaces to be joined. Such a material, it would seem, could be used to glue anything to anything. A universal adhesive.

Apart from the whimsical questions of how one would store such a universal adhesive (it's akin to the problem of the universal solvent, except that instead of asking, "what would you keep it in?" you ask, "how would you get the stopper out of the bottle?") there are a number of practical properties, besides surface free energy, to consider. For example, it is important that an adhesive not shrink excessively when it solidifies, particularly if it is a brittle material. Whether it solidifies by cooling from the molten stage, by evaporation of a solvent, or by polymerization, shrinkage stresses can be large enough to make the joint fail—by fracture of the adhesive itself—even before a load is applied. Moreover, the adhesive must not react chemically with the solid to form a product that would act as a weak boundary layer between the adhesive and the substrate.

But more important than these, if a universal adhesive is to be worthy of its name, it must be strong in the bulk, for if it fails, that's where it will fail. It is unlikely that our low-energy adhesive would be strong enough for every conceivable application; generally, such materials do not have a remarkably high cohesive strength. This is unfortunate, because the properties of any joint depend critically on the bulk properties of the adhesive. If the adhesive is brittle, the joint will be brittle; if the adhesive is elastic, the joint will be tough. For this reason, a rubbery adhesive with a low ultimate strength may, in certain instances, be more resistant to failure than a brittle adhesive with a higher ultimate. Because there is more area under its stress-strain diagram (see margin) the rubbery material can store more energy.

And when the joint breaks . . .

An even more dangerous conclusion to be drawn from the argument of surface free energies and spreading is to assume that just because the energetics are favorable for spreading, they guarantee the formation of a strong joint. Unfortunately, the factors involved in making a joint and breaking a joint are not directly related. It is one thing to control matters so that a proper interface will be formed; it is quite another to make a strong adhesive joint, for it is the adhesive material itself that fails, not the interface. The strength of a properly made adhesive joint depends largely on the flaws and stress concentrations in the adhesive and can be analyzed only through fracture theory.

With our understanding of adhesion and adhesive joints, we can go back and see how it applies to well-known adhesives. We can see, for example, that pressure-sensitive adhesives work because the adhesive material always remains fluid and is always capable of flowing (with the help of pressure) into intimate contact with the substrate. We can also see that animal glue works well on wood because the surface free energy of the wood is higher than that of the glue.

Only by careful stumbling

But aside from such questions, our understanding of the mechanism of adhesion has yet to have much influence on the practical matters of sticking two pieces of *A* together with a drop of *B*. But then, neither has any other scientific explanation of adhesion. People have been cooking up adhesives for centuries without knowing why two materials stick. Today, the discovery of new adhesives progresses generally with very little appreciation for prevailing theories of adhesion. As recently as ten years ago, scientists stumbled across a very interesting adhesive when checking the index of refraction of a new synthetic polymer. When they compressed the cyanoacrylate between the two prisms of their test instrument, they found they could no longer get the prisms apart—and a new adhesive was born.

Happenstance or not, it seems that the adhesives we've got are probably as good as any theory could have found for us. Particularly today. Modern adhesives have very few limitations; almost any two materials can be stuck together. Applications in the aircraft industry have progressed to the point where modern airplanes are almost more adhesives than rivets, and there are several types of aircraft flying today with well over three quarters of their external surface bonded on with adhesives. In automobiles, adhesives are now used to attach

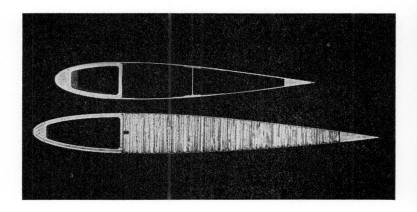

Fig. 2-79. Durable, long-lived helicopter blades would be almost impossible to make without adhesives; they have almost completely replaced wooden predecessors. In top photo, honeycomb blanket is laid over a paper-like film adhesive between leading and trailing edges. In middle photo, it is covered with aluminum upper surface and the entire assembly heat-cured in the lay-up press. Cross sections compare new honeycomb-core blade with older adhesive-bonded blade. (Courtesy Bell Helicopter Co.)

panels, glass, steel reinforcements, and trim, to the extent that some cars come off the assembly line carrying as much as 25 lb of adhesive.

In electronics, adhesives bond the conducting copper foil to printed circuit boards, and conducting adhesives are being tested for use as cold solder. In metal-working industries, adhesives join castings, extrusions, and sheet-metal parts, and a special adhesive often keeps bolts from backing out of their threads. In housing and construction, adhesives are used for everything from the bonding materials that hold the plies of plywood together to the stickum that bonds the component sheets of metal curtain-wall assemblies. And the laminated metal ski would be impossible without adhesives.

Many more things could be glued together that aren't. For example, adhesives have been tested in a variety of automotive applications—including a test vehicle made several years ago that was put together almost entirely with adhesives—but such applications often prove to be impractical for assembly-line manufacture. Clothing manufacturers are testing adhesives that may one day replace the stitches in the seams of garments and surgeons have already reported good results with an adhesive that closes incisions in blood vessels. Manufacturers of automobile and marine engines have also experimented with engines made by die casting engine halves and bonding them together. They claim the experiments were succesful but admit they were less interested in the practicalities than in seeing whether or not it could be done.

What's in the glue pot?

All of this sticking and gluing and pasting comes about mostly because of a new generation of adhesives that has grown up in the last few years. The new generation owes more to polymer chemistry than it does to theory. Indeed, the most exciting new adhesives are all synthetic polymers of one sort or another.

Synthetic polymers have several advantages over the traditional materials. One of these, surprisingly enough, is *not* low surface free energy. It is true that many polymers have a reasonably low surface free energy, but it's not remarkably low; epoxy, for example, is down around 47 dyne/cm which is somewhat lower than casein glue, but not significantly.

The most important feature of adhesives that set by polymerization is . . . just that. This mechanism of solidifying a liquid by stringing monomers together to form a rigid polymer has several advantages. In the first place, these adhesives generally don't shrink as much as adhesives that solidify by cooling or by drying. This means that there is a lower residual stress and, consequently, they can carry a larger working stress. In the second place, because they do not set by evaporation of a solvent, the inside of the joint cures just as rapidly as the outside. This is particularly important when the adhesive is trapped between two impermeable pieces of material. A cellulose cement between two pieces of aluminum might take weeks to set—and then would probably form a poor joint because of shrinkage. An epoxy, on the other hand, will polymerize clear through the joint in a matter of a few hours, at most. Or a polymer can be prepared that cures extremely fast (30 seconds or so) and would therefore be useful in applications that would have been impossible if it had been necessary to wait for the joint to cool or dry.

Another advantage of the polymers is the infinite variety of compounds that can be made this way, organic chemistry being what it is. An adhesive chemist can tailor the adhesive for each particular application, if need be. The epoxies, for example, make strong joints with aluminum, stainless, magnesium, and a number of other metals with average tensile-shear strengths somewhere around 3000 psi. The joints, however, are brittle and break quite easily when subjected to shock loading. The solution has been to combine the epoxy with a viscoelastic material like nylon, thus greatly increasing the toughness of the material without sacrificing much strength. Similar polymer materials using polyurethanes, phenolics, neoprenes, vinyls, epoxies, either singly or in combination, are also exploited for their adhesive properties.

So sticky they're dangerous

One of the most intriguing aspects of the polymer adhesive is the polymerization mechanism itself. Chemists have come up with a number of ingenious ways to trigger the curing cycle. The adhesive that keeps threaded fasteners from backing out of their threads, for example, is cured by suffocation; it is a special kind of material that remains fluid as long as it is exposed to air but sets up when trapped between the threads of a nut and bolt. Epoxies can be mixed on the job, in which case they will probably cure at room temperature, or they can be premixed by the adhesive manufacturer and cured by heat. A clever variation of this involves an epoxy that is premixed by the manufacturer, generally in the form of a film, and then immediately refrigerated to prevent curing. The user simply removes the material from its dry-ice packing, cuts the film to shape, clamps it between the mating parts, and allows it to cure at room temperature. Another variation is a heat-curing epoxy film that contains an integral resistance heater; just put it in place and plug it in.

Cyanoacrylate adhesives are another interesting material; they cure when they come in contact with hydroxyl ions, which is anywhere there is a moist surface, which is, in effect, anywhere. The adhesives are extremely fluid and set extremely fast (in less than a minute, usually). Because of these properties, they are almost dangerous to have around. If you squeeze a drop between two fingers for 30 seconds, you'll have to cut your fingers apart with a razor blade. It's an experiment you won't want to perform more than once.

Advanced kinds of stickum

The outcome of the search for better adhesives has been so successful that there are very few important adhesive needs left unfilled. Admittedly, it would be nice to have a room-temperature adhesive that would allow untreated Teflon and other low-energy materials to be bonded structurally to other materials, but the lack of it is not a particularly important impediment to progress. And, of course, we could always use a stronger adhesive—but this simply means that we want stronger plastics, and they aren't likely to be found lurking under convenient rocks (see "Tailor-Making Plastics," page 235).

There remains one area where the need for a better adhesive is critical. Missiles and supersonic aircraft can be made more efficiently if their structures are bonded, but these adhesives must withstand temperatures up to 500°F or so. Several years ago, the Armed Services set up a target to shoot at. They wanted an adhesive that would withstand 1000°F at 1000 psi for 1000 hours. So far, no one's come close. More recently, Armed Services spokesmen stated that they would be satisfied with an adhesive that could live at 500°F indefinitely . . . and it's hard to tell whether that's a tougher target or an easier one. About the best anyone's done so far is an adhesive that has been baking at 350°F for 4000 hours and seems to be getting stronger all the time.

High-temperature adhesives are generally made by starting with an organic polymer that can resist high temperatures for a short time—an epoxy-phenolic, for example—and curing it with a material that prevents oxidation. Arsenic pentoxide is an effective antioxidant, as is arsenic trisulfide. No one is quite certain how the antioxidants work, but experiments show a marked increase in the endurance of the adhesive at high temperature.

At one time, it was hoped that non-organic ceramic adhesives would offer the answer to the high-temperature problem. Tests showed that bonded joints could operate comfortably at 1000°F and actually became stronger with increasing temperature. But the ceramics proved to be almost hopelessly brittle—to the extent that they would break when merely dropped on the laboratory floor. Chemists found this property difficult to breed out. Brittleness is, in fact, a problem with high-temperature organic materials too, a property brought on by the high degree of crosslinking necessary to establish temperature resistance in certain polymers.

Perhaps an effective high-temperature adhesive will never be found. Perhaps we are pushing our luck and our theories to imagine that those universal forces of attraction that lie waiting within an atom's diameter of any substance can be brought into play for every assembling and mending job. Perhaps so. But we'd hate to think that nature had no surprises left for us.

Further reading

Your education in adhesives and adhesion is incomplete until you've sampled some of the other theories of sticking. You've been exposed to the adsorption theory; now look at the diffusion theory, summarized nicely in six pages by S. S. Voyutskii in *Adhesive Age* **5**, 30 (1962). The magazine, incidentally, is worth looking at if you want to keep abreast of developments in adhesives technology ($6/yr). An expanded version of Voyutskii's thesis has been published under the title *Autoadhesion and Adhesion of High Polymers* (Interscience, 1963, $15).

For different views of the adsorption theory and an enormous amount of additional information about adhesion see *The Science of Adhesive Joints* by Bikerman (Academic Press, 1961, $8) and *Adhesion and Adhesives*, edited by deBruyne and Houwink (Elsevier, 1951, $10). Either one could pass as a classic in the field of adhesives and both include theoretical as well as technological information, with technology getting perhaps the better part of the bargain. The deBruyne book is a collection of chapters written by individual authors but is better done than this sort of thing usually is. A revised edition is expected soon, edited this time by Houwink and Salomon, so wait, if you're buying. In this same category is *Adhesion* by Eley (Oxford U. Press, 1961, $9), which is a more scientific examination of the sticking phenomenon in terms of thermodynamics, rheology, surface roughness, physical chemistry.

If you're interested in digging further into

the adsorption theory, you should start at the beginning with London's "The General Theory of Molecular Forces," *Transactions of the Faraday Society* **33,** 8 (Jan. 1937), and "Van der Waals Forces" by Margenau, *Review of Modern Physics* **11,** 1 (Jan. 1939). Then, take a breather with deBruyne's entertaining and well-illustrated "The Action of Adhesives," *Scientific American* (Apr. 1962, p. 114), before plunging into "The Physics of Adhesion" by deBruyne, *Journal of Scientific Instruments* **24,** No. 2, 29 (1947). The paper in which Sharpe and Schonhorn first put forth some of their ideas, "Surface Energetics, Adhesion and Adhesive Joints," can be found in a special publication of the American Chemical Society, *Advances in Chemistry Series,* Vol. 43 (1964).

Two broad (and recent) reviews of the subject of adhesion are included in the bound volumes of the proceedings of two symposia. These are both quite well done and include papers by most of the prominent men in the field. The first, from a symposium held at Picatinny Arsenal in 1961, is titled *Symposium on Adhesives for Structural Applications* (Interscience, 1962, $6.25) and is mostly technological, while the second, from a symposium held at General Motors the same year, titled *Adhesion and Cohesion* (Elsevier, 1962, $11) is mostly theoretical.

Chapter 3

Technology

TRAFFIC

by Evan Herbert *

In Brief: *Vehicular traffic consists of independently controlled units. When they are densely concentrated, drivers' whims gel into a cooperative fluid—but one whose flow is more describable by stimulus-response equations than by physical laws of motion. There is an incompatibility among the geometry of roads, the vehicle-driver complex, traffic controls, and the law. But research leading to a theory of traffic flow may provide a more realistic basis for designs of roads, vehicles, and controls that may resolve the conflicts. Even without a theory, there is promise of some relief of congestion in computers that adapt the timing of signals to real-time traffic demands on a city street system. Longer range, the very causes of movement can be manipulated by rearranging building placement to simplify circulation patterns among these traffic generators.—E.H.*

■ There you sit, seat belt fastened, engine idling, in command of two tons of personal locomotion. Your automobile gives you freedom to travel where you want, when you want, and, unlike the aircraft pilot, you can grossly change your course without prior clearance. The road is yours and to assert your rights you're belligerent beyond your bumpers.

From your vantage point behind the wheel, you're an expert on traffic . . . at least the way most people are experts on politics, religion, and sex. In a sense, you are *the* expert. For the basic fact about highway traffic is that—unlike rail or air or water traffic—it is composed of small independently controlled units.

* Evan Herbert is Associate Editor of *International Science and Technology*.

But when traffic gets dense, free will is bent toward cooperation with the traffic stream.

However, your problem of personal mobility looks a little different to the traffic engineer; he tries to keep you moving.

Transportation and city planners have still another view of traffic. They must preserve the environment of a city as a decent place to live and work in the motor age.

Today, if you were to start with an empty field and commence to build a city, you would find no agreement among traffic engineers, transportation coordinators, and city planners about how to deal with its traffic problem.

Do we need to replace roads and highways with entirely new kinds of transportation systems for individuals . . . automatically controlled cars, vehicles running in troughs, or cars carried on conveyer belts? Or can we still vastly improve the present combination of roads, cars, and controls?

Actually, we don't know the answer to either question. Though we've learned to construct magnificent roads, they're engineering marvels only when they're empty.

What generates traffic? How does it flow under various conditions? Can drivers be made to conform to a traffic-control system, or should the control system adapt to the behavior of traffic?

Recently, an increasing number of scientists and engineers from many disciplines have begun to study parts of the traffic problem from rather different points of view. There are physicists who believe that methods of statistical mechanics can be applied to the difficult problem of describing the distribution of traffic on

for quantitative descriptions of traffic flow through bottlenecks, or under no-passing conditions.

As a science, traffic is still in an embryonic stage. With rare exceptions, most research money has been spent on developing longer lasting concrete, on signal sizes, on traffic counts that mostly amass meaningless data.

Let's look at typical parts of the problem as a motorist sees them.

Ready? Beep bee-ep!

The dilemma zone

Ahead of you at an intersection a signal light turns amber, a caution signal between green and red to warn a motorist it's time for a decision. But, even if you are familiar with this intersection, know how long the amber cycle is, you simply don't have enough information to make a satisfactory decision. If the amber is too short, you plunge into the dilemma zone (margin), an area near the intersection where you can't stop safely and you can't clear the crossing before red without speeding.

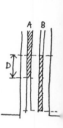

S - Stopping
D - Dilemma
A - Can't go
B - Can't sto

As you look ahead toward other intersections, signals seem to be turning from red to green progressively. How fast should you travel to stay with the green lights? Suddenly it doesn't matter, for there's a streetcar ahead, stopping to unload, so you can't pass.

Left turn ahead. You inch over to the center of the road and stop at the intersection, waiting for a gap in the oncoming traffic. Meanwhile, through traffic piles up behind you.

On the cross street now. And the lights no longer are a steady progression. You get a red signal at almost every intersection. At each corner you sit and wait, even when there is no other cross traffic at the intersections.

Finally, you're headed out of the city over a bridge ahead. It has only a single lane in each direction, but traffic seems moderate and moving rapidly on the approaches. As you begin to cross the traffic stream slows to a crawl. An accident perhaps? But there's no sign of any obstruction anywhere on the bridge as you reach the other side and pick up speed.

Did the bridge builder overestimate its capacity as on the 13-year-old Delaware River bridge at the southern end of the New Jersey Turnpike? It was designed for a daily flow of 21,000 vehicles by 1962, but now carries up to 60,000 vehicles. Perhaps better predictions never would have gotten the money to build the bridge at all. A twin of the $44 million first bridge will now cost $76 million. Initially, it may have been cheaper to lay foundations for additional lanes, like the Garden State Parkway Bridge over the Raritan River in New Jersey,

Fig. 3-1. New York or Paris, or almost anywhere these days, congestion seems the same. There's a mix of vehicles of various speed characteristics and drivers whose code of the road varies from conformity to sheer anarchy. In messes like these, individual will disappears into a cooperative traffic fluid. (Courtesy G. Ferguson (top) and J. Richardson)

TO EVERY MOTORIST

COMES HIS DAY

SO CALMLY WAIT

YOUR CHANCE

PEDESTRIANS HAVE

THE RIGHT OF WAY

WHEN IN THE

AMBULANCE

BURMA-SHAVE

a road. Some communications engineers see an analogy in the movement of morning rush-hour traffic from the suburbs to the city; to them, the flow of vehicles by streets, feeder roads, and expressways has much in common with the flow of subscriber messages via feeders and trunks to a telephone central.

Little is really known about the vehicle-driver combination and its interaction with other vehicles, the road itself, traffic signs, and controls. Psychologists and mathematicians are developing models of vehicle-driver behavior

or provide for an additional deck like the George Washington Bridge.

Now you come to the junction of several roads at a traffic circle, also known as a rotary and, most appropriately, a roundabout. You enter and leave on the periphery, but traffic from the right has priority, so you're gradually forced toward the center and around you go. You've heard that dense traffic has actually become physically locked up on such circles.

On the open highway now you conscientiously try to apply one of the first rules you learned for safe driving: Allow one car length between you and the car ahead for every 10 mph of speed. But try leaving an opening when traffic is dense and someone is sure to dart in front of you. Slacken speed to drop back to a safe distance and, whether you know it or not, your deceleration affects the car behind you. His slowing affects the next car, and so on, until somewhere in the serpentine chain of reaction, started from your slight slowing down, a car may reach a complete stop. Traffic movements like this, viewed from the air, resemble a huge accordion.

Let's leave the stall now and go back to look at typical problems you've encountered.

Incompatibility at the crossroads

What created the dilemma zone that put you in a situation beyond your judgment at the amber light? An analysis of the problem made by Herman, Olson, and Rothery of General Motors Research Laboratories, found a basic incompatibility of the amber light duration, geometry of the intersection, and traffic laws.

A commonly used rule of the traffic engineer's thumb for setting the amber phase allows one second for every 10 mph of approach speed. But this considers only stopping distance, not the width of the intersection nor the length of a vehicle—behemoth bus or beetle compact—and its acceleration or stopping characteristics coupled with driver-reaction time. The *effective* width of an intersection is the distance between a stopping line short of the corner and a clearing line beyond the far corner. This varies with the length of a vehicle and the duration of the amber signal.

If you decide to stop the moment you see the amber warning, you must decelerate as comfortably and safely as you can; depending on your approach speed and distance from the intersection at the onset of amber, this can mean a fairly sudden stop.

But suppose, because the road is slick or you're being followed too closely, you decide to go through the intersection in hopes of passing the clearing line completely before red. Can you accelerate fast enough, but still stay within the lawful maximum speed?

Few intersections now have adequate amber-phase durations to shorten or eliminate the dilemma zone. There are intersections where amber lasts only 1.5 seconds. Of course, there is the frequent argument that motorists treat longer amber lights as extensions of the green, but the GM study casts doubt that motorists behave differently at the amber except when placed at a severe disadvantage by a relatively long dilemma zone created by short signal phases. In England, traffic detectors in the road extend the green for a limited time for approaching vehicles that would otherwise be caught in a dilemma zone.

Homogenized traffic

How cars are distributed along a road after leaving a signalized intersection is of great importance for traffic control.

The phenomena of vehicles forming into platoons and platoon-diffusion behavior are related to coordination of successive traffic lights and achievement of smooth traffic flow.

Hydrodynamic models of traffic have been proposed and the wave behavior of platoons in heavy traffic has been described as analogous to the propagation of a shock front. Other theoretical models, more appropriate for medium traffic, are concerned with relative motion of the elements in a wave and give theoretical results for the arrival time of vehicles at a given point for the front of a platoon and the rear of a platoon.

There have been attempts to simulate the flow of traffic under various conditions by an analogy that hypothesizes vehicular flow on roads to be the same as the movement of fluids through pipes. But do cars trying to squeeze past an accident or waiting to merge with a fast-moving stream on an expressway enter the main highway because of a pressure buildup in the access road?

So, you can't really turn to the laws of motion to describe mathematically the way cars move down a road. While it is evident that vehicles in traffic no longer move as a matter of the drivers' free will, but as a cooperative phenomenon—the cooperation is a psychological phenomenon, one that is better described by stimulus-response equations. Drivers respond to the cars in front, to the cars behind, and to the cars alongside. The closer the proximities, the tighter the coupling of stimulus-response. In fact, a theoretical model of vehicular follow-the-leader movements might conceivably describe the behavior of a school of fish or a flight of birds.

How an entire population of automobiles be-

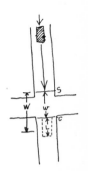

S- stopping line
C- clearing line
L- car length
w- effective width
W- physical width

haves is the subject of an interesting theory developed by Prof. Prigogine of the Université Libre de Bruxelles. His generalized approach to traffic flow is similar to the Boltzmann equation of the kinetic theory of gases. It predicts the critical traffic concentrations which result in a flow of vehicles being transformed from individual cars, operated according to each driver's free will, into the collective flow of a sort of cooperative fluid in which drivers are forced to behave within the restrictions of the community about them.

There may be some ways to describe this traffic fluid which will prove useful in solving real problems on the highway. For example, the average acceleration of all the members of the fluid community gives some indication of how traffic is moving. Drivers in a group of cars constantly make adjustments relative to one another—small but random accelerations and decelerations. The variance in the distribution function of a vehicle's acceleration pattern is called acceleration noise. Measured average noise can tell some useful things about the state of traffic fluid.

Consider what happens when you leave a safe spacing in fast-moving traffic. On a two-lane highway, you find cars from the slow lane moving over into the bigger headway spaces in the fast lane. So the fast lane is slowed by new spacing adjustments while the slow lane gains greater headway and becomes the fast lane—until a new oscillation of speeds begins.

Even in single lane travel, with no traffic, acceleration noise can be a clue to what affects the motion of the vehicle. In studies made in New York's Holland Tunnel, it turned out that confined conditions and narrow lanes caused acceleration noise to be almost double the dispersion from a perfect road value even with no traffic interference. Similarly, studies of acceleration noise on winding highways, or poorly surfaced roads can tell a good deal about how they will affect traffic flow.

A study of acceleration noise by Potts and Jones of the University of Adelaide, Australia, shows a correlation between high acceleration noise and the frequency of accidents on a given road or involving a given driver. Indeed, the acceleration mismatch of various vehicles in a line of traffic tends to increase driving hazards. This is reflected in a high-acceleration noise observed in Japan where there are a large number of rear-end collisions in mixed traffic composed of pedicabs and bicycles, automobiles, trucks, and buses of all sizes.

There is a significant correlation between the results of studies of the over-all motion properties of the traffic stream or macroscopic variables, with those studies that try to under-

Fig. 3-2. Newbury, a town of 30,000 in England, has paper mills and research labs nearby which make another 30,000 people dependent on this center. Desire lines for work journeys within town are dark grey, journeys with origin or destination outside town are in color. Compare this with constriction of actual traffic flow (right); through traffic is shown in color. (From Traffic in Towns, *permission of H.M. Stationery Office)*

stand the detailed behavior of individual vehicles following one another. Microscopic variables have been examined in car-following experiments by Herman, Rothery, and Potts on the General Motors test track in Warren, Michigan, and in the Holland Tunnel in cooperation with Edie and Foote of the Port of New York Authority. With two cars linked together by piano wire, they were able to record how they behaved relative to each other in spacing, speed, and acceleration.

The car-following theory evolved from these experiments gives limits to the values of sensitivity of response to stimuli in various densities of traffic and predicts the time lag of the response. The theory predicts instabilities that can lead to chain-reaction rear-end collisions of the sort that sometimes pile up a hundred cars on turnpikes and expressways.

The green wave

With valid testing of traffic-flow theories, it becomes possible to develop ways to make dense traffic move more freely. By introducing gaps in the traffic stream, thus forming groups of cars into platoons of limited dispersion, pulses of vehicles can be funneled along a road so that they arrive at intersections and pass through during a green-light cycle while the gaps between platoons arrive at the intersection during a red cycle. In effect, you as a motorist would be riding a green wave of lights.

On a one-way street, a platoon should be able to travel along at a constant rate—the speed of the advancing green light. In practice, though, some traffic engineers contend that total congestion—complete stoppage in all four directions when platoons hang over into intersections—occurs under lower traffic densities with the progressive system than when all the lights change simultaneously.

When the progressive system is applied to two-way streets, the interaction of control schemes with city planning becomes most apparent. Most cities are not neatly laid out as rectangular grids of streets. Intersections are not only irregular in spacing, but often occur at intervals, which make a rhythmic progression almost impossible in both directions at the same time.

Two-way progressive systems make it harder to clear crossing traffic, especially from unsignalized intersections because the traffic streams flow in staggered fashion in opposing directions on the same street.

Too short a signal cycle can reduce the traffic-handling capacity of a street because trucks may not keep up, pushing platoons back. Drivers who run faster than the green wave

reach the next intersection too early, thus joining onto the rear of the next platoon.

Clearly, a driver must fit into a progressive timing pattern and stay with it. A means of accomplishing this has been tried in Germany and in the United States. Strangely, it works better in Germany than in the U.S.

Presignals and signal funnels

To speed starting, Wolfgang von Stein, of Düsseldorf's Traffic department, has experimented with presignals placed 100 feet, the normal accelerating distance, before an intersection. A presignal gets the moving cars back of the intersection off to the same flying start as the stopped lead vehicles. Von Stein has also used presignals in Düsseldorf and in other parts of Germany to create "time islands" for streetcars that must stop where there is no room for loading islands.

Ordinarily, a streetcar may arrive at a signalized intersection just at the beginning of a green light. By stopping to load passengers, it stops all other traffic. A presignal ahead of the streetcar stop allows the streetcar to pass into the unloading zone only after all the nonrail-bound traffic has left. Then the presignal turns red when the intersection is red to keep the unloading zone clear.

While presignals like this also have been used to allow fire engines to leave their stations, they have wider implications to the city planners concerned with traffic. For there are cases in which the building of a public garage or industrial plant would have been prohibited because of the traffic jams they would create on already busy streets. But presignals enabled the regulation of queuing and turning traffic at these points.

Another type of turn presignal, now working in Toronto, Canada, is the advanced green. A flashing green at an intersection signals a driver that he may safely turn, since opposite direction traffic still has red. Toronto traffic engineers found the flashing an advantage over a simple green arrow because flashes of, say, three per second seem to hurry drivers into the turn.

The speed signal is a further refinement of the presignal. It is used to regulate the flow of traffic already ahead of intersections. Von Stein claims that in Düsseldorf it has increased the percentage of vehicles passing through an intersection without stopping from 55% to 77%. As shown in Fig. 3-3, a correct speed is indicated to a driver which will guarantee him a green light at the next intersection. This tends to aid the driver approaching a dilemma zone for he will know that he is not making the indicated speed and an amber-to-red light ahead

Fig. 3-3. This speed signal on highway leading into Düsseldorf tells a driver that for the next 600 m he should travel 60/km/h (37 mph) to be assured progressive green lights. (Courtesy W. von Stein)

will not be a surprise. All this seems to work toward a concept of "continuous" traffic control.

The introduction of speed signals has posed another problem of law, for they can change their meaning within a few seconds, particularly if they are actuated by the density and flow of traffic rather than from a fixed, pretimed pattern.

Groups of connected speed signals and presignals form signal funnels which channel vehicles, even including out-of-town drivers unfamiliar with the pattern, into free-flowing green waves. They can also be used to help synchronize coordinated-signal systems with different cycles, enabling a smooth changeover for the driver entering the city limits.

If hundreds of signal funnels work successfully in Germany, why is the traffic-pacer signal-funnel installation on Mound Road near Detroit less than a success? On recent days this motorist tried check rides during light and heavy traffic periods and found that other drivers simply ignored the indicated speeds, thus piling up at intersections. Admittedly the sample is small and based on observation, but it points up one example of driver behavior that needs measurement and analysis. One might conclude that the German driver is characteristically more obedient—but then, German traffic engineers visiting the United States

marvel at the ability of American traffic engineers to marshall drivers into lanes simply with a brush and a bucket of paint.

If markings, signs, traffic signals give visual stimuli to drivers, they need to be uniform in meaning if they are to induce uniform responses. Their size and placement is critical if a driver in a fast-moving vehicle is to have time to make decisions. Adherence to a uniform code is now mandatory in the United States whenever federal highway aid is given. But traffic directions in some cities are misleading and confusing. Recently the New York State Legislature took steps to compel New York City to conform to state and federal traffic sign codes but the Mayor says the changes would cost too much.

Can visual clues between leading and following cars—perhaps tiny traffic lights—give drivers enough information about acceleration, coasting and braking? Test track experiments at GM showed such lights reduced reaction time by 50%, thus permitting cars to follow closer with the same stability, or to follow at the old spacing with greater stability in the traffic stream.

Because excessive following distances don't make efficient use of available roads, and faulty following is a major contributing factor to more than one third of the accidents in the U.S.A., there may be considerable merit in giving advanced driver's licenses to skillful motorists. Incentives could be monetary in the form of substantially lower license fees and lower insurance rates.

If drivers cannot be encouraged or made to conform to a control system imposed upon them—and, from a systems point of view, there is no agreement on the best control pattern to impose—then it might be better to let the control system adapt to the traffic, or to put automatically controlled vehicles on the highway.

By detecting stationary or moving vehicles by pneumatic tubes, ultrasonics, radar, strain gages, magnets, or magnetometers, traffic can actuate signals. For years, England has employed traffic-actuated signals, but individual signals controlled by a highly localized pattern of traffic simply don't work when traffic is heavy. Traffic flow is an area problem.

Live traffic laboratories

Traffic counts that amass data about various roads fail to reveal the dynamic characteristics of a system—the volume and density of traffic, speed of vehicles—that change rapidly and unpredictably and are vastly different throughout the system at every instant.

So most signal systems based on traffic counts today have been designed for conditions which no longer exist, or never may have existed. Nor are static system characteristics, like road capacity, sufficiently accurate. The U.S. Highway Capacity Manual gives no data points, for they are scattered so widely that many of the graphs in it would seem to lose all significance. But, for the highway engineer, such curves become as useless as would be the International Critical Tables for the physicist if there were no hard data points.

However, "hard" research in traffic is vexingly difficult to do because of the grand scale of experiments needed to assure validity. Controlled experiments that seek, say, maximum values for the capacity of a roadway under various conditions may require miles of test track, expensive instrumentation, and hundreds of vehicles and drivers.

Yet, if traffic research seems costly, it is relatively cheap compared to the actual cost of roads. For roads are the only business that may operate at full capacity from the day they open . . . and be termed a failure.

While the mere existence of test tracks does not assure success, such facilities for scientific experimentation are sadly lacking in most countries. Perhaps the most active national laboratory is in England's Department of Scientific and Industrial Research. Its Road Research Laboratory has long conducted controlled experiments like the ones shown in Fig. 3-4.

For example, when designing a roundabout for the interweaving of traffic streams at a road junction, the traffic-handling capacity for a given design must be determined for various vehicle mixes. Put too many vehicles into a roundabout and they have been known to lock up like the puzzles with movable squares and just one empty space to slide them in. In January 1964, it took hours to jockey the only gap in a monumental jam toward a traffic circle exit at Eatontown, New Jersey.

To find the ultimate capacity of a roundabout, the Road Research Laboratory made a full-scale mock-up of one and fed up to 130 vehicles into it—cars, taxis, trucks of various sizes, double-decker buses. This particular test showed that 800 mixed motor vehicles/hour/10 ft of weaving width can be accommodated under ideal conditions. It also showed that trip times through the roundabout were longer when the flow exceeded 90% of the maximum value.

Experiments like this can lead to a way to prevent overloads that precipitate traffic circle lockups. Once you know the critical mass of vehicles to lock up a particular circle, detectors in the road can anticipate this point and actuate red signals to keep more traffic out.

Similarly, anticipating the point of conges-tion with detectors is part of a pilot project on the busy Eisenhower Expressway near Chicago. Expressway detectors located upstream from an entrance ramp monitor the occupancy of lanes; control of entering traffic commences when the center lane equals 15% occupancy.

Then a traffic light at the ramp begins to meter cars into the main stream of traffic at the rate of 13 vehicles/min. It turns green just long enough to let one car pass a starting line for its attempt to merge; then it turns red to hold back other cars until the foot of the ramp is clear again. The timid driver need only watch for gaps in the main stream of traffic, for there are no cars crowding him so close that he can't risk an emergency stop.

As center-lane traffic increases—this lane reflects the results of slowdown or increasing occupancy of the right lane—the metering rate decreases until, at 24% occupancy, it is 6 vehicle/min. When center main-lane occupancy reaches 25%, the ramp metering devices let through only 4 vehicles/min.

What do you do with traffic that can't enter the Expressway? Unlike many projects which end their responsibility for traffic at the edge of the road, the Chicago Area Expressway Surveillance Project, which developed this control system, is equally concerned with the arterial subsystems that feed the Expressway or receive vehicles from it.

This project was established in 1961 as a research program of the Illinois Division of Highways and is financed by federal, state, Cook County, and Chicago funds. Its objective is to develop, operate, and evaluate a pilot network information and control system to reduce travel time and to increase traffic flow over the Expressway *and* major street network systems.

So experimentation is not limited to the main highway; advising drivers how to go is part of the plan. Signs still seem to be the best method of communicating with the motorist on the move. One type with a changeable message (see Fig. 3-5) has been developed by the project engineers for installation on streets leading to the Expressway and on the Expressway itself when diversions to parallel streets are necessary due to congestion or accidents. The detection system and its associated analog computers change the color of the arrows to indicate the degree of congestion ahead.

The entire 5-mile pilot network-information control system is essentially a research tool using live traffic. Project Director Dolf May, Jr., is investigating the relationship between average travel time and traffic volume for various road links under controlled and uncontrolled conditions in an attempt to find the cause of significant changes. His group is com-

Fig. 3-4.
IN ENGLAND,
CONTROLLED
EXPERIMENTS
ON TEST TRACKS . . .
This aerial view shows part of Road Research Laboratory Track at Crowthorne, England. Central area being used for traffic experiment here is 900 ft in diameter. Single-lane capacity problem is being run on circular tracks with radii of 200 and 415 ft.

Temporary test track at Northolt Airport was site of controlled experiment to determine roundabout traffic capacity. Test of interweaving actions involved 130 vehicles.

Maximum capacity of a 60-ft approach to an intersection with mixed vehicles under test at Fighting Vehicles Research and Development Establishment.

Effect of goods (commercial) vehicles on capacity of an intersection with traffic signals is assessed by groups of light and heavy vehicles on two connected test circuits. Initially grouped by weight, the vehicles are gradually interchanged on the circuits until mixed like this.

Approach to 30-ft wide intersection is tested with pure-bred herd of mini-cars. All tests shown on this page were made by Road Research Laboratory, whose resourcefulness was not limited when it lacked its own test-track. (All photos courtesy Road Research Lab, H.M. Stationery Office)

This "kiss 'n run," a suburban commuter railroad station, is a traffic generator adjacent to the Eisenhower Expressway near Chicago. During rush hours twice a day, a peck on the cheek is prelude to a driver's struggle to merge with the traffic mainstream at the ramp in tinted area.

Here is what happens: If too many cars surge onto expressway via ramp, right lane slows, some through drivers then try other lanes. Center lane occupancy upstream is clue to congestion. So . . . . . .

Ultrasonic detectors are mounted on overpass identified by arrow at left. When center lane is more than 15% full, cars are metered onto highway at ramp downstream. Number of vehicles permitted to enter each minute decreases as lane occupancy increases.

Halted vehicle near foot of ramp has just been dispatched by green signal. Driver has free shot at merging, can stop suddenly without fear of rear-end collision, because signal will turn red to hold back rest of cars until he passes second detector (arrow and right).

Five-mile section of Eisenhower (formerly Congress Street) Expressway is monitored by analog computers of surveillance project studying total network of expressway and its arterial sub-systems. Signs near feeder streets are actuated by detector-computer system and advise motorists about congestion on approach ramps and main highway. (Courtesy Illinois Division of Highways)

paring link characteristics both physically and operationally; subsequently it plans to evaluate the effect of control on the total length of the Expressway and major arterial streets nearby.

Unfortunately, this systems view of traffic can never be seen by the expert behind the wheel. In the Road Research Laboratory's experiments with roundabouts, drivers' opinions of effectiveness were largely conditioned by the amount of queuing, rather than the layout itself. Movement, no matter how agonizingly slow, seems preferable to standing still for most drivers. Indeed, many traffic-signal systems are sold by economically justifying their ability to reduce the number of vehicle stops required of the tax-paying user. The American Association of State Highway Officials estimates each 15-sec passenger car stop from 30 mph costs roughly 1.5¢.

Stops are costly, too, even when they are not caused by traffic signals. Many kinds of start-stop congestion involve momentary halts followed by immediate acceleration, all of which consumes fuel, wears tires and brakes, adds maintenance costs. Each stop from 30 mph without standing delay can cost 0.75 cents. Few motorists consider such figures. Hand on the horn, foot on the gas pedal, they seek to shorten trip time wherever they go.

Computer cops

When you don't know enough about the static and dynamic properties of a system to design controls for it, the techniques of adaptive control and self-optimizing system may hold some promise for traffic.

Conceivably, a computer should be able to continually sample traffic situations on interrelated streets and to calculate the best sequence of signals at any given moment to keep traffic flowing—if the scientific knowledge is developed to tell it what to do. For nobody yet knows how to control an enormous network of moving traffic in a street system.

A computer is now solving a simple network problem near Crowthorne, England. At a fork in the main road, two alternate routes lead to the same town. Detectors determine the traffic loads on them and the computer posts the shortest trip time on a sign at the fork.

The first major attempt to give a large-scale computer master control of traffic is underway in Toronto, Canada, where a UNIVAC 1107 is now being hooked up to street detectors to take data simultaneously at 100 intersections. These detectors are scanned 64 per second for pulses indicating the passage of vehicles. The computer calculates traffic density, direction, and flow at individual intersections. From internally

stored tables of data that describe the street width, detector placement, turn prohibitions, parking restrictions, etc., of each intersection, the computer calculates the signal timing for the entire network of lights, as shown in Color Fig. 13.

In effect, the existing signals are to be put under central control, though each signal will be individually adjustable at any moment and can be operated according to different principles of traffic control. By repeated experimentation with signal timing, it is hoped to learn which routines work best for various conditions so they can be recalled by the computer whenever applicable. Ultimately this data-taking is expected to reveal how many combinations of how many conditions might exist at 1000 intersections in Toronto. If it turns out to be a manageable number for so large a network, then it must be decided what the computer should do under these conditions.

For example, signals along some routes could be set progressively for heavy one-way traffic out of the city during rush hour. When traffic becomes more random, the signal settings would favor the greatest density of traffic moving toward an intersection. If, say, there is an exodus to the country or to the beaches on a weekend, and it rains mid-Sunday afternoon, a computer can detect the rush of earlier return traffic and adopt signal routines to cope with it. Similarly, by instantaneous scanning of the detectors, it could see where traffic is in the way and calculate fastest routing between two points for fire engines responding to an emergency, meanwhile rerouting ordinary traffic away from the scene. It could also accommodate to local area generators of traffic like parades or concerts.

The development of master programs and subroutines for this system, now being carried on by Traffic Research Corporation, Toronto, uses the entire downtown area as a live traffic laboratory. With live traffic information inputs and signal-control instructions preserved on magnetic tape, the computer can retrieve data to later produce charts for analysis of possible control schemes and for future urban planning.

Traffic generators

Still another aspect of the traffic problem is revealed each time a new road is built: New traffic comes forth and creates new congestion. Why? Because roads are connecting links to human activities. Road systems inherited from the earliest days of travel are direct links from town center to town center. And, in towns and cities, traffic is a function of buildings in which human activities take place. Buildings generate traffic and are destinations for it.

COMPUTER COPS

(In One Second)

1. Read + Verify signal monitor

2. Read intersection vehicle sensors

3. Calculate QUEUE Lengths, volume, speed + density

4. Calculate signal timing based on traffic (3) and co-ordination parameters

5. Is it time to change signals?

YES   NO

6. change signal (optionally display new signal state)

7. Repeat steps 1 to 6 for all 1000 Intersections

8. Compute Co-ordination parameters based on area flow.

9. Record traffic data and signal commands on magnetic tape.

Nowhere is this simple principle made more clear—that traffic and buildings are two facets of the *same* problem—than in a study of long-term problems of traffic in towns for Great Britain's Ministry of Transport. The Buchanan Report, named for Colin D. Buchanan who led the study group which completed it last year, found that while Great Britain seems still at a comparatively early stage of the motor age— 6.6 million automobiles and 1.8 million motorcycles for 16.4 million families—it *is* an island. The vehicle density per unit mile of roadway is double that of the U.S. with no room for expansion.

It's not simply a matter of an area so filled up that buildings are obstructions to cutting more roads. The Buchanan Report finds the conflict between traffic and towns stems from the physical layout of cities and towns. But if the answer to compactness is dispersal of traffic generators, one need only look at Los Angeles, now 80 miles long, to realize that dispersal also complicates transportation problems by increasing the distances to be traveled. Cities and towns are attractive because their great concentration of people offers a wide range of employment, services, housing, and cultural pursuits. If these activities are traffic generators, then one approach to the problem is to manipulate the causes of movement by seeking new designs for towns.

If you disregard traffic just passing through towns, it turns out that the patterns traced by vehicles are closely related to the manner in which the buildings are arranged. These patterns are so complex that widening of the streets will have less effect on traffic flow than developing simpler flow patterns by grouping buildings according to the nature of traffic movements they generate.

The essence of this concept is that road networks are services to environments. A calculable relationship can be developed between the capacity of environmental areas to generate traffic and the capacity of distributory networks to serve them. When environmental areas and access ways are designed together—call it traffic architecture—established urban areas take on a new look and new towns tend to be cellular in concept.

The new towns

What does happen when an entirely new town is systematically built to master the motor age by relating activities and traffic to the city plan? Cumbernauld, Scotland, is one example of what is now being built. It has fewer miles of main road in proportion to its population than other towns planned for 70,000

people. Car ownership is assumed to be one per family.

Roads in Cumbernauld are built like high-powered expressways with elaborate intersections; they provide vehicles with a fast-flowing but circuitous approach to the town center. Pedestrian networks are completely separated and much more direct. Shops and other central area buildings are constructed on a deck while vehicles arrive and park beneath. But how well Cumbernauld copes with traffic will not be known until the city reaches its planned population.

Surprisingly, these concepts of traffic architecture turn out to be old rather than new. Leonardo da Vinci's notebooks show sketches of 15th century cities with two-level roads— one level for vehicles and the other for pedestrians. Venice, a self-contained city of 140,000 that has existed for centuries entirely without wheeled motor vehicles, has a distributory system of canals completely separated from pedestrian walkways.

"New town" traffic architecture appeared in the United States in 1928 at Radburn, New Jersey (see Fig. 3-6). The Radburn plan was never widely adopted in the U.S.A., but some of its features now crop up all over the world . . . in the multilevel separation of vehicles and traffic in Philadelphia's Penn Center, in Stockholm and its satellite city of Farsta, in rebuilt bombed-out cities like Rotterdam and Coventry.

Where the sweeping change of complete redevelopment has not been undertaken, particularly because of cost, cities like Copenhagen and Bremen have closed entire streets to vehicular traffic during business hours, turning them into pedestrian malls. Significantly, other older cities such as Washington, D.C., Stockholm, and Toronto are making plans to extend their mass transit systems, for even future roads of conventional design can only hold so much traffic.

Automatic highways

Among the arguments for reduced headway between moving vehicles is that it will let more vehicles per hour use a road. But since there is an interaction between individual driver-controlled vehicles in denser traffic, a number of schemes have been proposed for entirely new road systems which would achieve automatic spacing control.

Automatic vehicle guidance systems have been demonstrated by the Road Research Laboratory, General Motors, and RCA. However, a driver performs extremely complex tasks in a variety of driving situations . . . tasks that presently defy duplication by an automatic

Fig. 3-6. *A principle of town planning tried in Radburn, N.J., in 1928 is appearing in "new towns." Independent routes for motorists and pedestrians serve buildings grouped by the nature of the traffic they generate. Photo shows curious gradual abandonment of plan in Radburn, but Cumbernauld, Scotland, and Hook, England, are being constructed much like sketch above. Venice, Italy (below), is reminder of successful scheme providing separate primary and secondary distribution systems for pedestrians and vehicles. (Courtesy* Traffic in Towns *and Aeroservice Corp.)*

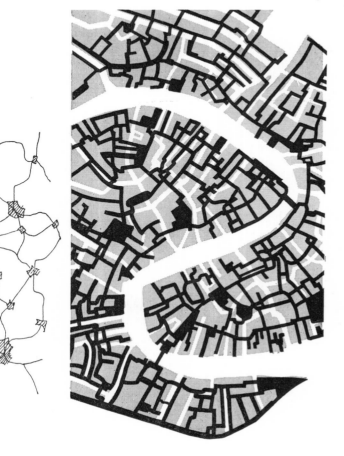

control system. To keep driving situations simple, automatic highways probably will be limited to driverless cars subject to central control of all vehicles in the system.

Another concept of the automatic highway has been proposed by Westinghouse Electric Corp. It reduces the headway between cars by loading them close together on sleds propelled by motors in the roadbed.

But one cannot even begin to evaluate such totally new concepts of individual transportation until they can be compared on equal terms. This is one of the objectives of a multimillion dollar research contract soon to be let by the Bureau of Public Roads, U.S. Department of Commerce. The objective of this contract will be a paper study toward development of a generalized model of individual transportation *systems* needed in the U.S. for the 1970's, hopefully making it possible to evaluate present and future concepts.

Elsewhere, as in England's Road Research Laboratory, at General Motors Technical Center in Michigan, at the University of Adelaide in Australia, at Cornell Aeronautical Laboratory, in the Operations Research Society there is a broadening of the research effort into traffic, a melding of interdisciplinary interests in what causes it and how it moves.

Ever so slowly, as if the research efforts

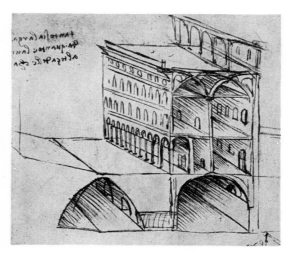

Fig. 3-7. *Simultaneous design of buildings that generate traffic and roads that carry it results in traffic architecture first suggested by da Vinci (above). Multi-level roads, mass transit, and pedestrian paths are at heart of Philadelphia's Penn Center (above, left) and Stockholm (left). In some cities, pedestrian malls are made by closing streets to vehicular traffic. (Courtesy Philadelphia City Planning Commission and American Swedish News Exchange)*

ing and instrumenting mockups is comparatively cheap insurance for an investment—like that in the U.S.A.—of a million dollars per mile for 41,000 miles of new roads.

Traffic presents a perplexing problem of living space and man-machine systems overlaid by social customs and laws; it needs microscopic and macroscopic examination that goes far beyond any ever attempted before.

Further reading

A bibliography of current literature on traffic and transportation is published by Northwestern University. This publication is particularly valuable for its listing of metropolitan area planning reports, usually hard to come by and worth reading because they are poles apart from microscopic views of the vehicle-driver-road problem.

An excellent volume of papers that deal with both microscopic and macroscopic views is *Theory of Traffic Flow,* the proceeding of a symposium held at General Motors Research Laboratories in 1959 (Elsevier, 1961, $9). Proceedings of a subsequent conference at the Road Research Laboratory in England are forthcoming.

The Transportation Sciences Section of the Operations Research Society of America holds meetings which bring together a mixture of scientists, traffic engineers, and city planners. Among the papers appearing in the society publication are "Nonlinear Follow-the-Leader Models of Traffic Flow," by Gazis, Herman, and Rothery (*Operations Research* **9,** No. 4, July–Aug. 1961). The most recent report on

were bogged down in their own traffic, more attempts are being made to ask the right questions, to design more meaningful experiments. For, after ten years as an embryonic field there are clearly signs that there can be a science of traffic. In addition to purely empirical approaches of the past, there is more organized research leading to theories that may have specific predictive values when adjusting the factors that affect traffic. This more fundamental research is coming almost exclusively from a new breed, not trained initially in traffic engineering, but in mathematics, physics, chemistry, etc.

If most traffic engineers are not similarly equipped to cope effectively with the problems of their own field, the fault may lie with universities that have trained them.

But, if bright, well-trained people are needed to develop a traffic science, so also do they need equipment to do experiments, and facilities in which they can be carefully performed. Traffic laboratories, like England's Road Research Lab, are almost nonexistent. In most places, it's against the law to conduct experiments on public roads. And, while controlled experiments on test tracks seem costly, build-

car-following studies by the General Motors group appears in "Vehicular Traffic Flow," *Scientific American*, Dec. 1963.

Don't pass up the eminently readable Buchanan Report, published as "Traffic in Towns" (Her Majesty's Stationery Office, 1963, $10). Even the charts and photos are intriguing.

A highly mathematical paper "On a Generalized Boltzmann-like Approach for Traffic Flow" by I. Prigogine et al. appeared in *Bulletin de la Classe des Sciences* **48**, Part 5 (Académie royale de Belgique, 1962).

Traffic Engineering and Control, published in the U.K., and *Strasse und Verkehr*, published in Germany, are two journals reflecting the work of traffic engineers. But you'll find other facets of traffic in articles appearing at random in the *American Behavioral Scientist* and the *Quarterly of Applied Mathematics*. Papers are published by the Inst. of Traffic Engineers and the Highway Research Board.

Aspects of the Toronto computer experiment are discussed in "The Control of Traffic Signals With an Electronic Computer" by L. Casciato (*Proceedings of the IFIP Congress 62*, North Holland). Traffic Research Corp. of Toronto (20 Spadina Rd.) has a color sound motion picture.

AIR TRAFFIC CONTROL

by William G. Osmun and Evan Herbert *

IN BRIEF: *Air traffic control seems deceptively simple because there are so many ways that parts of the problem can be isolated, defined, and solved. Each technique, each black box alone seems to be the starting point for a solution to the problem of coordinating the flights of many aircraft so they stay safely separated. But engineering them into a balanced man-machine system turns out to be an elusive task—mostly because the total problem has never been rigorously defined. It almost defies definition, because the parameters keep changing. Aircraft fly higher, faster. Users of the airspace make conflicting demands. Lightening the pilot's burden may overload the air traffic controller, or vice versa. Automatic communication and information processing is the answer recommended by a host of study groups. But after decades of studies, the pilots and controllers are still linked by a patchwork quilt of navigational systems, communications, radar of various vintages, anxious eyes in the cockpit, and some nervously chewed-on pencil stubs. —E.H.*

■ You've fastened your seat belt, the engines have started. So vast is the open sky above that these moments before you are airborne seem remote from any problems of air traffic.

Even with other aircraft aloft, the blue yonder is so wide that controlling traffic up there looks deceptively simple—more a matter of coordination than control: just ensure that aircraft flying from here to there stay far enough apart in position, altitude, and time.

And still make the buffer of space around each aircraft small enough so that you can accommodate simultaneously all the flights en route.

Yet parts of this apparently empty sky are sometimes so full of aircraft that they saturate human abilities to coordinate an orderly flow. When this happens, traffic in the air merely backs up . . . one hopes.

For none of the air traffic control schemes in use are completely foolproof or fail-safe.

In an age of technological triumphs that have sent men and women safely through space, it seems illogical that travel nearer the surface of this planet should not be more expeditious, less nerve-shattering. That in an age of pinpoint navigation of submarines and missiles, neither air traffic controllers nor pilots can always be sure of an aircraft's real position. That in a computer age, human beings doing hasty mental arithmetic are still at the heart of every air traffic control system. The skills and the judgment of these human beings still make air traffic control more an art than a science, though most of the components of a number of more automated systems are readily available.

For, domestically and internationally, the complexities of designing and instrumenting improved air traffic control systems are beset with political and economic difficulties that often overshadow the technological problems of achieving a satisfactory solution.

In the United States, where acute congestion in the air was publicly recognized only after a series of spectacular mid-air collisions, plan after plan for improving the system has been proffered by a ceaseless round of study groups. New systems are still at the planning stage in Europe, where national boundaries have long been overrun by jets in a matter of minutes

* William G. Osmun was Editor of *Business/Commercial Aviation* when this article was written; he is now on the staff of *Space/Aeronautics*. Evan Herbert is Associate Editor of *International Science and Technology*.

Fig. 3-8. To get a feel for the problem, try to resolve an air traffic control problem just as the controller sees it. His radar scope (top photo) shows six aircraft under his control. Markers known as shrimp boats point to the blips identifying these flights, though there may be a clutter of blips from uncontrolled flights in the area. The information printed in black on the scope photo is carried in the controller's head. Ready? It's 0958 hr and X500, which has just taken off from the airport at Sea Isle (SEI) is cleared by the control tower to fly toward the navigational radio fix at Kenton (ENO) while climbing to 2000 ft. He now asks for further clearance to fly at 9000 ft on airway. Victor 539: "Sea Isle approach control from Nan 500. Maintaining 2000 direct to Kenton. Request further clearance." All other traffic on the flight strips and radar is inbound at various speeds to ENO, wanting to land at SEI. Your problem: Give headings and altitudes to any or all aircraft so that Nan 500 (X500) can climb safely through oncoming aircraft and onto Victor 539 at the desired altitude. You have 1½ minutes and know only as much as a controller is given in the present operation of the air traffic system. Solution appears in Fig. 3-9. (Courtesy W. Osmun)

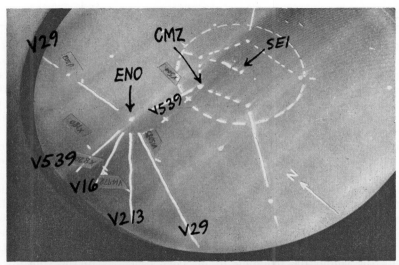

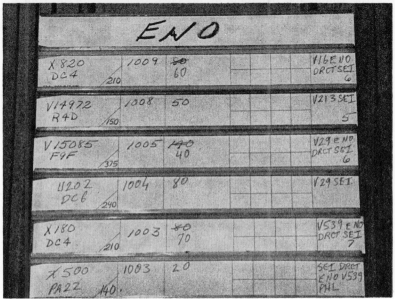

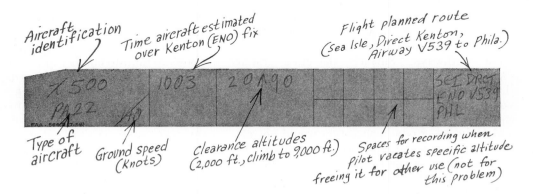

and where the approach lights at the end of a runway can glow brightly atop the soil of a neighboring country.

Over the busy North Atlantic air traffic complex, agreements about procedural and technological improvements among the member nations of the International Civil Aviation Organization, ICAO (a U.N. body), get ratified only after fancy political footwork, and adherence is still a problem. In this process, technically valid answers are often subordinated to sovereignty and economics.

Almost everywhere, the political cycle is shorter than the development cycle. Far too many research and development projects are killed off by changes in administration before they can be brought to fruition. The development cycle is long and tricky for a system that must satisfy a variety of users . . . civil and military, private and commercial, high-speed jets and low-speed propeller-driven aircraft, airplanes with every useful navigational aid and communications facility, and those carrying a minimum of such equipment.

So a philosophical definition of the problem —keeping a safe minimum separation among a maximum number of flights wanting to use the same airspace at the same time—is hardly rigorous enough to spell out the techniques and hardware which will solve it.

Airspace management requires compromising the conflicting demands of airspace users. There is a classic contest between airlines and private pilots for the use of the lowest 3000 ft of airspace, with private pilots wanting random, uncontrolled routing and airlines seeking the downward extension of controlled airways for low-level short-haul routes like Kansas City–Omaha or Paris–Brussels. Television towers intrude into paths of landing aircraft. Should the airports be moved or should the towers be confined to antenna farms?

Take-off

Technically, the air traffic problem begins on the ground, not in the air. It starts on the ramp, not on the runway, for your aircraft has already started to consume precious fuel once the engines have roared to life. Later, the amount of fuel remaining may become so critical as to drastically alter the altitude and routing of your aircraft.

At this moment, a local controller in the tower is watching you move away from the gate, observing your movements along taxiways, across busy runways, while he phases in movements of arriving aircraft along these same pathways. Surface detection radar (ASDE) can produce a scope image so fine that the controller can count the engines on your aircraft. But few major airports are equipped with ASDE. Given enough runways and taxiways, ground congestion would not affect movements in the air. But air traffic system designers can't control this factor, for most airports are municipally owned.

Now you're in take-off position, waiting for clearance from the tower. From here on, the pace of events will quicken, and the aircraft that safely stood only a few yards away on the ground will now have to be kept apart from yours by at least five minutes flight time, or 1000 ft of altitude—unless your flight is followed on radar, in which case only three miles horizontal separation is needed.

Safe separation is always the responsibility of the pilot; but if he elects to fly in controlled airspace, that is, along established airways, he makes what is in essence a contract with the air traffic control service. By filing his flight plan, he agrees to fly within certain tolerances at a certain altitude along a particular ground track according to a given schedule. Safe separation of all aircraft making a similar contract is then up to the air traffic controller, for pilots cannot always overcome poor visibility or detect the rapid closure of jets.

In good weather, there may be other aircraft in the same airspace flying under visual flight rules (VFR); separation from those aircraft is outside the controller's responsibility and is up to the controlled and uncontrolled pilots—see and be seen. Yet, at high altitudes, pilots approach each other at more than 1200 mph; an unobtrusive speck on the horizon may go unnoticed until it looms disastrously close.

As you thunder down the runway, you have little doubt that the controllers know their business, or that pilots know theirs. But now you're part of a vast man-machine system, a system so complex, so dynamic that nobody is really sure, beyond a shadow of a doubt, how an action in one part of the system may affect another part of the system.

Cowpaths in the sky

You're airborne now, and have been vectored (given headings) by the departure controller watching you on his radar to get you around other traffic and obstructions and up to the part of the sky in which you will fly.

Just how the sky is segmented for traffic control affects the capacity of the air traffic system and the machinery by which it operates. It also affects the navigation system aboard your aircraft.

If area control were exercised, you could choose an infinite number of paths between any two points in an area. What's actually used now is route, or airway control, which offers a finite number of paths between a limited number of points in the area. There are hundreds of airways criss-crossing the United States. Most of these are cowpaths in the sky . . . they've evolved from well-traveled routes. Traffic in channels seems easier to anticipate, easier to observe and control, though when you put it all through narrow pipes in the sky you're bound to get congestion.

So navigational systems are more than a pilot's tool; they're an integral part of the air traffic control system. En route now, in the part of the sky assigned to you by the air traffic center, are you really where you say you are? Within what tolerances? (On December 16, 1960, when United 862 collided with TWA

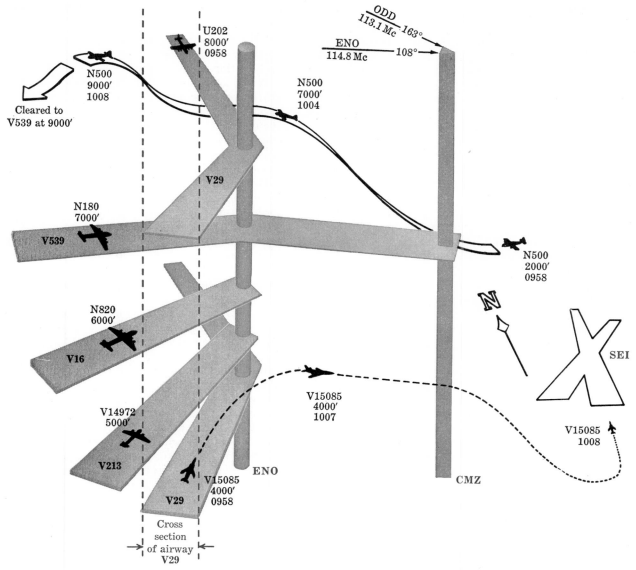

Fig. 3-9. This is how air traffic problem in Fig. 3-8 was solved by controller. "Nan 500. Turn right heading 300 degrees. Climb to and maintain 7000." When N500 (X500 in controller shorthand on strips) was clear of the airway, he would be vectored left to 270° until he was clear of traffic at 7000 ft or clear of Victor 29. Then he would be cleared to 9000 ft, reporting leaving 8000, when he would be turned left to 230° until he intercepted Victor 539 enroute to Philadelphia. V15085, a jet, was turned short of ENO to avoid conflict.

266 over Staten Island, the Civil Aeronautics Board concluded one aircraft was apparently not where it had been judged to be by the pilot or the controller. The damage suit is still in the courts.)

In the United States, ground navigational aids have been laid out on a route basis. An air traffic system tied down to the location of its ground stations stays somewhat inflexible; as traffic develops, a controller needs to rearrange routes, move faster aircraft around slower ones. That's not so easy with point-to-point navigation of airways.

The points are marked by VORs, very high-frequency radio range stations broadcasting

omnidirectional signals which establish an unlimited number of geographical tracks 360° around each station. The pilot may select any radial as his desired flight path and watch absolute (reference to north) VOR bearing indications on a 360° meter dial (see margin). He can fix his position by tuning to another VOR station and plotting the intersection of the two bearing radials. The traffic control system often uses the intersection of two radials as a reporting point or holding point. In rough terrain, though, VOR is troubled by reflections, so experiments are underway to cure them by improved antenna arrays.

VOR is the standard short-distance en route

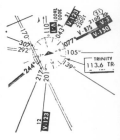

radio aid adopted by ICAO. There are over 800 stations in the United States alone, radio lighthouses covering more than 700 airways totaling over 355,000 miles.

Consider now that your aircraft and many others are flying nominally converging courses toward these stations (10 of the radials at Indianapolis are actual airways) and that the pilots have more difficulty in maintaining navigational accuracy the closer they get to a station because the radials get closer together. So the converging courses become collision courses, except for a traffic system separating them in altitude, time, and position.

Then why not parallel tracks in the sky? One could double the number of ground stations (at about $120,000 per VOR), but the tracks would still be fixed by the ground station locations. What would happen the next time more tracks were needed? Obviously, there's a limit to the number of tracks this network of ground stations can support. What's more, a network fixed by point-source navigation aids on the ground is fairly rigid.

An alternative—a navigational system that gives area coverage from central transmitting sites—has long been favored in some quarters outside the United States. With an area navigational system, an infinite number of tracks are possible and tracks can be changed at will by agreement between controllers and pilots, without adding or moving ground stations. Hyperbolic systems like Decca have long been proposed and a modernized high-altitude version of this system, called HARCO, is now under evaluation by Eurocontrol, a multination agency preparing to establish high-altitude air control over some of the most heavily traveled airspace in Europe.

Radio road signs

In addition to navigational systems that give direction for flying a course, there are fixed radio marker beacons that provide a pilot with positive indication (a beep or light) that he is over some specific point like "gates" for airport approach paths, or a convenient locale for delaying traffic in holding patterns.

Markers aren't needed as much by aircraft carrying distance measuring equipment. DME sends very short pulses of radio frequency energy from the aircraft to a selected ground station, usually located at a VOR. The interrogating pulses automatically trigger the ground station transmitter, essentially producing an artificial echo. The elapsed time between the interrogation and reply is measured precisely and displayed in mileage units on a cockpit indicator resembling an odometer.

Unlike directional radio navigation aids, DME does not depend on directive antenna arrays and does not suffer errors caused by propagational disturbances like reflection.

With accurate distance information from DME and bearing information from VOR, a pilot has a polar-coordinate radio-navigation system which tells him how far he is and in what direction from a known geographical point. Thus he can navigate more accurately, report his position to an air traffic controller.

Because position is available in the aircraft as an electrical signal, it can be fed to a pictorial display in the cockpit which superimposes the location of the aircraft as a spot of light moving across a map. Such devices have been shown to be very useful to a pilot in following flight paths specified by a traffic controller. The electrical signal may also be used by a simple analog computer to provide the pilot with left or right steering directions. He may fly offset straight paths which establish a system of parallel airways, or fly curved paths for holding and approach maneuvers.

But pilots cannot always rely on ground stations for navigational aid. For geographic or economic reasons, you simply can't put them the optimum 200 miles apart over large undeveloped land areas, in oceanic or polar regions. So the problem is to provide reliable propagation of navigational radio signals over distances of a thousand miles or more. Very low-frequency radio, around 100 kc, appears suited for this service despite the need for enormous ground antennas radiating high transmitter power in an already crowded and noisy portion of the radio spectrum. But there is still no agreement on what aids should be developed further for international adoption. Systems at various stages of development lie in laboratory limbo waiting for international agreement that may never come.

Meanwhile, long-distance air navigation relies on dead reckoning, in which the pilot estimates his present position by continually observing his speed and direction of travel from a known starting point.

To improve dead reckoning, Doppler navigation is used by military aircraft (see "The New Navigation," page 550). Inertial guidance is another dead-reckoning tool, but despite its success in military and space vehicles, until now it has been too bulky, too costly and complex for commercial aviation. Pan American Airways is currently testing inertial guidance for airline operations under a Federal Aviation Agency contract.

Because long-distance en-route navigation is still so imprecise, large blocks of airspace are maintained around each aircraft flying over, say, the North Atlantic. These days you can fly across the Atlantic in a subsonic jet in 6 to 9 hours. The airspace for the crossing appears so enormous that it is hard to realize its capacity is limited. But the most attractive arrival and departure schedules for eastbound and westbound aircraft cluster the traffic over the ocean at peak periods. The airlines also compete for assignment to the most economical (fuel-saving) upper levels of the narrow band between 28,000 and 41,000 feet. Also, there is a spread of positional uncertainties for which air traffic controllers must allow in keeping aircraft safely apart. Separation standards over the ocean, therefore, are greater than over land.

Cocoons of safe air

How many aircraft can a controller handle? How does he keep track? The answers involve the combined capacities of people, communications, automatic information-processing equipment, and the sheer hellishness of amalgamating them into a working system operating in an environment that varies continuously.

Recently, the Air Traffic Control Association, a U.S. organization of 7200 air traffic controllers, concluded that a controller can safely handle no more than *five* aircraft at one time, either in the terminal area or en route. All too often they handle more . . . sometimes as many as sixteen in peak traffic periods. In response to this recommended limit by ACTA, the FAA conceded that it was exceeded "occasionally," says it is currently studying the volume of traffic a controller can be expected to handle.

Can you reserve blocks of sky ahead of the moving flight and not permit the aircraft to enter the next block until it is positively clear? Since there can be only a finite number of blocks of a given size and shape of airspace, there is a limit to the number of aircraft that can be safely accommodated between two points en route. Or should you reserve a cocoon of airspace around the flight and monitor its progress to make sure that it doesn't impinge on a similar cocoon of airspace around any other flight?

How to use the airspace most efficiently, how to restructure the blocks, is part of the problem of redesigning today's air traffic system. It involves not only the precision with which the aircraft's position can be fixed and continuously monitored (radar permits the blocks to be shrunk) but also the ability of the pilot and his navigational equipment to stay within the confines of the block.

Yet more efficient management of air traffic means that coordinating actions from the ground must take place more rapidly than the speed of traffic through the air.

Pencil stubs and shrimp boats

What does a controller need to organize the flow of air traffic in a smooth, orderly, and safe fashion? He needs information about the identity, position, and altitude of the aircraft he must separate. He needs the means to store, display, and process this information. Processing involves computation of speeds, projection of future positions, and determination therefrom of potential conflicts—ATC terminology for the situation when two aircraft are separated by less airspace than the minimum specified in ATC procedures.

The controller needs to be able to query the pilot about his intentions and pass clearances to the pilot. And finally, the controller needs to be able to exchange information with other controllers responsible for bordering sectors.

How big these sectors should be is still a question mark of practicality. Faster aircraft may traverse a small sector so quickly that the pilot must negotiate more often for clearance to the next sector. That places a heavier communications burden on both pilot and controller, and on already busy radio channels. Shrinking the sector reduces the workload on the controller.

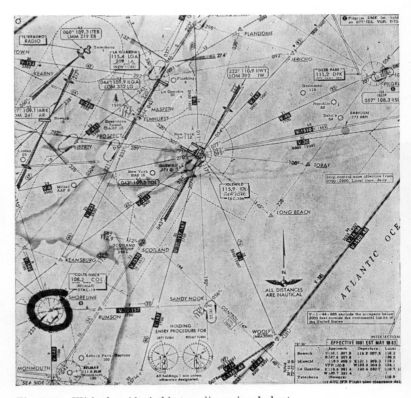

Fig. 3-10. With the aid of this two-dimensional chart, showing arrival and departure routes over New York terminal area, a pilot must imagine the three-dimensional view shown in Color Fig. 14. (Courtesy Jeppesen and Co.)

To a controller, your aircraft is the cryptic flight progress data on a narrow strip of paper, a spot of light on a radar scope, a disembodied voice in his headset. While the flight progress strip may be printed out in advance (the flight plan) by a computer, as it is in a few large centers like New York or Indianapolis, once your flight becomes active the strip still is updated by hand.

When data are transferred to another center, even by high-speed teletype, it still may take a quarter of an hour to distribute the strips physically to the proper controller's position. Some of the computer equipment being delivered to the FAA by International Business Machines will print out selectively on electric typewriters in various centers, but this printout is of flight plans, not updating of flight progress for the controller. Updating information comes from a pilot reporting his newest position over a fix, or from a radar screen watched by the controller.

Most of the United States and much of Europe is well-covered by radar. But many World War II battleship-type radars are still in en route air traffic control service. Some high-altitude flights fade out in a "black hole" above the antenna or between 20 and 30 miles away. Some fade out beyond 60 miles.

Which of possibly 200 aircraft within a 40-mile radius is yours on that scope? If the controller has your radar blip identified, he places a little numbered marker, a "shrimp boat," next to the blip and moves it along by hand. If he's not sure, your airplane may be asked to make an identifying procedural turn which he can see on the scope. This, of course, changes your rate of flow in traffic and your position relative to other aircraft.

For several years now, the FAA, the military, and many companies in the U.S. and Europe are experimenting with ways to present aircraft identity and altitude data electronically on the scope where it moves along with the appropriate blip; a computer may even extrapolate the aircraft's future route, predict conflicts and its sequence among aircraft approaching the same destination. But this technique still has problems. Controllers don't want all of this data all of the time—too much clutter—but they do want to interrogate electronically whenever they need vital data. And so far, nobody has figured out a simple, practical way to keep one blip from capturing the wrong data tag nearby when aircraft are over each other on the same track but at different altitudes, as in a holding stack.

Still, besides position, aircraft identity and altitude are what the controller needs. There may be a number of ways to give them to him automatically. Radar beacons have long been under consideration, though there is still no agreement on how they should be used. A beacon is a transponder, a receiver-transmitter carried by an aircraft which automatically sends out a coded reply whenever it receives a specific radar signal from the ground. It's an outgrowth of Identification Friend or Foe (IFF) of World War II. The reply signal strengthens the radar echo on the controller's scope, makes it easy to see despite distance of the target or cluttering echoes from rain clouds

Fig. 3-11. Aircraft also float in relative positions in Avco volumetric display. Light spots are generated directly on spinning electroluminescent panel at grid points designated by radar. Computer could add predicted paths (see Fig. 3-13) and alphanumeric indicators. Problems of manufacturing electroluminescent panels limit displays to about 30 × 20 in. and life of about 10,000 hr. Control room must be dark to view spots. (Courtesy Avco)

and the ground. Except that when the blip "blooms" on the scope, it sometimes covers three miles—so *precisely where* is the aircraft? To solve this problem, FAA is developing an electronic marker which will pinpoint the center of the blip.

However, the reply code could also uniquely identify the aircraft, that is, if there were enough codes available and a logic for their assignment had been developed.

The beacon's use of coded pulses offers temptation to use it for other tasks. For example, altitude measured from the ground is not as accurate as when measured from the aircraft and radioed to the air traffic controller. Pilots could be freed of altitude reporting over busy communications channels if the aircraft's altitude were transmitted automatically by the beacon. And then why not transmission of other data?

Questions like this—How much of a data link should a beacon be? Should it be the only link?—are still unresolved in the planning of air traffic control systems that contemplate the use of beacons as a tool.

The party line

Meanwhile, as the air route structure grows more complex, the number of compulsory position reporting points also grows. The faster an aircraft travels, the more rapidly it arrives at reporting points. But sheer volume of communications traffic is not the only problem for pilot and controller. The intelligibility of voice communications is sometimes so restricted by rapid speech (time is precious on a "party line"), by distortion, noise, or inaudibility that transmissions must be repeated, further adding to the load on present communications.

By 1966, certain bands will accommodate more channels through 50 kc spacing, rather than 100 kc spacing. There is also work in

progress at Martin-Marietta and Motorola on modulation schemes which are claimed to be capable of handling all communications requirements of civilian and military aircraft with only two wide-band frequency assignments of 4 Mc each, giving every aircraft and controller a private radio telephone number rather than several party lines for all. But more channels are only a partial solution; pilots and controllers must still take time to transmit or to listen—and to understand.

The plight of a controller at Frankfurt, Germany's Rhein Main airport is an extreme case. More than 40 airlines use this field, and German or English is not the native tongue of most of their pilots. So controllers and pilots must talk slowly, using up precious seconds to overcome even such language barriers as shades of meaning or a Texas drawl.

If you were now flying from, say, New York to Chicago, you would have to send 111 voice messages from the time you left the departure gate at Idlewild until you parked on the ramp at O'Hare. You'd pass through nine different control jurisdictions and make eight changes of communications frequency en route.

This would be cut in half by ACCESS (Aircraft Communication Electronic Signaling System), a data link proposed to the FAA by a Motorola-General Precision team. Rather than a pilot listening for a break in the constant stream of communications a controller is having with other aircraft, he can push a button in the cockpit that lights a request-to-talk indicator on the controller's console.

A typical clearance message exchange by voice runs almost a full minute: 20 sec for the clearance, the rest for queries, answers, and acknowledgment. The same exchange when digitized runs ½ sec for the clearance, 60 millisec request for acknowledgment, and 60 millisec for acknowledgment.

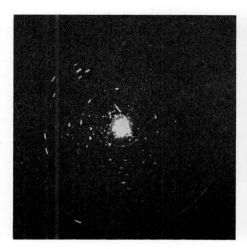 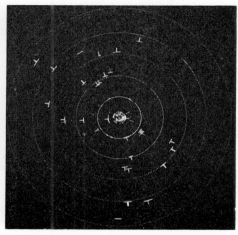

Fig. 3-12. Scope at left shows both stronger signals from beacon-equipped aircraft and ordinary radar echoes. But elongated beacon blip makes airplane look several miles long so center mark is added electronically (right) to pinpoint position. If beacon becomes data-link too, scope could automatically show aircraft identity and altitude next to each correct blip. (Courtesy Federal Aeronautics Administration)

For position reporting in ACCESS, a data processor on the ground keeps track of flight plans and interrogates an aircraft by radio 3 min prior to its estimated time of arrival over a fix. When the aircraft actually arrives over the fix, the pilot pushes a position report button which transmits a digital signal giving aircraft identity and time. The computer then calculates the estimated time of arrival over the next fix and sends a report by voice or to a cockpit teleprinter. The pilot acknowledges its correctness by pushing a button. If the aircraft fails to report over a fix within a certain time of his ETA, the controller is alerted by a warning light on his console.

Even more automation is said to be possible with ACCESS. Beacon codes could be changed automatically and radio receivers in the cockpit could be switched by ground station signals to new frequencies as the aircraft enters each new control sector.

All these communications chores are reasonably spaced in time during the en route portion of your trip, but both pilot and controller become incredibly busy as you enter the terminal area.

Final approach

Since you are flying toward the terminal, it would be ideal to simply descend along the straight track to your destination. But within a terminal area there are potential conflicts with other aircraft arriving or departing from different directions. The terminal area may begin

Fig. 3-13. Path-prediction display has been proposed by Avco to help controllers schedule, see projections two minutes ahead, and guide more aircraft to safe landings in congested terminal areas. (Courtesy Avco)

as far out as 40 miles from large cities that have metroplexes . . . multiple airports nearby, both civil and military. These are usually so close in flight time that the traffic at one airport affects the traffic at another.

So finer controls than used en route must be exercised over your altitude, speed, and path of approach to the runway. You'll be landed in a time-honored sequence of arrival: first come, first served. Yet the speed and size mix of today's air traffic makes sequencing of random arrivals rather inefficient.

If the landing acceptance rate of an airport—a factor determined by instrument landing aids, number of runways, high-speed turn-offs to clear them—is, say, one per minute, then the goal in peak traffic periods is to control the flow of traffic through the terminal area to funnel them into a final approach path one minute apart. But this gets tricky with mixed traffic; you can't let a large jet transport be followed too closely by a relatively small, light aircraft. Under certain conditions, wing tip vortices create severe turbulence in the wake of large aircraft. These move unpredictably with the wind and have caused fatal accidents to aircraft three or four miles behind.

To control separation and flow, controllers can ask pilots to travel at certain speeds, or to stretch out their flight paths so that they travel a longer route and take more time, or to hold a position by flying a tight racetrack pattern over a fix. Many aircraft may be stacked over a fix, each descending 1000 ft to the next lowest cleared altitude as the bottom aircraft is cleared to land.

The last ten miles will be traversed at a velocity (about 120 knots for jets) which will make for a precisely controlled rate of descent and lateral corrections to line the aircraft up with the runway. However, variations in this velocity can affect the spacing between leading and following aircraft. If you are, say, 19 sec late in touching down, the aircraft behind you may be more than half a mile closer. If he should have to pull up to go around again—running up to full power for most jets is like kicking a dinosaur in the tail—the aircraft takes a long time to react.

Clearly, then, for most efficient use of the landing facilities, the controller needs some aid to better prediction of terminal area flight paths. His en route predictions could be based on straight line projections, but here the flight paths are randomly curved and impossible to predict simply by direct computation. One solution to this has been proposed by Avco Corp.: a fast-time adaptive analog computer coupled to a flight simulator. This traces flight paths predicted for two minutes ahead of each blip on the radar scope, thus showing the anticipated separation of each aircraft.

Another proposal, by Sam Saint—an American Airlines jet captain and longtime ATC expert—uses a more simple computer to give approach controllers a "time to turn" for each aircraft lining up for a final approach. Saint also is a consultant to FAA, which is currently testing his concept in a simulator.

If your plane misses the final approach you're now making, you'll have to go around again, jockeying through terminal area traffic until you can re-enter the approach pattern in a satisfactory sequence. Missed approaches happen most often under marginal weather conditions, which means that the controller must vector your go-around on radar at a time when, say, a storm center moving across his scope may obscure other aircraft at a critical moment.

To this extent, automatic blind landing equipment would improve the landing rate in bad weather and would reduce the number of missed approaches. Experimentation and development work is currently underway in England, France and the U.S. on blind landing equipment and techniques. All three use refined versions of the present electronic navigational system or instrument landing system (ILS). But the British philosophy of committing the final few hundred feet of the landing entirely to the automatic systems contrasts sharply with the U.S. and French philosophy of permitting the human pilot to take over at any stage of the automatic landing.

But you've made it this time. You're on the runway at your destination, and as you taxi toward the gate, you wonder why, if newer technology already exists, it isn't now operational in the present air traffic control system.

When overloaded, automate

The fact is ". . . techniques are available to permit a solution of the traffic problems expected in the next two decades." The quotation is from one of the half dozen post-war plans for modernization of American aviation facilities. This one was dated May 1957.

Most of them take the same tack: the human elements in the system—pilots and controllers —are overloaded; therefore, provide automation wherever possible to relieve them of the routine tasks that could be done equally well by a machine. For monitoring routines, machines are more consistently on the alert, more tireless than men. The demands on the human elements in the air traffic control system almost reach saturation at times. How many hours of uninterrupted attention can a controller stand at full strain?

Dr. Heinz von Diringshofen, a German authority in aviation medicine, thinks that human reserves for peak performance peter out after two hours of such strain. Further studies of this human factor are being made in the United States; FAA's Civil Aeromedical Research Institute is testing the controller as a critical human subsystem. While today controllers are rotated through the most difficult control positions—a half hour is the maximum most controllers can stand in the tower radio position at O'Hare Field in Chicago—they still face periods of incredible tension during an 8-hour shift.

When, under these conditions, controllers making critical judgments of dynamic situations must rely on powers of memory and imagination to correlate and interpret data, it seems logical to turn to the superior memory and endurance of machines and to present the data they handle in graphic displays more suitable for swift, sure human decision. But make the information system evolutionary: give machines a back-up of hard-copy data so men can take over whenever there is a failure. And have the system fail gracefully, rather than all at once like the "one-hoss shay."

All of the controller's clerical chores are ripe targets for automation, and that includes upwards of three quarters of his work load. Prime target for automation has always been "data processing"—the recording, updating, computing and extrapolation that goes with aircraft flight plans and position reports. This is the information the controller has to digest *before* he can detect potential conflicts and issue clearances to resolve them. Automation of the conflict prediction task itself is still a long way off because the computer program is tricky to write. To date, no conflict prediction program has been completely debugged, and tested in an operational environment.

Experiments with computers for analyzing flight plans, calculating arrival times over fixes, and updating information have been carried on since 1953. The road to their operational use is paved with leftover black boxes tried with all good intent. For, engineering an information system is more than wiring equipment together. First the problem must be analyzed, the nature of the solution decided upon, and the means of solution carefully spelled out in a computer program.

If flying or control procedures are complex— as for approaches and holding—they are difficult to automate. If there are procedural ambiguities or lack of procedural precision in the way air traffic situations are resolved by humans, these will not be tolerated by machines. The mechanical requirements are well within the state of the information processing art, but

Fig. 3-14. London's Heathrow Airport ATC posts handwritten flight progress data by closed circuit TV. Dutch SATCO system is updated by controller keyboard, read-out is electromechanical display. (Courtesy Marconi Wireless and N. V. Hollandse Signaalapparaten)

the systems engineering has to be accomplished *before* the equipment is ordered.

Fail softly

If an electronic information system should fail, what happens to air traffic control operations? Redundancy of critical equipment is at the heart of every automation plan for ATC. But few computer engineering organizations in the world have had much experience with the tricky programming logic of how a standby computer takes over. And failures of electronically held data mean that the controller, pencil in hand again, must be able suddenly to pick up from hard copy of traffic information current at the time of failure. Moreover, if automatic

information processing and display will enable each controller to handle more traffic than the present manual system, a failure of such equipment could dangerously overload the controllers when there is a sudden reversion to manual.

Current FAA thinking about automation of data transfer between air and ground concentrates on a limited, one-way air-to-ground data transfer using the radar beacon system. Concern with a two-way automatic air-ground-air communications link (like Motorola's ACCESS or RCA's AGACS) is put off for the future. By contrast, Eurocontrol seeks an air-ground data link as part of its plan for high level area control. The HARCO technique now being studied features area navigational capability, with a data link.

Closely related to data processing and data transfer is the all-important matter of displaying data for the controller. For display techniques now exist to show virtually any information the computer can derive from data stored in its memory. But, as long as the choice of computer and the method of processing data are unresolved, practical development of optimum displays is difficult.

Starting in the middle

But how you go about engineering advanced automatic equipment into a compatible system depends on your concept of how it should be used operationally—on whether procedures already in use are to define the system, or whether the new system should define future procedures.

Ideally, a pilot should be able to fly wherever he wishes, subject only to another aircraft being there first. The ideal of random flight paths, however, imposes the severest demands on system technology. In the U.S., the point-to-point navigational capability of the VOR network would need DME added to it, pictorial displays, and off-course computers, before true area navigational coverage was possible. And controllers would need the most sophisticated data processing-transfer-and-display system to monitor and to control the potentially infinite number of flight paths.

Today's airways structure provides an orderly and more easily manageable concentration of traffic on the most-traveled routes.

Although the basic rules of keeping two aircraft apart are the same the world over, different procedures are possible in Australia, where the ground authority has both separation control and operational control of aircraft flights, than in Europe and North America, where operational control is the jealously guarded prerogative of the pilot.

In Germany, where civil air traffic control was built from the start by the Allied military, the problem of integrating civil and military traffic can be handled far differently than it could in England and elsewhere on the Continent, where the onset of an airways system meant depriving the military of their time-honored freedom of action in an airspace that was shrinking fast at jet speeds.

The civil-military problem crops up everywhere. How can both military and civil aircraft use the airspace, and be separated safely from each other without subjecting military flights to the confining limitations of civil procedures or making civil flights give up valuable airspace for unrestricted and exclusive military use? When is a strange blip on the radar scope an enemy bomber, or merely a lost airliner? Both air defense and air traffic control systems must be able to talk to each other and answer that question—fast.

In the French Centre de Controle du Nord at Orly Airport, control experts are using an IBM 650 computer and a data entry keyboard at the controller's position as a test bed to answer a fundamental question: "Is it reasonable to ask the controller to tell the machine what he knows?" No significant progress in lightening the controller's work load is possible until this question is resolved because, until the air-ground data link is fully automated, there is no device—except the human controller—to update computer information.

Today's controller has no such problem; updating is automatic: the scribbles he puts on flight progress strips record and display data already updated in his brain. Can the controller also update the computer without disturbing his control task—and if so, is his effort worth it?

If the French get an affirmative answer, then it is possible to build automatic data processing onto today's manual system in an evolutionary fashion. If the answer is negative, we'll need an automatic entry of data from aircraft in flight without resorting to the controller as an input device. This can either be based on the long-sought two-way automatic exchange of information via the air-ground data link (Eurocontrol approach), or a more limited one-way flow of information via the radar beacon system (U.S. plan).

Over the borders and far away

Born of the necessity for coordinating the flights of high-speed jets over Europe, Eurocontrol achieved treaty status in February 1963. The first concrete effort of Eurocontrol will be to take over responsibility for high-altitude control now exercised in national traffic control centers.

The North Atlantic air traffic complex seems less complicated because there are no national boundaries. The complex was examined recently, using operational analysis in a study regarded as a milestone in the application of these techniques to ATC. Predictably, where the study's conclusions cut across traditional operations preferences, they are now being kept at arm's length. But who is to say that the logic produced by a study group does in fact take into account all of the realities of practical day-to-day operations?

Study groups have long been at work in the U.S.A., where air traffic became a problem earliest, where more money and more people have been committed to more different solutions than anywhere else in the world.

Half a flight plan

Seven years have gone by since Congress passed the Federal Aviation Act of 1958, and set up the FAA—largely to provide the money and the organization to speed the development of a "modern" air traffic control system. How far have we come since then? More important, are we any closer to the design, development, and implementation of a future system than we were then?

Surprising as it may seem, the functional requirements for a modern ATC system were laid down as long as 15 years ago in the very first coordinated study of the problem. Subcommittee 31 of the Radio Technical Commission for Aeronautics then spelled out the need for automation of the controller's clerical duties, improved situation displays, and automation of the information exchange between controller and pilot. Most of the techniques were known even then.

For example, the use of secondary radar (the ATC radar beacon system) to give controllers automatically the position, identity, and altitude of an aircraft, was proposed by SC-31 and it is the cornerstone of the 1961 Project Beacon report—which set the guidelines for today's R&D effort.

Despite the fact that every committee, study group, team, or task force after SC-31 has reiterated the need for automating the controller's work load, his job today is still manual. Stripped of hardware improvements, the system is basically what it was ten years ago. As shown in Fig. 3-8, the controller must still record, store, and display flight progress information by writing on strips of paper.

Pilot to Parkinson: Help!

The most noticeable change that has taken place in air traffic control centers over the past seven or eight years is the great increase in number of controllers. Lacking mechanical tools to help the controller cope with the rising tide of aircraft movements, FAA has chosen to meet the increased work load by making control sectors smaller, adding more controllers. The multiplication of sectors and controllers creates fantastic requirements for communications, for coordination between controllers of adjacent sectors. Some Parkinson law may set a limit on the improvement made simply by adding more controllers.

Conceding that we have the technology, it seems much more advanced than our ability to formulate the problems to which this technology is a solution. What has been lacking is a rational method of selecting from among competing technologies. Without this, most studies and development efforts have dealt only with subsystems of basic problems. Indeed, black-box development has often preceded—even *generated*—problem definition. A climate of "black boxes looking for a problem to belong to" was worse in pre-FAA days, but it still seems to linger.

It would be unfair, indeed, to give the impression that effectively managing the ATC research and development effort is easy. As we have shown, air traffic control requires a complex family of man-machine interfaces. They're hard to define when the problem won't stand still. Aircraft performance ranges are broadening—from hovering helicopters to supersonic jets. Not only is the mix of these aircraft changing, but much of the uncontrolled (VFR) traffic shows up in airspace where controlled flights operate on instrument flight rules (IFR). In 1954, about 15% of the aircraft in the U.S. were controlled. In 1963, control has been extended to only about 25% of everything that flies, and even this is already straining the system (see Color Fig. 14 and Color Fig. 21 for a visual representation of this strain).

As long as the requirements that the ATC system has to satisfy are continually changing, the solution will never quite catch up with the problem. What's really needed, then, is a system that can cope with current demands made on it while it's being improved to keep ahead of the changing, growing requirements.

FAA has managed to mobilize the manpower and funds needed to push U.S. air traffic control up to the point where it can just keep up with today's requirements. The question is whether current FAA efforts will be enough to develop a system that can meet the demands of tomorrow's traffic and be responsive to the changing requirements of all users.

Its success, or failure, transcends the national boundaries of the United States because the way the U.S. solves its air traffic control problem may have great influence on the way similar problems can be handled elsewhere in the world.

Further reading

It's worth reading the full Civil Aeronautics Board Aircraft Accident Report on the mid-air collision over Staten Island, N.Y., in 1960 (CAB File No. 1-0083).

The present plan for ATC in the U.S. is required reading: "Design for the National Airspace Utilization System" (Federal Aviation Agency Systems R&D Service, Washington, D.C., 1962). Compare it with "National Requirements for Aviation Facilities—1956–1975," a more systems-oriented study (Govt. Printing Office, 4 vols).

"Project Beacon" is the engineering basis for the present plan (FAA-SRDS). "An Analysis of Project Beacon" was made in 1961 by the Air Traffic Service, FAA.

An excellent operation analysis of long-haul problems over the undeveloped areas is given in "Systems Analysis of the North Atlantic Air Traffic Complex" by Arcon Corp. (FAA-SRDS, Dec. 1962, and ASTIA AD-294610).

An analysis of current ATC problems and recommended improvements is contained in the report of Subcommittee 104 of the Radio Technical Commission for Aeronautics (RTCA Secretariat, N.W., Washington 25, D.C., June 1963, $1.25).

RTCA, a cooperative government-industry association of aeronautical telecommunications agencies, holds meetings on ATC problems; the International Civil Aviation Organization (Montreal) convenes an Air Traffic Automation Panel at various intervals.

Professionally interested people may arrange to visit an ATC center by writing to the chief controller, nearest FAA Regional Hq. The same qualification applies to viewing an ATC simulation at NAFEC, Atlantic City. Mention ATS Simulation Branch when writing to Tech. Inf. Div. FAA-SRDS.

If you can't visit an ATC center or be in a cockpit, you can *hear* the communications between pilot and controller on Aero Progress LP records: "LA to NY-VFR" ($14.95) and "In Radar Contact" ($5.98), Jeppesen & Co., Denver, Colo. Voice and data-link communications are dramatically compared in a booklet containing an LP record on ACCESS. A limited number of copies are available from Ken Martin, Teledata Div. Motorola.

HYPERSONIC FLIGHT TESTING

by Antonio Ferri *

IN BRIEF: *When a body moves through the air at a velocity exceeding 5 to 6 times the speed of sound, it is said to be in hypersonic flight. This regime is a rigorous one, much more so than the lower-velocity regimes of supersonic and transonic flight. For one thing, friction between the air and the body is sufficient to heat the surface beyond its melting point. For another, shock waves around the vehicle generate a region of high temperature and pressure in the gas flowing near the surface, thus setting up complex chemical reactions there. Hence theoretical analysis becomes extremely complex and must be buttressed in experiments run under simulated flight conditions. Such experimental techniques fall into three categories: ballistic ranges, where the model is launched into a controlled atmosphere; wind tunnels, where the model is fixed and the air moves; and combinations of the two. No one facility can simulate completely all flight conditions, both aerodynamic and chemical. Hence a family of complementary facilities has been devised.—F.P.*

■ As a technology expands, so must its lexicon. But few technologies grow in a predictable and orderly fashion. Thus the words we choose along the way are being constantly redefined to make them more useful.

In the early stages of high-speed aerodynamics, we described what we observed by means of three interchangeable adjectives: hyperacoustic, supersonic, and hypersonic. All three meant but one thing—that the observed phenomenon had occurred at a speed above the speed of sound. They differed only in their etymology; the first is all Greek, the second all Roman, and the last is Greco-Roman.

Today, however, the word hypersonic is used only in conjunction with flight speeds above 5 to 6 times the speed of sound, while supersonic now defines the flight velocity range above the speed of sound but below these values. The word hyperacoustic has become an anachronism.

The speed of sound in the flight medium is important in high-speed aerodynamics for a simple reason. It turns out that the flow around the body and the forces on it as it rushes through the medium are both dependent upon the Mach number—the ratio of the body's velocity to the speed at which a small disturb-

* Antonio Ferri is Professor of Aerodynamics at New York University, Director of the Guggenheim Aerospace Laboratories, and President of General Applied Science Laboratories, Inc., Westbury, New York.

ance, such as a sound wave, propagates in the medium. When the flight speed is high enough for the flow to be characterized as hypersonic, the fluid "streaming by" the body no longer behaves as a simple gas, and the nature of the flow becomes much more complex.

This flow is nicely illustrated by the shadowgraph of the flow around a conical body with a spherical nose shown in Fig. 3-15. The Mach number of this flow is of the order of 8. The photo indicates the existence of a demarcation front that starts near the nose of the model and extends far from the body. This front, called a shock wave, represents a sharp change of static pressure and temperature of the flow, and divides the undisturbed flow from that which is perturbed by the motion of the body. Because of the hypersonic speed of the body, any disturbances it produces cannot travel in front of the shock wave, but are restricted to the region behind it. The shape of the shock wave and the flow behind it are a function of the body's shape and its Mach number.

Why *hypersonic* aerodynamics anyway?

It is important to distinguish the very high-speed range of hypersonic velocities from the lower supersonic range because the problems to be solved in the design of a hypersonic vehicle are quite different, as are the technologies involved. The convenience of such classification has been recognized by the theoretical aerodynamicist, the vehicle designer, and the experimentalist alike, although for somewhat different reasons.

The theoretical aerodynamicist is happy to have a new speed regime defined because the simplifications that are valid when the Mach number is small are not valid at very high Mach numbers. However, by assuming large values for the Mach number, he can introduce different approximations into the equations of motion and thus simplify the analytical problem. This permits new types of analyses to be derived for some families of problems. But there are other difficulties. The theoretical aerodynamicist must consider chemical processes that occur in the flow which force him to abandon the assumption of a perfect, inert gas. These processes complicate the analyses severely and require different computational techniques—usually numerical ones.

For the vehicle designer, the problems related to hypersonic flight are quite different from those encountered at lower, supersonic speeds

 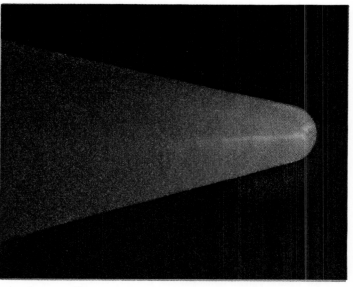

Fig. 3-15. Aircraft do not yet fly as rapidly as these two models, "in flight" above Mach 8 in an earthbound wind tunnel. This is the realm of the ballistic missile, the returning satellite or spacecraft. It's a harsh realm, for the hurtling body is accompanied by a steady shockwave (left) behind which are generated very high pressures and temperatures. One result is severe heating of the body itself (right). Another is ionized gases that disrupt communications. The most adroit theoreticians can probe these effects only so far. Then the experimentalist must lend a helping hand. (Courtesy Aerospace Institute, Brooklyn Polytechnic Institute, left; Gas Dynamics Laboratory, Princeton University)

because of the large aerodynamic heating produced at high speed by air friction on the body surface. The heat that penetrates beneath the surface is sufficient, in many cases, to melt and destroy the structure. To combat this situation, special care is taken to select aerodynamic shapes that will minimize the surface heating and to incorporate special cooling systems in the structure to absorb and dissipate the heat produced, thus maintaining tolerable temperatures in the structure.

The heat flux penetrating the vehicle is very large near the nose (Fig. 3-15), and at that point it is inversely proportional to the square root of the nose radius. Therefore, in order to reduce heat penetration, the nose on a hypersonic vehicle is made blunt rather than sharp. At lower speeds, where drag rather than heating is the major problem, the vehicle will have a sharp nose instead of a blunt one.

With the need to control heat flux looming so large in vehicle design, two basic approaches have been worked out. For long-duration flights, the so-called "active" cooling technique looks more practical; the heat that penetrates the structure is absorbed by a coolant—usually fuel —in a heat exchanger at the vehicle's surface, or it is dissipated by radiation. In some cases, both means are used.

In short-duration flights, "passive" cooling is preferred; the heat is absorbed either by the heat capacity of the body itself, or by the ablating material placed on its external surfaces.

The ablating material performs two functions: It absorbs the heat by changing its state, literally melting and vaporizing layer by layer; and, at the same time, the gases thus produced form a heat-absorbing film that moves along the body with the air flow (see "Ablation," page 535).

A closer look behind the shock wave

The strong shock wave generated near the nose of the body produces a very large temperature rise (and a pressure rise as well) in the region between the shock and the body. This abrupt change in temperature is, of course, more pronounced at low altitude—where the air is denser—than it is at high altitude, and it varies with vehicle velocity as sketched in the margin. In the presence of such high temperatures, the chemical composition of the air behind the shock changes. The oxygen and nitrogen molecules tend to dissociate to atomic form. Some of the particles become ionized, and a weak plasma is generated.

Now hypersonic flight usually occurs at high altitude so that the static pressure and density of the gas flowing near the body is low. For these conditions, the reaction rates for recombination of the dissociated and ionized gas are small; therefore when the flow re-accelerates, as it does by moving around the body, it does not immediately reach chemical equilibrium.

This departure from chemical equilibrium does not strongly affect the aerodynamic forces around the body, but it does affect the heat transfer to the body, and it strongly affects the ionization level of the flow and the intensity of the plasma around the vehicle. This is troublesome, for the plasma persists in the flow downstream of the nose and even in the wake of the vehicle. The resulting plasma shell shrouding the vehicle interferes with electromagnetic radiations reaching the vehicle or emanating from it, thus disrupting its comunication system. This effect was, in fact, the cause of the communications blackout experienced by the first Mercury capsule during re-entry. Radar signals are reflected by the vehicle's wake, thus the presence of the plasma in that region of the flow significantly increases the "radar cross section" of the vehicle—a big factor in missile defense.

Enter, the experimentalist

As you can appreciate, the theoretical analysis of all such problems is extremely difficult. Accordingly, the vehicle designer is forced to turn to the experimentalist for answers to his questions. For hypersonic flight, these are transformed into different classes of experimental problems. Principal among these are the determination of aerodynamic forces on different body shapes, along with heat transfer to these shapes in the absence of ablation; evaluating heat transfer when ablation *is* present; measuring thermal stresses in the structure; and studying the plasma field around bodies and its effect on radar cross section.

It would be nice if we had a single experimental facility in which we could investigate all these phenomena simultaneously. Such does not exist. However, we have evolved a family of different facilities—which I shall discuss later on—each of which is tailored to limited types of problems because it simulates only a few of the many parameters involved.

Why don't we simulate hypersonic flight completely? We don't because it would require testing a model of the same size as the vehicle, at the same relative velocity, and in a fluid having the same static pressure, temperature, and chemical composition as in flight. Fortunately, such extremes are necessary only when nonequilibrium chemical processes must be completely simulated. In such a case, the flow times—that is, the time required for a given particle to move between any two given points—must be the same in the test as in flight so as to keep the ratio of flow times to reaction times the same in both cases. Fortunately, it has been shown that nonequilibrium effects are not important in pressure and force determinations, and that for heat transfer measurements below Mach-25 corrections can be introduced easily.

When the chemical processes that occur are in equilibrium, and when the chemical properties of the flow depend only upon local conditions, then life is simpler and scaled down models can be tested. Even then, however, velocity, pressure, and composition of the air must be simulated in order to simulate the chemistry. It often transpires, however, that chemical phenomena need not be simulated at all, for chemical processes in hypersonic flight often take place only in a very localized region of the flow where high static temperature is reached. In such a case, the effect of chemistry is small and it can be investigated separately so that appropriate corrections can be made. Of course, the validity of the final results depends heavily on the investigator's understanding and ingenuity in selecting the right set of experiments and in introducing the chemical effects measured in one into the fluid-dynamic characteristics measured in the other.

Chemistry aside, the aerodynamic quantities of the flow and the forces on the actual vehicle can be obtained, to a first approximation, by simulating in the model test the values of the two main fluid-dynamic parameters—the Mach number and the Reynolds number—and by controlling the model's surface temperature. Just as the Mach number is the similarity parameter related to the propagation of pressure waves in the flow, so the Reynolds number is the parameter related to the viscous flow phenomena—and hence to the shear forces on the body and to the boundary-layer flow.

We recall that the Reynolds number is a nondimensional ratio: $R = VL\rho/\mu$, where L is a reference length of the vehicle, V the velocity of the stream, ρ the density of the undisturbed gas, and μ its viscosity. Complete aerodynamic similitude requires that the Reynolds number be the same in the test as in flight. Fortunately, however, most important aerodynamic coefficients—such as the drag and lift coefficients—vary but little with Reynolds number. Thus as long as the test is not run over a wide range of Reynolds number, it can be run at a smaller value of this parameter than the flight value without introducing much error. This much leeway can be a boon when attempting similitude at reasonable cost, for both air density and velocity can be lower.

Which kind of hypersonic facility to use?

There are two basic techniques for generating very high-speed flows (often called hypervelocity flows): ballistic ranges, and what I might loosely call wind tunnels. The aerodynamic phenomena in constant-velocity rectilinear flight are dependent only on the velocity of the body relative to the undisturbed air.

Therefore, other parameters being equal, aerodynamic forces and flow properties can be found either by moving the model with respect to the air, or by keeping the model stationary and moving the air past it.

In the ballistic range, the model is accelerated to the required velocity and is stabilized so that its orientation with respect to the velocity vector is known and invariant during the measurement period. If possible, instruments are placed in the model so that data on surface properties during flight can be transmitted to fixed receiving stations. Properties of the flow are observed by ground instruments which make their measurements at given fixed points. Because these positions with respect to the vehicle change with time, the instruments and the functioning of the vehicle must be carefully synchronized with respect to time and space.

In the wind tunnel, the flow is arranged so that its properties at any given point are constant with time. Since the model is fixed, it can be instrumented more elaborately. The key feature of the wind tunnel is that it must be capable of producing flows having uniform physical properties in the test section at the conditions required by the test.

Sometimes the ballistic range and the wind tunnel are combined. Here, a model is launched upstream of a wind tunnel that produces a flow at high velocity. Then the velocity of the model is added to that of the wind tunnel, and very high relative velocities can be obtained.

Ballistic ranges are very useful for determining flow properties by means of optical or electromagnetic devices. Hence this testing technique is often used for studying shock waves, wakes, and the related electromagnetic phenomena. However, the problem of instrumenting the moving model makes the ballistic range difficult to use when detailed information is sought on the properties of the flow and the pressure distribution on the model. For this kind of investigation, the wind tunnel is more appropriate. The combination of the two is finding wider use at very high Mach numbers.

The hypervelocity aerodynamic range

In a ballistic range, Fig. 3-16, a launcher or gun "fires" the model into the range, which is a tubular enclosure wherein the chemical composition, temperature, and pressure of the air are controlled so as to match the desired altitude and speed of sound. The model—usually

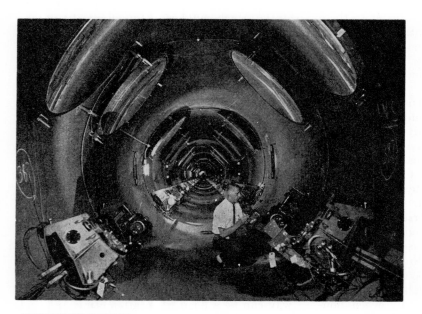

Fig. 3-16. In a ballistic range a model is fired into a test chamber maintained at controlled atmospheric conditions. Flight characteristics are observed by cameras stationed along trajectory. In facility at left, photocell detects model, triggers a spark lamp which illuminates model, whose shadow in mirror is photographed using reflected light. Each station has two cameras at right angles so that orientation of model can be determined. This Argus-eyed test chamber has 30-40 stations along its 1000-ft length. Model flies down the range at speeds up to 20,000 ft/sec. (Courtesy U.S. Naval Ordnance Laboratory, White Oak, Md.)

BALLISTIC RANGE

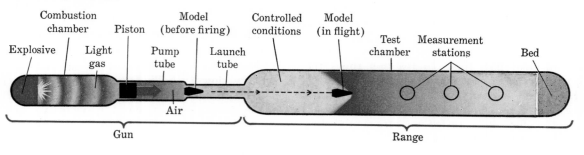

an axially or quasi-axially symmetric body without lift—flies down the range along a very nearly straight line. Aerodynamic drag gradually decreases its velocity, but this does not affect the instantaneous measurements.

At several stations along the way very accurate measurements are made of velocity, angle of attack and yaw, and physical integrity of the model in order to determine the flight parameters. At the same time, the physical properties of the flow around the model are measured to determine the characteristics of this flow. The spectroscopic, electromagnetic, and optical properties of the gas are used as the basis of measurement. In addition, schlieren and shadowgraph observations (see Fig. 3-15) of the over-all flow field are performed. Average aerodynamic forces are found from flight dynamics by measuring the body's position and angle as a function of time.

Inasmuch as hypersonic flight testing requires that the model be accelerated to velocities of the order of 20,000 to 30,000 ft/sec, a very special launcher must be used (an ordinary high-velocity rifle has a muzzle speed of 3000–4000 ft/sec). It is really a two-stage gun, as the diagram in Fig. 3-16 shows. A very high pressure is created in the first stage, usually called the driving tube, and the light gas therein then accelerates a piston placed at the end. This, in turn, compresses the gas in the second stage, often called the pump tube, and thus accelerates either the model or a "sabot" that carries the model in the launch tube. Model sizes are of the order of 1 in. in diameter.

Several methods for pressurizing the driving tube have been used. The explosive charge shown in the diagram can be replaced with a detonating mixture of oxygen and hydrogen in a helium atmosphere, or by an electrical discharge in helium gas. Light gases are desirable because we want the pressure buildup at the

piston to be as rapid as possible, which will be the case when the sonic velocity in the gas is high. To get this we use a low-density gas.

The hypersonic wind tunnel

The classical apparatus used for the measurement of aerodynamic forces is the wind tunnel, which is designed to produce a flow at the required velocity, pressure, and temperature. The flow must have uniform physical properties in the test region and must be free from turbulence. To do this, we discharge heated and compressed air from a reservoir through a nozzle which has been contoured to deliver a uniform flow at the point downstream where the model is situated. The model is stationary and can have a maximum dimension of several feet. The expansion in the nozzle is adiabatic and, if the nozzle has been designed efficiently, isentropic. Therefore, the pressure and temperature conditions in the reservoir required for the correct flow simulation are easily determined. These are termed the stagnation conditions for the test.

The stagnation conditions that we need in order to simulate the static (i.e., environmental) pressure, static temperature, and the flow velocity at different altitudes of flight are shown in Fig. 3-17. For very high-flight velocities, the correct representation of the actual environment requires us to compress and heat the air to be used in the tests to conditions that are extremely difficult to achieve. For example, to simulate conditions corresponding to those encountered by a vehicle re-entering the earth's atmosphere from a low-altitude, circular orbit (which means a velocity of about 25,000 ft/sec), the air must first be heated to about 13,000°K and compressed to about 20,000–30,000 atmospheres. This high-pressure obstacle is not universally appreciated.

Usually, wind tunnels are utilized to determine heat transfer, pressure distribution, and

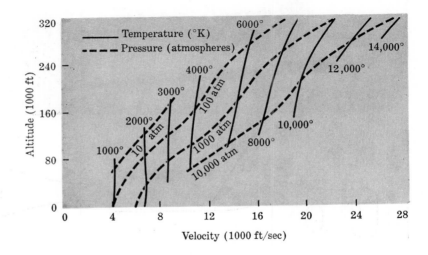

Fig. 3-17. The wind tunnel experimentalist states the conditions of flight—i.e., altitude and velocity—in terms of the pressure and temperature of the gas in the reservoir upstream of the nozzle. Hence the equivalent "stagnation" curves at right. Note the extremely high stagnation pressures and temperatures required to simulate flight completely at high altitude and velocity. No present facility can achieve these conditions, so hypersonic flight simulation is not complete.

$$v = \sqrt{\frac{kp}{\rho}}$$

$v = $ *sonic velocity*

$k = c_p/c_v$

$p = $ *pressure*

$\rho = $ *density*

force on complex shapes without simultaneous simulation of chemical effects. Therefore all that is required is the simulation of Reynolds number, Mach number, and such chemical parameters associated with wave propagation as the specific heat ratio of the flowing gas. As a consequence, the stagnation pressure and temperature required are much lower, and hence possible to achieve experimentally. With the present state of the art, short-duration wind tunnels are able to operate at stagnation pressures of 700 to 2000 atm, and stagnation temperatures of 1500 to 2500°K—permitting us to test at sufficiently high Reynolds numbers and at Mach numbers up to about 25.

The construction details of wind tunnels vary substantially from case to case. For tests at high Mach number, intermittent-type wind tunnels are widely used, Fig 3-18. Here, the air is compressed to high pressure, dried, then stored. This may take several minutes to a few hours. At the same time thermal energy is accumulated in a storage heater—usually a bed of pebbles heated either by resistance units or gas burners. Just before the test the storage heater is pressurized from the air reservoir to the required stagnation pressure.

To initiate the test, a throttling valve atop the now-pressurized heater is suddenly opened. The air surges through the heater, picking up heat as it goes, and expands through the nozzle. Its mass flow is controlled by the throat of the nozzle, and the pressure upstream of the

heater is kept constant by a pressure regulating valve. As the air sweeps by the model in the test section, it is moving very rapidly but at very low static pressure. Hence it must be discharged through a diffuser which slows the air before it reaches the vacuum system. Often a cooler is installed between the diffuser and the vacuum system to further decrease the volume that the vacuum system must handle. The duration of the test varies from a fraction of a second to several minutes, depending upon the test and the facility. Consequently, aerodynamic measurements are made with instruments designed to record automatically.

Shock tubes and shock tunnels

Wind tunnels do not permit us to obtain full simulation of the stagnation enthalpy of the air, hence in wind tunnel tests many of the chemical effects are neglected. The shock tube is a facility especially suited for the investigation of such effects. Its basic principle of operation is simple and is illustrated in Fig. 3-19.

In one section of the shock tube is a light gas, called the driver gas, which is heated before the test to high temperature and pressure. The gas in the so-called driven tube is air at relatively low pressure. As soon as the right conditions of pressure and temperature are reached in the driver tube, the diaphragm is exploded. The abrupt release of pressure sets up a shock wave that travels down the driven tube. The driver gas acts as a kind of expand-

Fig. 3-18. Wind tunnels have the advantage that stationary models can be instrumented easily. Stagnation conditions are limited, however, so that such facilities simulate Reynolds number only. Thus wind tunnels yield aerodynamic measurements primarily, with high-temperature chemical effects left for other complementary facilities. Photo shows Mach-10 tunnel that uses air compressed to 2000 psia and heated to 1500°F. Flow from nozzle (left) enters 50-in. dia. test section (right) and exits to vacuum tank (not shown). (Courtesy Arnold Engineering Development Center—USAF)

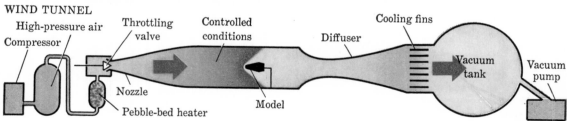

WIND TUNNEL
High-pressure air
Compressor
Throttling valve
Controlled conditions
Diffuser
Cooling fins
Vacuum tank
Vacuum pump
Nozzle
Pebble-bed heater
Model

ing piston, compressing the driven gas ahead of it so that the interface between the two moves downstream in the driven tube. The shock wave moves much faster than the interface, as shown in the "wave diagram" of Fig. 3-19.

When the shock wave reaches the end of the driven tube, which is essentially closed, the shock is reflected and moves upstream—thus further compressing the driven gas between it and the oncoming interface. During this adiabatic compression, the driven gas reaches zero velocity and very high pressure and temperature. The maximum pressure and temperature possible depend upon the initial conditions of the driven- and the driver-gas and upon the Mach number of the shock wave. Stagnation conditions thus produced involve pressures in the order of 2000 to 4000 atm and temperatures in the order of 10,000°K. Because of the limited pressures attainable for this high temperature, Reynolds number cannot be fully simulated.

The use that is made of the resulting compressed driven gas depends upon the kind of investigation being conducted. If we are interested in the chemical and physical properties of the driven gas at high pressure and temperature, then the driven tube is kept closed and the gas compressed at its end is analyzed. Such a facility is called a shock *tube*. For aerodynamic investigations, the closed end is used as a reservoir and a nozzle is attached, separated from the reservoir by a frangible diaphragm. In this case, the driven tube is then used to produce a high-stagnation enthalpy and pressure in the air before it is released through the nozzle, which is designed aerodynamically to produce uniform flow in the test

section. With a vacuum system attached, the device is then termed a shock *tunnel*, Fig. 3-20.

In both types of hypersonic shock facility the driver gas can be heated and compressed in different ways. Resistance heaters placed inside the driver tube are commonly used, but the process is slow, and only relatively high temperatures can be reached. Much higher stagnation temperatures (and hence enthalpies) can be achieved by combustion techniques: A controlled quantity of oxygen and hydrogen is added to the driver gas and the mixture ignited by electrical discharge.

Shock tunnels and shock tubes, by virtue of the fact that they can produce large pressure and temperature variation abruptly in a gas without contamination, are widely used for basic research in thermodynamics, chemical physics, and in physics. The main problem in any shock-tube or shock-tunnel investigation is, of course, the short duration of testing time that is imposed—a matter of a few milliseconds. By mounting a series of open-ended shock tubes on a rapidly rotating drum, in a sort of Gatling gun arrangement, test duration can be extended to more than 10 sec.

The hot-shot tunnel

The hot-shot tunnel is also a short-duration facility, similar in concept to the shock tunnel and created primarily for studying large chemical effects in hypersonic flows. Here, though, there is but one working fluid—air—which is heated abruptly in a high-pressure container by an electric arc. The apparatus consists of an arc chamber, followed by a nozzle and a test section which discharges into a vacuum chamber as shown in Fig. 3-21. A diaphragm divides the arc chamber from the nozzle. When the chamber has been pressurized

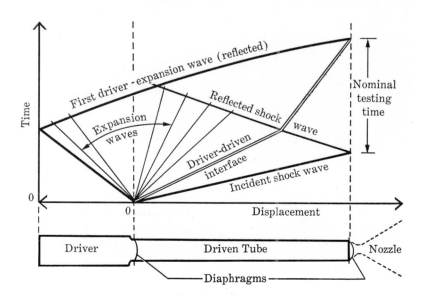

Fig. 3-19. Wave diagram shows rudiments of shock tunnel. As first diaphragm breaks at time zero, shock wave hurtles toward right end. Interface between two gases moves more slowly, compressing gas ahead of it. Shock wave reflected from end slows interface to velocity dependent on nozzle discharge rate. Test time is interval between shock wave's reflection and arrival of interface at nozzle. Driver is tuned so reflected expansion wave does not shorten test time. For shock tube, nozzle (dashed lines) is replaced by closed end.

Fig. 3-20. In hypersonic shock facilities, very high stagnation temperatures are achieved. These allow simulation of chemical effects. However, in this case, the Reynolds number cannot be fully simulated. Tunnel in photo has a 6-ft diameter test section, and achieves Mach-30 flow from 14,000°F gas in "reservoir" at end of shock tube. Flow is from shock tube (left), through nozzle (behind upright pipes), and into test chamber (far right). Vacuum tank is behind wall. (Courtesy Cornell Aeronautical Lab)

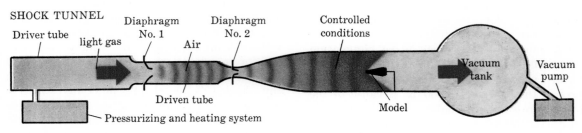

SHOCK TUNNEL

Driver tube · light gas · Diaphragm No. 1 · Air · Diaphragm No. 2 · Controlled conditions · Vacuum tank · Vacuum pump · Driven tube · Pressurizing and heating system · Model

Fig. 3-21. Hot-shot tunnels, in which a gas is heated and compressed by arc discharge, permit longer test times than shock tunnels. Here, SNAP nuclear power generator is inserted in 100-in., Mach-20 tunnel to simulate re-entry burnup. (Courtesy Arnold Engineering Development Center)

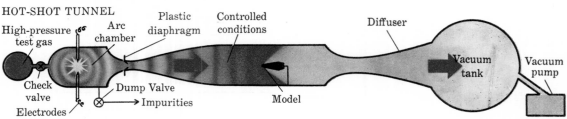

HOT-SHOT TUNNEL

High-pressure test gas · Arc chamber · Plastic diaphragm · Controlled conditions · Diffuser · Vacuum tank · Vacuum pump · Check valve · Dump Valve · Impurities · Electrodes · Model

with air to anywhere from 30 to 300 atm, and the nozzle evacuated to a high vacuum, then an arc is struck between two electrodes by discharge of electrical energy stored in a capacitor bank. The arc produces an abrupt temperature and pressure rise, which ruptures the diaphragm and injects air into the nozzle.

This type of facility permits an order of magnitude increase in testing time over the shock tunnel—a few hundredths of a second, rather than milliseconds, being typical. However, the electric discharge tends to produce evaporation of solid parts, mainly the electrodes, and this can introduce impurities in the flow around the model, particularly at high stagnation temperatures.

The arc-jet wind tunnel

In an effort to increase the time period during which high-enthalpy, high-speed gas flows can be studied, the arc-jet wind tunnel has been devised, Fig. 3-22. Here, the air is preheated in the chamber upstream of the nozzle by means of a continuous arc, and then is injected under pressure into the nozzle. The arc jet (see "Plasma Torches," page 458) is an efficient way to obtain a very high stagnation enthalpy in the air at moderate stagnation pressure; however, it has certain limitations for hypersonic flight testing.

First, there is the problem of contamination. The surface of the electrodes reaches a very high temperature, so that oxidation of the electrode material can produce contaminants in the flow. Hence, much work has gone into methods of reducing local electrode temperatures. One uses an external magnetic field to force the arc to rotate about the cylindrical electrode. In addition, the electrode is both cooled and partially shielded by an inert gas which is injected near the surface of the electrode.

The other major problem with the arc-jet tunnel concerns its unfavorable characteristics for aerodynamic testing. The flow properties are nonuniform in time and space, plasma oscillations exist in the arc, and the enthalpy distribution changes from point to point in the arc. Some uniformity can be gained by adding a settling chamber downstream, though this introduces losses. Chemical problems exist, too, for the gas entering the tunnel is highly dissociated and ionized and seldom reaches full chemical equilibrium at the model. Despite these and other problems, on which much development effort is being spent, the arc-jet wind tunnel appears to be the most promising device on the horizon for long-duration, high-enthalpy flows.

Fig. 3-22. Arc-jet wind tunnel uses plasma arc to superheat test air. Through window we see model ready for gas flow from nozzle (right). Plasma generator is at far right. Facility simulates hypersonic flight conditions for about 20 min. (Courtesy GE Space Sciences Lab)

Accelerators may solve some problems

In all the facilities for hypersonic flight-testing that I have described thus far, the air is brought to the required stagnation pressure and temperature before it is released in the nozzle to flow over the model. This has evident limitations when high Mach numbers are desired. The gas, heated to extreme temperatures, radiates and conducts heat to the walls, creating heat transfer problems both in the reservoir and the nozzle throat. The flow undergoes changes in chemical composition as it expands adiabatically through the nozzle. And at low pressures near the test region, the process of chemical recombination is slow and nonequilibrium conditions exist at the model.

Progress in solving these problems for very high-Mach-number testing has been slow, hence schemes are being investigated which do not require extremely high pressure and temperature. The basic principle here is to create body forces in a gas flow which has already attained high velocity, by one of the methods previously discussed.

Two accelerating schemes are presently being investigated, one using magnetohydrodynamic effects and the other using purely mechanical means. The MHD accelerator is simply a gaseous analog of the ordinary electric motor: the flowing gas, if it be made electrically conductive, acts as the rotor—the body to be accelerated. By passing a current through the fluid while it is in the presence of a magnetic field, an electromagnetic body force on the fluid is produced that depends upon the current and the magnetic field, and directed as sketched in the margin. Because an ionized gas has good electrical conductivity, the output of an arc-jet wind tunnel is usually employed as the input

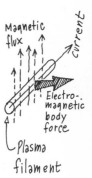

ARC-JET

E - Electrode
A - Arc
G - Test gas
V - Vortex chamber
I - Impurities
P - Plenum
PJ - Plasma jet

Magnetic flux
current
Electromagnetic body force
Plasma filament

to an MHD accelerator. The conductivity can be increased by seeding the gas stream with small amounts of easily ionizable material, though this creates some nonequilibrium effects in the test region.

The mechanical scheme for accelerating a flow already moving at high velocity involves superimposing on this velocity that of a body moving in the opposite direction. This is sketched in the margin. The stream of air encounters a curved passage moving opposite to it, also at high velocity. The oncoming air enters the passage, changes its direction of motion, and—if the turn is 180°—it emerges in the same direction as that of the passage. What's more important, the air leaving the passage does so at an increased absolute velocity. If losses are neglected, the velocity of the leaving stream is increased by an amount that is twice the velocity of the passage itself.

It is not absolutely necessary to apply body forces to the moving gas stream in order to achieve high-flow velocities. This is not a paradox if you keep in mind that what is desired is a very high velocity of flow *relative to the model*. Instead of keeping the model fixed, as in the two acceleration schemes just discussed, we can also move the model against the fast-moving gas stream. This is done by coupling a shock tunnel with a ballistic range. By launching a model at high velocity counter to the hypersonic gas flow emitted from a shock tube, we are able to achieve flow velocities relative to the model as high as 40,000 ft/sec, and 60,000 ft/sec seems feasible.

The measurement techniques for this type of facility (see Fig. 3-23) are similar to those described for ballistic ranges. However, the

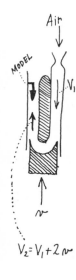

determination of the velocity relative to the model requires measurement of both the air velocity and that of the model, and is therefore subject to larger error.

In conclusion, I should like to make explicit an idea that I have tried to echo throughout this discussion—that all of these approaches to hypersonic flight testing are complementary and interdependent. This needs emphasis, for they all compete to a degree for funds and for public attention. They are all extremely expensive to build and very difficult to operate fruitfully—despite their apparent simplicity. Upon the ability of the investigator depends the correctness and usefulness of the results.

This is a situation that calls, I believe, for a balanced, programmatic approach: on the one hand, a large number of small, yet sophisticated facilities for the training of knowledgeable investigators; and on the other, a few large facilities in which these same investigators can probe intelligently the frontiers of hypersonic flight.

Further reading

The field of hypersonics has matured to the point where more and more books are becoming available. The one most closely related to our article is Riddell's *Hypersonic Research* (Ronald Press, 1959, $10). Two other useful volumes are *Hypersonic Aerodynamics* by Truitt (Academic Press, 1962, $10.50) and *Hypersonic Flow Theory* by Hayes and Probstein (Academic Press, 1959, $11.50).

To probe further into the intricacies of the several methods described in this article, the following reports and papers should prove useful. On ballistic ranges, see "Design of a Light-Gas Model Launcher for Hypersonic Research" by Anderson and Prince (AEDC-TDR-62-97, May 1962); request from Commander, Arnold Air Force Test Station, Tenn., Attention: AETI. A typical high-speed wind tunnel is detailed in "Hypersonic Facility of Polytechnic Institute of Brooklyn and Its Application to Problems of Hypersonic Flight" by Ferri and Libby (WADC-TR-57-369, Document AD-130809); obtain from ASTIA's Documentation Service Center, Arlington Hall Station, Arlington, Va.

Shock tunnels are well covered in "Summary of Shock Tunnel Development and Applications to Hypersonic Research" by Hertzberg et al., Air Force Office of Scientific Research TR-60-139, July 1961; request from R. Pandy, Cornell Aeronautical Lab, Buffalo 21, N.Y. The scope of information obtainable from shock tubes is shown in "Fundamental Data Obtained from Shock Tube Experiments," AGARDograph 41, edited by Ferri (Pergamon, 1961, $12). Chem-

Fig. 3-23. Countercurrent facility increases gas velocity relative to model by firing model into discharge from shock tunnel. Characteristics of model and of gas flow are measured from external observation posts along test section shown here. Model flies from right; gas flows from left. (Courtesy Ames Research Center, NASA)

ical effects are well covered in Kantrowitz's "Shock Tubes for High-Temperature Gas Kinetics," Avco-Everett Research Lab Report 141, Oct. 1962; request from AERL, Reports Distribution Dept., Everett, Mass.

On hot-shot tunnels, see "Development of Capacitance and Inductance Driven Hotshot Tunnels" by Lukasiewicz et al., available from Commander, Arnold Air Force Test Station, Tenn., Attention: AETI. A typical arc-jet facility is described in Petrie's "Investigations of a Plasma Wind Tunnel," ARL Report 62-419, Aug. 1962; write to Commander, Wright-Patterson Air Force Base, Ohio. Recent research using countercurrent technique is covered in "Ames Hypervelocity Free-Flight Research"

by Seiff, *Astronautics and Aerospace Engineering* **1**, 11 (Dec. 1963).

Papers detailing experimental procedures will be found in *Advances in Hypervelocity Techniques, Proceedings of the Second Symposium on Hypervelocity Techniques*, edited by Krill (Plenum Press, 1962, $19.50). For papers in first symposium, write A. Krill, U. of Denver. The third symposium was held in March 1964, also in Denver, but proceedings are not yet available. The First International Symposium on Fundamental Phenomena in Hypersonic Flow was held in June 1964, under the sponsorship of Cornell Aeronautical Lab, Buffalo, N.Y.; these proceedings, too, are so far unavailable.

RADIATION PROCESSING

by Daniel I. Cooper *

IN BRIEF: *Ionizing radiation is rapidly joining heat, pressure, and catalysts in the armory of agents for changing materials to man's ends. Dow Chemical, for example, uses a 2500-curie Co^{60} source to manufacture 10^6 lb/yr of ethyl bromide from hydrogen bromide and ethylene. And several manufacturers are using accelerators to crosslink polyethylene thus making it more heat-resistant. Semiconductor manufacturers produce defects with energetic electrons (a physical rather than a chemical effect) to improve diodes and transistors. More such products and processes are on the way to early commercial realization. In the longer term recoiling fission fragments might prove an economic source of the required ionizing radiation.*

The underlying processes are poorly understood, however. It's known that radiation produces ions, excited molecules, and free radicals, but the probabilities for these elementary processes have been measured in only a very few cases, and much remains to be learned about the ensuing reactions among these new chemical entities. Thus there is room for basic research as well as enlightened exploitation.—D.C.

■ An electron from even a modest accelerator has a million times the energy of a typical chemical bond, a hundred thousand times the energy required to ionize molecules. These big numbers underlie the impressive possibilities in the use of ionizing radiation to alter materials to man's ends. A growing list of radiation-produced materials (see the table on p. 330) attests that some companies have successfully made the long journey between impressive

possibility and money-making actuality. Radiation improvement is every bit as real as the radiation damage we hear so much about; indeed it is the other side of the same coin. Just as heat can improve some materials and ruin others, so can radiation.

But heat and nuclear radiation differ fundamentally in their mode of action: Heat is marked by sharing of the available energy among all the molecules in a system—the average share being relatively modest. The interaction of radiation with matter is characterized by the distribution of relatively large packets of energy to a few molecules lying along the paths of the irradiating particles. This energy is subsequently distributed through complex pathways—some of it is generally shared in the form of heat, but the chemically important part is usually restricted to a small fraction of the molecules.

Because heat energy is shared so generally, thermodynamic approaches are possible, and one can extrapolate with reasonable confidence from what is happening on a macroscopic basis to what is happening on a molecular basis. Thus if you heat ice till it melts, you can picture water molecules throughout the lattice receiving enough kinetic energy to overcome the intermolecular forces that tie them into a solid. Even when it is a more complex matter of shifting the rate of a reaction by altering the temperature of a chemical system there is a good body of reaction-kinetic theory to guide our predictions of what will occur. Not so with radiation; with radiation, generalizations are a lot harder to come by. Still, one of the first things Roentgen did was to note the chemical effects of his x-rays, and seventy years of ra-

* Daniel I. Cooper is Executive Editor of *International Science and Technology*.

	Product	Virtue
TODAY nuclear radiation is making these things...	Crosslinked polyethylene	Higher melting point
	Heat-shrinkable plastics	Easily applied coverings
	Ethyl bromide	Purer; cheaper
	Sterilized medical supplies	Simplified packaging; cheaper
	Faster semiconductor diodes	Controllable defect concentration
TOMORROW these radiation products may hit the market	Biodegradable detergents	Bacteria can attack in sewage
	Radiation-sterilized bacon	No refrigeration; FDA approved
	Wood-polymer "alloys"	Stronger; less water-absorbent
	Finishes on building materials	Save on curing time and space
	Cured latex products	More uniform; transparent

diation chemistry have left us with a considerable pile of facts about the ways in which radiation energy gets distributed in matter. We should look at that large, if untidy, structure of fact before we consider some of the particular irradiation processes in commercial use today.

Spreading it around

The first step in the transformation of radiation energy into chemical change is the ionization and excitation of the molecules of the medium by the electrons passing through it. I say electrons advisedly because, although electrons and gamma rays are both used as radiation sources today, the gamma rays undergo processes in which they give up most of their energy to an atomic electron, itself indistinguishable from one of those accelerated by machine. So for purposes of following the transformation of energy we need only consider electrons.

That a high-energy electron should ionize and excite molecules along its path is to be

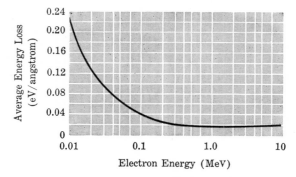

Fig. 3-24. The more energetic an electron the slower it loses energy. Rate of energy loss, or linear energy transfer, determines local concentration of excited molecules. (From A. O. Allen, Radiation Chemistry of Water and Aqueous Solutions, *Van Nostrand, 1961)*

expected; the electron is charged and it repels the electrons of stationary molecules and attracts their positively charged nuclei as it flies by. If the electron gets close enough to an atom of the molecule, the force can be great enough to completely eject an electron, ionizing the molecule, or else the atom can be raised to one of many excited states. Most molecules are unaffected, however—the electron goes by too quickly for them to respond—only about 1 in 1000 along the path of a 1-million-volt electron is ionized.

As the electron slows down it becomes more efficient at ionization because it spends more time near each atom and the *linear energy transfer* (or LET, as it is called) goes up correspondingly, as shown in Fig. 3-24. As a consequence of this, much of the ionization occurs in small "spurs" along the main track of the electron where a particularly large amount of energy has been given to one molecular electron that is then able to ionize and excite others in its neighborhood. This fact is important to the subsequent dispersal of the energy, as we shall see.

Of course the energy for these ionizations and excitations has come from the incident electron, and eventually it is slowed down and stopped. Thus, where once we had a fast electron we suddenly have a collection of ionized and excited molecules laid out along its path, clustered in occasional spurs.

In the course of excitation and ionization, the molecule may or may not break into two or more fragments. The break can occur at any of the bonds in the molecule, the weaker bonds being the more likely to break, in general. Thus the variety of molecules that are present, even in an originally homogeneous system, is now considerably increased. For example, the William H. Johnston Laboratories have found that the seemingly simple O_2 molecule breaks up in no less than 11 ways.

This proliferated profusion of pieces is now free to engage in reactions with each other or with the unaffected molecules that surround them. For example, a newly ionized molecule can pick up an electron from a neutral molecule with which it collides, becoming neutral thereby while ionizing the struck system. Or an excited molecule can transfer its energy to another, less hardy molecule that breaks up in the process. Obviously many of these fragments will be free radicals—atoms with unpaired electrons available to form covalent bonds, so the whole of free-radical chemistry is superimposed on the new chemistries of excited molecules and ions that I have been sketching above.

Just what products will finally result depends on the detail of the system being irradiated. If it is a liquid rather than a gas, the ions and their descendants will be more likely to react in the spur in which they were formed (though sometimes the energy can be channeled a long distance away through like molecules). If oxygen or some other molecule with a high electron affinity is present, it will tie up the electrons in negative ions and thus have an important effect on the radiation yields. Only small quantities of so-called free-radical scavengers will serve to drastically alter the nature of what is made.

Such is the complexity of radiation chemistry and such is our ignorance of the elementary reactions that make it up that all we have are a few guidelines, no all-embracing principles. Even so simple a question as whether radiation will lead to simpler or more complex molecules cannot be answered a priori. Radiolysis—the breaking up of molecules under irradiation—is as common as radiation synthesis—the building of new species. Where molecules do break up we find a certain correlation with bond strength or character. We do know, for example, that the chains of long-chain hydrocarbons will break if a main-chain carbon atom has no hydrogen atoms bonded to it (see table in the next column). Thus radiation crumbles Lucite while it strengthens polyethylene.

But if we are not able to enunciate general principles, it does not mean we are in total ignorance. Particularly in the postwar years the effects of radiation on a huge number of chemical systems have been recorded. The best of this work is unambiguous—free of the interfering effects of small quantities of impurity such as can easily wreak havoc in this field. And there has been a considerable elucidation of the basic processes—though there is much left to be done and the underlying mechanisms in the ra-

diation chemistry of even so basic a substance as water is still the subject of controversy.

The chemist, as Louis Hammett has pointed out ("Chemical Bond," page 184), must make progress even where he does not have a complete theory. The applied radiation chemist has gone ahead by making good use of the empirically measured yields of radiation-chemical reactions—the number of molecules of a particular sort formed or destroyed per unit energy input. To these yields he assigns the symbol G; for the unit of energy he uses 100 electron volts. G values range from fractions to 5 or 6 for endothermic reactions, but can be in the tens of thousands for reactions that are exothermic and can propagate as a chain reaction once initiated by radiation. Such high-G-value systems are the most likely to be successful commercially, and I will tell you shortly about the first such high-G radiation process to go commercial. I do want, first, to say something of the radiation side of radiation processing.

Insofar as there is nuclear physics in radiation processing it has to do with such matters as how deep the radiation penetrates into the product and how best to arrange radiation sources for optimum utilization of available energy. These matters are inherently much less complicated than heat transfer (which I, a nuclear physicist, have never understood). They are rapidly being reduced to handbook form by an Atomic Energy Commission eager to spur peaceable uses of its products. Still you will need some acquaintance with radiation to follow its uses, so here are some ABC's.

RADIATION EFFECTS ON TYPICAL POLYMERS

Degrade	*Crosslink*
$(-CH_2-CX_2-)_n$	$(-CH_2-CH_2-)_n$
$(-CHX-CHX-)_n$	$(-CH_2-CHX-)_n$
$(-CHX-CX_2-)_n$	
$(-CX_2-CX_2-)_n$	
Teflon $(-CF_2-CF_2)_n$	Polyethylene $(-CH_2-CH_2-)_n$
Polymethylmethacrylate $(-CH_2-CCH_3COOCH_3-)_n$	Polystyrene $(-CH_2-CHPh-)_n$
Polyisobutylene $(-CH_2-C(CH_3)_2-)_n$	Polyvinylfluoride $(-CH_2CHF-)_n$
Polyvinylidene Chloride $(-CHCl-CHCl-)_n$	Polyvinyl Alcohol $(CH_2-CHOH-)_n$

Courtesy R. Timmerman, Radiation Dynamics, Westbury, N.Y.

PATHWAYS IN RADIATION CHEMISTRY

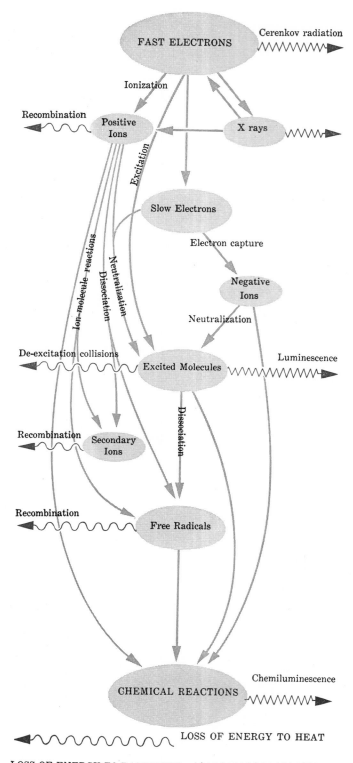

Fig. 3-25. Radiation chemistry begins with production of ions and excited molecules by incident fast electrons. These ions and excited molecules and the negative ions, secondary positive ions, and free radicals

It's as simple as α, β, γ, and e

To start with you can forget about neutrons, protons, alpha particles, mesons, and strange particles of various kinds and focus on just two nuclear entities—gamma rays and high-energy electrons. The point is that all the others are either too expensive to make, or induce radioactivity, or are insufficiently penetrating to be useful in industry. (I've overstated things. There is long-range research interest in using the ionizing power of fission fragments to initiate chemical reactions. Chemonuclear reactors based on this idea are under investigation at Brookhaven, Aerojet General, and Rensselaer Polytech.) The gamma rays are, of course, high-energy quanta of electromagnetic radiation. They can be created when accelerator electrons hit a target or emitted by a radioactive nucleus (cobalt-60 is the radioisotope most commonly used). The high-energy electrons receive their energy by being accelerated in a suitable accelerator—imagine a foot-long evacuated cylinder with a heated cathode at one end and a million volt potential along it and you've got a sufficient picture for now. The electron is negatively charged and, at these energies, travels with pretty much the speed of light.

The gamma rays are more penetrating than the electrons; what's more, they differ in the mode of penetration. The electrons have a short and fairly definite range; the gamma rays are absorbed exponentially (as is light) and an appropriate measure of penetration is the distance required for the intensity of a gamma-ray beam to be reduced by $1/e$. The numbers are something like this: a two-million-volt (2-Mev) electron, one that has been accelerated through a potential of 2 million volts, has a range of 1 cm in water; a 2-Mev gamma ray has a $1/e$ length of 20 cm in the same medium. Obviously the electron is better suited to the irradiation of relatively thin products—sheet, tube, wire—and the gamma ray to the irradiation of bulk matter—such as sewage, molasses, hospital supplies, to mention some current candidates.

Different units are used to measure the number of particles coming from these two sorts of sources: For the electrons it is simply the current of electrons delivered to the target—typical values range between 5 and 30 milliamperes, depending on voltage. For the gamma rays the unit used is the curie, which clearly harks back to the early days of radioactivity. The curie was

that they produce can enter into chemical reactions (bottom). At every stage energy can be lost to collisions (= heat) or escape as low-energy radiation. (Courtesy D. Harmer, Dow Chemical Co., Midland, Mich.)

first set forth as the number of disintegrations per second in a 1-gram radium source and is now defined as precisely 3.7×10^{10} disintegrations per second.

While Mme. Curie gave her lifetime, and eventually her life, to the separation of a few curies of activity, today's nuclear reactors can produce hundreds and thousands of curies just by soaking up excess neutrons in cobalt-59 to make radioactive cobalt-60. Kilocurie sources are common today, and the first megacurie source is in operation.

On today's technology, accelerators are much more intense sources of radiation than are radioisotopes. But intensity is not the only consideration, and for some applications the high flux of the accelerator is a handicap.

The thing you're really interested in is the amount of energy deposited per unit of mass of the material being irradiated. Here the pertinent unit is the rad, defined as 100 ergs of radiation energy absorbed per gram of material. It's descended from the roentgen, the unit that you hear about in biological and medical uses, which explains why we speak of the *dose* of radiation even to inanimate objects. Assuming that all radiation energy is absorbed in the material being irradiated (which is hardly ever the case, usual efficiencies are under 50%) one can equate electron and gamma-ray source strengths to dosage rates: 1 milliamp of 1-million-volt electrons = 70 kilocuries of Co^{60} gamma rays = 1 kilowatt = 800 megarad-pounds per hour.

Since a dose of 0.1 megarads is typical of what you need to do interesting things in radiation processing (the actual range is quite broad: 10 kilorads to 100 megarads) you can see that a source with the power output of a toaster can process some 8000 lb/hr of product. Thus there exist sources capable of readily providing the necessary energy input to matter to make things happen. Let's look into some of the things that *are* happening.

Dave Harmer's marvelous pot

Out in Midland, Michigan, there is a 40-gallon nickel pot, sitting ingloriously some 4 ft underground in a steel-lined pit, that is converting some of this radiation-chemistry talk into real dollars for Dow Chemical Co. Into the pot are fed streams of hydrogen bromide and ethylene gas, out of it comes ethyl bromide, a water-white, sweet-smelling liquid reagent that the chemical industry likes well enough to buy from Dow at 40¢/lb. Dow's little pot can make 1-million lb/yr of the stuff.

The secret of the pot is:

$$BBr + C_2H_4 \rightarrow C_2H_5Br$$

where the arrow represents the catalytic contribution of a modest 2500-curie cobalt-60 source disposed in 60 rods, each a foot long, encased in stainless steel. The reason that so little cobalt can get so much done is that it supplies bromine atoms for a chain reaction, viz.:

$$HBr \rightarrow H + Br$$

$$Br + CH_2-CH_2 \rightarrow BrCH_2-CH_2$$

followed by

$$BrCH_2-CH_2 + HBr \rightarrow BrCH_2CH_3 +' Br$$

This obliging pair of free-radical reactions (the boldface symbols are free radicals) succeeds in converting one molecule of ethylene and one of hydrogen bromide into the desired product and, at the same time, restores a bromine free radical to do the same thing over again. So efficient is the process that the gaseous ingredients bubbling up through their liquid product are completely consumed before they reach the top, and no bubbles break through the surface. Occasionally—on the average after about 10,000 of the steps outlined—a Br has the misfortune to meet up with an H and gets downgraded to HBr. That's where the cobalt source comes in—it breaks up HBr molecules into fresh pairs of free radicals at a rate sufficient to keep the party going. Without the source the reaction would not go, and the input gases would bubble away uselessly.

Dow had for years been making ethyl bromide by a conventional process involving the reaction of HBr with alcohol.

$$HBr + C_2H_5OH \rightarrow C_2H_5Br + H_2O$$

But this process, as even a physicist can see, consumes alcohol and produces by-product water that must be gotten rid of. Worse yet the alcohol has a way of carrying over into the product ethyl bromide, and even some of the HBr gets taken up in the water. So a catalyzed process was clearly superior—but why not a chemical catalyst or a photochemical process? It turns out that the available catalysts are easily destroyed by water and/or must be replaced or cleaned up and recycled. And ultraviolet photocatalysis loses because of (1) the cost of power for arc lamps and (2) the difficulty of keeping the optical path clear so that the uv can get at the reactants.

Dow is delighted with the process. It works well, the product is over 98% pure, there have been no troubles with the source, and part of one man's time suffices to run the whole apparatus, outlined in Fig. 3-26.

More revealing for radiation chemistry are the problems that were experienced in first starting up the process. It took five days for

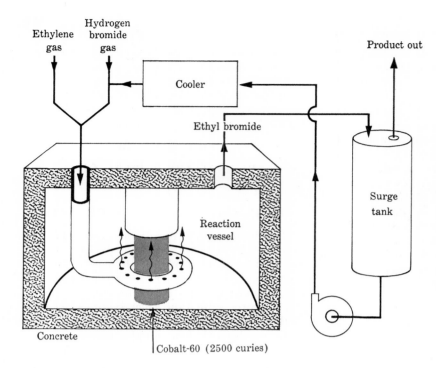

Ethylene gas

Hydrogen bromide gas

Cooler

Product out

Ethyl bromide

Reaction vessel

Surge tank

Concrete

Cobalt-60 (2500 curies)

Fig. 3-26. Making ethyl bromide the easy way. Ethylene and hydrogen bromide gases are fed to cobalt-60 irradiator, where they combine to form liquid ethyl bromide under catalytic action of radiation-produced atomic bromine. Some of the product is recirculated, since reaction goes best in presence of cooled liquid. Residence time of liquid in reaction vessel is 2 min; one man runs the process, simplified here. (Courtesy D. Harmer, Dow Chemical Co., Midland, Mich.)

the system to be freed of impurities (principally iron contamination from the piping) that entered into reactions with the all-important free radicals, stealing them from the system.

Radiation and polymers

Some of the most interesting and fruitful work on radiation processing has been application of accelerator electrons to improve polymers. Crosslinking the polymer chains of polyethylene to improve its properties is the principal commercial success of radiation processing. A host of other plastics have been irradiated to improve their dyeability, printability, or other properties—some of these are on or close to the marketplace. Others are flops. But polyethylene is an unqualified success.

The irradiation of polyethylene is the basis of a multimillion dollar business that includes,

among others, the production of shrinkable foods wrap by the Cryovac Division of W. R. Grace, mass production of heat-resistant wire and shrinkable fittings by Raychem of Redwood City, California, and Radiation Materials Inc. of New York, and service irradiation of high-temperature material for printed-circuit boards and the like by Radiation Dynamics, Westbury, L.I., Electronized Chemicals of Burlington, Mass., and others.

The basic idea in crosslinking of polyethylene is easily diagrammed as it is in Fig. 3-27. But how crosslinking occurs is little understood. Unirradiated polyethylene consists of "half ethylene" (i.e., CH_2) molecules linked together via their carbon atoms in very long chains—perhaps a thousand molecules to a chain. The properties of the bulk material are determined principally by the forces between

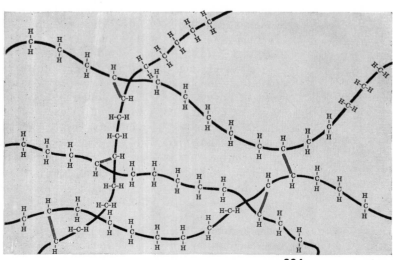

Fig. 3-27. Crosslinking in polyethylene. Radiation breaks off H atoms along polymer chains opening way to strong C-C bonds (color). (Courtesy G. Adler)

chains—as is suggested by the fact that butane, which has the same basic formula as paraffin but shorter chains, is a liquid while paraffin is a wax. But these forces between chains are relatively weak, molecular forces rather than true chemical bonds.

Radiation can produce true bonds between chains in several ways. In polyethylene, it can excite or ionize one of the molecules causing a hydrogen to separate from the chain at some point. This leaves an unsatisfied carbon bond (an unpaired electron, an alkyl free radical, if you will) and a free hydrogen atom, itself a free radical, as shown in the margin. The hydrogen atom usually has enough energy to move away from its former site and rob a hydrogen atom from another chain forming H_2 gas. Often the hydrogen picks up the first hydrogen atom it encounters, which ensures that there will be unpaired carbon bonds close by each other; such bond proximity helps, since the chains themselves have limited mobility. Now the radicals formed can link up in a strong C-C bond from chain to chain.

The result of these processes, carried out many times over, is a linking of the polymers into an interlocked network, which, as you would expect, has a higher melting point than the unirradiated material. Specifically the melting point goes from the 135°C that is typical of even the best "high-density" polyethylene to 325°C, the temperature at which polyethylene decomposes.

Notice that not every bond is affected, only a small percentage are. But this still crosslinks most chains and makes these very drastic improvements in the properties of irradiated polyethylene. In fact, it's this that makes radiation economic in this application.

The result has been a godsend to the aerospace and defense industries who need high-temperature wire for missile electronics but prefer to stay away from Teflon insulations, which are not only more expensive (a trivial consideration in that business) but which, because of their waxy surface, don't take well to being encapsulated. The wire at 2¢/ft is still too expensive for most civilian applications, but anyone who has groaned when a soldering iron inadvertently melted polyvinyl chloride insulation will welcome its early introduction to a more general market.

Even more remarkable than heat resistance is the shrink memory that radiation can impart to polyethylene. The manufacturing procedure is simple. One takes the irradiated polyethylene and heats it to the temperature at which the *un*irradiated form would melt. Then the plastic is stretched or molded to the desired size and cooled while in the stretched state. Now it is

only necessary to heat the polythylene above the unirradiated melting point once more, and the plastic will remember its original shape.

On a molecular basis what has happened is this: heating the irradiated polyethylene above its unirradiated melting point has overcome the relatively weak molecular forces that ordinarily cause it to be solid. The irradiation-produced crosslinks are still present, however, and the resultant material acts like an elastomer that can readily be stretched to any desired size. If the polyethylene is cooled in the stretched state these molecular bonds are re-established and the material freezes in its stretched state. However, further heating at any subsequent time can loosen these bonds once more, restoring the rubberiness so that the crosslinking bonds can pull the material back into the "remembered" state of lower energy (see margin sketches).

The Cryovac Division of the W. R. Grace Co. uses these ideas to make a polyethylene food wrap. The food processor need only heat the film gently and it will shrink to form a skin-tight, clear, tough wrapping such as is essential for today's supermarkets. Grace can make upwards of 3-million lb/yr of the film at its South Carolina facility, a facility, incidentally, that is rumored to have 8 GE accelerators. I say rumored because Grace is very close-mouthed about the operation—a disease that is very common among those who are sitting on a good thing in irradiation.

The same idea is being put to industrial use by the other companies I mentioned earlier with a series of ingenious products that can easily slip into place in the stretched condition but then form a tight seal when heated. For example, one can insulate splices in electrical wiring this way (see Color Fig. 15) or make up whole harnesses of complex wiring layouts that are entirely sealed. It is even possible to perform mechanical work in areas inaccessible by other means.

The memory cuts both ways, too—a folded polyethylene form will remember its unfolded condition. Anyone want to erect antennas in space?

Nor is the trick restricted to polyethylene. Polyvinylchloride, fluorocarbons, and neoprene rubber have been made heat-shrinkable by suitable irradiation with accelerator electrons.

Radiation can also be used to graft one polymer system onto another. For example polypropylene is a promising fiber—cheap, strong, lightweight. But it won't take dyes and feels greasy. However, researchers at American Cyanimid have used radiation to graft chloromethylstyrene to the polypropylene and end up with a material that has none of these disadvantages.

START
IRRADIATE
HEAT
STRETCH WHILE HOT

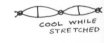

COOL WHILE STRETCHED
REHEAT

A new series of wood alloys

An even more startling "copolymer" is that obtained by irradiating wood impregnated with a suitable monomer. This line of research, to the best of my knowledge, started in the Soviet Union at the Karpov Institute of Physical Chemistry and elsewhere, but the most vigorous pursuit of the subject is now going forward under the aegis of J. A. Kent at West Virginia University with AEC support.

What Kent does is to vacuum impregnate wood with monomers such as methyl methacrylate, styrene, vinyl acetate, and others. Then up to one part of monomer per part of wood is irradiated to a total dose of 0.5 megarads. (Entirely typical of this business is the fact that Kent's most recent work permitted dropping the required dose by a factor of 10 simply by irradiating under a blanket of nitrogen gas—apparently it displaces oxygen, a free-radical scavenger that inhibits the polymerization.) The radiation serves to polymerize the monomer. Whether it forms copolymers with the cellulosic polymers that are wood is still open to question.

The changes in the macroscopic properties of the wood are unmistakable though. The new wood-polymer "alloys" are so hard that soft pine feels like rock maple. They are stronger and more water-resistant. This last causes the wood to have greater dimensional stability (though long-term changes are still present).

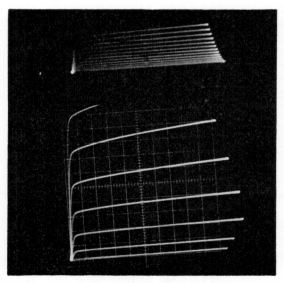

Fig. 3-28. Transistor characteristics before (bot.) and after irradiation. What's plotted (automatically, on an oscilloscope, the way EE's do) is collector current as a function of collector-emitter potential for various values of base current (see margin). Radiation decreases current gains $\beta = I_c/I_b$, *which is sometimes desirable. (Courtesy J. Olander, Electronized Chemical Corp., Burlington, Mass.)*

The wood alloys can be sawed, drilled, and sanded pretty much the same as conventional woods. What one has, in short, is a new material—more expensive than wood, to be sure, but sufficiently promising to make specialized applications possible.

The AEC's Isotopes Development Division is passing out samples of the stuff these days in an attempt to encourage applications—dies, shoe lasts, bowling pins are some of the candidates, but the winning application may still be lurking in someone's worry box. Here, as elsewhere in the growing line of radiation-produced products, is an answer looking for a problem.

Gamma rays look like the logical kind of radiation for bulk work on wood, but there's also a lot of excitement these days about the use of machine electrons to bond plywood and to cure the finishes on other building materials. Here an important consideration is that drying time is nil—radiation-cured paints or even powders polymerized in place obviate the long infrared ovens or voluminous drying areas required with the present product. No one is saying very much, but at least one such product is thought to be near term.

Faster, faster ye diodes

Lest it seem that all of radiation processing is chemical, let me tell you of some important semiconductor applications. These involve changes in crystal structure rather than chemical composition. You see, an electron of about 1-Mev energy will, on the average, come close enough to at least one silicon atom to knock it out of its normal position in the lattice. This produces a vacancy and, in the nearby position to which the silicon atom is initially displaced, an interstitial atom. These lattice defects—or more properly their descendants—have an effect on the electronic properties of the semiconductor. In essence they provide new recombination centers for the holes and electrons that carry the current in a transistor or diode. This has the effect of reducing the carrier "lifetime" and thereby of increasing the speed of the device and decreasing its amplification or gain.

To increase speed always seems like a good thing, but who would want to throw away gain? It turns out that lots of semiconductor manufacturers would. The point is that many applications call for a low-gain transistor—and the manufacturer would rather degrade a high-gain unit than have to set up the procedures for making yet another type. One company has 23 different types that all derive from the same manufactured unit by the use of varying amounts and depths of electron irradiation (see Fig. 3-28).

A more recent electronic application of radia-

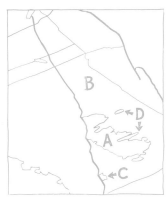

Color Fig. 17. Postirradiation polymerization of acrylamide crystals is here revealed by polarizing microscope (magnification 350×). Crystal is colorless; color arises from interference in birefringent monomer when placed between crossed polarizers. Polymer itself is amorphous, so color depends on amount of unpolymerized acrylamide in light path. In purple area (A), reaction has progressed to a greater extent than in surrounding blue-green area (B). Color changes usually start near defects (C) and proceed till only small residual areas (D) are left unreacted. See "Radiation Processing," in Chapter 3. (Courtesy G. Adler and R. F. Smith, Brookhaven National Laboratory, Upton, N.Y.)

Color Fig. 18. Semiconductor device made by neutron transmutation doping. Neutrons passing through slit in cadmium die (left) transmuted some of silicon-30 to phosphorus-31, making that region n-type. Subsequent etching reveals well-defined silvery n region. Gold plating permits soldering leads. Background: 1-mm squares. See "Radiation Processing," in Chapter 3. (Courtesy Fundamental Methods, Inc., New York)

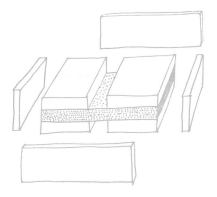

Color Figs. 19 and 20. The dome of the Roman Pantheon, in this Panini painting (from the National Gallery of Art), is a 142-ft. hemisphere made of concrete sandwiched between blocks of masonry. Cutaway view shows how thickness of dome tapers from base to crown. See "Modern Concrete Design," in Chapter 3. (Courtesy Panini, National Gallery of Art, Washington, D.C., Samuel H. Kress Collection, left; Bettman Archive, below)

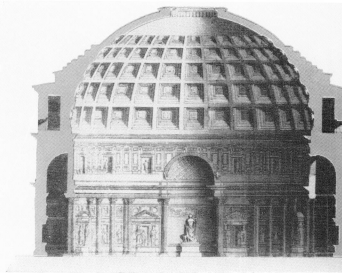

Color Fig. 21. Model of volumetric display developed by International Telephone and Telegraph to show controller the spatial relationship of aircraft around a terminal area. Spots of projected light, color-coded by flight level, are positioned by signals from three-dimensional radar or a computer. Grid lines of light can be superimposed. U.S. Air Force has just contracted for further development of this device. See "Air Traffic Control," in Chapter 3. (Courtesy Int. Tel. and Tel. Corp.)

tion to semiconductors is the work of Fundamental Methods Associates of New York in fabricating semiconductor devices by neutron-transmutation doping. Neutrons absorbed in silicon 30 (say) transmute it to phosphorus-31, which makes silicon n-type. The spatial distribution of these transmutation-induced impurities is controlled by enclosing the semiconductor blank in an appropriate die of neutron-absorbing material (e.g., cadmium) which lets neutrons go through only at appropriate slits (Color Fig. 18). The semiconductor is subsequently annealed to remove nontransmutation defects produced by fast neutrons and gamma rays.

One drawback: radioactivity is induced in the devices, and a two-month cooling period is required for the radioactivity to decay to background. But Fundamental Methods have produced p-n-p "sandwich" configurations in silicon with characteristics (e.g., arbitrary shapes of n and p regions) not achievable with conventional methods. One of the first experimental units, produced in the Oak Ridge Research Reactor, is shown in Color Fig. 17.

Bringing home the bacon

Perhaps the most promising application of large-scale radiation, in terms of eventual economic significance, is its use to preserve food. The way is fraught with difficulties—particularly nontechnical difficulties involving marketing patterns and consumer acceptance—but progress is being made.

The facts are as follows: radiation can be used to disinfest grains, to improve storage qualities (e.g., by suppressing sprouting in potatoes), and to pasteurize or even sterilize foods. This can be done, in a great number of cases, without deleterious effects—the foods look and taste and metabolize substantially like unirradiated foods.

The Canadians have already approved for human consumption potatoes irradiated to 10,000 rads (to inhibit sprouting) and seem to be moving towards commercial realization of the process. (They test marketed 10^6 lb in the fall of 1962 with good results.) Typical of the complexity of achieving economic realization of such a technique is that not all potatoes are to be irradiated (there's a chemical-spraying process that's cheaper for field use and irradiation can reduce the ability of the potato to heal bruises received during handling). Only the part of the crop to be stored for most of the winter, the part that most needs to resist sprouting, gets the treatment. Other promising candidates are strawberries (see Color Fig. 16) and papayas, according to Prof. Edward Maxie of the U. of California at Davis, the principal AEC contractor on fruit irradiation. Typical of the state of flux and complexity of this field is that until recently peaches were regarded as good candidates, too, but radiation seems to loosen the skins of some varieties—there are variations with the particular variety of peaches that suggest more work is needed. In addition, there are some impressive chemicals that will extend shelf life.

A more clear-cut advantage exists in the pasteurization of seafood. A 250–450-kilorad dose of cobalt-60 gamma rays can triple the refrigerated shelf life of fresh haddock and clams. A mere 50 kilorads will double the iced-storage life of shrimp and also control the "black spot" discoloration that results from the action of phenol oxidases. Here there are no competitive chemical preservatives.

It all looks promising enough that AEC has under construction in Gloucester, Mass., a Marine Products Development Irradiator that will permit the fisheries industry to gain experience with this new preservation technique. Actually, preservation would be most effective if done on shipboard, or in factory-type mother ships, but here one runs into the traditional small-enterprise patterns of the fishing industry.

An army travels on its stomach

Antedating the AEC program, with the goal of *sterilization* of foods to permit long-term storage without refrigeration is a program run by the U.S. Army. Centered around an impressive $1.8-million laboratory in Natick, Mass., the Army program has covered a broad range of foods and extensive feeding and acceptability tests. Irradiated bacon (4.5 megarads), developed in the Army program, has been cleared for human consumption by the Food and Drug Administration. The bacon looks and tastes like ordinary bacon—even better, some claim—but it will keep for months without refrigeration. There are obvious advantages to a military force that can serve good-as-fresh foodstuffs to its soldiers without the logistic complications of refrigeration, but the Army, like the civilian population, has its resistances, and complete irradiated diets lie off in the future.

Speaking of sterilization, one of the most successful applications of radiation has been to the sterilization of medical supplies. Surgical sutures, disposable hypodermics and catheter sets, human bones, artificial arteries, and bioabsorbable sponges are among the wide range of products that are being freed of bacteria by a 2.5-megarad dose. The fact that no heat is required makes it possible to sterilize heat-sensitive materials and to use simpler and cheaper packaging.

One future possibility is the irradiation of

JP-4 jet fuel to inhibit growth of bacteria that clog lines and corrode storage tanks. Another is the irradiation of raw molasses to kill a rope-forming bacterium that degrades the product. Also very promising—and OK'd by the FDA—is the low-dose (20-kilorad) irradiation of wheat and wheat products to rid them of insects. The dose interferes with the reproductive cycle and is also sufficient to sterilize the eggs and larvae. Incidentally, a related idea is the basis of the successful use of radiation to rid the Southwestern United States of the screwworm fly by releasing large numbers of radiation-sterilized (in the sexual sense) male flies that could entertain but not impregnate normal females.

Putting radiation to work

This is a good point to depart from a recounting of the wonderful things radiation can do to consider the practical questions of how to put it to work: of radiation sources, their economics, and their suppliers.

Probably the most useful thing I can tell you about radiation sources is that they are now a commercially available, if specialized, item and therefore there is no lack of interested parties to educate you by explaining the merits of their type of irradiator. More than that there are dozens of irradiation facilities that will be glad to conduct exploratory research on possible application of radiation to your problems. Still, you ought to have some idea of the lay of the radiation land to guide your normal protective instincts, so here are some of the realities of the business as I see them.

For one thing there is a basic choice between accelerator electron (or x-ray) sources and isotope gamma-ray sources. There was a time when the advocates of each tried to convince you that the other was useless; nowadays there seems to be an uneasy truce that recognizes at least some applications that are best suited to each. The electron accelerators tend to be natural for applications that require high power and low penetration. The gamma-ray, cobalt-60 sources look best when power requirement is low but penetration must be high. Thus, for example, electron accelerators dominate the market for irradiation of thin polyethylene film to high doses while gamma rays are best for the sterilization of bulky bales of goat hair. Gamma rays are right for the Dow ethyl bromide process because (1) the radiation power required (2500 curies of cobalt-60, equivalent to 35 W) is too low to sustain the high capital cost of an accelerator and (2) the reaction goes best in liquid, which gammas can penetrate better than electrons.

What about economics? Any figures must necessarily be rough, since commercial experience in this field is limited. One 10-kW accelerator costs $100,000; a 30-kW machine costs about $150,000. The shielding and utilities required to put the larger machine into your plant will run about $50,000–$100,000, depending on the details of the process. These high capital costs make it desirable to keep the facility operating more than one shift per day, and the numbers there are $10,000 per operator per shift with an equal amount for overhead. (The expectation, though, is that the operator would be free to work on other parts of the process, so his costs should not be allocated solely to the accelerator.) The amount to chalk up to maintenance is one of the tough questions; $15,000 per year is typical of the numbers manufacturers quote for the more powerful machines—advocates of cobalt irradiators insist these figures will be higher. Putting all the numbers in and using a 10-year depreciation one comes up with costs per kilowatt-hour of the order of 50¢–$1. This is a lot more than that amount of thermal energy would cost you, but this is a very fancy form of energy. The only meaningful economics is what it will cost per unit of your product.

A direct comparison with cobalt-60 irradiators is difficult since cobalt technology just isn't up in the 30-kW range yet. Based on their present experience in the 100-kilocurie range, designers are willing to extrapolate to 1-megacurie (= 14 kW) units. The costs, I'm told, might be $550,000 for the encapsulated cobalt, $300,000 for irradiator, shielding, and conveyor system, $20,000 per operator year for personnel and their overhead, and $5000 for maintenance. The unit energy cost is then some $6/kWhr. This is higher than for accelerators, but, as I pointed out before, the difference is often taken up by factors reflecting differences in irradiation geometry.

The battle still rages on the matter of maintenance economics. One of the landmarks here is the switch by the Ethicon Corp. from microwave linear accelerators (used and still used for their first suture-sterilization plant) to cobalt-60 for follow-on plants under construction in San Angelo, Texas, and Somerville, N.J. Ethicon found the maintenance costs of the accelerator high (though they still made a profit) and also had troubles maintaining dose uniformity because the accelerator output was so intense. Isotope people seize on this as evidence for their side, but accelerator proponents point out that Ethicon came along "too early" with their first installation and that today's accelerators would behave more reliably.

For example, the folks at High Voltage Engineering Corp. acknowledge that only now do they have a truly industrial accelerator. The Van de Graaff generators and microwave linear accelerators that have been their mainstay till now are basically intended for research use, where there's always a spare Ph.D. around for debugging and where outages are accepted as part of the hazards of research. In their new Insulating-Core Transformer machines, also invented by Professor Van de Graaff, they have a machine that has none of the moving belts and delicate microwave tubes of the aforementioned (Figs. 3-29 and 3-30). Thus High Voltage now has something that truly competes with GE's resonance transformer machine, which has walked off with most of the industrial business to date. Radiation Dynamics, a spunky competitor to HVEC, also puts out a machine

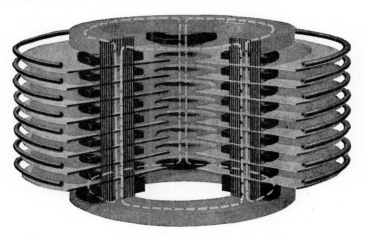

Fig. 3-30. In generating half of Insulating Core Transformer accelerator, alternating (60-cycle) current in primary windings around bottom of each of three legs produces magnetic flux (dashed lines) that induces currents in stacked secondary coils, electrically insulated from each other. These currents are rectified by solid-state diodes, resistors, and capacitors on each deck, producing about 30 kV dc per stage. (Courtesy High Voltage Engineering Corp.)

Fig. 3-29. Accelerating half of new Insulating Core Transformer accelerator. Electron beam starts from cathode within shiny aluminum electrode, is accelerated down evacuated tube (largely hidden by parallel equipotential planes), and spread magnetically before emerging at snout below. High voltage, generated in other half (see Fig. 3-30), is fed in through connector at top. In operation, accelerator is enclosed in pressure vessel that contains insulating gas. (Courtesy High Voltage Engineering Corp.)

free of moving parts in its Dynamitron, so there are several accelerator alternatives today.

Another interesting aspect of the new High Voltage machine is that the voltage source is separated from the accelerating tube, the two being connected by extra-high-voltage cable. This makes the accelerator proper smaller, more easily shielded, and more easily serviced (usually accelerator tubes are not good for more than 2000 hr).

Cobalt has gotten a lift in recent years from two sources: AEC has dropped the price of cobalt, in lots greater than 100,000 curies, from $1 to 50¢ per curie; also, large sources have been installed and proved industrially acceptable. The largest source to date is the 1.3-megacurie source at the Army's Natick laboratory. An even larger source is being assembled at a radiation development center, which the AEC has set up at Brookhaven National Laboratory specifically to advance the technology of large-source handling and of radiation engineering. One of the projects of the center is the preparation of a radiation engineering handbook that will cover all aspects of irradiator design and use.

Such U.S. encouragement is particularly necessary because, in recent years, much of the business for large cobalt irradiators has been going to the British and the Canadians. The Canadians, in particular, offer through Atomic Energy of Canada, Ltd., an integrated service that includes designing the irradiator, building it, and irradiating and encapsulating the cobalt

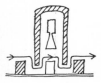

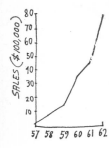

for it. For complex historical and political reasons no such integrated service has been available in the U.S., though that situation is likely to change in view of this pressure from the North.

For both cobalt and accelerators there is an increasing appreciation of the need to have the irradiator fit in with standard industrial practice. Thus, for example, in the new irradiation service facility at Electronized Chemicals Co. in Burlington, Mass., the maze that is required to combine access to the accelerator with protection from scattered radiation is built in the form of vertical steps rather than horizontal jogs (see margin) to permit the straight-through operation characteristic of most production lines. Thus the irradiator designer needs not only to provide the desired dose to the product at a dose rate such that the residence time is economic and the source is used efficiently, but he needs to fit the irradiator into the operating pattern of the plant.

How *many* plants there will be depends on how real the advantages of radiation turn out to be.

If you ask me . . .

Looking back on this article and on my renewed acquaintance with the field of large-scale radiation applications, I have some reactions that I'd like to leave with you in an opinionated epilogue:

I think it's clear that there is real industrial potential in this not-so-new source of energy. I think it is equally clear that much of what has been accomplished so far can be chalked up to luck or the obvious opportunities in a virgin field. The need from here on out is for research that is thoughtful, research that attempts to take as much from radiation chemistry and a fundamental, mechanistic view of radiation effects as our limited understanding permits. This seems to be happening—radiation programs are being guided by research understanding rather than by something the Chairman of the Board saw in *The Wall Street Journal* that morning.

There are some very exciting pure-research opportunities in radiation chemistry. It's abundantly clear that where so much is unknown much fun can be had. I'm sure our understanding of the mechanisms of chemical reactions of all sorts will be deepened by what we learn from the radiation-chemical systems with their extra degrees of freedom. One thing—and this is pure hunch—we may learn is that we have a "sleeper" in gas-discharge chemistry. After all, why go to million-volt electrons to create 100-volt ions when you can get the same ions out of a modest gas discharge.

Finally I wonder what is wrong with industry—American industry in particular. There are some reasonably clear opportunities to make money out of radiation processing. But there has been an awful lot of inertia in going after these opportunities; I suspect that the traditions of the quick return on investment and playing it safe have cut into our free-enterprise responses. To rouse those healthy entrepreneurial instincts I have embellished the outer margin with a final and intriguing sketch: the sales curve of the Raychem Corp., which, in 1959, decided to go into the irradiated-wire business. They've made a bundle.

Further reading

This article provides a brief introduction to radiation chemistry, which underlies the whole subject of radiation processing. Fortunately a very good book on the subject has recently come out. It is *An Introduction to Radiation Chemistry* by Spinks and Woods (Wiley, 1964, $12). A classic, recently revised, is *Radiation Chemistry of Gases* by Lind (Reinhold, 1961, $12). Proof of the complexity of H_2O is that a whole book—a good book—is devoted to its radiation chemistry: *The Radiation Chemistry of Water and Aqueous Solutions* by Allen (Van Nostrand, 1961, $6). Also very good is Swallow's *Radiation Chemistry of Organic Compounds* (Pergamon, 1960, $17.50).

One of the very finest books in this or any field is Chapiro's *Radiation Chemistry of Polymeric Systems* (Wiley-Interscience, 1962, $21). Shorter and simpler is Bovey's *The Effects of Ionizing Radiation on Natural and Synthetic High Polymers* (Wiley-Interscience, 1958, $9). An excellent book by a radiation pioneer is *Atomic Radiation and Polymers* by Charlesby (Pergamon, 1960, $15).

There have been excellent reviews of topics in radiation chemistry in each *Annual Review of Physical Chemistry* (Annual Reviews, $7) for the past five years at least.

Apparently, the only textbook on industrial radiation processing is *Massive Radiation Techniques,* edited by Sidney Jefferson (George Newnes, Ltd., England, 1964, 70/). The International Atomic Energy Agency has just issued the proceedings of a conference on radiation processing, *Industrial Uses of Large Radiation Sources* (IAEA, Vienna, 1963, in two volumes, $8.50 each). The proceedings of an earlier conference, partly outdated but useful in spots, are in *Large Radiation Sources in Industry* (IAEA, 1960, in two volumes, $4.50 each).

The AEC has just added *Isotopes and Radiation Technology* to its list of quarterly progress reviews (Supt. of Documents, Washington 25, D.C., $2/year). It joins such journals as *Radia-*

tion Research, Nucleonics, Journal of Polymer Science, and *Journal of Applied Radiation and Isotopes* as the principal sources of information on this ill-defined field.

The man at the AEC to talk to if you've got ideas about new applications for radiation is Joe Machurek, 202-HA7-7831, ext. 5271. The annual Buyers' Guide of *Nucleonics* (330 W. 42 St., New York 36, $2) lists companies who manufacture accelerators, encapsulate cobalt-60, consult in the radiation field, and otherwise stand ready to help you explore this subject. The 1963/64 issue also lists irradiation facilities available on a commercial basis.

SIZING SOLID PARTICLES

by Brian Kaye *

IN BRIEF: *Technologies in which fine particles play a vital role are legion and more appear on the scene each year. Crucial to understanding particle behavior is often the size of the particles involved or the distribution of various sizes in a mixture. Size may be determined "directly"—by examining individual particles over a meaningful sample, by detecting the effect of their presence in a moving stream of fluid, by sieving them, by observing their rate of fall in a viscous fluid, or by washing them into fractions for examination. There are powerful "indirect" methods as well, in which a surface area of a bed of particles is calculated. In one of these, area is determined from the measured resistance a fluid encounters in permeating the bed; in another, area is found by measuring the amount of gas adsorbed as a monolayer on the bed's surface. In both, particle size is then deduced from the calculated total surface area. All the methods have their advantages and limitations, most of which become apparent once the basic concepts of the methods are understood.—F.P.*

■ It requires but a moment's reflection to appreciate the ubiquity of particulate matter in our environment. Imagine standing barefoot on an ocean beach scanning the star-swept heavens. The celestial particles our eyes perceive many light-years away are, of course, very large. Those small sand particles between our toes are, despite their smallness to us, near the middle of the cosmic size scale: we know that the whole realm of atomic and subatomic particles remains—beyond and beneath our conventional ken.

It is the particles in this "middle" range that interest me professionally, and it is the measurement of their size to which I propose to introduce you here. The exact definition of how small a small particle is need not concern us unduly. Suffice it to say that they are large enough for us to perceive with our unaided senses (our toes, if you will), but small when compared with common objects in our terrestrial environment. And they are of great importance industrially—be they submicron-sized paint pigments, or crushed ore particles several millimeters in diameter.

But it is not my purpose to regale you with examples of the important role small particles play in diverse disciplines—ceramics, powder metallurgy, food processing, air pollution, concrete construction, astronomy, and criminology, to suggest a few. This is a story in itself that has been amply and vividly told (see "Further reading"). And there are experts in all these areas who have a firm grasp of particle technology and the complexities of size measurement it entails.

My concern rests, rather, with those of you to whom matters particular are presenting new, perhaps perplexing problems in your work. Typifying this predicament is the chap now designing some device for future use on the possibly powdery surface of the moon. Or, he may be a criminologist intent on identifying a certain clay as characteristic of the scene of a crime. Perhaps he is a metallurgist frustrated in his attempts to find a suitable abrasive polish for a new alloy he is trying to inspect metallographically.

Whatever the task, it is very often vitally necessary to know the size of the particles one deals with. It may be, as in food processing, that what counts is the homogeneity of particle size. Or, as in concrete, we may wish to control the distribution of several different-sized particles—cement, sand, gravel—within the mix. The question immediately becomes this: What methods of measurement are available, and how do we choose among them? To answer this question, it is first essential to consider some of the many concepts of size as used in particle technology.

Size is a many-splendored thing

One of the biggest stumbling blocks is that we always want instinctively to convert the idea of "a particle" to that of "a *spherical* particle." Few particles, of course, are of this

* Brian Kaye is currently conducting powder studies at the IIT Research Institute, Chicago, Illinois.

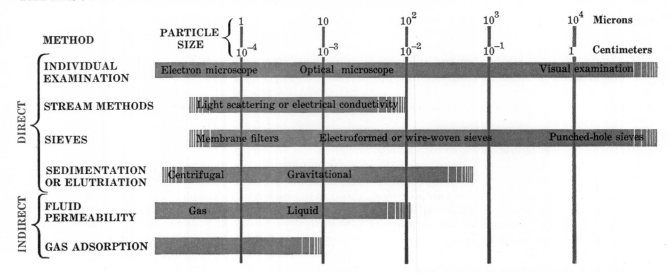

Fig. 3-31. *All sizing techniques do not cover all size ranges. The direct methods span the widest range, and this—plus the relative ease of operation and interpretation of results—makes them widely used. The indirect methods have their advantages, though, as the text explains.*

handy geometry. Nonetheless, the subconscious wish remains, and we can thus often overlook the fact that the size of *nonspherical* particles has no unique meaning unless the method of measurement is clearly specified.

To illustrate, consider the simple cylindrical particle sketched in Fig. 3-32. What is the size of this particle? If it were large enough to hold between our fingers, we could measure its dimensions and specify its shape and volume. However, if it were only one of many small particles, requiring measurement by sieving, its "effective sieve size" would be 2 units as set by the sieve. If it were small and had been collected on a microscope slide by, say, settlement from the atmosphere, then it might lie on its side and appear as a rectangle 4 units long.

Dispersed in a heavy-mineral-oil film on the slide, it could have any profile intermediate between 2 and 4 units. In fact, a uniform dispersion of many such identical cylinders would appear, upon microscopic examination, to consist of many different shapes and sizes.

In theory such difficulties can be overcome by measuring more than one dimension of the particle. In practice this is rarely possible. Most measurement schemes depend upon observations of some other property of the particle, as we shall see, and the measurement is then converted by some appropriate relationship to an "equivalent" particle diameter. Such relationships can be devised from theory, from empiricism based on much observation, or from some simple ideal comparator. As an example of the last of these, it is common practice when viewing particles under a microscope to compare the projected area of the particle with those of a series of circles drawn on a transparent disk and inserted into the eyepiece. In this case, the effective-size parameter reported in the literature becomes the diameter of the circle of equal area. In the case of our cylindrical particle on its side, the particle "size" would be an equivalent radius of $\sqrt{2/\pi}$. This number, by itself, would not be very revealing. To make any real sense, it should be accompanied by details showing how the measurement was made.

Know thy methods of measurement

Given the crucial role of method in size determination and specification, it is important for the neophyte to have a firm grasp of the physical basis and limitations of the commonly used methods. The best way to do this, and

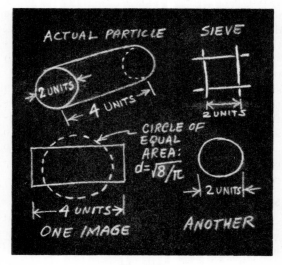

Fig. 3-32.

still avoid the paralyzing detail which emerges when you begin to examine specific techniques, is to discuss the six major groups into which such techniques fall. These are shown in Fig. 3-31, and are correlated rather roughly with the range of particle size to which they are applied.

In the group of methods I have called "direct," measurements are made on some size-dependent parameter of the particle. The physical basis of methods based on individual examination of particles is self-evident, and I have touched upon certain aspects of these earlier. In the *stream* methods, a fluid bearing the particles to be sized is drawn past a sensing device which is designed to monitor continuously some physical property of the fluid—such as its capacity for scattering light. The presence of the particles creates a discontinuity in this property, and its magnitude is related to some particle parameter so that a size distribution can be obtained. *Sieving* segregates the particles into size groups by means of screens having known aperture sizes. In *sedimentation* methods, the particles settle through a static fluid, whilst in *elutriation* techniques the fluid moves and separates the particles into two fractions—those carried along by the fluid and those too heavy to permit this.

The first group of "indirect" methods—the *permeability* techniques—uses the fact that the resistance offered to a fluid passing through a porous compact of particles is related to the pore structure of the compact. By making certain assumptions, the pore structure can be related to the size distribution of the powder comprising it; hence by measuring the flow resistance an average particle size can be calculated. The basic concept involved in the other indirect method—*gas adsorption*—is simple: If the quantity of gas required to cover a powder with a complete monolayer of gas molecules is known by observation, then the powder surface area can be calculated using the cross-sectional area of the gas molecules. Once we have the area, it is possible to calculate an "effective mean size."

A measurement is only as good as the sample

I shall have more to say about each of these broad methods of analysis in a moment, but first a few words are in order on the crucial importance of sampling technique. That the sample of powder to be analyzed should be representative of the parent supply is one of those truisms that is honored in the breach more often than not. The reason is usually that the laboratory is remote from the process plant and the sampling is often carried out by personnel with little or no understanding of the purpose for which the sample is required.

A victim of this situation more than once, I recall clearly one typical instance. After I had spent much time and effort analyzing a metal powder sample, the results were challenged; I analyzed a second sample—with different results. Perhaps I was an incompetent analyst? Subsequent investigation showed that the first sample had been scooped from the top of a drum of powder which had been sitting for a while atop a vibrating table. The second sample was scooped from the same drum after perhaps half its contents had been used. The analytical results were only too true! Since then, I have often wondered how many failures in correlating performance of metal powder parts with measured distribution of the particles in them can be traced to unsatisfactory sampling procedures.

Complex procedures have been evolved for sampling from large quantities of powders, but my interest here lies in what might be called secondary, or analytical sampling problems. In short, what kinds of problems must one watch out for when an adequate sample from the source is at hand, and the analytical process—in itself a sampling process—is about to begin. I think these problems can be best elucidated by a bit more thorough examination of the various analytical techniques themselves.

A view through the microscope

Direct individual examination of particles or their images has the advantage that information can be obtained on particle shape and surface characteristics. Thus, microscopic examination is always a good supplement to the other methods. It has an important disadvantage with most heterogeneous powders, though, in that too much work is required with present methods of analysis to obtain a measured distribution that has the required confidence limits.

Many of the discussions of the microscopic method in the literature pertain to powders having relatively few different size ranges within them. The resultant compact scatter bands can give a false sense of security to the investigator who is not mathematically inclined. This is because as the number of size ranges increases, the relative frequency of occurrence of the larger particles is reduced.

This problem is illustrated by the table on p. 344, in which two different size distributions are shown, each split into ten equal-sized groups with the relative frequencies of particles in each group displayed alongside. For distribution *B*, the relative frequency of the smallest and largest particles is only $479:1890 = 1:4$, so that in a series of microscopic measurements on 500 particles a sufficient number of large particles would be encountered. For distribution *A*, how-

TWO TYPICAL POWDER-SIZE DISTRIBUTIONS

(n = *number of particles in each size group for a sample of 10,000 particles*)

Distribution A		Distribution B	
Size group	n *value*	*Size group*	n *value*
0–1.0	9514	6.0–6.4	1890
1.0–2.0	352	6.4–6.8	1568
2.0–3.0	76	6.8–7.2	1314
3.0–4.0	28	7.2–7.6	1112
4.0–5.0	13	7.6–8.0	950
5.0–6.0	7	8.0–8.4	818
6.0–7.0	4	8.4–8.8	708
7.0–8.0	3	8.8–9.2	618
8.0–9.0	2	9.2–9.6	543
9.0–10.0	1	9.6–10.0	479
	10,000		10,000

Note: Particle sizes are in arbitrary units.

ever, the chances of encountering a large particle are very small even if 10,000 particles were measured. It can be imagined that the adoption of the measurement procedure evolved for type B to a sample of powder A could cause serious difficulties because the man at the microscope would probably be reluctant to repeat a series of 500 measurements for comparative purposes.

Establishing a satisfactory counting procedure for any but the narrow size-range powders is a complex problem, requiring the aid of a competent statistician, and should not be undertaken lightly. When examining reported microscopic measurement data, the manner of its acquisition should be carefully scrutinized. If it is not given, the claimed confidence levels may be optimistic. There are several automatic microscopes available that can handle large numbers of particles and hence reduce this aspect of statistical error, but they are often too expensive for the average laboratory.

One way to reduce viewing fatigue is the use of the concept of statistical diameters—mathematical conventions that describe readily measured averages. Two of the most commonly used are sketched in Fig. 3-33.

The *Martin's* diameter is the mean length of a line that intercepts the particle image and divides it into equal areas; the bisecting line is always taken parallel to the direction of traverse. The *Feret's* diameter is the mean distance between two tangents on opposite sides of the particle image, the tangents being drawn perpendicular to the direction of traverse.

As you can see, the use of statistical diameters removes the need for constant realignment of the eyepiece reticule to measure a particular dimension of the particle—say, its length. The magnitude of a statistical diam-

eter is a function of the particle's shape; indeed, the ratio of two different diameters—for example, the Martin's and Feret's—have been used as shape factors to describe particle size. The trouble is that as yet there is little information to indicate how many particles should be counted, using statistical diameters, to achieve a given confidence level. However, I expect the future will see wider use of the shape-factor approach, particularly when the automatic microscope becomes more easily available.

Because slide preparation requires very small quantities of powder—as little as a milligram from a kilogram—sampling problems can be difficult. Each situation will have its own complications, but I cannot stress too highly that care be exercised in setting up a sampling procedure. For example, the size of a fragile particle can easily be changed in the process of preparing the slide. Other factors which influence accuracy, and on which we need more information, are operator bias, his inevitable fatigue, and the manner in which he selects his field of view.

Particles + moving fluid = stream

As noted earlier, most measurement schemes involve some property of the particle that is related to its size. In the stream methods, a fluid carrying the particles is passed through a device that senses the discontinuities in the properties of the stream due to the presence of varying-sized particles. There are a number of physical effects used, and more are under study. In some, the manner in which light is scattered by the particles is measured and correlated with size; in others, the change in

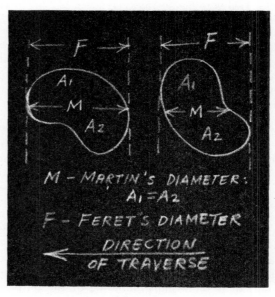

Fig. 3-33.

electrical resistance of a fluid column when a particle is present serves as the basis of measurement. There is current interest in analysis methods based on sound measurements—either using reflection effects or, as in the newest laboratory techniques, using the sound generated by the particles themselves as they move with the fluid. Neither of these techniques is used widely as yet because they are still in the development stage. In general all devices for stream analysis are relatively expensive because of the associated electronics.

I would like to focus briefly on one of the more commonly used stream methods, for it illustrates some problems common to all stream devices. This is the Coulter Counter, whose basic components are sketched in Fig. 3-34.

The sensing zone is a small orifice between two portions of a particle suspension held in a wide outer vessel and a narrow inner one. Two electrodes, one on each side of the orifice, permit the measurement of resistance in the orifice zone. When a particle is drawn through the orifice by the electrically conducting fluid, it replaces its own volume of electrolyte and there occurs a change in the resistance between the electrodes. Such changes are measured and recorded electronically, and a particle-size distribution is obtained.

This method can be accurate, but operational or environmental quirks can easily arise to obscure the results. This can be as simple as electrical noise from a nearby stirring motor; if the counter electronics are not shielded adequately, the device may register fine particles that do not exist. Or, if the suspension is not stirred adequately, the large heavy particles may settle and those passing through the orifice will not be wholly representative of the mix. Keep in mind that the suspension must be very dilute so that only one particle is present in the orifice at once. This, coupled with the fact that rarely can the particles be seen, means that insufficient stirring could increase the apparent fineness of the powder.

I cite this example because it is so typical of the kind of conditions that can lead to false confidence in the results of analyses from "black boxes," even though the basic experiment is repeated many times. So often a device for size analysis utilizes principles outside the formal training of the investigator, and he can easily become mesmerized by knobs and buttons into accepting on faith the results that emerge. A simple point, but so often overlooked these days.

Sieving is deceptively simple

I am sure that a suggestion to investigate sieving theory and practice would bring forth little enthusiasm from any industrial sponsor.

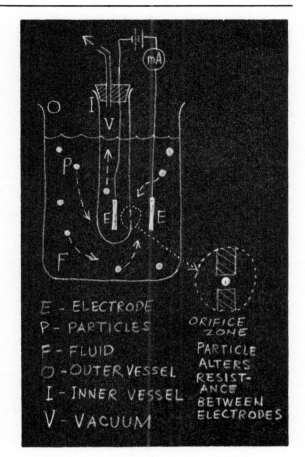

E - ELECTRODE
P - PARTICLES
F - FLUID
O - OUTER VESSEL
I - INNER VESSEL
V - VACUUM

ORIFICE ZONE
PARTICLE ALTERS RESISTANCE BETWEEN ELECTRODES

Fig. 3-34.

Surely, we know all about sieving. In point of fact, very little is known about basic sieving theory—with its complex interactions of different-sized particles as they try to pass through the apertures of the sieve. In sieve analysis, the size distribution of a powder is obtained by measuring the weight of powder fractions retained in a series of grids of decreasing aperture size. The grids can be manufactured in different ways, each having its own influence on the sieving action.

The advantages of sieve analysis are several and important. Large quantities of powder can be used and so sampling error can be minimized. The equipment is cheap, easily maintained, reasonably robust, and simple to operate. The main problem is deciding when sieving is complete, that is, when the particles are fully separated into oversize and undersize. Then, too, it's just not possible to make a perfect sieve: even the best ones have a finite range of aperture sizes present. Fine meshes are easily damaged, and such damage is difficult to detect with the naked eye.

If we use sieves in good condition, and if we follow standardized procedure, then sieve analysis will yield precise, reproducible results.

Ignore these if's, and chaos will reign. If not convinced by this, try circulating a sample of powder to different analysts giving no other instructions than to sieve the powder and report the results. The disparities will show you how essential it is in inter-laboratory testing (say, between producer and user of a powder) to agree upon a standardized sieving procedure—including selection and calibration of the sieves used. Indeed, most industrial nations have established standards for the manufacture and use of sieves, although there is still a need for rapid methods of calibrating and testing sieve surfaces.

The case of the falling particles

Sedimentation is the most important of the fourth, and last group of direct methods of particle-size analysis. It is based on a study of the speed at which particles fall through a viscous fluid. In practice, this boils down to observing the time required for particles to settle through a predetermined distance, h. If we know this time, t, then an "equivalent particle diameter," d, can be computed from the Stokes equation for a sphere falling steadily under the influence of gravity through a fluid of viscosity η:

$$d^2 = 18\eta h/(\rho_P - \rho_F)gt$$

In this equation, ρ_P is the density of the particle, and ρ_F is that of the fluid.

For the Stokes equation to be valid, even for spherical particles, the flow around the falling particle should be streamlined, and the particle should fall through the fluid remote from other particles. Usually, the falling speeds used are low enough for the first of these conditions to be satisfied; however, it is not possible to satisfy completely the second condition.

A series of measurements on single particles falling through the fluid would be ideal, except that the detection of their movement would be difficult with the usual sensing devices. In point of fact, we do not observe falling speeds at all, but rather changes in the concentration of particles at the end of the falling height, h, at different times. Thus, we have to compromise between the ideal concentration (one particle) and one that our device can sense accurately.

In general, concentrations between 1 and 2% by volume have been used, except for the case where concentration is measured by observing the attenuation of a beam of light; here, much lower concentrations can be used. However, recent work on the interaction between particles falling in a viscous fluid indicates that concentrations lower than 0.1% should be used if very high accuracy is desired.

This important point is nicely illustrated by results obtained in experiments carried out by R. P. Boardman and myself while studying particle interactions at Nottingham and District Technical College in England. Instead of particles, we used small glass spheres. The measured velocity of a single *red*-glass sphere falling through a large bath of heavy mineral oil was taken as its ideal Stokes velocity. We then measured the velocity of this same red sphere as it fell through different concentrations of *white*-glass spheres in the same oil.

The average ratio of the two velocities, when plotted against particle concentration as sketched in Fig. 3-35, then gave a surprising view of the importance of concentration in sedimentation analysis. You'll note that the maximum increase in velocity (greatest deviation from a ratio of unity) occurred near 1 to 2%—precisely the region where much sedimentation analysis is conventionally done. We concluded that to get accuracy by sedimentation methods, a great deal more will have to be known about just how particles interact in a fluid.

But sedimentation analysis is more than getting the right concentration and calculating some size-dependent parameter from the fall characteristics. Two other major factors are involved: adequately dispersing the particles in the suspension, and accurately measuring changes in concentration at the bottom of the fall.

There are two kinds of suspension systems possible, and on each it's possible to carry out measurements in two ways. The resultant four systems are sketched in Fig. 3-36, and are largely self-evident. Whatever the suspension system, however, the effect of the dispersion method must be checked. For example, high-velocity gas jets are often used when the sedi-

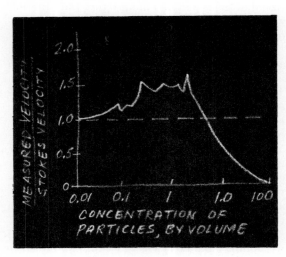

Fig. 3-35.

menting fluid is a gas, but the jet action may cause the powder to become strongly charged so that electrostatic effects may actually retard settling action. If the fluid medium is a liquid, mechanical agitation is rarely an adequate dispersing means and a surface-active agent has to be used. The concentration of this agent can, in turn, alter the settling behavior and hence should always be reported with any sedimentation data. A good general rule to follow is to choose a dispersion method whose severity is of the same magnitude as that to which the powder will be subjected when processed. For instance, if a paint powder is being analyzed that will, in practice, be simply stirred into water—then you would do the same when preparing the sample for sedimentation analysis.

But what is the concentration, sir?

I mentioned earlier that we do not actually observe the settling time of a particle in the suspension. Indeed, we cannot always see them individually. We can determine the time they take to fall, however, by observing how fast they build up in our chosen observation layer. That is, we measure the change in concentration in this layer with time.

Of the many techniques for measuring concentrations of particles in suspension, I shall mention but two. Perhaps the simplest principle to use is that of buoyancy, so it's not surprising that hydrometers are widely used. They are cheap, simple, and robust; however, they are usually long and over this length a density gradient can easily exist, hence the resolution obtained is not good. There are also other practical and theoretical objections to their use. To improve the technique, a Danish ceramist named Berg developed miniature hydrometers which are completely submerged in the suspension. The main problem with these so-called "divers" is that their position must be monitored magnetically or electronically.

In the frequently used pipette technique, the suspension concentrations are determined directly by withdrawing a sample by means of a fixed volume pipette and measuring the solids content gravimetrically or chemically. It is simple and low-cost, so the pipette method is perhaps the most commonly used method in sedimentation analysis. It was also one of the earliest techniques to be developed and has consequently acquired an aura of sanctity. You will often find a new method of analysis compared with "the pipette method" and when agreement between the two is good, the assumption is implicit that the new method is satisfactory.

It turns out that there are a surprising number of factors that can influence pipette meas-

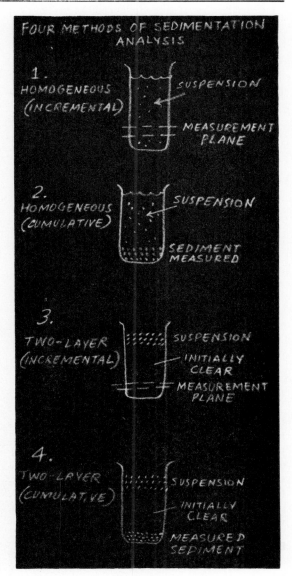

Fig. 3-36.

urements, and unless procedural detail is given, a vague reference to "the pipette method" is of little value in judging the worth of published data. Let me just cite two of the many trouble spots. If the pipette is left in the suspension, particles near the stem will not fall in the same manner as those away from it. Accordingly, there will be density differences near the measuring zone and convection currents will develop around the tip of the pipette. Then, too, the flow velocities into the mouth of the pipette from the measurement zone—actually a sphere rather than a thin slice, as shown in Fig. 3-37—will determine whether all particle sizes are sampled efficiently. Thus, if the operator sucks too slowly, the fine particles will be overestimated because the larger ones will not be drawn into the orifice of the pipette.

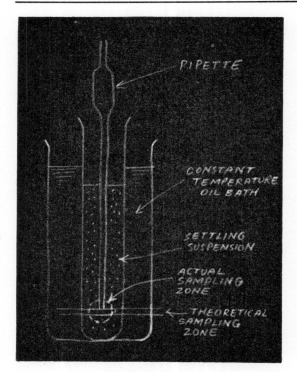

Fig. 3-37.

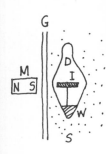

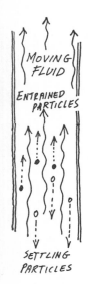

D – Diver
W – Weight
I – Iron plate
G – Glass wall
S – Suspension
M – Magnet

MOVING
FLUID
ENTRAINED
PARTICLES

SETTLING
PARTICLES

The story is pretty much the same no matter what the method of concentration analysis used in sedimentation: there has to be a compromise between ease of operation, time needed, expense of equipment, precision desired, the sample size needed for analysis and other factors. For many methods, a satisfactory compromise has been worked out; for others, much work remains to be done.

Elutriation, the reverse of sedimentation

Problems of elutriation methods are basically the same as those in sedimentation techniques in that the major problems of particle dispersion and particle dynamics are common to both. Elutriation—literally washing out—is the process of separating powders into fractions of different mean diameter by suspending the particles in a moving fluid. In a vertical elutriator, for example, the fluid moves upward through a column as sketched in the margin. For a specific fluid velocity, particles smaller than a given size move upward with the fluid whilst the larger particles settle. Size analysis is carried out by using different velocities (analogous to different sieves) to split the powder into different fractions which can then be weighed directly.

Elutriation has the advantage that fractions thus prepared can be examined directly by secondary methods such as microscope analysis. However, as in sieving, the fractionation of individual particles does not always occur sharply

with respect to the theoretical partition diameter, and it is sometimes hard to tell when fractionation of a given particle size is complete.

Enter, the indirect methods of analysis

You will recall that in permeability techniques the surface area of a powder can be calculated from the resistance offered to the flow of a fluid through a plug of powder. From this surface area the size of the particles making up the plug is deduced. I shall not go into the various relationships between pressure drop and surface area, and between area and particle size, for these are available in any book on the subject. It must be stressed, however, that what we are measuring is the permeability of the plug, and that consequently the validity of the area determined from it is no better than the validity of the assumptions made when interpreting the permeability data.

The methods as a group have several advantages. The equipment is cheap and usually robust. A sample in the order of grams is required so that sampling problems are comparatively simple. And lastly, the method is rapid. But serious difficulties can be encountered when comparing powders that contain widely different size ranges.

Suppose, for example, that we are investigating the sintering behavior of different powders of the same metal. We could vary the powder by removing the coarse grains from it, but under some circumstances this could result in an apparent *decrease* in the surface area per gram—the opposite to what we would expect. The measured surface area per gram might apparently decrease because the removal of coarse particles could leave a loosely packed powder through which the fluid could easily permeate. In reality, with the coarse particles present, the smaller particles would closely interpack with them, the powder bed would be dense so that a low permeability (i.e., a high-surface area) would be recorded.

So if the technique is used to compare products of a similar size distribution—say, samples from a ball mill at successive time intervals—then it can be very useful; but if it is used with widely different powder types, anomalous results can be obtained.

In the last sizing technique I want to mention—gas adsorption—we again calculate the surface area of a bed of particles, but one which has been covered by a complete monolayer of gas molecules. The surface area of the powder is calculated from the known cross-sectional area of the gas molecules. The study of gas adsorption is itself a complete branch of surface chemistry, and little useful comment on the various methods used can be given here. The important point to keep in mind is that although gas-adsorption techniques measure directly the surface area available for chemical or physical reaction, any derived measure of particle size from such data must be interpreted with the greatest care.

This point can be simply illustrated by considering a cube of sugar as a "particle." Because of its porous structure, it has a high-surface area for solution reaction. From this area we could readily calculate the "equivalent effective surface diameter," that is, the diameter of a particle of a monosized powder one gram of which would have the same surface area as one gram of sugar. It's quite obvious, however, that we would hesitate to use this effective diameter to predict sedimentation dynamics of the actual sugar cube in, say, a viscous mineral oil. This is obvious because it's on a macroscopic scale. However, with particles of a size not visible to the naked eye, the inconsistency in using the "equivalent" diameters from gas adsorption data to predict sedimentation dynamics is often not so obvious.

Tomorrow, and tomorrow, and tomorrow

Despite such subtleties, and there are many spread among the methods I have discussed and some I have not, it's becoming apparent that most of the basic methods of sizing particles have been explored—at least tentatively. K. T. Whitby, a particle technologist at the University of Minnesota, put it most succinctly in his recent remark on sedimentation methods: "There are no new methods, only new investigators with new compromises." With but a little stretching, in my judgment, his comment could easily extend to the whole field of size analysis.

In the coming years, as the importance and vigor of particle technology mounts, the major efforts will probably be in optimizing analytical procedures. Already, the American Society for Testing and Materials and the Society for Analytical Chemistry have subcommittees dealing with size analysis. In England, the subject is being taught on the post-graduate level at the Bradford Institute of Technology, and a professor of Powder Science has been appointed at Kings College, London University. There are growing centers of research both here and abroad. It's even possible we shall see established the ultimate in scientific respectability— a "Journal of Powder Technology." I'm all for respectability in this business if it means better accuracy all round. Let's just hope that when such a journal comes its liveliness quotient is high!

Further reading

A delightfully written (and illustrated) overview of fine-particles research is the 3rd quarter, 1961 issue of the *Stanford Research Institute Journal* (SRI, Dept. 300, Menlo Park, Calif.). In it are articles showing the nature of particle technology and its role in production, in agriculture, in health and disease, and in the atmosphere, together with a useful chart showing characteristics of particles and dispersoids. In 1962 a symposium on industrial powder technology was held in England; its proceedings are quite useful, and were published as "Powders in Industry," a special publication of the Society of Chemical Industry (14 Belgrave Sq., London). For a slim, single book covering both techniques and the statistics that must accompany their successful application, see *Fine Particle Measurement: Size, Surface, and Pore Volume* by Orr and DallaValle (Macmillan, 1959, $12). For the mathematically inclined, there is Herdan's *Small Particle Statistics* (Butterworths, 2nd Ed., 1961, $12). To appreciate the pattern of research in the field, see *Symposium on Particle Size Measurement* (ASTM Special Publication No. 234, 1958). It's available from the American Society for Testing and Materials (1916 Race St., Philadelphia), and it is particularly illuminating on the problem of comparing results between processors of powders and the laboratories which measure them. Currently available commercial instruments for particle-size analysis are reviewed in the July 1963 issue of *R&D for Industry*.

ULTRASOUND IN INDUSTRY

by Ronald G. Neswald *

IN BRIEF: *Experimenters and industrial ultrasonographers entering the sonic field in the last few decades have come upon a rich legacy of predicted exploitable effects just waiting for the right materials and techniques to come along.*

* Ronald G. Neswald is a former Associate Editor of *International Science and Technology.*

With the advent of modern (particularly sonar) needs and the concomitant development of new (e.g., electrostrictive and magnetostrictive) materials and the electronic and acoustic techniques to implement them, the business grew rapidly. The generation and processing, the reflection, refraction, delay, and dispersion of high-frequency sound waves led to an impres-

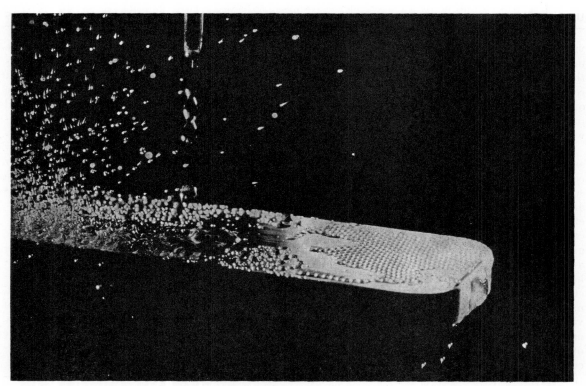

Fig. 3-38. Sonic, but not quite ultra-, this vibrating bar, driven by a power amplifier and a large voice-coil, can control chemical reaction rates. Above, liquid falling on the bar is broken by intense surface waves into droplets whose size depends on frequency of excitation. Since chemical reaction rates vary with surface: volume ratio, the frequency controls reaction rate. Note nodes—quiet places on the bar where droplets gather. Thermoplastic stearic acid pellets below were formed from liquid (at 1500 cps, right; 500 cps, left) and cooled in falling. (Courtesy N. C. Pickering)

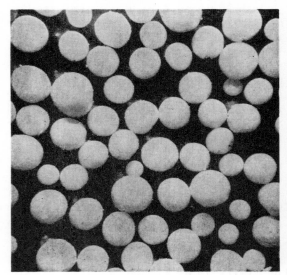
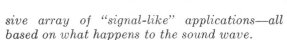

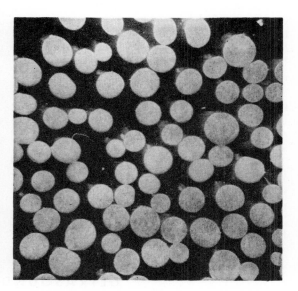

sive array of "signal-like" applications—all based on what happens to the sound wave.

Of course, ultrasound also makes its mark on matter; if the sound is sufficiently intense, radical disruptive effects occur. The effects range from cavitation in liquids and plasticity increases in metals to sonoluminescence and coagulation. Many effects have been observed and several have been applied industrially. But this is where classical theory leaves off.

Clearly, what's now needed is a D'Alembert of cavitation, a Chladni of sonic mixing, a Rayleigh of the effects of high-intensity sound. —R.G.N.

■ In days of old, before space became so headily and incestuously intertwined with time that it tangled back on its own warped self, its various "continua" shot through with wormholes and chopped up into quanta, Nature was a pretty unsophisticated anthropomorphic simpleton. She abhorred vacua, favored simple symmetries, and, when pinched, punched or otherwise perturbed, she reacted in kind with restoring forces, which (to a first approximation) were proportional to the magnitude of the original disturbances. The LeChatelier-Braun principle in chemical solutions, Lenz's law in electrical circuits, Hooke's law in mechanical systems reigned supreme.

Anthropomorphically, even then, there was always some reaction time, and often an observable overreaction. And, of course, there was the entirely natural tendency for the reacting system to flail about and involve any immediate (and, ultimately, all available) systems in the reaction. In those times, Nature was more material than she now appears; virtually all physical media exhibited these properties of elasticity, elastic lag (also called relaxation time), and coupling among systems and among degrees of freedom within systems. This was fortunate for ultrasonics and, indeed, for all mechanical-type mechanics. For, whatever may have been the forces that held the constituent particles of those eighteenth- and nineteenth-century fluids and solids to their relative positions, the prosaic reaction was the means by which vibrations and other cooperative mass motions were propagated.

From that basic notion of a piece of reality (i.e., a mass) perturbed from its equilibrium position in an elastic medium (e.g., from its place along the spring in the top margin sketch), it has long been traditional to develop the idea of a single mode of vibration. The concept of a relaxation, of an elastic lag or phase shift between a disturbance and the resulting restoring force, led Rayleigh, in the last century, to recognize that some of the energy of the disturbance would be dissipated. His idea was that "an equalization of the different sorts of energy" would occur in a gas as translational energy of molecules was transformed into other, rotational, modes. He even predicted that this would show up as an absorption of sound—but that's getting ahead of our story.

Big waves from little jiggles grow

As the succeeding sketches in the margin suggest, coupling one vibration mode to another and then another ultimately leads to the progressive disturbance through a homogeneous elastic medium (which is represented by the heavy spring in the last sketch). That is, starting with a displacement y, at some distance x along a springy medium, and considering successively smaller portions of the spring-mass

system (so that $\delta x \to 0$), ultimately gives rise to the wave equation

$$\delta^2 y / \delta t^2 = c^2 (\delta^2 y / \delta x^2)$$

The progressive disturbance described by all this is a *wave*, and it travels through the medium with a wave velocity given by $c^2 = k/m$. The most familiar of these progressive disturbances periodically repeats the same pattern as it travels through the medium. Its pattern of displacement, y, with distance, x, and time is $y = a \sin n(x - ct)$; everybody calls it the common sine wave.

Our sine wave, wriggling its way along the length of the massive spring in the margin, is a fine example of a longitudinal wave. It's the same periodic disturbance that's called a "sound wave" in elementary-physics courses, where it is usually presented as a compression wave in air, the series of compressions and rarefactions marching across the top of Fig. 3-39. But the present argument covers that case too; we haven't said a word yet about what those restoring forces really are, about whether those springs represent electrical or magnetic forces in crystals or forces due to local pressure gradients in fluids like air or sea water.

What's sauce longitudinally is sauce transversely

The argument holds for any elastic forces, exotic or mundane, in any distensible media. In fact, those conceptual springs might even represent real springs, just as long as they are free to change their lengths in response to a disturbance. For our purposes, sonic waves are even more general than that.

The wave doesn't have to be longitudinal, with its particle displacement along the direction of wave propagation, and the medium needn't necessarily change its length. In one of the simplest other modes of vibration, our massive spring is plucked so that an element moves perpendicular to the spring axis, and generates a transverse wave that travels along the axis. Furthermore, if we use a material with a finite Poisson's ratio, we can, in general, expect coupling between vibration modes due to shearing forces and those due to tensile forces. As you might imagine, this can lead to a large family of complex paths for an individual mass element to trace out. Anisotropies and discontinuities give rise to still other complex modes. The most common of these is the Rayleigh surface wave of Fig. 3-39, which results from unbalanced forces at the surface of a solid, where a layer of molecules experiences internal forces on one side and much smaller fluid restraining forces on the other.

All these modes—and many more—are sonic

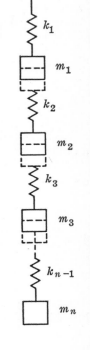

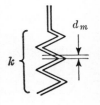

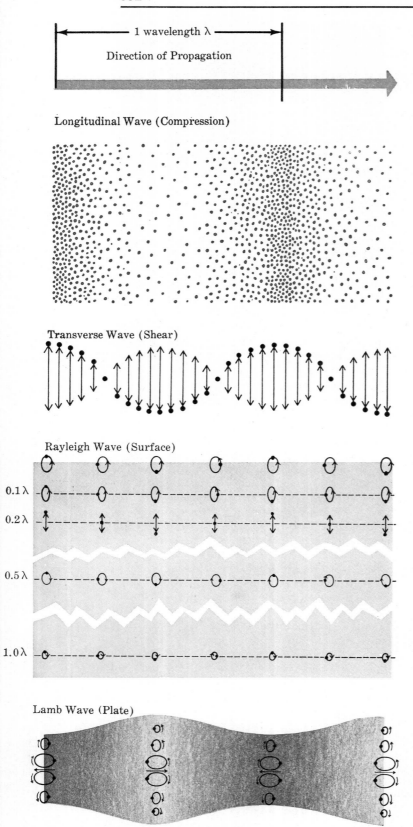

1 wavelength λ

Direction of Propagation

Longitudinal Wave (Compression)

Transverse Wave (Shear)

Rayleigh Wave (Surface)

0.1λ

0.2λ

0.5λ

1.0λ

Lamb Wave (Plate)

Fig. 3-39. Particle motions in any but the simplest waves are very complex. Asymmetrical restoring forces near solid surfaces give rise to Rayleigh modes that

waves. In fact, any progressive periodic or even aperiodic disturbance of the mass elements of an elastic medium from their equilibrium positions qualifies. That is, any physical movement of matter that affects neighboring hunks of matter, through restoring forces, is grist for sonic transducers. Transducers don't absolutely require periodic phenomena; they will usually respond to transients. Still the practice of industrial ultrasonics generally—but by no means always—involves periodicity.

So that's the sonics part of our title; the ultra part of the term is a bit more vague. The lower-frequency boundary of ultrasonics has been variously and arbitrarily defined as 10 kc/sec or as "a few megacycles" in a recent government bibliography. However, to illustrate how arbitrary any dividing line must be, I could point out the same document includes some work done as low as 100 kc/sec. At one time, it was fashionable in the industry to call ultrasound anything above the frequency range of human perception. But Haeff and Knox reported that they have recorded and measured human perception of sounds above 100 kc/sec, so the "above-human perception" criterion may go out of style, particularly among manufacturers of ultrasonic cleaners, emulsifiers, and similar equipment in the 20-to-100 kc/sec range. Let us just say that ultra means anything out of the range of your hi-fi, but not necessarily so.

On the high-frequency side, the tendency has been to call a vibration above a few hundred or 1000 Mc/sec hypersonic. It's a reasonable place for another foggy, arbitrary line: The techniques, both theoretical and experimental, tend to be quite different at such frequencies; it's hard to work in fluids (for which the theory tells us to expect sound absorption to vary as f^2), and in solids (where most of the absorption mechanisms also vary as high powers of frequency). Besides, sound travels through most gases (at most conditions) with velocities of the order of a few hundred m/sec, through most liquids at around a thousand m/sec, and through most solids at a few thousand m/sec. Since $c = \lambda f$ for any wave, the wavelengths at a few thousand Mc/sec are very small fractions (hundredths or thousandths) of millimeters; this allows for new tricks, but disallows many of the old ones.

One result of all this has been a great flurry of basic materials studies and theoretical work in that challenging range, where sonic wavelengths—unlike electromagnetic waves of simi-

diminish rapidly at distances of the order of a wavelength below the surface. Many types of symmetrical and asymmetrical Lamb waves can be used for the quality control of sheet and plate stock.

lar frequency—can be much greater than an electron's mean free paths, and where interactions between sonic modes and various degrees of freedom of electrons and nuclei can be observed. And, of course, there's the exciting prospect of watching the experimental frequencies climb, in spite of all the difficulties, toward the relaxation frequencies (in most metals, around 10^{12} cps) beyond which the materials can't follow an input sound. (The IEEE ultrasonics symposium in 1963 included several papers by people working with sonic waves near 10 gigacycles—10^{10} cps.) But, as enticing as all this is (and it has, in fact, enticed a goodly number of EEs into the ranks of the solid-state physicists), it's at least as far removed from today's industrial practice in sophistication as it is in frequency.

Another result of this dichotomy has been an apparent de-emphasis of industrial ultrasonic problems in professional engineering symposia. No visitor to a typical recent meeting would have had to listen hard to pick out several disappointed engineers who had come with orphaned problems of genuine technical merit and broad economic significance and who sat through what was a very un-engineering, but glamorous and exciting, session. The prognosis is more of same.

You might read into the foregoing that the engineer, charged with accomplishing a precise industrial purpose using ultrasonics, is in a pretty dismal position, confounded by an intractable jumble of coupled vibration modes, his problems scorned by his most obvious sources of help. That's not entirely the case; there are many things in his favor. Paramount among these are the early giants who worked this field. (Beyer has commented that, regardless of major field, just about every great name in physics, from Mersenne and Bernoulli through to Einstein and Landau, has published some contribution in acoustics somewhere in his career.) And very good work, especially in transducers and materials properties, has been going on for two or three decades now. Then, too, there are rich and transferrable lores from other fields, e.g., geometrical optics $\longleftrightarrow$ geometrical sonics.

To be more specific, let's consider the problem of separating the various modes in a very common application of ultrasonics; one based, simply enough, on the progressive nature of sound waves.

The accomplished use of delay

I said that sound travels through most materials at from a few hundred to a few thousand m/sec—about 10^{-5} the velocity of light. Almost as soon as people had need for such things, this suggested the use of ultrasonic delay lines, to store (for times of the order of milliseconds) small packets of information in the form of sonic wave trains traveling through metals, glasses, or fluids. An early and still important application is in moving-target radars, where there is an important need to deemphasize reflections from stationary objects.

Returning echoes are ultrasonically delayed by the inverse of the radar pulse repetition rate; they are then bucked against signals from succeeding pulses, so that echoes from a stationary reflector (with its unchanging echo return times) are very largely canceled out.

Other applications—in computers and other places—have combined to make the delay line an important part of the ultrasound business. A reminder of the possibilities of this important area is General Telephone & Telegraph's flat display screen (Fig. 3-41) which, in effect, uses the intersection of pulses on two or three orthogonal delay-lines to locate spots of piezoelectric activity for exciting an electroluminescent phosphor. (The possibilities of this

Fig. 3-40. A lesson in geometrical sonics is Van Heel's theory on why whales become stranded on gently sloping beaches. The idea is that sound pulses from the whale's navigation system glance off the bottom and keep going without being reflected back to the whale, and that the ambiguous result is interpreted as an open sea, until . . . (Courtesy Marineland of Florida)

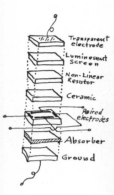

Fig. 3-41. Sonic pulses define spots on an electroluminescent display screen. Transducers send orthogonal sonic pulses into a ceramic sheet. Because the ceramic is piezoelectric, electric charges accompany the sonic pulses, as they move across the sheet. Where waves from each axis cross, the total charge is sufficient to excite the phosphor. (A nonlinear resistance enhances the difference between light and dark on the screen.) Timing the pulses controls spot position. (Courtesy General Telephone and Telegraph)

both longitudinal and transverse components. Unless these modes are sorted out somehow, a train of sound waves introduced into a face of a typical metal or quartz ultrasonic delay-line would show up at the output end as the result of a longitudinal wave (with a velocity of around 5200 m/sec, for quartz), followed by a transverse wave (which made the trip at some 60–70% of that velocity) and a miscellany of other modes. (Incidentally, as you'd imagine, the mode with the slower propagation velocity is often of special interest in a device whose purpose is to generate time delays.)

Fortunately, there is a ready answer to mode separation; it lies in Snell's Law, which holds for geometrical sonics as it does for geometrical optics. Referring to the margin sketch, you'll see that when a sound wave meets a discontinuity in its medium, part of it is reflected and part is refracted and the sines of the beam angles (with respect to the normal to the interface) are proportional to the velocities involved. The proportions of incident sound that are reflected and transmitted depend on the relative acoustic impedances, the ρc's, of the two media. Thus, we have a reflection coefficient

$$R = (\rho_1 c_1 - \rho_2 c_2)/(\rho_1 c_1 + \rho_2 c_2)$$

and a transmission coefficient

$$T = 1 - R = 2\rho_2 c_2/(\rho_1 c_1 + \rho_2 c_2)$$

In particular, the newly arisen (slower) shear wave shown is refracted less than the longitudinal wave. To carry the optical analogy still further, if the incoming sound beam is adjusted to some critical angle, the longitudinal wave will be refracted at 90° to the normal, so that the shear wave becomes the dominant mode still remaining in the block. Or, the shear wave itself could be refracted to the point where some other mode (typically, the next in line would be the Rayleigh surface wave) is dominant.

Ultrasonic delay lines have other complications, of course. For example, the fact that sonic velocity is not necessarily independent of frequency, leads to the phenomenon of group velocity. The various Fourier components of a typical 5-μ/sec pulse form a group of frequencies whose group velocity may be quite different from the velocity of the (say, 4 Mc) component of the train. The resulting effect is a dispersion of arrival times that depends on $\partial c/\partial f$, the variation of sonic velocity with frequency, and an effective group velocity c' that differs from velocity of the component wave in this way:

$$(1/c') - (1/c) = (f/c^2)(\partial c/\partial f)$$

scheme, as a flat-faced solid-state TV screen, among other things, has been an obvious spur to the activities in this area.)

The strain, in main, is not on just one plane

The problem of sorting out a jumble of modes arises from the partial conversion of longitudinal and other modes of vibration into still other modes. You don't have to go through the analytical rationale to see intuitively that the forces acting on a mass element can be very different for its various degrees of freedom and that this will give rise to different amounts of attenuation and different velocities of sonic propagation for the various modes. For example, the velocities of longitudinal and shear modes are

$$c_1 = [(\Lambda + 2\mu)/\rho]^{1/2} \text{ and } c_s = (\mu/\rho)^{1/2}$$

where ρ is the density and Λ and μ are the Lamé elastic constants; Λ is called the plate modulus and μ the shearing modulus. These relationships are often used to determine the elastic properties of difficult samples.

Now the mode equations I just cited are for an isotropic medium. For *each axis* of an anisotropic, there are moduli (and resultant modes); this means 21 elastic constants for, say, a cubic crystal leading to 3 particle velocities (and 3 waves) which, except in special cases, will have

Commonly, plots of c and c' against wavelength for such a "dispersive" material have the form shown in the margin. Even in these dispersive delay lines, the geometric model holds, and, in fact, the sound is piped around in what amounts to ultrasonic waveguides.

An echo for detection

Inherent in the geometric notion of sound is a vast array of ultrasonic detection, inspection, and selection schemes.

A straightforward scheme is the echo-type flaw-detector, and one of the most straightforward of those is a flaw-detector working into a fairly homogeneous mushy medium of uniform pressure and temperature to detect reflections from objects of radically different density. Such a medium, while much more attenuating than a solid, has the advantage that it will support virtually no spurious (particularly shear) modes to obscure the echo from the initial pulse. The result shown in Fig. 3-42 is a trace of a stone found in somebody's kidney with a commercial flaw-detector using 1000 pulses/sec of 1.6 Mc/sec sound. (Kidney stones tend to move around during surgery, thus hampering x-radiography.)

Of course, these ultrasonic detectors have been developed for many materials and many purposes, using various frequencies (as in optics, wavelength governs resolution), echo intervalometers, and transducer arrangements. Some determine fat profiles of cattle or wall thickness of corroded pipe; some are fathometers and fishfinders; some locate fissures in welds and some measure road pavement thickness or monitor plastic sheet stock. There are scanning arrangements which trace the outlines of discontinuities (some produce sonoradiographs) and systems for determining the structural qualities of concrete in situ. Other gadgets gage the homogeneity of things by measuring the Rayleigh scattering (i.e., the f^4-dependent attenuation due to the scattering) of sound by a population of discontinuities such as grain boundaries, pores, and foreign inclusions. But many an inspector or sonar operator would envy the clean, unequivocal trace at top of Fig. 3-42.

The mechanical inspector, using Rayleigh waves to search for hidden surface cracks or Lamb waves to examine sheet stock, has mode conversion and multiple paths to allow for, but the sonar operator (let's say he's a peaceful oceanographer) meets geometrical acoustics on other grounds.

Alpha is for attenuation

For one thing, the distances in open water are so great that attenuation (especially in the

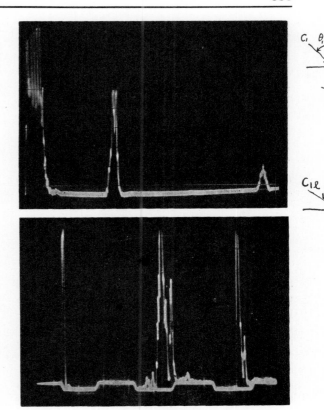

Fig. 3-42. An echo from a kidney stone (top) is representative of a growing number of medical applications for sonic flaw-detectors. (The near and far walls of the kidney are the extreme pulses.) The record, made with a commercial 1.6 Mc/s flaw-detector, is cleaner than the typical record of flaws in an iron pipe (bottom) largely because of severe attenuation of extraneous modes in the fleshy medium. (Courtesy Branson Instruments; Smith's Industrial)

face of sea noise) is a big problem; that old α-term is a major frequency-limiting factor in such equipment. I noted earlier that sound is attenuated in liquids roughly as the square of frequency (and even faster in water).

But in real cases, the picture is somewhat complicated by the effects of pressure and temperature on both attenuation and velocity ("Underwater Sound," page 625). Some of these effects have been capitalized on in ultrasonic flowmeters which need not impede flow to measure it and in thermometers that indicate average temperatures across their fields of view. In fact, the first equation presented to students of sound in fluids is

$$\text{velocity} = \text{bulk modulus/density}$$

and just about anything that influences these terms (e.g., anything that introduces a shear modulus in addition to the bulk modulus, or that changes density by changing liquid structure, or by dissolving other matter in the

STANDING
WAVE
BUGABOO

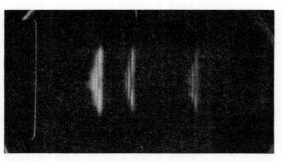

Fig. 3-43. This multiple exposure shows Schlieren images of the alternative condensations and rarefactions of a 2.25 Mc/sec sonic pulse, as it moves from the transducer at left. After delay-times of 25, 33.5, 47.5 and 60.5 μ-sec, the grating pattern remains intact. (Courtesy Battelle Memorial Institute)

medium) will have its repercussions on sound propagation. The open sea is a still more complicated environment; in addition to the aforementioned effects, there are problems of top and bottom reflections (and effects of the irregularity of these surfaces on sound reflection at different frequencies)—see the whale in Fig. 3-40. There are also the effects of ambient sea noise (sonar calculations for real equipments are typically run for various sea states), and even fish noises to be considered. I remember a sensitive sonar apparatus that prematurely hit the surplus market when it was found that fish, attracted to the hydrophone, were overdriving the associated amplifiers.

Handling all these nonlinear effects in the sonically inhomogeneous ocean is a challenging business to say the least, and it is fortunate for the developers of this field that computers such as Sperry's analog sound-ray tracer and special-purpose digital programs are available. Since, at the distances involved, beam shape and dispersion are important too, such computation aids have also been applied to the design of transducer arrays. In fact, the designers of sonar transducer arrays often sound like radar antenna people, and, because of the convenience of the scale factors involved (especially wavelength), there are numerous examples of sonar models of the designs for major radar undertakings.

Perhaps the most exciting recent development in this area stems from one of the bugaboos that haunts sonar and radar designers alike and follows from the most general solution to the wave equation from which we started. The solution for displacement

$$y = f(x - ct) + g(x + ct)$$

contains both a progressive term and a regressive term. If they're both present (the regressive term coming from a reflection) in,

say, a sine wave, then periodic spots will exist where the displacement is always zero. The spots of zero displacement are called nodes; the general configuration is called a standing wave. Long before ultrafast photography (as in Fig. 3-43) made ultrasound visible, the stationary stratifications of maximum and minimum density standing waves supported by elastic materials were illuminated by oblique lights and measured to determine wavelength.

Then in 1932, Debye and Sears reported on the diffraction of collimated monochromatic light by such an ultrasonic "phase grating." Recently the effect has been applied to special-purpose optical shutters. DeMaria has used it to control the optical path of a laser, and the "ultrasonic grating" appears to have the makings of a laser modulator, as well as of a variable-spacing diffraction grating. Of course, the ratio of the speed of light to the speed of sound is so great that such effects also occur, on the fly, without standing waves—in effect, with a grating moving at the speed of sound. But then it's harder to work with.

Whatever happened to Ultraschall

With all this well-established sophistication, a natural question is why the industrial application of ultrasound has been so halting. Certainly there are unresolved issues involved in hitching the classical theory to reality, issues such as the higher-order elastic effects being explored in nonlinear materials. But, although some brilliant experimental work was carried on in the thirties (particularly in Germany), the applications art has been delayed more by other factors.

The most obvious was lack of good equipment. Sonics involves moving masses, and the most common modes involve reciprocating particle paths. Well, as any cam-designer will testify, it's not at all easy to reciprocate mechanically anything of any size at $10^{3\,or\,4}$ to $10^{6\,or\,7}$ cps. Even at the very small displacements usually encountered, the accelerations and local forces involved are well beyond common experience. To illustrate: For a fairly modest 20 kc/s generator radiating sound into water, with an intensity, I, of 5 watts/cm², Crawford worked out the peak acceleration from

$$A = f\sqrt{2\rho c I}/2\pi\rho c$$

It turned out to be some 3.4×10^6 cm/sec² (that's 3500 g), although the displacement

$$x = A/4\pi^2 f^2 = \text{only } 2 \times 10^{-4} \text{ cm}$$

By the time the frequency reaches 1 mc/s, an intensity of 10 watts/cm² results in accelerations of some quarter million g!

There's another lesson in these equations; that is the frequency-dependence of any acceleration-determined or displacement-determined mechanisms that might be (or might have been) experimentally studied for comparison with theory. For an example, see Fig. 3-38.

Now that doesn't say you can't exhibit all kinds of industrially or medically beneficial effects with a broad, unstable, uncontrolled ultrasonic spectrum; it just says that progress in understanding what you are doing may be hampered considerably. A similar, though possibly more restricted, case could be made for the significance of sonic intensity. Considering the difficulties of work with strictly mechanical displacements and the need for stable frequency and intensity, I regard with considerable admiration the temerity of researchers who worked in pre-electronic days at frequencies in the tens and hundreds of kc/sec.

Whistling up a storm

There *are* electronic-less, ultrasonic devices, however, and an important class of industrial sound generators, especially high-powered low-frequency generators, can be said to date back to Galton's whistle of 1883. Galton's gadget was an edge-tone generator, using the same effect which shows up when you blow over the edge of your knife blade: The impinging gas stream oscillates back and forth across the edge at a frequency that is proportional to the jet velocity and inversely proportional to the distance between the jet nozzle and the edge, but Galton's edge outlined a resonant cavity.

Since the output depends on gas velocity and an alignment of the device, the frequency will depend on the amplitude. Still, edge-tone whistles have reached frequencies as high as 170 kc/s and provided a base for the development of several classes of whistles, some samples of which are currently pouring several hundred and in some cases a few thousand watts of sonic power into chemical processes.

An important step along the way was the whistle Hartman developed in Denmark, in which the jet velocity exceeded the velocity of sound as it loaded gas into a resonant cavity. The pressure in the cavity periodically built up to a critical point at which the gas was violently expelled. One such whistle delivered 160 watts at 10 kc/s (but only 6 watts at 50 kc). While they are capable of delivering quite respectable powers, such devices have much less stable frequency and power than the less traumatic noisemakers.

Whistling in the dark

Many modifications of these early whistles have been made, and some of those developed for particular classes of applications (especially applications to chemical reaction rate control, gas treatment, drying, foaming, emulsification, etc.) are hardly recognizable as whistles. For example, there are atomizers, such as the old Sonic Engineering device, which use a resonant vibrating reed to tune their whistlings.

There are also stem jet whistles, with a stem or rod concentric with the jet nozzle and resonant chamber that somehow increases the efficiency of the whistle, so comparatively low jet pressures of less than 10 or 20 psi can produce industrially useful outputs. There are vortex whistles, in which the motion of the gas stream is helical within the chamber, the gas rotation time (see margin) determining frequency; in Hungary, Gregus has developed a liquid version of it.

Another interesting whistle wrinkle is the power generator in Fig. 3-44 intended for use as an atomizer. This device (by Astrosonics,

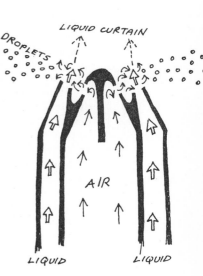

VORTEX WHISTLE (VONNEGUT)

Fig. 3-44. In sonic whistles of this type, air (or other gas) impinges on a resonant cavity, alternately filling and erupting from it. The gas leaves the cavity turbulently, and encounters a concentric film of liquid, breaking the film into droplets with a frequency-dependent distribution of sizes. (Courtesy Astrosonics)

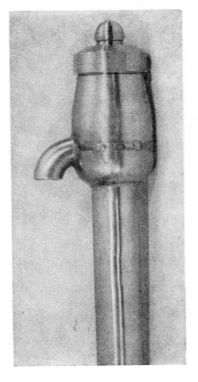

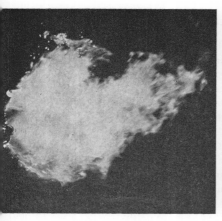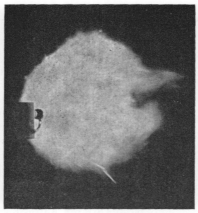

Fig. 3-45. As the sizes of the fuel droplets produced by this sonic atomizer are reduced, the flame burns hotter, cleaner and more efficiently. In the final frame, No. 2 fuel oil is burning with the smoglessness of gas. (Courtesy N. C. Pickering)

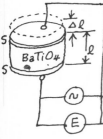

Ferro-
electricity

S = Silver
electrodes

$\Delta l \propto E^2$

E = electric
field

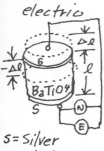

Piezo-
electric

S = Silver
electrodes

$\Delta l \propto E$

E = electric
field

Inc.) is also a turbulence generator. Sound generated by a high-pressure gas jet erupting periodically from a resonant cavity (which includes part of the gas stream envelope, as well as the metal chamber) gives rise to turbulence swirls which can be used to atomize a cylindrical curtain of liquid flowing past from the outer slit ring.

Most of these whistles have their uses, of course, wherever a large amount of relatively cheap unfussy sound must be generated in a fluid—with no question asked. But they're aerodynamic nightmares to analyze; their design is mostly cut-and-try. The predictability of their properties and their sensitivity to temperature, nozzle pressure, and mechanical tolerances, and to evil spells cast by competitors, are just about what you'd expect. Still, these sonic blunderbusses are no-moving-parts devices—except for the excited medium—and that's worth a lot.

In theoretical crudity, they are kin to rotary sirens, which utilize rotating disks with several hundred ports to modulate the escape of gas through other ports in the stationary members. (Port shape and other geometrical considerations are reminiscent of similar mystiques in the whistle business.) But for rotating sirens, the problem is complicated by the difficulties of economical realization: These machines rotate at 20,000 RPM and higher, and some of them are pretty big. Spacings between rotors and stators are often fractions of a millimeter and quite critical.

The intensities available are potentially quite high, in the tens of kilowatts at low frequencies. Power falls off at higher frequencies, because, while intensity demands large port areas, high frequencies demand many ports per revolution—and the rotational speed restricts rotor diameter.

Because of these limitations, rotary sirens have enjoyed rather limited popularity as an industrial or a research tool in this country. However, since the war, they have created quite a stir in eastern Europe, particularly Poland, where several variable frequency sirens, using rotor speed control and interchangeable disks, have been applied to fume-agglomeration and gas-cleaning tasks.

Still, the rotary siren never quite became the quick, cheap, versatile, and stable sound source required for its wide use in industrial ultrasonics. Indeed, it could not possibly have, until fairly recent developments in machine-work made faster rotation possible.

Many of the same difficulties apply to the electrodynamic (voice-coil in a magnetic field) speaker art, which was wedded to the compressed-air siren by Altec-Lansing when they replaced the siren's rotor-stator combination with a big reciprocating voice-coil. A typical unit delivers 2.5 kw at 500 cps and 1 kw at 1 kc. In this unit 100 watts of electric power modulates an airflow of 150 ft³/min at 25 psi.

Necessity as the fosterer of electronics

Thus far, we have considered equipment for moving gases rapidly to and fro, and, in some cases, for moving liquids. It's less a matter of coincidence than a matter of relative agility that electrons have supplanted gas molecules in most jobs calling for intricate and fast footwork; electrons are easier to start, stop, count, and control, especially at high frequencies. While Kirchhoff and Helmholtz and Rayleigh may have dreamed about what effects might be observed in acoustical fields of many megacycles/sec, experiment had to wait until 1917. That was when Langevin excited a piezoelectric quartz crystal at its resonance with an oscillating electric current from a vacuum tube circuit—and demonstrated that the resonant mechanical distortion of a crystal by an applied field could form the basis of a large family of transducers and resonant circuit elements.

Piezoelectric transducers using quartz, tourmaline, Rochelle salt, and ammonium dihydrogen phosphate (ADP)—rapidly followed by magnetostrictive transducers using alloys of iron, nickel, and cobalt—very quickly coupled progress in experimental ultrasonics to progress in electronics.

These electrical devices could provide stable sound sources of narrow bandwidth over a wide range of frequencies. But, while such materials provided researchers with a lot of interesting results, there were severe material limitations on their commercial exploitation.

The early magnetostrictive materials had considerable conversion losses. Their hysteresis and eddy-currents heated them up. Furthermore, the geometry of the exciting coils and their fields tended to preclude the excitation of disks; the most straightforward approaches used long rods or tubes driven longitudinally. Since resonance is inversely proportional to the length, these devices had disappointingly low upper frequency limits.

Except for quartz, most piezoelectric materials were incapable of sustaining high power densities without fracture—especially in the thin slabs and disks that can resonate at high frequencies. Others turned out to be hygroscopic, and still others exhibited instabilities or spurious oscillation modes. Quartz itself, while very stable and free of most of these problems, is far from the most efficient converter of electricity to sound.

The government giveth and the government taketh away

The naval significance of these sound-generating materials was very apparent. Ultrasonic research therefore derived considerable support from military agencies—but the deployment of the available resources in men and materials was skewed to reflect the interests of government sponsors, and in some instances progress was classified, stockpiled and otherwise priced out of the open market.

On the other side of the ledger is the rapid military development of transducer design techniques. Some examples: shaping of sonic beams, with arrays of transducers; techniques for loading transducers and for coupling them to other materials; magnetic biasing schemes for linearizing magnetostrictive materials; methods for reducing eddy current and hysteresis losses; sonic lenses; and a host of circuit advances.

Additionally, we owe to sonar-inspired sponsorship much of the forced-draft development of the very valuable class of ferroelectric ceramics. These materials exhibit very large changes in dimensions with applied electric

field; they can serve as piezoelectric materials several hundred times as active as quartz. Such ceramic materials can be cast into various sizes and shapes to generate focused beams of high intensity. And, of course, the effect is reversible—reversible enough for a project to be under way (at U.S. Sonics Corp.) to convert the acoustical noise from jet engines into useful electrical energy.

Analogous work on such materials as piezomagnetic ferrites may give the piezoelectrics a bit of competition in the megacycle region. The combined effect through the past decade has been a steady progression of increasingly efficient transducers onto the market at prices that should encourage their incorporation into industrial and even household items. Today, as you talk to people in the industry, it's quite common to find companies which have been doing fine in the military sonic business harboring dreams of ultrasonic remote control gadgets (the radio spectrum is getting more and more crowded), or of ultrasonic denture cleaners, or fishfinders.

Of course, these things are only possible to the extent that the attendant circuitry follows suit. And in many applications (and despite stricter requirements for radio-noise suppression), circuit package prices have come down along with transducer costs.

Illustratively, Locklin at Battelle is studying the feasibility, for the American Petroleum Institute, of an ultrasonic fuel-treatment apparatus for installation in residential oil burners. A little ultrasound—typically 5–15 watts at 50 or 60 kc/sec—improves combustion efficiency considerably by breaking up fuel droplets. Estimates of the price of a home unit range from Locklin's own goal of about $15 to a pessimistic $39.50. A few years ago, before transistorized power oscillators were available to drive transducers, those prices would have been some five times that.

It now seems we have one answer to that question posed a while back, the one about why widespread applications in this field have been so slow in coming. There certainly *were* equipment impediments to industrial applications in this field, and there are probably still some, somewhere. But, except perhaps for really high-powered requirements with special restrictions, those equipment voids are now fairly uncommon. The problem, apparently, lies elsewhere. In fact, there is a sense in which the readily available equipment came altogether too soon.

To see what I mean, you needn't look farther than the recent history of one of the most common of all applications of ultrasound.

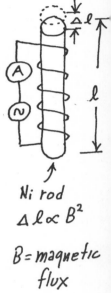

Magnetostriction

Ni rod

$\Delta \ell \propto B^2$

$B =$ magnetic flux

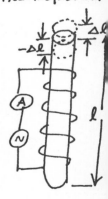

Piezomagnetism

$\Delta \ell \propto B$

$B =$ magnetic field

On coming clean and other traumas

A while back, I mentioned the dependence of acceleration on frequency and the tremendous accelerations arising with increasing frequency. It stands to reason that if you put a particle into a sound field in a fluid, part of that acceleration will be imparted to the particle—and the smaller the particle, the larger the amplitude of its motion. Obviously, it would seem, if you put a large article which is loosely

Fig. 3-46. The comparatively short wavelengths of sound above a Mc/sec facilitates much more local irradiation than is possible with nonionizing radio waves. Because the sound can be focused with shaped transducers and lenses (shown here positioned directly above the tips of a head-holder), internal brain matter can be selectively treated without affecting intervening cells. W. J. and C. J. Fry have experimentally demonstrated cures of Parkinsonian and similar maladies by inducing small internal lesions with this equipment. Reduced power yields temporary effects, for mapping purposes. (Courtesy University of Illinois)

coupled to a small particle into the sound field, the article and the particle would tend to separate. Any small streaming in the fluid, such as is often found in ultrasonic tanks operating at frequencies around 500 kc/sec, would sweep the particle away from its larger host.

So the way to get into the ultrasonic cleaning business back in the late 40's or the early 50's was to build simple power oscillators from surplus transmitter components and use them to drive transducers at frequencies around ½ Mc/sec. Many people did. The only trouble was that such things didn't clean. But cleanliness being so near to godliness, it was a long time before the mystique was challenged. Meanwhile, many cleaners were built and sold and installed.

Actually, the principal mechanism of cleaning is now agreed to be cavitation. That $\sqrt{2\rho cI}$ term you saw in Crawford's formula above is the peak pressure of the sound wave in the fluid. Working out the numbers for 5 watt/cm² in water yields a peak pressure of some 3.8 atmospheres. Local pressures, which are that much greater than atmospheric, will produce gas-filled or vapor-filled voids—bubbles. Like the particles we postulated earlier, the bubbles pick up energy from the accelerating liquid. Eventually, they implode, producing shock waves at pressures much higher than the initiating pressure. Anything nearby is jolted; if it's dirt, fine. If it's a poorly plated lead on your microcircuit, you lose.

Even today the cleaning mechanism itself is still not understood well enough to guarantee that such things as this (or outright corrosion, or other damage mechanisms) will or won't be important in several applications; this uncertainty has even led to discontinuance of ultrasonic cleaning in some places. As a matter of fact and in spite of recent progress in explaining the nucleation of cavitation bubbles (particularly, Sette's work on cosmic rays and cavitation nuclei), the cavitation itself—its temperature dependence in various fluids, etc.—is not well understood.

Now the reason I chased through a popular but erroneous theory about the mechanism of sonic cleaning isn't because I'm against particle displacements. Actually, the chances are that Fry's neurosurgical effect alluded to in Fig. 3-46 is a displacement mechanism. My point was that cleaning is an example of a large class of industrially important and technically challenging sonic effects which were not well understood when the classical theory was handed down. Many of these effects are outside the realm of the classical theory, in that they're "traumatic" action. But lots aren't.

Another important member of this category is ultrasonic machining (Fig. 3-47), in which cavitation plays an as yet undefined role. Here again, the mechanism of just how the machining takes place has not been established to everyone's satisfaction, and in this it resembles the situation for ultrasonic welding. The popular explanation now for ultrasonic machining is that the tool crushes an abrasive between the work and the tool point and that the abrasive chips out small bits of the work as the tool hammers away with something like 100 watts at 20 kc/sec. Whether the cavitation accompanying ultrasonic machining actually blasts out little cavities in the course of bubble collapse or whether the bubbles just move the abrasive around and against the work is still an open question.

As a matter of fact, a review of the review articles on the various gross mechanical effects of ultrasound turns up a disconcerting number of proposed, observed, and marketed effects, for which the mechanisms are still open questions. The fields of aerosol coagulation and dust precipitation (despite Schmolukowski's early theoretical work on relative displacements of large and small particles in the acoustic field) suggest a couple of answers to our naive initial question about the reasons for the limited application of ultrasonics to industrial purposes.

An indicative state-of-the-art review article by Boucher in *Chemical Engineering* for October, '61, points out just how complex the problems are, and then goes on: "Numerous acoustic dust precipitation plants using rotary sirens were built in the U.S. during the ultrasonic craze, and several papers describing these installations have been published. As none of these plants are still in operation, we will confine our discussion to more reliable and economical installations that have been built abroad in recent years . . ." particularly in central and eastern Europe.

All this is not to say that the application of power ultrasonics to material treatment is entirely black magic; nor is it to say that there aren't good people following fruitful and promising lines. There are. The very formidable problems involved in sonically induced coagulation and precipitation have been tackled, with encouraging results, in the last few years by Inoue in Japan and by others elsewhere. But it's still a long, long way from handbook engineering.

Along metallurgical lines, we see a similar situation. Blaha and Langenecker's (1955) observation that ultrasonic stress imposed on zinc reduces its yield stress has been taken up by many workers here and abroad with a view to increasing the plasticity of a number of metals

during such operations as wire- and tube-drawing.

However, the yield strength reduction doesn't occur for all metals and alloys, or under all conditions. Here again, although some progress has been reported by Langenecker himself and others, the mechanisms involved are not well enough understood to permit formulation of a complete theory. Langenecker lists six mechanisms of various importances for sound absorption by dislocations alone. Besides these, there is a surface effect—a reduction of interfacial friction between tools and workpiece.

Ultrasonic grain refinement of solidifying metals is another such case. Sonic agitation of solidifying welds has been investigated for many years, and generators capable of delivering tens of kilowatts of sonic power into melts of several tons have been developed (a recent wrinkle is the introduction of the sonic energy through vibrating furnace electrodes). If the theory were as high-powered as the generators, this method too might well be in widespread use, but it's not at all clear how much of the grain refinement is due to fragmentation and dispersal of initial crystals, how much is due to induced supercooling, or to cavitation in weld pools, or to other effects.

The pattern is quite general. Although some progress has been made in understanding a few mechanical effects of sound on materials, the

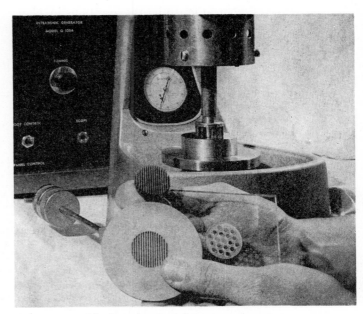

Fig. 3-47. With the advent of intense sonic sources, such as mechanical transformers, ultrasonic impact grinding with slurries of abrasives has enabled fabrication of intricate shapes from many hard materials. Theory's lacking, but an empirical lore has developed. The mechanism here differs from that of the mandrill in Fig. 3-46. (Courtesy Gulton Mfg.)

picture is much the same for emulsification and dispersion as it is for precipitation and agglomeration. It's the same for ultrasonic eggbeaters as for ultrasonic defoamers and the same for gadgets that polymerize polysyllabic siloxanes on Tuesdays and depolymerize them on Wednesdays.

There's a lot of beautiful equipment available—efficient tranducers that can operate at several hundred degrees, power amplifiers that can continuously sweep from 50 cps to many Mc/sec, phased transducer arrays, horns, lenses and reflectors for concentrating sonic energy, and many things more. "Signal" ultrasonics is in comparatively good shape—a boon from classic theory. But before ultrasonics graduates from the try-it-and-see-if-it-helps stage to legitimate entry in the engineering handbooks, some basic questions must be answered.

Further reading

There are some classics that show why there are classicists; Rayleigh's two-volume "The Theory of Sound" is a case in point (most recently, Dover, 1945, paperbound $4). Further, if you like to trace developments of rich lines of thought, you'll enjoy D. C. Miller's "Anecdotal History of the Science of Sound," which itself is a classic. Unfortunately, it's out of print, but the trip to the library is worth it, and while you're in the catalog file, you can look up his "Sound Waves: Their Shape and Speed," for a graphical grasp on the gyrations involved in the various modes. Actually, there's an important thesis that notions of waves and all that they imply to modern physics were mainly carried along by acoustical engineers from their inception by the early Stoics to the last century; the point is nicely made by Kilgour in his "Vitruvius and the Early History of Wave Theory," an article in the Summer 1963 issue of *Technology and Culture*, the quarterly of the Society for the History of Technology. There are also many more recent treatises such as the standard American text, *Sonics* by Hueter and Bolt (Wiley, 1955, $11) and the more recent *Ultrasonic Physics* by Richardson (Elsevier, 1962, $5.50), who wrote the earlier British standard text and edited a series of volumes on the technical aspects of sound for the same publisher. But still the best recent 157 pages I've found on this subject is the authoritative Third Section of the *American Institute of Physics Handbook* (McGraw-Hill, 1963, $30). The case with ultrasonic technology is less encouraging; since Bergmann's prewar *"Der Ultraschall,"* which is now found only in libraries or in the locked bookcases of oldtimers, nothing has come along to match it. Carlin's *Ultrasonics* (McGraw-Hill, 1960, $11.50) and Goldman's *Ultrasonic Technology* (Reinhold, 1962, $11) and the Russian Babikov's *Ultrasonics and Its Industrial Applications* (Consultants Bureau, 1960, $10) all reflect the dilemma of mating practice and reality. I recommend a new international periodical, *Ultrasonics* (Iliffe Publications, London), as an excellent source for good practical reviews.

SOLIDS IN PIPES

by Ludwig Koch *

IN BRIEF: *Transport of solids in pipes is a natural outgrowth of successful pipelining of oil and natural gas over long distances. Solids in the form of particles ranging from 50 microns to several inches in diameter can be transported hydraulically so long as the liquid carrying them in slurry form moves rapidly enough to prevent their settling. For slurries that settle easily at rest, there is a certain "critical velocity" above which the solids will remain in suspension. Here, the energy lost due to pipe friction is usually a minimum, allowing the heterogeneous mixture to be pumped at optimum total energy input. Other slurries are homogeneous, containing enough fines to impede the settling of the larger particles so long as the flow is turbulent. When the particles are too large or the velocity too low, a flow that is homogeneous can change to one that is heterogeneous, or even to a flow where some solids settle and form a stationary or sliding bed, while others go skipping along on top. Power requirements to maintain requisite fluid velocities are high for all these regimes, so a new concept has emerged: slug or capsule pipelining. Here, solids are introduced as large, coherent segments of the moving stream. They move faster than the average fluid velocity, but can be transported slower than solids in suspension. Thus, with a concentrated "train" of slugs or capsules, the same throughput is possible at much lower power cost. Work still underway on slug and capsule flow may prove to be the genesis of a new generation of pipeline transportation.—F.P.*

* Ludwig Koch, now Research Scientist with the Continental Oil Co., Ponca City, Oklahoma, wrote this article while with the Colorado School of Mines Research Foundation, Golden, Colorado.

■ The long distance transportation of fluids, particularly oil, by pipeline has long been regarded as a means of moving large volumes at astonishingly low cost. The economy inherent in pipelining can be attributed to the continuity and reliability of the pumping operation, the low manpower requirements per ton-mile, and the low operating and maintenance costs per ton-mile. These advantages have created a widespread interest in the pumping of solid-fluid suspensions, or slurries, over long distances.

However, while the science and technology of fluid pipelining is quite advanced and sophisticated, the principles of solids pipelining have not yet progressed past the stage of semiempirical formulas. Although these expressions describe the complex flow characteristics of solid-fluid systems fairly well, much diligent research and development work is still required to extend their present limitations, and to bring the technology of solids pipelining on a par with that of fluids. Further, there are economic considerations which retard the ready acceptance of the hydraulic transportation of solids. Among these I would say three appear to be the most serious:

- Much energy is required to maintain the suspension of solids in the flowing fluid, especially when the solid particles being transported are coarse and of high density.
- Some solids become contaminated through direct contact with the fluid or lose in commercial value through degradation and attrition during transport.
- Considerable cost may be connected with the preparation of a pumpable solid-fluid suspension and with the separation of the suspended solids from the fluid at the discharge end.

Nevertheless, slurry pipelines have a present-day potential where very large tonnages of a bulk commodity have to be transported over a long distance. Over medium distances of 10 to 100 miles pipelines cannot usually compete with existing modes of transportation—truck, rail, and barge. For short hauls, slurry pipelines are becoming increasingly attractive, although the coming "supertrucks" will certainly be competitive. But, regardless of distance, there are three situations where pipelines are able to compete: in areas where freight rates are above the national average; in inaccessible areas where pipelines can considerably shorten the total haul distance; and in areas where there are no established means of transport.

One reason why pipelining of solids is still a restricted method is that to date no way of transporting different materials through the same pipeline has been devised. If this problem could be solved, the pumping of different commodities on a common-carrier basis might become a reality. One approach looks promising:

At the Research Council of Alberta, Canada, experiments are being conducted to determine the feasibility of transporting capsules or capsule-shaped solids through pipelines, as well as solids in the form of consolidated slugs. Coal, sulphur, and potash have been transported experimentally in slug form. It can be seen that by such means the separation of solids from the carrier fluid is greatly simplified. More about these interesting and significant techniques later.

Some historical parallels

At this point I should like to point out the similarity between the early history of oil pipelining and the development of solids pipelines to date.

The first oil pipeline was built near Titusville, Pa., in 1865 by a young man named Samuel van Syckel who borrowed $30,000 for a 6-mile-long,

Fig. 3-48. Poised serenely over Utah's Evacuation Creek, this 600-ft suspension bridge of 6 in. pipe forms but one link in a 72-mile pipeline that carries gilsonite, a kind of solidified crude oil. Other links are the pulverizers at Bonanza, Utah, that grind the ore and add it to the carrying water, the pumping station at the mine, and the separation and drying equipment at Grand Junction, Colorado where the gilsonite is retrieved as it flows from the pipeline at a rate of 700 dry tons per day. Slurry pipelines like this may be tomorrow's common carriers if problems both technical and legal can be solved. (Courtesy American Gilsonite Co.)

2-inch pipeline transporting 800 barrels per day at $1 per barrel. Although the teamsters opposed this and other lines, and battles were even fought over them, oil pipelines soon became the accepted mode of oil transport. They were originally owned and controlled by the railroads, but later on the stronger refiners acquired or built pipelines to use as levers in rate negotiations with the railroads.

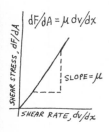

Today's oil pipelines are marvels of automation, transporting different petroleum products at different times through the same pipe and even feeding relevant data automatically into computers for control and accounting purposes. And yet they transport a gallon of oil from Texas to New York for less than the cost of a post card.

The first solids pipelines were used by miners during the gold rush in California as a means of raising gold-bearing gravel to the sluice boxes. In the 1890's pipelines were used in Pennsylvania to dispose of anthracite wastes, while in 1915 coal was successfully transported hydraulically from river barges to a power station in London, England. Since then the transport of solids in pipelines has become an accepted mode of transportation in the dredging, phosphate, and sand and gravel industries. Other industries have been hesitant in their acceptance of this transport method, except for a few outstanding pipeline installations. Among the exceptions are a 108-mile long pipeline transporting coal, a 72-mile long pipeline transporting gilsonite, and a 14-mile long pipeline transporting copper-ore concentrates. These, and at least 60 other pipelines here and abroad, to my knowledge, are now operating successfully and transport a variety of materials ranging from sugar cane to iron-ore wastes, from wood pulp to smelter slag.

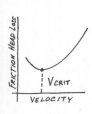

Where then do solids pipelines stand now in comparison with the development of oil pipelines? Let's look at the previously mentioned 108-mile-long coal pipeline. It was built by the Consolidation Coal Company in 1957 after years of research and hesitation in order to fight the high cost of rail transportation which at that time could add as much as 100% to the cost of coal at the mine. It operated successfully for six years until it was moth-balled in the spring of 1963—not because the pipeline failed, but because the railroads had lowered their freight rates. This lone successful coal pipeline and the threat of more to come have been enough to lower coal freight rates as much as 50% in the eastern U.S.

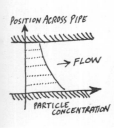

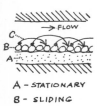

Fluids, real and ideal

In order to understand the problems involved in the hydraulic transportation of solids

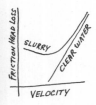

in pipelines, I should like to turn now to a discussion of the hydraulic characteristics of solid-fluid suspensions.

When we apply a shearing stress to an ideal fluid in order to make it flow, it will deform at a uniform shear rate that is proportional to the shearing stress. Most true liquids and all gases will behave under such a stress like an ideal fluid in that they can be characterized by a single physical quantity, the viscosity μ. It represents the slope of the straight line which results when the shear stress is plotted against the shear rate, as sketched in the margin. These fluids are called "Newtonian." In other liquids, such as solutions, colloids, and suspensions, viscosity is dependent upon the rate of shear imposed and in some cases upon the *duration* of shear. These are the "non-Newtonian" fluids.

The problem with pipeline slurries is that they can belong to either of the two broad fluid categories: suspensions of solid particles behave similar to Newtonian fluids at low concentrations, changing to one of the non-Newtonian types above a certain critical concentration. This critical concentration depends on the size and shape of the solid particle, the degree of dispersion, as well as on the density of the solids in the suspension.

Early investigators of flowing solid suspensions in water quickly recognized the existence of different flow conditions or regimes (which I'll discuss later on), and of a critical or economical velocity which coincided with the lowest energy loss due to friction, as sketched in the margin. Clearly, the objective is to find this velocity for any given suspension so that pumping can occur with minimum loss of head due to friction. Research on flow at high velocities reveals that the friction head loss in any pipeline approaches that of clear water at the same high velocity, as shown in the third sketch. This work also showed that the particles tend to settle in the pipe, as might be expected, thus creating a concentration gradient across the pipe section (see sketch) and that the settling particles induce turbulence of their own which is added to the general turbulence of the flow. The result is that, in many cases, coarse solid particles are transported by rolling or jumping along the bottom of the pipe, as in the marginal sketch. This mode of flow is now usually called flow by saltation.

Numerous researchers have contributed to the development of working formulas that attempt to describe the flow behavior of specific non-Newtonian fluids or non-Newtonian fluids in general. However, all these investigations and formulas are only applicable to suspensions of very fine particles, say below 30 microns. It includes emulsions, pastes, sludges—in short, truly *homogeneous* mixtures of solids and liquids which cannot be easily separated mechanically.

Slurries are different

While these fluids are of great interest to the chemical and process engineer, they are of little importance in the field of hydraulic transportation of solids as I am discussing it here. Bulk commodities will usually be in the form of particles larger than 50 microns, the lower limit of conventional, large-scale pulverizing equipment being 35 μ. Suspensions of this type are generally called slurries. When the particles in the liquid exceed 50 μ, gravitational and inertial forces acting on them become increasingly important and overshadow the viscous forces that are of prime importance in truly homogeneous mixtures.

While in homogeneous mixtures the solid-plus-liquid phase behaves like a single-phase fluid, in slurries the solid and liquid phases usually maintain their individual properties. These, in turn, influence the flow behavior, and so the mixture being pumped must be treated as a two-phase fluid. The simplest classification of slurries is therefore based on the behavior of the solid phase at rest under the influence of gravitational *and* viscous forces: if the viscous forces of the liquid can prevent or greatly attenuate the gravity settling of the solid phase, the slurry is called *non-settling* and will present no major problem in pipeline transportation. Examples are slurries of finely crushed coal, limestone, or colloidal clays.

There are two ways of achieving such a low settling rate, and thus an essentially *homogeneous* slurry: first, the solids can be ground so that the largest particle will not achieve a *free fall* velocity greater than some arbitrary value (usually 0.005 ft/sec). This is hard to do economically in practice. The second method is to obstruct settling by increasing solids concentration so that the settling velocity decreases considerably due to interaction of particles.

This effect is especially noticeable in slurries with *mixed* particle sizes. Here the fine fractions slow down the settling velocity of the larger fractions, similar to the buoyant action of a heavy liquid. Thus it is possible to suspend a certain percentage of *large* particles in a slurry containing a certain amount of fine particles at an over-all solids concentration where the particles, if uniformly sized at some intermediate diameter, would still settle under free-fall conditions (see the marginal sketch).

At present, however, the greater number of all operating solids pipelines are transporting *settling* slurries—medium-crushed coal, metallic ores and concentrates, sand silt, and gravel. The reason for this is that either the particle size is simply too large, the solids concentration is too low for proper particle interaction, or the material is too much of one size and thus does not include the fine particle fractions necessary to form a supporting medium.

In such a heterogeneous slurry we are dealing definitely with a two-phase system in which each component retains its own identity and characteristics. Life would be immensely simpler if all pipeline slurries could be carefully composed so as to be nonsettling. But this would require the added financial burden of complex sizing and mixing equipment, along with controls for same.

The practical problem of friction

Now that we have some idea of the different kinds of slurries that are transportable by pipelining, let's examine what happens when they are put into the pipe. First, we have the problem of friction that occurs within the slurry itself. A slurry of a given concentration flowing in a pipe of given diameter will lose a certain amount of head (energy) due to friction, the exact amount of loss depending on the flow velocity. For each pipe-diameter–concentration combination there will be, as suggested earlier, a flow velocity which will give a minimum of friction head loss and, consequently, require a minimum of pump energy to sustain flow. For the same pipe-diameter–concentration combination there will also be, for the most practical case—that of settling slurries—a flow velocity below which the solid particles will settle out on the bottom of the pipe. When this occurs the slurry flow becomes unstable.

The problem of designing a solids pipeline, therefore, can be stated as follows: *Find a flow velocity which will prevent settling yet require a minimum of pump energy for a pipe-diameter–concentration combination that will transport the required dry tons per day.*

Since the quantity of solids to be transported as well as the properties of the fluid and solid phase are usually pieces of stated information, the design problem boils down to the determination of the "critical" velocity and the required pump energy for a number of pipe-diameter–concentration combinations.

The *critical flow velocity* is simply the velocity below which solid particles begin to drop out of suspension and form a deposit on the bottom of the pipe. It is determined experimentally in a test loop of the sort pictured in Fig. 3-49. At velocities greater than the critical velocity all solid particles will move through the pipeline in full suspension. The *required pump energy* per lb of solids is the sum of the

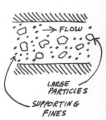

LARGE PARTICLES

SUPPORTING FINES

Fig. 3-49. In an arrangement of test lines as disarmingly simple as this one in Grenoble, France, the proof of any pipeline pudding is revealed. Most practical slurries will deposit solids if flow velocity drops below a "critical" value, thus choking the pipeline as discussed in text. By measuring the pressure drop as an actual slurry flows in a full-sized pipe, this and other changes in flow regime can be quickly discerned. (Courtesy Soc. Grenobloise d'Etudes et d'Applications hydraulique)

static head, or difference in elevation between pipeline terminals, *and* the friction head. It is expressed in terms of pump pressure necessary to maintain the flow of a given volume of slurry through a pipeline of known dimensions.

The static head is, of course, known. Thus prediction of the friction head loss, or pressure gradient, is the main problem of all pipelining. However, due to the very complex nature of the relationship between friction head loss, flow velocity, pipe diameter, solids concentration, and particle characteristics, no single comprehensive formula has been advanced to date which would allow the calculation of pressure gradients for all flow conditions. The difficulty is that the existing theoretical formulas are based on laboratory and pilot-plant experiments in which slurries with uniformly sized particles were used. This simple situation is not achieved in practice for reasons of process-equipment expenses alluded to earlier.

Most recent investigations suggest an additive relationship between the friction head loss due to the fluid and the friction head loss due to the suspended solid particles. Thus, the total friction head loss is composed of two parts—one expressing the rate at which potential energy is *dissipated* to maintain the flow of the *liquid,* the second expressing the rate at which

potential energy is *supplied* to maintain the *solids* in suspension.

One of the best known correlations, and one which is quite typical for the general form of slurry-flow equations, was proposed by the French investigators Durand and Condolios. They found that the head loss in the slurry mixture h_m and the loss in the clear carrying water h_w are related as follows:

$$h_m - h_w = \phi C h_w$$

That is, the increase in the friction loss in the pipe due to the introduction of the solid particles $(h_m - h_w)$ is proportional to the clear water head loss h_w, the concentration C of solids by volume, and a nondimensional factor ϕ. This last factor turned out, not unexpectedly, to be a function of the Froude number $V/\sqrt{gD}$ for any flow at velocity V in a pipe of diameter D, as well as of the size and specific gravity S of the solid material.

By changing the above equation into the dimensionless form beloved by the hydrodynamicist, we can see this factor ϕ more clearly

$$(h_w - h_w)/C h_w = \phi$$
$$= K[\sqrt{C_d} V^2/gD(S-1)]^{-3/2}$$

In this form, the only unfamiliar items are K, a numerical factor depending upon solids concentration and particle geometry, and C_d, the drag coefficient of the solid particles—a function of particle density, size, and settling velocity in water. This equation, which applies *only* to settling slurries, is based on several hundred test points and has been confirmed in this or similar form since it was published in 1952. Other useful formulas have been proposed by Newitt in Britain and other researchers.

In introducing this equation, my intention is not to show you how to design a pipeline; rather, it is to indicate the physical basis of the friction loss–velocity curves shown in Fig. 3-50. The left-hand plot shows the general characteristics of a settling heterogeneous slurry; the one at the right is of a nonsettling homogeneous slurry. Both diagrams represent the flow characteristics, as determined by tests, for a given water-solids slurry and pipe size at varying flow velocities and solids concentrations. Similar diagrams can be drawn for other materials and pipes of different diameters.

We can observe several features of these curves that are characteristic of all slurry flow. The friction head loss is, of course, always greater than that for clear water. But the lower the flow velocity, the more chance for particle interaction, and hence the higher the friction head loss. As we would expect, too, the more

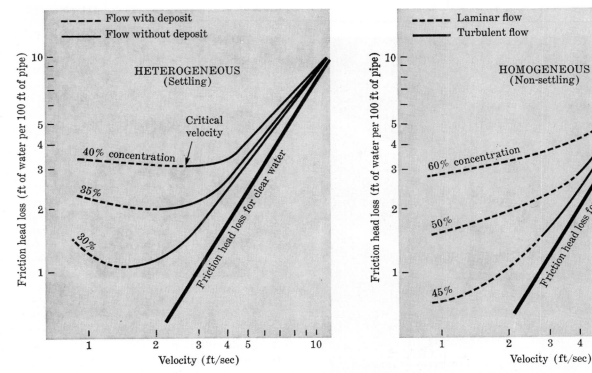

Fig. 3-50. Slurries come in two basic kinds, depending upon how they behave at rest. Most common is the heterogeneous (left chart), two-phase slurry from which particles settle rather rapidly. In a pipe, its velocity must be kept above the critical value to avoid deposits that constrict the pipe and increase energy losses. Less common is the homogeneous (right chart) slurry that settles more slowly, but must be pumped at turbulent flow velocities to retain its nonsettling characteristics.

solids we put into the slurry the higher the energy loss.

Moving from high to low velocity, we observe that at a certain value the slurry curve will either begin to level off or go through a minimum depending on whether a nonsettling or a settling slurry is being pumped. In the case of a nonsettling slurry the velocity at which the slurry curves begin to level off marks the transition from turbulent to laminar flow. One always tries to keep the velocity above this point, in the turbulent region, for here the particles will remain in suspension and the head loss will be closest to that of clear water.

In the case of a settling slurry—by far the most common one—the velocity which coincides with the minimum friction head-loss conditions is usually very close to the critical velocity at which a moving bed of particles begins to form at the bottom of the pipe. The slight tendency of friction head losses to increase as the velocity is further reduced indicates a growing deposit of solids in the pipe with a consequent reduction in free pipe area. Therefore, we pump settling slurries at velocities higher than critical —which usually means the flow is turbulent— but not too much higher, for the critical velocity usually corresponds to the most economical velocity.

Flow regimes and particle size

If one thinks of the flowing carrier fluid as a means of at once keeping the solid particles from settling and transporting them along, clearly there can be transitions in flow as we vary the speed of the fluid and the size of the particles therein. There are, in fact, more or less definite regimes of flow that are quite different from one another.

Based on experiments by Newitt in England, and Grovier and Charles in Canada, four significant regimes emerge as shown in Fig. 3-51. We are concerned with bulk commodities whose particle sizes generally exceed 50 microns, or about 0.002 in. in diameter. If we focus on a velocity of, say, 10 ft/sec we see that for small particles the flow can be either homogeneous or it can be heterogeneous. In operation, we try to choose our conditions (in this case, particle size) so that we could be well away from the transition zone between two regimes. If we get too close, the flow may change abruptly from one to the other, thus changing the head loss and hence the load on the pumping system.

Now if the particle size is increased to, say, 200 microns, or about 0.08 in. in diameter, we see an even more serious situation. We approach a sort of "triple point" where the flow can move

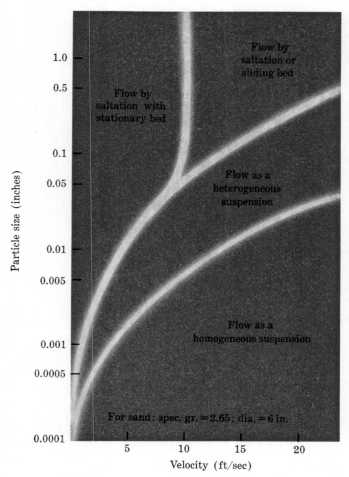

Fig. 3-51. *Different modes or regimes of slurry flow are hard to define precisely. Clearly, those with larger particles will flow differently from those with finer particles; slow-moving ones will behave differently from the swift. Diagrammed above are four regimes of flow that have been observed, as discussed in text.*

into either of two regimes. A velocity less than 10 ft/sec is insufficient to carry much of the material along, so most of it remains on the bottom as a stationary bed. What material moves does so by successive bounces or jumps on top—the saltation mode mentioned earlier. Thus the flow area becomes restricted and losses go up. With a bit higher velocity, these same bouncing particles can move into suspension and thus be carried forward, the next layers move by saltation and, indeed, the whole bed may receive enough energy to move or slide.

You will have noted that the flow-regime diagram used as an example is for one material —sand of a particular weight in a specific pipe. Most bulk commodities are not so uniformly graded; they are mixtures of many different sizes of the same solid. So a diagram of regimes has to be constructed for each.

Solid + fluid = slurry

Up to this point, I have discussed primarily the problems connected with the hydraulics of a solids pipeline; let us look briefly at the desired properties of solids and fluids, and at the composition of a suitable slurry. The physical aspects—pump selection, selection of pipe material and type, wear and corrosion—are important, but quite secondary to the concepts involved, and so will not be treated here.

Solids pipeline installations operating at present are transporting a wide variety of materials and, within certain limits, most any solid bulk commodity can be transported hydraulically. The gilsonite pipeline pictured in Fig. 3-48 transports a solid hydrocarbon with a specific gravity of 1.05; another pipeline transports copper concentrates with a specific gravity of 4.2. While the density of the solid material alone is no deterrent, it becomes important when considered together with the particle size and size distribution.

In general, a heavy material must be transported in a much finer size than a light material in order to achieve similar economics, although gravel and phosphate rock are being pumped in pieces several inches in diameter. When pumping solids which have to be dewatered at the discharge end, the degradation or attrition during transport becomes important. If the solid material is friable and tends to produce an appreciable amount of fines in the micron sizes, this fact might make dewatering a rather costly job.

To date, most slurry pipelines are operated with water as the fluid phase. The process and chemical industry is an exception and uses a wide range of fluids to transport solids, such as catalysts, over short distances within the plant proper. The *ideal* fluid would have a density close to that of the solids to be transported and would, at the same time, have a low viscosity and would not react with the solids. Such fluids exist but, unfortunately, they can hardly ever compete in cost with the "common carrier"—water.

If a liquid can be found to transport a pumpable solid, and the pipeline idea is still alive, it is time to composite a slurry. For coarse and heavy material such as clean gravel, there is very little that can be done to improve the flow characteristics of the slurry that is not already known to experienced dredge operators. But there is much room for improvement when the material contains fractions ranging from less than 5 mm to micron sizes.

The main parameters for tinkering are viscosity, settling behavior, and wear characteristics, all of which are markedly influenced by

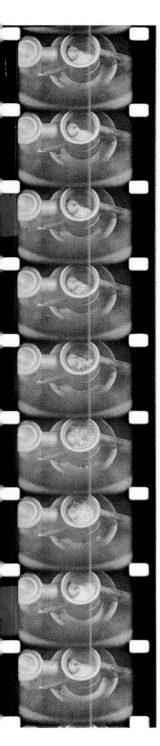

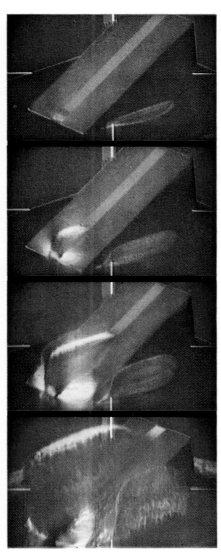

Color Fig. 22. A view (left) that even the most sophisticated auto buff rarely sees: you're looking down the throat of a carburetor to examine the jet squirt. Blue line is superimposed scope trace. Contrast these relatively slow exposures (¹⁄₄₄₀₀th sec) from an 1100 frame/sec strip with the ultrahigh-speed records (right) of an exploding band of pentolite. These are selected frames exposed at 0.1 μsec. Argon flash bombs illuminated the pentolite, which shows as yellow ribbon. See "Ultrahigh-Speed Photography," in Chapter 3. (Courtesy F. Bowditch, General Motors Research, left; M. Sultanoff, U.S. Army Ballistics Research Laboratories)

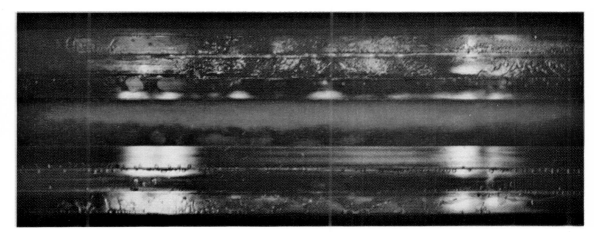

Color Fig. 23. You are looking at the edge of a sheet of paper being formed in a flume. The dark fibers of cellulose are in a red dye suspension flowing at 1800 ft./min. This polariscopic study of laminar shear flow was exposed 0.1 μsec by xenon flash. See "Ultrahigh-Speed Photography," in Chapter 3. (Courtesy E. L. Scott, Mead Paper Co.)

Color Fig. 24. Control pulpit of Welsh hot-strip steel mill overlooks rolling line longer than nine football fields. Digital computer (below right) is located in another building where it predicts initial setpoints for multivariable analog controller, monitors data from sensors and recalculates new regulator setpoints as steel is rolled. In more simple, though still automatic, mode of control an operator in control room right would assign trol room (right) would assign setpoints to multivariable controller. Under completely manual control, an operator would be assigned to each roughing or finishing stand along the process line. See "Modern Process Control," in Chapter 6.

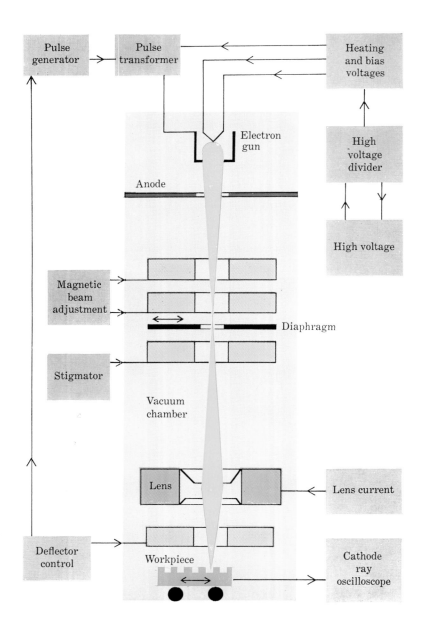

Color Fig. 25. You can also machine with electrons — hurled from a high-voltage electron gun (top), collimated, shaped, aligned, and focussed by magnetic optics (center), and finally halted by the work surface (bottom). Giving up their kinetic energy as heat, the impacting electrons melt and vaporize a thin surface layer. Pulsing the beam at high frequency prevents deeper melting; deflecting it allows holes or slots of any desired shape to be "cut." Machining rate is much lower than for even spark-discharge machining, but tiny, delicate parts are easily worked on. See "Nontraditional Machining," in Chapter 3. (Courtesy Hamilton-Standard)

the density, particle size, particle size distribution, and the concentration of the solid material. The slurry viscosity should be as low as possible which requires a *low* solids concentration and a *minimum* of micronsize fines. On the other hand, solid particles should stay in suspension even if agitation or turbulence is removed temporarily, which requires a *high* solids concentration and a *maximum* of super fines. Highly concentrated slurries of fine material are, in general, also desirable from a pipe wear standpoint because abrasion of the pipe wall usually increases with particle size.

The slurry composition, in short, is of such importance to the technical and economic feasibility of a solids pipeline that much experimentation is necessary before the decision can be made to employ this method of transport. This may even extend to chemical treatment of the slurry to modify its flow characteristics. Certain dispensing agents, usually complex poly-phosphates, create repulsive forces between the fine particles—thus keeping them separated and releasing absorbed water that would otherwise be immobilized through natural flocculation.

Up from slurries?

The success of slurry pipelining all over the world, and in particular the excellent results obtained in the U.S. with long solids pipelines, has convinced many, myself included, that this new mode of transport is here to stay. One need only reflect upon the profound impact that oil and gas (and more recently, coal) pipelines have had on the economy of many countries. Still, the capital costs are high and the competition from more conventional methods of transport is keen. Consequently, solids pipelines may be slow in developing unless some way can be found to make them useful. Looming particularly large here is the fact that slurry pipelines can only carry a single commodity, and then only in fairly large quantity. Railroads, on the other hand, can carry different commodities in varying quantities.

The question, therefore, is how to make the solids pipeline a truly "common" carrier. The answer may lie in the technique mentioned at the beginning of the article—that of hydraulically driving capsules or slugs of solid material through a pipeline. This could also reduce, if not eliminate, the problem of separating the solids from the carrier fluid at the end of the pipeline.

A case of serendipity

Surprisingly, the idea of transporting capsules or slugs hydraulically did not emerge as an extension of the pneumatic tube method familiar to department stores and postal systems. Rather, it arose from the observations of two oil pipeline researchers, Hodgson and Charles, at the Research Council of Alberta in Edmonton, Canada. They were studying the flow characteristics of water mixed with oil of the same density to determine whether the water, being of lower viscosity, could be made to flow at the pipe wall and thus facilitate the flow of the oil (see sketch).

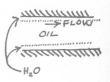

It turned out that oil would indeed flow concentrically within a water annulus, and with a lower friction head loss as well. But the interesting observation was that if slugs or bubbles of oil formed, they would flow along in a stable manner and with a diameter of 60–90% of the pipe's internal diameter, as sketched in the margin. Moreover, two significant characteristics of this intriguing behavior became apparent after studying it over a wide range of flows: the oil slugs moved *faster* than the supporting water, and the friction-head loss of the oil slug-water mixture proved to be less than that of the water alone (under turbulent conditions) at the same volumetric flow.

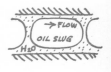

The obvious question arose: could the oil slugs or bubbles be replaced with solid material of the same shapes and total density? Further, would solid slugs or spheres having density greater than the supporting fluid also flow as easily? If both questions could be answered affirmatively, the way might be open to a new, third generation—after fluids and slurries—of pipeline transportation.

The two Canadian researchers and their co-workers analyzed the problem both theoretically and experimentally. They built a small-scale line of plastic pipe equipped with a capsule injection chamber similar to that used for inserting scraper capsules into oil pipelines. They proceeded then to tests and calculations on hollow plastic capsules, loaded with lead shot or mercury, as well as on solid slugs and spheres of both aluminum and steel.

The results, using both water and oils of different viscosities, proved most encouraging. As predicted, the various solid shapes flow pretty much as the oil slugs do in water. And the capsules heavier than the supporting fluid move at speeds faster than the average fluid by itself—so long as the capsule's diameter is about 90% of the flow diameter.

This work also revealed one very significant advantage of slug or capsule pipelining over slurry pipelining. If they are of the right size, slugs and capsules can apparently be hydraulically transported at practically any velocity commensurate with the desired rate of solids movement, whereas a solid in slurry form has to move quite rapidly to prevent settling. This is important, for power is proportional to the cube of velocity. Hence it appears that solids can be piped in slug or capsule form economically by pumping them at *low velocity* but at quite *high concentration* within the pipe.

Perishables in pipelines?

All this is, of course, based on quite small-scale work. The Research Council's test line was only 1¼ in. in diameter and 35 ft long, though big enough to evaluate the concept. However, an initial economic study was conducted in parallel which indicates some tantalizing possibilities. Although capital costs would be higher than for a slurry pipeline, because of locks around pumping stations as well as injection and retrieval openings, process equipment at the end would be largely eliminated. Thus it may prove possible economically to cast sulfur, say, into slugs that could be moved hydraulically in special pipelines, or even in existing oil pipelines. Canada alone anticipates a production of some 2 million tons per year of this commodity in its Western regions. Calculations show that a 10 in. pipeline could handle this solids throughput adequately.

Fig. 3-52. What on earth are these chaps doing? They're getting set to test the solids capsule concept in an existing oil pipeline. The capsule being injected at Sundre, Alberta, Canada, contains radioactive material for tracing purposes, hence the gingerly handling (right) and the Geiger counter (left). This capsule was retrieved at Rimbey, Alberta, 70 miles away. This and other tests suggest that slugs of solid commodities, or capsules containing damageable ones, might be transported over long distances through oil or water pipelines. (Courtesy Research Council of Alberta)

Other possibilities for slug or capsule transport include coal, phosphate, potash, metal ores, or refined metals. Even wheat is being seriously considered, for the Canadians move some 12 million tons per year of it over exceedingly long distances from the Western plains. Here, however, a serious product degradation problem would have to be surmounted. What is needed is a tough, cheap, disposable plastic film or, perhaps, a system of reusable capsules for protecting the wheat (or other delicate commodities like chemicals, for that matter) during transport.

Although slug and capsule pipelining have not yet been tried on a large scale, the cost barriers look formidable. It would seem that an intermediate development might be more likely until the new concept is proved out competitively. Large amounts of water are needed in large pipeline operations, and often it must be totally clarified before it can be discharged into rivers or lakes. To sidestep this problem, the slurry technique will more probably be extended by adding a recirculating system, with the partially clarified carrying fluid (not necessarily water) returning to the source. Such a fluid would contain a large percentage of fines which would permit large chunks (small slugs, in effect) to be transported at low, economical velocities. The solid chunks to be transported would be fed into the pressurized "dense medium" just after the pump delivery.

Withal, slug and capsule pipelining appears to be a promising extension of slurry transportation which is, in itself, a radical but potent departure from existing modes of transport. As with all such departures that require extensive capital, each type or both will flower only if the economic need is there.

There are legal problems as well. Pipelines as a class have not been granted the right of eminent domain in most states, though oil and gas pipelines have. Only two states, West Virginia and Utah, have passed laws granting this right to coal pipelines considered to be in the public interest. Most eastern states have rejected such legislation. The Administration introduced a bill in the 87th Congress to grant the federal right of eminent domain to coal pipelines, but no action has been taken. Pipelines for other commodities will surely follow if coal pipelines can gain the necessary right-of-way.

Despite these obstacles of capital and law, the technical and economic underpinnings of each pipeline technique are being carefully constructed against the day when conditions demand their adoption. I feel assured that this day is not far off.

Further reading

The only source in book form is *The Transportation of Solids in Steel Pipelines* (Colorado School of Mines Research Foundation, Golden, Colo., 1963, $3.50). This handbook, which the author helped to prepare, summarizes current theories and their application. It also lists some 250 references, and gives details on 52 successful pipelines all over the world. In shorter form, but with more attention to underlying theory, the same ground is nicely covered in two sets of recent articles. One is a group of three by two French investigators, Condolios and Chapus, published sequentially starting in the June 24, 1963, issue of *Chem. Eng.* as "Solids Pipelines." The first is "Transporting Solid Materials in Pipelines," followed by "Designing Solids-Handling Pipelines" and "Operating Solids Pipelines." The second set is a group of two by three Canadian researchers, Ellis, Redberger, and Bolt in *Indus. & Eng. Chem.*, Aug. and Sept. 1963, under the general title of "Trans-porting Solids by Pipeline." The first is "Slurries" and the second "Capsules and Slugs" which covers the unique work on this latter concept done at the Research Council of Alberta, Edmonton, Canada. See also "The Pipeline Flow of Capsules—Potential Industrial Applications" by Hodgson and Bolt, available from RCA or from the Engineering Institute of Canada, Montreal. To focus on a specific commodity, write to Mr. Eric Reichl, Consolidated Coal Co., Library, Pa., for two papers: "The Coal Pipeline" by Hanson and Regan, and "Some Comments on Coal Pipelines" by Reichl. The first describes the original Cadiz-Cleveland, Ohio, pipeline; the second is a lively account of operating experience with it. Readers interested in legal and economic aspects would profit from "Report to the Panel on Civilian Technology on Coal Slurry Pipelines" (Dept. of the Interior, Washington, D.C., May 1, 1963). And for some really blue-sky thinking, see "People Through Pipes?" a letter to Communications Center, *Intern. Sci. Tech.*, Dec. 1962.

MODERN CONCRETE DESIGN

by Paul Gugliotta *

IN BRIEF: *The introduction of shell structures and shell mathematics to concrete design has changed the face of modern architecture. Such thin, graceful shapes are possible, not only by improving the strength of concrete, but by changing some fundamental design concepts. The beams in a conventional design, for example, carry maximum compressive stress only in the top surface, and maximum tensile stress only in the reinforcing bars near the bottom surface, while the concrete in the rest of the beam loafs. In a shell, the concrete is shaped so that stresses are uniform across the entire thickness (or thinness, if you like) of the shell; all the concrete in the structure works equally hard to support the load. However, such shapes are easier to talk about than they are to design. In recent years, the introduction of prefabrication, and the development of new shapes and materials have greatly expanded the use of concrete.—C.J.L.*

■ One of the most striking modern buildings in the city of Rome is the Palazzetto dello Sport, a sports arena erected in 1957 for the 1960 Olympic Games and built almost entirely of concrete. One mile and eighteen centuries away stands the classic Pantheon, built in 120 A.D. by the Roman Emperor Hadrian, using concrete as an essential part of its masonry structure. (See Color Figs. 12, 19, and 20 for details of these structures.)

Although concrete is basic to both buildings, there is clearly a difference in the way it was used to shape each of them. The Pantheon's powerful hemispherical dome tapers from a thickness of nearly 20 feet at the base to several feet at the top. By contrast, the roof of the Palazzetto is a graceful parabolic shell. It is as light and compliant as it appears, being only slightly more than 1 in. thick. Despite their different thicknesses, the domes of the two buildings span nearly the same area.

Such a contrast in thickness-to-span ratios would be understandable if today's concrete were significantly stronger than that used in Roman times. But concrete has changed very little in 27 centuries of use. Modern concrete is, of course, reinforced with steel (some of it is reinforced with pretensioned steel, further increasing its strength). However, even this is not sufficient to explain the difference between the structures.

The principal difference is a difference in fundamental design concepts. In recent years, architectural engineers have developed a sounder understanding of how a concrete structure works—a realization that concrete

* Paul Gugliotta, who studied under Pier Luigi Nervi in Italy, is a member of Juster and Gugliotta, architectural, engineering, and planning consultation firm in New York.

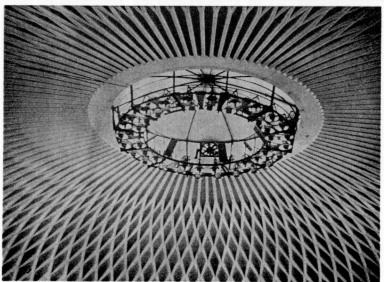

Figs. 3-53 and 3-54. The Palazetto dello Sport (Small Sports Palace) in Rome, designed by A. Vitelozzi and Pier Luigi Nervi, features a parabolic concrete shell roof 197 ft. in diameter. It is composed of 1620 precast concrete tiles about 1 in. thick. (Courtesy Museum of Modern Art, top; Richard Olmsted)

is, after all, not just a melted stone to be cast into shapes that serve as replacements for steel beams or masonry walls, but that it has a unique form and shape in which it functions best. Of fundamental importance is the appreciation that concrete is most efficient when it is fashioned into continuous, one-piece structures that carry loads by distributing them among all the members of the structure.

The boldest expression of such syntactic design is to be found in the thin shells built in the last few years. Here, in a manner similar to the stressed-skin designs common in aircraft and space vehicles, the entire structure carries a share of the load purely by virtue of its geometry. Although the dimensions of the inch-thick shell of the Palazzetto dello Sport, for example, seem entirely too fragile for concrete, the building itself does not appear flimsy or delicate. In the shell, concrete has been formed into a shape that expresses purely what it does. Even the untutored eye can see the compressive loads being collected and directed to the buttresses.

Glued-together stone

Concrete today, as in Roman times, consists of a mixture of cement, rock, and sand, the rock and sand being referred to as the aggregate. The cement serves simply to glue the aggregate together and is generally the weakest of the ingredients. There are various kinds of cement, the most common being portland cement, which is made from a mixture of limestone and clay fired together and ground to a fine powder. Similarly, there are various kinds of aggregates, varying in size from fine sand to large stones, and in shape from jagged to smooth. For high strength, aggregate should have sharp edges and be graded so that small aggregate fills the voids between large aggregate, creating an interlocked material.

In general, the strength of concrete is directly proportional to the amount of cement, the density of the mixture, and the size and gradation of aggregate, and is inversely proportional to the amount of mixing water. The amount of water forces a compromise: if the mixture is too dry, it will not flow between forms and around reinforcing bars, and if it is too wet, it will be too weak after it sets. Typically, fully cured, high-strength concrete will withstand about 8000 psi in compression and about 500 psi in tension (in design, the allowable tensile stress is usually assumed to be zero).

To anyone who thinks of concrete as a static, rigid material, it comes as a surprise to learn that it is one of the most difficult materials for a designer to work with. For one thing, he has to deal with a long curing period, after pouring, before the material reaches full strength. Unlike a flour-and-water paste, concrete does not harden by drying out, but hardens because of a complex chemical reaction between the water and the cement. In fact, it hardens faster under water than it does in air. And like a thermosetting resin, the hardened cement cannot be ground up and restored to its original form, nor can it be dissolved by water or other common solvents. A fortunate thing, too, for it is this last property that gives it its resistance to weathering.

The chemical reaction that takes place in curing (about which little is known) is a slow one and may actually require several years before the concrete is fully cured. In construction, however, it is customary to assume that concrete has reached full strength after 28 days, and that after 7 days it is sufficiently cured to remove the forms. The curing period is a construction difficulty that takes some planning and may well affect the kind of structure that can be built. There are a number of cases on record where forms have been removed too soon, causing the concrete to sag beyond the point of salvage.

Hidden sources of stress

The concrete designer has another problem few designers face. Concrete shrinks as it cures, the amount of shrinkage varying from 0.05 to 0.10%. In continuous structures, this shrinkage can create large stresses unless the designer has provided means for dissipating them. When a large concrete apartment building was constructed for a New York housing project recently, the contractors left a 2-ft vertical gap between two halves of the building to minimize shrinkage stresses. Only after the concrete in the entire building had cured was the concrete poured to fill the gap.

Internal stresses can also come from temperature changes in the structure. Concrete has a high thermal expansion coefficient; if a beam subjected to a 40°F temperature rise is not allowed to expand, a stress of about 700 psi will develop—and this is over half of the normal allowable working stress. Expansion could be absorbed in expansion joints, but not without limiting the structure's continuity. The problem is complicated because temperatures are generally not uniform over the structure: a slab in the sun may be much hotter than the beam it is shading, and the beam itself may be much hotter on the outside than on the inside.

Added to all these difficulties is the fact that concrete, being manufactured on the job, cannot be expected to have consistent properties from batch to batch. Moreover, the weather, the humidity, and other uncontrolled factors can contribute other variations to the properties of the final material.

In the designer's favor (for the most part) is another unusual and often unrecognized property of concrete. Unlike most other materials, concrete is not an elastic medium. It is an elastoplastic material—that creeps slightly under constant stress. This plastic deformation is normally double the magnitude of the initial elastic deformation. Although plastic deformation creates problems, causing elements to sag when they were not intended to, it is also an advantage.

Plastic flow acts as a kind of built-in safety factor. Deflections that would cause stresses beyond the allowable maximum based on elastic assumptions do not, in fact, occur because the concrete creeps and redistributes the stresses. Overloaded members can relax, transferring excess load to another part of the structure, thus avoiding actual failure.

An understanding of plastic flow in concrete has led recently to the introduction of ultimate-strength design in place of the customary elastic-design considerations. In elastic design, of a beam, for example (see Fig. 3-55), maximum allowable compressive stress (ultimate stress divided by a suitable safety factor) is allowed to occur only at the top surface of the beam. (The designer assumes that the entire tensile stress is carried by the reinforcing steel.) Ultimate-strength design limits the maximum load (not stress) to a safe proportion of the failure load. The net result is a more efficient design that utilizes the material's reserve strength.

Why build in concrete?

Considering its vanishingly small tensile strength and the complexities in the pouring and hardening process, concrete would hardly seem to be the ideal material for building thin shell-like roofs, huge unsupported domes, sweeping cantilevered canopies, and other shapes that leave very little margin for error. In recent years, such problems have been worked out largely because concrete offers many other attractive features.

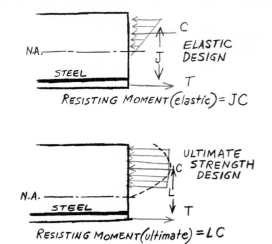

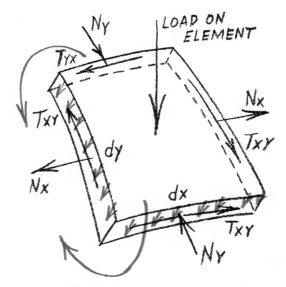

Fig. 3-55. Design standards now permit engineers to take advantage of concrete's plastic flow properties in strength analysis. The conventional elastic design assumes that compressive stress distribution is triangular (upper sketch), like any other elastic material. But concrete is not elastic; it flows plastically at higher stresses, as shown by the parabolic curve in the lower sketch. In the new ultimate-strength design, the designer approximates this parabolic distribution with an empirical distribution of compressive stresses (rectangle in lower sketch). The concrete, in either case, presumably carries no tensile stresses.

In the first place, concrete is cheap. The raw materials—sand, rock, limestone, clay—occur naturally and abundantly the world over. Moreover, concrete is fire-resistant (most building codes require that structural steel be encased in concrete to protect it from heat), is resistant to weathering, offers effective damping of vibration and shock, and (of increasing importance) acts as an efficient shield for ionizing radiation.

To the architect, concrete's most attractive feature is its versatility. It can be molded into one shape as easily as it can be molded into another. Shapes that would be prohibitively expensive or even impossible in steel are entirely practical in concrete. Doubly curved surfaces, bent or twisted beams with intricate cutouts, slabs with sections cut away where loads are light—all these are available to the designer who chooses to work in concrete.

Concrete's greatest deficiency—its lack of tensile strength—is not difficult to correct. Reinforcement with steel is, of course, a common and rather obvious solution. Nearly all concrete structures built today are strengthened with imbedded reinforcing rods that become integrated with the concrete when it shrinks during curing.

Prestressed concrete is a more efficient and more recent solution to the problem. It is made by compressing the concrete between pre-tensioned reinforcing rods so that the concrete carries an initial compressive load. Prestressing makes better use of concrete's properties because this initial compressive load permits members to resist larger loads without developing tensile stresses (see marginal sketch). Effectively, the prestress is a bias; it moves the initial stress to a more favorable value between the allowable extremes of tension and compression.

Strong like an egg shell

Beams, whether prestressed or simply reinforced, represent only one way to span a space. A more efficient, more spectacular, and, in many ways, more difficult way is the thin shell. Like the old egg-shell trick in which the contestant attempts to crush an egg by squeezing it in his hand, a thin concrete shell, reinforced with steel, is exceedingly strong when subjected to a uniform external load.

In contrast with a beam, all parts of the material in an ideal shell work equally hard against the load. The beam is inefficient because stress varies from maximum tension on the bottom to maximum compression on the top, and zero stress in between. In a shell, the load-bearing surface is shaped so that a cross-section of the shell at any point is in a uniform state of stress.

The ideal shell is a pure membrane—a soap bubble, if you like. In a membrane, there are no bending moments, no transverse shear forces (see Fig. 3-56), and no radial restraints at the

Fig. 3-56. The ideal shell structure carries only direct membrane stresses. Free-body diagram of membrane segment shows pure tensile and compressive forces accompanied by tangential shears. In actual concrete shell, there are also bending moments and transverse shear forces (color).

edges. Real shells, of course, cannot conform too closely to this ideal. Unbalanced loadings, restraints imposed by the supports, and necessary stiffeners introduce bending moments and transverse shear forces.

The analysis of real shells is an extremely complex mathematical exercise. Most designers today rely on computers for the preliminary analysis, but even with computers, there are too many unknowns, too many indeterminate quantities, to make a complete analysis. Elastic models of the proposed structure help to confirm theoretical calculations, but it is always difficult to relate stress and strain in the model to that in the real structure. In the end experience and intuition become as important to the design as theory and experiment. An intuitive feel for concrete's peculiar properties is one mark of the successful designer. Pier Luigi Nervi, the celebrated Italian engineer who has been working with concrete for nearly 50 years, looks upon the design process as a kind of collaborative enterprise between himself and the concrete. "Mainly because of plastic flow," he explains in his book *Structures*, "a concrete structure tries with admirable docility to adapt itself to our calculations . . . and it even tries to correct our deficiencies and errors."

The shell, like the arch (which is a two-dimensional special case of a shell), should be shaped in the form of a parabola if a uniform load is to be transformed into pure tensile and compressive membrane stresses. Moreover, the shell must be flexible so that it can distort to conform to nonuniform wind loads or other live loads. It is only through distortion that shell stresses can continue to remain pure membrane stresses. A shell would develop moments in the skin if if were unable to deflect when subjected to nonuniform loads.

The need for flexibility creates several problems. Although the shell must be flexible, it must also be stiff enough to prevent buckling. A well-designed shell is a compromise between one that is so stiff it will not distort, and one that is so flexible it will not prevent the shell from buckling in compression.

The designer faces another problem at the points where the shell meets the ground, or where it attaches to its supporting structure. These supports must necessarily be rigid, which means that bending moments will be developed in this area when the shell distorts (see margin). The usual solution is to increase the thickness of the shell at its base. An ingenious solution is shown in the photograph of the Palazzetto dello Sport (Fig. 3-53). Notice that the edges of the shell are scalloped. Besides being an attractive

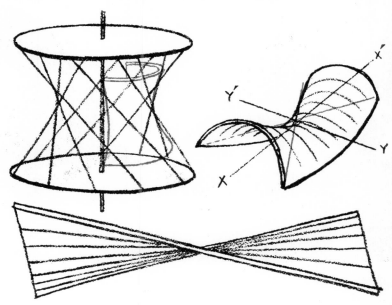

Fig. 3-57. Hyperbolic paraboloids simplify shell construction because they are composed of straight lines. The sketches above illustrate various ways of generating such a surface. The classic example—a parabola with open ends down sliding along a parabola with open ends up—is at upper right. Planes parallel to xx'-yy' intersect the surface along hyperbolas— hence the name hyperbolic paraboloid.

way to treat the edges of the shell, the scallops serve as stiffeners to resist the bending moments that develop at the edges. They also allow more light to enter the building and, as a bonus, act to divert rain water to points where it can be conveniently guttered away.

Although concrete is well suited to the construction of shell structures, it is not economical if the wooden formwork is too elaborate or too expensive. The techniques for putting the structure up are at least as important as the techniques for making it work once it is in place. One of the simplest shell forms to erect is the hyperbolic paraboloid. Mathematically, a hyperbolic paraboloid is the surface generated when a downward curving parabola is translated along an upward curving parabola. The advantage of this shape is that it can be formed entirely from straight lines (although this may be difficult to imagine without a model in front of you) and can therefore be molded on forms composed of straight wooden boards.

The hyperbolic paraboloid is quite easy to analyze, its shape producing constant tension, compression and shear throughout when uniformly loaded. Consequently, the shell is very efficient. Felix Candella, a Mexican architectural engineer, has been a leading exponent of concrete hyperbolic paraboloid shells, extolling their relatively simple mathematics and construction.

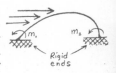

Fig. 3-58. Restaurant at Xochimilco, Mexico, by Felix Candella, was easier to design and build than it looks. Because each of the arched shells is a hyperbolic-paraboloid, formwork was built of straight boards. (Courtesy Jane Doggett and Dorothy Jackson, Architectural Graphics Associates)

Shells a piece at a time

Pier Luigi Nervi is responsible for two developments that have greatly broadened the horizons for concrete shell construction. In 1940, Prof. Nervi designed and built six aircraft hangars for the Italian air force. In the first of these, the framework for the roof was composed of a gridwork of poured-in-place arches. In the later designs, the framework was built entirely of prefabricated concrete elements. These prefabricated trusses were placed to form the gridwork of arches and assembled by electrically welding the reinforcing rods protruding from the ends. After welding, concrete was poured into the joints to form a continuous concrete and steel network. This frame was then covered with narrow, corrugated, concrete slabs.

During the war, the hangars were destroyed by the Germans to prevent them from falling into Allied hands. Heavy charges were set off at the base of the supporting buttresses causing the roof to drop to the ground in one piece, like an enormous umbrella. When Prof. Nervi examined the joints, he found that none had broken and most had not even cracked. Similar methods of prefabrication have since simplified the construction of many complex architectural forms and, through mass production of identical elements, have reduced the cost of erecting continuous concrete structures.

Professor Nervi's most recent contribution to the construction of thin shells is the invention of ferrocemento, a kind of half-steel, half-concrete material with some properties characteristic of both. Ferrocemento is made by plastering concrete through an armature made of light reinforcing rods sandwiched between sev-

Fig. 3-59. This aircraft hangar, designed and built by Pier Luigi Nervi in 1940, is one of the first examples of prefabricated concrete construction. Roof trusses were individually precast, then assembled by welding the reinforcing bars and pouring concrete into the joint. (Courtesy Pier Luigi Nervi, top; Vasari-Rome)

eral layers of wire mesh. In a sense, it is simply a thin sheet of reinforced concrete containing an unusually large proportion of steel. But because the steel is uniformly distributed, the composite acts more like a low-grade steel than a concrete. It is as strong in tension as it is in compression and therefore well suited for molding prefabricated shell elements.

One of the first applications of ferrocemento appears in the roof of the Turin exhibition building's main hall, built in 1949 (Fig. 3-60). The arched shell is made up of many identical corrugated ferrocemento beams, supported in their final position and then continuously connected by pouring concrete tendons in the joints between the elements. The corrugations make the shell strong even though the thickness to

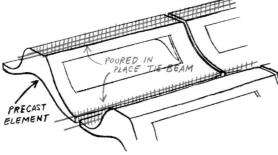

Fig. 3-60. The thin-shell roof of this exhibition hall in Turin, Italy is made of prefabricated ferrocemento elements with poured-in-place reinforced arches connecting the peaks and valleys of the undulations. The shell, designed and built by Prof. Nervi in 1948, spans 300 feet. (Courtesy Nervi Moncalvo)

span ratio is only 1:2500 (compared with 1:150 for the typical arched-beam cylinder roof). The lightness of the shell is emphasized by a multitude of openings pierced in the corrugations, flooding the hall with natural light.

A more recent application of ferrocemento in shells is shown in the dome of the Palazzetto. Here, ferrocemento was first prefabricated in the form of tiles shaped like inverted, diamond-shaped cake pans. By laying these tiles over skeleton framework shaped in the form of the shell, they could be interconnected by pouring concrete into the gaps between tiles. The result is a dome that looks smooth from the outside but on the inside carries an intricate lace work of ribs where tile lips meet.

One of the more surprising applications of ferrocemento is the construction of ship hulls. The hull of Prof. Nervi's private ketch *Nennele* is built entirely of reinforced concrete, from keel to superstructure. The concrete has proven to be completely watertight, the bilges remaining dry in all seasons. Damage to the hull can be easily repaired by patching with concrete.

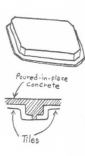

Steamed beams and plastic cements

We are just beginning to learn how to use concrete's traditional properties to best advantage. Meantime, new types of concrete with totally different properties point the way toward an even greater variety of structural forms. Recent research has yielded a number of promising new developments.

The Russians have recently revived the autoclave method of making concrete. In this process, a sand and lime mixture with low water content is steam-cured at high pressures for several hours. The resulting concrete has strengths above 10,000 psi. The size of individual units is limited by the size of the autoclave, but these units are extremely strong and light and lend themselves to all types of prefabricated concrete construction.

The laboratories are now experimenting with concrete mixes that expand upon curing. Such mixtures will be useful for casting self-prestressing beams and slabs. They may also lead to the development of a practical concrete that does not change dimension when curing, thus eliminating a major source of problems in concrete construction. Nonshrinking concretes made by mixing a carefully controlled quantity of iron filings with the concrete mix are already available. The expansion of the iron as it oxidizes compensates for the normal shrinkage of the cement. These mixtures are expensive, however, and useful only for special applications.

Concretes that use an epoxy adhesive in place

Fig. 3-61. Concrete less than ½ in. thick forms the hull of Prof. Nervi's own 40-ft ketch, Nennele. The ferrocemento hull was built by shaping several layers of wire mesh into the hull form, then plastering concrete through from the inside and smoothing it off on the outside. (Courtesy Nervi, Vasari-Rome, top; Architectural Forum)

of the normal portland cement are also under investigation. Because of the greater cohesive strength of the epoxy, such mixtures may eventually be useful for pouring extremely thin, lightweight shells. Epoxies are also being used

to join prefabricated concrete elements. Some day, it may be possible to erect an entire building by simply gluing precast concrete elements together.

Further reading

Even if your interest in concrete architecture goes no deeper than the esthetics of design, you will be well rewarded by simply thumbing through some of the beautifully illustrated books now available. Nervi's latest book, *Buildings, Projects, Structures: 1953–1963* (Praeger, 1963, $15), is essentially a picture book containing a complete collection of photographs and sketches for structures he built in the last 10 years. His earlier book, *Structures* (Dodge, 1956, $6.95), contains examples of earlier works along with a readable explanation of his design philosophy.

For a broader view, also thoroughly illustrated, see *Reinforced Concrete in Architecture* by A. A. Raafat (Reinhold, 1958, $7.50). It examines recent technological advances and presents examples of the architecture these advances make possible. Also in this picture-book category are two recently published books: *Candela: The Shell Builder* by Colin Faber (Reinhold, 1963, $16.50) and *Shell Architecture* by Jurgen Joedicke (Reinhold, 1963, $22.50).

The classic book on shell mathematics is *Elementary Statics of Shells* by Alf Pfluger (Dodge, 1961, $8.75). The first edition was published nearly 50 years ago but its recent translation from the original German underscores its present-day usefulness. For another treatment of shell design, see the chapter on shells by M. G. Salvadori in *Architectural Engineering* (Dodge, 1955, $12.75).

The bible of the prestressed concrete world is *Design of Prestressed Concrete Structures* by T. Y. Lin (Wiley, 1955, $11.50). For the architect, however, it is rather more theoretical than practical. To learn more about concrete itself, what kind of stuff it is, how it is made, look up *Concrete Technology*, in 2 vols. by D. F. Orchard (Wiley, 1962, $19.25). Another recent book on this topic is *Concrete Properties and Manufacture* by T. N. W. Akroyd (Pergamon, 1962, $12.50).

ULTRAHIGH-SPEED PHOTOGRAPHY

by Kenneth R. Coleman *

IN BRIEF: *The faster high-speed photography becomes, the more valuable it can be to analyze movement or to detect rapid change. New tech-*

niques facilitate ultrahigh-speed pictures with exposures of 50 microseconds or less. High-speed phenomena such as flow in chemical plants, the dynamics of stress-strain, the rotation of a pinch of plasma become the camera's targets. But the experimenter is more than just

* Kenneth R. Coleman is with the Atomic Weapons Research Establishment of the United Kingdom Atomic Energy Authority, Aldermaston, England.

a sophisticated cameraman, for photographic data-taking becomes part of the experiment itself. An object can be lit briefly by extremely bright sparks or high-intensity gas discharges, but the self-illumination of a hot flame requires a laser flash to produce a meaningful photographic record. Records are frames or streaks of data.—E.H.

■ Where has the light come from?
How long has it taken?
Can you imagine taking a flash photograph and finding it necessary to ask these questions?

High-speed photography in the past few years has progressed to the point that the finite velocity of light itself has become not only a problem but a tool to illuminate objects a chosen distance from the camera without photographing nearer or further objects.

While high-speed photography is not new, a number of techniques have been developed which push it into an entirely new region—of *ultra*high speed—where exposure times range from less than 50 microseconds to as short as a few nanoseconds.

Why so fast?

How movements take place and the analysis of movement is the main purpose of high-speed photography. If you make exposures short enough in a sequence of motion picture frames, the movement will not be blurred. Run the frame rate up high enough and you can play back a view of the movement in "slow motion." In this article, I shall be concerned with the

ultrahigh speed, even though I find it convenient to dispense with the word "ultra." (See Color Figs. 22, 23, and 29 for some vivid results of the ultrahigh-speed technique.)

While 3000 frames per second has been fast enough to investigate the movement of solid bodies, this speed simply would not satisfy, say, a plasma physicist. He may ask for ten pictures in 0.2 μsec because he has noticed something he did not expect between the first two frames from his rotating mirror camera (10^7 frames per second).

Other experimenters may wish to investigate flow in chemical plants or combustion chambers. In many fields, the problems to be solved by high-speed photography involve extremely rapid change rather than direct movement alone. The analysis of an electric arc—trapped in its sputtering passage in the photographic records in Fig. 3-67—can lead to methods of minimizing the damage it causes through arc suppression or by making it take a safe channel. Often it is necessary to determine the rate of change of stress as it is distributed through a solid body. These changes can be so rapid that only framing rates greater than 10^6 per second can "freeze" the changes in the photoelasticity fringes.

Your first brush with ultrahigh-speed photography should not be too frightening if you bear in mind that the problems are analogous to the low-speed snapshot and movie photography with which we are all familiar. First you must decide how fast your photography must

Fig. 3-62. Spectacular shots like this bullet in mid-flight are usually the most popular impressions of high-speed photography, though the ingenious setups apply equally well to scientific data-taking. The shutter of the camera, a conventional Speed Graphic, was opened in a darkened room. When the rifle was fired, a microphone picked up the sound and triggered a xenon flash of ½ μsec duration. (Courtesy H. Edgerton)

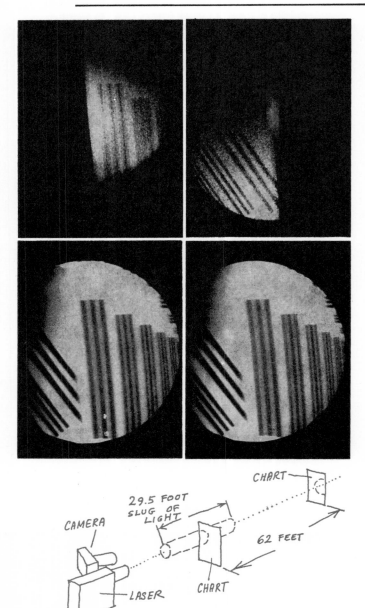

Fig. 3-63. You can light near but not far, and vice versa, with a laser flash. In the frame at top left, a 30-nanosec pulse lights the near chart. In next frame, top right, a 30-nanosec piece of light 29.5 ft. long illuminates only the far chart. Ordinary flash, as below, cannot discriminate. (Courtesy K. Coleman)

be; that the motion of the image on the film should be less than the degree of spatial resolution provided by the optical system.

Given this short an exposure, you must then determine the amount of light that must be present to give a usable image; this is a function of the brightness of the object (if self-luminous) and the sensitivity of the film. If the object is not self-luminous then you have an extra measure of control—the intensity of the light source you use. It is seldom possible

to optimize speed, exposure, and definition together.

There are extremely fast cameras, of course, like the Fastax by Wollensak, the Dynafax by Beckman and Whitley, ranging up into the ultrafast like the STL Image Converter, Beckman and Whitley 189 and the Barr and Stroud CP5. But simply getting modern cameras, or even a good photographer, is only half the battle. For the experiment itself determines how the cameras become data-taking tools of the scientist.

Look for the bit

While in its broadest sense, photography is writing with light, more advanced experiments require photography to become an integral part of the physical measurement. I find it valuable to think of that problem of physical measurement in terms of an information-theory approach. Any object that we photograph provides information on five "channels": three of these are the spatial coordinates of the object, a fourth is the intensity of light emitted (or reflected) from it, and a fifth very broad channel is the spectral distribution of the light. Our recording medium—black-and-white photographic film—has only three channels: two spatial coordinates and the density of the recorded image.

However, we have a choice of how this information can be used by sampling it in various ways. Familiar snapshot photography samples space, producing a single photographic record in two dimensions of space plus the brightness of the object at any point. A third space dimension can be added only by further samples, as is approximated in stereophotography.

In a record (I shall drop the adjective "photographic") from a spectrograph, the space dimensions represent wavelength and the length of the slit. If the image is scanned along the film surface over the length of the slit, this space dimension is transformed into time, thus making the photographic instrument a time-resolving spectrograph. Similarly, the record from a streak camera, which we'll describe later, represents time by one direction, a space dimension by the other, and intensity by density distribution.

In experiments one seeks recording channels with the greatest dynamic range. For example, the available dynamic range of photographic film today limits one recording channel because it is somewhat more than two orders in density while the bit capacity in the space dimensions is about 500/in. There may be many more bits of information in the light emitted from the object being photographed.

And then there was light

It is essential to understand the differences between using the light emitted from a self-luminous object and using the light reflected from an object by external illumination.

Self-luminous objects like plasmas or incandescent burning gases to a large extent fix the apparatus used for their observation. The instantaneous temperature of such objects determines the spectral region of maximum sensitivity required and the dynamic range is fixed by the corresponding range of luminance or luminous intensity—this is a photometric quantity which our eyes treat as "brightness."

The commonest light for high-speed photography is the xenon flash. It comes in all sizes from small portable models up to systems big enough to photograph a circus. The flash lasts from several milliseconds to as short as ten microseconds, the time between flashes is limited by de-ionization time to about 100 μsec. If longer periods of light are required at extreme energies, xenon flash tubes are not particularly convenient because they overheat.

An explosive charge—in the wide-open spaces —is an excellent energy store, and, in a flash bomb, that energy is transferred with reasonable efficiency into a luminous shock wave in a suitable gas, like argon. Light is emitted in this way for a period of 10–20 μsec.

A laser flash

The number of photons per unit area, per unit bandwidth, per unit time emitted by a laser is several orders greater than from any other light source because the bandspread is so small. Photographing by laser light through a narrow-band optical filter with maximum transmission at the laser wavelength gives the opportunity to discriminate against the self-light of a hot, incandescent object. By this means it is possible to examine solid, liquid, or powder surfaces with flash illumination even though the surface is much hotter than the surface of the sun.

A number of simple, high-speed, photographic systems depend upon shadowgraphs—shadow-like images—filmed with a light source, field lens and a simple camera. Their great advantage is that they are quite economical with the available light. One of the earliest forms of such a really high-speed camera is the Cranz-Schardin system (see margin). In this system the light sources need only be quite small so they are usually sparks, which give submicro-second flashes.

Shadowgraphs can also be taken using an x-ray source. This is the only way of using x-rays for high-speed photography because

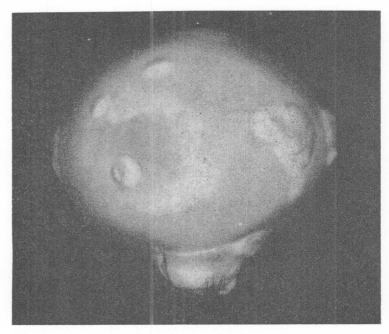

Fig. 3-64. In an unusually early state of ugliness, this nuclear device bursting on a tower was captured at 200,000 frames/sec by a rotating mirror framing camera. One frame in sequence of 140. (Courtesy K. Coleman)

there is no chance of focusing the radiation if it has any real penetrating power. The effective size of the source needs to be quite small and should preferably be less than 1 mm square. Fast shuttering of x-rays is very difficult so the exposure time has to be defined completely by the characteristics of the source.

Fairly low-energy x-rays can be obtained by a simple extension of known vacuum-tube methods, electrons from a heated filament bombarding a heavy metal target. These energies, up to 100 keV, are too low to penetrate very thick ($>\frac{1}{10}$ in.) bodies sufficiently, and the last few years have seen the laboratory development and exploitation of fast x-ray tubes up to 3 MeV. These are pulsed electrically, producing x-ray flashes of 0.5 to 2 microseconds. There are also commercial tubes capable of giving unit density on film, with an exposure time of 0.2 μsec even after penetrating 150 mm of aluminum. These cost about $20–30 thousand for a system.

Blinking a camera eye

While controlling the light source is one way of time-sampling in a camera system, you can also shutter the light flux at the camera itself. The closed-open-closed mechanical shutter, familiar to anyone who has handled an ordinary camera, interposes an opaque body or deflects a mirror positioned in the light path.

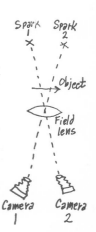

A very fast shutter must be of extremely light parts making very small movements. The fastest commercial mechanical shutter, the Japanese Optiper HS Citizen, covers a 4.5 mm diameter in 300 μsec. At higher speeds, moving-part shutters are actuated either by explosive charges or by magnetic actions triggered by capacitor discharge.

Even faster obscuration is attained by an exploding wire shutter. As thin wires are vaporized by discharging a capacitor through them, a thin metal film is explosively deposited on one or more optical surfaces in about 30 μsec. Open-closed devices like this are called capping shutters and are required with flash tubes, which nearly always emit a low level of light for long periods after the main flash.

Other types of capping shutters include a shatter shutter which, in its simplest form, is a 30 mm disk of optical glass between two windows in a steel box. A small detonator on the rim of the disk shatters it in about ten microseconds, leaving it effectively opaque much like a lump of sugar in appearance.

A large number of high-speed photographic groups use the scatter shutter, a small capsule of petroleum jelly mixed with lampblack. It is burst by an exploding wire or charge and splatters an opaque cover over a 30 mm diameter in 50 microseconds. The emission from this type of shutter can be an embarrassment to owners of adjacent instruments.

A number of nonmechanical capping shutters depend on various optical phenomena under electronic control—hence the term "electro-optical" shutters. The most common of these is the Kerr cell.

The Kerr effect is the bi-refringence produced by an electric field in a dielectric which changes the polarization state of the light going through it. Drawbacks of the Kerr cell shutter are that its polarizers absorb 80% of the light and a fairly high-voltage pulse (15–40 kV) is required unless the plates are very close together. Exposure times are 5–10 nsec.

Special requirements, in explosive research, for example, have led to the development of multishot, fully engineered Kerr cell cameras. A great advantage of the electronic shutter is that the sequence of firing and the exposure times can be preset. A light trigger, in the form of a photomultiplier and differentiating circuit, can start the sequence as soon as the light level is sufficient for photography.

The Faraday cell provides a shuttering effect derived from a rotation of the polarization plane of light passing through a liquid, solid, or gas through which a magnetic field is passing. It is simpler to make than a Kerr cell; it only requires a coil and a rod of very dense glass, but the necessary high-current pulses through this coil limit the speed of operation to about 1 μsec.

Framing cameras

It is difficult to record in density and the two space dimensions with sufficient sharpness and tonal range to completely satisfy the eye at picture-taking rates greater than 10^6 pictures per second. The most successful cameras form a stationary image of the event at the surface of a rotating mirror. The rotation of the mirror sweeps the light from this image over a sequence of lenses, each focused on its own part of the film, forming a sequence of pictures along the entire film.

However, the rotating mirror is inertial and cannot be accelerated instantaneously, making it hard to synchronize with the event as required in some experiments. To solve the problem "continuous access" cameras have been built. These have complicated optical systems which ensure that the mirror is in a taking position at every angle of rotation; then a capping shutter can provide the required synchronization. There are usually two separate optical trains at right angles to each other, so that when the mirror has its edge toward one set of optics, it squarely faces the other set.

Scientists in the Soviet Union have developed rotating mirror cameras using a multiple-reflection approach that keeps the rotation speeds of the mirrors fairly low, presumably to avoid trouble with bearings. Despite this they have been able to achieve high framing rates by using the mirror surfaces several times, thus increasing the optical lever effect. A pair of mirrors rotates at the same speed but in opposite directions. As a result the angular velocity of each mirror can be as small as one-twentieth of the angular velocity of the optical path. As might be expected, the usuable angular field is very small with this method.

A streak of data

To increase the number of pictures that can be taken of each event involves too much duplication of equipment if single-shot cameras must be used. It would be like making movies in the way animated cartoons are made from a succession of still pictures. A solution to this problem is to open and close a Kerr cell repeatedly in front of a camera through which the film can be moved rapidly. In practice the most usual system of this type is a simple film holder in the form of a robust drum made of high-tensile strength material. This drum can be rotated by air or helium-powered turbines at a near to bursting speed, but the exposure

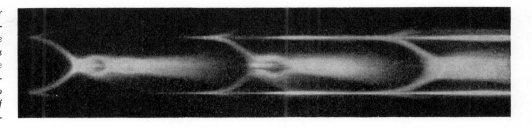

Fig. 3-65. This streak or smear of data is an electrical discharge through deuterium. The event was photographed by a streak camera with a slit image swept along the film by a rotating mirror. Time is easy to measure along the length of the strip. (Courtesy K. Coleman)

time can be sufficiently short that there is no blurring due to rapid motion of the film.

The drum of this apparatus can be used to take useful records in a rather different way. Suppose that there is some kind of symmetry to be expected in an event, say, a discharge between two plane parallel electrodes, so that we need record only one space dimension. This event can be focused on a slit mounted very near the film and drum surface. The slit is perpendicular to the direction of motion but, of course, parallel to the space dimension of the event that is to be recorded. In this way we get a record in which the measurement along the strip of film is time and the measurement across the strip is space. Such a record is called a "streak" or "smear" photograph.

An alternative means of obtaining streak photographs is to use a rotating mirror to sweep a slit image along the film. This gives much better time resolution because the mirror acts as an optical lever which bends the light through twice the angle through which the mirror itself rotates. Cameras of this type resolve better than 10 nanosec for a film record 19 in. long (or 25 μsec).

Time-resolved spectrographs

The high-speed mirrors and drums developed for use in streak or framing cameras have also been used in other scientific instruments. Plasma physics in particular needs time-resolved spectrographs so that rapid changes in spectral-line widths (from which one can deduce plasma temperatures) can be measured. Drum cameras and mirror-streak cameras are most suitable for this purpose with the addition of a dispersing system. A small region of the source is focused via a spectrograph across the slit of the camera. The record then has a spectrum across its width and time along its length. If you have a rotating mirror unit available there is a fairly cheap and quick way of doing the job. The mirror is arranged to sweep the image of the source along the slit of a laboratory spectrograph.

It has recently become important to extend the capability of these instruments right down into the vacuum ultraviolet because of the high temperatures attained in plasmas. The problems of running high-speed mirrors in vacua of 10^{-7} torr had been considerable but have been

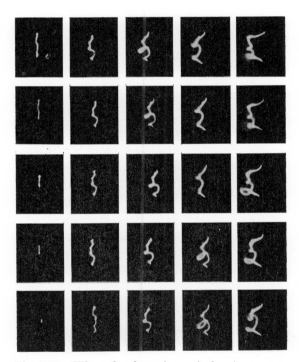

Fig. 3-66. The surface of this incandescent tungsten filament would have been impossible to record as you see it here without a laser flash to overcome the self-luminosity of the glowing wire. (Courtesy K. Coleman)

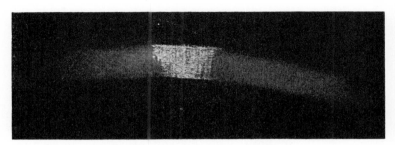

Fig. 3-67. When the damaging wriggle of an ac arc is revealed, you can channel it or even suppress it. Though wormlike in appearance, this phenomenon required 20-μsec exposures. (Courtesy K. Coleman)

surmounted. Time-resolved spectra are now obtained extending below 1000 Å.

Dissecting an image

While rotating-mirror cameras are highly complex pieces of mechanical and optical engineering, they are justified by the large amount

Fig. 3-68. A framing camera captured this axial view of thetatron discharge in deuterium. Each frame was exposed for 0.12 µsec. Zero time is at left; the first visible record of implosion is at 0.24 µsec and the last at 5.20 µsec. (Courtesy G. B. Niblett)

of information they can collect per second. However, when less information is required, and an event, such as a "wriggling arc," does not have the symmetry that would make streak photography a solution, a simple but elegant technique called image dissection can be used.

The image can be considered as a number of finite spots of light of various intensities, just like the 14,161 ink spots per square inch in the photoengraving on these pages.

A similar way to dissect an image so that it occupies less of the total frame is to put a grid over the film to cover, say, nine tenths of the area. Successive pictures could then be taken by moving the grid one tenth of the frame at a time. While this method loses 90 percent of the light, a lenticular plate—which looks like embossed rows of convex lenses—instead of the grid, will use much more of the light collected by the camera lens. The RKS.2 lenticular plate camera developed at the Leningrad Institute of Cinematographic Engineers takes 250 pictures at rates up to 10^5 frames per second with continuous access. Another lenticular plate camera by J. S. Courtney-Pratt of Bell Laboratories takes multiple-shadowgraph records by separated spark sources. These are read back by placing the film record behind the plate and illuminating from each source position. There is also a lenticular film, Kodak 5209, which can be used as a combination of lenticular plate and film.

As you can see, these methods of putting a number of successive pictures into a frame area

normally used for a single, more finely detailed, picture are ways to overcome the mechanical limits of moving film from frame to frame at such high speeds that it tears.

In some image-dissection methods there is much less scanning movement. Rather than spreading the entire image out in two dimensions over an entire frame, it is much easier to dissect the image (see Fig. 3-69) and lay the pieces out in, say, a straight line.

A bundle of glass fibres can be tightly packed at one end and a picture focused on it. At the other end of the bundle, the individual fibres can be spread out into a number of straight lines and mounted several fibre diameters apart. The picture can be unscrambled by playing back through the same system.

Image tube cameras

The greatest scope for development of new high-speed recording systems is inherent in the electronic image tube. Such image tubes have held much promise for many years, but it is only recently that a camera—the STL Image Converter—built around a tube designed especially for high-speed photography, has been available commercially. Fundamentally, an image tube consists of a light-sensitive surface which emits electrons where light falls on it, an electron lens to focus these electrons, and a phosphorescent screen onto which these electrons can fall.

Image tubes can have several favourable features. The light sensitive surfaces are 10% efficient—about a hundred times more efficient than photographic emulsions.

Furthermore, there can be a light gain—the output picture can be brighter than the input

FIBRE OPTI DISSECTO

Fig. 3-69. Each of these pictures has a different number of image elements. Each element is arbitrarily of the same density (black). The photographs were made through a fiber-optics image dissector and are all of the same scene but with increasing numbers of fibers. Notice that when there are as few as 900 elements, you can barely distinguish major features of the scene. (Courtesy H. Schardin)

picture. There can be a wavelength transformation—the (monochromatic) output picture can be different in wavelength from the input. We can shutter image tubes easily because electrons are much easier to interrupt, accelerate and deflect than light beams.

The property of light amplification is a distinct advantage of the image tube but it is important to realize that amplification will not improve signal-to-noise ratio. Poor signal-to-noise ratio at the primary receptor cannot be corrected by greater gain. Actually, the greater sensitivity of the primary receptor is the reason why image tubes are fundamentally two orders better than film cameras. With film you throw away 99.9% of the primary photons; with photoemissive tubes you throw away 90%.

The first important image tube used for high-speed photography was the Mullard ME1201. It is justifiably famous and a type still in use. This tube is focused magnetically and can be switched on and off in less than 100 nanosec. Switching is not difficult because this tube operates at a rather low voltage, 6 kV. Much greater light gain can be obtained by tube voltages around 15–20 kV, but switching becomes more of a problem when a tube operates at these higher voltages.

Soviet designers have built electronic camera tubes requiring much lower voltages to operate a deflection shutter. The electron lens is arranged so that there is a region of crossover, just like a point focus in light optics. If an aperture is put at this position the electron beam can be deflected across it. Thus electrons only reach the screen during the instant the beam crosses the aperture.

The electronic image tube can be used either as a streak camera or a framing camera. As a streak camera, the time resolution can be better than 1 nanosec and by adding a dispersing system, a prism or a grating, time-resolved spectra can be recorded at that speed. As a framing camera the only disadvantage is the fairly small number of frames that can be displayed on the screen of the tube.

New tubes now appearing in the laboratories are capable of more than five pictures in sequence with exposure times of a few nanoseconds. At first, one wonders why such fast tubes are needed since they approach the region where velocity of light must be considered. After all, light travels only 1 ft in a nanosecond. However, it is clear from records of rotating-mirror

cameras at top speed that valuable information *is* being missed between the early frames on a number of events. This is particularly true of spark discharges and also of the faster-moving pre-pinch stage of plasmas. It is also likely that there will be a whole new field for image-tube applications in the development of lasers because the exponential buildup of output from each region takes place in nanosecond times. Any information leading to a more even distribution of output over the surface would be of extreme value. This gain in efficiency can be used at lower speeds to photograph bright objects such as interferometer patterns. In this context, interference spectroscopy experiments are nearly always short of light. One experiment which we have performed is to photograph a Fabry-Perot interferometer pattern with microsecond exposures to study the detailed changes in incident radiation. This is a "black cat in the coal cellar" problem.

When recording discharges, it is immediately found that the majority of the information is contained in the ultraviolet and vacuum-ultraviolet regions of the spectrum. There have been rotating-mirror cameras specially developed or modified for this region, but there is a limit set by the short-wavelength cut-off of photographic emulsions. On the other hand, the photoemissive surfaces used in image tubes can be chosen to maintain efficiency right down into the vacuum ultraviolet, beyond even the wavelength where the last windows fail to transmit and the tube and the experiment have to be built together in one vacuum unit.

What's ahead?

What are the limits on what can be done? First of all, the number of photons per second is limited by the event, so that there is a fundamental limit on the information obtainable by our processes. Secondly, the velocity of light is finite so that ultimately there is an uncertainty about the order in which extreme events took place. Finally, and this is a point frequently missed, there is the vexatious scattering of light.

One of the biggest problems in photography is the investigation of an object surrounded by a medium which scatters for some reason. The best optical solution, so far, brings together several of the techniques of high-speed photography. The light source is a laser because it is extremely bright, it is directional, and can be of very short (nanosecond) duration. The camera is an image tube because it is sensitive and has an exposure time the same order as the light pulse.

The camera shutter is opened at exactly the correct time interval after the light pulse has been fired so that the light has had time to travel to the object and then back to the camera. This method discriminates in favour of the light scattered off the object itself and so improves the signal with respect to the noise, that is, the light scattered everywhere else. One would even be able to see better in a fog which, in a way, is the purpose of high-speed photography.

Further reading

An up-to-date review of ultrahigh-speed photography with a very full group of references appears as a "Report on Progress in Physics 1963" (Inst. of Physics and Physical Soc., 47 Belgrave Square, London S.W. 1).

Carefully indexed and well-edited conference proceedings of the biennial congresses on high-speed photography are available from various publishers: fourth congress 1958 (Hellwich, Darmstadt, Germany, 1959), fifth congress 1960 (SMPTE, 1962), sixth congress 1962 (Willink, Haarlem, Netherlands, 1963). Earlier work is described by Chesterman in *The Photographic Study of Rapid Events* (Oxford U. Press, 1951, $4.50) and by Courtney-Pratt in *Reports on Progress in Physics 1957*. An excellent and useful book covering the slower speed range is *Engineering and Scientific High-Speed Photography* by Hyzer (Macmillan, 1962, $15).

Those embroiled in ultrahigh-speed photography often discuss their work at meetings of the Royal Photographic Society, the Optical Society of America, the Society of Motion Picture and Television Engineers, the Institute of Electrical and Electronic Engineers, the Society of Photographic Scientists and Engineers, Society of Scientific Photography of Japan and the physical societies of various countries.

Journals that carry articles on various aspects of ultrahigh-speed photography include *Applied Optics, Optica Acta, Journal of Photographic Science, Journal of Scientific Instruments, The Review of Scientific Instruments, Journal of the Society of Motion Picture and Television Engineers, Proceedings and Transactions of the IEEE, Probory i Teknika Eksperimenta, Soviet Physics—JETP.*

MEASURING TEMPERATURE

by Lawrence G. Rubin *

IN BRIEF: *The trouble with any measurement is the inevitable mismatch between the messiness of reality and the purity of the abstractions used to describe it. Of this truism, thermometry is the exemplar.*

Of course, any physical property (length, electrical resistance, stiffness, etc.) that changes with temperature can make a thermometer, but that leaves you dependent on material purity and experimental details. So, long ago, Kelvin came up with a thermodynamic scale that went upward from $-273°C$ using the $PV = RT$ gas law. Then all you had to do was to keep track of P and V and find a perfect gas, and . . .

Realities led to the adoption of the International Practical Temperature Scale, a set of boiling and freezing points and three thermometers to interpolate between them. Using these standard thermometers—a resistance bulb, a thermocouple and a radiation-law device—for various ranges, absolute measurement accuracies better than $10^{-6}°C$ have been achieved (at the triple point of water), and national laboratory calibrations to within $10^{-4}°C$ can be provided (in some parts of the scale). But the practical scale is discontinuous and limited in range, and as if that weren't trouble enough, the budding pyrometrist must cope with another reality, instrumentation error, largely because, after all, everything is temperature sensitive.—R.G.N.

* Lawrence G. Rubin is now Group Leader of Instrumentation and Operations at the National Magnet Laboratory, Massachusetts Institute of Technology. When preparing this article, he was Manager of the Instrumentation Group at Raytheon Research.

■ One of J. C. Maxwell's less well-known contributions to science and engineering is a brief but elegant definition of temperature: "The temperature of a body is its thermal state considered with reference to its ability to communicate heat to other bodies." Interestingly, while this definition relates our earliest personal experiences with hot and cold objects (such as mixing bath water) to the thermodynamic view of heat as a transferable form of energy, it is unsatisfactory from a practical pyrometrist's viewpoint.

The difficulty is that, although temperature is one of the primary quantities, along with mass, length, and time, it is more subtle conceptually and much more difficult to define. Besides, temperature is an *intensive* parameter; it has the same value in a part of a system as it has in the entire system, i.e., it is independent of mass. All this has led to a multiplicity of temperature scales—thermodynamic scales, practical temperature scales (and others).

The awful truth about temperature

Any temperature measuring system must establish *both* a reference temperature and a rule for measuring the differences between the reference and any other temperatures. Early inventors of temperature scales failed to provide for interpolation between their reference points. As a result, while at least two fixed points were established to define their scales, no two thermometer-makers could have had their instruments in agreement at any but the fixed points unless they used identical thermometric materials. However, assuming the rules were obeyed, then (in principle) nearly any property of a material which changes with temperature in a well-defined way can serve as a thermometer, and a temperature scale based on the changes of this property can be defined, as a result of the zeroth law of thermodynamics shown in the margin.

To get around this dependence on the material used and the specific details of the experiment, thermodynamic temperature scales were devised.

Let's first recall that, as a consequence of the second law of thermodynamics, there is a tendency on the part of nature to become more disordered, to proceed toward a state of greater entropy. Formally, the thermodynamicists write: $dS = dQ/T$, which gives the entropy change, dS, of a system that absorbs an infinitesimal amount of heat energy dQ_R (expressed as an inexact differential) during a *reversible* process at temperature T. This leads to a second definition of temperature: It is the amount of heat energy that must be added to an object to increase its entropy by one unit.

Kelvin proposed an embodiment of the second law of thermodynamics, in which he used the Carnot cycle of a perfect, reversible heat engine taking heat Q_1 from one infinite capacity heat reservoir and putting heat Q_2 into the other. Then the temperatures, T_1 and T_2, of the two reservoirs are

$$T_1/T_2 = -Q_1/Q_2$$

In other words, the *ratio* of the temperatures of the heat reservoirs is defined as equal to the *ratio* of the heat absorbed from the two reservoirs. A thermodynamic scale can then be completely defined by establishing one fixed point, or a fixed interval.

Acting on a suggestion made by Joule, Kelvin chose his scale so that it would be simply related to the then existing centigrade scale. As a result, $T_K = t_C + 273$, where the 273 was based on the experimentally observed coefficients of expansion of various gases (using the conventional T for absolute, and t for empirical temperatures). In 1954, the thermodynamic scale was adjusted slightly by choosing the temperature of the triple point of water to be 273.16°K exactly. This temperature, the state at which solid, liquid, and vapor phases of water are in equilibrium, can be measured to within error of about 2×10^{-4} degree.

But it's not all as simple as that; we must realize that the thermodynamic concept of temperature is an idealization, based on equilibrium (remember that zeroth law) in reversible processes. Since these conditions are more the exception than the rule, the universally accepted definition of temperature does not apply completely. This difficulty is uncommon in the measurement of other quantities. However, even in an nonequilibrium condition a temperature can be assigned as long as the *microscopic* distribution of energy does not differ significantly from the equilibrium distribution at the temperature. (See Katchalsky's "Nonequilibrium Thermodynamics," page 194.)

All these peculiarities of temperature have led several practitioners of the thermometric art to identify the conceptual difficulties I mentioned at the onset, even though most of those problems are rarely encountered in practice. Illustrative is McNish's warning that "It is of limited meaning to say that one degree in the neighborhood of 0°K is equal to one degree near 273°K."

Acknowledging this, but armed with the fact that this thermodynamic scale is the same as that defined by the gas equation $PV = RT$, one can reduce Kelvin's scale to practice. In fact, at the present time, the gas thermometer is the primary instrument for realizing the thermodynamic scale—over the range where gas thermometers work.

But don't think we're limited to the gas equation for determining thermodynamic temperature. There are several thermodynamic ways to determine temperature which have nothing to do with gas thermometers. Two of them are the paramagnetic scale for very low temperatures and the Planck radiation law for high thermodynamic temperatures.

Thermo-idealities and measurement realities

Unfortunately for gas thermometry, the ideal gas is just an abstraction. To correct for differences between real and ideal gases, we use the empirical fact that, at constant tempera-

Zeroth Law of Thermodynamics

If two bodies are each in thermal equilibrium with a third, they are in thermal equilibrium with each other

Table 1. FIXED TEMPERATURE POINTS ON FOUR COMMON SCALES

Significant points	Kelvin scale (°K)	Centigrade scale (°C)	Fahrenheit scale (°F)	Rankine scale (°R)	
Absolute zero	0	−273.16	−459.72	0	
Helium boils	4.2	−269	−452	7.6	
Hydrogen boils	20	−253	−423	36	⎫ NBS Provisional scale (platinum RT)
Nitrogen boils	77	−196	−321	139	⎬
Oxygen boils	*90*	*−183*	*−297*	*162*	⎭
Carbon dioxide sublimes	195	−78	−109	350	⎫
Triple point of water	*273.16*	*0.0100*	*32.018*	*491.71*	⎬ Pt resistance thermometer
Zinc melts	*693*	*420*	*787*	*1246*	
Sulfur boils	718	445	832	1291	⎭
Antimony melts	*903*	*630*	*1166*	*1625*	⎫
Silver melts	1234	961	1762	2221	⎬ Pt-Pt + Rh thermocouple
Gold melts	*1336*	*1063*	*1945*	*2404*	⎭
Platinum melts	2047	1774	3224	3683	⎫
Tungsten melts	3643	3370	6098	6558	⎬ Planck's radiation law
Tungsten boils	6173	5900	10,652	11,112	⎭

ture, every real gas exhibits the ideal constant pressure-volume product as the limit of zero pressure is approached. Although a great deal of effort has gone into this work, gas thermometry remains difficult and tedious, generally unsuited to practical needs.

And so, in 1927, the International Practical Temperature Scale (IPTS) was instituted (with important revisions in 1948 and minor ones since then) to represent the thermodynamic scale as closely as possible in a practical way. The IPTS is defined by fixed points (italic in Table 1) and rules for interpolation between them and extrapolation beyond. At one point, the triple point of water, both scales are in exact agreement. All these points were assigned on the basis of gas thermometer measurements performed as accurately as the state of the art permitted. As you see from Figs. 3-70 and 3-75, interpolation between the fixed points

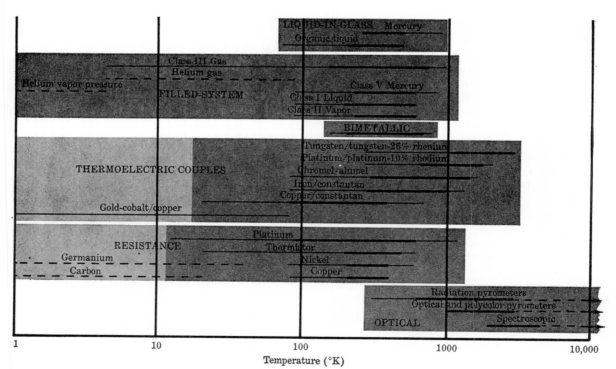

Fig. 3-70. Not shown, on this chart of common thermometers in their applicable ranges, are many of the more exotic devices—oscillating crystals that change their resonance with temperature, pyroelectric crystals that respond to thermal stress by producing voltages across their faces, paramagnetic salts for cryogenic use, temperature-sensitive transistors that act as their own amplifiers, and rattlesnake infrared detectors. These thermometers are ranged vertically in order of their popularity (number of installations).

is arrived at by different methods for different ranges. I'll go into more detail about these methods later.

Although the IPTS is actually nothing more than a practical standard *empirical* temperature scale, its advantages have been very important indeed: Now any competent laboratory can calibrate a thermometer in terms of the fixed point standards—without reference to any other laboratory, but with confidence that the results will be consistent and in agreement with thermometers calibrated by all other competent laboratories. This is the most basic requirement for any measurement system.

No upper limit is assigned to the IPTS, but the present lower limit is 90.19°K. By calibrating a series of platinum resistance thermometers, PRT's (the change in resistance of platinum with temperature is a well-established and stable standard) against a helium gas thermometer, the National Bureau of Standards has established a "provisional" scale between 11° and 90°K. Continuing research is aimed at defining the scale in this region in terms of

fixed points for pure materials and at increasing measurement precision, particularly below 20°K. Semiconductor RT's, because of their intrinsically high sensitivity, show great promise here. (The right-hand side of Fig. 3-71 shows how they compare with metals like platinum and tungsten.) Although their reputation for reliability and precision is not as great as that of the PRT, they are fast closing the gap.

Resistors as thermometers

The most accurate of all temperature-sensing devices—permitting measurements to be made within an accuracy of about 10^{-4}°C at room temperature—is based on the fact that the electrical resistance of any material depends on its temperature. Suitably chosen and prepared materials will vary in a well-defined and calibratable manner with temperature. The resistance is usually measured with various bridge or with potentiometric techniques (which employ constant current sources and precision potentiometers).

Of all metals, platinum is the most appro-

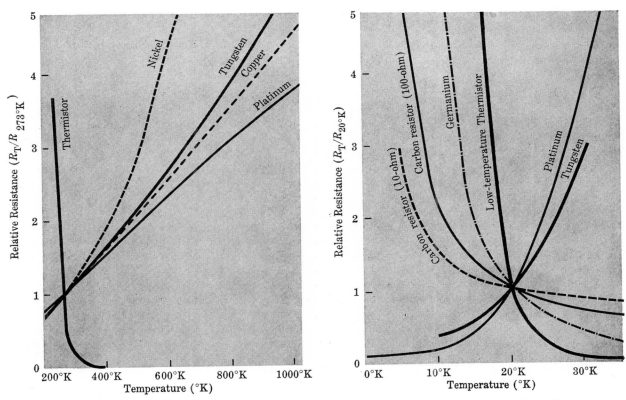

Fig. 3-71. Copper, and more commonly, nickel wire are widely used industrially; Cu provides linear output over a wide range, while Ni has comparatively high sensitivity. They both provide an inexpensive means of measuring temperature over the range from about −100°C to +200°C. As high as 1200°C (in protective atmospheres) the refractory metals are used. For high sensitivity resistance thermometry, semiconductors are the thing—particularly at low temperatures, where their negative R-t coefficients show to advantage against the decreasing sensitivities of metals.

$$R_t = R_0 + \delta\left(\frac{t}{100}-1\right)\frac{t}{100} + \beta\left(\frac{t}{100}-1\right)\left(\frac{t}{100}\right)^3$$

$$t = \frac{R_t - R_0}{\alpha R_0}$$

**Callendar–
Van Dusen
equation**

$R_t = $ resistance @ t

$R_0 = $ resistance @ $0°C$

$\alpha, \beta, \delta = $ constants

$\beta = 0$ @ $t \geq 0°C$

priate because it is commercially available in pure form, is easily worked, and is relatively indifferent to environmental conditions. In a pure, fully annealed and strain-free state, it has an especially stable and reproducible relationship between resistance and temperature. Perhaps the best reason for platinum's suitability is the simplicity of this R-t relationship, the Callendar-Van Dusen equation shown in the margin, which holds over a very wide temperature range. Once an individual platinum-resistance thermometer has been calibrated at the oxygen, ice, steam, and sulfur points, it can then be counted on at *any* temperature between the oxygen and sulfur points by determining the R_t/R_0 ratio.

In fact, this thermometer is used as *the* realization of the IPTS from 90° to 903°K. In that exalted realm, only the most highly pedigreed PRT's are permitted to roam. Such units begin with ultrapure platinum, drawn into wire with utmost care to maintain its purity. The wire is then formed into a coil, which is supported so as to be relatively immune to mechanical effects caused by differential thermal expansion and free from contact with any materials which might contaminate the temperature-sensing element.

It is then mounted in a helium-filled, glass-sealed platinum tube along with pairs of platinum current and potential leads. The construction is such as to minimize time lag and the heating effect of the measuring circuit. Of course, for those whose requirements allow for lower precision, PRT's are also made commercially in various convenient and rugged (and less expensive) forms. But The National Bureau of Standards provides calibration services only for the high precision units; such an accurate PRT setup may run to several thousand dollars.

Another group of resistance thermometers utilizes elements made of semiconducting materials. Included in this category are thermistors, carbon resistors, and doped germanium units, almost all of which have a characteristic resistance decrease with increasing temperatures. (See right-hand side of Fig. 3-71.)

All very nice—but

Thermistors (a contraction for Thermally Sensitive Resistors) are made of mixtures, mainly of the oxides, but also of sulfides and silicates of various metals. They are as much as ten times as sensitive as metal RT's—although their R-t relationship is far less linear, exponential in fact—and come in pin-head sizes with rapid thermal response (1-millisec time constants). However, such very small

thermal mass can lead to problems; if the measuring current is not strictly limited, I^2R heating of any resistance by the measuring current can occur.

In a small resistance element, which cannot readily conduct away its self-generated heat, the problem can be very severe. Large thermometer elements—resistors, thermistors (or, for that matter, any other contacting thermometer system) present the budding pyrometrist with other discrepancies between the meter reading relayed to him by his system and the temperature of what he is trying to measure.

Not the least of these is a consequence of the fact that no temperature-measuring device can do more than transmit information as to the thermal state which it *itself* attains, what it "sees." (And, it's *not* considered good practice, nor are the necessary data usually available, to correct a poor installation by the use of computed correction factors.) To minimize this problem, an obvious precaution is to provide good thermal contact between the sensitive portion of the sensor and the subject. But there are times when the thermometer may perturb the conditions of the subject—for instance, heavy gage lead wires or a thick protection tube may conduct heat toward or away from a small specimen, or may not allow the sensor to respond fast enough to follow the fluctuations of a small specimen.

Of course, neither of the latter two precautions is vital when dealing with systems of large thermal mass, such as production kilns, rolling mills, or steam boilers, but in such places we may meet with other problems—such as the effects of long leads in the circuit.

Most relatively inexpensive thermistor devices require no corrections for lead-wire resistance because of their (usually) high resistances, and most have a large energy output per degree temperature change as a favorable result of their large R-t coefficient. But in order to cover a wide temperature range, several thermistors usually are required, because a high sensitivity and nonlinear R-t characteristic will cause an individual unit to swing from an inconveniently low to an inconveniently high resistance if the temperature span is too great.

Most thermistors are used between $-100°C$ and $+300°C$, but special compositions have greatly extended this range—as high as $1600°C$ and as low as $4.2°K$. Their reputation for calibration stability is poor; while it is true they cannot compare in this respect with a PRT, they can be quite stable when properly aged before use, and particularly when their use is limited to temperatures between $-50°$ and $+100°C$.

The ordinary carbon-composition radio resistor, in sizes from one-tenth to one watt, and room temperature resistance values of about 2 to 150 ohms, exhibits a large increase of resistance from about 20°K downward. Below 20°K, a semi-empirical equation (margin) developed by Clement applies to them. When the constants are determined by calibration, reproducibilities of about 0.2% are feasible from 1° to 20°K. At the He (4.2°K) and H_2 (20°K) points, the repeatability is 0.1%, even with warming and recooling cycles between observations.

About the only drawbacks of carbon resistors are a loss of sensitivity above 20°K and the adverse influence of stray radio fields in applications much below 4.2°K. In general, however, their characteristics, taken with their small size (the $\frac{1}{10}$ W variety is $\frac{1}{8}$ in. long and $\frac{1}{16}$ in. in diameter) and extremely low cost (about 10¢), make carbon RT's very handy for cryogenic workers.

Sometimes, particularly below 20°K, and even more so below 4.2°K, reproducibilities of 0.1% are insufficient to provide practical secondary standards to supplement thermodynamic methods. To make possible the future extension of the IPTS to very low temperatures, both arsenic- and gallium-doped germanium elements have been fabricated with the necessary precautions to avoid mechanical strain, contamination, and the effects of stray resistance. At this writing, various labs have reported reproducibilities ranging from 0.0001° to 0.001° at 4°K. But I should point out that the 0.0001° figure approaches the state-of-the-art limits of measurement.

No simple formula is known for the *R-t* relationship of these units, so interpolation is somewhat complex. However, the thermometer apparently requires only a single calibration; this, together with the availability of high-speed computers for reducing the measurement data, serves to minimize this problem.

Present commercial units cover the range from about 1° to 40°K. While they undoubtedly will be improved, they already offer solid performance as either supplements to, or replacements for, other cryogenic thermometers. These RT's, made of semiconductors and metallic oxides, etc., are especially valuable at low temperatures where the low resistances of metals, which usually result in feeble signals, would get them into other troubles.

Not the least of these problems is the contribution of thermoelectric voltages generated where leads and contacts meet. Experience, dating back since Seebeck's discovery of thermoelectricity in 1821, has shown that, whenever two junctions formed of two dissimilar homogeneous materials are held at different temperatures, a voltage is generated which depends on the temperatures and on the materials involved.

The Seebeck effect is actually the algebraic sum of the Peltier and Thomson effects. The Peltier effect is the change in heat content of a circuit when a current flows across its junctions; the Thomson effect is the change in the heat content of a single metallic conductor when a current flows along it through a temperature gradient. Seebeck emf's, along with most other stray voltages, are, of course, additive and independent of the signal strengths of temperature (and other) sensors. But this bane of resistance thermometry is the basis of thermoelectric thermometry.

Thermoelectric-ometry

Since the Seebeck emf is measurable either by a millivoltmeter or potentiometer, it provides a means of thermometry. A reference temperature such as an ice bath is established for one of the junctions, the other junction is exposed to some unknown temperature, and the emf that is developed will vary directly and only with the unknown temperature.

In order to take advantage of this thermoelectric thermometer, many empirical relationships and many advanced materials have been developed. This has been difficult because of ignorance of some of the fundamentals, including the mechanism by which heat is converted into electrical energy and how emf varies with temperature. However, it is only fair to point out that numerous experimental and theoretical studies have made considerable gains in determining the origin of the emf's in a thermoelectric circuit and their interrelationships.

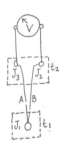

In the circuit in the margin, the thermocouple "measuring junction" J_1 is connected to a meter M with lead wires C. Two junctions J_2 and J_3 are formed where the leads attach to the wires that form J_1. If J_1, J_2, and J_3 are all at the same temperature, there will be no emf at M; if all three are at different temperatures, the total emf is the algebraic sum of the emf's developed at each junction. In the most common case, J_2 and J_3 will be at the same (reference) temperature t_2, and the emf at M is proportional to $t_2 - t_1$. The important point here is that the emf is independent of the presence of the third material C as long as J_2 and J_3 are at the same temperature.

Seebeck's original circuit used wires of copper and antimony. Of all the practically limitless combinations of materials available to us since then, relatively few have been put to use. These have been chosen on the basis of their thermoelectric output, stability, reproducibility, homogeneity, electrical conductivity, immunity to various chemical environments, melting points, ease of fabrication, and their cost. The principal classes of thermocouples in current use are charted in Fig. 3-72. (Also included for comparison is a 'couple of pyrolytic graphite against one of its alloys.)

For any thermocouple (TC), one can always generate an emf versus temperature as accurately as desired, depending on how carefully the calibration is performed. However, for the common TC's, the usual procedure is to use reference tables of emf vs. *t*, which represent the *nominal* characteristics of particular types. Thus, even if you've taken all the necessary precautions to eliminate reading errors, stray emf's, etc., you are still limited by the errors of the reference table. The total errors are functions of the type of TC, its wire gage, tempera-

ture range and environments and range from ¼ to several percent.

With accuracy in mind, let us once again think of the marginal on p. 391. Sometimes copper wire leads are used to connect M to junctions J_2 and J_3. As I said, this is all right no matter what A and B are if J_2 and J_3 are held at a constant reference temperature by an ice bath, triple point cell, thermoelectric cooler, or controlled oven, etc.

In industry, it's customary to employ cold junction compensation to compensate for changes of the reference junction. In this case, the TC wire should extend from J_1 directly to M, where possible. Sometimes, the expense entailed by long runs is excessive, so lower-cost extension wires may be used. Special compositions are available to match some TC's, at the probable temperatures of their junctions to the

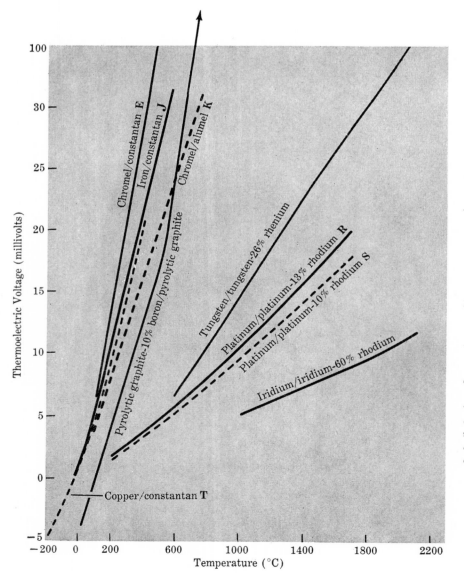

Fig. 3-72. The bold letters are Instrument Society of America designations for thermocouple classes. Of all these common thermocouples, the type S (platinum-platinum +10% rhodium) thermocouple is the most important for scientific use. Often called the Le-Chatelier 'couple, it is used for defining the ITPS from 630.5°C to 1063°C. The interpolation equation, with a reference junction at 0°C, gives the output voltage, $E = a + bt + ct^2$. The constants are determined by calibration at the freezing points of gold and silver and by a platinum resistance thermometer reading at 630.5°C.

Pyrographite thermocouples really do have that enormous output. Pyrographite against its alloys can produce tenths of a volt at a couple thousand degrees.

extension leads; other TC materials are used as their own extension wires, although a change in wire gage may be appropriate.

TC circuits aren't limited to this simple arrangement; differential measurements can be made with a circuit having junctions at t_1 and t_3: $E_{bb} \propto \Delta t = t_3 - t_1$. Or N similar TC's may be connected in series to form a thermopile with a sensitivity N times that of a single thermocouple. If N thermocouples are connected in parallel with the proper precautions, the emf generated will correspond to the *mean* of the temperatures of all the junctions. All sorts of other arrangements are possible, as you would expect.

As with any transducer, many inobvious errors in the final measurement can result from poor instrumentation practices. Thermocouples, particularly when used with amplifiers, indicators, recorders, and controllers, are prone to ground-loop and leakage errors, problems with stray fields, etc. When *emf* is measured with current-measuring devices, such as galvanometers (as is usual in low-cost installations), the indications vary with meter errors and with resistances in the circuit—which may change from time to time.

These difficulties, along with mechanical and thermal abuse, are almost always enhanced at high temperatures. But for all these problems, if proper care and good indicators are used in association with stable, well-made TC's, the success attained depends almost entirely upon the ability of the observer to bring the thermocouple junctions to the specimen temperatures. This apparently simple requirement can be troublesome enough, particularly at high temperatures, to make contacting-thermometers impractical, and to lead us to. . . .

Radiation pyrometry of all kinds

Since all substances at temperatures above absolute zero radiate electromagnetic energy as a result of the atomic and molecular agitation, we have radiation pyrometry. The power emitted per unit area is $W = \epsilon\sigma T^4$ watts/cm² where σ, the Stefan-Boltzmann constant is in watts/cm²/°K⁴, and T is in degrees K. The dimensionless factor ϵ, called the total emissivity or emittance, is defined as the ratio of the radiation of the surface in question to what would be emitted by an otherwise comparable blackbody, i.e., another idealization, one that absorbs all incident radiation. (Some substances such as soot and platinum black do approach $\epsilon = 1$ very closely.) Both total intensity and spectral distribution of the emitted energy depend only on the temperature of a blackbody in the manner postulated by Planck in 1900; this forms the

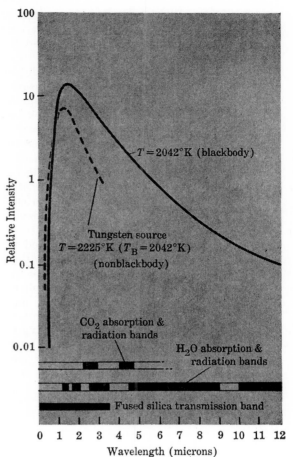

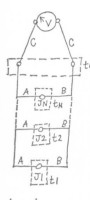

Averaging thermocouple circuit

Fig. 3-73. *Most radiation pyrometry depends on the spectral distribution of the radiation. The solid curve plots radiation of a blackbody (for which $\epsilon = 1$) at $T = 2042°$ K. A non-blackbody tungsten source has a different curve because its $\epsilon = F(\lambda) < 1$. The blackbody at temperature $T_B = 2042°$ K, has the same radiant output (point P) at 6500 Å as does the tungsten source at temperature $T = 2225°$ K. Shown below are typical absorption bands of materials which may interfere with the accuracy of pyrometry.*

basis of the thermodynamic scale at high temperatures.

By measuring its radiant power over some very large spectral range, it is possible to measure the temperature of a source. This may be done by focusing the emitted radiation on an absorbing area, called the receiver. The temperature of the receiver rises until its own rate of heat loss is equal to its rate of absorption. This equilibrium temperature is seldom more than 30° to 40°C higher than the ambient, even for a very intense source. The significant fact is that, after equilibrium has been reached, a change in T of the source will change the t of the receiver, albeit by much less, through the medium of the emitted radiation. This so-called total, or panchromatic, radiation pyrometry is

one form of Planck's Eq:

$$E(\lambda_1 T)\,\Delta\lambda = e(\lambda_1 T)\,C_1\lambda^{-5}[\exp(C_2/\lambda T)-1]$$

the simplest and perhaps the easiest radiation pyrometry to use and understand, but it isn't the basis of the IPTS because it is also the least accurate.

There are several schemes for transducing the temperature information of the receiver. Most commonly, a sensitive thermocouple or thermopile is connected to a small blackened metallic disk acting as a receiver. The receiver can also be a strip of blackened platinum or semiconductor resistor forming one arm of a resistance bridge; then it's called a bolometer. There are occasions when the receiver is a bimetallic spiral actuating a pointer, or a capsule, called a Golay cell, in which gas pressure changes with temperature.

In more general terms, there is no need for the source radiation to be translated into thermal changes at all. Photosensitive detectors (e.g., photoconductors and photomultipliers) will respond directly to radiation. They have much shorter response times and potentially higher sensitivities (but sensitivity varies widely with wavelength). In fact, the bandwidths of photosensitive detectors vary con-

siderably and exhibit a wide variety of spectral peaks. At any rate, thermoelectric radiation detectors are the most widely used in their class and have the advantages of ruggedness, relative immunity from damage by high ambient temperature and their sensitivity over wide wavelength ranges.

There are problems associated with the design of thermoelectric radiation pyrometers, but many of these have been alleviated. Evacuated interiors to reduce convection losses, fine support and lead wires to reduce conduction losses, electrical or thermal compensation for variations in ambient temperature, and proper optical design to match receiver to the source are some of these. There remains selective absorption of radiation by the atmosphere, windows, lenses, mirrors, and by the receiver itself. For measuring the low temperatures, lens and window materials must be restricted to those that transmit the long wavelengths where most of the power is concentrated.

Much can be accounted for in calibration. However, disturbances in the radiation path, such as smoke, haze, and soot, and emissivity

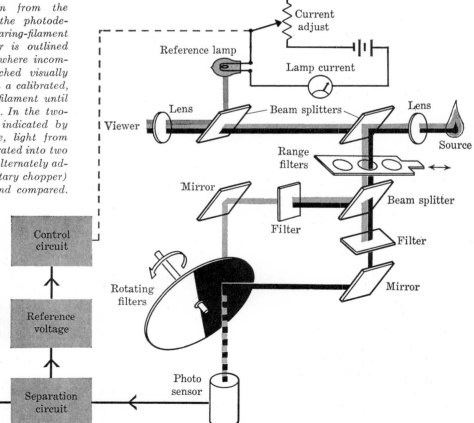

Fig. 3-74. This nonexistent all-in-one pyrometer becomes a total radiation device if all the filters are removed and all incident radiation from the source falls on the photodetector. A disappearing-filament optical pyrometer is outlined in the top path, where incoming light is matched visually against light from a calibrated, adjustable lamp filament until the images merge. In the two-color pyrometer, indicated by the lower scheme, light from the source is separated into two bands, which are alternately admitted (by the rotary chopper) to the detector and compared.

$$\frac{N(t)}{N(Au)} = \frac{\int_0^\infty [E_\lambda]_t V_\lambda \, d\lambda}{\int_0^\infty [E_\lambda]_{Au} V_\lambda \, d\lambda}$$

$N(t) =$
spectral
radiance

$= 1063°C$

$273.15°C$

$1.438 \, cm \, deg$

variations of the source are basic limitations that remain to plague this instrument. Nevertheless, for automatic control applications, where an economical means of operator-free, continuous measurement at a distance is required, the total radiation pyrometer is commonly used.

Absolute measurements of radiant power are hard to make precisely, but the ratio of two radiant powers, where one is a standard known temperature, serves to define a scale. That's how the IPTS was established beyond the gold point. The defining equation is given in the margin in terms of a quantity $N(t)$, the spectral radiance, which is basically just E, taken in a particular direction, and per unit solid angle.

That equation has meaning only when it is decided just what wavelength, λ, is to be used. The decision will depend on the measuring device, usually the disappearing filament optical pyrometer, in which the unknown source is imaged onto a reference source and both observed through a microscope. The reference, the filament of a small vacuum lamp, can be made to "disappear" into the unknown source by varying the lamp current. Filters are used to reduce the apparent source t if it is higher than the maximum obtainable lamp temperature (about 1500°C). If the instrument has been calibrated, and if the source is a blackbody, matching the brightness by varying the lamp current will give a temperature determination on the IPTS.

A fairly well-defined "effective wavelength" is achieved in the optical pyrometer by a filter, usually red, nominally centered at 6500 Angstroms. Red is used because it works at lower temperatures, because stable sharp-cutoff filters are available in this range, and because higher observer relative luminous efficiencies are available there. The observer or, more particularly, his eye sets the fundamental limitation in the precision attainable in visual optical pyrometry. Within its range (4000–7000 Å), the normal eye can match brightness well enough to reduce the uncertainty to as little as 0.2°C at 1400°C, 1.6°C at 800°C, and 1 to 1.5°C at 2900°C.

So far, we've considered only blackbody sources. This is not the limitation it might seem, since for many purposes, blackbody conditions can be simulated well enough by simply drilling a small hole into a solid or by inserting a small cavity in a molten substance. However, there are still many cases where measurements of nonblackbodies must be made. If you used an optical (sometimes called a brightness) pyrometer in such a case, you would get a "brightness temperature" T_b of the nonblackbody, specified at 6500 Å. By definition, this means

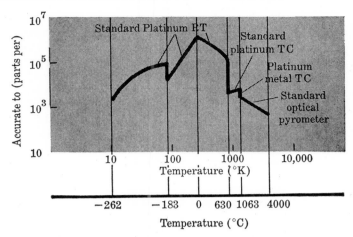

Fig. 3-75. The accuracies in reproducing various parts of the international temperature scale at NBS (1955 data here) point up the scale discontinuities at fixed reference points and the errors assigned to each of the three standard thermometers. Note the high accuracy shown for the resistance thermometer at the triple point of water—attributable to the accuracy with which that point can be reproduced. (Courtesy R. Neswald)

the temperature at which a blackbody will emit the same amount of radiation—over a small $\Delta\lambda$ around 6500 Å—as does the nonblackbody at *true* temperature T. Since, at any T, nonblackbodies always radiate less energy than blackbodies, the T_b of an object is always less than true T, and if you know its emissivity, you can correct for it. (See Fig. 3-73.)

Another practical method utilizes color, or polychromatic, pyrometry. The color temperature of a nonblackbody may be defined as the temperature to which it is necessary to heat a blackbody so that its radiation will match the visual color of the nonblackbody. In particular, if we choose two wavelengths (colors), $\lambda_2 > \lambda_1$, in the 4000 to 7000 Å range, we can measure a T_C by taking the ratio of powers radiated from an incandescent body at the wavelengths λ_1 and λ_2.

For most common materials, ϵ is a slowly decreasing function of λ in the visual spectrum. For those materials, T_C is slightly higher than T; for example, the T_C of tungsten is 8°–24°C higher than its T in the range 800° to 1500°C. In the same range, the monochromatic (brightness) pyrometer gives answers from 41° to as much as 123° *lower* than T. However, for some important materials, $T > T_C$. There are a number of both laboratory and commercial models of two-color or ratio pyrometers; all introduce some complexity to gain direct (often linear) read-out and high sensitivity. Some instruments use three or more colors, and require measuring multiple ratios. This scheme, along with shifting the λ's to other regions (such as to the infrared), will often reduce errors caused by anomalous variations of ϵ with λ.

Fevers, baths, and calorimeters

As a group, the glass-stem, vapor-pressure, liquid- and gas-filled, and bimetal thermometers hanging on walls and dipped in pots all over the world probably account for the majority of temperature measurement installations. The most popular is the liquid-in-glass thermometer, using mercury, toluene, alcohol, or pentane (which has been used down to $-196°C$). Some read correctly only when the bulb and entire liquid-filled stem are exposed to the environment to be measured; others require only the bulb and a short length of the stem to be immersed. Because the partial-immersion types are often used with greatly different stem and bulb temperature, they are not as accurate as total-immersion types. Granting that some units are more expensive and complex than others of their class, it is safe to say that liquid-in-glass thermometers owe their popularity to low cost, simplicity, high reliability, and long life (assuming accidental breakage to be the exception rather than the rule).

Bimetal thermometers, using the differential expansion of two metals, have many advantages over liquid-in-glass thermometers. They are available in both short- and long-temperature spans; they usually can be over-ranged without harm (if the elastic limits of the materials aren't exceeded); they will retain their accuracy (as high as $\frac{1}{2}\%$) indefinitely if handled with reasonable care and are easy to reset if calibration is necessary; they are easier to read, less subject to breakage and do not require stem corrections. Some go as high as $500°C$, but below $-100°C$ their sensitivity drops off rapidly because the expansion coefficients of metals approach each other.

Filled-system thermometers, using the temperature-induced expansion of liquids or gases, all make common use of a bulb, a connecting capillary and a mechanism (usually a bourdon tube) which responds to changes in pressure or volume of the filling fluid. The bourdon is linked to a pointer or pen to provide readout on a suitable scale or chart. Some incorporate a compensating capillary and bourdon tube to correct for ambient changes along the capillary and at the case.

Other ways to sound out the temperature

The velocity of sound in a perfect gas is related to the Kelvin T by $v^2 = \gamma RT/M$ where γ is the specific heat ratio, R the universal gas constant, and M the molecular weight of the gas. In a typical experiment, two transducers are spaced at a known distance, with circuitry for continuously measuring the transit time of an ultrasonic wave generated by one transducer and received by the other. This reduces temperature measurement to time measurement, a great advantage because of the accuracy with which time can be determined.

In addition, because the gas itself is the thermometer element, very rapid temperature changes can be followed, and errors normally introduced by thermometer elements (heat leaks, thermal lags, etc.) are absent. Of course, there are the attendant difficulties: departure of the gas from ideality; the necessity for accurately determining γ; the dependence of v on pressure, which must therefore be corrected; and the fact that instead of measuring point temperature, an *average* temperature over the path is being determined. Temperature-dependent sonic velocity effects are also exploited in liquids and solids, and in fact have been used to measure the temperatures of bodies of water (to within $0.1°C$) and to make temperature-sensitive crystal oscillators that detect changes as small as $10^{-5}°C$.

Just as a mechanical stress applied to a piezoelectric material will produce a measureable electric charge, so will a thermal stress applied to a pyroelectric material. This pyroelectric effect has been utilized in thermometers that are sensitive to *microdegree* temperature changes. Materials of high pyroelectric coefficients have been studied from $4.2°K$ (colemanite) to more than $1400°C$ (barium zirconium metaniobate).

Ranging from the magnetic practical temperature scale (where adiabatic demagnetization effects in certain salts define temperatures as low as $0.005°K$) to the pseudotemperatures of "thermal" plasmas and beyond (there is a beyond, in the cores of some stars), there are as many possible thermometers as temperature-sensitive effects (e.g., see Goldanskii's "Using the Mossbauer Effect," page 31) and as many thermometric materials as those that exhibit these effects (even electromagnetic blackbody radiation has a significant thermal capacity around $10^7°K$). As numerous as are the methods of thermometry, there are almost as many criteria to be applied in selecting one of these methods for a particular application. One may have to consider accuracy, stability, sensitivity, reproducibility, speed of response, reliability, life, linearity of output, temperature range of usability, ease of reading, simplicity, safety, size and weight, adaptability to automatic recording and/or control, first cost and maintenance cost, etc. Perhaps in no other branch of measurement technology is it more appropriate that we "let the user beware."

Further reading

To see how simple and straightforward the notions of temperature can be when presented on a classroom basis by a thermodynamicist, glance back over your college thermo text, or see Zemansky's *Heat and Thermodynamics* (McGraw-Hill, 1957, $9.50—25¢ extra for the answers). Then compare that with the three-volume set *Temperature, Its Measurement and Control in Science and Industry*, to see how the thermometrists view the subject. Vols. 1 and 2 went out of print about the middle of 1963, but all 2600-odd pages of Vol. 3 attest to the problems and the activities in this field. Of particular relevance to our article are Part 1, *Basic Concepts, Standards and Methods*, edited by Brickwedde, and Part 2, *Applied Methods and Instruments* (Reinhold, 1962, $27.50 and $29.50, respectively).

The budding pyrometrist mentioned in the article would profit well by ready access to a copy of *Temperature Measurement in Engineering* by Baker and others (Wiley, Vol. 1, 1953, $4.95; Vol. 2, 1961, $13.50) and he should also see Lion's *Instrumentation in Scientific Research* (McGraw-Hill, 1959, $10.75). If his problems involve heat conduction or temperature transients, he should find Schneider's *Temperature Response Charts* (Wiley, 1963, $7.50) of considerable help, while if his work is in the range of radiation pyrometry, he should see Harrison's *Radiation Pyrometry and Its Underlying Principles of Heat Transfer* (Wiley, 1960, $12). There's also a wealth of valuable material available from the manufacturers of measurement apparatus; an excellent example is *Thermoelectric Thermometry* by Dike (Leeds & Northrup Co., Philadelphia, Pa.).

If your interest is still general, you'll find Benedict's "Temperature and Its Measurement" and McNish's "Fundamentals of Measurement" useful. (See *Electrotechnology's* Science & Engineering Series, July 1963 and May 1963, respectively.) Also check the 700 references listed in the Sept. 1963 Supplement to NBS Monograph 27, *Bibliography of Temperature Measurement*.

NONTRADITIONAL MACHINING

by Ford Park *

IN BRIEF: *Traditionally, metals and alloys have been machined by the shearing action of a sharp tool forced against the work. Yet in recent years, work materials have become almost as strong and hard as the cutting tools. Machining thus takes longer, tools wear out faster, and costs begin to climb. Since the early 1950's the search has been on for metal removal techniques that are independent of workpiece strength. We now have, in various stages of development and use, machining methods that will handle the most intractable of materials. They fall into four categories—thermal, chemical, electrochemical, and impactive—according to the means they use to transfer the needed energy. Just about every physical effect known is being explored in order to find new and versatile methods that will automatically machine metal into accurate and complex shapes.—F.P.*

■ The old gaffer being brought up to date in the cartoon in Fig. 3-76 was, indeed, born thirty years too soon for the spot he's in. For shrewd, experienced, and adaptable as he is, it's a sad fact of life that the Bull of the Woods would probably be an anachronism in the machine shop of the near future.

*Ford Park is Associate Editor of *International Science and Technology*.

This is not to say that laser beams are going to machine spur gears—either now or for a long time to come. It is to say that the traditional foundation of machining is rapidly being enlarged to encompass physical processes that many of the machine shop foremen of the recent war years would be hard put to understand and exploit.

Since the Second World War some remarkable machining techniques have been developed that bear little resemblance—in their principles of metal removal—to the traditional metal cutting machines familiar to most of us. The qualifier is important, for a quick glance into a modern machine shop (or, maybe, one a few years off) can be misleading. The array of machine tools looks about the same, for when metal is removed to make a shape, workpiece and "tool" must still dance in tune.

But stay a while and the differences become apparent. For one thing, the machines look leaner, less muscular. And so they are, for they are nibblers by nature—removing but a little metal at a time. As a consequence, they are quieter (and slower) even though the power levels involved in removing metal in near-atomic amounts must by necessity be larger. Less dominant as you listen is the keening whine of the high-speed lathe, or the com-

BULL OF THE WOODS

W — Work
T — Tool
SP — Shear Plane
CD — Cut Depth

pulsive shudder of the heavy shaper. Replacing these are the quiet murmur of bubbling fluids, the low-pitched whir of recirculating pumps, the insistent buzz of high-frequency arcs and transducers, and the ta-pocket, ta-pocketing of the vacuum pump.

Even the machine shop smells of beloved memory have changed. The nose avidly searches for the exhilarating pungency of smoking metal and lubricant, only to have first success obliterated by the odor of strange but more purposeful chemicals—electrolytes, dielectrics, solvents.

And the chips? The prideful, ever-sharp, in-the-soles-of-the-shoes evidence of work accomplished? Gone. Replaced by myriad metal particles and washed down drainpipes wrought by the fancy of some new machine tool designer-cum-chemical engineer. Chips, alas, have become crud.

Materials are harder than ever to machine

What would the Bull of the Woods say about this description of the machine shop of tomorrow? After some muttering about how things "ain't what they usta be," he'd probably mutter some more about the slide-rule boys in white coats. On second thought, though, the Bull would probably welcome them—once it became evident that they held the key to getting some of the tough jobs out the door.

It's a fact that the boys in the white coats are ever more in evidence on the machine shop floor. And their tribe will increase, for more and more machining tasks are proving too diffi-

cult for traditional methods based on the formation of a chip ahead of a cutting edge.

Chip formation requires that the cutting tool be harder than the workpiece. For as the cutting edge advances, the material ahead of it is compressed and the ultimate shear strength is reached and exceeded. As the workpiece material successively shears along its shear planes (see sketch) and plastically flows, a gross amount of material is separated from the work and escapes along the tool face.

One difficulty arises when the strength, abrasiveness, and brittleness of the work approach those of the tool—as is the case with many of the high-strength, high-temperature materials developed for aerospace needs. There has been a regular procession of these, starting with titanium in the early fifties and continuing on through the high-strength steels to the refractory alloys of current interest.

The difficulty becomes manifest in an economic way. The producibility engineer—to earn his keep—has to devise ways of cutting these metals at reasonable speeds to prevent labor costs from skyrocketing, while retaining sufficient tool life to keep tool costs in line. These two factors are fundamentally at odds with each other, as expressed in Taylor's classic equation VT^n = constant. As you try to cut at faster speeds V, tool life T between regrinds inexorably decreases because of the greater heating at the tool. As workpiece strength and hardness go up, this clash between speed and tool life becomes accentuated.

Industry has succeeded brilliantly over the last few decades in staving off a final impasse in this situation. In stronger tool materials alone progress has been steady and fruitful. Recent years have seen the timely intervention of sintered carbide tools, cermets, and—most recently—ceramic cutting edges. And there is still potential in this area for improving cutting efficiency.

There have been gains in other areas too. Research into the influence of cutting tool geometry—such seemingly simple changes as negative- instead of positive-rake on carbide tools—has increased tool life by a factor of three every ten years over the last two decades. Cutting fluids are continually improving, as well, though their potential for sharply increasing cutting speeds appears limited.

The environment in which traditional metal cutting occurs holds much promise for progress. Take temperature, for example. It's only an accident of nature that we machine at about 70°F. Recent research has shown that by heating the workpiece locally just ahead of the tool to about 800–900°F, and thus weakening the work material, the cutting speed can be increased three-fold or more. And conversely, cooling the cutting tool cryogenically, so as to dissipate frictional heat, may have a similar effect by prolonging tool life.

Wanted: accuracy, gentleness, versatility

Despite the optimism engendered by these and other developments, the ineluctable paradox remains: designers are imploring materials specialists to develop materials of greater strength; but with such strength usually comes greater hardness and hence more headaches for the machinist.

To this trend, one must add three more—all of them born of the imperatives of the aerospace business, yet having their effects throughout the metalworking industry.

The tolerances on machined parts—from bearings to waveguides—are becoming ever-tighter. And this is forcing the metal removal processes to higher and higher levels of accuracy—millionths of an inch instead of tenths of thousandths 15 years ago.

Hand in hand with this trend is the greater incidence of complex configurations in today's manufacturing—from turbine buckets to automotive stamping dies—which means modern machine tools must be ever more versatile.

The demand for more delicate and Lilliputian machined parts, often from extremely brittle materials, is rising as well. This, in turn, requires machining techniques that exert little or no force on the work, a characteristic not found in traditional edge-cutting methods.

The cumulative effect of these trends on design practice has been profound. Not so long ago, the engineer designed his part with a sharp eye on what the machinist could produce. Now, as often as not, most of the designer's ingenuity goes into functional aspects, and manufacturing takes the hindmost.

What's in a name?

In these circumstances it is not surprising to find that the search is on for alternative methods of machining—methods that are not constrained by the mechanical properties of the work. We now have, in various stages of development and commercial acceptance, a whole family of metal removal processes—techniques that utilize other than chip-forming principles to machine the toughest materials into complex and delicate shapes having excellent tolerances. And more will be forthcoming as soon as ideas for removing metal can be drawn from other disciplines, sorted out, and the best ones tried.

It's time now for a careful look at this new family, to see what principles its various members employ, to assay their advantages and limitations, and to get a feeling for what kinds of tasks they are now performing. In doing so, I shall be keeping in mind that look of somewhat glum astonishment displayed by the Bull of the Woods in our opening cartoon, and the sardonic anticipation shown by his machine shop hands. For if the new machining methods cannot satisfy at least their needs, born of long experience in turning out the work, they are sure to remain largely methods of limited utility.

Because the alternative machining methods are, by and large, so different from established metal cutting techniques, I've chosen to characterize them as "nontraditional." Some have called them "unconventional," but woe be in this business to the man who so describes *any* process that has earned its first shiny dollar on even the most modest semicommercial basis.

Roughly speaking, these techniques—whatever their status—can be pigeonholed into four categories: those that depend upon softening, melting, or evaporation of the work, those that dissolve metal by chemical action, those that remove it by electrochemical processes, and those that "machine" by erosion or abrasive impact. This is more or less the narrative order I shall follow.

Thermal machining with sparks

Of the new methods that are based on the local application of intense heat, by far the most successful carries an electrical cognomen. This is electrical discharge machining, more

graphically described as spark erosion, spark machining, or capacitor-discharge machining.

Scientists have been tinkering with electrical sparks since the time of Ben Franklin and Joseph Priestley. Svedberg, in 1906, disintegrated metals with sparks, and electric-arc methods of cutting metals appear in the patent literature of the thirties. It remained for two Soviet investigators, B. R. and N. I. Lazarenko, to develop a viable metalworking process based upon the repeated application of high-energy sparks on a metal surface.

Developed during the Second World War, electrical discharge machining (EDM for short) was truly an alternative method. Facing a shortage of diamond abrasive, the Soviets simply had to find another way; necessity really was the maternal force of ancient usage.

The solution was to discharge the stored electrical energy in a capacitor bank across two electrodes—one the negative tool and the other the positive workpiece. The energy transferred in this manner turned out to be sufficient to remove a tiny piece of the workpiece surface. By repeating this event thousands of times per second, a "tool" could be made to remove or erode as much material as a cutting edge—though much more slowly.

But the really fascinating aspect of this novel nibbler, in the light of today's needs, is that it performs equally well on both hard and soft materials—so long as they are electrical conductors (Fig. 3-77). No longer is the tool engineer faced with the problem of finding cutting edges tougher than the workpiece. He has other tooling troubles, as we shall see, but the

old bugaboo of ever-increasing workpiece strength need concern him no more.

A major caveat must be entered here, for the long-suffering tool engineer's problems are always Janus-faced. Although he now has tools that can machine any metal or alloy, they must do so much more slowly. If we take steel as a standard, while the traditional lathe is hungrily taking off metal at 10–30 in.³/min or more, the EDM machine will be nibbling away at an equally inexorable, but much more modest 0.1 in.³/min or slightly more. But if we change to a more formidable, aerospace material—say, an alloy with a Brinell hardness of over 400—then the situation changes swiftly. The EDM machine nibbles on at the same rate, while the lathe is reduced to relative economic impotence. As Aesop related: if conditions are right, the mouse *can* triumph.

Now machine tools aren't animals, and metaphors can be misleading. How *does* metal get removed by EDM, as shown in Fig. 3-78? Here we enter the murky waters of controversy, though by now most investigators agree that the general ideas set out by the Soviet inventors in 1943 are substantially correct. In essence, the process works about as follows.

The mechanism of metal removal

The capacitor bank is first charged by an appropriate current control. The tool and workpiece are immersed in a dielectric fluid—usually an ordinary hydrocarbon- or mineral-oil. Then the tool is brought toward the workpiece until the gap between them is about 0.001 in. When the voltage across the closest asperi-

Fig. 3-77. Spark machining "cuts" metals by discharging electrical energy stored in a capacitor bank across a thin gap between tool (cathode) and work (anode). With the tool held close to (but not touching) the work by a servo control, thousands of sparks per second are generated. By vaporizing tiny craters, they erode the tool shape into the work. Fluid flushes "chips" away, confines the spark. Tool can be brass, steel, graphite, or powdered metal.

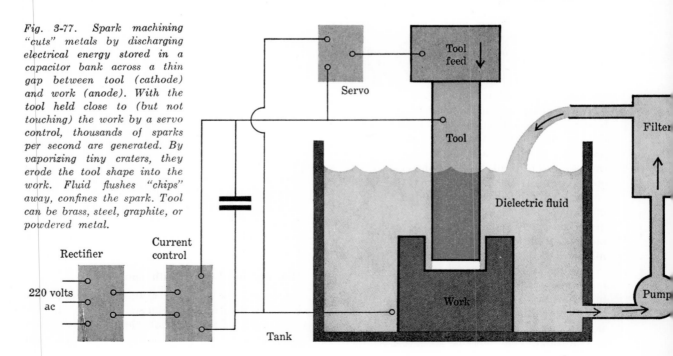

Fig. 3-78. A spark discharge like this, multiplied many times over per second, will machine at a rate of 0.1 to 0.3 in.³/min—slowly compared with what conventional cutting tools can do on ductile metals. At hardnesses above 400 Brinell, however, spark erosion machines the faster. Shown here is a steel tool discharging against a steel workpiece, a combination chosen to show the violent ejection of incandescent particles. Sparking in a liquid constrains the discharge, raises its temperature and its ability to cut metal. (Courtesy Cincinnati Milling Machine Co.)

ties reaches about 70 volts, the intense electric field between them ionizes the dielectric and initiates the discharge.

At this moment a narrow channel of continuous conductivity is formed in the dielectric through which begins to flow an avalanche of electrons. This current impulse, or discharge, is assisted in its initiation by minute conductive particles in the fluid, and takes place in less than a microsecond.

Because so much energy is abruptly transferred through such a tiny space, the dielectric fluid vaporizes and partly decomposes. The discharge channel thus enlarges and the stream of electrons passing through it accelerates—generating as it goes a strong magnetic field. Ions of the fluid are thus drawn at high velocity toward the channel axis, compressing it in a pinch effect, and raising its temperature to perhaps 10,000°C.

The effect of this discharge phenomenon is to soften, melt, and partially vaporize the workpiece surface at the anode end of the current channel. One major question as yet unresolved is precisely how the local heating occurs. Is it due to the stream of high-velocity electrons impacting the surface and rendering up their kinetic energy as heat? Or is there some complex mechanism by which the heat in the plasma is transferred to the surface?

Whatever the electro-thermal mechanism, the surface material is in a condition to be moved. And the forces are there to move it, for the plasma pressure in the spark channel has reached thousands of atmospheres. When the current is interrupted at the end of the discharge, the pressure drops and the channel collapses explosively—somehow ejecting metal in all directions (Fig. 3-78) and leaving a tiny crater. Ejected metal solidifies upon impact with the surrounding fluid. The debris is then swept out of the gap by the moving dielectric

fluid, and down the drain to be filtered out and removed—a totally new kind of chip, indeed!

Many discharges do useful work

What I have described above rather roughly is, of course, only a single discharge. Visualize, if you will, a current control system capable of generating up to 500,000 of such discharges per second. These will occur at random over the tool face at whatever points thereon are closest to the workpiece surface. Over a period of time, then, the shape of the tool electrode can be reproduced in the workpiece with a predictable degree of overcut.

By ingenious design of the tool electrode a whole host of tasks can be performed by spark machining. If you wish an irregularly shaped, through hole (see sketch), you can trepan it simply by forming a tool out of sheet metal much as you'd create a cookie cutter. If you desire a forging die, machine a master of the part you want to make from some easy-to-cut metal, and spark-erode the die cavity to match it. Is your workpiece a delicate structure like metal honeycomb? Spark machining will shape it free of burrs. Do you have a lot of holes you want to drill simultaneously in a complex shape? Make your own spark machine with multiple electrodes à la Fig. 3-79. Even a moving wire can be used as a tool electrode.

And so it goes. But the tool engineer is not home scot-free as I noted earlier. Even though the primary erosion occurs at the workpiece end of the spark channel, the fact that the discharge is confined in a tiny gap has its effect on the tool. In short, the tool is subject to erosion as well, though usually not as much as on the work itself.

By judicious selection of tool material, the wear on the tool can be kept to as low as $\frac{1}{10}$ of the metal removed from the work. The wear factor must, of course, be taken into account

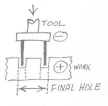

EDM TREPANNING

WHERE'S TH' CHIPS?

in any job, and the need for changing tools—atop the already relatively slow rate of metal removal—is one of EDM's limitations.

Since the quantity of metal removed is proportional to the energy per discharge times the number of discharges per second, EDM machining rates are varied by selectively changing one or the other of these quantities. But there is a hitch. If a higher average-pulse energy is chosen, more material will be removed, to be sure, but the individual crater size will be greater and the surface finish will be rougher.

Metal removal rates up to about 0.3 in.^{3}/min are now quite realistic, but you've got to take a surface finish of 500 microinches (arithmetic average) or more with it. Cut the pulse-energy level, and your finish can drop to below 10 microin., but you'll machine perhaps 1000 times more slowly. It's the old story, familiar to the Bull of the Woods and anyone else reared on traditional machining: finer finishes go hand in hand with lower metal removal rates.

A question of surface damage

As you might expect, spark erosion—thermal in nature as it is—has an effect on the properties of the workpiece surface. Metallographic studies show that the melting and resolidification of the surface layers can be enough to change the surface to a harder microstructure—particularly at the higher removal rates. Whether this is classed as "damage" or as "better wear resistance" depends, of course, upon the application. But the user should be aware that changes can and do occur. Indeed, spark hardening of tools by a process akin to EDM is a well-established shop technique in Europe and the USSR.

One intriguing feature of current EDM research into higher metal-removal rates deserves mention. This is the increasingly important role being discovered for the dielectric fluid. Until recently, the fluid was regarded primarily as a medium for clearing the electrode gap of "chips," and secondarily as a means of confining the spark channel. But with new insights being gained into the electron avalanche concept of discharge initiation, it appears possible to improve machining rates by improving the dielectric fluid so as to make ionization easier to achieve.

Machining with electron beams

While the importance of electron impact in spark machining is open to some question, there is one nontraditional machining process where its role has been established beyond a peradventure. This is electron beam machining, also called electron beam milling or electron beam cutting.

The device used at present for generating and ordering electrons in a manner suitable for metal removal is one akin to the electron beam microscope. The electron "gun" is basically a triode—with a cathode emitter, a grid for controlling beam current, and a plate anode for accelerating purposes. Electrons emitted in a cloud from the filament are accelerated through a 150,000 volt potential difference between cathode and anode. Leaving the anode, the emitted electrons may be moving toward the work at more than half the speed of light—and thus have much potential (kinetic as it is) for doing work.

There remains, however, much disciplining to be done, for electrons are essentially vagrants. There must be a vacuum (usually about 10^{-4} torr) to reduce the chances of their collision with deflecting gas molecules. Then there must be a series of magnetic coils to align the electron beam, give it a circular cross section, refocus it to diameters as low as 0.0005 in. at the workpiece, and to deflect the beam over the surface as desired. (Color Fig. 25 shows a configuration that satisfies these requirements.)

We have here, then, the elements of a powerful, yet agile thermal machine tool: by impacting a tiny area with a high-velocity stream of electrons, power densities in the order of 10^9 watts/cm^2 can be delivered to the work; since high-velocity electrons are absorbed (i.e., give up their kinetic energy as heat) in a very thin layer of the impacted surface, this power input can be employed to generate local temperatures beyond the melting point of any known material; and with all the controls electronic in nature—the shape, size, position, and duration of the electron beam can be altered precisely and in a matter of microseconds.

The importance of being impulsive

Let's examine this matter of short-time variation of beam characteristics a bit more closely, for it lies at the very root of the electron beam's success as a "cutting" instrument. The problem in metal removal, as distinct from melting or welding, is to be able to vaporize a geometrically exact amount of material without melting the metal that lies beneath. By pulsing the beam on and off, subjecting the workpiece to short bursts of great energy, this can be accomplished.

The prediction that this would be possible came from K. H. Steigerwald at the Zeiss Co. where much of the development of the e-b machining process occurred. After assuming that an electron beam had "bored" through a material to some depth, Steigerwald computed the distribution of incident energy to the various thermal processes that must consume it. Some of the energy goes to heating a thin layer at the cavity bottom, some to melting this layer, some to vaporizing it. Additional heat is lost by radiation, and more is conducted into the material beneath the machining site. It turned out that, at the temperatures generated by beam impact, most of the energy went into heating, melting, and (most particularly) vaporizing the thin layer. Much less energy was lost by conduction into the metal (see sketch).

The question then was: would a pulsed beam of electrons possibly fit these favorable circumstances? It would. Steigerwald computed that by applying the very high power-density beam to a surface of tungsten, for example, the thin layer in which the electrons would give up their energy as heat could be raised to the melting point by a beam exposure of only 10^{-8} sec. On the other hand, the time to conduct away sufficient heat to melt material only a few microns deeper proved to be of the order of 10^{-5} sec. Thus, he showed that there would be ample time to vaporize and remove the absorption layer before deeper layers were melted.

And this is how it works out in practice. Short bursts (10^{-6} sec in duration) of the beam are used to "drill" holes down to 0.0005 in. in

diameter, and to "mill" slots as small as 0.001 in. wide in almost any material. Holes less than 0.050 in. diameter are drilled almost instantaneously in materials up to 0.050 in. thickness. In heavier metals, up to $\frac{3}{8}$ in. thick, drilling such holes takes a little longer.

For holes or slots of complicated shape, the work can be programmed about beneath the electron beam as it cuts. Or, as in a recent innovation, the beam itself can be programmed with the signal from a phototube that has received light from a template illuminated by the scanning beam of a cathode-ray tube.

With electronic legerdemain of this sort, and with the highly localized character of the machining action, it is clear that e-b machining is ideally suited for intricate, miniaturized work. This is its long suit, and we should not think of this method as useful for machining gross areas such as the cavity in a stamping die for an auto top.

A perusal of the literature shows just what kinds of tasks e-b machining is now doing with its very low metal-removal rate—in the order of 0.00005 in.^{3}/min, as compared to 0.1 in.^{3}/min and above for EDM. We find tiny holes being drilled in stainless fuel-injection nozzles, sapphire jewel bearings, and TV-gun electrode assemblies. Thin slots are being milled in ferrite components for computers. The programming technique is being used to cut complex and miniscule extrusion dies for synthetic fibers, and to machine circuits in the thin films of miniaturized electronic modules.

Toward lower cost e-b machine tools?

The chief obstacle to the broader application of e-b machining, aside from low metal-removal rate, would appear to be the relatively high cost of the equipment. This derives from the precise apparatus needed to generate, align, shape, focus, and control the beam. It may be that a new and simpler method for generating a collimated beam of electrons will have some impact in this area. This is the plasma electron beam announced in 1962 by both GE and The Martin Co. (Color Fig. 26).

The essential innovation in the new technique is the source of the electrons. Here, it is a *cold* cathode (rather than a heated filament) in the shape of a tin can. Placed in a gas like argon at a low pressure (1–10 microns) and negatively charged with about 20,000 volts, the hollow cathode generates a plasma of positive gas ions and free electrons within it. So long as the voltage is applied, the plasma will be maintained in the can, and the electrons can be accelerated toward the workpiece through a hole in the can's bottom.

Electron formation in the can is augmented

E-B ENERGY
GOES INTO:

H+M - HEATING AND MELTING
V - VAPORIZATION
R - RADIATION
C - CONDUCTION

by several mechanisms. Those positive ions present initially in the surrounding gas are attracted up into the cathode where, by virtue of their higher energy, they knock electrons off the inside. Also, the cathode plasma glows with radiation, the ultraviolet portion of which knocks further electrons loose inside the cathode by photoemission.

The collimated beam itself helps to sustain electron formation, for as it collides with gas molecules more positive ions are formed—some of which, in turn, travel to the cathode to knock off more electrons. Other ions stay at the core of the beam, neutralizing the tendency of the negatively charged electrons to scatter from each other. By this mechanism, beams up to 30 in. long have been generated that display little spreading.

For machining purposes, as we have seen, high-power densities are necessary. Although the plasma electron beam is small in diameter, it must be focused electromagnetically (here cost begins to creep back in) to reduce the diameter to 0.010 in. or below. This done, power densities as high as 10^7 watts/cm² can be achieved. This is not as great—because of the larger spot size—as the 10^9 watts/cm² obtainable with the Zeiss-type e-b machines, but it is sufficient to vaporize any material. And by adding a grid within the cathode, as has been done at GE's Advanced Technology Lab, the beam can be pulsed—another requisite for machining with the electron beam.

Laser machining—up from razor blades

The young fellow demonstrating the experimental laser machining device to the Bull of the Woods in Fig. 3-76 is probably using a razor blade as a target. As Peter Franken pointed out in an earlier article ("High-Energy Lasers," page 135), this has already become a classic experiment.

Well, the laser is slowly climbing out of this gimmicky category, and is being carefully explored as a metal-removal tool that shows promise of someday competing with the electron beam process. The main advantage, of course, is that the energy densities—especially of focused laser beams—are comparable and can be achieved without the presence of a vacuum.

The laser is an ingenious device for converting electrical energy into an intense and narrow beam of monochromatic light or infrared energy. In pulsed lasers, the only type used in machining work, the electrical energy from a bank of capacitors is discharged through a gas-filled flashlamp. The resulting intense flash of white light is focused on the laser material—often a ruby rod—in such a way that it becomes excited, or optically "pumped."

The characteristics of the laser material change when sufficient light energy has been absorbed by it. Rather than sitting there absorbing light, it becomes an optical amplifier. Equipped with reflective coatings at both ends, the laser rod has built into it a feedback mechanism. After the light has thus been amplified by rebounding from end to end, the system oscillates—that is, a signal emerges through one end of the laser material (only partially reflecting) in the form of a thin pencil of light. At once monochromatic, directional, and coherent—the beam is intense and narrow enough to produce, unfocused, power densities in the order of 10^8 watts/cm².

It is this high-power density that renders the laser beam useful in cutting, for it can be used to vaporize any material in a manner akin to e-b machining. There is a basic difference (aside from the nature of the beam) however. In e-b machining the electron beam can be pulsed repeatedly, quickly, and easily according to the most suitable program for the workpiece. The light beam from a solid-state laser, however, delivers its energy in one burst of a few milliseconds duration. The second burst cannot be repeated until the laser material is cool and ready to receive the pulse—a matter of 1–10 seconds or so with present-day equipment.

This time delay is not an insurmountable obstacle to machining, however. The laser beam can be focused through simple optical arrangement to provide ample power density for drilling 0.015 in. diameter holes in metal thicknesses up to ⅛ in. in a single burst (ordinary steel, for example) or in a few bursts (the higher melting-point metals).

Laser impact still a mystery

The precise mechanism of metal removal is not as well understood as it is for other nontraditional machining techniques. Some of the material is vaporized without question, and some is blown out of the cavity by the vapor as hot chunks of molten globules (Fig. 3-80). But how the beam energy is distributed among the various thermal processes is poorly understood.

Recent high-speed motion pictures taken by D. A. Buddenhagen and co-workers at Hughes Aircraft Co. labs have revealed the metal removal action with considerable clarity. As a result, reports Buddenhagen, "We now have much less understanding of what is going on than we had before."

Despite the deepening mystery at the fundamental level, investigators are finding that a whole family of materials—from tungsten to porcelain to even the tougher plastics—can be pierced with fine holes and still show little damage to the adjacent material (Fig. 3-81).

Laser beams will certainly not cut spur gears, but there is much they could do in the way of commercial drilling tasks if the twin problems that plague solid-state lasers could be solved. One is that of thermal inefficiency: far too much (99%) electrical energy goes into heating the laser material to the point of impotence, necessitating external cooling varying complexity to maintain reasonable discharge rates. The second problem is the short life of the xenon flash lamps—5 to 5000 shots depending upon energy level.

Plasma torch = forceless machining?

Suspicious and skeptical as the Bull of the Woods might be over the prospects for laser beams, electron beams, and even spark discharges, there is one thermal source for machining that would warm the cockles of his heart. This is the plasma torch, and he'd cotton to it because of its superficial similarity to the oxy-acetylene torches so widely used in his day (and now) for cutting plate.

There is a substantial difference, however,

Fig. 3-80. Here's what the Bull of the Woods would see if the white-coated young man in Fig. 3-76 were to complete his demonstration. The high-energy laser is the newest of the nontraditional machining methods, though it's still an experimental way to drill holes. Here, a 10-joule burst from a ruby laser takes less than a millisecond to boil a 0.020 in. diameter hole in a tungsten sheet. (Courtesy Hughes Aircraft Co.)

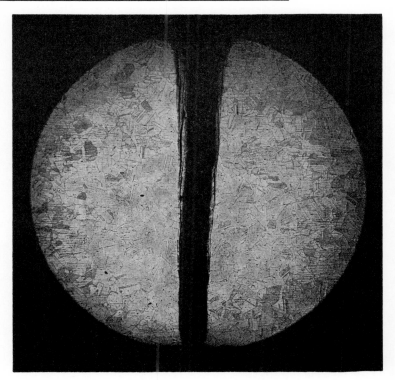

Fig. 3-81. You can almost count the 8 laser bursts that "cut" this hole by the layers of molten metal splashed up the side. Last molten metal dropped out bottom as this 0.015 in. diameter hole penetrated the ⅛ in. thick stainless. Drilling apparently occurs by reflection of incident energy from later bursts off the hole wall. Note the lack of thermal damage to metal adjacent to the hole. (Courtesy D. Williams, GE Advanced Technology Laboratory)

for the plasma torch uses enormous quantities of electricity to drive the temperature of a *single* gas to levels far exceeding those possible by ordinary combustion. Practically, this is done in four basic ways (see sketches).

Such devices (see "Plasma Torches," page 458) can deliver power densities in the order of 10^4 watts/cm^2 to the surface of the workpiece. This is considerably lower than that transferred by either the electron beam or the laser beam. However, it is a whole order of magnitude higher than that available from the oxy-acetylene flame, and it provides surface temperatures of 6000° to 20,000°K. This is quite sufficient to melt the difficult-to-machine metals.

The charm of the plasma torch as a possible machine tool lies in the fact that these high temperatures can be achieved over a significant area—say, up to 0.5 in. in diameter. Further, the hot gas stream is emitted from the torch at high velocity. This suggests that the metal made molten by its temperature might be removed by its impact without applying much force to the workpiece as a whole.

DC ARC

DC PLASMA TORCH
(NON-TRANSFERRED ARC)

DC PLASMA TORCH
(TRANSFERRED ARC)

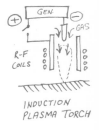

INDUCTION
PLASMA TORCH

Some positive results

How does it work out in practice? Well, several companies have attempted the relatively simple operation of lathe-turning using the plasma torch, and the results are rather startling. At the Linde Company, R. L. O'Brien found, for example, that in turning materials such as high-nickel alloys, refractory alloys such as René 41, and the Hastelloy alloys, metal could be removed 5–10 times faster than with edge-cutting tools. And just as significant, the power per in.^{3} removed per unit of time proved to be the same or lower.

But what about precision? Removing metal this way at, say, 5 in.^{3}/min is a right smart advance over even spark machining. But isn't the plasma torch really a kind of thermal plow, capable only of gross work? Here, too, there have been advances. For example, two years ago researchers at Pratt & Whitney began to work on plasma-torch machining. As an early step, W. G. Voorhees and W. P. Luscher carefully analyzed the energy balances at the work site as the torch moved along it (Fig. 3-82). They succeeded in deriving equations that predict the shape and size of the "cut" in terms of the torch speed and angle, thermal properties of the metal, and the energy density of the flame.

Over a multitude of tests, these equations

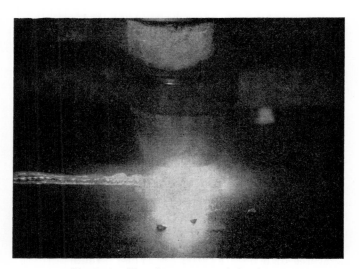

Fig. 3-82. The plasma arc torch has been around since 1955, but only recently has it been investigated as a possible tool for metal removal. Here, "chips" of molten mild steel are sent flying as a transferred-arc torch cuts a groove ¼ in. wide at 120 in./min (with ±0.004 in. tolerance). Torch would normally be inclined backward to blow metal from the melt zone. Though torch uses an inert gas to blanket removal site, cutting metals prone to oxidation can prove difficult unless area behind torch is cooled with a water film. (Courtesy A. Kiely, Pratt and Whitney Co.)

have proven quite accurate and, indeed, correlate quite nicely with the material-removal rates found in ablation theory for space vehicles re-entering the earth's atmosphere (see "Ablation," page 535).

Thus the prospects for plasma torch machining look cautiously bright at the moment. Practical problems of articulating the torch over the workpiece, of starting, maintaining, and stopping it at will, remain. If these can be solved, we may see a thermal machine tool developed that can find a useful place in the machining of difficult metals and alloys at significant cutting rates.

Better machining . . . through chemistry

Despite their natural ability to overcome the "hardness barrier," the thermal machining processes display certain limitations. Some of them are intermittent and therefore slow; most of them tend to vaporize the metal, thus consuming more energy than is really needed; and most of them must put up with considerable inefficiencies and side effects because thermal energy is difficult to direct only to the process of metal removal.

It is natural, therefore, to consider whether alternate machining techniques based on chemical- rather than thermal-action might offer the possibility of side-stepping some of these difficulties.

Is it possible to "corrode" a piece of metal to a shape desired and thus "machine" it? It turns out that it is. And with the assistance of electrical energy, it's possible to machine the hard metals faster than they can be machined with cutting edges, and many times faster than is possible with spark machining.

The key nontraditional machining process in this area is called electrochemical machining, which I shall abbreviate here to its more common nickname of ECM. It is also termed electrolytic machining, but this is a less desirable cognomen since it is often taken, erroneously, to include spark machining.

In ECM, both tool and workpiece are conductive and, with a suitable electrolyte between them, form opposite electrodes of an electrolytic cell. The workpiece is the anode, connected as it is to the positive terminal of a dc power source. The cathodic tool is connected to the negative terminal and is cut beforehand to a shape identical (or nearly so) with that desired in the work.

When a driving emf is supplied across the electrodes, electrons flow from the anode, through the external circuit, to the cathode. The electrons most easily moved are the ones belonging to the atoms of metal at the surface of the workpiece. Remaining behind at the work surface are positive metal ions. This condition of electrical instability must be stabilized. So, in obedience to Faraday's laws, the ions leave the work surface and combine with the electrolyte in a reaction,

metal atom + solution anions

= metal salt + electrons

Depending upon the electrolyte, the salt that is formed can be either an oxide or a hydroxide. This aside, the above anodic reaction produces an excess of electrons in the circuit. To keep the current flowing, this anodic reaction at the workpiece must be accompanied by a corresponding cathodic reaction at the tool. The excess electrons are used up there in a reaction like this

cations + electrons = atoms

Since aqueous solutions are used in most electrolytic machining, the cathodic reaction above results in the discharge of hydrogen atoms at the cathode. And so the current flow continues: electronic flow in the external circuit; ionic conductance in the electrolyte (Fig. 3-83).

Electroplating's a kissin' cousin

How can this be any different from the established processes of electroplating or electropolishing? The answer lies in the different conditions under which the electrolytic action occurs. Electroplating is a slow metal removal process (anodically speaking) because metal salts leave the anode by diffusion and until they have left, no fresh salts can be formed.

Although Faraday's laws tell us that the amount of metal removed can be increased precisely in proportion as the current density is increased, doing this achieves nothing but IR heating unless the flow of reaction products away from the metal removal site can be increased markedly. This applies to the cathode as well, for if H_2 gas is allowed to accumulate, both of the required reactions for electrolysis will be impeded.

The solution—and the factor on which successful ECM rests—is to increase the flow of electrolyte through the electrode gap. It must flow fast enough so that the reaction products are swept away and so that enough fresh electrolyte is brought into the gap to support current densities high enough to remove metal from the anode at a respectable rate.

By cleverly designing tools and fixtures (see marginal sketches), developers of the ECM process have achieved electrolyte flows in the tiny gap (0.001 to 0.020 in.) up to 200 miles per hour. This may require pressures to 600 psi which calls for pretty hefty pumps.

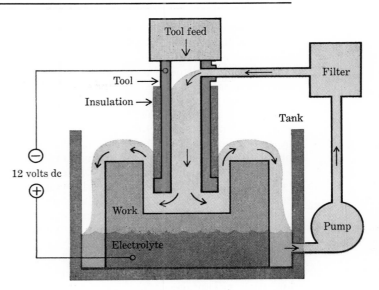

Fig. 3-83. Electrochemical machining shapes metal by a rapid deplating action wherein the tool is the cathode and the work the anode of an electrolytic cell, whence its alternate name "anodic cutting." Electrolyte is pumped rapidly through the gap to flush out "chips" and to bring fresh electrolyte in, so that high-current densities can be sustained. The main charm of ECM is its higher removal rate, compared to spark machining. It is, however, a less precise method.

Combining high flow of electrolyte with current densities of several thousand amps/in.²— far above what the electroplater is used to— makes it possible to remove metal at rates in excess of those possible by spark machining. Currents of 10,000 amps are common. Spread over a 10 in.² area, this results in a removal rate of 1 in.³/min—quite a respectable figure when cutting materials harder than 400 BHN. At this hardness level, edge-cutting tools can remove metal only one-half as fast.

ECM has its problems

We can see quite readily why ECM has a metal-removal rate that is higher than for EDM, for the electrolyte is constantly working away on the surface—whereas you can't have two sparks occurring at the same point at the same time. The continuous action of the electrolyte over the entire workface is the root of one difficulty with ECM, however. And this is that the tool shape cannot be reproduced in the work as precisely or as uniformly.

Spark machining can hold tolerances of ±0.0005 in. in corners, whereas for ECM a good present figure would be ±0.001 in. This problem of precision is further complicated by the difficulty in constraining the high-current field to the work area as the electrolyte goes racing through the thin gap. This puts a premium on careful tool and fixture design, fig

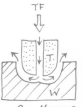

RIB METHOD

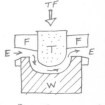

FLOW-THROUGH METHOD

W- WORK
T- TOOL
F- FIXTURE
TF- TOOL FEED

that the distorting effects of electrolyte turbulence can be avoided. In effect, each tool must be "barbered" for the job.

Atop the problems of moderate precision and fairly expensive tooling, one has with ECM the problem of power consumption. Electrolysis is a greedy process, and in this case it consumes power at an awesome clip: some 160 hp/in.^{3}/min, as compared to 40 for spark machining, about 10 for heavy-duty grinding, and only 1 hp/in.^{3}/min for lathe turning. This is not unexpected, since of all the nontraditional machining processes ECM is the one that functions at the atomic level where bond strengths are the greatest. It is indeed fortunate that, as machine shop commodities go, power is cheap.

So we have in electrochemical machining a nontraditional process with certain limitations, but with advantages where they count when shaping the difficult metals: a respectable machining rate at present, limited only by the machine designers' ability to transfer electrically induced heat out of the electrolyte (it must not boil); tools that do not wear, or become plated; surfaces that are free from surface damage (at least for most alloys) and unwanted burrs (Fig. 3-84); and the ability to duplicate parts over and over.

If one is willing to put up with (or pay for) the stringent measures that go with a process like this that requires corrosive fluids, one can perform the same broad tasks possible with EDM—cavity sinking, drilling, broaching, trepanning, turning, and so on. And, like spark

machining, ECM's ability to produce contoured shapes by lowering a matching tool "into" the workpiece suggests the possibility of direct competition in some applications with numerically controlled traditional machine tools in the not-so-distant future.

Electrolytic grinding

There is a variant on electrolytic machining that is of interest since it couples electrolytic action, as described above, with the mechanical action of an abrasive wheel. Here, the cathode is a rotating wheel—usually metal-bonded for conductivity—in which abrasive particles are embedded. The work is the anode as usual. The electrolytic cell is the gap between the wheel (either its face or its edge) and the workpiece as sketched in the margin.

Actually, the term "electrolytic grinding" is a bit of a misnomer, for the metal removal mechanism is perhaps 95% electrolytic in nature. The surface being machined is flushed with the electrolyte—usually a neutral aqueous solution of salts such as sodium nitrate or sodium nitrite. These fluids tend to form a passivating film on the work that inhibits further electrolysis. Thus the main purpose of the abrasive is to break up this film.

Chemical machining sans electricity

Machining with chemicals need not require the consumption of lots of electricity—if you've got plenty of time to spare, and not much material to remove. Not much in *depth*, that is.

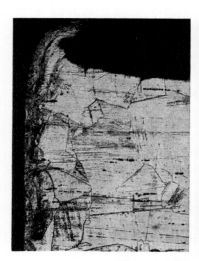

Fig. 3-84. These photomicrographs compare the effects of drilling a 0.030 in. diameter hole in a tough Co-Ni-Cr alloy by three different methods. You're looking at the top right-hand corner of the hole cross section. The hole at left was drilled in 1 min with a conventional twist drill, which left a burr and a 0.002 in. thick layer of distorted metal. The spark-machined hole (center) took 4 min, has no burr, but displays a 0.002 in. thick layer of resolidified metal along its surface. When electrochemically machined, the hole was drilled in 0.8 min, is free of both burr and transformed layer next to hole. (Courtesy M. Davis and C. Allison, CMM)

→| 0.004 |←

Margin diagram:
AW
E →
W   ⊖
⊕
↓ E

ELECTROLYTIC GRINDING
W—WORK
AW—ABRASIVE WHEEL
E—ELECTROLYTE

For the process of industrial etching known as chemical milling was developed expressly for taking shallow cuts from large areas of aircraft and missile structures so as to optimize weight.

In brief, the process involves the covering of the part to be machined with an oxidation-resistant coating, then the hand removal of this masking from the areas to be machined, followed by the pickling of the thus masked part to remove surface oxides, the dipping of the part into a suitable etchant, and—finally—a rinsing and inspecting operation.

Now this procedure sounds quite simple and, in principle, it is—particularly for the less dense and more easily oxidizable metals like aluminum and magnesium. But these are the structural materials of yesterday's aerospace technology. The stronger metals and alloys of today are also much more resistant to chemical attack. They're denser, too, which means material must be used more efficiently in airborne use. Tolerances are thus tighter, thousandths now instead of hundredths.

All this means that the milling chemist has been pressed to the utmost to come up with oxidants powerful enough to do the metal-etching job and, at the same time, to devise maskants that will protect the areas not requiring machining (including tanks and allied equipment).

There is much more than the raw materials problem, for during the chemical milling process the control chemist must change the balance of his ingredients—usually combinations of raw acids—to match the increasing metal concentration in his solution. Furthermore, it's becoming apparent that even different heat treatments of the same alloy can require different etchants.

Although there exists no universal etchant for all the newer metals and alloys, the chemical milling specialist can perform a variety of tasks with his present and growing array of acid combinations. He can etch to depths up to 0.5 in., though he's got to do it slowly—at about 0.001 in./min. A depth of some 0.060 in. is more characteristic of the process (the deeper the cut, the poorer the tolerance; shallow cuts can be controlled to ±0.001 in.). Sheets, extrusions, or formed sections can be tapered gradually or in steps.

In short, if the geometric variations you want are for the most part gentle and cover a large area, chemical milling is one nontraditional metal removal technique worth checking into. And if, while doing so, you could invent an automated, accurate way of applying the maskant, the chemical milling industry would be much in your debt.

Impact machining—an ancient process

If the raison d'être of many of the nontraditional machining methods rests upon the need to side-step the ever-increasing hardness of modern materials, surely there should be a machining technique that exploits that very hardness. There is, indeed, and it shares with electron beam machining the distinction of being a precision "cutting" process that does not require the workpiece to be electrically conductive. This method, however, drives tiny, sharp-edged particles, rather than electrons, into the work to achieve material removal.

It's called ultrasonic machining because the energy is supplied by a magnetostrictive transducer that oscillates a tool coupled to it at frequencies well above the audible range. This vibration takes place along the axis of the tool and, when amplified mechanically, it may be as much as 0.004 in. at the tool tip.

Boron carbide abrasive particles, introduced between the tool tip and the workpiece in a slurry, receive this vibrational energy and impart it in turn to the workpiece in a chipping action greatly akin to rock drilling. Slowly, the continuous action of many particles over many impact cycles produces a cavity the same shape and size (within thousandths) as the tool (Fig. 3-85). With this technique holes can be pro-

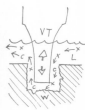

VT- VIBRATING TOOL
W- WORK
X- ABRASIVE
C- CHIPS

Fig. 3-85. This is the business end of an ultrasonic machine tool. The upper end of the cone is driven by a magnetostrictive transducer (not shown) so that the tip vibrates up and down at frequencies above the audible range. In operation, the gap between them is nearly closed and is flooded with an abrasive slurry (draining away here). The vibrating tool drives particles into the work, abrading the surface and thus "machining" the shape of the tool into the workpiece. (Courtesy Sheffield Corp.)

duced ranging from 0.001 in. to 3.5 in. in diameter. Depths up to 5 in. are possible.

We have here, then, a modern variant on the method used by the ancients to pound holes through brittle rock with tools of ductile copper. Now, ductile steel tools are used to machine ultrasonically a steadily growing list of materials. By this method, semiconductor wafers are diced, carbide stamping dies are cut, ferrite and oxide ceramics are shaped for electronics uses. Glass, quartz, hardened tool steels, high-pressure plastic laminates, and even some of the refractory metals can be machined this way.

Ultrasonic machining itself goes back to the forties in origin. Despite even this relative longevity, the precise mechanism of metal removal has not been pinned down to this day. There are four logical gross actions at work: the high-velocity impact of the particles against the work, the repeated hammering of these into the surface by the tool, cavitation, and chemical action derived from the slurry fluid used.

A few years ago, M. C. Shaw and his co-workers at MIT concluded after careful theoretical analysis that the first two actions are the pertinent ones and that of these the hammering action is the most significant. This analysis, however, assumed a hard, brittle work surface acted upon by a conventional aqueous slurry of boron carbide particles. The question of how material might be removed ultrasonically from a ductile surface was not considered in this analysis. It has, in fact, been long assumed that ultrasonic machining was simply of no use on soft materials like mild steel and brass. However, in recent experiments at Therm, Inc., W. Pentland has found that these materials can sometimes be machined this way faster in the annealed state than when hardened. This suggests that plastic flow may, under certain circumstances, predominate over brittle fracture—that the abrasive particles can act as miniature cutting edges rather than as wedges that break off tiny pieces of work.

The fluid slurry has several important roles to play. In addition to bringing abrasive to the work site by capillary action, it cools both tool and work, and provides an appropriate acoustic coupling between them so that energy can be transferred efficiently. Furthermore, the cavitation that occurs on the work surface as the tool withdraws on the up-cycle helps to recirculate the slurry.

Cavitation may do more. Pentland has found evidence that it can materially assist in the metal-removal process, though this requires more study. In addition, by switching to a slurry that uses a liquid metal instead of water as the carrying fluid, he has been able to embrittle some work surfaces so as to enhance the cutting action.

What all this means is that there is apparently no one removal mechanism that predominates under all conditions in ultrasonic machining. It means, too, that further scrutiny of the fundamental processes involved is in order. The payoff may be worth it—for the principal difficulty with ultrasonic machining is its low removal rate: about 0.02 in.^{3}/min, comparable to that of electron beam machining. This is, in part, a problem of finding a better way to generate and transfer higher levels of vibratory energy, for present transducers are limited in output.

One thing is clear: if the rate problem can be licked—through better transducers, embrittling techniques, or more thorough knowledge of the removal mechanism itself—ultrasonic machining could easily move into the ranks of mass-production piercing and engraving tools.

A peek into the crystal ball

With this rather detailed examination of eight promising nontraditional machining methods, I have sought to show how the problem of metal removal is being attacked on many fronts. I do not wish to leave the impression that these are the only possible approaches. They are not. A number of possibilities are being explored. Some examples:

MEBBE MENTAL TELEPATH NEXT!

- A beam of high-energy ions would make a good metal-removal tool. Since the ion has a greater mass than the electron by far, a beam of high-velocity ions would be able to punch its way through air—obviating the vacuum needed in e-b machining.
- A thin, high-pressure jet of water will cut through lumber, coal, brick, solid-propellant, and the like. On metal the effect is minor. If an abrasive could be added, without damaging the nozzle, perhaps metal could be cut.
- Suddenly applied magnetic-field forces look attractive, if only because they are already being used to form sheet metal (see "High Energy Rate Metalworking," page 421). Can they be coupled to a surface so as to remove metal in a controlled manner?
- Some metals undergo a drop in their shear flow stress when pulsed laterally by a sinusoidal shear stress while under static compression. Perhaps an oscillating cutting tool could produce plastic flow at greatly reduced stresses using this "Fitzgerald effect."
- Shock waves can be used to transform metal, shape it, break it, even weld it (see "Shock Waves in Solids," page 80). It might be possible to remove controlled quantities of metal

from a surface by harnessing the energy from shock waves applied at high frequency.

There is, I believe, a general recognition in metalworking circles that fresh winds should blow freely—that cutting tomorrow's materials into complex shapes with ever-increasing tolerances is going to tax technical ingenuity to the utmost. A start has been made, and a new class of metal-removal techniques is emerging in response to the demand for closer control over the manufacturing process as a whole.

In the years ahead we can expect this family to grow. Not only can we look ahead to new energy sources along with the refinement of existing ones. There is sure to be close scrutiny of the whole metalworking matrix: Can the materials to be machined be modified in some manner beforehand to enhance the effect of a given machining technique? Is it possible to make the environment in which the process operates more favorable? Can the transfer of energy—whatever its form—be made more efficient? Should the part be formed by a metal-removal process at all? These questions should be, and are being pondered.

Coupled with these new ways of looking at the fabrication process itself, we can expect the evolution of a more intimate relationship between the engineer who designs the part to be machined and the system of men, machines, and controls that ultimately makes it. Soon, perhaps, the engineer-designer will be able to communicate his design concepts directly to a computer in language that will set to work the new machining processes I have described.

It may not be machining by mental telepathy, but to the Bull of the Woods and his men it'll be the next thing to it.

Further reading

Indispensable to anyone approaching advanced machining methods are three short readable reports prepared for DOD by the NAS-NRC Materials Advisory Board. They are available to qualified requesters from the Defense Documentation Center, Cameron Station, Va., as: "Alternative Methods for Machining" (AD-256377), "State of the Art on Machining" (AD-276915), and "Recommended Research Programs" (AD-285277).

For a thorough scrutiny of the present problems facing the metalworking industry, see a hefty volume *"International Research in Production Engineering."* It contains a very good section on electrical machining methods (ASME, 345 E. 47 St., N.Y.C., $25).

A broad search for possible new techniques of metal removal is presented in Rosenthal's four progress reports on Project NEOS, "A General Study of Processes for the Realization of Design Configurations in Materials" (written under Air Force contract AF 33(600)-42921, obtainable from E. Chester, Cornell Aeronautical Lab).

A prescient and gracefully written bit of crystal ball gazing is Merchant's "10 Years Ahead—What's in It for Metalworking?" (*American Machinist*, May 18, 1959). See also Battelle DMIC Report No. 75, "Review of Some Unconventional Methods of Machining" (OTS, document PB-161225 for 50¢).

On EDM, the most comprehensive single volume is "Electro-Discharge Machining," interim report ASD-TDR-7-745 (IR I) on work done at Cincinnati Milling Machine Co. under Air Force contract AF 33(600)-42282. Available to qualified requesters from ASTIA's Documentation Service Center, Arlington Hall Station, Arlington, Va. See also B. R. Lazarenko's "Physical Principles of Electro-Spark Metalworking," available in English from Translation Services Branch, Foreign Technology Div., WPAFB, Ohio, as FTD-TT-61-186/1 + 2 + 4.

A thorough discussion of e-b machining will be found in Chap. 7 of *Introduction to Electron Beam Technology*, edited by Bakish (Wiley, 1962). See also Moore's "Electron Beam as a Machine Tool," paper SP62-30, ASTME, Detroit, Mich., and write W. D. Hirst, Advanced Technology Lab, GE, Schenectady, N.Y., for Stauffer's "Modulated Plasma Electron Beams."

On laser machining, see Buddenhagen's "Lasers and Their Metallurgical Applications" (from ASTME or write D. H. Buddenhagen at Hughes Aircraft Co., Newport Beach, Calif.

Electrochemical machining is discussed interestingly in "Electrochemical Machining of Metals," *Battelle Tech. Review*, **12**, No. 1 (1963). For latest research results, see "Electrolytic Machining," interim report ASD-7-6486-IR I, covering work for the Air Force at GE under contract AF 33(657)-8794, available from ASTIA.

If machining with chemicals intrigues you, see H. Muller's "Chemical Milling of Exotic Materials," ASTME paper 486, or write him at Turco Products, Inc., P. O. Box 1055, Wilmington, Calif., for his "Chem-Mill Design Manual," which covers this patented process licensed by North American Aviation to Turco for sublicensing purposes.

On plasma torch machining, get O'Brien's "Applications of the Plasma Arc," ASTME paper SP63-56, and write to Mr. A. Snyder, Pratt & Whitney Co., West Hartford, Conn., for a summary of their latest work.

One comprehensive review of ultrasonic machining is Shaw's "Ultrasonic Grinding" in the Swiss journal *Microtechnic*, **10**, No. 6 (1956).

Recent experimental work of interest is covered in a WPAFB interim report by W. Pentland of Therm, Inc., Ithaca, N.Y. Informative

company brochures can be obtained from G. Barker, Raytheon Co., Lexington, Mass., and C. Nobis, Sheffield Co., Dayton, Ohio.

VAPOR-PHASE METALLURGY

by Robert Bakish *

IN BRIEF: *There are three main ways to make a material from its atomic building blocks. One is to deposit them from ionic solution by electrodeposition. Another is to condense them on the surface from the vapor phase. Both are established industrial processes. The third method is to deposit the atoms after extracting them from their volatile compounds by surface-catalyzed decomposition, reduction, or synthesis. Called variously gas plating, chemical vapor deposition, vapor-phase metallurgy, this technique has the advantages of greater speed, throwing power, and deposits free from pores. It has the disadvantages of currently expensive raw materials, occasional toxicity problems, product anisotropy, and the need for heated substrates to catalyze the reactions. Nevertheless, it is being used in many fields: semiconductors, microelectronics, high-purity materials, refractory materials, oxidation-resistant coatings for materials that corrode easily. It could be adapted for coating strip steel or building large metal shapes if problems of film nucleation and growth could be solved. The answers lie in the secrets of the crystalline state.—F.P.*

■ It's been called by a number of names: gas plating, pyrolytic deposition, molecular deposition, vapor forming, chemical vapor deposition, to cite a few. But I don't wish to debate the semantic merits of each here, because names of metallurgical processes can be a rather subjective matter. For my purpose, it will suffice to call the interesting and increasingly important process I'm going to discuss simply—vapor-phase metallurgy.

What do I mean by this? In essence, I mean a technology based on the ability to break down certain compounds, after converting them to a gaseous state, and to deposit materials thus extracted from them as either thin films or thick coatings. These deposited materials can be metallic or nonmetallic, and for this reason I'm not going to bear down hard on the word "metallurgy" in what follows.

Vapor-phase metallurgy is a chemical-reaction type of deposition process that can be thought of as a complementary to electroplat-

* Oriented toward vapor-phase metallurgy, thermo-electric materials, and electrochemical processes, Robert Bakish is a consulting engineer in Englewood, New Jersey.

ing and vacuum evaporation. As we shall see shortly, it can do certain tasks these established processes cannot. Still, it is thus far too complex and expensive a process to compete with them in the everyday jobs they do so well: plating of hardware, automobile parts, plastics, optical surfaces, and the like.

This kind of metallurgy is old in the sense that its rudiments are all well known and have been applied to the production of certain metals—mainly nickel and the refractory metals—for many years. But it is new in many respects: A spectrum of unusual tasks, such as the synthesis of compound semiconductor materials, are being attempted with it. The technical problems raised by these new tasks are stimulating research into a number of questions—for example, the exact nature of such vapor-phase deposited structures as the chromium crystal bar of Fig. 3-86. It is new also in that, under the stimulus of need, many new source materials, like the metal-organics, are being brought into play.

It seems to me that vapor-phase metallurgy can be most succinctly described as the production of deposits by means of surface-catalyzed thermal-decomposition or reduction of a variety of volatile compounds in their gaseous state. This suggests the kind of equipment that is needed, the basic elements of which are sketched in the margin: a retort in which to volatilize the compound containing the material we want, a carrier gas to take the vapor to a working chamber, a hot substrate on which to deposit the extract, and an exhaust to dispose of the by-products of the reaction.

Such a system can be as small as a bench-sized setup of laboratory glassware for growing experimental semiconductor films. Or, it can be as large as any small pilot-scale chemical plant, with steel retorts big enough to build refractory structures as large as a man for rockets and re-entry vehicles. And, if we adapted the process to, say, the coating of steel strip—a promising possibility—the equipment to do so might fill a room 20 ft by 20 ft. But this is getting ahead of my story. Let's look first at the deposition process itself.

Deposition, atom by atom

Inasmuch as the vapor phase is the key to this process, imagine for a moment a compound

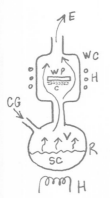

SC - Source Compound
CG - Carrier gas
R - Retort
V - Vapor
WC - Work chamber
H - Heater
C - Coating
E - Exhaust
WP - Workpiece

Fig. 3-86. This bar of ultrapure chromium crystals was built up on a hot tube by thermal decomposition of chromium iodide vapor. Cr of this purity (less than 10 ppm impurities) may lead to Cr alloys with improved ductility. (Courtesy J. M. Blocher, Battelle Memorial Institute)

that has been volatilized. By virtue of their thermal energy, the molecules of this vapor will fill the volume that constrains them. If, in the course of their random travels, the molecules hit a surface that is at a temperature equal to their decomposition temperature, the molecules will break down into constituent parts. If one of them is a metallic substance, a metallic atom will deposit on the surface, while the remaining atoms will continue their restless wandering.

More specifically, suppose we had a vapor of compound AB which breaks down into A and B atoms. At the equilibrium state, the following reaction will take place:

$$AB \rightleftarrows A + B$$

This reaction will be reversible even at the decomposition temperature *except* when we have a hot surface present. Such a surface catalyzes the decomposition process, shifts the equilibrium to the right, and allows one of the constituent atoms, say *A*, to be deposited. Increased temperature also shifts the equilibrium, as will the simultaneous presence of the temperature and a catalyzing surface.

In this manner, then, we can generate from certain compounds an atom-by-atom, surface-catalyzed deposition of useful constituents contained in these compounds. One of the great advantages of this vapor-phase metallurgy is that the product is always the result of an interaction that takes place on an atomic or molecular scale. It is a product with theoretical density and, when the reaction takes place properly, it is impervious. And, as I shall note shortly, vapor-phase processes can deposit such products by reduction or synthesis of volatile raw materials, as well as by decomposition, thus increasing the number of possible useful reactions.

Before examining some of these, it is important that we recall the two alternate and quite well-established processes which permit us to deposit metals and, in a few cases, non-metals. The first of these, and probably the oldest, is the process of electroplating (and its variant, electroforming) in which we have the reduction of a metal from a metal-ion containing solution. A typical reaction here might be that for copper:

$$Cu^{++} + 2e^- = Cu\ metal$$

413

The main limiting factor that concerns us here is that in electrolytic processes only metallic materials can be deposited.

Vacuum evaporation or metallizing is the second alternate process. It is purely physical in nature, involving as it does the vaporization of the material to be deposited and its recondensation on an appropriate substrate. We might express this "reaction" as follows:

$$Solid \xrightarrow{heat} Liquid \xrightarrow{heat} Vapor \rightarrow Solid + heat$$

Its primary disadvantage lies in the fact that deposition takes place in a vacuum, so that the material moves from source to substrate only by line-of-sight. This is a problem which can be partially overcome by clever geometrical disposition of the source material within the chamber, however.

One might reasonably ask: why use a vapor-phase chemical deposition process rather than one of these two established alternatives? One reason is that there is really no other way of manufacturing pore-free deposits of certain metals. Coatings made from the refractory metals are an example; they can't be electroplated from water solutions, and their high melting points make metallizing difficult.

The second, and just as vital, reason is that we can now prepare materials like the so-called pyrolytic deposits and the refractory oxides which we were in no position to make by alternate means. Thirdly, because the compound vapor tends to completely surround the object being plated, we have "throwing power" (an electroplating term) superior to that of any other process.

And finally, an important commercial consideration: these vapor-phase processes permit some of the highest rates of material build-up. Rates up to some 20 mil/hr are possible, and, in some cases, this is almost a two-fold increase in yield over either of the two alternate techniques.

Resources and reactions

From what kinds of compounds can we deposit materials by vapor-phase metallurgy? The tabulation in Fig. 3-87 shows some common deposits and whence they originate. We see that three broad groups are available: the inorganic halides, the purely organic compounds (for deposition of carbon, principally), and a fairly recent group—the so-called metal-organics. This last group includes, in addition to the alkyl and carbonyl families represented in the table, the aryls, arenes, arakyls, acetylacetonates, and cyclopentadienyls.

Sometimes classed with the metal-organics are the silanes (not shown in the table) which are vital to the vapor-phase deposition of a certain type of semiconductor film wherein the interaction between atomic structure of the deposit and of the substrate influences the film morphology significantly. Aside from such epitaxial films, silanes are employed to deposit silicon oxide films for electrical insulation purposes.

The table will give you a feel for the wide variety of compounds available, but it represents only a tiny fraction of the source materials under active study. More of them are cited in the bibliographical section at the end of the article. Despite this variety, I am certain that there exists on the organic chemists' shelves a whole host of compounds not as yet considered for vapor-phase deposition work. Perhaps an inventory is in order?

TYPICAL MATERIALS DEPOSITED BY VAPOR-PHASE METHOD

You can deposit this material…	from the compound listed in this column…	which appears in the form of a…	Compound is heated in retort to this temp. (°C)…	and deposited on workpiece at this temp. (°C)…	by the following process…
Tungsten, W	Tungsten hexafluoride, WF_6	gas	R.T.	300-600	Reduction of inorganic halide
Tantalum, Ta	Tantalum pentachloride, $TaCl_5$	solid	180	900-1400	
Silicon, Si	Silicon tetra-iodide, SiI_4	liquid	250	700-1200	
Iron, Fe	Iron pentachloride, $FeCl_5$	solid	300	1000	
Carbon, C (pyrolytic form)	Methane, CH_4	gas	R.T.	1000-2500	Decomposition of organic compound
	Acetylene, C_2H_2	gas	R.T.	1000-2500	
Aluminum, Al	Tri-isobutyl-aluminum, $Al(CH_3)_3$	gas	160	265	Decomposition of metal-organic compound
Nickel, Ni	Nickel carbonyl, $Ni(CO)_4$	liquid	40	>100	
Iron, Fe	Iron carbonyl, $Fe(CO)_5$	liquid	100	180-300	

Fig. 3-87. A few of the many materials deposited by vapor-phase metallurgy. Source compounds are inorganic halides, organics, and metal-organics. Decomposition or reduction are common deposition methods, but synthesis is also used. Note that a heated substrate is required—not the case in electroplating and vacuum evaporation.

To beneficiate these diverse compounds, a number of vapor-phase processing conditions have been adopted, Fig. 3-88. The decomposition reaction mentioned earlier is the simplest way of getting a useful product. An outstanding example is the decomposition of nickel carbonyl to get copper-free nickel. This is the essence of the Mond process, really the grandpapa of vapor-phase metallurgy since it was invented back in 1888. The most interesting, and even unique, feature of this process is that one of the decomposition products, CO, is recovered, recirculated, and used for the production of additional carbonyl—thus helping to produce nickel metal continuously.

Iron carbonyl can be similarly decomposed so as to produce iron, and a glance at the table indicates that here too we are dealing with a compound having a low decomposition temperature. This suggests that deposits from iron carbonyl could be used to construct magnetic films. In addition, we already know that carbonyl-deposited iron has corrosion resistance superior to that of iron deposited by alternate

methods. The reason for this is not entirely clear, though absorbed CO from the carbonyl may be responsible.

As suggested above, the carbonyls have been around a long time. A decomposition process of more recent vintage, one that has vapor plating enthusiasts champing at the bit, is the protection of steel and other corrosion-susceptible materials with aluminum or chromium. Economics is the obstacle here, however. The aluminum compounds that can be used, including the alkyl aluminum listed in the table, are too expensive. If we could produce these compounds cheaply, we might conceivably get such a coating process on an economic basis. Chromium coatings are in a similar situation. Excellent chrome plating can be laid down by the decomposition of chromium dicumene. In both cases, the nonporous nature of the coating will always permit a slightly higher price, but the classic vicious circle is there: to get compound cost down, volume production is needed; but volume won't come until the price is right.

In the case of carbon deposition, on the other

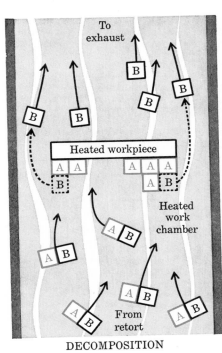
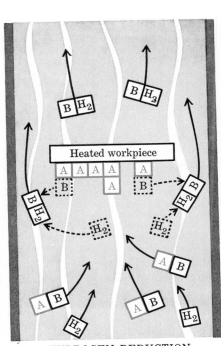
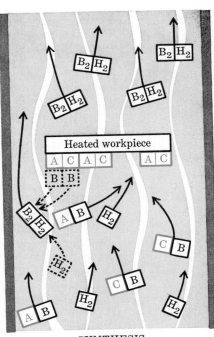

DECOMPOSITION

$$AB \xrightarrow{heat} A + B$$

HYDROGEN REDUCTION

$$AB + H_2 \xrightarrow{heat} A + BH_2$$

SYNTHESIS

$$AB + CB + H_2 \xrightarrow{heat} AC + B_2H_2$$

A B	= Compound AB containing product A
C B	= Compound CB containing product C
A C	= Resulting deposit = A
H₂	= Reducing gas
B₂ H₂	= Gaseous by-product

Carrier gas

Fig. 3-88. The three methods of vapor-phase metallurgy: decomposition, reduction, and synthesis. In each, atoms of material to be deposited are thermally dissociated from their compound vapors and deposited on hot workpiece (and on walls as well). Deposited layer then forms hot substrate for further reaction. Carrier gas can be reducing gas itself.

Fig. 3-89. You can deposit massive structures like these, as well as thin films, by vapor deposition techniques. Shown is an experimental rocket nozzle made of pyrolytic graphite, extracted by decomposition from methane or acetylene gas. Thick deposits become freestanding structures when substrate (mandrel or mold) is removed. Pebbled appearance of surface here shows ends of columnar pyrolytic structure. (Courtesy R. J. Diefendorf, GE Research Laboratories)

hand, the economics are favorable, for the source materials—methane and acetylene—are readily available. Decomposition of these materials is the basis for a fast-growing industry —vapor-phase deposition of anisotropic carbons. These materials are of great interest because of their unusual thermal and electrical properties at high temperature.

However, I focus on them briefly here for a different reason: they are an excellent example of how large structures, not just thin films, can be constructed by vapor-phase deposition techniques. What makes such massive structures as the one in Fig. 3-89 commercially feasible, of course, is the high deposition rate compared to other processes. There are other methods for making large shapes—for example, machining or sintering in situ (see "Powder Fabrication," page 465). But the product, whether a graphite or a metal, has very different properties.

Reduction and synthesis

The reduction reaction is the second of the important reactions governing vapor-phase metallurgy processes. The most common reducing agent is hydrogen, and we might express the essence of this reaction symbolically as:

$$AB + H_2 \rightleftarrows A + BH_2$$

It usually takes place at elevated temperature, where the equilibrium can be easily displaced to the right. The hydrogen has a greater affinity for the B constituent of the compound than for the A constituent, which we seek.

This reaction is employed to make many pure metals. For example, all the halides tabulated in Fig. 3-87 will yield their respective metals this way. In the 1930's, van Arkel and de Boer developed their iodide process for titanium and zirconium, and began what has become today's refractory metals industry.

In the last year or two, reduction of tung-

sten hexafluoride has been used to deposit refractory coatings on graphite shapes used in rocket engines. Such coatings, though resistant to hot exhaust gases, have had a tendency to crack because of thermal expansion mismatch with the graphite. More recently, WF_6 is being reduced to yield experimental quantities of bulk tungsten. On a production basis, we find both titanium and niobium being produced from their respective chlorides.

An extension of the reduction reaction is the so-called co-reduction of one or more compounds simultaneously. The compounds to be co-reduced must be chosen so that no interreaction tendencies between the species occur at the reduction temperature. Direct co-reduction of mixed halides appears quite promising. For example, tantalum and niobium appear in most minerals together, and it might just be that we could make Ta-Nb alloys by co-reducing their chlorides in the vapor phase. More commonly, semiconducting alloys of silicon and germanium are easily made by co-reduction of their halides.

The third important vapor-phase reaction is synthesis, where two or more compounds are recombined into a single complex compound of desirable properties. The following reaction will express the simplest of these, a binary synthesis:

$$AB + CB + H_2 \rightleftarrows AC + B_2H_2$$

where the compound of recombination AC is desired for deposition, and B_2H_2 is waste.

Although ternary and quarternary deposits are not impossible, we are dealing here with a somewhat more complex problem. For each new compound product, the precise conditions must be established that will shift the reaction from left to right profitably. Consequently, work has barely begun on vapor-phase deposition of such complex compounds; binary reactions look promising enough.

Synthesis, like co-reduction, is accomplished

most easily when we interact compounds of the same or related families. A good example is the preparation of the so-called intermetallic compounds for semiconductor applications, using the halides as raw materials. Indium telluride (In-Te) and indium antimonide (In-Sb) are two of many such compounds that have been made in this way. Such compound semiconductors are being studied intensively as suitable materials for thermoelectric generation of electric power from heat, and for other electronic applications.

There are several intriguing factors linking thermoelectric semiconductors of this type with vapor-phase metallurgy. First is the fact that comparatively thick (up to about ¼ in.) deposits are needed in thermoelectric devices—a requirement that can be met economically by vapor plating. Secondly, synthesis during the deposition process itself would sidestep the danger of partial decomposition that might occur if the intermetallic compound was made first and deposited later by vacuum evaporation. This is important, for the properties of intermetallics vary sharply with slight changes in composition.

And finally, a most desirable practical advantage: thermoelectric modules could be vapor-plated in situ, in pre-set patterns, just as thin-film circuits are built up by metalizing. These factors, plus the flexibility by which various compositions can be made and tried out, are sure to bring forth some startling developments in thermoelectric generators.

Synthesis from the vapor phase is also being tried with materials normally created by decomposition. For example, metallic halides and hydrocarbon gases are being interacted to form pyrolytic graphite "alloys" containing tantalum, niobium, zirconium, and molybdenum. Similarly, pyrolytic carbides of metals such as niobium, zirconium, hafnium, and tantalum are being formed. The goal here, of course, is composite metals that provide suitable electronic materials at very high temperatures—well in excess of the 200°C limit on current solid-state devices.

A matter of choice

The type of reaction—decomposition, reduction, or synthesis—is an important criterion in selecting the right compound for vapor deposition, but not the sole one. Suppose we wish to deposit high-purity iron. The tabulation of Fig. 3-87 shows that we might simply decompose iron carbonyl at a relatively low temperature of 200°C. Or we might use the hydrogen reduction of iron chloride at a much higher temperature, 1000°C. On the basis of reaction, the first and simpler of the two would be the choice.

However, in selecting the carbonyl we would have to give up the goal of extreme purity, for the carbonyl iron almost invariably contains some residual carbon. This would not, of course, be true with the halide iron.

Both these compounds happen to be good ones. They possess almost all of the features one likes to see in a vapor-phase compound. They have good volatility, they can be obtained pure (iron carbonyl) or extremely pure (iron chloride), and they are not unreasonably priced. Both are quite stable, although somewhat hygroscopic. They are only mildly toxic and can be handled without undue precautions. Both decompose completely, leading to a product of good purity. The large difference between their evaporation temperature and their decomposition and reduction temperature, respectively, assures efficient vapor transfer from the retort to the work chamber.

Now consider nickel carbonyl, $Ni(CO)_4$, also listed in the table. This is a good compound by all the criteria discussed for the iron compounds. It is even better from the point of view of volatility, and its very low decomposition temperature makes it easy to use. However, nickel carbonyl is one of the most toxic compounds known, and should not be used unless extreme protective measures are taken.

All the halides face a common difficulty as source materials because of their great sensitivity to moisture and to oxidation. Under these conditions they convert to oxyhalides, useless materials because they are so stable they cannot be volatilized with ease. It should be noted, too, that most of the metal-organic compounds are very susceptible to oxidation. Some are pyrophoric and even explosive.

While on the matter of compounds and their suitability for vapor-phase metallurgy, I should like to emphasize one point concerning decomposition temperature. Chemists and metallurgists have quite different notions as to what this temperature is for a given compound. The difficulty arises from the matter of rate. The chemist usually wants to know at what temperature will the compound *begin* to break down. In vapor-phase metallurgy, success or failure turns on *how fast* breakdown takes place. So, in selecting source materials, always look beyond the normally listed decomposition temperature to that temperature (usually higher) at which the reaction proceeds at a significant rate.

Don't overlook nonmetallic deposits

I mentioned at the outset that the discussion would not be limited to metal depositions. One nonmetal (really a semimetal) has been discussed—pyrolytic graphite. Vapor-phase deposition is also an efficient way to make dense ceramics. Beryllia, zirconia, alumina, and magnesia, for example, are often laid down from their respective halides—mostly chlorides.

Such deposits are having a profound impact on many problems of advanced materials technology. The coating of nuclear fuel materials is an excellent recent example of this, and it also shows how vapor deposition can couple nicely with an established beneficiation process. By passing the appropriate hot-compound vapors through a bed containing fine particles of uranium (or its oxides or carbides), we can now apply protective coatings of alumina, beryllia, or pyrolytic graphite (see Fig. 3-90). When these coated particles are consolidated by powder fabrication techniques, we have fuel elements better able to retain their fission products and to remain stable in the difficult environment of a reactor.

Using the gas-fluidized bed method of coating particles, we are in a position to re-examine the whole area of metal-ceramics, the so-called cermets that showed so much promise a few years

back. Perhaps ceramic-coated metal powders (or the reverse) will provide the elusive optimum conditions of bonding that can turn the sintered metal-ceramic into an unqualified success.

One method of strengthening ceramic structures is to reinforce them with a network of higher-strength fibers, leading to the so-called fiber composites. Here, vapor-phase metallurgy has one answer, because ultrahigh-strength metal whiskers can be grown by the reduction of metal halides. More than 15 halides have been used for this purpose, and whiskers have been grown 1–50 microns in diameter and up to 5 cm in length. Their advantage as reinforcing agents is that they are essentially free of dislocations and thus their strength approaches the theoretical strength of their base metals.

Problems and opportunities

While introducing a number of different application areas into this narrative, I do not wish to imply that vapor-phase metallurgy is without its problems, or that it is a cure-all process. Neither is true. It is a process that complements both vacuum evaporation and electroplating, and it has its limitations. I have mentioned the problems of economics and occasional toxicity. Let's examine a few others.

From a practical standpoint, the most important of these stems directly from the need for temperatures above ambient to make the vapor processes work. This means that many substrates of interest cannot be coated this way. For example, we could not lay down any of the coating materials tabulated in Fig. 3-87 (with the possible exception of nickel from its carbonyl) on paper, textile fibers, or the many industrially useful plastics without doing some structural damage.

The temperatures to which such materials can be exposed are climbing steadily but slowly. Yet, the real need is for source compounds having high volatilities at much lower temperatures of decomposition or reduction than exist at the present time. Indeed, no more fruitful area of research for the chemist in support of vapor-phase metallurgy can be imagined.

A second practical problem derives from a virtue of the vapor-phase processes. Since the reacting gas completely surrounds any object placed in the work chamber, the surface we coat can be of any shape—the gas can reach the deepest recess. However, when we are interested in uniformity of coating thickness, then we must make sure the surface-catalyzed reaction takes place evenly on all surfaces. Thus, the gas flow must be arranged properly by means of baffles or moving jets, for example,

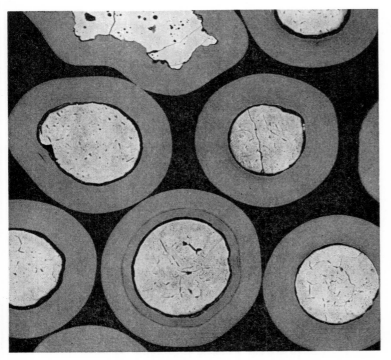

Fig. 3-90. Float hot particles in a stream of gas that contains the coating element desired, and you can deposit a thin, uniform layer on each, like the 125 micron coating of pyrolytic graphite on these uranium carbide particles. This fluidized bed method may soon be used to coat fine particles for dispersion hardening in metals, and for extracting niobium from $NbCl_5$ seed particles. (Courtesy J. M. Blocher, Battelle Memorial Institute)

as sketched in the margin. Both electroplating and vacuum evaporation have analogous problems of deposit accessibility.

When we turn to the vapor deposition of free-standing structures, we have other problems that interfere with production rates. Freestanding objects, like that of Fig. 3-89, must be deposited in molds or on mandrels which must then be removed. This is a problem best resolved by designing split molds (or mandrels) or molds that can be dissolved or destroyed without attacking the deposit. Graphite, copper, or glass are the most commonly used materials for this purpose.

And finally, there is the broad question of the structural nature of the products deposited from vapor-phase reactions. Because of the variety of source compounds, reactions we can choose, and the conditions for them, we encounter a great variety of deposited structures. From deposits of very fine and random grain size (i.e., the metal oxides), we can go all the way to single crystals having considerable order and freedom from dislocations (i.e., the metal whiskers).

The problem is to control these various structures in the making so that they fit our needs. For example, many vapor-deposited materials tend to grow in columnar form at right angles to the substrate, but these structures link together poorly one to another. In the case of pyrolytic graphite, this is a boon, for the resulting anisotropy gives good heat conduction along the surface of deposition (thus allowing heat to dissipate fast laterally), and poor conduction toward the surface (thus protecting it from thermal damage). But the accompanying anisotropy in mechanical strength is a disadvantage. Indeed, in the case of tungsten protective coatings, mechanical weakness along the surface leading to cracks is one source of unexpectedly poor performance.

Of all the problems in structure control, perhaps the most demanding are those imposed by semiconductor requirements. Here, we seek special orientations, low concentrations of imperfections, and the ability to attain these goals while still controlling composition closely. We still don't know, for example, precisely what role impurities (i.e., doping agents) play in the morphology of the deposits laid down for semiconductor uses. Until we understand more fully just how nucleation and crystal growth occurs

from the various vapor-phase reactions, we cannot intelligently exploit this technique for tomorrow's transistors, rectifiers, solar cells, and microelectronic circuits.

Further reading

Since the advent of semiconductors, the vapor-deposition field has sprawled rapidly, and unified references are hard to find. For example, the only book in the field, *Vapor Plating* by Powell, Campbell, and Gonser (Wiley, 1955, $5.50) is quite out of date. The authors are preparing a new edition some three times as long as the first.

In the meantime, for a single volume reference, get hold of Report No. 170 from Battelle's Defense Metal Information Center called "Chemical Vapor Deposition" (document AD 281887, OTS, Dept. of Commerce, Washington, D.C., $2.25). A summary of this report appears in the March 1963 issue of Battelle Technical Review entitled "Chemical Vapor Deposition—A Rediscovered Tool for Molecular Engineering," by Blocher.

A short review, emphasizing experimental setups as well as applications, is "Vapor-Phase Metallurgy and Ceramics" by Bakish, Gellar, and Marinow, *Jour. of Metals*, Oct. 1962.

A useful, concise listing of important papers *and patents* since 1958 is Coughlen's "Bibliography of Materials Plating by Thermal Decomposition of Gases or Vapors," University of California (Lawrence Radiation Lab) Report No. 6997, prepared for the AEC (OTS, 50¢). The included patent listing is particularly valuable since, in a fast-moving field, useful technical articles often lag patent disclosures.

The diversity of the field can be sensed also from the variety of articles from *International Science and Technology* which have dealt with related aspects. In addition to the one cited in the text ("Powder Fabrication"), you should also check (along with their bibliographies) the following: "Pyrolitic Graphite," Aug. 1962; "Electricity from Heat," March 1962; "Metal Oxides Ceramics," Feb. 1962; "Thin Films," Feb. 1962; and "Protective Coatings," Aug. 1962.

For those readers interested in attempting vapor plating themselves, source compound information can be found in Kaufman's *Handbook of Organometallic Compounds* (Van Nostrand, 1961, $27.50).

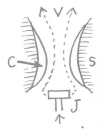

Stationary jet gives uneven coating:

C – coating
S – substrate
V – Vapor
J – Jet

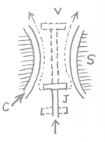

Moving jet gives even coating:

Baffles direct gas into recess:

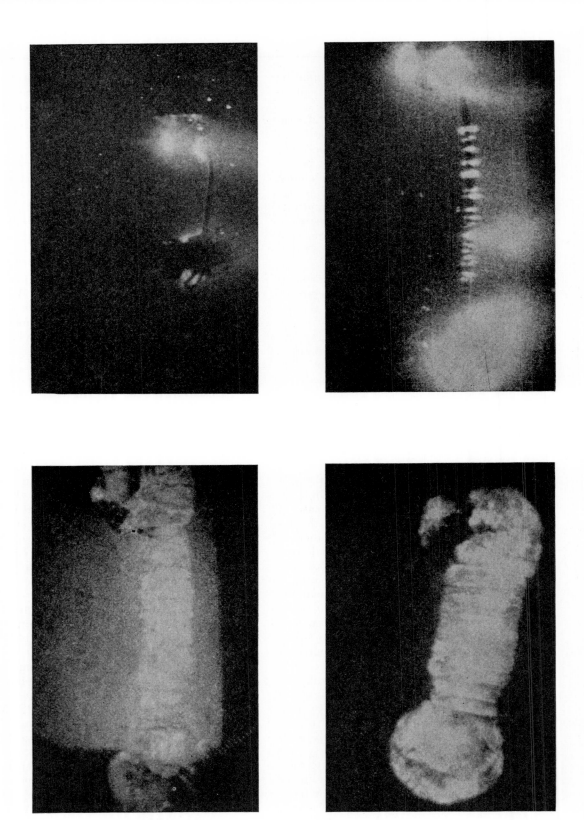

Fig. 3-91. *Reading left to right and* **top to bottom,** *four events in the life of a wire exploding under water during electrical discharge at Republic Aviation. First, wire glows at 10 μsec after capacitor-stored energy surges through it. Then, at 20 μsec, vaporization begins. After 40 μsec, the wire is vaporized, and a plasma channel forms. Finally, at 50 μsec, the channel begins to expand. (Courtesy Republic Aviation Corp.)*

Fig. 3-92. Pressures generated by electrical discharges like that in Fig. 3-91 can deform metal into shapes like this piece made at Electro-Hydraulics Corp. Note that steps usually done separately—forming, flanging, trimming, and punching—are done here in one operation. (Courtesy Hans Basken)

HIGH ENERGY RATE METALWORKING

by Ford Park *

IN BRIEF: *The requirements today for things shaped from metal are more severe than ever before: They must be more precise, more intricately shaped, in sizes that often strain the capacity of conventional metalworking equipment.*

Most often confronted with such problems, the aerospace industry is leading the attack on them with a variety of new metalworking techniques—all characterized by unusually high rates of energy input. You can now shape metals in microseconds with high transient pressures generated by rapidly releasing energy from explosives, combustible gas mixtures, compressed gases, or from high-voltage capacitor banks.

These methods are becoming economical enough to interest other industries. But we still don't know precisely how they deform metals so effectively. The answer may lie in dislocation theory. Once we know for sure, the high energy rate processes, and the more conventional ones they supplement, will become even more efficient and economical. Then metalworking can accelerate its progress from an art to a science. —F.P.

■ The wire you see exploding under water in Fig. 3-91 is a giant fuse—the final release mechanism for enormous quantities of electrical energy stored in capacitors. The atom bomblike plasma cloud that results may endure for several hundred microseconds. But in the first microsecond of its life, pressures in the order of 10,000 atmospheres may be generated. Though quickly attenuated by the surrounding water, this pressure pulse is easily transmitted to a metal workpiece immersed in the water—plastically deforming it into a waiting die. The result: a useful, close-tolerance metal part like the one illustrated in Fig. 3-92—produced in a fraction of a second.

* Ford Park is Associate Editor of *International Science and Technology*.

This "electrohydraulic" technique is but one of several new methods of working metals faster than they have ever been worked before by application of high transient pressures. The source of the high pressure is varied and ingenious: Instead of releasing stored electrical energy into an explodable wire, it can also be released at open electrodes—creating a high peak energy spark. Or the current can be pulsed through a magnetic coil, inducing a current in the workpiece that interacts with the magnetic field to do the work. In one of the more developed techniques, pressure pulses are generated by explosives detonated at or near the workpiece. Slower-burning propellants and explosive gas mixtures, ignited in closed die systems, are also employed in production today. And the mechanical press has not been overlooked: sophisticated presses are now available in which the sudden release of compressed gas drives a lightweight ram at very high velocities at the workpiece.

The feature that all these techniques have in common is the application of a high pressure over a given area so that the metal moves enough to take a permanent set in a very short time. Expressed dimensionally, this characteristic is simply (lb/sq in.)(sq in.)(in./sec), which reduces to the rate of energy input (in.-lb/sec) to the workpiece—certainly a common enough feature in any metalworking process. Here, however, pressures as high as several thousand lb/sq in. or deformation times as low as a few microseconds are sufficient to lift the energy rate for these processes into an order of magnitude far above that of the conventional metalworking techniques.

For example, a fraction of a pound of high explosive can release some 10^6 in.-lbs of energy to form a metal part at a rate 20,000 times the release rate of a conventional heavy-duty press. This points up one of the key features of these processes: their ability to deliver large amounts of power at relatively low cost. And the availability of these high-energy rates offers an opportunity to form many of the new metals and alloys—materials that have been developed to resist extreme environments, but that have proved most difficult to shape.

Before turning to the question of how these at high energy rate processes work, it is important to point out that they have features other than their energy characteristics that make them desirable additions to the spectrum of metalworking techniques—regardless of the material being formed. These include such considerations as reduced tooling costs, the ability to form re-entrant corners, to shape metal in a vacuum or in place in a subassembly, to true up already fabricated structures, or to add cutouts or stiffening beads to them. Such seemingly mundane problems are the stuff of ordinary everyday engineering producibility. Without the means for solving them, many of today's product designs would not emerge.

Two other factors of vital practical importance should be mentioned before the processes themselves are examined.

First of these is the more uniform manner in which the impacting pressure introduces forming energy into the workpiece, compared to conventional metalworking practice. In a sense, you can think of the fluid pressure (except in the case of the high-speed ram) as a flexible punch that imparts energy to all particles of the workpiece simultaneously. There is some argument about whether the transmitting fluid pushes the workpiece into all portions of the die, or whether it simply acts as a coupling medium to allow the pressure waves to get the metal moving. Whatever the precise mechanism, the male die has been sidestepped. This means that much of the complex system of localized yielding and redistribution of stresses by point-to-point plastic flow is avoided. With high energy input to all parts of the workpiece, plastic flow in one degree or other can start quickly in many parts of the metal. As long as the *relative* velocity between adjacent particles does not exceed a critical value—from one hundred to several hundred ft/sec, depending upon the metal—the part will not fracture before it hits the die and is formed.

The second major factor, as suggested earlier, is economic in nature and relates to producibility requirements. For example, consider the "impossible" sizes of metal components required these days, particularly in the aerospace industry. To build a mechanical press large enough to form a bulkhead some 30-odd feet in diameter for the next generation of liquid-propelled space vehicles is clearly out of the question from a cost standpoint. But to detonate a few pounds of high explosive underwater near a metal blank

stretched over a suitable open die has the potential of accomplishing this task at modest cost. At the other end of the production-rate spectrum the picture is less clear—except in the case of forging, where any sidestepping of machining costs is a boon. Still, if a pressure pulse can be generated by spark discharge at rate of one per second—and this is the rate being achieved now with commercial equipment—then the possibilities for meeting the high production rates of, say, the auto industry are great.

A detailed comparison of the various high energy rate processes for the purpose of selecting one of them for a given task within the production spectrum is beyond the purpose and scope of this survey. However, the table on page 423 will give a qualitative feel for their interrelationship so that the following discussion of each technique, and how it works, will have some perspective.

Forming with explosives

Explosive forming is the oldest of the high energy rate metalworking techniques, going back before the turn of this century. Then, it was used for embossing, engraving, and, legend has it, for the manufacture of that pre-suffrage bit of Americana—the brass spittoon. In the last five years, the method has experienced a renaissance stimulated by the special needs of the aerospace industry for large metal structures, often of hard-to-work materials.

A typical example is the production of a hyperbolic radar reflector. The problem faced here by the Columbus Division of North American Aviation was to make the reflecting "skin" of a radar antenna which would ultimately be assembled in an adhesive-bonded sandwich construction. The solution, in brief, was to cast and machine a large Kirksite (zinc base alloy) die, clamp the specially rolled 6061 aluminum alloy blank over it, suspend a suitable configuration of Primacord explosive over the blank, immerse the assembly in a pool of water, and detonate the explosive—thus forming the part.

The result: a 10-ft diameter, 0.160-in. thick reflector, formed to the correct shape and tolerance required for the antenna. The cost: less than $8500, over 95% of which was the cost of the material and the die. Actual forming of the reflector consumed some 40-odd man hours. The cost of the explosive to provide the forming energy: less than $3. At such a price, the energy to form large metal parts is well within the reach of anyone.

There are two distinctly different types of explosives used in metal forming: high explosives and low explosives or propellants. High explosives are characterized by detona-

SUMMARY OF HIGH ENERGY RATE METALWORKING TECHNIQUES

		EXPLOSIVE FORMING			PNEUMATIC-MECHANICAL	ELECTRIC DISCHARGE		
		High explosives	Propellants	Gas Mixtures	High pressure gas	Exploding wire	Spark discharge	Magnetic field
Source characteristics	Method of energy release	Chemical detonation	Chemical burning	Chemical burning	Quick-release valve	Vaporization of wire	Ionization of medium	Collapsing magnetic field
	Energy-transfer medium	Water, air, sand	Air, water	Gas	Air	Water, air	Water, air	Air
	Pressure-wave velocity, ft/sec	4,000–25,000	1,000–8,000	1,000–8,000	50–200	20,000	20,000	10,000–20,000
	Pressure-wave duration	Microseconds	Milliseconds	Milliseconds	Milliseconds	Microseconds	Microseconds	Microseconds
Adaptability	Location of facility	Remote	Separate	Separate	Unrestricted	Separate	Separate	Separate
	Part diameter limits	10 ft.	5 ft.	5 ft.	Present: 1.5 ft. Future: 3 ft.	Present: 5 ft. Future: 10 ft.	Present: 3 ft. Future: 5 ft.	Present: 1 ft. Future: 4 ft.
	Shape versatility	Good	Good	Fair	Excellent	Good	Good	Fair
	Uses for technique reported to date	Blanking, coining, powder compacting, cutting, embossing, drawing, expanding, flanging, hardening, joining, sizing, stretching	Bulging, compacting, sizing, stud driving, machining	Bulging, stretching, sizing	Compacting, drawing, extruding, forging, stretching, upsetting	Bulging, stretching, sizing	Bulging, stretching, sizing, coining, embossing, expanding	Swaging, joining, shrinking
	Main advantage	Large part size	Hand tool	Pressure control	Precision forgings	Reproducibility	Operating Ease	Swaging operations
Process selection factors	Capital investment	Low to medium	Low	Medium	Medium to high	Medium to high	Medium to high	Medium to high
	Tooling costs	Low	Medium	High	Medium	Medium	Medium	High
	Operating costs	High	Low to medium	High	Low	Medium	Medium	Medium
	Energy costs	Low to medium	Medium to high	Very low	Low	High	High	High
	Cycle time, present:	High	Medium	High	Low	High	Medium	Medium
	future:	Medium	Medium	Medium	Very low	Low	Very low	Low
	Safety considerations	Only trained personnel should operate			Conventional guards & interlocks	Restricted access and safety interlock required as with all high voltage equipment.		
Typical suppliers	Equipment or energy sources	American Cyanamid Co. Atlas Chemical Industries Chromalloy Corp. (Propellex Div.) E. I. DuPont de Nemours Hercules Powder Co. Olin Mathieson Chemical Corp. The Ensign-Bickford Co.			General Dynamics Corp. (Advanced Products Dept.) Ken-O-Matic Corp. (Los Angeles) U.S. Industries (Clearing Div.)	Electro-Dynamics Inc. (Detroit) • Electro-Hydraulics Corp. (Ft. Worth) • Electronic-Acoustic Research Inc. (Santa Barbara) • General Electric Co. • General Dynamics (Advanced Products Dept.—*spark*) • General Dynamics (General Atomic Div.—*magnetic*) • Westinghouse Electric Corp.		
Areas requiring development	Practical	• Charge standardization • Elimination of blasting caps • Tooling methods for large dies • Process and design data	• Improved reproducibility • Elimination of heavy dies	• Mixture control • Chamber shape for consistent firing • Elimination of heavy dies	• New tooling concepts and materials • Methods for slowing extrusions • Larger capacity machines	• Improved switching devices • Equipment cost reduction	• Longer-lasting electrodes • Better control of discharge characteristics	• Permanent coil designs • Development for use on nontubular parts
	Theoretical & experimental	Effect of high strain rates on metal properties; A comprehensive analysis for high energy rate deformation and formability of metals; Complete energy balance for all processes; Investigation of shock-wave attenuation in various media; A systematic method of tool design for high-energy-rate processes; Proper metallurgical treatments for metals formed by these processes; Fundamental investigation of the transition from burning to detonation in gas mixtures; Development of better measuring devices for high pressures.						

(a)

(b)

(c)

(d)

(e)

Fig. 3-93. Steps in explosive forming: (a) cast and machine die; (b) clamp metal blank in place; (c) suspend explosive over blank; (d) immerse, and detonate explosive; (e) remove the formed part, and inspect. (Courtesy North American Aviation)

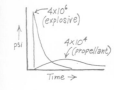

tion—extremely fast rates of reaction and high pressures. Low explosives, on the other hand, deflagrate—burning more slowly and developing much lower pressures. Whether the explosive detonates or deflagrates, the energy released is about the same: roughly 1000 calories per gram (or 1.6 megajoules per lb), not all of which, of course, is available for forming the part.

When a high explosive detonates, pressures developed at its surface can be as high as 4 million psi and last for a microsecond or so. A short distance away, the pressure is much lower, but its duration is longer. Propellants, when properly confined, build up pressures too,

but here they are in the order of 40,000 psi, and the pulse endures for milliseconds rather than microseconds.

Explosive forming operations fall into three categories: First, those in which a high explosive is detonated in contact with the workpiece—a system used to harden steels, compact metal powders, weld metals or cut them. Second, those in which sheet metal structures are sized or formed by drawing, using high explosives detonated in air or in water at some "standoff" distance from the blank. And third, those in which a closed system is used, with the pressure being generated by propellants or low explosives.

Fig. 3-94. Explosive forming is also done in closed dies. Here, engine exhaust duct is formed at Rohr Corp. from 321 stainless steel 0.025 in. thick. (Courtesy Rohr Corp.)

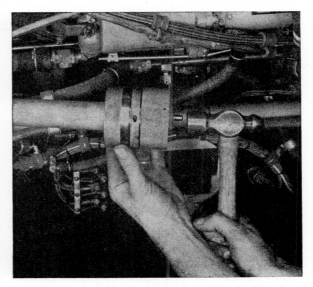

Fig. 3-95. Propellants adapt easily to hand tools. Above, AM 350 tubing to be brazed is expanded in place at Rohr by exploding a cartridge in a special tool. (Courtesy Rohr Corp.)

It is the last two categories that have most importance for the present subject. Here, the pressure and momentum of the explosion products are transmitted to the workpiece through the coupling medium in the form of a shock wave—a high pressure wave with a discontinuous jump at the front, and a more or less rapid decline of pressure following. As shown by the velocities in the table, such a wave travels very rapidly.

Just how effective this wave is in deforming the metal depends upon many factors. If the explosive is near the water surface, for example, the question arises as to whether reflected waves from the water-air interface will affect the "working" pressure wave unduly before it impacts the blank. Or, a reflection from a nearby solid surface may affect the shock wave. Assuming that an effective amount of energy arrives successfully at the workpiece, and that there is effective acoustic coupling between them, it is now a question of interaction between the wave and the blank (which interaction is, in turn, influenced by the material properties and the die shape) that determines whether the part will be formed successfully.

When the pressure wave impacts the blank it splits into a transmitted wave and a reflected wave. The transmitted wave gives up part of its energy to the material, the rest being reflected back from the far side. Further energy is given up by the reflected wave, which in turn reflects from the front surface—setting up a series of reverberations. The energy transfer process is quite complex, but the end result is to put the blank into motion and to set up a pressure difference between the front and back surfaces. Plastic deformation of the workpiece arises from the combined action of the kinetic energy imparted to it and the pressure energy applied.

The uses of contact explosives

If the explosive is detonated in intimate contact with the workpiece, then the agents that bring about change are shock waves generated within the metal itself. As indicated earlier, pressures generated at the explosive surface—and hence in this case at the metal surface—are in the order of several million psi. Such high pressures set up exceedingly high stresses just inside the metal. The transient stress distribution thus generated is transmitted at high velocity throughout the metal—producing fracture, plastic flow, work-hardening, or other effects depending upon the metal-explosive system.

Since the peregrinations of transient stress waves in solids have been largely charted (see "Further reading"), we shall not concern ourselves with them here. It is interesting to note, however, that because of these extreme internal pressures and their short duration, these interactions are not ones with which metallurgists and others concerned with metal forming are ordinarily familiar. There is thus a whole new environment for metallurgical investigation, since through clever design of the metal-explosive system it is possible to control very precisely the distributions and durations of these pressures.

This technique is currently being used to work-harden alloys for abrasion-resistant applications. Manganese steels, for example, resist abrasion well but are difficult to work-harden deeply. By detonating a sheet of explosive on the surface, parts such as teeth for excavating shovels can be work-hardened to a depth of ¼ in. and more, thereby greatly increasing abrasion resistance. Specific patterns of failure induced by contact explosives can also be employed to split ingots by simultaneously detonating charges on opposite faces; or the tenacious internal scale on heating pipes can be jarred loose by detonating explosives on the outer surface.

Perhaps the most interesting work lies ahead, however, in the realm of the metallurgical unknown. One good example, stemming from research at Stanford Research Institute on explosive welding of dissimilar metals, is the possibility of inducing extremely high diffusion rates by means of contact explosives. Investigators at SRI, in trying to drive plates of copper and gold together explosively to form a weld, have discovered that the intermetallic compound $AuCu_3$ forms in the weld zone. Since the process consumed roughly one microsecond, and the temperatures apparently did not get very high, the existence of this diffusion process indicates that it may be possible to alloy metals —even carry out high-pressure chemical reactions—without the high temperature normally required. The exact mechanism of these very high diffusion rates, and the precise pressures and temperatures that exist, need more study.

Forming with burning gas mixtures

By igniting a mixture of hydrogen and oxygen in a closed die, metal parts can be formed by a process akin to explosive forming by propellants. With gas mixtures, however, the energy source assumes the shape of the container and becomes, if it can be ignited in a fairly uniform manner, a charge of optimum shape. This technique is used as a supplement to more conventional explosive forming techniques, being brought into play when the part to be formed is thin and likely to rupture under uneven pressure distribution, or when production rates are high enough to make open-tank explosive forming uneconomical.

A typical setup at The Boeing Company, where the technique was developed, is shown in Fig. 3-96. This method can start with either a flat sheet or with the part roughly preformed to shape before firing. In the case of the missile part shown in the die here, the preform was simply a welded right cone. The ends of the die chamber serve to seal the interior of the preform to create a combustion chamber, and to provide entry to the interior for the gas mixture.

When the right initial pressure—from 1 to 10 atm—is reached, the mixture is fired with a glow wire or a simple spark plug. Burning takes place continuously in successive concentric spheres until the peak pressure is reached at the container wall. Heat transfer to the wall then cools the combustion gas so that the pressure drops slowly to atmospheric. Forming pressures attained are much lower than for explosive propellant forming—in the order of a few hundred psi.

Other gases such as methane or ethane can be employed as fuels. Hydrogen, however, is relatively cheap, is a simple and predictable element, and its reaction with oxygen is well known and catalogued. A typical mixture would be: 3 parts hydrogen, 1 part oxygen, and 1 part nitrogen—this last constituent being a diluent which can also be argon or carbon dioxide. The purpose of the diluent is to provide greater control over the reaction and its duration, and, particularly, to prevent unstable detonation and the unpredictable overpressures that can result therefrom. This problem of unexpected transition from deflagration to detonation is a complex one. In addition, there is a paucity of information on such transitions, and further research on the precise mechanism would be most useful since dies for the process could be made lighter if the conditions for transition could be avoided.

The high-speed ram for metalworking

Pneumatic-mechanical systems for high energy rate metalworking employ compressed gas, suddenly released, as an energy source. Conceptually, high-speed ram devices have much more in common with conventional presses than with the fluid-pressure techniques we have been discussing. However, they belong in this survey because the rate of energy available from these devices is so high, some five times as high as that available from conventionally designed presses. Though below that available from explosives or spark discharges, the energy

Fig. 3-96. Heavy closed dies like this one at The Boeing Co. are required to form metals with explosive gas mixtures. Note valving system for adjusting gas mixture properly. (Courtesy Boeing Co.)

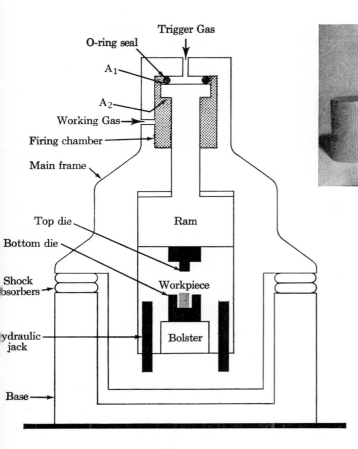

Labels on diagram (top to bottom, left):
Trigger Gas
O-ring seal
A_1
A_2
Working Gas
Firing chamber
Main frame
Top die
Bottom die
Shock absorbers
Hydraulic jack
Base
Ram
Workpiece
Bolster

Fig. 3-97. *High speed press of the type sketched at left forged the corner, shown above, for fuel tank on Convair 880 jet transport. Pictured at left is the aluminum alloy billet; at center, corner is partly formed; at right, the finished part. High pressure gas, applied to the ram by sudden opening of O-ring, drives the ram toward the billet at high speed. Part was formed in three blows by Precision Forge Co., Santa Monica. (Courtesy General Dynamics)*

rate that is available is sufficient to forge, extrude, compact, or stamp metals that are quite hard to shape on the slower machines.

Before we examine what kinds of tasks the high-speed presses are performing, let's get an idea of how a typical press of this type works. As shown in Fig. 3-97, high pressure gas—air or nitrogen at about 2000 psi—holds a ram in position while the workpiece is inserted in one die-half. Full working-gas pressure is prevented from acting over the entire ram area by a pressure seal, here a rubber O-ring. With area A_2 designed to be greater than area A_1 surrounding the seal, the ram is held in a "cocked" position.

Now the device is ready for firing. By cracking the seal, done here by introducing a small surge of "trigger" gas through an orifice inside the O-ring, the high pressure gas is applied to the full driving area. Since this is much larger than the differential area over which the high pressure acts to just barely support the ram, a large unbalanced force is generated. This drives the ram containing the other die-half at high velocity—in the order of 100 ft/sec—toward the workpiece. The same driving force acts upward against the main frame, accelerating the workpiece toward the approaching ram. The ram and main frame must have equal momenta at impact. In this particular device, designed by the Advanced Products Department of General Dynamics Corp., a light mass at

high downward velocity impacts a heavy mass at low upward velocity.

The energy at impact may be in the order of 200,000 ft-lb, absorbed by the workpiece in a few milliseconds. Any slight excess energy is dissipated in the shock absorbers. Between hits, hydraulic jacks lift the ram, compressing the working gas and cocking the device for the next impact. Other machines (see table, page 423) utilize essentially the same principles, but the details of triggering, mass-velocity distribution, and fluid flow vary. Machines available vary in size, and cost on the order of $25,000 to $70,000.

Most of the metalworking being done on these fast presses lies in the forging area. In addition to increased forgeability of materials like the alloy steels, titanium, the super-alloys, and refractory metals, this method permits parts with no draft to be made—a considerable advantage in many designs. Often, the as-forged part is to finished dimension, thus avoiding considerable machining costs, particularly on the harder-to-machine alloys. Most important, perhaps, is the close control over metal grain flow that is possible with the high forging pressure—a factor critical in the design of high speed rotating structures like turbine wheels. Beyond forging, high energy rate presses are turning out precise short extrusions, small sheet metal parts, and powder metal compacts of unusually high density—up to 100% of theoretical in some cases.

Electrical discharge metal forming

This survey began with a brief description of one of the newest types of high energy rate metalworking—exploding-wire electro-hydraulic forming. This is but one of three forming techniques that are based on the conversion of electrical energy stored in high voltage capacitors into mechanical energy in the form of a transient high pressure pulse. Apart from exploding a wire, this mechanical energy can be generated by jumping capacitor current across two electrodes under water, or by pulsing it through a coil to produce a rapidly changing magnetic field coupled inductively with the workpiece. The nomenclature is a bit fluid at present, but for purposes of discussion here the first two methods will be termed "electrohydraulic" or "electrospark" forming. The magnetic technique we'll simply call electromagnetic forming.

In all of these processes, the energy available at the outset of the conversion process is given by the familiar voltage-energy relation for capacitors: $E = CV^2/2$, where C is the combined capacitance of the system. With energy E a function of the square of voltage V, it is natural to find considerable interest in high voltage sources for metal forming in order to avoid excessive cost for capacitance C. However, the hazards of working with high voltages are well known, so that production equipment, now in the 5–15 kv range, will probably not exceed 50 kv in the future.

Laboratory-sized units are available with energy outputs ranging from about 10,000 joules to 50,000 joules, with their costs varying from about $7000 to less than $20,000. Production units, on the other hand, cover about the same joule output range, but cost in the order of $10,000 to $30,000. The difference in

cost lies essentially in the additional electrical equipment necessary to provide rapid recharging of the bank—as quickly as 1 second for some production machines, up to 25 seconds for experimental devices.

Building pressure with the electrospark

Assuming we have a suitable source of stored electrical energy that can be quickly released, let us examine what happens, in broad terms, when the switch is thrown. If an initiating wire or ribbon is used, as in Fig. 3-91, the surge of current heats, melts, vaporizes, and then ionizes the metal to form a thin plasma channel. The precise mechanism of this "explosion" is not known as yet, though it is being studied extensively. Using a wire is an advantage in that it can serve to shape the initial plasma channel to fit the geometry of the part being formed. Forming the channel with just a spark jumping between electrodes avoids the need for replacing the wire each time, thus reducing cycle time between shots.

In the earlier stages, the plasma channel absorbs most of the electrical energy input since it has an enormous capacity for storing energy in the form of particle activation, ionization, dissociation, and so on. Pouring so much energy into the channel, confined as it is by the surrounding water, raises its temperature and starts it expanding rapidly. The high inertia of the confining water opposes this expansion, so that much of the high pressure pulse in the

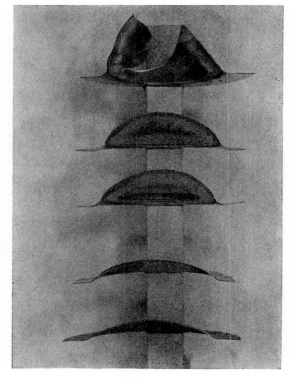

Fig. 3-98. Focusable spark electrode, designed with flat face by Rohr Corp., after 50 firings. Put the electrode 1.5 in. away from aluminum blank (bottom right) and you get little deformation; put it 6 in. away (top right) and you get fracture. (Courtesy Rohr Corp.)

channel is transmitted to the water as a shock wave. This wave, transmitted to the workpiece, helps to set its motion toward the die in much the same way as described earlier for explosive forming. Far behind the shock pressure, the channel continues to expand, providing additional pressure energy to help in the forming process. It is estimated that the total energy input to the water divides about equally between the shock wave and the expanding bubble.

While questions of energy distribution are, indeed, important, much work is proceeding in the area of configurations for electrodes, their material, how they are placed in relation to the metal to be formed, and the like. Investigators at Rohr Corp. and at Electro-Dynamics, Inc., for example, have found that startling differences in the degree of metalworking can be wrought by fairly minor changes in transducer design or position. A typical electrode and the changes it produced in a simple case are shown in Figs. 3-98 and 3-99. In short, it looks as if commercial progress in electrospark forming will come from basic research on the physics of the process, coupled with better techniques for focusing the available energy and improvement in existing energy source equipment.

Forming with electromagnetics

The newest of the high energy rate metalworking processes is electromagnetic forming. This technique is also sometimes referred to as inductive-repulsion forming, since the forces generated to shape the metal are derived from the interplay of two transient magnetic fields. One of these is generated by pulsing electrical energy through a "working" coil surrounding the workpiece. The other is generated, following Faraday's law, by the inductive influence of the transient working flux on the adjacent workpiece. This induces an emf in the metal to be deformed, causing current to flow in it in the opposite direction to that flowing in the working coil, as shown in Fig. 3-100. The existence of this current in the primary magnetic field results, by Lenz's law, in a force at right angles to the flux and to the current. This force, if large enough, can be used to deform the metal. The coil, of course, experiences an equal but opposite force.

Since the magnetic energy available to do the forming is proportional to the square of the magnetic field intensity, the creation of a sudden, intense magnetic field in the working coil is an excellent way of generating such a large force. Figures 3-101, 3-102, and 3-103 show this. Here, the working coil is literally exploding under the influence of magnetically generated

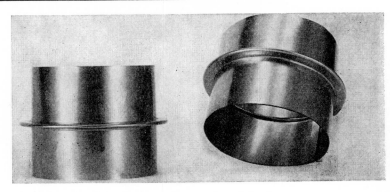

Fig. 3-99. Spark energy can be employed to form re-entrant shapes, as shown by this coil of stainless with a deep bellows configuration formed in center by Electro-Dynamics Inc. (Courtesy Electro-Dynamics, Inc.)

pressure. At the same time, the workpiece collapses onto a mandrel.

By such an arrangement, a variety of swaging operations can be performed. The energy source for this task is essentially the same as that used in electrospark forming. How much energy is transferred to the workpiece depends primarily upon the voltage applied to the coil, the duration of the current pulse, and the magnetic coupling between the pulsed coil and the workpiece.

It is important to note that the workpiece need not be magnetic; it merely needs to be electrically conductive. The efficiency of energy transfer suffers, however, when low conductivity materials like stainless steels are electromagnetically formed. This can be obviated by wrapping the workpiece with a thin layer of copper sheet— a technique that also applies when the workpiece is a ceramic body.

The working coil need not, of course, be expendable, for the coil can be designed to counter the destructive effects of both mechanical forces of dilation and thermal breakdown from ohmic heating. This can be done by reinforcing the coil—even prestressing it—by cooling the magnet externally, or by designing the coil itself so that self-cancelling force fields are set up within it.

Why form at high energy rates?

Now that we know how the various high energy rate processes work, it is useful to examine briefly the basic mechanism of plastic deformation to get some insight into why they are able to form many metals so readily (see "Plastic Deformation," page 50). Central to this is the theory of dislocations. Until fairly recently, metallurgists have been puzzled by the fact that the shear stress to cause slip in a single crystal is several orders of magnitude less than that calculated on the basis of shifting one layer of atoms in the crystal structure en masse to the next adjacent site. It has long been observed, however, that plastic deformation does not occur uniformly; rather, it occurs on just a few selected planes even though the same shear stress is applied to all of them. The evidence for this is the grouping of these active slip planes into the familiar slip bands that appear at the surface of many plastically deformed crystals.

The theory of dislocations provides an explanation for this behavior: Slip takes place sequentially rather than simultaneously because of imperfections in the crystal structure. Simplest of these imperfections, and the one deemed most influential in the slip process, is the edge dislocation sketched in the margin. The key feature of the edge dislocation is the abrupt termination of a row of atoms or, put another way, the existence of an extra half-row of atoms in the lattice. The term "edge" dislocation arises naturally, because a three-dimensional body is composed of many atom planes, and the ends of the extra half-rows in these planes form the edge.

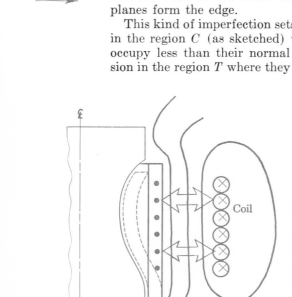

This kind of imperfection sets up compression in the region C (as sketched) where the atoms occupy less than their normal space, and tension in the region T where they are more widely

spaced than usual. Application of a shear stress, as shown, relieves this local situation by shifting the dislocation to an adjacent region. The energy required to move the dislocation in this manner is apparently not very high. If there are many such dislocations—the number in undeformed crystals is in the order of 10^6 per sq cm—there is ample opportunity for the lattice to be nudged along in "jumps" under shear stresses much less than that required to cause whole atom shifts in a perfect structure.

Thus, one of the most interesting and important features of the edge dislocation appears to be its ability to move a crystal structure—facilitating slip. And the more dislocations there are, the easier slip becomes—up to a point. Plastic deformation, once started, does not continue effortlessly: additional stress is needed to produce further deformation. This is workhardening, and it occurs in both pure metals and alloys.

The curious thing is that work-hardening is accompanied by an *increase* in the number of dislocations: densities of 10^{12} dislocations per sq cm have been observed in heavily workhardened metals. Apparently, existing dislocations have a way of expanding and subdividing to form new ones. Since any impediment to the easy movement of dislocations will stiffen (work-harden) the metal, it would appear that this spawning of dislocations can create a "traffic jam" on an atomic scale. Dislocations can get locked in place by getting tangled with other dislocations. The road blocks can be second-phase particles in two-phase systems, or

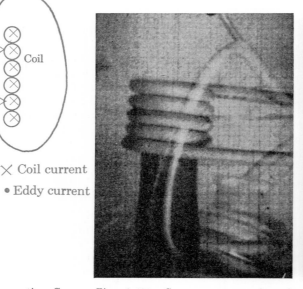

Fig. 3-100. *Swaging by magnetics. Confined magnetic field interacts with induced current in workpiece to set up deforming force.*

Fig. 3-101. *Current surges through coil, generating magnetic pressures up to 50,000 psi, swaging tube in 10–20 μsec. (Courtesy General Dynamics)*

Fig. 3-102. *Expendable coil bulges under radial pressure and influence of ohmic heating. Insulation soon begins to deteriorate. (Courtesy General Dynamics)*

they can be solute atoms of the interstitial or substitutional variety.

The importance of velocity

In conventional metalworking processes, where the metal is moved plastically at velocities of perhaps 15 ft/sec, these obstructive mechanisms make production an intermittent process for many metals: First you form to a certain hardness level, then you relieve the distorted lattice by annealing. Unless the metal can be worked hot, so that the relieving process can go along with the forming process, this stop-and-go procedure to avoid fracture is time-consuming. If the forming process is accelerated a bit, even more work-hardening results—the stress to cause plastic flow increases some 15–30% (as long as the temperature is below the recrystallization point).

Contrast this with high energy rate metalworking where the metal moves at some 100–200 ft/sec. By introducing energy to the workpiece suddenly by means of fast-moving pressure waves, previously intractable metals and alloys can be plastically deformed without fracturing by excessive work-hardening. How can this be? How can the multiplying dislocations avoid getting entangled with each other, or with other obstacles, and thus retain their desirable characteristics as slip devices?

This question has not yet been answered. However, recent theoretical analysis of the problem indicates that the dominance of kinetic energy of a fast-moving dislocation over its potential energy can alter the usual force field

between it and dislocations of similar kind. Instead of repelling each other, they are attracted to one another. Thus it may be that there exists a coalescing process by which many small dislocations may collect to form larger dislocations—permitting slip rather than further work-hardening to occur. The trouble with this is that the dislocation velocities required for this force inversion to occur are very near—near sonic velocity—and it seems doubtful that such velocities are attained in high energy rate metalworking. It may turn out that the increase in work-hardening experience at higher rates of deformation is actually a *stabilizing* mechanism, so that the localized thinning that leads to fracture in more conventional metalworking processes cannot occur until the entire workpiece is ready to dissipate its kinetic energy into plastic deformation.

These are only two conceivable mechanisms for metal deformation at high energy rates. There are certainly others. One thing the experts agree upon so far: there is plenty of room for further research—both theoretical and experimental—before the mystery is completely unraveled.

Further reading

The literature of this field is enormous. The best guide to it is *High Energy Rate Metal Working Bibliography*, a new index over 200 pages long, with all items annotated, coded, and catalogued in 10 major sections. This document carries two identifying numbers: an Army Ordnance number: ORD-241; and a North Ameri-

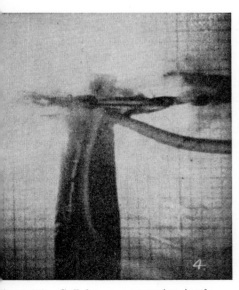

Fig. 3-103. Coil lets go, scattering insulation and wire in all directions. High speed motion pictures by General Dynamics/Convair. (Courtesy General Dynamics)

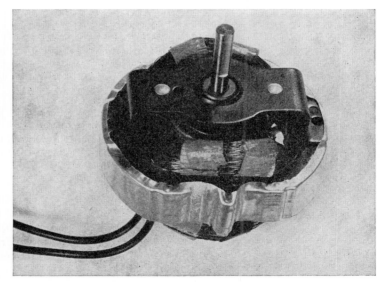

Fig. 3-104. This motor, clamped with a crimped metal strip, could be assembled on the moon, since magnetic method, designed by General Atomic Div. of General Dynamics will work in a vacuum. (Courtesy General Dynamics)

can Aviation number: NA62H-46. Plans for making it widely available have not yet been completed. If interested, write to D. E. Strohecker, the chief compiler, at Battelle Memorial Institute. Copies are available to qualified contractors at ASTIA. An abbreviated bibliography is: Office of Technical Services SB-441 (revised), *Explosive Metal Forming* (10¢).

Many papers on all phases of the subject have been given at three seminars run by American Society of Tool and Manufacturing Engineers, 10700 Puritan Ave., Detroit 38, Mich. Write to Col. L. Fletcher at ASTME for lists of papers, bound volumes, and prices. For information on metal behavior, you could see, for a starter, any good up-to-date text on physical metallurgy, for example: *Physical Metallurgy* by Chalmers (Wiley, 1959, $12.50). For more advanced thinking in this area, get *Response of Metals to High Velocity Deformation*, ed. by Shewmon and Zackay, AIME Conference Vol. 9 (Interscience, 1961, $18); the survey paper, "High Velocity Dislocations," by Weertman, is particularly interesting. See also *Basic Parameters of Metal Behavior Under High Rate Forming*, an Arthur D. Little report to Watertown Arsenal (No. WAL-TR 11.2/20, available from OTS, $2.25).

On explosive forming, the first complete book is *Explosive Working of Metals* by Rinehart and Pearson (Pergamon Press, 1962). A short, readable survey is: *Explosive Metalworking* by Simons, DMIC memo No. 71 (OTS No. PB 161221, 50¢). For much practical information see *High Energy Rate Metal Forming*, a Lockheed Aircraft Corp. report by Pipher, Rardin, and Richter (OTS No. PB 171896, $6).

On electrical discharge forming, DMIC memo No. 70, *High-velocity Metalworking Processes Based on Sudden Discharge of Electrical Energy* by Wagner and Boulger (OTS PB 161220, 50¢), presents a good overview. A historical survey, including a summary of significant Soviet work, is Dunleavy's article "Hydrospark Forming—Evolution of the Process," *Tool Engineers*, March 1960. Some recent Air Force research is covered in Republic Aviation Corp. report 7-844 (IV), *Capacitor Discharge Metal Forming*, available to contractors from ASTIA. Detailed papers on sparks initiated by heated wires will be found in *Exploding Wires*, ed. by Chace and Moore (Plenum Press, 1959, $9.50). For underwater plasmas, see "Experimental Investigation of a High-Energy, High-Pressure Arc Plasma" by Martin, *J. of Appl. Phys.*, **31**, 2, p. 255 (1960). Magnetic forming is well covered in DMIC memo No. 70 (above) and Brower's article "Magnetic Pulse Forming," SAE paper 479B, Jan. 1962.

Papers on pneumatic-mechanical metal forming will be found in the ASTME seminar papers cited above, which also include a thorough paper on "Explosive Forming with Gas Mixtures" by Lingen and Cruver (paper No. SP62-02).

NUCLEAR POWER TODAY

by Chauncey Starr *

IN BRIEF: *Nearly two score electric-power stations are today deriving their energy from the fission of uranium. From the many possible arrangements of fissionable fuel, moderator, and coolant that can constitute a chain-reacting system, five types have emerged as the principal contenders for full-scale electric power generation. These are: the pressurized-water, the closely related boiling-water, the heavy-water-moderated organic-cooled, the gas-cooled graphite-moderated and the sodium-cooled graphite-moderated. The author favors the last, pointing to its high operating temperature and consequent high efficiency, its low operating pressure, and its usefulness as a development tool for the sodium-coolant technology required for fast-breeder reactors, which, everyone agrees, will be needed someday.—D.C.*

* Chauncey Starr is President of Atomics International Division of North American Aviation, Inc., Canoga Park, California.

■ In the early days of the U.S. nuclear energy program there existed in some quarters an almost mystical faith in the benefits to mankind that would arise from the peaceful use of the atom. There also existed another position, a more informed technical and engineering opinion, which did not anticipate magical developments, but was able to foresee the possibility of practical, economic benefits from nuclear power following a reasonably long term, sound development program. Those who expected magic from the atom are still awaiting their prize. But those who have approached the new technology more realistically are now beginning to realize the fruits of their labors. A practical new source of energy to help meet the world's increasing power needs is now at hand.

That there should have been overoptimism appears reasonable when you consider the dramatically small amount of nuclear fuel required to produce large quantities of energy.

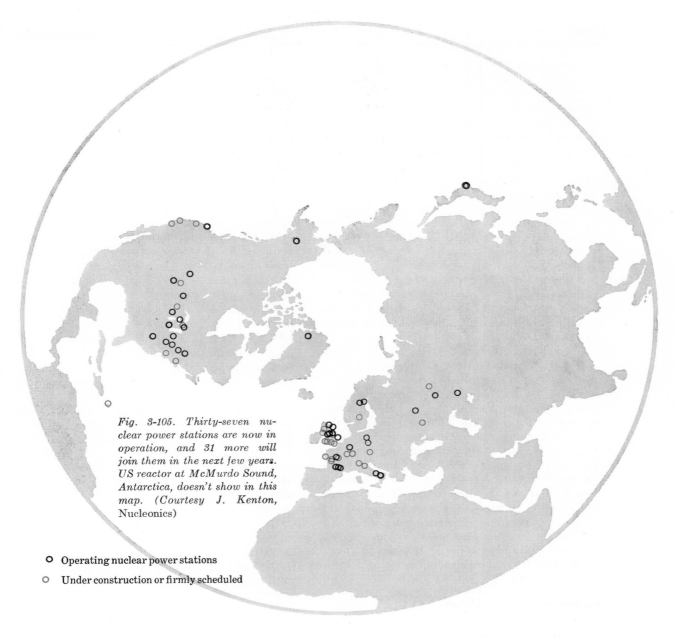

Fig. 3-105. Thirty-seven nuclear power stations are now in operation, and 31 more will join them in the next few years. US reactor at McMurdo Sound, Antarctica, doesn't show in this map. (Courtesy J. Kenton, Nucleonics)

○ Operating nuclear power stations

○ Under construction or firmly scheduled

My favorite way of portraying this is to point out that a cubic inch of the isotope uranium-235 can release energy equal to that contained in 22 railroad cars of coal holding a total of 1600 tons. This very great concentration of energy reflects, of course, the fact that the ultimate source of the energy is nuclear. Nuclear energies tend to be about one million times the chemical energies available from changes in the electron orbital structure as conventional fuels are burned.

Not only are nuclear fuels a very compact source of energy, but they also are potentially a very high-temperature source. The upper limit is set by the energy of the nuclear fragments produced after fission—it comes to millions of degrees.

But it is difficult to benefit from this dramatically compact form of energy in a prac-

tical device. The present limit for the temperature of steam generated by nuclear reactors is much more modest—about 1200°F, set principally by materials limitations. Similar practical limitations of heat transfer and structural strength cause nuclear reactors to be larger and more complex than the energy concentration of their fuel might suggest. In addition the penetrating radiations associated with the operation of a reactor require that several feet of heavy shielding surround the nuclear core.

These engineering constraints have been met, however, in a growing list of operating nuclear power stations all over the world (see Fig. 3-105). Nuclear power is a reality today; what's more it is fast becoming economically competitive with power derived from fossil fuels. I believe that further development of nuclear power technology will cause the price of nuclear power to drop below that currently associated with conventional plants in many areas of the country. This doesn't mean all new power plants will soon be nuclear; that depends on how well coal plants meet this new competition. However, I'm confident that the cost of electricity will go down, and a significant reduction in the cost of a basic commodity such as electric power can make a tremendous direct and indirect contribution to our standard of living.

Because of the growing importance of nuclear power, because its rich technology should be shared more broadly with the entire technical community, and because that technology will only benefit from a feedback of information and interest on the part of those outside the nuclear field, I've tried to set forth here the basic present technical and economic situation of nuclear power for large central electric power plants.

A good way to start thinking about nuclear reactors is in terms of neutron physics—what it takes to keep a controlled chain reaction going, ignoring, for the moment, the problems of removing the heat generated or of holding things in place. An assemblage of fissionable material is necessary but not sufficient—one may also need a moderator to slow the neutrons down and thus (for reasons we shall see shortly) make more efficient use of the available fissionable atoms. You also need control rods to regulate the reaction, reflectors to return some of the neutrons that would otherwise leak out of the core of the reactor, and possibly some nonfissionable but fertile material that can be converted into fuel through the alchemy of nuclear transformation.

Fission and what follows

The fundamental process of nuclear power generation is the splitting or fission of the nuclei of certain heavy atoms by neutrons. The bombarding neutron enters the nucleus, makes it unstable, and causes it to disrupt into two or more pieces. The very considerable energy released by the disruption of the fissioned nucleus shows up in the kinetic energy of the fission fragments and the energy of the radiation and neutrons that are released. In today's power reactors essentially all of this energy is degraded to thermal energy and used as such to raise steam with which to drive turbines. Direct conversion of nuclear energy to electricity is still in the experimental stage, and I don't see it being applied to large power stations for years, if ever.

All heavy nuclei are not equally likely to fission when bombarded with neutrons. The two isotopes that constitute most of uranium as it is found in nature differ drastically in this regard. Uranium-238, which is the more abundant of the two (99.2% of all U atoms), can be fissioned only by fast neutrons, such as are produced in fission, not at all by low-energy, "slow" neutrons. In fact, at low and intermediate energies U^{238} is a troublesomely good absorber of neutrons—soaking them up without fissioning. Uranium-235, whose natural abundance is only 0.7%, is readily fissioned, particularly by low-energy neutrons.

It is possible to base a chain-reacting system on natural uranium with its small quota of U^{235}, but one has to be careful to conserve neutrons. Most U.S. reactors employ fuel made from uranium that has gone through a gaseous diffusion plant to be slightly enriched—up to 5%—in its U^{235} content.

What makes a chain reaction possible is that an average of 2.5 neutrons is emitted by each U^{235} nucleus that is fissioned. Since the fissioning of subsequent U^{235} nuclei requires only one neutron per nucleus, the 1.5 "excess" neutrons provide a margin to ensure a self-sustaining chain reaction.

There are two broad classes of nuclear reactors known by the speed of their neutrons as fast and slow (or thermal). They are distinguished by the choice of whether (1) to use highly enriched, highly concentrated fuel and have the chain reaction proceed with the fast neutrons that are produced in fission or (2) to provide materials that will slow down the neutrons so that they are more effective at fissioning, and thus less concentrated, slightly enriched fuel can serve.

The slowing-down process is simple, conceptually. The neutrons born of fission have kinetic energies some tens of millions of times higher than the average kinetic energy of the atoms of the reactor core in which they move. Thus in elastic collisions with those atoms (or, more properly, the nuclei of those atoms), a fast neutron will lose energy; its kinetic energy will be reduced; its velocity grow more moderate. Through such elastic collisions it comes in thermal equilibrium with the structure in which it moves. Because light atoms are more efficient at slowing neutrons, low-atomic-weight materials such as water or beryllium or carbon are used as neutron moderators.

Neutrons then diffuse through the lattice, moving much like atoms in a low-pressure gas. One may be absorbed by a nucleus of the structure, in which case the principal result is to make that nucleus radioactive. Or a neutron may enter a fissionable atom, in which case fission follows immediately, and the chain reaction is maintained (Fig. 3-106).

The chain reaction can be controlled and regulated by the use of control devices whose

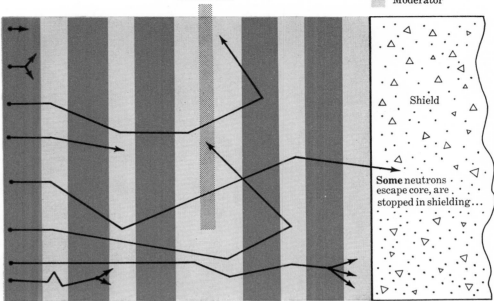

Of the fast neutrons born in fission in a fuel element...

...A few cause additional fissions before they slow down...

Most are slowed down by collisions with atoms of the moderator...

Some of these are absorbed while slowing down...

The rest come to thermal equilibrium with and diffuse through the reactor core...

Some of these diffusing neutrons are captured in moderator or core structure...

The rest, enough to keep the chain reaction going, are captured in fuel and cause fission, producing the next generation of neutrons...

Control rod

Fuel element

Moderator

Shield

Some neutrons escape core, are stopped in shielding...

Fig. 3-106. The reactor designer's problem is to ensure that, on the average, 1 of the approximately 2.5 neutrons released in the fission of a uranium nucleus survives to cause fission in yet another U235 nucleus. To do this economically while meeting structural and heat-removal requirements is the essential challenge. (Courtesy R. Moeller)

basic purpose is to regulate the number of neutrons which they absorb and thus the neutron losses from the complete cycle. These "control rods" are used to adjust the nuclear "reactivity" of the system. They contain some elements such as cadmium, boron, and hafnium, which has a high probability for capturing slow neutrons. This probability is usually given in terms of the effective target area (cross section) displayed by the struck nucleus and is measured in barns. A barn is 10^{-24} cm², which will seem awfully small, but a cadmium atom has a cross section of 2550 barns and there are lots of cadmium atoms in a rod.

Unfortunately most structural materials also have a significant neutron-capture cross section. Such parasitic absorption makes it that much harder to maintain a chain reaction. To minimize it we restrict the amount and type of structural materials in the nuclear reactor. Zirconium and certain of its alloys are often used for reactor structures or to clad fuel elements. Type 304 stainless steel is another common choice, though it absorbs more neutrons than zirconium.

New fuel for the burning

Of course neutron absorption is not always undesirable. As we have seen, it is desirable as a means of reactivity control. Absorption is also sometimes desirable when either uranium-238 or thorium absorbs the neutron. When this happens, *new fuel is made.*

The absorption of a neutron by uranium-238 produces plutonium-239. The absorption of a neutron by thorium produces uranium-233. Both of these products are fissionable and can be used as fuel. Thus there are two classes of reactor fuel material: those that are "fissionable" (uranium-233, uranium-235, and plutonium-239) and those we call "fertile" because neutron capture makes them fissionable (uranium-238 and thorium-232).

If one atom of new fuel is produced for every atom fissioned, then the reactor has a "conversion ratio" of one. Leakage and parasitic absorption reduce the conversion ratio in most slow-neutron or "thermal" reactors to something like 0.5–0.8. But at the neutron energies that typify fast reactors almost all materials have a negligible capture cross section. This leads to the minimizing of parasitic absorption and allows an increase in the conversion ratio. If the conversion ratio exceeds 1.0, then the reactor is a "breeder" and produces more fuel than it consumes. Conversion ratios of about 1.1 to 1.2 can be obtained using plutonium as the fuel in a fast reactor. Thermal breeders are theoretically feasible, but, due to very high parasitic neutron absorption of slow neutrons, it is very difficult to achieve high conversion ratios.

The only large operational fast reactor with any hope of breeding is being operated by the British at Dounreay. The Enrico Fermi reactor near Detroit, Mich., should also breed when in

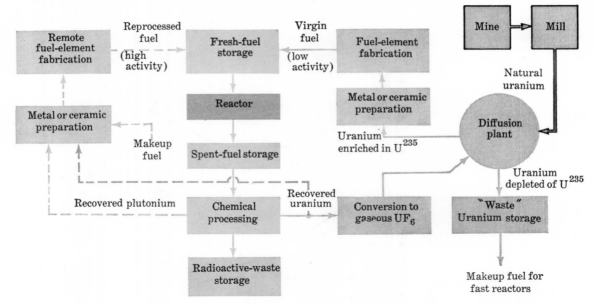

Fig. 3-107. Rather than the simple linear sequence of mine to boiler to ash heap that characterizes the fuel cycle of a coal-fired power plant, the nuclear-fuel cycle is complex and truly cyclical. Dashed loops will become important only when plutonium manufactured in breeder reactors becomes important as a fuel. (Courtesy W. Prokos)

full operation. The Experimental Breeder Reactor-II, at the National Reactor Testing Station in Idaho, should demonstrate breeding beyond question. The Russians started operation of a small experimental fast reactor, the BR-5, in 1959; this reactor, however, was not designed for breeding.

The advent of the fast reactor will reduce the demand on uranium ore and on diffusion-plant facilities but will cause an increasing reliance on fuel-reprocessing facilities. The operational status of fast reactors will depend on timely, efficient reprocessing of spent fuel in fertile materials to recover plutonium and uranium-233 (see Fig. 3-107). Already progress is being made toward establishing privately owned, commercially operated fuel reprocessing facilities in upper New York State.

Conversion or breeding is an important di-

vidend, but the principal function of the reactor is to produce power.

Power-producing process

In both fast and thermal reactors heat is produced by fission, absorption of gamma rays, and the conversion of the kinetic energy of particles and fission fragments. This heat must be removed, thus necessitating the use of a coolant. (Several coolants are compared in Fig. 3-108.) The heat from the coolant can be used to produce steam which in turn can produce electricity through the use of conventional turbogenerators. Seen from the turbine's point of view the nuclear reactor is nothing more than a boiler. It is here that the new nuclear technology meets the "old" technology of turbogenerators. In fact, it is ironic that most nuclear reactors produce steam at temperatures and

Liquid	Nuclear properties	Heat-transfer properties	Volumetric specific heat (Btu/ft^3/°F)	Stability (temperature and radiation)	Handling	Relative pumping power
Pressurized water	Good	Good	74	Some dissociation	No serious	1.0
Sodium	Good	Excellent	17	Stable	Chemical reaction with water	1.04
Lithium	Poor	Very good	31	Stable	Same as for Na and NaK	0.68
Terphenyls	Good	Poor	35	Some dissociation		—

Fig. 3-108. How common reactor coolants compare.

pressures below those of modern fossil fuel plants. Turbine manufacturers had to dig in their files for 1930 designs when the new nuclear reactors came along.

The many choices

Given no more constraints than those imposed by the need to keep a chain reaction going and to extract the resultant heat, it is startling how many different sorts of reactors are possible. For the basic fissioning isotope one has a choice of U^{233}, U^{235}, or Pu^{239}, and this fuel can be in the form of metal, alloy, or other compound. For the moderator (if one elects to have a thermal reactor) the choice ranges from such common substances as light or heavy water and graphite to more exotic materials such as beryllium and zirconium hydride. Similar choices are possible for the coolant and structural materials, as is suggested in Fig. 3-109.

Beyond that one has a variety of ways to bring these elements together: they can all be combined homogeneously in a solution, the fuel can be its own coolant by circulating through the reactor, etc., etc. Most of these reactor types have been thought of and quite a few of them have been the subject of experiment in the years that atomic power has been under development. Some of them may yet be the subject of renewed interest, but for now the realities of materials limitations and of economics have limited the reactor types that are receiving serious consideration to about six. Some views of two of them are given in Color Figs. 27 and 31. Color Figs. 28 and 30 depict nuclear fuel elements and their handling.

I've shown the flow diagrams and systems characteristics for the big six in Fig. 3-110. Let me describe each of them to you, briefly.

The pressurized-water reactor. In this reactor the coolant and moderator are the same—water under pressure high enough ($\sim$2000 psi) that it will not boil even at the 600°F temperatures reached in the core. Fuel is usually UO_2 in the form of pellets that are assembled into tubes that are further combined into arrays of such tubes known as fuel elements (an example is shown in Color Fig. 30). The fuel material is usually UO_2, since uranium metal would react with the water if the protective tubing developed even a small leak. Examples of this reactor are the Shippingport and Yankee plants; all the U.S. atomic submarines use a reactor of this type. Westinghouse and Babcock & Wilcox are the companies most closely associated with this concept in the United States.

The boiling-water reactor. This reactor is very similar to the pressurized-water reactor except that the pressure is somewhat lower, allowing the water to boil in the core. One striking advantage of this approach is that the resulting steam can be fed directly to the turbine generator—no heat exchanger is needed, little radioactivity carries over to the turbines. Reactors of this type are in operation at Commonwealth Edison of Chicago's Dresden plant and several other locations here and abroad. General Electric and Allis-Chalmers are the

MATERIALS SUITABLE FOR NUCLEAR REACTORS

Function in Reactor	Materials to use for... ...Thermal Reactor	...Fast Reactor
Fuel (U^{235}, U^{233}, Pu^{239})	Natural or enriched uranium as metal, alloy, oxide, or carbide	Plutonium or enriched uranium as metal, alloy, oxide, or carbide
Fertile Material (U^{238}, Th^{232})	Uranium or thorium as metal, alloy, oxide, or carbide	Uranium or thorium as metal, alloy, oxide, or carbide
Moderator	Hydrogen (as hydride, water, or organic); graphite; beryllium	None
Coolant	Water, organics, sodium or gas (He or CO_2)	Sodium or gas
Core Structure	Zirconium, aluminum, steels	No significant nuclear limitation
Control Rod	Boron, cadmium, europium, or gadolinium as elements, alloys, oxides, or carbides	None

Fig. 3-109. Multiplicity of choices for reactor components is magnified by the multiplicity of possible forms and arrangements. Many reactor types are possible. Only a few are technically and economically attractive.

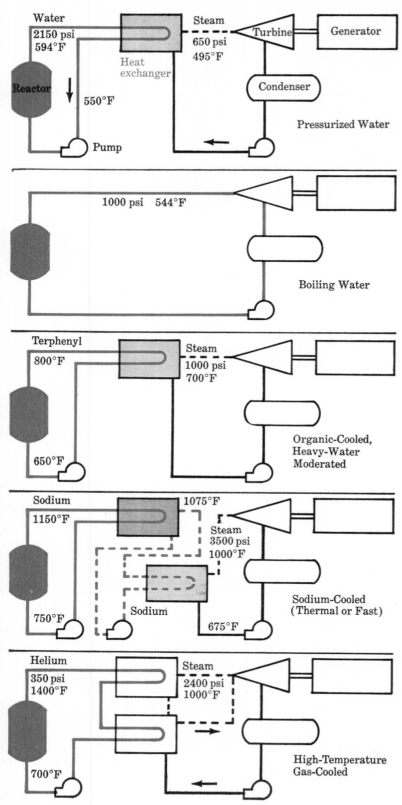

Fig. 3-110. Basic steam-raising cycle of power reactors varies with the reactor type. Boiling-water reactor, for example, feeds steam directly to turbine, while all other types have one or more intermediate heat exchangers. Steam conditions (temperature and pressure) are comparable with modern coal-fired stations only for sodium- and gas-cooled types. Cycle for fast breeder is same as that for sodium-cooled thermal reactor. (Courtesy W. Prokos)

companies that have adopted this type of reactor.

The gas-cooled reactor. This is the reactor type favored by the British in their large nuclear power stations. They use natural-uranium fuel, a graphite moderator and CO_2 gas as a coolant. In the United States the General Atomic Division of General Dynamics has pursued this concept using enriched uranium carbide as fuel and helium as a coolant. A reactor employing these principles is being constructed at Peach Bottom, Pa., and another is being constructed at Oak Ridge National Laboratory to provide electricity to the TVA grid.

Heavy-water natural-uranium reactor. Another reactor that can use natural uranium as a fuel is one that uses heavy water as a moderator. (It is impossible to sustain a chain reaction using natural uranium and ordinary water as a moderator.) Atomic Energy of Canada, Ltd., under W. B. Lewis, has been in the forefront of the development of this concept; my company, Atomics International, has had an interest, too, in a scheme in which heavy water is used as the moderator but the cooling is done with an organic liquid, terphenyl.

The sodium graphite reactor. Here graphite does the moderating, the liquid sodium does the cooling. This is one of the reactor types that I favor—the operating temperature can be much higher than in water-cooled reactors, matching the best steam conditions of modern turbines, and yet the pressure is close to atmospheric. Also, since sodium is favored as a coolant for fast-breeder reactors, experience with this reactor type will pave the way for the breeder reactors we'll need in the future. A 75-MW reactor of this type is in the early stages of operating in a plant built for the AEC for operation by the Consumer Public Power District of Hallam, Nebraska (see Color Fig. 27 and Fig. 3-111).

The fast-breeder reactor. This system uses fast neutrons for fissioning and thus has no moderator. Like the sodium-graphite reactor it will produce high-temperature steam using low-pressure sodium as a coolant. Considerable work must be done to understand the nuclear behavior of fast reactors and to develop adequate reactor controls. This reactor system's potential low-power cost and breeding capability mark it as the thoroughbred in the stable.

Each of the reactor systems that we have been considering has its own characteristic advantages. The fairest and most equitable comparison can be made by an economic analysis—how many mills per kilowatt-hour. The cost will have two principal components: that arising from the capital cost required to build the plant in the first place and that arising from the cost of fuel and of operation and mainte-

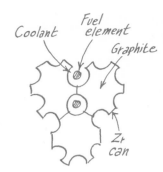

Coolant
Fuel element
Graphite
Zr can

Fig. 3-111. Nuclear reactor cores are characteristically regular arrays of fuel elements, surrounded by moderator (to slow neutrons). Heat generated in fission is removed by coolant that flows past the hot fuel elements. Shown here is the core of the sodium-graphite reactor at Hallam, Neb., during construction. (Courtesy Atomics International)

nance. In a general way you can appreciate that power costs will go down if: the cost of the plant goes down and if the plant is kept running as large a fraction of the time as is possible (load factors of 80–90% are usually assumed and achieved with nuclear power plants). Similarly the contribution of fuel cost will be lower if uranium and its fabrication into fuel elements costs less. So far the economics parallels that of conventional coal-fired power stations. But there are differences, and I'd like to discuss these and show the effects of certain reactor characteristics on reactor economics.

Burnup, efficiency, conversion ratio

In most reactor systems the fuel consists of uranium slightly enriched in the 235 isotope. In the course of reactor operation the U^{235} is fissioned and burned up. But typically it is not possible to burn up all the U^{235}; long before that happens the diminished amount of U^{235} and the neutron-absorbing power of some of the fission products make it impossible to continue the chain reaction. Or else the fuel element suffers so much radiation damage from the neutrons and fission fragments coursing through it that it no longer has the required physical integrity. It is as if coal were removed from a furnace well before it was completely burned.

However, the uranium in spent fuel is still enriched, and some of the U^{238} will have been converted into plutonium through the capture of a neutron. Thus it pays to submit the spent fuel to a reprocessing plant where uranium and plutonium are chemically separated from the fission products and made available for use in new fuel elements. The initial fabrication and reprocessing of fuel is, as you might imagine, a fairly complex and costly process, so it be-

comes desirable to increase the residence time of the fuel in the reactor, to allow a greater burnup.

I show, in Fig. 3-112, the effect on the fuel cost of increasing the burnup from 10,000 to 25,000 Megawatt-days per tonne of contained uranium (tonne = metric ton = 2200 lb). Although it is not shown on Fig. 3-112 and the precise point is not known it appears that 25,000 MW-d/tonne burnup is, roughly, an economic minimum for thermal reactors. The optimum burnup is determined by the balance of economic factors that provide a minimum fuel-cycle cost. As the time in the reactor (or burnup) increases, costs are reduced by prorating the initial fuel-fabrication cost, reactor refueling down-time, and reprocessing costs over an increased power output. These savings, however, are not proportional to the time in the reactor. As a practical matter, the increased costs of the higher enrichment (and consequent increased fabrication cost) necessary to keep the chain reaction going to higher burnups balance the rate of savings at some point. Since I fully expect fabrication and reprocessing costs to go down with increasing experience, the economic optimum burnup for a thermal reactor will probably decrease in the future. There are additional effects contributing to the trend, but, nevertheless, there is a large difference between the 25,000 MW-d/tonne for today's thermal reactors and the 0.4 MW-d/tonne for coal.

Another factor that contributes to cost is the thermal efficiency of the entire plant, that is the ratio of the electricity produced to the heat energy released in the reactor. The heat energy is proportional to the number of atoms of fuel that are fissioned, so that the thermal efficiency measures how much of the fission energy goes into useful electricity and how much goes into

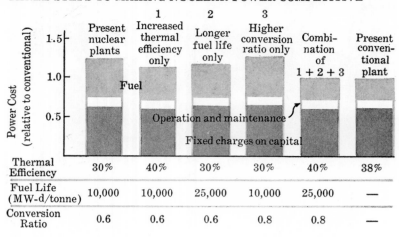

	Present nuclear plants	1 Increased thermal efficiency only	2 Longer fuel life only	3 Higher conversion ratio only	Combination of 1 + 2 + 3	Present conventional plant
Thermal Efficiency	30%	40%	30%	30%	40%	38%
Fuel Life (MW-d/tonne)	10,000	10,000	25,000	10,000	25,000	—
Conversion Ratio	0.6	0.6	0.6	0.8	0.8	—

Fig. 3-112. What will it take to make nuclear power plants competitive with conventional plants powered by fossil fuels? Increasing temperature of operation will lead to increased thermal efficiency; reaching optimum fuel life of about 25,000 MW-days/tonne will help, too. Raising conversion ratio (number of Pu239 nuclei created by neutron capture in U238 per fission of U235) lowers net fuel cost also.

waste heat that is removed by the cooling water of the steam plant. High thermal efficiency is desirable from these three standpoints: (1) it increases the kilowatt hours of electricity that are produced during a given fuel burnup; (2) it reduces the necessity for cooling water and the capital investment required for cooling-water facilities; (3) it reduces the size and cost of turbines for a given electrical power rating. The effects of an increase in thermal efficiency from 30% (which is typical of most of the present current reactors) to 40% (which is better than the best of today's conventional plants can do) is to reduce the cost of power by 10%, as shown in Fig. 3-112.

The conversion ratio (number of Pu nuclei formed per U235 nucleus fissioned) also has a noticeable effect upon the cost, though less than the effect derived from increasing thermal efficiency or prolonging fuel life. The effect comes from two aspects: some of the plutonium that is formed from U238 is fissioned when struck by a neutron while still in the reactor, and some of the plutonium remains when the fuel elements are removed for refueling. This unburned plutonium can be sold to the government.

Typical of the economic complexity of the reactor business, the government's price for plutonium has varied from $30 per gram to $8 per gram. Due to the vagaries of government purchasing, we cannot predict how this price will vary until a free market is established by creating a demand for plutonium as fuel in fast reactors. This will come in a few decades and we are predicting now that the price of plutonium will be about $15–20 per gram (1963 dollars) on the free market when supply and demand are balanced.

Another economic change that is imminent is the change from government to private ownership of U235 over the next decade. The low government leasing charges (4¾%) now in effect will of necessity be increased under

private ownership. This apparent predictable increase in costs could be partially offset by new methods of financing and technical developments that will allow the reduction of fuel inventories.

If all three improvements of which I have spoken—increased thermal efficiency, longer fuel life, and higher conversion ratio—are obtained, the cost of nuclear power becomes comparable with that from the conventional station I've chosen for my standard. This symbolizes qualitatively the fact that nuclear power is becoming economically competitive, at least in New England and California, where fossil-fuel costs are high because they are so far from the coal fields.

A more precise comparison is provided by the actual working experience with some of the reactors already on line. Perhaps the happiest experience has been with the Yankee reactor, located in Rowe, Mass. It is, they tell me, producing electricity for under 10 mills/kWh as compared with a New England area cost of 8–10 mills/kWh from coal-fired plants. The costs of power from Yankee are expected to drop further with a third core that is being installed. Operation has been very smooth, safe, and dependable.

This leads us to the comparison of the economics of reactor types that I promised at the beginning of the preceding section. A caveat is in order at the outset: each reactor type has its partisans. I am partisan to the sodium-cooled graphite-moderated concept and to the sodium-cooled fast breeder for the long range. I am also convinced that the natural-uranium heavy-water-moderated organic-cooled system will eventually play a role for large power stations.

Comparative economics

I have tried, in making the comparison that follows, to apply the same criteria to all reactor types. But there inevitably enters an extrapolation to the probable characteristics of these reactor types in the near future.

In making that extrapolation I have used the best information available and tried to be equally optimistic in all cases, but obviously judgment enters. Each reactor type is compared after extrapolating to the same degree of technological refinement. The extrapolation is greater in some cases than in others. We have operating experience with full-scale pressurized- and boiling-water reactors; there is only prototype experience for the others. In particular I assume, in the case of the fast-breeder reactor, the future solution of several present technological problems. Some factors are fixed however: the comparison is for 500-MW plants, privately financed, with uranium oxide costing $8/lb and plutonium credited at $8/g.

With that long explanation out of the way, here are the costs of nuclear power from the leading reactor types as they might be from comparably developed plants.

Reactor Type	Projected cost (mills/kWh)
Fast (Pu-Pu) breeder	4.24
Thermal reactors:	
Sodium graphite	5.02
Fast (U^{235}-Pu) breeder	5.10
Organic-cooled, heavy-water-moderated	5.13
Advanced PWR	5.57

It is evident from this table that there is ample economic justification for encouraging the development of fast-breeder reactors. However they are unlikely to be available until the technological problems I assumed solved are in fact solved.

It is also evident that the sodium-graphite reactor is an exciting near-term economic prospect.

To achieve the projected power costs indicated in this analysis, we must continue the research, development, and construction of experimental prototypes that are required to realize the potential of these approaches.

There is at present considerable confidence in the dependability of water-moderated and -cooled plants based on the performance of three operating units: Shippingport, Yankee, and Dresden. The next step is to bring the same degree of confidence to the more advanced reactor types, such as the sodium-graphite and gas-cooled systems.

This is being done, in our case, by the continued operation of the Sodium Reactor Experiment that first produced power for Southern California in 1957. This reactor, though until recently the highest-temperature power reactor in the U.S., is now being modified to

provide very advanced conditions and high temperatures for systems experience and component testing. Just recently the Hallam Plant attained full power, producing the highest quality steam at the highest efficiencies of any nuclear plant in this country. The gas-cooled system is being brought to a higher degree of confidence by the construction of the Experimental Gas-Cooled Reactor at Oak Ridge and the Peach Bottom plant near Philadelphia.

From the long-range standpoint, it is apparent that our power economy will include nuclear reactor systems which will produce steam conditions capable of taking full advantage of the metallurgical and technical advances in power generating equipment and utilizing the fertile uranium-238 and thorium fuels. These future reactors must be able to produce more usable fissionable material than they consume if we are to make best use of our uranium resources. The reactor system can be described in general terms today. I believe it will be one that uses fast neutrons for fission, is sodium-cooled, and will probably use carbides or oxides of uranium and plutonium as fuel. It will be in excess of 500 MW in size and will have an efficiency exceeding any plant in operation today. To realize this reactor system will require many years of orderly development from the broadest possible technological base.

One question that always comes up when nuclear power is discussed is the matter of safety. Safety is a relative matter. It is possible to make nuclear reactors as safe to the public as any other part of industry. The nuclear industry and government have developed the safety aspects of a nuclear reactor to the point where only an external catastrophic occurrence would violate a plant's integrity.

A word about safety

Vaguely aware that the source of energy in the controlled chain reaction of a nuclear reactor is the same as that in the uncontrolled chain reaction of an atomic bomb, the man in the street links the two, if only subconsciously. In actuality these fears are unjustified. It just isn't possible to have the same sort of explosive energy release even if all the uranium and moderator were brought together in an optimum configuration. Besides, it is characteristic of chain-reacting systems that an increase in temperature slows the chain reaction—one has to take very special measures to see that a bomb stays together.

While there is no danger of a Hiroshima-type explosion in a nuclear reactor there is, in principle, the possibility of the power in the reactor increasing very suddenly, melting fuel elements, and expelling them with the radioactive coolant from the reactor core. Several steps are taken to guard against this possibility. For one thing the control rods that are the first line of defense against such a reactor runaway are equipped with fail-safe, fast-acting controls. For another the reactor is generally designed to shut itself down (by means of such mechanisms as the heating of the moderator, which quickly raises the average neutron energy thereby decreasing the cross section for further fissions). And all of today's power reactors have a mechanism for retaining the radioactivity that might be released in such a reactor "incident." These devices range from the giant containment shells that have given water-reactor buildings their characteristic silhouette to pressure-suppression systems that will condense the radioactive steam that would be formed.

Some reactor types have certain inherently safe characteristics. This is illustrated by sodium-cooled reactors where no significant reactor pressures are involved and where the coolant dissipates the heat and suppresses fission products so effectively. As a matter of record, a partial meltdown of fuel elements has occurred in a sodium-cooled reactor. Not only was the public unaware of the event, but the reactor operators, with all their detection and control equipment, noticed only a slight operational perturbation.

The Atomic Energy Commission has long had a vigorous research program to explore problems of reactor safety. The AEC also carefully analyzes, with the help of an Advisory Committee on Reactor Safeguards, the safety features of all reactors. Reactor manufacturers, conscious of their responsibility, have cooperated, despite the fact that nuclear power could be noticeably less expensive, even economic today, if extensive safety measures were not required. A remaining task of both industry and government is the education of the public in matters concerning nuclear reactor safety, to make the public aware of the tremendous pains that have been taken to ensure the safety of nuclear power plants. This question of the public attitude will become particularly important in the years ahead as the number of nuclear power plants grows and as designers seek sites closer to large cities.

Is it worth all the effort?

From the very beginning of our national nuclear power program in 1946, its hope and justification lay in the economic benefits it might bestow on our nation. I believe our faith is being answered by the recent and positive indications from the utility industry, both public and private, that nuclear power is demonstrably competitive with fossil fuels in several major areas of the country. In those areas where fossil fuels have not been available at low cost, and where there are major industrial and population centers, several utilities have taken active steps for the immediate construction of nuclear plants. Further, these utilities have announced their intention to emphasize nuclear plants in their construction plans for the seventies.

These steps are being taken on a sound business basis, and presage the era of economic development which we in the atomic industry have been anticipating for the past decade. Also, the effect of future competition by nuclear plants is being directly felt by the fossil fuel industry, and the economic benefits of such stimulation are becoming increasingly evident to the whole power industry, indeed the entire economy.

If one considers that 777 billion kWh of electricity were sold to the U.S. public in 1962, the effect of a drop of 1 mill/kWh in power costs is a change in cost to consumers of $777 million each year. A decade hence this figure will be twice as large due to the anticipated doubling rate of power production. The future (direct and indirect) effects of nuclear power may well result in even more significant cost reductions. When these savings are compared with past expenditures of $2 billion made by government and industry in the development of nuclear technology, it becomes evident that the potential economic benefits to the people of the U.S. provide ample justification for our past expenditures and compelling rationale for a continued vigorous program.

Further reading

There is, if anything, too much literature on nuclear power. Fortunately it has been superbly recorded and controlled over the years by *Nuclear Science Abstracts,* AEC's bimonthly abstract journal for the field of Atomic Energy and related subjects (at your library or Govt. Printing Office, $22/yr.)

For those starting out, an easy introduction to the concepts of nuclear physics and of nuclear energy is Ellis' *Nuclear Technology for Engineers* (McGraw-Hill, 1959, $9.50). More advanced, but still accessible to the nonspecialist, are any of the many textbooks bearing variants of the title "Introduction to Nuclear Engineering," say R. Stephenson's (McGraw-Hill, $9.50). Up to date and excellent is Glasstone and Sesonske's *Nuclear Reactor Engineering* (Van Nostrand, 1963, $9.50). A classic on the neutronics of reactors, one of the best, is Glasstone and Edlund's *Elements of Nuclear Reactor Theory* (Van Nostrand, 1952, $5.50).

Worthy of mention is Weinberg and Wigner's *Physical Theory of Neutron Chain Reactors* (U. of Chicago Press, 1958, $15).

The periodical literature of atomic energy is as international as the interest in the subject. Here in the United States *Nuclear Science and Engineering* (comes with $18/yr membership in the American Nuclear Society), *Nucleonics* (McGraw-Hill, $8/yr), and the AEC's quarterly *Technical Progress Reviews* (there are four: *Nuclear Safety Power Reactor Technology*, *Reactor Materials*, and *Reactor Fuel Processing*—each $2/yr from GPO) are the important ones. In the USSR there's *Atomnaya Energya* (available in English translation from Consultant's Bureau). In England, there are *Nuclear Power* and *Nuclear Engineering*, in France the CEA *Bulletin*, in Germany, *Atomwirtschaft*, in Italy, *Energia Nucleare;* etc.

The reactors Dr. Starr discusses have been described at length in many AEC reports, tersely in a series of Reactor Foldouts available from *Nucleonics* for 25¢ each, and in a series of books prepared by AEC for the 1958 Geneva Conference and available from Addison Wesley.

If your company has more than passing interest in the nuclear field, it should belong to the Atomic Industrial Forum; write them at 850 3rd Ave., N.Y.C.

An excellent source of information on the political, technical, and economic aspects of atomic energy are the records of the hearings of the Joint Committee on Atomic Energy; especially "Development, Growth and State of the Atomic Energy Industry" (GPO, 1963, $1.25). To stay current, scan the annual AEC reports to Congress (GPO).

SUPERCONDUCTING MAGNETS

by J. K. Hulm, B. S. Chandrasekhar, and H. Riemersma*

IN BRIEF: *Until two years ago, it was believed that superconductors and magnetic fields wouldn't mix. But then came a special superconductor that could survive large magnetic fields—and the new magnet was born. Magnetwire superconductors differ from ordinary superconductors in their transition from the superconducting to the nonsuperconducting state. They don't switch all at once when exposed to magnetic fields, but change first to a partially superconducting state. Enough superconductivity remains at fields of 100 kilogauss or more to sustain a very large current.*

Making magnets from these materials has, however, been fraught with difficulties. The metals are hard and brittle and very difficult to handle. Currents have been much less than expected from laboratory tests. For some reason coils of wire don't perform as well as short pieces. And ways must be found to protect the coil from the energy released when it accidentally returns to the resistive state while carrying current. Nevertheless the research worker can now manipulate fields in the tens of kilogauss without having to pay for them in terms of a huge initial cost for capital equipment or a large electric bill.—C.J.L.

■ Given: A material that remains superconducting in high magnetic fields.

*J. K. Hulm and H. Riemersma are engaged in superconducting magnet studies at Westinghouse Electric Corp., Pittsburgh, Pennsylvania. A former colleague at Westinghouse, B. S. Chandrasekhar is now Professor of Physics at Western Reserve University, Cleveland, Ohio.

Problem: Make a superconducting magnet.

A trivial problem, really. Simply wind the material into a coil, submerge it in a bath of liquid helium, and run a current through it.

Or so we thought. And so, presumably, did everyone else in the superconducting business.

The solution proved to be far from trivial. We spent six months learning how to draw long pieces of magnet wire from an ingot of exceedingly stubborn material. And once we had succeeded, we found that coils wound from this wire would carry only a fraction of the current expected from tests on the wire before it was wound. Consequently, maximum fields were disappointingly low. We did know that if we pushed the coil beyond its maximum current it would change back to a normal conductor, despite low temperatures. But we were not prepared to find that, once this happened, the coil was sometimes worthless for further superconducting magnet experiments.

It is now two years later. Some of these mysteries have been cleared up; others still remain. But we have gained some proficiency in the art of winding superconducting magnets. Enough so that we have been able to make superconducting coils with current densities up to 100,000 amp/cm²—a density that would melt an ordinary copper conductor. Steady fields of over 100 kilogauss have been created with the wire we've drawn. And with new materials, now in a number of research laboratories, it seems likely the superconducting magnets will penetrate well into the region between 100 and 200 kG.

With the prospect of creating such large fields with coils that are small, light, and consume no power, technology has followed closely on science. Applications in nuclear accelerators, energy storage devices, fusion power machines, magnetohydrodynamic generators, rocket engines have been studied. Most of these, however, will have to await further improvement in magnet performance before their practicality can be tested. Meanwhile, other applications, particularly those in which the magnets create fields for research experiments, have already proved their usefulness, broadening the whole spectrum of high-magnetic-field research in the laboratory.

Power is zero, except . . .

High fields, small volume, low weight—superconducting magnets offer all of these, but their most engaging feature remains their low power consumption. "Low" is the proper word; despite zero resistance, power consumption is not zero. For to compare superconducting magnets with conventional magnets, it is necessary to include the power required to keep them at superconducting temperatures. This, in the ideal case, would be about 20 watts, which is approximately the amount of heat that would leak through the walls of the dewar for a magnet with a 20-in.³ working volume. But liquid-helium refrigerators drawing 20 W do not exist. Realistically, then, minimum power requirements are about 5 kilowatts.

For a 100-kG field this is still a trivial amount of power. A comparable conventional magnet having a water-cooled-copper coil would draw about 1000 kW. And even a liquid-hydrogen-cooled aluminum coil, which wastes less power because resistance is lower at these temperatures, would draw about 100 kW (for comparison, see Fig. 3-113).

These meager power requirements alone are sufficient to make the superconducting magnet attractive in applications where power is at a premium—in space, for example. But even where there is an abundance of power, the superconducting magnet would win out on economic grounds since the capital cost of a high-field magnet installation rises steeply with the power level. With further development it is expected that the cost of superconducting wire, which now averages about one dollar per gram, and the expenses of elaborate cryogenic equipment, can be substantially reduced. It is further hoped that high-field working volumes can be increased; those so far achieved for a 70-kG magnet amount to only a few cubic centimeters.

The development that triggered the interest in superconducting magnets was the announcement, in 1961, that certain superconductors could carry extremely large currents in high-magnetic fields, without losing their superconductivity. Until this time, it had been assumed that even a moderate magnetic field would choke off all superconducting current. Working with a niobium-tin compound, Kunzler, Buehler, Hsu, and Wernick of Bell Laboratories showed that short samples of this material could be made to carry 10^5 amp/cm² in fields as high as 88 kG. Once physicists were awakened to the possibilities, other materials were soon tested—principally the niobium-zirconium alloys—and also found to be suitable for magnets.

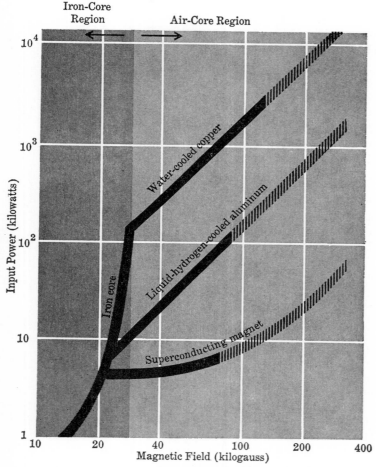

Fig. 3-113. *By comparison with conventional magnets, superconducting magnets are strikingly efficient. They are unrivaled except in the low-field range where the field-concentrating effect of an ironcore (before saturation) creates more gauss per watt input. And they would be more economical there, too, but minimum power for a liquid-helium refrigerator is about 5000 watts. At high fields, liquid-hydrogen-cooled aluminum coils offer an intermediate-power range, but power there is mostly refrigeration, too. All curves are for magnets with a 20-in.³ working volume.*

The undesirable ideal

Besides their ability to remain superconducting in large magnetic fields, the new materials had properties that were distinctly different from those associated with the "ideal" superconductors.

This notion of "ideal" had slowly emerged from studies of superconducting materials over a period of 40 years. All good superconductors, it was assumed, had four distinguishing properties:

First, they have zero resistivity—or at least so little resistance that it cannot be measured with the most sensitive instruments. It appears that resistivity is at most less than 10^{-22} ohm-cm (the best normal metals—even at very low temperatures—have resistivities of 10^{-9} to 10^{-10} ohm-cm) and is very likely zero.

Second, they are diamagnetic—flux is completely excluded from the interior of the superconductor up to its critical field, at which point the material goes "normal" and complete flux penetration occurs. This effect is called the Meissner effect and is reversible.

Third, externally applied magnetic fields do not stop abruptly at the surface but decay exponentially over a finite distance. Even in a superconductor, surface currents over a finite depth are needed to cancel the magnetic field. The $1/e$ point on the decay curve is known as the penetration depth, λ, and is characteristically in the range between 10^{-5} and 10^{-6} cm.

Fourth, superconductivity can be destroyed by passing a current through a superconducting wire. When this current creates a magnetic field equal to the critical field the material changes to its nonsuperconducting state. This critical current is defined by the equation $I_c = 5rH_c$, called Silsbee's rule, where the current, I_c, is in amps, r is the radius of the conductor in cm, and H_c is the critical field in gauss. When an external field is added to that created by the current in the wire, the situation becomes somewhat more complex, but the critical field observed when the two fields are simply added is usually quite close to that observed with the current alone.

The delinquents

Alas, as more materials were found to be superconducting, it was discovered that very few behaved as the set of "ideal" properties said they should. It is true that well-annealed, properly shaped, pure single crystals of a few superconductors such as tin and indium did indeed behave like ideal superconductors. But the vast majority were delinquents. They showed gradual transitions from the superconducting to the normal state, with increasing temperature or magnetic field. Flux exclusion at fields below the critical value was sometimes incomplete, and removal of the field occasionally left a paramagnetic moment frozen in the sample. Critical currents showed a great variety of dependence upon sample size and applied field, but rarely anything satisfying Silsbee's rule.

At first, rather than discard the idea of ideal superconductors, physicists chose another course. The fault, they said, lay in the condition of the materials. If samples of nonideal superconductors could be prepared in a well-annealed, homogenous, single-crystal form, then these superconductors would also behave as ideal ones. Send these ill-behaved materials to the zone-refining school, as it were, and all would become well-mannered.

With a better understanding of the properties of these nonideal superconductors, and with advances in the theory of superconductivity, these notions began to change. A significant step in the understanding of nonideal superconductors was made with the theory proposed by the Soviet physicists V. L. Ginzburg and L. D. Landau in 1950. More recently, several of their compatriots, notably A. A. Abrikosov and L. P. Gor'kov, have extended this theory. In keeping with the current passion for acronyms, the collective work of this group is referred to as the GLAG theory. The GLAG theory is a phenomenological theory; it seeks to explain the superconducting mechanism in nonideal superconductors in terms of their macroscopic properties. In that way, it is unlike the superconductivity theory proposed by Bardeen, Cooper, and Schrieffer, which forms the basis of our microscopic knowledge of ideal superconductors. But there is no disagreement between the two theories. Indeed, Gor'kov showed that the GLAG theory was consistent in all respects with the BCS theory and, in fact followed from it.

The two classes

The significant contribution of the GLAG theory was to show that there are not one, but two classes of superconductors. One class, called superconductors of the first kind, includes all of the original ideal superconductors plus those with properties that are close to the ideal. The second class, called superconductors of the second kind, contains those materials that depart markedly from the "ideal." These two classes correspond, in most cases, to what have been referred to as "soft" and "hard" superconductors, respectively, but these terms are not precise and should probably be dropped. All high-field superconducting magnet materials, including the original niobium-tin compound, are superconductors of the second kind.

The principal difference between the two types lies in the mode of transition from the superconducting state to the normal state. Superconductors of the first kind have a sharp transition with increasing field; below a certain magnetic field strength the sample is entirely superconducting and above that field strength, it is entirely normal. Superconductors of the second kind show a gradual transition; between the entirely superconducting and

the entirely normal states there is a "mixed" state in which the sample is partially superconducting and partially normal. It is the electronic structure of the material that permits this mixed state to occur. In thermodynamic terms (see Fig. 3-114) the mixed state will occur whenever it represents a condition of lowest free energy.

Were it not for this departure from the previously established "ideal," superconducting magnets would be impossible. Superconductors of the first kind are useless for magnets; they switch to the normal state at fields usually no greater than a few thousand gauss. In superconductors of the second kind, the mixed state permits the material to remain substantially superconducting to fields of perhaps 200 kG or higher.

Unfortunately, not all superconductors of the second kind are suitable for magnets. For example, well-annealed, single crystals of such superconductors as pure niobium, lead alloys, and the niobium-tantalum alloys assume a mixed structure, but it quickly changes to an all-normal material at relatively low fields. C. J. Gorter suggested that they break down because of the Lorentz force a magnetic field exerts on a current. This Lorentz force squeezes the superconducting regions down until they eventually disappear. Good magnet materials have discontinuities in them that serve to pin the superconducting regions against the action of the Lorentz forces. These are typified by materials that have been heavily cold-worked or contain other sources of lattice strain such as dislocations, vacancies, or interstitial atoms.

Present materials have limitations

For the most part, only two superconductors of the second kind—Nb_3Sn and the alloys of Nb-Zr—have been extensively investigated as superconducting magnet materials. Both have limitations, but, despite these difficulties, both have made successful electromagnets.

The principal limitation of Nb_3Sn is its mechanical hardness. Because it is so brittle, a variety of fabrication techniques have been proposed but the most successful from the point of view of magnet construction appears to be the original method worked out by Kunzler, Buehler, Hsu, and Wernick. In this process, a niobium tube containing elemental niobium and tin is first wound into a coil and then heat treated to form the niobium-tin compound, neatly avoiding the problem of winding a brittle wire. Although the method is effective, once wound, the magnets cannot be unwound to make modifications or to inspect the cause of failures without damage to the superconducting core. Furthermore, the presence of a niobium

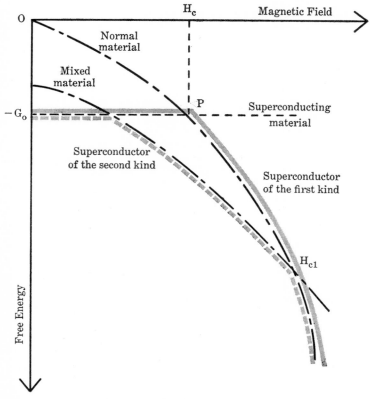

Fig. 3-114. A plot of thermodynamic free energies shows why there are two kinds of superconductors. The two kinds are represented by a composite of three curves, corresponding to three different states. "Normal material" curve falls with increasing field, according to the relationship $G = -H^2/8\pi$, because flux penetrates the material. "Superconducting material" curve, begins at lower free energy, does not change with field because flux does not penetrate. "Mixed state" has intermediate energy at zero field and drops slower because there is only partial flux penetration. The position of this third curve depends on the electronic structure of the material. Assume that a particular superconducting material has a mixed-state curve that lies above point P. Because any system always seeks a condition of minimum free energy, the material will not assume the mixed state at any value of field and the material will be a superconductor of the first kind (solid line). If the electronic structure is such that the curve falls below P, the material is a superconductor of the second kind (dashed line) and complete transition to the normal state will not occur until H_{c1} (perhaps as high as 200 kilogauss).

tube, which does not carry superconducting current and is typically two to three times the diameter of the core, reduces the effective current density by a corresponding factor of four to nine.

Another method, developed by Hanak and Cody of RCA, is to deposit Nb_3Sn in the form of a thin film on metallic tape; these films show good high-field properties and appear to hold promise for magnet applications.

The upper critical field for Nb_3Sn has not yet been determined experimentally, but it is certainly greater than 200 kG. It therefore looks at the moment like the most promising material for use at the highest fields, despite fabrication problems.

Niobium-zirconium superconducting wire, on the other hand, with zirconium present in the range from 25 to 75%, is limited to critical fields between 70–100 kG. The alloy containing 25% zirconium is widely used for building commercial superconducting magnets for fields up to 60 kG. The materials are hard and the metallurgical problems of working with them are quite serious, but with some effort long lengths of wire can be drawn. This material can be handled quite roughly without deterioration of superconducting properties.

Better materials

The search for better high-field superconductors goes on. The exploration has been carried out mainly in that great fertile plain of the Periodic System, the transition metal series. Many have contributed to the search; one of the most active explorers has been B. T. Matthias originally from Bell Laboratories but now at the U. of California.

Besides Nb_3Sn, the other attractive members of the β-tungsten group include Nb_3Al, V_3Sn, and V_3Ga. There are also several compounds of potential interest in the sigma-phase and alpha-manganese structures, although none of these has transition temperatures quite as high as the β-tungsten group. But the problem of brittleness remains. The critical matter is not the difficulty of winding a brittle wire, but the problem of building a magnet that is capable of withstanding cooling and mechanical shock without damage.

With alloys, the crucial question is: can critical fields be pushed well over 100 kG? Because there is a rough correspondence between transition temperature and critical field, the answer seems to hinge on finding higher transition temperatures. If they can be pushed out of the top alloy range (12–15°K) to the top compound range (17–18°K), we might approach 200 kG with alloys.

Besides their gradual transition from the

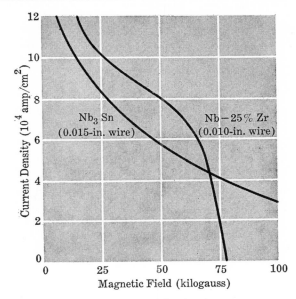

Fig. 3-115. Critical current density in magnet super-conductors decreases nonlinearly with applied field. The Nb_3Sn curve shows effective densities for a 0.006-in.-dia. superconducting core surrounded by a 0.015-in.-dia. nonsuperconducting niobium sheath.

superconducting to the normal states, superconductors of the second kind depart from the properties of the first kind in another way—a way that has much significance for the designer of superconducting magnets. In most superconductors of the first kind, the critical current is the current that corresponds to the critical field, and when there is an externally applied field, this field and the field created by the current should equal the critical field. By contrast, superconductors of the second kind have no such well-defined relationship between the applied field and critical current (Fig. 3-115). More important, at some values of applied field, magnet superconductors cannot carry nearly the current they could if the two fields were linearly related.

For a magnet with a field of 100 kG and a winding of reasonable thickness—less than three feet, say—the critical current density must be at least 1000 amp/cm². Such currents are possible in Nb_3Sn at fields greater than 100 kG but Nb-25% Zr reaches current densities of 1000-amp/cm² at about 70 kG.

The degradation mystery

It would be enough if the decrease in critical current density with increasing field were the only problem facing the magnet designer. But the designer must deal with an even more serious problem.

It was observed with the very first magnets wound from Nb-Zr wire that, for a given field, coils of wire had a much lower critical current

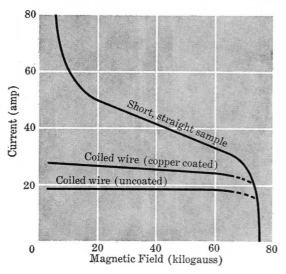

Fig. 3-116. *A mystery: Why do straight samples of a wire perform better than inductive coils of the same wire. This "degradation effect" is not yet satisfactorily explained although some proposed theories fit the observations rather closely. With copper coating, there is some recovery, but it is not complete. The curves here are for 0.010-in. diameter Nb-25%-Zr wire.*

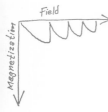

than a short straight sample of the same wire. This degradation of critical current has been shown to be dependent on both the strength of the applied field and the composition of the alloy. Although the work of the Bell Laboratories group indicates that degradation in Nb_3Sn is negligible, the experience with coils wound from this material is insufficient to conclude that degradation never occurs.

Degradation is bad enough in cold-worked Nb-25%-Zr wire; it is disastrous in heat treated wire. A straight piece of 0.010-in. diameter cold-worked alloy may be able to carry 50 amp in a 20 kG field, whereas a magnet wound from the same wire can carry only 20 amp. But if that wire is annealed at 700°C for a few hours, the straight sample may increase its current-carrying capacity to 200 amp while the coiled form falls to a paltry 4 amp. A decrease in available critical current from 50 to 20 amp is a disappointment; a drop from 200 to 4 amp is surely a catastrophe.

This effect makes the coil bulkier than one feels it ought to be to produce a given field. A good number of amperes are somehow mislaid when the wire is wound into a coil and all of us in the magnet business would like to reclaim them.

Empirically, we have found that some of the lost amperes can be regained by spacing the superconducting windings farther apart, and particularly by separating the windings with a layer of high-conductivity metal such as copper. These methods give a somewhat higher

critical current (Fig. 3-116), but it is still far short of that observed in a short straight sample. And it is not certain why it works.

One of the first thoughts that occurred to everyone who came up against the degradation effect was that the superconducting wire is of nonuniform quality along its length, and that a long piece of wire is more likely to have a weak spot than a short piece. But our experiments on noninductively wound coils show that 1000 ft of wire carry almost the same current as a short sample, while the same wire, wound into an inductive coil, showed the characteristic degradation.

The flux-jump model

It is our feeling now that the explanation must lie primarily in the phenomenon of "flux-jumping." Flux jumping frequently occurs when a sample of Nb-Zr or Nb_3Sn is subjected to an increasing external field. As the field increases, the field that penetrates the normal portions of the sample does not increase smoothly, but in jumps, as in the margin. At each of these jumps, a pulse of heat is released in the sample and appears as a temperature rise. In some instances, the heat may be enough to send the sample momentarily normal. But in the case of a small sample immersed in liquid helium and carrying no current, the heat is rapidly carried away, the sample recovers its superconductivity, and the B-H curve continues its saw-toothed course.

In a magnet, the effect of the flux jumps can be expected to be different than in a small sample. The distribution of field across the coil varies from a maximum at the center to a lower value at the outer turns, and may even pass through zero and be negative in the outer turns if the coil is large and flat. As the current increases, flux jumps occur in a complex pattern that depends on the current and field at every point. Not every one of these jumps drives the corresponding section normal, even momentarily. And should a transitory normality occur, it may decay and superconductivity be restored before the normal portion can grow by joule heating. But as the current continues to increase, there will be a point where heat from a flux jump sends a portion of the coil normal, and this heat, combined with joule heating in the normal portion, triggers the coil normal.

We are putting forth this model tentatively; it does make some of the observed phenomena reasonable, but it leaves others as mysterious as ever. To its credit there is the observation that a magnet rarely goes normal at the point where it would be expected—the point of highest field, at the middle of the innermost winding. This, if the model is correct, is because the critical flux jump could well be at some point which is seeing a much lower field.

Some problems still elude explanation. In testing short samples, for example, we often get the same results when a given current is applied and then the field slowly increased as when the order is reversed. If the flux-jumping model is correct, one would expect that the constant-field, increasing-current test would give higher critical currents since the flux jumps would have already occurred.

The persistent mode

As might be expected, firing up a superconducting magnet is more complicated than simply throwing the switch; the wire has zero resistance and it would seem that any voltage across the coil should cause an infinite current to flow. In practice, current is limited by the internal resistance in the power supply, the inductance of the coil, and the resistance of the nonsuperconducting leads outside the dewar. The usual practice is to connect the power supply—which may be any d-c source from an automobile battery to a welding generator—through a current-control resistor.

To set a persistent current circulating, we simply put a superconducting short across the power leads of the magnet before the coil is put in the dewar. During runup, this wire is kept normal by heating it with a small heating coil. When maximum current is flowing in the magnet, we shut off the heater, the shorting wire returns to the superconducting state, and the persistent current is established. We have maintained the persistent current mode this way in a 50 kG coil for several days without detectable drop in field. To shut down the magnet, we simply reconnect the power supply and reverse the startup procedure.

When superconductivity vanishes

Beyond the critical-current threshold lies the resistive realm of normal conductivity. When a coil is pushed into this region the freely circulating current meets a rapidly growing resistance, and the energy stored is quickly dissipated, in the form of heat. For the small research magnets we are working with, the effect is not necessarily disastrous. There is no explosion in the usual sense; the worst that can happen is that the coil burns out. For larger coils, normalization is accompanied by a loud bang caused by the vaporization of liquid helium that has permeated the windings.

In small magnets, resistive heating, which may raise the temperature by 100°K, is generally not harmful. It is the voltage induced by rapid decay that can cause the most damage. As in any pure inductance, the voltage induced

is proportional to the rate of current decay according to the relationship

$$V = -L \, dI/dt$$

With a moderate inductance and a rapid decrease of current, this voltage can be large enough to cause arcing between windings—splattering metal around and creating permanent shorts. Interlayer insulation will solve this problem if voltages are not too large, but as coils get larger and inductances grow, V will increase unless steps are taken to slow down the current decay.

Rate of current decay is ultimately controlled by the speed at which the normal region grows—the propagation velocity of the interface between normal and superconducting regions. This propagation velocity is, in turn, dependent on the power to be dissipated and the thermal properties of the winding. The driving power is essentially $J^2\rho_n$, where J is the current in the windings and ρ_n is the specific resistivity of the winding material in the normal state.

The magnitude of the current is determined by the magnetic field requirements, but there

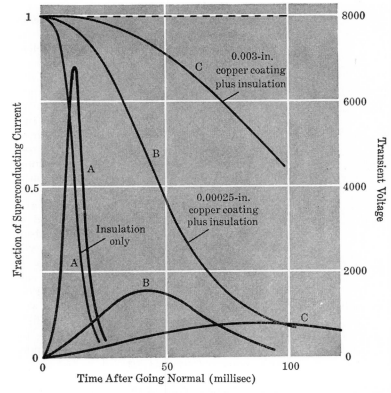

Fig. 3-117. *Current decays rapidly when superconductivity breaks down under the stress of a magnetic field. In an inductive magnet coil the rapid current change generates voltages large enough to arc across windings. Various thicknesses of copper on the superconductor (curves B & C) slow down current decay by providing a low-resistance path around the nonsuperconducting area. The curves are for a 50-kG coil with a 5-henry inductance.*

is nothing to prevent us from reducing the effective value of ρ_n, by placing a high-conductivity normal metal in parallel with the superconductor. Thus, when normalization begins, magnet current will switch from the superconducting path, which is now highly resistive, to the low-resistance normal path. A thin coating of copper, for example, in addition to the normal insulation, will produce a substantial reduction in V.

Propagation velocity cannot be changed much by tinkering with the thermal conductivity and heat capacity of the wire without also diluting the windings with nonsuperconducting material. The thermal conductivity along the wire is essentially fixed. But the thermal conductivity transverse to the wire may be reduced by suitable thermal insulation. With this heat barrier, normal resistance is injected at a reduced rate.

Magnets for research

Even with the small superconducting magnets being wound today, there are many experiments in solid-state physics where high fields in low volumes are of great interest. Examples are studies of the Fermi surface in metals by de Haas-van Alphen measurements and magnetotransport experiments. Superconducting magnets have already been used for electron paramagnetic resonance and nuclear magnetic resonance studies. Investigations of magnetic materials, particularly those with low susceptibilities, will be easier with the new magnet. Many other "small magnet" applications of this type could be listed, but it suffices to remark that the superconducting magnet comprises an important new research tool which will probably find its way into almost every basic science laboratory in the near future.

Cryogenics itself will benefit from the new magnet because a new key has been found to the world below 1°K—the region close to absolute zero. These temperatures can be achieved most readily by magnetic cooling, a process in which heat is absorbed in a paramagnetic salt by quickly removing a magnetic field. Formerly, to get into this business in a serious way required a large power station for the high-field magnet and a small river to cool it. One is not quite ready to scrap these tools, but the poor man's demagnetizer has arrived in the supermagnet.

The influence of magnetic fields on chemical reaction rates has already become a subject of more intensive study under the stimulus of more readily available high field strengths. Finally, in the life sciences, little is known about the influence of high magnetic fields on living organisms, but preliminary studies suggest that the occurrence of certain anomalous cell processes can be greatly modified by the presence of a field. Studies of these effects will be made much easier with magnets that are small and inexpensive to operate.

Further reading

Two classics on superconductivity are *Superconductivity*, by Shoenberg (Cambridge U. Press, 1962) and *Superfluids*, Vol. 1: *Macroscopic Theory of Superconductivity*, by London (Wiley, 1950). These two books taken together represent the state of knowledge ten years ago, and provide the necessary foundation for understanding subsequent developments. A concise, up-to-date survey of the field is contained in *Superconductivity*, by Lynton (Wiley, 1962), which also contains the only pedagogical treatment in English of recent Russian theoretical work. An excellent elementary account of the Bardeen, Cooper, and Schrieffer theory was given by Cooper in the *Am. J. Phys.*, **28**, 91 (1960). To go deeper into the theory, one should consult the articles by Bardeen in *Handbuch der Physik*, Vol. 15 (Springer-Verlag, 1956), and by Bardeen and Schrieffer in *Progress in Low Temperature Physics*, Vol. 3, edited by Gorter (North-Holland, 1961). The reader should be warned that the last two articles require a comprehensive background in theoretical physics for their understanding.

An International Conference on High Magnetic Fields was held at MIT in Nov. 1961, and the proceedings have been published as a book, *High Magnetic Fields* (MIT Press and Wiley, 1962). This book contains comprehensive accounts of the generation of high magnetic fields both by conventional means and by using superconductors, and applications to various physical problems.

Publications on superconducting electrotechnology are quite sparse. Perhaps the best source of information is the proceedings of the annual conference on cryogenic engineering, *Advances in Cryogenic Engineering*, ed. by Timmerhaus (Plenum Press). Discussions of superconducting magnets, motors, rectifiers, and other devices appear in Vol. 5 (1960), 6 (1961), and 7 (1962).

Special techniques are obviously needed for operating equipment and doing experiments at very low temperatures. These techniques are discussed in *Cryogenic Engineering*, by Scott (Van Nostrand, 1959) and in *Experimental Techniques in Low Temperature Physics*, by White (Oxford U. Press, 1959).

HIGH-SPEED SHIPS

by Edward V. Lewis *

IN BRIEF: *At speeds above 40 knots, the deep-running submarine is a formidable and elusive naval vehicle. The surface ship might overtake it if hull forms could be designed to cope better with two problems: One is the resistance set up by the disturbance that the hull itself generates as it slices through the water. The other is the dangerous pitching and heaving that occurs in stormy seas as the ship tries to move at high speed through them. Naval architects have conceived of many unusual hull forms, and are testing them in model tanks. Three that have emerged as promising are the extra slender destroyer hull, the slender ship with deep, large bulbs at bow and stern, and a radically new one—the semi-submarine—a ship whose hull would ride totally submerged near the sea's surface, but with hydrofoil-like struts projecting through it. What is needed now is money to design and build prototypes based on these concepts that will use the latest technology in air-breathing power plants, propulsion devices, and electronically controlled stabilization systems. Such an effort will show what the future of the surface ship will be for military tasks requiring great mobility.—F.P.*

■ In recent years the introduction of nuclear power has opened up tremendous possibilities for high-speed submarines operating freely beneath the surface of the sea. And fascinating new vehicles have appeared that skim over its surface on hydrofoils or on cushions of air. Now, naval architects and engineers are inquiring whether or not new developments in technology can lead to new concepts in fast surface ships. The answer is "yes," but before considering specific cases it may be well to discuss the reasons that have led to the avoidance of the sea surface in some types of craft.

Although all vehicles must cope with friction in some form, one particular disadvantage that confronts the surface ship is the added resistance or drag associated with the generation of waves. This resistance can be minimized but never eliminated. The establishment and maintenance of a train of waves requires an expenditure of energy that reveals itself in the added power required to drive the ship. Physically, this means that the integration of the longitudinal components of pressure on the surface of the forebody of the ship exceeds that on the

* Edward V. Lewis is Assistant to the President at Webb Institute of Naval Architecture, Glen Cove, Long Island, New York.

afterbody. One can observe the buildup of a bow wave on any fast ship, and the lack of an equal buildup at the stern.

One way to avoid this disadvantageous wave-making resistance is to go below the surface, as a submarine does. In fact, if a well-formed body moves through a fluid at great depth, the only resistance to motion is friction; the integrated pressures on the afterbody balance those on the forebody.

The other disadvantage confronting the surface ship is the waves which always disturb the surface of the sea, and which offer real restrictions on speed—not to say discomfort—in case of storms. Of course, a submarine at great depth is unaffected by storms raging above which may be of real concern to the surface mariner. Thus, for certain military missions, the submarine is the answer—especially when the requirement of stealth is added to those of speed and insensitivity to waves.

But for many duties it is important to remain on the surface: launching of aircraft, use of radar, communication with land bases, ships, or aircraft. Furthermore, submarines are limited in the types of power plant they can use. Existing nuclear plants are heavy, space-consuming, and expensive. Plants making use of air—steam, gas turbines, or diesels—are obviously unsuited.

Limits on vehicle speed

So we may return to the original question of whether or not new concepts in surface ships might give them a renewed place in the scheme of things. The answer is in the affirmative—*if* we can develop hull forms to reduce wave-making resistance specifically, and *if* these same hull forms are good performers in rough seas.

The minimization of wave-making resistance would, in itself, be a tremendous boon in our quest for higher speed. Deferring for a while the question of rough sea behavior, what limits would there be, then, to increasing speed, whether on the surface or just below it? For any craft, the frictional resistance provides the one inescapable limit. Since it is the *least* resistance a body can experience, frictional drag offers a frame of reference for the performance of real ships. Let's see just how.

If we compute the installed power P required to move a completely submerged body of gross weight W and density ρ_b at a velocity V through a fluid of density ρ_f, the resulting equation for the specific power has this dimensionless form:

$$\frac{P}{WV} = \text{const.} \times \frac{V^2/gl}{\rho_b/\rho_f} \times \frac{S}{v^{2/3}} \times \frac{1}{\eta}$$

The term l in this equation is the cube root of the submerged volume and is an index of the size of the body, S is its wetted area, and v its volume. Factor η is the propulsive efficiency.

The left-hand side can be thought of in several ways. We may interpret it in terms of resistance R, since the installed power $P = RV/\eta$. Hence P/WV becomes $R/W\eta$. To the naval architect, R/W is the *resistance per lb* of vehicle weight or displacement. It is also approximately the *thrust per lb* that must be provided to propel the vehicle. To the aeronautical engineer, P/WV is really η times the reciprocal of L/D, the familiar *Lift/Drag* ratio.

For completely submerged ships—subs, bathyspheres, torpedoes (and dirigibles, for that matter)—the weight of the vehicle and

that of the displaced fluid are identical. Thus, the density ratio $\rho_b/\rho_f = 1$. For surface ships, it's the immersed volume that counts, and the density ratio of unity can be applied here as well.

To create our frame of reference, based on frictional resistance, we choose an ideal shape —namely, a sphere. This shape has the minimum possible ratio of the wetted surface to the volume $(S/v^{2/3})$, and thus—for any given *speed ratio* V^2/gl and density ratio—will require the least driving thrust per lb of vehicle. So putting our spherical "vehicle" into water, and choosing an ideal propulsive efficiency of $\eta = 1$, reduces our P/WV equation to the following simple dimensionless form:

$$P/WV = \text{const.} \times V^2/gl$$

Much can be learned from plotting the specific power P/WV against speed V on a log-log diagram, as was done in 1950 by Gabrielli and von Karman. The sphere equation is a straight line with a slope of 2. Actually, a family of such straight lines, for $\rho_b/\rho_f = 1$, must be plotted to account for different values of size l. This has been done in Fig. 3-118.

These lines represent definite limit lines for a particular value of the density ratio. No matter what refinements of form may be adopted, a vehicle moving in a fluid under turbulent flow conditions cannot perform any better than the ideal sphere whose size (volume$^{1/3}$) equals the l-value for that vehicle. Put another way, it is impossible for any buoyant vehicle to operate at speeds to the *right* of its l-value line.

The influence of wave-making

We can now see the influence of various losses faced by actual ships, including wave-making resistance. On Fig. 3-118 are operating points for several ships—from a PT-boat to a large tanker. For one of these, a World War II destroyer, the actual curve of P/WV is plotted. Note that at low speeds, 10–15 knots, the curve almost coincides with the line for the $l = 50$ ft of the destroyer. In other words, at low speeds the destroyer generates few waves, and the thrust per lb required to move it through the water at these velocities is quite close to that for an ideal sphere.

As soon as greater speed is attempted, however, the deleterious effect of wave-making resistance is evident: the destroyer's curve falls away from the ideal sphere line, until its designed speed of some 30 knots is reached. The arrow indicates the speed gap that exists between the operating point and the ideal sphere line of the destroyer. Although curves are not shown for the other vehicles spotted on the

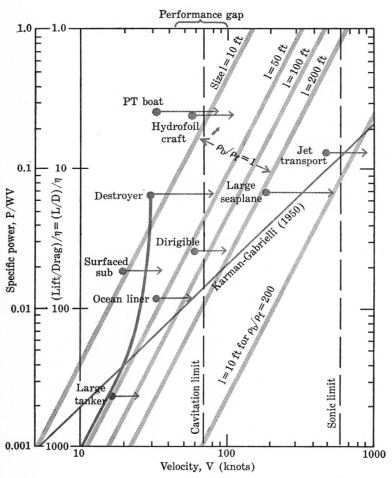

Fig. 3-118. *Specific power required by actual ships is compared here with that needed to drag ideal spheres of equivalent size (lines of slope = 2) through water. Destroyer curve deviates from its ideal sphere line because of wave-making resistance. See text for discussion of this chart.*

diagram, each has an arrow indicating the position of its size line.

The plot, and the equation from which it is drawn, clearly show that attainable speed for all vehicles is limited both by available power and by size. Velocity V can be increased by the brute force method of increasing installed power—keeping the vehicle size the same. Or, the thrust per lb of vehicle can be kept constant, and speed increased by increasing size.

Modern technology is quite able to provide the increase in size or in power required to increase the speed of water craft, *provided* power is not wasted in overcoming wave-making resistance. We'll see shortly how the naval architect is trying to keep such wastage down.

A final point about Fig. 3-118. On it appears the original limit line drawn by Gabrielli and von Karman in 1950. This line formed an envelope of all the specific power-velocity curves of vehicles then extant, but it did *not* represent a barrier for possible new vehicles. Some already have penetrated it; for example, the large tanker, as shown here. Thus the G-K line was not a real limit, only an empirical "state-of-the-art" line. It did not take into account the two factors of size and density.

The other limit lines for buoyant vehicles (and a line for aircraft which has been added at $\rho_b/\rho_f = 200$) *do* have a physical basis: speed may be increased by an increase in size, as in the case of the tanker, or by a decrease in fluid density, as in the case of the airplane.

The new, low-resistance hull forms

Now we are in a position to examine briefly some of the new hull forms being devised by naval architects to reduce wave-making resistance. There are three promising approaches suggested by the previous discussion: (1) to modify the form of the hull in such a way as to cancel the original waves by other waves, (2) to make the hull longer and more slender in order to reduce the wave disturbance, or (3) to put a large part of the hull far enough below the surface to reduce wave-making.

The first method is typified by the so-called "bulbous bow" which is found on all large U.S. Naval vessels and passenger liners, as well as on many cargo ships and tankers. Recent consideration has been given to much larger bulbs in the hope of having a more drastic effect on wave-making. The theory is that a bulb near the surface will generate its own train of waves and, if properly shaped and located somewhat forward of the bow of the ship, its wave train can partially cancel the ship's bow wave train. This would reduce resistance.

In actual practice, however, no simple shape can exactly counteract the somewhat complex wave configuration created by a hull. An example is the so-called Escort Research ship, profiled in the margin, which was developed by the Navy's Bureau of Ships but not yet built.

Large-bulb ship (Escort Research)

The second technique for reducing wave-making resistance—making the ship longer and more slender—is an approach that has been followed generally in the past. Figure 3-119 shows this historical trend based on data gathered by Ridgely-Nevitt of Webb Institute. Naval ships are, of course, the fastest available today. For any given value of size (that is, displacement), we see that the faster vessels have the lowest ratio of size-to-length. In other words, greater length means greater speed. The reason is that wave-making resistance goes up with the ratio $V/\sqrt{gL}$, which the naval architect calls the Froude number. Hence, if both length L and speed V are increased, we can keep the Froude number from increasing, thus avoiding excessive change in wave-making resistance.

Keeping resistance low by the third method

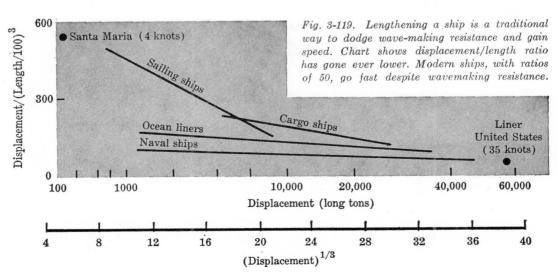

Fig. 3-119. *Lengthening a ship is a traditional way to dodge wave-making resistance and gain speed. Chart shows displacement/length ratio has gone ever lower. Modern ships, with ratios of 50, go fast despite wavemaking resistance.*

of putting much of the hull beneath the surface is difficult. To do this, it is necessary to go quite far below the surface to have a significant effect. Further, the amount of hull projecting through the surface, for purposes of navigation and supplying air and exhaust for the engines, must be kept to a minimum. The resistance of any appreciable projection may cancel the advantage of the submerged hull.

An example of this type of proposed craft is the semi-submarine, one form of which has a main hull that rides submerged to avoid surface limitations on speed. It has surface-piercing hydrofoils to aid stability and accommodate engine air intake and exhaust. Taking advantage of the light machinery weight possible with advanced, air-breathing power plants of the steam- or gas-turbine type, this new ship form offers the possibility of bursts of speed greater than modern nuclear or electric submarines can attain. It cannot maintain such bursts of speed for long periods of time, however, because of the need to conserve fuel.

A question of power

Before we turn to the question of ship behavior in storm seas, it is of interest to look

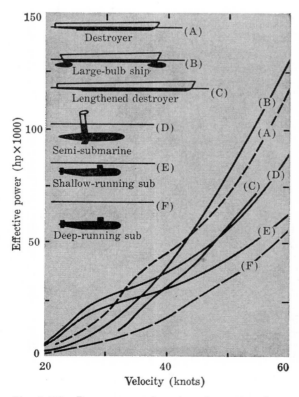

Fig. 3-120. *Power comparison in calm water shows semi-submarine offers potentially large reduction in power as against conventional destroyer. Humps in curves show speeds where surface wave effects are accentuated.*

briefly at the comparative powering requirements of the three new ship concepts. This is done in Fig. 3-120, where the effective horsepower is plotted against vehicle speed for calm-water operation. EHP is simply the power, $P\eta/550$, needed to overcome the total resistance to motion through the water, neglecting propulsion losses. Each craft shown is calculated in comparison with a DD-692 (World War II) class destroyer, whose displacement of some 2880 tons is considered reasonable for high-speed surface craft.

The two dashed lines, one for the conventional destroyer and the other for a deep-running sub, are shown as limiting cases. The submarine, of course, has the lowest resistance and we see that even at a speed of 60 knots, the EHP would not be astronomical. However, it is difficult to pack this much power into a small enough volume to drive a submarine of this displacement at such high speed. Indeed, higher power per cubic foot (and per lb, as well) should be, in my opinion, the next goal for designers of naval nuclear power plants.

We see that the lengthened destroyer and the semi-submarine have comparable performances, which suggests that the former would be the simplest solution to the high-speed problem: the semi-sub, with its submerged hull, presents problems in hull design and stability that do not, at first glance, seem worth the effort. However, when rough sea performance at high speeds is considered, we sense that the surface-ship approach may not, in fact, be the simplest. The large-bulb ship shows up well here up to about 40 knots and, as we shall see, it has excellent rough-water characteristics. A vehicle of this type could be designed to fall to the right of the conventional destroyer at speeds beyond 40 knots.

The cruel sea

Of course, it is not enough for a surface or near-the-surface ship to show favorable calm-water resistance at high speed. To compete with a deeply submerged submarine, the ship must be able to maintain good speed in rough storm seas. This may be, in part, a powering problem. However, in high-speed craft, it is usually mainly a matter of avoiding or minimizing ship motions and indirect effects—such as wet decks, slamming of the bow after it breaks free of the water, propeller racing, and so on. Hence, the ideal craft is one that gives the best compromise between low resistance and very good performance in rough water.

Ship motions are usually resolved into six components for study, as sketched in the margin: the angular motion of roll, yaw, and pitch and the translatory motions of heave, surge, and sway. Some are more troublesome than others, but when one or two are reduced the others are apt to become more noticeable.

Rolling has received particular attention ever since steam replaced sails and the steady-effect of canvas was lost. Because the forces involved in rolling are small, these amplitudes can be reduced drastically by various antirolling devices: the bilge keel, which adds damping; controllable fins, particularly effective at high speed like the control surfaces on an airplane; and antiroll tanks, internal water tanks that are designed to absorb the wave energy by sloshing the water back and forth instead of rolling the ship.

Heaving and pitching motions are the most difficult to overcome and present the worst problems because they involve large vertical accelerations and cause shipping of water, slamming and propeller racing. So, we will focus on these two motion modes, and assume there are methods for handling the others.

Model research in regular head seas has brought out the fact that amplitudes of motion are greatest near synchronism between the period of encounter with the waves—which depends on ship speed—and a ship's natural period of oscillation. Furthermore, phase relationships leading to wet decks and slamming are also characteristic of synchronism.

Thus, there are two possible methods by which significant reduction of pitching and heaving amplitudes can be sought: one is to avoid resonance with the waves; the other is to reduce the magnification effect that causes increased amplitudes near resonance.

Although damping devices such as bow fins can reduce the magnification effect somewhat, the most effective method of reducing motions is by avoiding synchronism. We can see several ways by which this might be accomplished by looking at the conditions for synchronous pitching in a seaway.

For this, we will use the simplest, most severe case—that of regular head seas. A basic parameter involved in the resonant oscillation of a ship's hull in response to waves is the dimensionless period ratio $T/\sqrt{L/g}$, where T is the natural period of oscillation of the hull in pitch or heave. The condition for synchronism with a wave of any particular length is a function of this period ratio and another dimensionless ratio, $V/\sqrt{gL}$, the familiar Froude number.

Without delving into the equation form of the resonance relationship, we see it plotted in Fig. 3-121. The different curves represent the conditions for synchronism, in regular head seas, with waves of different length compared to the ship's length L.

One can naturally ask, what about the irregular storm seas faced by real mariners—both modern and ancient? Oceanographers have shown that storm seas can be considered as a spectrum of a great many regular wave trains of varying length and direction, all superimposed on one another (see marginal sketch). They have also confirmed the observation of seamen that shorter waves are formed first in a storm. As the wind continues to blow, longer component waves are formed without seriously affecting the smaller ones. Thus, we can think of a storm sea as one in which, crudely speaking, all of the synchronous curves of Fig. 3-121 apply *simultaneously*.

What about the response of ships to such a spectrum of waves? Model tests have shown us that it is resonance with waves of length roughly equal to the ship's length or longer that causes the greatest difficulties. Hence, the curve on Fig. 3-121 representing a ratio of wave length to ship length equal to *one* forms a sort of natural boundary for comfortable ship oper-

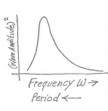

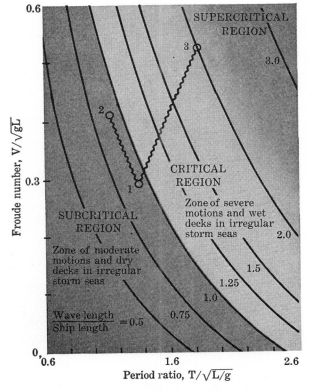

Fig. 3-121. Two ways to increase speed in storms. A ship operating near the critical region of resonance with long storm waves (point 1) can be made longer to reduce period ratio, thus permitting faster, subcritical operation (point 2). Or, it can be reshaped for a longer pitching period, permitting much faster, supercritical operation (point 3). Exact wave length for supercritical region is imprecise, depends on storm duration.

ation. When a given ship is operating at a speed *below* this line, it will face synchronism only with waves of length shorter than itself—lengths that tests tell us do not produce serious motion. In this region, the operation of the vessel is termed *subcritical*. The time-honored method of easing a ship in a rough sea is therefore to reduce speed.

The new ship forms in rough seas

We can now look at ways by which we might avoid the critical region without reducing speed, and how the new ship forms discussed earlier might fit in with this objective. Looking at Fig. 3-121, we can see two possibilities.

One alternative is to use hull proportions that raise the critical speed limit of the ship, and thus permit higher *subcritical* speeds. This means increasing the length of the ship in relation to displacement, which gives a reduced period ratio $T/\sqrt{L/g}$. A ship can then go at higher speeds before resonant response to waves of near ship length is experienced.

Our interest, however, is in rough sea speeds in excess of what present destroyers can maintain—say 40–50 knots, rather than about 20 knots. What chance does the ship-lengthening idea have of accomplishing this? In brief, not much. Model tests have been run on destroyer hulls 25% longer than a conventional DD-692 class destroyer. The tests showed that in a storm in which the conventional destroyer could attain a speed of 20 knots, the longer vessel could reach 30 knots, a fair increase (actually, from point 1 to point 2 on Fig. 3-121). However, to go further in this direction to even higher speed, the designer would be confronted with severe problems of stability, structure, and below-decks arrangement. Going to longer, thinner hulls, then, does not seem the answer to very high speeds.

The second alternative looks far more prom-

ising: to cross the critical region into a region of operation where the ship's period of encounter with the longest important wave component is shorter than its natural pitching period. The basic idea is simply to attain high ship speed *together with* a long natural pitching period—in effect, increasing the period ratio $T/\sqrt{L/g}$ of Fig. 3-121. Thus, we might operate at point 3 rather than at point 1. This region, at the upper right of the diagram, is termed the *supercritical* region. In essence, a ship operating at speeds and geometry that put it in that region is too sluggish to respond to the wave crests speeding by—very much as a fast-moving automobile does not respond to a washboard road.

Of our three unusual ship forms, the slender hull with large bulbs at both ends can certainly be considered a potential supercritical ship: its hull form is specifically designed for high speed, and the bulbed hull form that reduces wave-making resistance also increases the moment of inertia on which a longer natural pitching period depends.

Figure 3-122 shows a large-bulb ship model whose hull form was adjusted with a longer natural pitching period in mind. The result, in terms of pitching motions, is shown in the marginal sketch, which is based on a model test comparison with a conventional destroyer. We note that the pitch amplitude at speeds above 20 knots is substantially lower than for the destroyer. This is what we want, but one price of supercritical operation on the surface of the sea is apparent: with reduced bow motion, such a ship would tend to plunge through the waves rather than ride over them, creating above-decks structural problems.

These tests, run at Davidson Laboratory, are a natural outgrowth of the Navy's work on the Escort Research ship cited earlier. This was originally designed as an optimum ship for

Large-bulb ship

Pitch amplitude

D

B

25   50
Speed (knots)

D = Destroyer
B = Large-bulb ship

Fig. 3-122. The bulb ship, one type of supercritical hull form, is under test here in a long, regular head sea with waves twice ship length. Note how hull plunges through waves with little pitching because of its long natural period of oscillation. Bulbs that give this sluggish response are sketched in margin. In photo, forward bulb can just be seen. (Courtesy P. Van Mater, Davidson Laboratory)

sonor detection and tracking of subs. As such, it had a large sonar "bulb" below and partly forward of the bow. For quiet propulsion, electrically powered propellers were placed in a nacelle below and aft of the stern. Tests at David Taylor Model Basin showed calm-water resistance could be made quite low, and that the bulbs made the pitching period long enough to permit supercritical operation in rough seas.

These tests suggest that such a vessel could nicely complement a conventional destroyer escort: under calm seas, both could maintain high speed; under rough seas, the bulb ship could maintain "attack" speed while the destroyer, at slower speeds, could continue to "listen" for the hunted sub. Hopefully, a ship of this type will be built, for it would allow the Navy to evaluate a kind of "team" performance that might prove invaluable.

The semi-submarine

The most radical of the three new ship forms, the semi-submarine, looks even better in high-speed seagoing performance since it is mostly beneath the stormy surface. Model tests on this new concept are just getting underway, but simulated runs on the analog computer indicate a very long natural pitching period—some 20 seconds, compared with about 5 seconds for a destroyer. Thus, the longer wave components in a head sea should not cause trouble.

In a calm sea or in following waves, the semi-sub may experience other difficulties. The problem here is one of providing vertical control so that the ship will run about level, for there are interactions between the surface and a body running near it at high speed. The answer may lie in automatic control of stern planes in combination with a Vee-strut arrangement like that sketched in the margin. These struts would improve vertical control in much the same way surface-piercing foils control height on a hydrofoil craft. The stern planes would take care of local perturbations. Much thinking on the semi-submarine is, in fact, a blend of submarine and hydrofoil experience.

Don't give up the ship

From this brief review, it should be apparent that there are promising directions to be followed in developing new types of surface ships for naval uses. I say "naval" advisedly, for the question naturally arises as to the potential of these new ship forms for cargo transport. The answer is, bluntly, none. The manufacturer is already paying too much for high-speed transport on the sea, whereas the real competitive bottleneck he faces is getting his goods on and off present-day ships efficiently. But this is another story completely.

I have endeavored to explain how, for military purposes, the barriers to high speed on the ocean's surface might be overcome. Such influencing aspects as power plant development, payload considerations, and propulsion devices have barely been touched upon. While money is spent to develop hydrofoil craft, ground-effect machines, and new sub forms, my message is an old but still urgent one:

"Don't give up the ship!"

Further reading

You might start with Dugan's *The Great Iron Ship* (Harper's, 1953, $3.95), a colorful but accurate account of an audacious attempt, over 100 years ago, to solve the high-speed ship problem by a tremendous increase in size. In a fascinating paper titled "Ships" by the late Kenneth Davidson, *Proc. of 9th International Congress of Applied Mechanics, 1956,* the history of ships is traced briefly from earliest times, emphasizing growth of size and speed.

Two novel over-the-water vehicles, GEMs and hydrofoils, were surveyed in 1962 in two articles, respectively, in *International Science and Technology:* "Near-Surface Vehicles" in February, and "Hydrofoil Ships" in March. A brief but quite broad overview of how the U.S. Navy looks at unconventional ships is in Oakley's "High-Performance Ships—Promises and Problems," *Proc. of 3rd Symposium on Naval Hydrodynamics* (ONR document ACR-65, Supt. of Documents, Washington, D.C., $3.50).

Present understanding of the sea surface and ship performance thereon are detailed in Korvin-Kroukovsky's book *Theory of Sea-Keeping* (Soc. of Naval Architects and Marine Engineers, SNAME, 74 Trinity Place, New York, 1961, $15). St. Denis and Pierson show how a ship's motion in rough sea is the sum of responses to individual wave components in "On the Motions of Ships in Confused Seas," *Trans. SNAME,* **61** (1953). These theories are verified and applied in Lewis's "Ship Speeds in Irregular Seas," *Trans. SNAME,* **63** (1955). *Trans. SNAME,* Vol. 70, contains two papers of interest: One, "Wave-Making Resistance of Ships" by Inui, shows how this problem can be studied through photos of model-ship wave patterns; the other, "A Comparative Evaluation of Novel Ship Forms" by Mandel, is a detailed study of seven new ship forms, including the three covered in this article.

The practical engineering problems facing the semi-submarine are nicely summarized in "Semi-submerged Ships for High-Speed Operation in Rough Seas" by Lewis and Breslin, *3rd Symposium on Naval Hydrodynamics* (see above). Recent test data on a proposed semi-sub are reported in "Research on High-Speed

Semi-Submarine

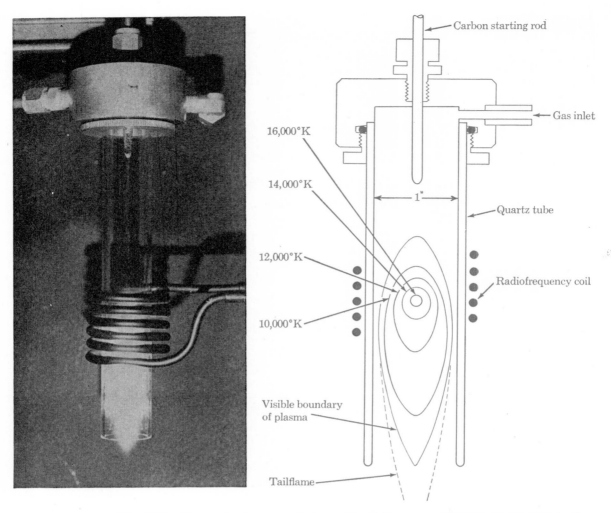

Labels on figure:
- Carbon starting rod
- Gas inlet
- 16,000°K
- 14,000°K
- 1"
- Quartz tube
- 12,000°K
- Radiofrequency coil
- 10,000°K
- Visible boundary of plasma
- Tailflame

Fig. 3-123. Plasma torch can reach temperatures in excess of 20,000° K. Heating is done electrically, with a radiofrequency induction coil. Carbon rod is needed only for starting. It's heated by the stray electric field of the induction coil and in turn heats the gas till it can support the discharge. Temperatures shown were measured spectroscopically for a torch operated at a power of 15 kw. (Courtesy MIT, Lincoln Laboratory)

Ship Forms" by Uram, given at a 1962 symposium at Stevens Institute of Technology, Hoboken, N.J. Copies are exhausted, but requests may be sent to Mr. H. MacDonald, c/o Davidson Laboratory at Stevens.

Finally, an interesting movie, *The Fluid Dynamics of Drag,* prepared by Shapiro of MIT,

is available from the Physical Sciences Study Committee, Watertown, Mass., on a rental basis. Prof. Shapiro has written a companion book, *Shape and Flow,* available in paperback (Doubleday, 1962, 95¢); it's a very stimulating little tutorial volume that reflects Shapiro's abiding enthusiasm for fluid mechanics.

PLASMA TORCHES

*by Thomas B. Reed **

IN BRIEF: *The limitation that molecular dissociation sets on the temperatures achievable through combustion can be circumvented by using electrical heating methods. This has long been done in welding arcs and the like, but the*

* Thomas B. Reed does research on plasmas and superconductors at the Lincoln Laboratory of Massachusetts Institute of Technology, Lexington, Massachusetts.

electrodes required for such discharges imposed many limitations. These were overcome in part by the dc plasma torch, essentially an arc discharge with a hole cut in one of the electrodes. The new, radiofrequency electrodeless discharge is even better for many purposes. Operating with argon gas it can reach temperatures above 20,000°K with outputs of perhaps ten kilowatts. By flowing the gases through, a torch effect is produced. Operation is simple and reliable; both 2.5- and 10-kw generators operating at a standard induction-heating frequency of 4 megacycles have been used; over half of the power supplied ends up in the plasma. Applications include growing crystals, spraying coatings, spectroscopy, and high-temperature chemistry. —D.C.

■ One of the hallmarks of today's rapidly advancing technology is our interest in ever higher temperatures. I'd like to tell here about the induction plasma torch, a simple method for using high-frequency electrical power to generate very high temperatures—temperatures four to five times higher than can be achieved by chemical combustion.

It has been interesting to watch the technological growth of the induction plasma torch. In this country three companies have started selling commercial models of the torch, none much different from that to be described in this article. But until 1964 all torches in this country were of the do-it-yourself variety, and the number of laboratories that used them has been estimated at several hundred. Events were quite different in Europe, interestingly enough, where few people built their own. One company has been selling torches there for two years now, mostly for melting refractory metals. In this country uses are primarily crystal growth, general research, and powder densification. Some laboratories are exploring their use for welding, chemical synthesis, and spray coating. Many are confident that the most important applications are yet to come.

Just what is a plasma?

The word "plasma" was coined in 1928 by Irving Langmuir of the General Electric Laboratory. He was working on the sorts of low-pressure electric discharges that have since become familiar in fluorescent tubes and neon signs. In these discharges the luminous, conducting gas spreads pervasively throughout the vacuum system. Thus "plasma" seemed a good name, by analogy with biological fluids that pervade all parts of an organism and can be expressed (Greek *plassein*, to mold) from any part of it.

Nowadays the word plasma covers a wide range of conditions in electrically conducting gases, from those low-pressure discharges to the fully ionized, extremely high-temperature plasmas that are associated with thermonuclear research. The exact nature of the plasma depends on the gas used, its pressure, and the energy supplied it. While plasmas are most easily generated electrically, they can be made in many other ways, for example plasmas are found in the shock wave of re-entering rockets.

For the purposes of this article it is necessary only to distinguish between low-pressure plasmas, such as we find in fluorescent lights, and thermal plasmas (also called high-pressure plasmas), most familiar in the electric arc. Figure 3-124 illustrates the differences and similarities of low-pressure and thermal plasmas. Both kinds of plasma are electrically neutral, since there are substantially equal numbers of electrons and gas ions present. The positively charged ions and the negatively charged electrons are accelerated in opposite directions by the applied electrical field. Because electrons are so much lighter, they move much faster than the ions and transfer their energy to the atoms and ions on collision. Accelerating atoms

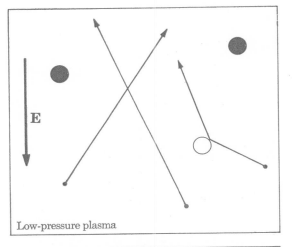

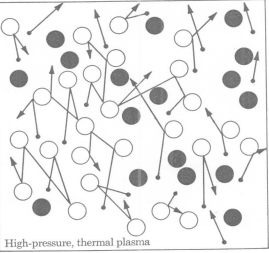

Fig. 3-124. Because collisions are 1000 times more frequent (per atom) at the higher pressure, electrons can share kinetic energy they get from applied electric field, E. As a result, electrons, atoms, and ions are substantially in thermal equilibrium. (Courtesy MIT, Lincoln Laboratory)

with electrons is like moving a bowling ball with bullets, since the atoms are about 50,000 times as heavy as the electrons and the electrons can only transfer 1/50,000th of their energy in each elastic collision.

In low-pressure plasmas—10^{-3} atm or less—collisions are relatively rare, and an electron travels a considerable distance between collisions. When it finally collides with an atom, it has gained enough energy from the electric field to produce an ion by knocking off an electron or at least to excite the atom and cause it subsequently to emit light. Therefore these low-pressure plasmas make excellent light sources, since most of the energy is used for making light rather than heat.

In the high-pressure plasmas—say 1 atm or more—the mean free path of the electron between collisions is a thousand times smaller and there are a thousand more collisions per atom per second. Although the amount of kinetic-energy transfer between electrons and atoms is still small per collision, there are enough collisions to distribute the energy uniformly among the electrons, atoms, and ions. Hence the name "thermal" plasma, which refers to the thermal equilibrium among the particles owing to the high collision rate.

One consequence of this equilibrium is that in describing thermal plasmas, the details of individual collisions become unimportant; the degree of ionization and total energy of the plasma are what count. This is why low-pressure-plasma scientists speak an atomistic language—mean free path, collision cross section, etc.—while the thermal-plasma school speaks a thermodynamic language, discussing heat and mass flow and energy-temperature

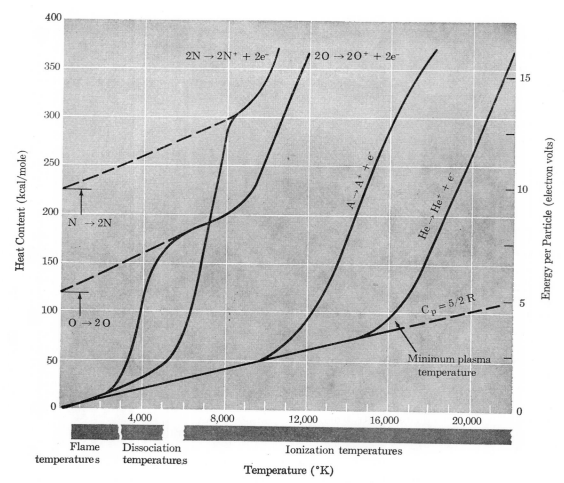

Fig. 3-125. This plot of energy content of gases as a function of temperature tells a lot about flames, both plasma and chemical. Curve for hydrogen, typical of diatomic gases, starts at left with region characterized by heating of the molecular gas. This is followed by section of steeper slope where molecules dissociate into atoms. As this dissociated gas gets even hotter, energy content of some atoms is sufficient for ionization to set in. Plasma torches operate at this very high temperature; chemical flames are limited to below dissociation temperature of their combustion product. (Courtesy MIT, Lincoln Laboratory)

relationships in the plasma. Another consequence is that the temperatures will be quite high, typically 6000° to 20,000°K.

This becomes clear when you examine the relation between the energy of a gas and its temperature, shown in Fig. 3-125. This relationship is very important in determining the high-temperature behavior of gases, plasmas, and chemical flames. As one adds energy to a gas, the temperature rises proportionally as long as all the energy is used only to heat the atoms of molecules. There is no dissociation, much less ionization, and the thermal energy increases linearly with temperature.

At higher temperatures, in the range 3000°–6000°K, diatomic molecules such as H_2 have enough energy to break their chemical bonds

$$H_2 + 103 \text{ kcal/mole} \rightarrow 2H$$

Since such a gas has a specific heat of about 7 kcal/mole/1000°C and thus takes 18 kcal/mole to reach the 2500°K dissociation temperature of H_2, we see that about seven times as much energy is necessary to carry a gas through the dissociation range as is needed to reach it.

Further energy input causes the dissociated atoms to ionize, according to the equation

$$H + 310 \text{ kcal/mole} \rightarrow H^+ + e^-$$

Monatomic gases such as argon, of course, do not dissociate in the chemical sense, but ionize directly at somewhat higher temperatures. In the case of argon

$$A + 361 \text{ kcal/mole} \rightarrow A^+ + e^-$$

These considerations help one understand the limit that nature sets on flame temperatures. For example an oxy-hydrogen flame derives its energy from the formation of molecules of water from molecules of hydrogen and oxygen gas, which releases heat

$$H_2 + \tfrac{1}{2}O_2 \rightarrow H_2O \text{ (gas)} + 57.8 \text{ kcal/mole}$$

The temperature of such a flame, depending as it does on the *formation* of water, cannot correspond to a high degree of molecular *dissociation* of water. In fact the flame temperature is stabilized at the toe of the molecular-dissociation curve for water. The oxy-cyanogen flame

$$C_2N_2 + O_2 \rightarrow 2CO + N_2$$

has the highest known flame temperature, 4850°K, for any common gas. This is because both CO and N_2 are extremely stable molecules; N_2 has a dissociation energy of 225 kcal/mole; CO, 257.

The hottest flames are then those whose combustion products are very stable, have high dissociation temperatures.

The temperatures found in thermal plasmas are not so limited, as can also be understood from the energy-temperature relationship shown in Fig. 3-125. Their temperatures lie above the toe of the corresponding ionization curve, typically at a point where the percent of atoms that are ionized is 10–50%.

At higher temperatures the conductivity reaches a limiting value near 100 (ohm-cm)$^{-1}$ (which is a value about that of carbon) since ionization of the gas beyond 50% is counteracted by the thermal expansion of the gas. And clearly the temperature can't be much lower if we are to have a conducting plasma at all, for the electrical conductivity of the gas depends primarily on the number of electrons and ions, and the conductivity will fall off rapidly at lower temperatures.

So plasmas are inherently much hotter than chemical flames—four to five times hotter. But how do we go about heating them up—what is the plasma equivalent of combustion?

Generating and heating plasmas

The simplest and oldest electrical method of generating a plasma is the familiar arc wherein an ac or dc current of tens to thousands of amperes is passed through a gas space between two electrodes, thus heating and maintaining the plasma. This method, which is used in all arc welding, in carbon-arc searchlights, and in the electric furnace, has the advantage of simplicity, but the plasma is "caught" between the electrodes and cannot be used independently of the electrodes.

The second method is that employed in the dc plasma torch, shown in the second marginal sketch. Imagine a hole to be drilled in the lower electrode of the simple arc and gas forced around the upper electrode and through this hole. Since the gas must pass through the arc, it will be heated to arc temperatures before leaving the torch.

The electrode-type plasma torch so formed has the advantage that the plasma can be used independently of the electrodes, and the plasma gas can be accelerated to high velocities. Although practical forms of this torch were first operated only in 1955, they are already in use for welding, cutting, and spraying metals and nonmetals, chemical reactions, re-entry simulation, and propulsion.

As do arcs, these dc torches have certain drawbacks for plasma generation, chiefly associated with the electrodes. Since the electrodes often operate at elevated temperatures, only certain gases can be used between them. Also the electrodes are at much lower temperatures than the plasmas so that they cool the plasma. Finally there are often problems associated with

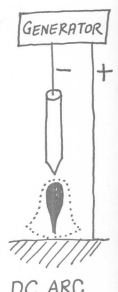

DC ARC

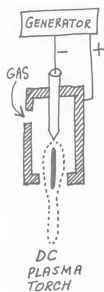

DC PLASMA TORCH

getting the electrons to and from the electrodes, and the electrodes may be damaged in the process.

Why not try induction heating?

These difficulties with electrodes are eliminated by generating plasmas without electrodes. This new method of heating gases can best be understood in the same terms in which the initial discovery was made. I had been working with dc plasma for a number of years before I joined the solid-state division at the Lincoln Laboratory. In my early months here, I worked with the floating-zone technique for purifying semiconductor silicon. In that method induction heating maintains a liquid zone in a solid rod of silicon. Since induction heating was so good for heating electrical conductors such as metals or carbon and since a thermal plasma is a good conductor, I wondered why induction heating couldn't be used for heating plasmas. It obviously couldn't be, I reasoned, or others would be doing it.

To find out *why* it couldn't, I set a 50-ampere dc "pilot" arc going between two tungsten electrodes placed at the center of an induction heating coil. The whole affair was surrounded by a quartz tube to maintain an argon atmosphere. When the high-frequency power was turned on, the ¼-in.-diameter pilot plasma became a 1-in. ball of plasma with a long plasma flame extending 8 in. beyond the coils.

So induction *could* be used.

In both cases, a high-frequency current flows

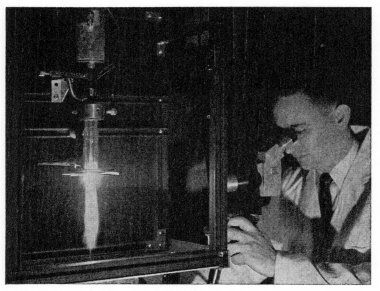

Fig. 3-126. Technician uses long-focus microscope to observe crystal growth in plasma torch. Temperature of visible boundary of the plasma is typically about 9000° K; however spectroscopic measurements reveal interior temperatures upwards of 20,000° K. (Courtesy MIT, Lincoln Laboratory)

in a cylindrical coil. The load to be heated is placed in the center of the coil, and behaves like a 1-turn shorted secondary of a transformer with n times the current flow of the n-turn primary. Typical values are 1 to 5 turns in the primary and 500 amperes in the plasma.

As in many other processes, starting a plasma is a separate problem from running it after it's started. Just as some pumps must be primed, the internal combustion engine requires a self-starter, a stick of dynamite needs a detonator, and the dc arc needs a spark or direct contact to start, so it is necessary to generate a small volume of plasma before the induction coil can couple to the gas. The pilot arc I used in my first experiment is the most easily visualized method of starting. In later work it was found sufficient to place a tantalum wire or carbon rod in the center of the coil. This is heated by the radiofrequency induction coil and in turn heats the gas around it, making it more conductive and concentrating the field. In the crystal-growing torch there is a water-cooled tube feeding powder to the crystal; the plasma will start from this also. Since it takes less energy to reach ionizing temperatures in argon than any other common gas (Fig. 3-125), the plasma starts much more easily in argon than any other gas. Once started it can be switched to any other gas if enough power is available to heat and dissociate it.

In any radiofrequency heating application an important design parameter is the skin depth, the depth in the material at which the current has decreased to $1/e$ times the value at the surface. The skin depth is inversely proportional to the square root of the frequency times conductivity and for a well-ionized plasma is about 3 mm at 4 megacycles. If this skin depth is comparable with or smaller than the plasma, heating efficiency is high, but if it is much larger the efficiency will be low. The plasmas we generate are about 2 cm across, so that we use 4-Mc frequency satisfactorily, but cannot operate at 400 kc. (These are standard radiofrequency heating frequencies.) A frequency of 100 Mc produces a doughnut of plasma because the skin depth is small, but would probably be quite suitable for a much smaller plasma, while 400 kc might be appropriate to a very large plasma.

We have used both 2.5- and 10-kw generators (costing $2200 and $11,000 respectively) for growing crystals with our plasmas. We have operated plasmas at as low as 500 w and as high as 15 kw (in a water-cooled torch). The gas flow ranges from 15 to 60 ft³/hr. We find that 50–60% of the power drawn by the generator winds up in our plasmas.

On viewing an operating induction plasma torch (Fig. 3-126), one can easily distinguish two areas of hot gas. The plasma proper is the area of high ionization and extremely bright gas within the coil, the temperature of its outer surface is about 9000°K. This is much too bright to observe with the naked eye, which is fortunate in a way, because the dark glasses necessary to view it comfortably also cut out the dangerous and insidious ultraviolet radiation. Lack of ultraviolet protection for the eyes can cause the "sandy eye" familiar to any welder who works without his goggles. The ultraviolet can also cause anywhere from a mild Florida tan to a third-degree burn of the skin, depending on exposure. Below the plasma proper, extends roughly 1–20 in. of plasma flame (the length depends on the degree of turbulent mixing with the air). This tail flame is generally not highly luminous when the torch is run on one of the permanent gases, but when metal ions are added it can be almost as bright as the plasma proper.

Since cold gas is being continually forced through the plasma, one other requirement for stable operation is a recirculation of ionized gas in the plasma region. Feeding the gas in uniformly can blow the plasma out of the radio-frequency coils. The simplest form of recirculation is achieved by introducing the gas tangentially above the plasma so that it forms a low-pressure area in the center. We have seen the luminous plasma extend several inches upstream from the coil in this setup.

What's it good for?

Uses for thermal plasmas can be grouped in several categories. The largest number of applications depend on the transfer of heat and momentum from the high-temperature gases, and lead to such applications as cutting and welding, spraying and coating, and crystal growing.

Chemical synthesis in plasma torches will depend on the chemical composition and characteristics of the gases as well as their temperature and energy content. There is ample precedent: in the early days of electric arcs, they were used for generating NO_2 from air to make nitric acid. And during the Second World War, the German war machine obtained much of its acetylene for synthetic rubber from the Hüls process using a forerunner of the present dc plasma torches to crack natural gases directly. A number of groups are now working on generation of acetylene, hydrogen peroxide, hydrogen cyanide, and similar highly endothermic molecules in plasma torches.

Other applications envision the use of plasmas in conjunction with magnetohydrodynamic or thermoelectric effects for generation of power or propulsion.

The induction plasma torch has a number of unique characteristics that will make it the preferred method of plasma generation for some of the above applications but which may handicap it for other applications. The most immediate advantage is the lack of electrodes in the induction torch. The plasma devices with electrodes work quite well in some gases, such as argon and helium, not as well with hydrogen and nitrogen, and generally not at all with oxygen, air, or water vapor, because of thermal, chemical, and high-electric-field attack on the electrodes. Another advantage to the lack of electrodes in the induction torch is that in many processes—such as growing crystals, spraying coatings, or synthesizing chemicals—it is necessary to feed gas, powder, or wire into the plasma, preferably along the axis. Unfortunately, the electrode is located on the axis so that it is necessary to feed the materials in from the side, which is much more difficult.

Growing crystals with plasma torches

Since its first successful operation in mid-1960, we have used the induction plasma torch primarily as a source of very high-temperature gases for growing crystals. Our geometry, shown in the margin, is closely analogous to the Verneuil technique used to grow synthetic sapphire. In the Verneuil process, powders are dropped through an oxy-hydrogen flame onto a molten cap of the crystal being grown through a ¼-inch, water-cooled tube. The use of a water-cooled, ¼-inch rod to inject powders through the plasma onto the growing crystal keeps the powders from evaporating in the plasma and gives even more stability to the flame. This has been our most important change for crystal growth, and it helps considerably. As the cap freezes the starting rod or seed is slowly withdrawn, forming a single crystal boule. The Verneuil technique can grow oxide crystals melting in the range 500°–2300°C.

We have used the plasma torch to grow sapphire, but we have also used it to grow stabilized zirconia crystals which melt at about 2600°C, too high a temperature for the conventional Verneuil technique. We have also grown single metallic crystals of metallic niobium (melting point, 2400°C) which cannot be grown in flames because it would be oxidized. Figure 3-127 shows a zirconia crystal being grown by this process. I feel confident that the induction plasma flames will take the place of chemical flames in crystal growth and many allied processes.

One difficulty we sometimes encountered in crystal growth was that the plasma was too hot for the powder injected through the plasma, and the powders vaporized completely. This

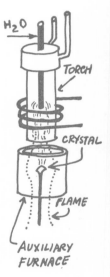

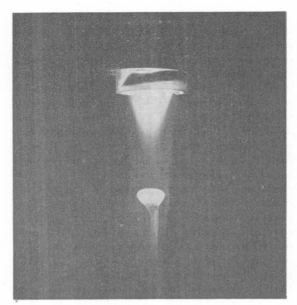

Fig. 3-127. Crystals can be grown with aid of plasma torch. Powder injected into gas stream is melted on passing through the plasma, recondenses on striking seed rod placed in tail flame. (Courtesy MIT, Lincoln Laboratory)

suggests two areas of application in spectroscopy. Spectroscopists are in need of stable heat sources to vaporize and excite the atomic and molecular spectra of the elements. At the temperature levels shown in Fig. 3-123, the band spectra of molecules will be excited in the cooler plasma flame regions while the simpler atomic spectra will be found in the hot central plasma region.

The complete vaporization and dissociation of molecules can also be used to produce new compounds and study chemical reactions at very high temperatures. Chemicals such as acetylene have been produced in very high yields in the dc plasma torches; I'm sure the induction plasma torch will also be used for high-temperature chemistry.

The uses mentioned so far are applicable with the torch in its present form. In this form, however, the heat is spread over a relatively large area, and the flames have relatively low velocities and little momentum. These characteristics, which make it suitable for crystal growth and chemical reactions, make it too diffuse for applications, such as welding, cutting,

and metal spraying. For these uses, it will be necessary to concentrate comparable powers in flames of smaller cross section either by using higher frequencies to generate smaller plasmas, or by forcing the plasmas through a nozzle of suitable shape and material.

The clean and open nature of induction plasma generation suggests its use in the more esoteric field of plasma research, where it may contribute to magnetohydrodynamic power generation, to confining plasmas magnetically, and to generating ultrahigh temperatures. Time and the ingenuity of scientists and engineers will show us the possibilities and limitations of induction plasma generation.

Further reading

In digging deeper into the subject of thermal plasmas, one soon discovers that the majority of plasma literature is either on low pressure or on thermonuclear plasmas. The best scientific and technological survey of the properties of thermal plasmas and the properties of arcs is in German: Finkelnburg and Maecker, "Elektrische Bögen und thermische Plasma," *Handbuch der Physik*, Vol. 22, pp. 254–444 (Springer-Verlag, 1956, $32). Another survey of electric arc technology is given in Somerville's *The Electric Arc* (Wiley, 1959).

There are few survey articles on dc plasma generation. One is "Recent Advances in Electric Arc Plasma Generation Technology," by John and Bade, *J. Am. Rocket Soc.* **31,** 4 (1961).

The only early work on induction thermal plasmas was done in the course of Russian radar research in Leningrad in 1941–1942; see G. I. Babat, "Electrodeless Discharges and Some Allied Problems," *Inst. of Elect. Eng. III* **94,** 27 (1947). More recently T. B. Reed has written "Induction-Coupled Plasma Torch," *J. Appl. Phys.* **32,** 821 (1961), "Growth of Refractory Crystals Using the Induction Plasma Torch," *J. Appl. Phys.* **32,** 2534 (1961), "Heat Transfer Intensity from Induction Plasma Flames and Oxy-Hydrogen Flames," *J. Appl. Phys.* **34,** 2226 (1963), "High-Power Low-Density Induction Plasmas," *J. Appl. Phys.* **34,** 3146 (1963), and "Recent Developments in Plasma Generation," in *Proceedings of the National Electronic Conference,* at Northwestern University, Chicago, October 1963.

POWDER FABRICATION

by George Dieter *

IN BRIEF: *Essentially, metals can be prepared for shaping into useful objects in just two ways: casting or powder techniques. The latter route is chosen when melting presents difficulties, when phase relationships need to be sidestepped, or when machining costs must be avoided. Traditionally, particulate materials are converted to useful shapes by compacting and sintering, sometimes followed by a deformation process such as coining. These are complex processes, still imperfectly understood. In recent years, traditional techniques have been adapted to manufacture of larger structures, some on a continuous basis. Hard-to-handle materials like the refractory metals are now rolled and forged from billets made by powder methods. Ordinary sheet steel can be made by a new process called powder rolling. Composite materials with unusual properties are being created from mixtures of particulate materials. Free-standing bodies can be constructed from sprayed powders. Even the centuries-old techniques of ceramics are being adapted to modern demands for structures that will withstand extreme environments. In short, the barriers are breaking down between the fields of metals, ceramics, and polymers, and a new technology is being born.—F.P.*

■ The old art of powder metallurgy is changing rapidly. No longer is the practice limited to the relatively small parts that can be produced with a punch and a die in a press. The field has acquired new dimensions: a host of techniques—some old, some new—are being adapted to fabricate large objects from particulate material. In the search for new materials with unusual properties, powder fabrication methods are being applied not just to metal powders, but to ceramic and intermetallic-compound powders, polymer powders, and combinations and mixtures of these. The term *powder technology* is probably a more apt description of what is going on today than the old term powder metallurgy.

Let me be more specific by citing some of the fruits of this burgeoning technology:

Figure 3-128 is a comparison between two methods of manufacturing sheet metal. One is the conventional mill procedure in which a steel ingot from the open hearth furnace is heated and rolled to the thickness desired. The other is a new method, one which starts with the same iron ore, but converts this into iron powder

which is then compacted, sintered, and rolled into sheet steel. This process is now in just the pilot plant stage, but it may well offer a way to supplement present mill capacity at roughly half of the capitalization required for present integrated steel plants.

Or consider more exotic materials than iron and steel. Much of the recent success in applying difficult-to-handle metals like tungsten, molybdenum, and beryllium in large structures is made possible by the use of powder technology. Now, rough billets made from powders of these metals are a first step to forging and extruding them into useful shapes.

Then there are entirely new classes of materials with startling properties that have been spawned by powder technology. One example is a series of new creep-resistant alloys based on the hardening effect of dispersed oxides within a ductile metal matrix. Another is a high-temperature bearing material in the form of sintered nickel impregnated with dry lubricant powders.

Why make things from powder?

The two major methods of primary production of useable materials are casting and powder fabrication. By and large, melting, followed by casting, has been the predominant method because of its economic advantages. Fabrication of solid bodies from powders, without going through the molten phase, has been used where there are technical difficulties with melting. These might be (1) a high melting point, (2) easy contamination of the molten metal by the atmosphere, or by the crucible or mold material, and (3) the formation of a large grain size and/or segregated structure in solidification which makes it difficult to roll or extrude the material later.

Because of these problems, powder techniques were devised many years ago for the primary production in small quantities of the high-melting-point, refractory metals like tungsten and molybdenum. The development of a powder fabrication process for making tungsten wire by Coolidge in 1909 made the incandescent lamp a practical reality.

A second important advantage of powder fabrication is the ability to produce alloys or combinations of materials (for example, of metals with ceramics) that are not controlled by phase diagram relationships, as would be the case with a solidifying liquid. The ability

* George Dieter is Head of the Department of Metallurgical Engineering at Drexel Institute of Technology, Philadelphia, Pennsylvania.

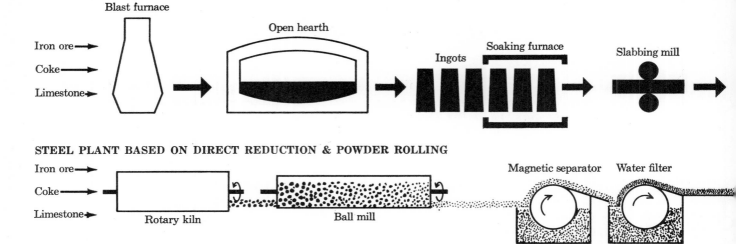

STEEL PLANT BASED ON CONVENTIONAL TECHNIQUES

STEEL PLANT BASED ON DIRECT REDUCTION & POWDER ROLLING

Fig. 3-128. Steel strip rolled continuously from powdered metal? It's a possibility, as shown in this comparison with a conventional strip mill of today. Success will depend on development of an economical, large-scale method for making iron powder. One way may be the direct reduction of iron ore shown here.

to produce materials with special properties has long been an important feature of conventional powder metallurgy, evident in such established examples as copper-carbon brushes for electrical motors, self-lubricating bearings of graphite and bronze, brake-band materials, and metal-ceramic cutting tools.

A third compelling reason for the use of powder fabrication methods is economy. Small structural parts such as gears, spacers, journal bearings, and so on can be made to close tolerances by pressing and sintering of powders. The chief economic advantage lies in the elimination or minimization of machining. Moreover, with the development of fabrication techniques for large dense shapes from metal powders, it begins to look as though a new area of economic incentive is arising for powder fabrication. Since powder fabrication of mill shapes such as sheet, bar, and tubing will require fewer processing steps than if the same products were made from a cast ingot, savings in processing costs and scrap loss should be possible, to say nothing of lower capital investment.

Where do powders come from?

Without suitable supplies of raw material in powder form, none of these ideas would be feasible commercially. You can produce powders in many ways, which fall under three main headings: physical, chemical, and electrolytic, as summarized below:

The simplest physical method is disintegration of a solid body by machining, grinding, or filing. Better control over particle size can be obtained by crushing and ball-milling, a method most suited to brittle materials such as oxides

and carbides. Ductile materials can be pulverized by stamping or hammering, but the particles become flakes that are unsuited to powder fabrication. Some of the latest innovations in the art of pulverizing such as impact milling, fluid energy milling, and vibro-energy milling are also being used. For example, with impact milling, it is possible to produce coarse powder from a soft material like polystyrene.

Spherical powder, or shot, can be obtained by pouring a fine stream of molten metal into water. This technique is also widely employed for making pre-alloyed metal powders such as stainless steel and Fe-Ni magnetic alloys. Another method of powder manufacture, used for very fine powders, is vacuum evaporation, followed by condensation.

There are many chemical techniques for making metal powders. The preponderant tonnage today is iron powder, and much of this is made by the direct reduction of the metal oxide with a hydrocarbon gas or with carbon. As noted in Fig. 3-128, the success of the powder rolling process for making sheet steel rests upon the direct reduction process. Hydrogen reduction of oxides and chlorides is also an important step in the making of tungsten and molybdenum powder. Powders are also produced by the thermal decomposition of a metal carbonyl, or by the precipitation of a metal from a solution of one of its salts by a metal higher in the electromotive series. And an important development is the production of Ni, Co, and Cu powders by the pressure leaching of ammoniacal solution of ore concentrates or scrap. Such hydrometallurgy techniques offer the possibility

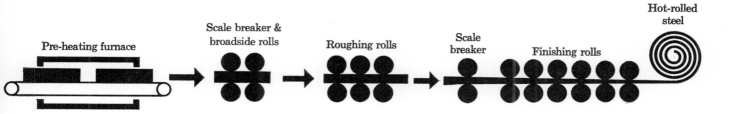

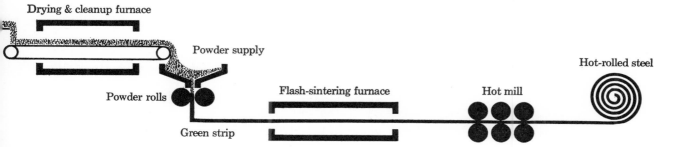

of an economical source of high-purity powders, a major obstacle to the wider use of powder fabrication methods generally.

Electrodeposition from solution or from fused salts (see "Molten Salts," page 257) is used to make powders in a wide variety of metals. Generally, powders made in this way tend to have a dendritic or tree-like shape.

What can we do with a pile of powder?

The conversion of a pile of powder into a useful shape generally follows three steps: (1) compaction, (2) sintering, and (3) densification by coining, rolling, or extrusion. In compaction, the particles are compressed into a shape. A good portion of its volume is pore space, and while some of the air has been expelled during compaction, part is trapped. At this stage there is point- and line-contact between particles, with relatively low forces of attraction between particles. There is also mechanical locking between particles, especially if they are ductile. These factors combine to give a "green" strength which allows the compact to be handled without breaking.

In sintering at elevated temperatures, the porous body lowers its energy state by reducing its surface area. Shrinkage occurs and the voids round off. The trapped gases must either diffuse out of the compact or go into solution in the metal, otherwise problems of gross porosity arise. Under optimum conditions, essentially zero porosity can be obtained by sintering. However, it is often more expedient either to leave a small residual porosity or to close it up by a plastic deformation operation.

The mechanics of compaction

The bonding produced by cold pressing of powders results from cold welding at points of contact between particles. Fundamental studies on why such cold welding takes place have not been carried out to any great extent as yet. However, extrapolations from bonding and adhesion studies on more macroscopic bodies show that shearing between particles is an essential ingredient. Cleanliness of the surface, the nature and amount of surface oxide, and the area of contact between particles are also important. The size of the particles will, of course, influence total surface area, as shown in Fig. 3-129. Smaller particles offer more contact points for welding and more surface area for reaction during sintering. On the other hand, the increased surface area enhances the possibility of surface contamination such as oxidation.

Compaction usually consists of combinations of any of three mechanisms, as shown in the margin. Relative densities (compared to the 100% density of a wrought material) of over 90% are readily obtained by compaction.

Aside from the problem of achieving cold-welding or its equivalent in a compact, there is the problem of pressure distribution. Pressure is not transmitted readily through a bed of powder, as it is through a liquid, so that pressure gradients (and corresponding density gradients) must be expected in conventional die compaction. This limits the effective length-to-diameter ratio to about 8:1. This problem can be combatted, in part, by adding a lubricant to the powder.

One way of removing the size restriction is to

COMPACTION MECHANISMS

1) by rearrangement...

before

after

2) by fragmentation...

before

after

3) by plastic flow...

before

after

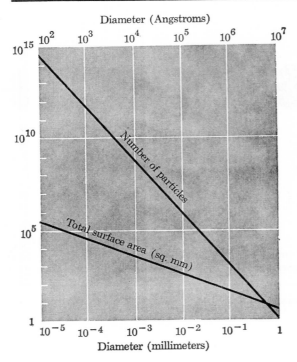

Fig. 3-129. As powder particles get smaller, the number you can pack into a given volume goes up, as does the total surface area available for bonding. Curves above are calculated on basis of equal-sized spherical particles contained in a spherical volume, 1 mm in dia. (Courtesy W. D. Jones)

contain the powder in a channel and press it periodically as it moves along under the punch. This has been done on an experimental basis at Westinghouse to produce long rectangular plates. Continuously compacting the powder into a sheet by feeding it into a rolling mill is a more practical method. This process of powder rolling, which was mentioned earlier, will be discussed further shortly.

Another method of compaction involves hydrostatic pressure. The powder is packed into an elastomeric or polymeric sheath and the air evacuated. The filled, sealed envelope is then pressurized in an appropriate vessel to hydraulic pressures of 50,000 psi or more. In addition to providing more uniform density, and thereby minimizing differential shrinking during sintering that might crack brittle materials, the method allows fabrication of fairly complex shapes that could not be compressed in or ejected from a die. Cylinders, tubes, and flat plates can be made this way in sizes that are uneconomical by die compaction because of tooling and press costs.

For compaction of refractory materials like carbides, nitrides, and oxides, researchers have been seeking to combine high temperature with hydrostatic pressure. Equipment for doing this

has been developed over the last few years at Battelle for the pressure bonding of dissimilar metals in nuclear fuel elements. In this autoclave, the steel walls are kept cool and temperature is provided by an internal heater well-insulated from the pressure shell. Using inert gases as the pressurizing medium, pressures of 15,000 psi can be achieved today at temperatures of 3000 F. For the near future, 50,000 psi at 5400 F are expected. By this technique, densification can be carried out at temperatures several hundred degrees below normal sintering temperature for cold-pressed compacts. This means materials can be made having finer grain size and more uniform structure.

High-energy-rate techniques play a part in compaction, too. For many years, Kennametal Inc. has compacted cemented carbide powders by inserting them, sealed in a rubber bag, in the chamber of a 14-in. naval gun barrel that is partially filled with water. Detonation of a propellant charge generates the needed hydrostatic pressure. Using contact explosives for compaction is a possibility, for it offers a cheap way to make compacts of nearly theoretical density in sizes even larger than can currently be made by hydrostatic compaction. Much more needs to be known, however, about the mechanics of shock-wave propagation in a particulate medium (especially how this controls internal cracking), and the response of explosively compacted material to sintering treatments.

An old technique has new possibilities

Although compacting powders in a heated die—called hot-pressing—is not new, it is being used more frequently today because of the demand for special materials. As temperature increases, the yield stress of materials decreases and they behave in a more nearly viscous manner. In this way, hot-pressing achieves compacts of higher density at lower pressure. Certain refractories like nitrides and borides are hot-pressed because they cannot be consolidated to high density by simple cold-pressing and sintering treatments. Property directionality is much less in hot-pressed parts, and they can be made in large diameters without excessively large presses. Forging billets 60-in. in diameter and 5-in. thick have been made from beryllium powder by hot-pressing in a vacuum.

The major obstacle to wider use of this method of compacting is the inadequacy of existing die materials. Steel dies can be used to about 20,000 psi at 1100 F. Graphite dies can go to higher temperatures, to about 4000 F, but pressures must be kept below 3000 psi and contamination of the powder from the graphite must be considered. A really suitable die material with improved strength at elevated temperature, oxidation resistance, and thermal shock resistance is not yet available. Hot-pressing, thus far, is a slow process because heating to temperature requires time.

Sintering increases compact density

In conventional powder metallurgy, a sintering treatment follows compaction. It is in this critical step that the properties of the final structure are established. In some of the newer concepts of powder fabrication of metals, extensive plastic deformation by rolling or extrusion produces the densification, and sintering is thus not of great importance. However, with brittle materials like ceramics and intermetallic compounds that cannot be plastically deformed much, sintering is still vital in controlling final properties. An alternative, just mentioned above, is to combine compaction and sintering by the process of hot-pressing.

The driving force for the densification that occurs on sintering is the decrease in surface area and the lowering of the surface free energy by the elimination of vapor-solid interfaces. The kinds of changes in pore structure that can occur are shown in the margin.

At least four material transport processes can act during sintering. They are (1) evaporation and condensation, (2) surface diffusion, (3) volume diffusion, and (4) ordinary bulk flow deformation. While the first two processes contribute to bonding and to rounding of pores, they do not produce any shrinkage and densification because atoms are simply transported from one internal surface to another. Thus, there is no change in the distance between centers of particles.

Volume diffusion of atoms through the crystal lattice is the chief mechanism of densification. Such internal diffusion is made possible by the presence and mobility of vacant lattice sites. During sintering, atoms flow through the lattice to the "neck" region, while vacancies move in the opposite direction, as sketched in the margin. The neck region acts as a vacancy source, and the grain boundary that inevitably forms between particles is the vacancy sink. Thus, as atoms migrate from the grain boundaries between particles to the neck regions building up between them, the particle centers are able to move toward each other, which causes the gross structure to densify.

Complete densification, or elimination of porosity, is difficult to achieve in sintering. One obstacle is that in the later stages of sintering, as pores are being eliminated rapidly, they are no longer able to anchor grain boundaries (much as surface tension holds a liquid droplet in shape) and to thus prevent grain growth.

When this happens, isolated pores are likely to be trapped inside one of the growing grains, out of contact with the grain boundaries. Then the rate of shrinkage will be greatly reduced because normal transport mechanisms are blocked, and it will be impossible to reach 100% density by sintering. Fortunately, it has been discovered recently by researchers at General Electric that dispersion of small amounts of additive retards grain growth to the point where porosity can be completely eliminated. For example, adding 0.25% by weight of magnesium oxide to aluminum oxide permits production of nearly porosity-free, translucent aluminum by a sintering process alone.

Liquid phase sintering gets a new twist

Very effective densification is possible if the sintering is carried out so that one of the constituents in the compact is in the liquid phase. This technique has been used for years to make WC-Co cemented carbides and porous bronze bearings. The mechanism consists of solution and reprecipitation of the solid constituent to give a high density and, usually, an increased grain size. For the method to work effectively, the solid phase must have a certain amount of solubility in the liquid phase at the sintering temperature, and must be wetted by the liquid phase.

Studies of the interfacial energies in the wetting of a solid by metal have resulted in new materials that can be made by liquid phase sintering. We know that nonwetting systems can be made to wet only by decreasing the solid-liquid interfacial energy γ_{SL} (see marginal sketch). Fortunately, minor third-element additions can have a strong effect on this energy factor. A good example is the recent discovery by Humenik of Ford Motor Co. that small amounts of calcium allow iron to wet graphite. By this means, metal-bonded graphite materials containing up to 90% graphite are available for electrical bearing and high-temperature applications.

What about alloys by powder fabrication?

Most powder fabricated alloys are made from prealloyed powder prepared by atomization of a molten stream, or by pulverizing a brittle alloy. However, another way might be to mix elemental powders of the alloy's constituents in the proper amount, and then sinter the mixed compact until a homogeneous chemical composition is achieved by mutual diffusion of the elements. If the alloy consists of more than two elements, it might be possible to introduce all of the alloying elements into the base metal in the form of a complex master alloy powder.

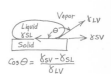

Sintering modes

In this mode, pore shape changes, size does not.

starting here...

In this mode, pore changes shape, gets smaller.

and smaller.

$$\cos\theta = \frac{\gamma_{SV} - \gamma_{SL}}{\gamma_{LV}}$$

Densification Mechanisms

1) by evaporation + condensation...

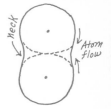

2) by volume diffusion...

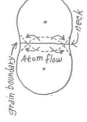

Prolonged sintering would be required for chemical homogeneity.

If, in the future, powder rolling becomes well established, this alloying technique might be carried a step further. It should be possible, for example, to shape such an alloy while it is in the *partially* homogenized condition where the ductile matrix particles will flow readily around the brittle master alloy particles. Once densification and shape have been obtained, then a final homogenization treatment would provide the desired alloy composition.

Whither powder rolling?

One of the important developments that has freed powder metallurgy from the confines of die compaction was the realization that powder could be fed into a rolling mill and extracted as a coherent "green" sheet. The last ten years have seen a great deal of experimentation with this process, and we now know that nearly any ductile metal powder can be rolled into strip or sheet.

At the beginning of this article, Fig. 3-128 showed schematically how powder rolling might be adapted to full-scale sheet steel production. Let's examine a little more fully just what pilot plant studies have revealed.

Following compaction into green strip by powder rolling, the strip is either flash sintered to give strength for coiling and rerolling, or it is hot-rolled to close up most of the porosity. Because of this porosity in the green strip, it is necessary to carry out these initial operations in a protective atmosphere to prevent interior oxidation. It has been found that a 100% dense sheet with suitable grain size and mechanical properties can be produced by either (1) sintering followed by alternate cold-rolling and an-

nealing, or (2) hot-rolling followed by at least one cold-rolling and annealing treatment.

The real potential for powder rolling lies in the production of high tonnage sheet from low-carbon steel, stainless steel, and copper at lower cost. There are obvious savings in scrap and processing costs if a 0.060-in. sheet can be rolled *continuously* from a 0.20-in. thick green sheet instead of from a 24-in. thick ingot on a *batch* basis.

A number of steel companies are currently studying powder rolling of sheet and strip. There seems to be no question that the initial capital investment for a powder rolling mill would be lower than for a conventional mill of the same capacity. Researchers at Republic Steel Corp., for example, estimate a total potential saving of up to 50% when the whole process—ore to sheet—is considered. The key to such economies appears to be the production of an iron powder with suitable powder rolling characteristics and proper purity at a price per pound that is competitive with iron produced via the blast furnace. Such a source of powder supply has not yet been achieved, despite advances in direct reduction of ore.

It is important to remember, in thinking about the future of powder rolling, that while it may often be advantageous to avoid melting, the absence of a molten stage eliminates the chance for a cheap refining and upgrading of the material being processed—slagging out impurities, for example. Wherever powder rolling is being practiced commercially, it is either because the process produces a material with superior or unusual properties, or because a chemical method for making the powder is available on economic terms (see Fig. 3-130).

The largest commercial application of powder rolling is the $23 million copper plant being built in the Philippines. The plant uses a chemical leaching and gas reduction process to make copper powder from the ore, and this is then converted into strip by powder rolling. Designed to produce annually 14,000 tons of strip, tubing, and wire, the plant is estimated to have a capital cost 50% less than for a conventional smelter and rolling mill. And it will be economical with about one-quarter the capacity needed to justify a conventional plant.

Hot-working of powder compacts

Powder extrusion combines the elements of hot compaction and hot mechanical deformation in three different, but related techniques: In the simplest of these, the heated extrusion chamber is filled with loose powder. The ram compacts the powder, and the severe deformation on passing through the extrusion die completes the densification. Fine-grained mag-

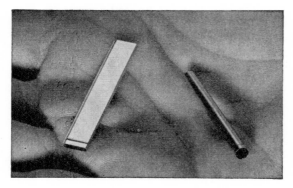

Fig. 3-130. Here are delicate cathodes for electron tubes, formed from a nickel alloy produced by powder rolling. The reasons for choosing such an alloy are typical: nickel powder of special purity was available, and the powder method permitted close control over the alloy composition. (Courtesy Sylvania Chemical and Metallurgical Division)

nesium alloys are made in this way. In the second method, a low-porosity billet is prepared by hydrostatic compaction, hot-pressing, or cold-pressing and sintering. The billet is then extruded into the shape desired. This method is used with many of the refractory metals. Extruding the powder after it has been compacted and sealed in a can of dissimilar metal, the third of the hot-working methods, makes it possible to extrude powders that are easily contaminated by air, or that are toxic, pyrophoric, or radioactive. Usually the can is removed after extrusion, although in some types of nuclear fuel elements the can is designed to remain in place as a cladding. Much of the pioneering in the hot-working of powders was, in fact, done to fabricate such fuel elements.

It may seem startling, at first glance, that sintered powder compacts are strong enough to take the deformation that occurs in forging. That this is so will be seen in Fig. 3-131 which shows a dish being forged at Wyman-Gordon from beryllium powder that was initially compacted in a stainless steel can. Hot-coining of powder compacts into dense parts with close dimensional tolerances is a potentially useful method for making turbine blades. This approach was tried, but was abandoned when the powder parts did not show enough ductility. However, with improved powder purity and new methods of deformation such as high-energy-rate forming, it should be tried again.

Powder fabrication without compaction

A number of techniques have come into general use that do not require compaction as one of the processing steps. This suggests that economies can be made in the manufacture of large complex shapes.

Slip casting is an old process used in the ceramic industry to produce objects from clay. More recently, it has been applied to oxide, carbide, and metal powders. Finely divided powders are dispersed in a liquid, and the slip is poured into an absorbent mold. As the fluid is absorbed, the powder agglomerates and forms a shape with enough green strength to be extracted from the mold. Careful drying and sintering produce bonding and strength.

Recently, slip casting has been used to make a variety of shapes from tungsten powder, as well as the carbides, borides, and oxides. Chromium-alumina cermet structures have been made this way for a number of years. A new and interesting adaptation of the process, developed by G. J. Comstock, uses suction rolls to consolidate a slip of fine metal powders into a green strip suitable for sintering and re-rolling. This process is claimed to be less complicated than powder rolling. However, with this

Fig. 3-131. Powders can be press-forged into shape, too. Here, a beryllium bowl is lifted from a 50,000-ton press. To forge Be powder, it is encased in a stainless steel container, heated to nearly 2000°F, then densified and hot-worked in the press. The container is then removed and the forged part machined to size. (Courtesy Wyman-Gordon Co.)

possible exception, slip casting still requires a craftsman's touch, but the potential of the technique for fabricating hard-to-work materials may lead to its improvement.

Powder-water mixtures have been used for centuries for making articles without pressing. The principal powder ingredient has been clay. With brittle powders, where a simple water mixture won't hold together, binders such as wax, starch, and polyvinyl alcohol have been added so that they could be cold-compacted or extruded as paste. Binders also give rigidity for sintering, then decompose and volatilize at sintering temperature.

Fabrication of metal powder structures this way appears to have been almost overlooked. Limited experiments with solutions of polystyrene or polyethylene as binders for metal powders have been reported by W. D. Jones of F. W. Berk Ltd., England. Good results were obtained, but distortion was experienced with large objects. So many polymer systems are available for investigation that it seems likely that improved binders with a range of viscosity and decomposition temperatures could be developed. This method might prove very useful for large shapes that do not have to be 100% dense, for providing preforms for hot-coining, or for large billets that could be hot-worked into mill products.

Sintering loose powder in a mold without any compaction may prove perfectly acceptable for certain applications. This method has been

Fig. 3-132. Composite materials are being powder fabricated these days to withstand extreme environments. Above, electrical contacts made from a new composite of tungsten and silver are tested under a surge current of 30,000 amps to check erosion resistance under service stresses. (Courtesy Fansteel Metallurgical Corp.)

used for years for making filters. Nonporous objects can be made this way provided great care and control is exercised over particle size distribution so as to give maximum density of loose powder combined with maximum contact area and minimum pore size.

Metal spraying, either in a plasma arc or in a flame, is an unusual method for construct-

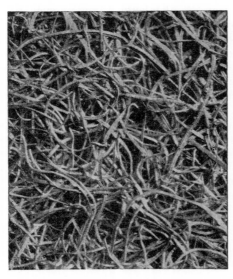

Fig. 3-133. Particulate materials need not be spherical; they can be fibrous as well. Above is a felt of 430 stainless steel fibers, 0.006 in. in mean diameter, sintered together into a rigid structure. Density is 5% of theoretical, but felt density can go as high as 95%. (Courtesy The Huyck Corp.)

ing particulate structures without compaction. By building up layers of oxides, carbides, nitrides or metals on a removable metal mandrel, it is possible to make free-standing bodies. The lamellar grain structure that results from spraying recrystallizes during sintering to give a desirable equiaxed grain structure in the final part.

New materials—another bonus

The freedom from phase diagram relationships granted by powder fabrication opens up the possibility of making new materials with unusual properties. Let's examine a potpourri of some of the more intriguing developments.

The dispersion-hardened alloys, which show so much promise as high-temperature materials, can currently only be made by a powder fabrication route. These are fine dispersions of oxides or other inert particles in a ductile matrix. One example is DuPont's recently announced TD-nickel series. Another is a series of chromium-magnesium oxide composites developed by Bendix, which are rather remarkable since they display considerable tensile ductility, whereas chromium alone is quite brittle at room temperature. With such materials becoming established, it should not be long before dispersion hardening is applied to tool steels, stainless steels, and age-hardening high-temperature alloys.

Ductile metals are being used to bond together refractory metals that are brittle at room temperature. Here, the composite is produced either by coating the refractory particles with ductile metal before compaction, or by infiltrating a porous compact of the refractory metal with the liquid metal. Typical combinations are W-Ag, W-Ni, and Be-Ag. Ductility imparted by the second metal makes possible machining in the sintered state. Originally developed for rocket nozzles, these composites may find uses as electrical contacts, Fig. 3-132, and as high-temperature bearings.

Another unusual composite, developed by Ilikon, Inc., combines dry lubricant powders such as MoS_2 and WS_2 with a nickel matrix to produce a high-temperature bearing material that remains stable to 700 C.

Researchers at Armour Research and at the Huyck Corp. have found that it is possible to make metal particles quite different from equiaxed powders—fibers with L/D's from 10 to 1000. They have formed these fibers into a felt by slurry molding or random layering. Sintering then bonds the points of intersection into a structure that is much like a random, three-dimensional, welded truss. This results in a tough, low-density material with completely inter-connected porosity, as shown in Fig. 3-133.

Such a matrix can be combined with many materials that need strengthening, from lead to brittle ceramics.

Some needs for the future

Such are some of the fruits from powder fabrication's recent development. I have tried to indicate along the way that the future growth of this new technology depends more on active application of existing concepts and ideas than on further theoretical developments. Certainly, greater emphasis needs to be given to economical ways to produce metals and ceramics in powder form. For metal alloy powders, an improvement over existing atomization methods, both in cost and in freedom from oxidation, would be a welcome development. There is room for great inventiveness in equipment design and in modification of existing techniques. It would help to have, for example: high-speed hot presses incorporating better mold materials; a cheap inert coating to protect porous metal billets from the atmosphere during hot-working; a system for hot-powder rolling in an inert atmosphere to avoid canning. In short, let your imagination go.

Further reading

A good idea of the mathematical relationships in powder compaction is given in "An Analysis of Powder Compaction Phenomena" by R. W. Heckel, *Trans. Metall. Soc. of AIME*, **221**, 1001 (1961), for metals, and "Compaction Behavior for Several Ceramic Powders" by A. R. Cooper and L. E. Eaton, *Amer. Ceramic Soc.*, **45**, 98 (1962), for ceramics. *Ceramic Fabrication Processes* by W. D. Kingery et al.

(Wiley, 1958, $9.50) discusses such important processes as hydrostatic compaction, hot-pressing, and slip casting. Hot hydrostatic compaction techniques are fully discussed in "Gas Pressure Bonding," DMIC Report 159, Battelle, 1961.

An up-to-date discussion of the theory of sintering has been published by R. L. Coble, *Jour. Appl. Phys.* **32**, 287 (1961). See also *Factors Affecting Sintering* by L. L. Seigle and A. L. Pranatis in the book *Powder Metallurgy in Nuclear Engineering* (Amer. Soc. for Metals, 1958). This same volume includes articles on powder fabrication by hot-pressing, extrusion, and rolling. Powder rolling is also discussed in *Metall. Rev.*, **4**, 14 (1959).

Until about 1952, the most complete work on the subject, covering both theoretical and practical aspects, was C. G. Goetzel's *Treatise on Powder Metallurgy* (Interscience, 3 vols., $77). A newer book, and a somewhat less formidable one, that contains reviews of the entire field of powder metallurgy is W. D. Jones' *Fundamentals of Powder Metallurgy* (St. Martin's, 1960, $30). Also see *Powder Metallurgy* by W. J. Leszynski (Interscience, 1961, $25). Many aspects of ceramic powder fabrication are covered in *Introduction to Ceramics* by W. D. Kingery (Wiley, 1960, $15). Current literature in the field can be followed best in the monthly magazine *Metal Powder Report* published by Powder Metallurgy Ltd., London, and in the quarterly journals *Powder Metallurgy* (Brit. Iron & Steel Inst.) and *Planseeberichte für Pulvermetallurgie* published by Metallwerke Plansee, Reutte, Austria.

Chapter 4

Rocketry, Space, and Astronomy

MARS

by W. W. Kellogg *

IN BRIEF: *Mars is the one planet in the solar system likely to support life something like the terrestrial kind. But if life exists there it must accommodate itself to an environment that's extremely harsh by earthly standards. Mean temperatures at the Martian equator, for example, are −35° to −45°C. Furthermore, the Martian atmosphere seems singularly lacking in oxygen (perhaps 0.1% by volume) and water vapor (Arizona's desert air is like a Turkish bath by comparison).*

Nevertheless, changes in color and polarization of Mars' dark areas that coincide with seasonal waxing and waning of the white (ice?) polar caps, persistence of the dark areas through the years, and recent discovery in them of spectral evidence of organic molecules combine to suggest that all of Mars is not as barren of life as its red dusty deserts of limonite seem to be. Fly-by space probes, ingeniously instrumented landing probes, and trained eyes at good telescopes—backed by brains—soon may answer this and a host of equally important geophysical questions.—S.T.

■ Conditions on Mars are quite different from those on earth—but perhaps not *so* different as to rule out the possibility that life exists there. Should this chance prove to be a fact, its many profound implications—religious, philosophical, scientific, and practical—must engage every thinking person's fancy.

* While preparing this article, W. W. Kellogg functioned as head of the Planetary Sciences Department at the RAND Corp. He is now Associate Director of the National Center for Atmospheric Research, Boulder, Colorado.

Yet there are several other excellent reasons why Mars always has excited the passionate interest of planetary scientists. For one, Mars is the easiest planet to see properly, as Color Fig. 32 clearly attests. Mars—unlike Venus (see "Venus," page 483) and the larger planets Jupiter, Saturn, Uranus, and Neptune—has a relatively cloud-free atmosphere, allowing us to see its surface. On it we can see varied and peculiar markings; we can watch them rotate through the 24-hour Martian day (Color Fig. 33 indicates Martian day is 24 h, 37 m, 22.7 s, ± 0.2 s) and change through the seasons; and we can even observe changing "weather" patterns in the Martian atmosphere.

Such good seeing enables us to make some fair guesses about the composition of Mars' atmosphere and surface, its temperature and climate, and its interior and geologic past. And now the day is near when we will be able to check our guesses.

On November 1, 1962, the USSR launched the Mars I space probe on a long elliptical flight path that was planned to intercept Mars —passing some 11,000 km distant—during the summer of 1963. However, a defect in the probe's orientation system made it impossible to apply an essential mid-course correction, and a dead fragment of the earth passed silently by Mars at a distance of more than 200,000 km. But there will be other attempts, of course, by both the U.S. and the USSR, and we hope for an early fly-by of Mars as successful as was the U.S. Mariner II's trip to Venus.

With all the talk about going to Mars, it is most pertinent to ask: What will we look for when we get there? What more would we like

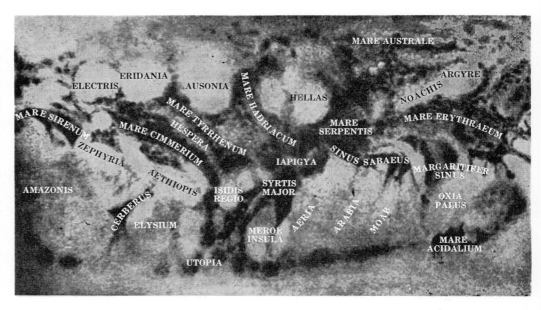

Fig. 4-1. Even superb photographs like those shown in Color Figs. 32 and 33, taken with the best telescopes, can resolve no feature on the surface of Mars smaller than 300 to 400 km across, because the earth's atmosphere distorts the image. Such a picture of the earth would not show Long Island or Sicily, though it might barely indicate Cuba and Ireland. But at rare, brief instants when seeing is excellent, the eye and pen of a trained observer can resolve the dark areas, as shown here, into groups of spots or granules that may be as small as 100 km across. (Courtesy J. H. Focas)

to know? The answers arise from knowledge already gained in decades of study from earth-bound observatories. And it may surprise some to learn that a great many of the needed observations do not require a space probe, but merely await astronomers with an interest in Mars and access to a good telescope.

The Martian landscape: the big picture

For example, the best photographs of Mars, Color Figs. 32 and 33, show clearly that there are dark areas, called "maria," although they are not oceans, yellow-red areas, often referred to—probably correctly—as "deserts," and white areas, called "polar caps," though they may not be snow and ice. But only rarely does the resolution of photographs made with even the best telescopes permit a singular feature on Mars smaller than 300 to 400 km to be distinguished. Such a fuzzy picture of the earth would not show Long Island or Sicily, and would barely indicate the land masses of Cuba and Ireland. Certainly no cities or other signs of man's presence would be visible, even if we knew what to look for.

The reason for this disappointingly poor resolving power, of course, is distortion and image motion caused by the earth's atmosphere. The human eye looking through a telescope can sometimes do better than a camera, since a trained observer who also is skilled with a drawing pen can take advantage of those instants when the image is clear. An example of what astronomers can see and record at such moments is shown in Fig. 4-1, drawn by J. H. Focas of The National Observatory of Athens. Here the dark areas of the photographs are resolved into discrete groups of small dark dots or granules, the smallest perhaps 100 km across, this being about the absolute limit of resolution of Martian features.

With the present quality of our pictures we cannot see mountains on Mars, nor even the shadows of mountains comparable in size with those on earth. Yet we can see clouds that sometimes stay in one place for many days; this is a common feature in our own atmosphere where air rising over mountains is continuously cooled to its dew point to form persistent clouds. And we can recognize extensive cloud masses on Mars that have a sharp edge which reappears at the same location in successive years. This is also a familiar event on earth where a moving air mass with clouds is held back by a mountain range. Figure 4-2, for example, a picture taken by Tiros I, shows just

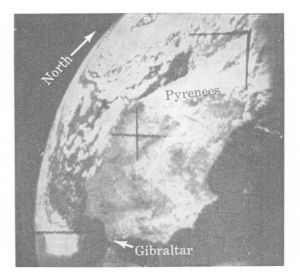

Fig. 4-2. Tiros picture shows characteristically sharp edges to extensive clouds at the Pyrenees, where mountains block clouds' passage. On Mars, similar sharp edges to clouds recur at same places each year, suggesting presence of mountains. (Courtesy National Aeronautics and Space Administration)

this happening as the Pyrenees hold back a cloud mass over southern France.

Such meteorological observations are the most convincing evidence that there are mountains on Mars, and they tend to confirm geological speculations about Mars' past which make presence of mountains reasonable.

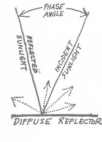

Mars is only about half as large as the earth and just a tenth as massive. Yet in spite of these differences it is almost certain that Mars has a hot molten core like ours (though its size is unknown), and it follows that there must have been some vulcanism and some mountain-building readjustments in its crust (see "The Earth's Crust," page 570). Since rock-weathering and erosion on Mars must be much less than on earth, with no rain (not much water there, as we'll see shortly) and a much thinner (and oxygen-poor) atmosphere, any mountains that formed would be preserved longer; the reasoning is much like that applied to the moon (see "The Moon," page 492).

The Martian landscape: the fine details

Oddly enough, though astronomers cannot resolve Martian mountains in their telescopes, they can deduce something about the fine structure of the surface and its composition.

Any surface material on the sunlit side of a planet yields its own spectrum of reflected and scattered sunlight in both the visible and near infrared. As seen from above the atmosphere which overlies the surface, however, this reflection spectrum characteristic of the surface is twice complicated and attenuated by absorption features—once as incident sunlight passes through the Martian atmosphere to reach the surface, and again as the reflected and scattered

sunlight passes out through the atmosphere on its way to us. Furthermore, absorption spectra of ordinary, heterogeneous surface materials are rarely as sharp as absorption spectra of gases and some pure crystals; this also makes interpretation difficult. But we still can get a hint about substances on the surface of Mars in this way.

Another extremely valuable optical characteristic of solids is their ability to polarize light that they reflect diffusely. The degree or amount of polarization depends in a characteristic way on the angle between the incident and reflected light, the "phase angle" (see marginal sketch), and on the texture of the reflecting surface.

Polarization curves of various parts of the Martian surface can be compared with polarization curves of known surfaces—either on the earth or in the laboratory—in an attempt to identify substances on Mars. Although this kind of materials identification is not certain, since different substances have rather similar polarization curves, and errors in observation are appreciable, it is certainly a most useful technique to use until such time as we can land and make more definite determinations. And it has led to some significant conclusions.

One conclusion is that the reddish-yellow desert areas are covered with powdered limonite, a hydrated iron oxide, $Fe_2O_3 \cdot nH_2O$. Not only does its color seem right, but no other geologically possible material that we know of on earth gives polarization curves similar to those of the Martian deserts.

Dead deserts and dark areas that "live"

Another, more exciting observation shows that while the polarization of the deserts does not vary with season or time of year, the polarization of the dark markings does. For a phase angle of 25° it shows pronounced and rather rapid changes in the spring, summer, and fall of the Martian year, as shown in Fig. 4-3. Dollfus—French astronomer and author of many of these polarization studies—attributed this vernal change to the appearance of a surface covering of small plants, scattered over the ground like a powder, which grew to larger size with the appearance in the spring of water vapor coming from the evaporating polar caps. But there are other interpretations possible, as we'll see farther on.

All that's ice isn't water

The brilliantly white polar caps are the most pronounced features of the Martian disk. They show on drawings made by Cassini as early as 1666 and by Huygens in 1672, and it was early noticed that they grew and shrank with the

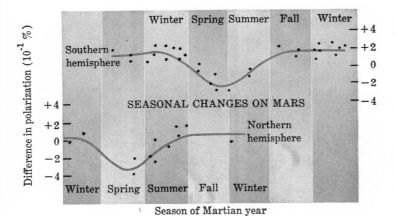

Fig. 4-3. *The extent to which sunlight reflected from Martian deserts is polarized does not vary significantly through the Martian year. But polarization of the dark areas does change markedly with the seasons, as shown in this plot of the difference in polarization between the two areas.*

Martian seasons, though Sir William Herschel about 100 years later was the first to carefully document the remarkable seasonal changes in the polar cap. The polar caps have long been taken by many as evidence for water on Mars; now we are not so sure. Infrared reflection spectra, and polarization measurements of the polar caps in the visible range (Fig. 4-4), are consistent with those obtained from laboratory-surface coverings of hoarfrost, sublimated water vapor deposited as a solid, under reduced pressure similar to that on the surface of Mars. That a conventional ice cap is possible is also suggested by results obtained in Martian environmental-simulation studies (Fig. 4-5), though temperatures on Mars may be low enough near the winter solstice to deposit a CO_2 (dry ice) sublimate as well as H_2O.

The belief in ice caps has been shaken by an alternate suggestion made recently by the Kiesses (husband and wife) and Corliss that the deposits may be sublimates of nitrogen tetroxide, N_2O_4, instead of either H_2O or CO_2. This idea is still being debated and cannot be set aside lightly, in view of the fact that there is apparently so very little water vapor in the atmosphere. Oxides of nitrogen also can account more effectively for several other peculiarities of the Martian atmosphere—some of its cloud forms, its color, and the so-called "blue haze"— that we'll talk more of in a moment.

Whether the polar caps are hoarfrost, dry ice, or some other sublimating crystal such as N_2O_4 remains a question, but remaining also is the fact that in the fall a great whitish cloud forms over a large part of the polar region. It persists through the early winter, then starts to dissipate, and in the spring the polar cap itself is revealed. With the coming of spring and disappearance of the cloudy veil, the polar cap begins to shrink, gradually withdrawing towards the poles in an irregular way as if there were valleys and mountain ranges that caused the "snow" to linger longer in some spots than in others.

The rites of spring

Some observers claim that there is a blue belt around the polar cap as it recedes, and they have referred to it as liquid water flowing from the melting ice. The existence of the blue belts may be real, but it cannot be liquid water, because we know that the vapor pressure on Mars is too low to permit liquid water on the surface—and these "water" bodies would have to be quite extensive, remember, to be seen at all. The belts may in fact be illusions, since other astronomers report repeated failure in attempts to see them at appropriate times of the year.

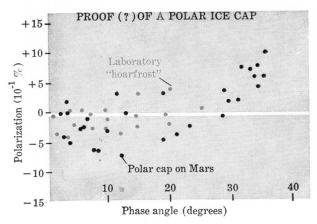

Fig. 4-4. Availability of water vapor on Mars is suggested but not proved by diffuse data shown here, comparing polarization of light from Mars' polar cap with that from hoarfrost deposited in laboratory, under low pressure—80 millibars—like that on surface of Mars.

According to the N_2O_4-sublimate theory of polar cap composition, referred to a moment ago, the belts may be higher oxides of nitrogen such as N_2O_3 and N_4O_6. These form a greenish-blue liquid at around 0°C and below. Still, the blue-green belt remains one of the many puzzles of Mars.

Another is the nature of the distinctive changes which occur in the spring—in the dark areas of the hemisphere in which the polar cap

Fig. 4-5. In this tank used to simulate Martian environments at NASA's Ames Research Center, the white substance at rear, ice, is growing across the surface and within the pore spaces of simulated soil mixture, limonite and sand, dark material in foreground. Temperature at far end approximates that of Martian poles, −100°C, while "equator" end at lower edge is held at +30°C. Simulator uses appropriate mixture of H_2O, CO_2, N_2, and argon to grow the "polar cap" under "Martian" pressure of 0.1 atm. (Courtesy NASA)

is melting or subliming. One such change, that in polarization, has already been described; at the same time, dark areas near the cap become still darker and more strongly colored, changing from predominantly neutral gray to pastel tones of brown or, more rarely, green or blue. (The color seems to depend to some extent on the astronomer.) The darkening of the maria progresses towards the equator through the spring, the intensity of darkening decreasing as the equator is approached by the "wave of darkening." But the wave finally does reach and cross the equatorial belt at the summer solstice, though with much reduced intensity. Shortly after this, a similar wave of darkening begins with the early spring and runs its course as summer comes to the opposite polar hemisphere. This results in an annual change in darkness of the maria at middle latitudes, and a twice-yearly change in the equatorial zone.

Many believe that this seasonal darkening of the maria, accompanied by the change in the polarization of the light they reflect (Fig. 4-3), must be due to movement or diffusion of some constituent (such as water vapor) in the atmosphere—rather than one on the ground—from the polar regions toward the equator as spring yields to summer. They argue that the relatively uniform speed of the progression, about 35 km per day, is too fast for any such change to propagate along the surface; nor does it seem to be much affected by surface barriers or topography. This conclusion seems entirely reasonable on the face of it. Yet meteorologists who have considered the matter are puzzled, since it is most difficult to describe a reasonable atmospheric circulation scheme that would bring air from the polar regions along the surface at such a remarkably steady rate—and all the way across the equator. In fact, as we will see shortly, a circulation that would be consistent with the thermal structure of Mars' atmosphere would tend to move air in just the opposite direction—from the equator poleward

—as the solstice approached and as the spring hemisphere grew warmer. Clearly, we cannot talk about the landscape of Mars much further without treating its atmosphere, since the two interact with each other in so many ways.

Cloudy days and dust storms

The most commonly observed changes in the Martian sky are of the same sort that we would expect on earth—dust storms and clouds. But there are some other changes that are probably peculiar to Mars.

Dust storms are identified by the fact that the atmosphere—viewed in natural light—takes on somewhat the same color as the orange-colored deserts; and at the same time the dark surface markings may be obscured for days on end in photographs taken in either blue or red light. The fact that we cannot see the surface in red light indicates either that the dust probably consists of particles over one micron in size, or else it is quite dense; otherwise we could see through it to some extent in red or near-infrared light. On some occasions dust storms have been seen to start in a localized region and spread to cover most of the planet with a yellow-orange pall. This seems to have occurred in 1956, for example (Fig. 4-6), during the period of opposition, when good observations of the surface could have been made but were frustrated for several weeks by just such a dust storm.

White or yellowish clouds are another feature of the Martian sky. As mentioned previously, the polar caps are covered with such a white veil in the fall and winter. In the spring when this white veil dissipates to reveal the polar cap itself, the cap sometimes looks tinged with yellow, from dust, perhaps. Still another frequently observed whitish cloud form is seen at the sunrise terminator, the boundary between day and night, suggesting a nocturnal fog or low cloud that dissipates with the rising of the sun.

VAST YELLOW CLOUDS OBSCURE THE SURFACE

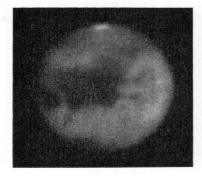 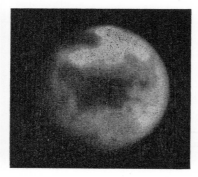

Fig. 4-6. In two photographs of the same face of Mars, taken through a red filter, the left one—taken in 1941—illustrates normal appearance of surface in yellow-red wavelengths with atmosphere free of clouds. The right one—taken in 1956— shows red clouds obscuring one third of the surface. Probable cause? Dust storms. (Courtesy E. C. Slipher, Lowell Observatory)

It is still a matter for debate whether these and other clouds are ice crystals, dry ice, or nitrogen tetroxide.

There would be no question about their composition if water *vapor* were sufficiently abundant in the atmosphere of Mars.

What about water in the atmosphere?

We don't know for sure just how much there is. Two of the most recent estimates of its abundance yield results that differ by a factor of ten or more. The higher of the two estimates calls for about 0.008 g per cm² of surface area of precipitable water in the Martian atmosphere; if it turns out to be correct the whitish clouds could be made of ice crystals. But if the lower estimate prevails—it ranges from 0.0005 to 0.001 g cm^{-2} of water vapor over the poles to even less over the equator—it becomes hard to imagine such an extremely small amount of water vapor forming a layer of ice clouds.

In either case, in comparison with the desert air over the American Southwest, for example, Martian air is extremely dry; nobody expects either rain or snow on Mars. And in case the lower estimate is right, we would not expect the polar caps to be hoarfrost either.

Perhaps, then, the answer will turn out to lie in the oxides of nitrogen hypothesis, mentioned a while back. Nitrogen, in fact, is thought (by default; it hasn't been spectroscopically detected) to be the atmosphere's chief constituent, making up at least 50% of its volume. Oxygen, on the other hand, comprises less than 0.1%, with perhaps 5 to 10% of argon plus CO_2 comprising most of the rest. It's possible that nitric oxide (NO_2) can be created in the high atmosphere of Mars by the action of ultraviolet rays in sunlight. Once a little NO_2 has

been created in this way, a reversible chemical change can take place:

$$NO_2 - \text{heat} \leftrightharpoons N_2O_4 + \text{heat}$$

where the tetroxide form is favored by cold-temperature conditions. Since NO_2 is a brownish gas, and N_2O_4 is a light yellow solid, the transition can create either whitish clouds or a light yellow surface deposit—such as sometimes tinges the polar caps—when the air temperature is cold enough as it is at the polar caps.

One of the strong points in favor of the NO_2–N_2O_4 theory is that it may explain one of the most intriguing mysteries of Mars, the phenomenon of the "blue clearing."

Why so smoggy in "blue" poor Mars

It has long been noted (Fig. 4-7) that pictures of Mars taken in red or yellow light showed surface detail best, that pictures in blue light (effectively <4500 Å) showed greatly reduced contrast, and pictures in the near ultraviolet were usually almost featureless. Occasionally, however, for periods of a day or two, and beginning quite abruptly, pictures in the blue or near ultraviolet do show surface features over all or part of the disk. It is as if an ever-present haze in the lower atmosphere of Mars—which itself must appear reddish, since it absorbs in the blue—suddenly coagulated or settled out or changed its optical properties over a wide area.

One suggestion seeks to explain the blue haze as made of fine carbon particles which have the right optical properties, and it calls upon small changes in their density to account for the clearings. These postulated—not observed—carbon particles could come from the dissociation of carbon dioxide by solar ultraviolet radiation. Another ingenious theory attributes the blue-

THE MYSTERY OF THE BLUE HAZE

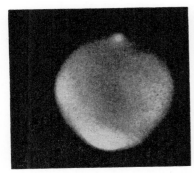 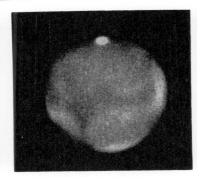 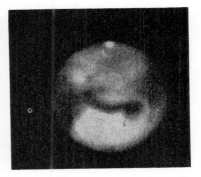

Fig. 4-7. Photograph taken in blue light (left), effectively <4500 Å, shows surface obscured by planet-wide layer of atmospheric haze, which itself would appear reddish. Haze occasionally clears (center), usually for a few hours to a few days at a time. Comparison photograph taken in yellow light (right) shows normal surface markings. (Courtesy E. C. Slipher, Lowell Observatory)

absorbing and scattering haze to fluorescing ions such as CO^+, CO_2^+, and N_2^+ in the higher atmosphere (see "Environmental Electricity," page 583), and infers changes in the flux of ionizing particles coming from the sun to change their concentration and clear the "haze." But C. Sagan has put forth some convincing arguments against this idea.

Still other theories invoke absorption by meteoritic dust or orange-yellow surface dust, but all have serious shortcomings. One not unreasonable theory envisions scattering from tiny ice (H_2O) crystals as the cause of the haze, with clearing explained by a temperature increase of about 10°C that vaporizes the crystals. This is similar to the nitric oxide theory, which also would explain the blue clearing by a small warming of the lower atmosphere leading to a small decrease in the number of yellow N_2O_4 particles.

Low pressure there, but fair winds blow

Although the question of the blue haze may seem far removed from practical matters, it is not. The presence of small haze particles in the Martian sky greatly complicates both of the main methods heretofore used to calculate the total depth of atmosphere and, from this, the atmospheric pressure on the surface of Mars. Yet an accurate value for the surface pressure is essential before we can properly design an atmospheric-entry capsule for Mars. Both methods involve measuring the amount of sunlight scattered by atmospheric molecules, and haze particles which also scatter sunlight cause overestimation of surface pressure. De-

spite this the best estimates by each of the methods did concur on a surface pressure of about 85 millibars (in contrast to the earth's average surface pressure of about 1000 millibars, and equivalent to about 17 km of altitude on earth).

Until very recently it had been thought that the error in this estimate was no more than about a factor of two. But a newer method of estimation—one based on infrared absorption features of CO_2—is independent of the sources of error introduced by haze particles, and leads to a pressure estimate less than one quarter of the earlier value; that is, a pressure less than 20 millibars (equivalent to an altitude of more than 26 km on earth). Until such differences in values for surface pressure are resolved this crucial design parameter for any proposed entry capsule cannot be finally specified.

As for the atmospheric circulation patterns on Mars, dust storms and changing cloud masses certainly indicate that there are winds, but we can only speculate about the details of this circulation. Several meteorologists have attempted to apply to Mars some of the knowledge derived from studies of the earth's atmosphere and from laboratory observations of fluid circulation in rotating tanks. Yale Mintz, UCLA meteorologist, thinks that during certain seasons of the year, near the equinoxes, there may be cyclonic and anticyclonic storm systems analogous to those on earth (Fig. 4-8), whose movements are accompanied, as on earth, by a strong, steady "jet stream" in the upper atmosphere (see "Tomorrow's Weather," page 610). These are the periods when, as on earth, the equatorial regions are warmer than the poles (Fig. 4-9). In contrast to this earthlike temperature distribution, however, which depends on our ice-covered poles remaining colder than the equator even in summer, near the solstices on Mars the summer pole becomes the warmest region on the planet (Fig. 4-10). And during this period Mars' circulation pattern must be quite unlike that on earth.

Because the temperature rises almost continuously all the way from the very cold winter pole to the region around the summer pole, the winds probably cause a lively—and unearthly—exchange of air across the equator. In fact, this across-the-equator wind must exist to explain the apparent exchange between northern and southern hemispheres of the substance making up the polar caps (whatever it may be) and the progression of it—or of an effect caused by it—equatorward in the spring, as evidenced by the maria's wave of darkening.

There is just one difficulty with this tidy concept. The direction of air flow is wrong at

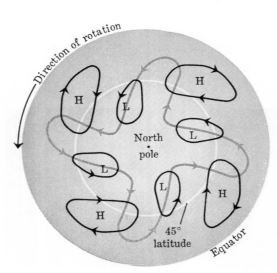

Fig. 4-8. At certain seasons of the Martian year, near the time of the equinoxes, atmospheric circulation may be like that on earth, with upper-air planetary wave or "jet stream" guiding the migratory high- and low-pressure cells at surface. (Courtesy Yale Mintz)

the surface. One would expect, on a simple model of the circulation as sketched in the margin, that the surface air would flow *towards* the summer pole along the surface, drawn by the thermal low in pressure over the warmest region. However, at this season of the year the darkening wave in the maria is moving relentlessly *away* from the warmer region, crossing the equator at the time of the solstice, and moving towards the winter pole before it dies out. This paradoxical situation demands more study, as do so many other aspects of Mars, especially ones relating to the possibility of life's existence there.

The possibility of life

In evaluating whether life can exist on Mars there are four bits of evidence that must be explained by those who uphold the negative view. None of these bits alone in any sense *proves* there is life on Mars: however, each phenomenon in concert with the others is hard to explain except by hypothesizing a form of living plant life, one that might be analogous to terrestrial forms in some respects, though necessarily different in order to survive the environment of the Martian surface, so low in water, oxygen, and temperature and possibly subject to a very high ultraviolet flux.

One piece of evidence is the "wave of darkening," explained by many as the response in the spring of some sort of vegetation to increased humidity (or nitric oxide?) in the atmosphere during sublimation of the polar cap. A second is the changing polarization of the dark areas in the spring. Both could be due to growth of small organic particles.

But both of these first two lines of evidence also can be "explained"—no less effectively and no more so than by hypothesizing life—by invoking color, textural, and size changes in unspecified hygroscopic salts which respond to slight seasonal changes in humidity. Less subject to this ambiguity is a third piece of evidence—the persistence of the dark areas through the years in the face of the recurring dust storms which would, in the absence of rain, finally tend to cover them with material the same color as the deserts. They could be high plateaus swept clean by frequent winds, of course, but the better explanation seems to be that vegetation persistently grows up through the perpetually shifting dust.

Perhaps the most compelling piece of evidence for life—our fourth bit—is the recent discovery by W. Sinton, of the Lowell Observatory, of absorption features in the 3.4- to 3.7-micron infrared range of radiation reflected from the dark areas on Mars that can be attributed to vibrational transitions in known

organic molecular bonds. The best—but not unambiguous—fit for the particular absorption spectrum observed is the substance acetalde-

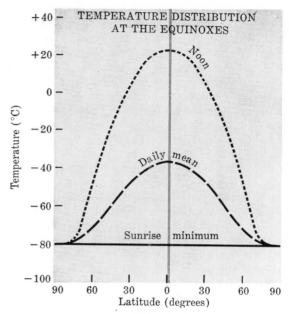

Fig. 4-9. At time of the equinoxes Mars' equator is warmer than poles, as on earth throughout the year, accounting for earthlike circulation of air on Mars—Fig. 4-8—at these times. But at solstices, Fig. 4-10, heat and air flow on Mars differs. (Courtesy Yale Mintz)

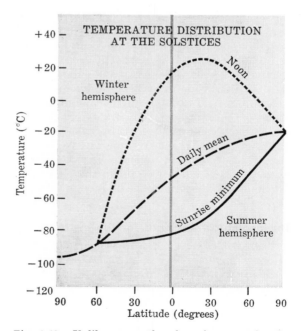

Fig. 4-10. Unlike on earth, where ice-covered poles remain colder than equator even in summer, Mars' summer pole becomes warmest region on the planet. This makes circulation on Mars at this time uniquely Martian. See margin. (Courtesy Yale Mintz)

hyde. And this is an especially interesting substance from the point of view of possible life forms, since an acetaldehyde molecule breaks down under ultraviolet radiation to form sugar-like molecules. However, this interpretation has not gone unchallenged. The spectral identification of organic matter on Mars has been questioned recently by D. G. Rea, T. Belsky, and M. Calvin (University of California, Berkeley), who studied the reflection characteristics of a variety of solid organic substances and concluded in a paper presented to COSPAR (Warsaw, June, 1963) "the assignment of the features to organic matter, implying the presence of life on the Martian maria, is found to be improbable." Just to keep the subject alive, and as a good example of the power of unfettered thinking, we should note the verbal reply of Carl Sagan to the COSPAR paper referred to above (we are paraphrasing): Acetaldehyde is a gas, not a solid, and could be held in little silicate capsules formed by the Martian vegetation. Silica (and there may be other substances just as good) transmits ultraviolet radiation, permitting a kind of photosynthesis to take place in the gas-filled cavity, in which acetaldehyde is broken down to form sugar. At least (he added) let us not be too hasty in discarding the evidence for organic matter on Mars; we should not have preconceived ideas about a life form that we know so little about.

There are many other facets to this fascinating subject, of course. One recent development, for example, has been the demonstration in several laboratories in the U.S. that some simple anaerobic micro-organisms—particularly spore-forming bacteria of the genus *Clostridium*—can survive in a soil subjected to a simulated Martian climate. They must have organic material to feed on, but with the nutrient available the warm period during the Martian "day" is long enough for a complete growth cycle to occur, and they can then survive the intense cold of "night" as spores. It appears that we can no longer say (as has been said in the past) that life under conditions to be found on Mars is *impossible.*

The geological evidence for life on Mars

There is one most important geological aspect of Mars' history as a planet that needs to be settled before we can do much more theorizing about life: Was Mars always as arid as it is now? It is usually assumed, and with good reason, that life on earth originated in the oceans or in lakes. Presumably this would have been so on Mars as well. But it is certain there are no oceans or permanent lakes on Mars now. Could there once have been some, long ago in the early history of the planet?

The answer is not known, but it should be one of the first geological studies to be made. Possibly the presence of ancient seas would be detectable from high resolution pictures radioed back to earth from fly-by orbiting probes. Certainly the answer will be clear when our instruments can probe the surface. Beds of limestone, salt flats, collections of wave-rounded pebbles, signs of ancient beaches, and other evidence indicating former seas should all be rather easy to find, if they exist on Mars, and they would tell us that we now see a planet that was once much more like the earth than it is now, a planet that is in the process of losing the last vestiges of the more volatile portions of its atmosphere—H_2 and O_2.

If we do *not* find evidence of former oceans, then it will indeed be difficult—and fascinating—to explain any life we do find on Mars.

Certainly one of the prime aims of early probes to Mars will be to search for life forms there. It may be possible to learn something from fly-by probes, by a combination of high-resolution TV photography and spectroscopic observations of the maria. But the main advance will come when the first successful landing on the surface takes place. A number of ingenious experiments are under development—under the beguiling code names of Gulliver (Cal Tech), Multivator (Stanford Medical School), and Wolftrap (U. of Rochester)—for determining whether there are carbon-based life forms on Mars that can propagate in organic nutrients similar to those which nourish terrestrial life.

So the observations and the theoretical arguments go on, with a growing optimism that life will be found on Mars, an optimism in which, as you may have guessed, I share.

Further reading

Just for the nostalgic fun of it, take a look at the pair of books that stimulated so much popular interest back when the world was very young—*Mars* (Houghton Mifflin, 1896) and *Mars and Its Canals* (Macmillan, 1906)—both by Sir Percival Lowell. Then move into the twentieth century with a vengeance with Kellogg and Sagan's excellent reviews, "The Atmospheres of Mars and Venus" (NAS-NRC Publication 944, 1962) and "The Terrestrial Planets," in the *Annual Review of Astronomy and Astrophysics,* Vol. 1, 1963. Another standard reference is the book *Physics of the Planet Mars* by G. H. De Vaucouleurs (Macmillan, 1954). To bring this up to date, see the appropriate parts of *Physics of the Planets, Proceedings of the 11th International Astrophysical Symposium,* Liège, Belgium, 1962 (Memoires de la

Société Royal des Sciences de Liège, 5th Series, Vol. 7, 1963). A pair of volumes from the U. of Chicago Press that should be old friends to readers in the planetary sciences also offer pertinent chapters: *The Atmosphere of the Earth and Planets*, edited by Kuiper (1952) and *Planets and Satellites*, edited by Kuiper and Middlehurst (1961). In the latter see especially the chapters by Dollfus, Petit, Sinton, and Finsen. Sinton also contributes "Further Evidence of Vegetation on Mars," an article in *Science* **130**, 1234 (1959). Also in *Science* **136**, 17 (1962) is Salisbury's review of the life question, "Martian Biology." For a spectacular array of pictures and commentary derived from a lifetime of

study, see Slipher's *A Photographic History of Mars, 1905–1961* (Lowell Observatory and the Air Force Aeronautical Chart and Information Center, 1962). Don't, in any case, overlook two excellent and brief compenda of information from industrial sources. One is Report SM-43634 of the Douglas Aircraft Co., entitled "Physical Properties of the Planet Mars," the other is the "Proceedings of the Lunar and Planetary Exploration Colloquium," North American Aviation, 1961. There's also a series of concise RAND Corp. reports—R-402-JPL, RM-3885-PR, RM-2567 among them—which review various aspects of the Martian environment and how to get things done in it.

VENUS

by Carl Sagan *

In Brief: *Hidden beneath its cover of clouds, the planet Venus steadfastly maintained its air of ineluctable mystery—until the last few years. Within this short period, earth-based observations of its radio microwave spectrum, its cloud-top temperatures, and its radar reflectivity—along with refined interpretation of its spectrum in the middle infrared—have combined to render it less mysterious, but no less puzzling. Prior to the well-publicized voyage of the Mariner R-2 spacecraft, no fewer than four different models for the surface of the planet could be reasonably defended: desert, swamp, ocean of carbonated water, or ocean of oil. Similarly, at least three model atmospheres were tenable—the so-called greenhouse, aeolosphere, and ionospheric models. Though earth-based evidence gave a narrow edge to a desert surface, overlain by a greenhouse atmosphere, it could not decisively choose among the alternatives. Mariner has narrowed the range of uncertainty.—S.T.*

■ The planet Venus is in some ways the earth's twin. It has about the same mass and radius, and its gravitational attraction is only slightly less. Yet despite such coincidences, Venus and the other nearby worlds are profoundly dissimilar. Each poses its own challenges to understanding, and for each we must seek unique solutions. Although it is easy to draw analogies from our experience on earth to interpret the limited data we have for Venus, upon closer inspection these analogies usually fail.

Next to the Moon, Venus is our closest neighbor in the solar system, yet we are more com-

pletely baffled by many of its attributes than we are by those of our more distant neighbor Mars. The surfaces of the Moon (see "The Moon," page 492) and Mars can be directly observed with telescopes, and at least moderately accurate descriptions of their physical environments were made by early visual observers. But behind its thick shroud of clouds, the surface features of Venus have remained an enigma.

Until the last few years, the available information was so sketchy that several highly contradictory views of conditions on Venus could be entertained, as suggested by Figs. 4-11 through 4-14. Recent radio observations, however, and the successful flyby of Venus by the Mariner R-2 spacecraft on December 14, 1962, have narrowed the range of speculation considerably.

Mariner represents the first successful attempt by the inhabitants of the earth to probe directly from a close distance (about 20,000 miles) the physical environment of another world. The spacecraft's scientific payload included two experiments exclusively designed for the planetary encounter—microwave and infrared radiometers. An account of the difficulties experienced by Mariner on its way to Venus reads like "The Perils of Pauline." While the spacecraft did not work as well as had been hoped, it has provided a substantial amount of new information. The flight of Mariner represents a remarkable success, both in science and in engineering, for the National Aeronautics and Space Administration. The Mariner results will be discussed in the appropriate sections below. It is fair to state at the outset that all questions about Venus have not been answered, and that it will take future generations of spacecraft to rigorously specify the environment of Venus.

* Carl Sagan is Assistant Professor of Astronomy at Harvard, and a staff member of the Smithsonian Astrophysical Observatory in Cambridge, Massachusetts.

Figs. 4-11 through 4-14. In one early view surface was pictured as swamp, filled with primitive fernlike plants, and thick cloud cover was assumed to be water. If, instead, clouds are windblown dust, surface might be arid and hot. Desert scene is also compatible with calm, clear ovenlike atmosphere below high ice clouds. But one alternate explanation for abundant CO_2 suggests surface covered by a mildly carbonated ocean. Another invokes oceans of surplus partially oxidized hydrocarbons left over from primordial atmosphere, beneath thick clouds of oily smog.

Surmises and speculation

The obscuring cloud cover of Venus was the first planetary feature observed through the telescope. Astronomers at the turn of this century decided, by terrestrial analogy, that the clouds must be made of water. And since no breaks in the clouds had ever been observed, they concluded that the clouds were very thick, and that, consequently, the abundance of water on Venus was very great. The presence of so much water somehow suggested—by analogy with terrestrial coal-forming swamps of Carboniferous times—that Venus was a steamy swamp, perhaps populated by primitive plants and small reptiles (Fig. 4-11).

The insecure foundations of this argument were clearly demonstrated when the expected great abundance of water vapor was sought by spectroscopy. The early searches were entirely unsuccessful, and it soon became obvious that, at least in the regions of the atmosphere then accessible to terrestrial observation, water was not present in large amounts. But if the clouds were not water, then what were they? The alternative idea arose that large amounts of finely pulverized dust were stirred up from the surface and swept by strong winds high into the atmosphere, creating a permanent pall in the sky of Venus. The surface was then arid, dusty, windswept, and probably rather hot (Fig. 4-12).

In later years, this model of Venus received support from the spectroscopic discovery of large amounts of carbon dioxide in the atmosphere of Venus. The reasoning behind this is simple. It is believed that the carbon dioxide balance is maintained on the earth by a process known as the Urey equilibrium, a sample reaction of which is

$$MgSiO_3 + CO_2 \overset{H_2O}{\rightleftarrows} MgCO_3 + SiO_2$$

On our planet, carbon dioxide outgassed from the interior of the earth through geologic time reacts with crustal silicate minerals (see "The Earth's Crust," page 570) to form carbonate minerals and quartz sand. But this equilibrium is attained only in the presence of surface liquid water. Now the equilibrium pressure of carbon dioxide for the earth, computed from the Urey equilibrium, is indeed within an order of magnitude of the observed partial pressure of CO_2 in the earth's atmosphere. But the greater probable partial pressure of carbon dioxide on Venus is incompatible with the Urey equilibrium at ordinary temperatures. The failure of the Urey equilibrium on Venus was attributed to the lack of water there, in agreement with the desert model.

However, this argument was completely turned around when it was suggested that failure of the Urey equilibrium on Venus may be due, not to unavailability of water, but to unavailability of the silicate minerals with which the abundant carbon dioxide was to react. Silicates conceivably might be unavailable if, for example, they were entirely covered by a global ocean (Fig. 4-13). Carbon dioxide outgassed from the interior would find nothing to react with, and would therefore remain in the atmosphere; and solution of carbon dioxide in the oceans would make them mildly carbonated. This planetary Seltzer ocean was rather at variance with the windswept desert model.

An entirely different attempt to explain the high carbon dioxide partial pressures invokes a presumed reaction in the early history of the planet between hydrocarbons and water vapor that is photodissociated in the upper atmosphere. The hydrogen released by dissociation preferentially escapes into space because of its low mass. But the oxygen which remains behind proceeds to oxidize the hydrocarbons according to reactions such as

$$CH_4 + O_2 \rightarrow CO_2 + 2H_2$$

In the case of a primordial excess of water, the hydrocarbons are all oxidized to carbon dioxide, and the excess water appears as O_2 and as H_2O in the later history of the planet. But in the opposite case, where there is an excess of hydrocarbons, all the water is used in oxidizing the hydrocarbons to CO_2, and therefore no free water or molecular oxygen appears. In this view of Venus, our difficulty in detecting H_2O and O_2 in the Venus atmosphere implies that the surface is covered with oil, overlain by smog (Fig. 4-14).

That four such diverse pictures of the surface conditions on Venus could seriously be entertained at the same time is an indication of the paucity of real data prior to 1956. In that

year observations were made at the Naval Research Laboratory in Washington indicating that somewhere on Venus there is a source which emits radio microwaves characteristic of a radiating black body whose temperature is about 600°K. The microwave spectrum, and its phase and time variations, are the keys to present models of the physical environment of Venus.

Microwaves, the key to the puzzle

The intensity of microwave radiation received from Venus at wavelengths between 3 and 21 cm is, within experimental error, inversely proportional to the square of the wavelength. This indeed indicates that, at least in this longer wavelength region, Venus is radiating as a black body. The equivalent black-body temperature when Venus nears its closest approach to the earth is around 600°K (see sketch in margin). But at the much shorter millimeter wavelengths also emitted by Venus, the indi-

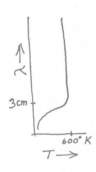

A CURRENT VIEW
OF CONDITIONS IN THE
ILLUMINATED HEMISPHERE OF VENUS

Fig. 4-15. To an observer on the ground, patches of clear sky seen through rare breaks in clouds may look yellowish-green, because of enhanced light-scattering effects in Venus' dense atmosphere. The scene otherwise would look rather dull, because of overcast. But high temperature of rocks (>600°K) might make the surface incandescent.

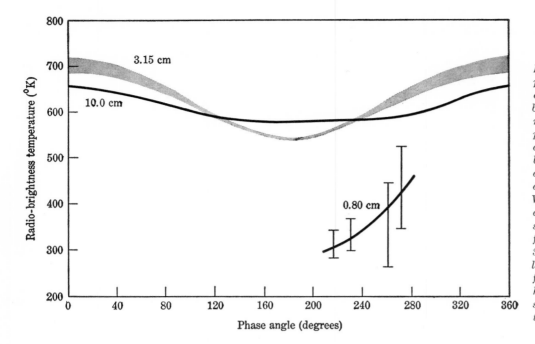

Fig. 4-16. Much recent interpretation of the environment on Venus depends on earthbase observations of radio microwave emission from the planet at various wavelengths, and at various times in its orbit around the sun. Phase angle referred to, left, is the angle between the lines sun-Venus and Venus-earth; lower angles place Venus on the far side of the sun, as viewed from earth. Quality of data at 3.15 cm and 10 cm is good, but lower temperatures deduced from shorter 0.80-cm waves have high probable errors, shown by vertical lines. See text for discussion.

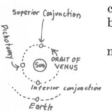

cated temperatures are considerably lower—being only about 350° between 4 and 8 mm.

Actually the surface temperatures on Venus must be even hotter than 600°K. Figure 4-16

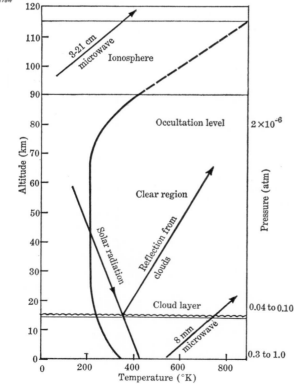

Fig. 4-17. Ionospheric model for atmosphere assumes that higher temperatures indicated by longer microwaves (see Fig. 4-16) result from acceleration of free electrons near other charged particles in a dense ionosphere. But at millimeter wavelengths, cooler surface of the planet shows through. (after NAS-NRC Publication No. 944)

shows more recent observations of the microwave emission from Venus at times other than inferior conjunction. (The sketch in the margin will make the astronomical terminology clear.) The abscissa of Fig. 4-16 is the phase angle, the angle Sun-Venus-Earth. Small phase angles refer to times when Venus lies on the far side of the sun with respect to the earth, near superior conjunction. Only then does one see the full illuminated hemisphere of Venus. The mean equivalent black-body temperature of this bright side at centimeter wavelengths is between 660° and 730°K, as shown by Fig. 4-16. And these are minimum temperatures; radar reflection and other data suggest that the true surface temperatures must be some 10% higher than this.

A model for an atmosphere

There have been several attempts to explain the microwave observations. In one attempt, the surface is the 600°K-plus source, and the lower temperatures deduced at millimeter wavelengths are due to absorption, by the atmosphere and the clouds, of radiation from the source at the surface. Alternatively, the ionosphere may be semiopaque at centimeter wavelengths, radiating there at the higher temperatures by free-free emission; that is, by the acceleration of free electrons in the vicinity of other charged particles with the consequent emission of centimeter microwaves. On this latter assumption, a model ionosphere can be constructed which is transparent below 3 cm, so that the cooler surface of the planet itself begins to show through the ionosphere at millimeter wavelengths. In this ionospheric model for the atmosphere (Fig. 4-17) the average surface temperature—in the dark hemisphere—might be as low as 350°K.

The essential distinction between the ionospheric model and other models is suggested in the marginal sketches. The ionospheric model in essence calls for a dense ionosphere and a cooler (350°K—still hot by terrestrial standards) surface. In contrast, other models such as the greenhouse and aeolosphere models shown in Figs. 4-18 and 4-19—to be discussed in a moment—postulate a less dense ionosphere coupled with a hotter emitting surface.

Microwave scanning from Mariner

Observations made even with very large earth-based radio telescopes are most conveniently performed near inferior conjunction. Because of the inverse square law, the intensity of microwave radiation from Venus decreases very rapidly after inferior conjunction. Thus the greater part of our information applies to the dark hemisphere of Venus, the side which is away from the sun. To make matters worse, the angular resolution of radio telescopes is so poor, that even with the largest single radio telescopes, a solid angle many times larger than that subtended by Venus is perceived. Until recently, the variation of microwave intensity over the full disk of Venus has never been observed from the surface of the earth. There is now the very exciting prospect of actually determining the temperature distribution over the disk of Venus by microwave interferometry. When two radio telescopes are used in tandem, as an interferometer, much greater angular resolutions become possible. But the first reliable measures of the variation of brightness temperature over the disk of Venus were obtained by Mariner.

As Mariner passed Venus, its microwave radiometer scanned the full disk at two wavelengths—13.5 and 19 mm. There were several important reasons for selecting these particular wavelengths. In the electromagnetic spectrum, 13.5 mm is one of the wavelengths at which water absorbs microwave radiation. If there is water present in the atmosphere of Venus, it will absorb some of the 13.5-mm radiation—if this radiation is coming from the surface of Venus. When the water abundance exceeds a certain minimum concentration, Venus would appear to be colder at 13.5 mm than at 19 mm, where there is no water-absorption.

Alternatively, suppose that the high-temperature source is above the surface, as in the ionospheric model, and again, Venus is to be scanned at 19 mm. In the ionospheric model, we remember, a wavelength of 19 mm is a spectral region for which the ionosphere is partially transparent. Therefore, as we look towards the center of the disk, we should see some radiation from the ionosphere, and some radiation from the underlying cooler surface.

As we look towards the edge, due to the slant path of the radiation which we receive, there will be a proportionately larger contribution from the hot ionosphere, and, therefore, a higher temperature will be deduced. Thus, on the ionospheric model, we should expect limb-brightening—that is, higher temperatures as the edge of the disk is approached. In the models that have a thin ionosphere and a hot surface, on the other hand, limb-darkening should be observed—in this case, because we see more of the cooler, overlying absorber as we look towards the limb than we do as we look towards the center of the disk.

Although the 13.5 mm observations of Venus made by Mariner are still being processed and interpreted, the 19 mm data have been reduced. Venus showed a distinct limb-darkening—no limb-brightening at all—and as a result, we can be quite confident that the ionospheric model does not apply to Venus. But we must then explain the high surface temperatures that this result implies.

The problem of the hot surface

The temperature of a hypothetical airless planetary surface can generally be predicted if we know the reflectivity of the surface and the flux of solar radiation reaching the planet, the local solar constant. If the solar constant is S, and the reflectivity averaged over all wavelengths is A, then $S(1 - A)$ units of solar energy will be absorbed per unit surface area and per unit time. At equilibrium, this is also the flux radiated back to space. The temperature can then be found from

$$\sigma T^4 = \tfrac{1}{4} S(1 - A)$$

The factor $\tfrac{1}{4}$ expresses the fact that a rotating planet has an effective area πr^2 for intercepting sunlight, while an area $4\pi r^2$ radiates back to space; σ is the Stefan-Boltzmann constant. Knowing the solar constant for the earth, the distances of Venus and the earth from the sun, and the visual reflectivity of the *clouds* of Venus, the average temperature on Venus on this simplified basis should be about 235°K.

Now this in fact is very close to the *cloud top* temperatures of Venus deduced in the middle infrared by placing thermocouples at the foci of large telescopes. But it is still much less than the temperatures deduced for the surface of Venus in any of the models. The attempt to explain this difference leads us to consider models alternative to the ionospheric one we have discussed.

Greenhouse effects and the infrared scan

One possible source of higher surface temperatures is the familiar greenhouse effect. When visible radiation penetrates the windows

Absorption by Atmosphere + clouds
OTHER MODELS
surface
$T \rightarrow$

surface
Ionospheric free-free emission
$T \rightarrow$

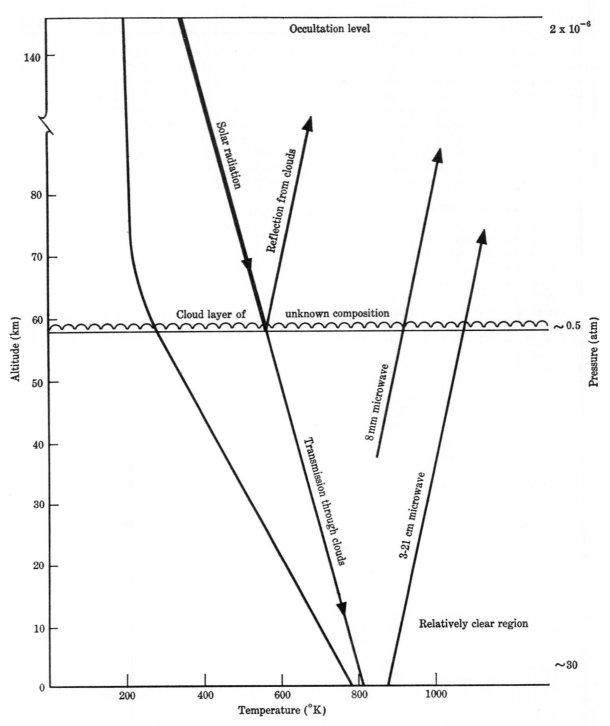

Fig. 4-18. *In contrast to the ionospheric model (Fig. 4-17), greenhouse model atmosphere postulates a less dense ionosphere and a hotter emitting surface for the planet. Heating of surface is thought to result from greenhouse effect caused by absorption characteristics of the abundant CO_2 and other molecules in the Venus atmosphere, and the effect of clouds. (after NAS-NRC Publication No. 944)*

of a greenhouse, it strikes the soil and heats it. The warm soil reradiates, however, primarily in the infrared region of the spectrum. And infrared radiation does not easily pass through the glass windows of the greenhouse. The temperature inside the greenhouse thus

rises until an equilibrium between incoming and outgoing radiation is achieved.

Now carbon dioxide, the only gas definitely identified in the atmosphere of Venus, has strong absorption bands in the infrared, like glass, although it is largely transparent in the visible. The large amounts of carbon dioxide present on Venus must raise the surface temperatures to very high values by such a mechanism (Fig. 4-18). However, unless the pressures on Venus are very high, CO_2 alone is probably not capable of bringing the temperatures to 600°K.

If water were present in somewhat greater quantities than exist on earth, or if other appropriate absorbers were available in the Venus atmosphere, the greenhouse model would probably be an acceptable explanation for the high surface temperature. However, the abundance of water vapor in the upper parts of the atmosphere of Venus seems less than one part in 10^5 by volume, although its existence has recently been confirmed by high-altitude balloon spectroscopy.

The infrared radiometers aboard Mariner were designed in part to help evaluate the merits of the greenhouse model. The infrared radiometers operated in the 8–9 and the 10–10.8 micron regions of the spectrum. The reason for selection of these wavelengths is that the atmosphere is probably transparent (except for clouds) to the passage of 8–9 μ radiation; but at 10–10.8 μ the lower atmosphere would be hidden by the presence of CO_2 which absorbs strongly in this wavelength interval. Therefore, if there are significant breaks in the cloud cover on Venus, the shorter wave infrared, not absorbed by CO_2, would arise from a much greater depth in the atmosphere than would the longer wavelengths. Thus, if there are breaks in the clouds, a substantial difference in pattern as well as temperature would have been detected between measurements in the infrared at the two wavelengths.

If, on the other hand, the temperatures obtained at both infrared wavelengths follow a similar pattern, the inference can be made that all of the radiant energy detected comes from the cloud tops, and that there are no detectable breaks in the cloud cover.

Detection of substantial leaks of radiation from the hot lower atmosphere would vitiate the greenhouse model. No such breaks were detected, although the topographical resolution over the disk of Venus obtained by Mariner R-2 was much less than had been hoped for. The results are thus consistent with the greenhouse model, but do not provide a critical test of it. Measurements of limb-darkening in the 10 μ region can, in principle, be used to distinguish among various models of the structure of the clouds of Venus and the composition of the atmosphere above the clouds. The distinction among various models of the clouds and upper atmosphere can be made, however, only if observations very close to the limb, where

substantial limb-darkening is expected, can be obtained. This demands better infrared topographical resolution than can be obtained from the earth, and is a natural experiment for future generations of Venus probes.

Dust storms, electron densities, and life

An alternative source of heating the surface of Venus arises in the aeolosphere model (Fig. 4-19). Here, the visible clouds are composed of dust whipped up from the surface by great winds. The circulation of gas and dust in the atmosphere transports momentum downwards. In this model, the atmosphere is a monster heat engine for converting solar radiation into surface friction.

The aeolosphere model also has its problems: first in explaining how such a circulation scheme could work; second in explaining the observed microwave phase effects shown in Fig. 4-16. The model assumes the pall of dust on Venus to be so thick that no sunlight reaches the surface. Therefore, the surface temperature responds

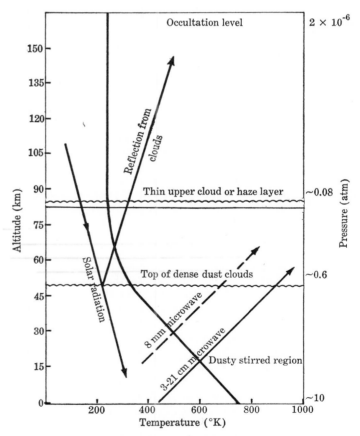

Fig. 4-19. Alternative to greenhouse heating of Venus surface is suggested in aeolosphere model. Here, solar radiation ultimately heats the surface by friction—through intermediate mechanism of high winds that blow dust over the surface and stir up visible dust clouds as well. (after NAS-NRC Publication No. 944)

very sluggishly to a change in the intensity of sunlight. The aeolosphere model then predicts that the temperatures on the bright side and on the dark side of Venus should be within a few degrees of each other; the observations contradict this prediction.

In both the greenhouse and aeolosphere models, the low or vanishing abundance of surface water and the very high surface temperatures appear to make life based on familiar biochemistry very unlikely. But the ionospheric model, with much lower surface temperatures, did hold out a hope for life on Venus. For the ionospheric model to work, however, very high electron densities in the ionosphere were required. Such electron densities could only be achieved if the magnetic field on Venus were so low that protons streaming in from the sun penetrated the atmosphere and ionized it, instead of being deflected by the magnetic field, as occurs at the earth.

The condition that would have to be satisfied for the ionospheric model to work can be expressed in another way, by the inequality shown in the margin. B is the magnetic field strength, n the proton number density, m the proton mass, and v the proton velocity.

$$\tfrac{1}{2}nmv^2 > B^2/8\pi$$

During its planetary encounter the magnetometer on Mariner in fact showed no rise in the average value of the magnetic field near Venus above that in interplanetary space, down to the limit of instrumental sensitivity— 5 gammas. By way of contrast, the earth has a magnetic field of about 30,000 γ at the equator, and 50,000 γ at the poles.

Evidence derived from the particle counters aboard similarly indicates that magnetically trapped particles—analogous to those of earth's Van Allen belts—are absent on Venus. While these observations do not prove that Venus has no magnetic field, they do demonstrate that if one exists, its strength must be very small.

However, in addition to the low or vanishing magnetic field strength needed to satisfy the above inequality, very large values for the solar proton wind are also required. But the electrostatic analyzer aboard Mariner, that monitored the solar plasma flux throughout the 109-day voyage to Venus, reported values that were too low, even in the light of Venus' very weak magnetic field, to lend support to the ionospheric model.

Interestingly enough, not all of the evidence inimical to the ionospheric model derives from timely and spectacular space-probe astronomy. Perhaps the most telling argument comes from a recent deskbound reanalysis of spectroscopic plates of Venus that were taken at the Mount Wilson Observatory way back in 1932.

The importance of old-fashioned thinking

These important findings by H. Spinrad show that the temperatures in the lower atmosphere on Venus are very high, consistent with surface temperatures of 600°K or more. The plates he used remained unanalyzed in observatory files for 30 years. It is interesting to conjecture how many other important discoveries are lying hidden in existing observations, awaiting only the person who can properly interpret them. Spinrad found a consistent pattern of pressure and temperature appeared in the 7820-Angstrom rotation-vibration band of carbon dioxide. The temperature can be determined from the relative intensities of the rotational components of the spectral band; and the pressures can be estimated from the contours of the rotational lines. The carbon dioxide molecule is undergoing both vibrational and rotational motion (see marginal sketch) as it absorbs and reemits solar radiation. And the higher the local temperatures are, the greater will be the excitation of higher-lying rotational levels. On the other hand, the greater the local pressures are, the broader will be the contours of the spectral lines. On Venus, higher temperatures go with higher pressures. An obvious interpretation is that at 7820 Å the cloud cover of Venus is variable, so that on some days one sees, on the average, to greater depths than on others. The highest temperature–pressure point deduced in this way is 430°K and 5.6 atm. Thus it is now rather certain that the surface temperatures and the surface pressures are both very high on Venus, virtually eliminating the ionospheric model. Furthermore, the absence of limb-brightening, reported by Mariner R-2, provides the *coup de grâce* to this model.

This matter of atmospheric pressure on Venus is worth a closer look. Our current conception of how Venus will look to the first man who gets there (Fig. 4-15) depends, in part, on it.

High pressure, greenish sky, red sun

In the original formulations of the greenhouse, aeolosphere, and ionospheric models, the surface pressures derived were of the order of a few atmospheres. Current estimates, based on various arguments, place the surface pressure of Venus at between 10 and 50 atm.

Such high surface pressures have several interesting consequences. On the earth the sky is blue because of Rayleigh scattering. The air molecules scatter short wavelength light (blue) more efficiently than long wavelength light (red). Thus blue light is preferentially scattered out of the beam of incident sunlight; and the sky appears blue because of multiple scattering of the blue wavelengths removed from the beam. But the sun looks red, especially near the horizon, because red light remains in the beam.

If we were to increase the surface pressure on earth some 10 to 50 times, such color effects would be enhanced. On a cloudless day on Venus, with such high pressures, the sky would have a yellowish-green cast. At the zenith, the sun would appear deep brick red, and it would be extinguished long before reaching the observer's horizon. Actually, cloudless days on Venus seem to be very rare, as is borne out by our inability to see breaks in the cloud cover with earth-based optical telescopes. The pressure-enhanced color effects would be washed out, and the predominant colors on the surface of Venus on an average overcast day should be dull grey, provided that sufficient light to see penetrates at all. Figure 4.15 attempts to portray the scene that might greet the eyes of the first man on Venus.

Night and day—how long?

The absence of Doppler shifts in the visible wavelengths at the limb of Venus (as suggested in the margin) shows that it is rotating more slowly than once every five terrestrial days. However, observations made of features resembling weather bands in ultraviolet photographs of Venus (Fig. 4-20) have been interpreted to give a period of rotation of several weeks; but for a variety of reasons, these conclusions are uncertain.

The best hope for determining the period of rotation of Venus, the length of the Venus day, is from analysis of Doppler broadening of radar pulses returned from Venus. Analysis of such observations performed in the Soviet Union gave a period of rotation less than eleven days. But analysis of similar observations made in the United States gives periods of rotation approximately equal to the period of revolution of Venus around the sun—225 days. And the most recent radar results suggest the rotation might even be retrograde, a phenomenon unique in the inner solar system.

This question of Venus' rotation rate is intimately tied to several other intriguing questions. If Venus rotates very slowly, what prevents the surface and lower atmosphere on the dark side from cooling to more equable temperatures than they do (as indicated by Fig. 4-16) during the long night? Or, expressed another way, what is the source of the energy which maintains the high-surface temperatures even on the dark side? And, similarly puzzling, why are the indicated temperatures for the cloud tops very nearly the same on both the illuminated and dark hemispheres?

Fig. 4-20. Ultraviolet photograph of Venus shows vague markings in cloud cover that have been interpreted as possibly being weather bands. Time-lapse observations of such features can be interpreted to yield figure for period of rotation, but such results are uncertain (from F. E. Ross, Astrophys. J., **68**, 57, (1928), courtesy R. S. Richardson)

The variation of radio-brightness temperature with phase angle (Fig. 4-16) provides direct evidence that, on an assumed non-synchronously rotating Venus, the surface does indeed cool at night. The diurnal temperature variation on Venus, as shown in Fig. 4-16, is much greater when observed at a wavelength of 3.15 cm than when observed at 10 cm. But the 10 cm radiation should arise from greater depths below the surface of Venus than the 3.15 cm radiation, just as, within the surface of the earth, the thermal wave becomes damped with depth. The 3.15 cm and 10.0 cm curves in Fig. 4-16 are just what is to be expected if the surface of Venus has thermal properties characteristic of dry powders.

Something about the body of Venus

The relatively long period of rotation of Venus needs explaining. Planets are believed to form from clouds of gas and dust which are initially slowly rotating and which rapidly condense. Conservation of angular momentum causes them to rotate faster as they contract. The same is presumably true of forming satellites. Yet every satellite in the solar system rotates synchronously, always keeping the same face towards its planet. Similarly, Mercury keeps the same face towards the sun. Synchronous rotation is caused by tidal friction, a torque exerted by the larger body on the smaller through body or surface tides. The tidal force declines very rapidly with distance. Mercury is very close to the sun and there, evidently, the tide-raising forces have been effective.

But Venus is much farther from the sun. It is not clear why tides should be so much more efficient for Venus than for earth. This circumstance may be related to the expectation that hotter Venus has a more extensive liquid core, onto which tide-raising forces may couple.

Mariner performed yeoman service. It was designed to aid in resolving among conflicting models for the planet. In the understandable delight and fanfare over Mariner's success, let us not forget to give quieter acclaim to the models—the rational guide for our scientific exploration programs—and in the most practical sense, the determinants of the scientific payload that will be carried on Mariner's progeny.

Further reading

There are certain books that are always a good point of departure for an excursion into a new subject. In the planetary sciences these include such standbys as *The Planets: Their Origin and Development* by H. Urey (Yale U. Press, 1952); *The Atmospheres of the Earth and Planets,* Kuiper ed. (U. of Chicago Press, 1952); and *Planets and Satellites,* Kuiper and Middlehurst eds. (U. of Chicago Press, 1961).

All of these contain pertinent chapters on the perplexing puzzles of Venus.

More sharply focused on Venus is a report of the U.S. Space Science Board entitled "The Atmospheres of Mars and Venus," by Carl Sagan and W. W. Kellogg, NAS-NRC publication No. 944, 1961. In the *Proceedings of the Eleventh International Astrophysical Colloquium* (P. Swings ed., Liège, in press) can be found some of the more recent thinking on the problems of Venus by representatives of many nations. This work includes, in particular, an excellent review of the radioastronomical data.

More recent reports include Sagan and Kellogg's "The Terrestrial Planets," in *Ann. Rev. Astron. Astrophys.* **1,** 325, edited by L. Goldberg (Academic Press, 1963); "The Mariner II Infrared Radiometer Experiment," by S. C. Chase, L. D. Kaplan, and G. Neugebauer in *J.G.R.* **68,** 6157 (1963); and "The Mariner 2 Microwave Radiometer Experiment and Results," by Barath, Barrett, Copeland, Jones, and Lilley in *Astronom. J.* **69,** 49 (1964).

Much of the remainder of the Venus story must be hunted down in the periodical literature: *Astrophys. J. Planetary and Space Science,* and scattered numbers of *J. Geophys. Research.* But you can never tell for sure, because, for example, Sagan's discussion of the very high pressures in the lower atmosphere of Venus, and of their consequences, is in *Icarus,* **1,** 151, 1962. And Spinrad's superb discovery that high temperatures can be observed in the infrared part of the spectrum appeared in *Publ. Astron. Soc. Pacific,* **74,** 187 (1962).

THE MOON

by A. G. W. Cameron *

IN BRIEF: *The moon has been an object of speculation and observation for centuries. Locked in its airless wastes are important clues to how the solar system was formed. But a new note of urgency has entered lunar studies; some day a man is going to have to survive there.*

Viewed in this light, our knowledge seems all too meager. Some facts are certain—the moon's size, shape, distance, density, and lack of atmosphere have been determined with great precision. But sophisticated methods for studying the moon have produced a great deal of contradictory evidence. And so theories proliferate over such vital questions as the moon's com-

position, its internal structure, and the origin of its surface features.

Lunar probes will provide the most satisfactory way yet—short of going there—for investigating our satellite. They will carry radiation detectors and seismographs, and will be able to analyze samples of the lunar surface. In this way, we hope to fill the worst gaps in our knowledge about the moon before we commit a man to that alien environment.—S.J.B.

* A. G. W. Cameron pursues lunar and related studies at the Institute for Space Studies, a branch of NASA's Goddard Space Flight Center, Greenbelt, Maryland.

■ In the next decade or so, the moon will move from the realm of astronomy into the realm of geography. Contradictory evidence and controversial speculation will yield to direct investigation and hard fact. But before the first man sets foot on the moon's surface, lunar probes may permit us to extend our meager knowledge of lunar properties and to resolve the worst

Fig. 4-21. *Composite moon, formed by merging photograph of moon at first quarter with one of moon at last quarter, provides high resolution of surface features except at edges. On photograph of full moon, detail tends to be washed out completely. Smooth, dark areas are the maria; lighter areas, called highlands, show extremely high density of craters and other features. Most of moon's surface features are believed to have formed as the result of an intense bombardment 4.5 billion years ago; maria probably formed at end of this bombardment, obliterating some of earlier markings. Much lower bombardment rate which has taken place since can be estimated from number of craters on maria. Dark region at lower right is Mare Imbrium. Above it is Copernicus, a large crater whose prominent ray system consists of fine debris sprayed out when crater was formed. (Courtesy Lick Observatory, University of California)*

conflicts in our interpretation of the evidence we have.

Certainly, we will not be exploring just another landscape; it will be a new kind of landscape. For we can expect the atmosphereless moon to have undergone processes unlike any to which the earth has been subject. Yet it is also true that much of the moon's strangeness results from its being a small, dead world which has undergone little change since it was formed. Unlike the earth, the moon has preserved a record of the early history of the solar system. Consequently it is an important object of study for those seeking to solve the mystery of how the sun and planets were formed, as well

as for those trying to figure out ways to keep a man alive on its surface.

From telescopes to lunar probes

Our investigation of the lunar record began when mankind acquired the telescope. Observers with fairly large instruments prepared elaborate drawings of lunar features that could not be seen with the naked eye. When astronomical photography became possible, it became clear that most of the detailed drawings of lunar features bore only a superficial resemblance to the lunar photographs.

Turbulence in the upper atmosphere severely limits the amount of detail that can be resolved on the moon, regardless of how large the astronomical telescope may be. The best lunar photographs resolve objects with diameters of about half a mile—not often considered "fine detail" in terrestrial investigations.

In recent years many other methods have been used to investigate the moon. These include some very sophisticated analyses of electromagnetic radiation in many different wavelength regions coming from the moon. Infrared and radar data support the evidence in the visible spectrum that the moon's surface does not resemble anything on earth. There are also deductions that can be made from the details of the lunar motion about the earth. And we have seen preliminary results of lunar investigations by Russian spacecraft.

The United States is about to embark on an extensive series of lunar investigations that will pave the way for a manned lunar landing by the end of the decade. There are three basic stages of planned investigation that we can designate by the names of the spacecraft that will carry them out: Ranger, Surveyor, and Prospector. Ranger is a basic spacecraft designed to take instruments toward a crash landing on the moon. Surveyor will have the ability to bring 250 lb of instruments to a soft landing on the lunar surface. It will be equipped with a drill that will enable an extensive chemical and physical analysis of one spot on the lunar surface to be carried out. Prospector will include a vehicle capable of roaming around the lunar surface to carry out similar analyses at many places. This vehicle may also be of assistance in establishing a base in support of the lunar landing. Possibly it may be able to fire some lunar samples to earth for extensive analysis in the laboratory.

How high the moon

In principle, one of the simplest observations that can be made about the moon is its position in the sky. Not only can this be accurately determined by modern instruments, but also records of ancient eclipses tell us where the moon was at certain special times in the past. From studies of this kind we deduce that the angular momentum of the earth-moon system is being redistributed; the rotation of the earth is slowing down and the earth-moon distance is increasing.

This corresponds to a dissipation of energy from the mechanical motion of some 3.2×10^{19} ergs/sec, according to a study by W. Munk and G. J. F. MacDonald. They show that if this rate has remained constant in the past, the moon would have receded from a distance of 100,000 km to 384,000 km in only 1.3 billion years. But the age of the earth is estimated at 4.5 billion years. In that length of time, the moon would have had to recede even farther than it has, so that we must question our assumption that the earth and the moon have always been members of the same dynamical system.

Has the rate of energy dissipation remained constant in the past? Sir Harold Jeffreys argued many years ago that the mechanism of the dissipation was in the action of tides in the shallow seas of the earth. Since the seas have changed enormously during the earth's history, we can't extrapolate into the past.

However, Munk and MacDonald have reviewed the evidence for the shallow-seas hypothesis. Looking at modern data, they have concluded that the energy dissipated by this mechanism is too small by at least a factor three to account for the measured dissipation. They suggest instead that most of the energy is dissipated by tides within the solid earth. Such tides would be practically unaffected by changes in the surface topography of the earth. Moreover, the closer the moon and earth are, the greater the rate of dissipation is. If this nonlinear effect is taken into account, the moon would have receded to its present distance in even less than 1.3 billion years. Munk and MacDonald therefore suggest that the moon has been captured by the earth relatively recently in its history. Clearly we need more evidence for this than the imperfectly understood dissipation processes, but we are warned right at the outset that we should have a wide open mind about the moon.

It's not green cheese—but what is it?

Another lunar quantity that is easily measured is the mean density, since we know the mass of the moon from the nature of its motion, and we know the dimensions accurately from measurements. The mean uncompressed density is about 3.34 gm/cm³. H. C. Urey has emphasized the smallness of this value compared with common stone meteorite densities of 3.6 to 3.8 gm/cm³, and especially compared with the earth's mean density of 5.5 gm/cm³. There has been a tendency in recent years, also following a suggestion of Urey, to postulate that the common stone meteorites containing rounded glassy inclusions (the chondritic meteorites) are reasonably good samples of the nonvolatile constituents of the solar system. But the low density of the moon indicates that it cannot have a simple chondritic composition.

How might lunar composition differ with respect to meteorites? Urey suspects that the moon is deficient in iron relative to the chondrites. Spectroscopic evidence indicates that the sun itself may have a lower ratio of iron to silicon than do the chondrites. If this suggestion is correct, then in fact the moon would be a better sample of nonvolatile solar system material, than the chondritic meteorites.

J. A. Wood has suggested that the moon has a low density because its iron content has undergone greater oxidation than the earth's. But it is then necessary to explain how this difference came about. One proposal is that the earth and moon were both formed from fully oxidized materials, and that extensive melting subsequently reduced the iron oxide in the earth and allowed the oxygen to escape. Another possibility is that the earth formed first from unoxidized materials, and the moon collected subsequently from materials which had undergone longer exposure to gases in the gaseous nebula from which the solar system formed. There are many other theories, but the evidence is insufficient to prove or disprove any one of them.

Other suggestions have been that the moon may contain substantial quantities of water or graphite in its interior; 2 to 3% of water or 7 to 11% of graphite would account for the low density. Urey has pointed out some difficulties with these suggestions: Since water lowers the melting point of silicates, we should expect to see extensive and persistent lava flows on the surface; there is no evidence for these. Similarly, carbon reduces iron and silicon oxides, and the density should be increased after the resulting gases have escaped.

Before we can distinguish among the various pictures of the formation of the moon, we need to find out what the composition is; we could then narrow the range of possibilities for the origin of the earth-moon system.

Arguments for a rigid moon

The moon is not a perfect sphere and thus has three unequal moments of inertia (as sketched in the margin). The largest moment C is about the axis of rotation, the second largest B along the tangent to the orbit, and the smallest A in the direction of the earth. These moments are much more unequal than they would be if the moon were in hydrostatic equilibrium. Hence either the moon has a complicated variation of density with angle, or else the outer layers of the moon support stresses of 10 to 100 bars (1 bar = 10^6 dyne/cm^2 = 14.7 lb/in^2). Variations in the surface elevations of the moon of 1 to 2 km over considerable areas also lead to the conclusion that the moon is rigid. If the outer layers of the earth were subjected to similar stresses, the stresses would be relieved by deformation in less than a million years.

Since the crust is so rigid it is unlikely that the outer regions of the moon are very hot.

This in turn implies that no significant components of the outer portions of the moon can be near the melting point. We would then expect little lunar volcanism of the terrestrial type, in which melted rock is brought to the surface from only a few tens of kilometers below the surface.

MacDonald and others have carried out extensive calculations on the thermal history of a moon of assumed chondritic composition. If the moon is assumed to be formed cold (0°C), then due to radioactive heating as may be seen in Fig. 4-22, temperatures well over 1500°C are reached at the center, and after a lunar history of 3 billion years, iron will be melted everywhere below a depth of about 500 km. The melting point of diopside, a silicate, may not actually be exceeded anywhere, but would be so nearly equaled over most of the lunar interior that one would expect the silicate materials to be very plastic and easily deformed.

If similar calculations are made with the moon at a higher initial temperature, then correspondingly larger central temperatures are reached after 4.5 billion years. Thermal conductivities are much too small for any appreciable amount of heat to escape.

This extensive melting in the interior seems incompatible with the large height difference supported by the moon. Thus it seems likely that the radioactive heating in the moon must have been considerably less than that assumed in the calculations. Since the isotope potassium-40 is the main source of radioactive heat in the earth and meteorites, the moon probably has a deficiency of potassium. Alternatively, the moon could have been melted and chemically

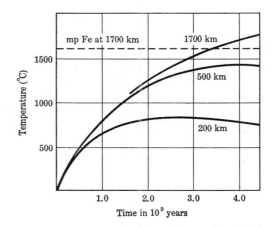

Fig. 4-22. *Calculations by G. J. F. MacDonald show development of temperature with time at various depths if moon were formed at 0°C, and had chondritic composition. Melting point of iron, indicated by dashed line, would be exceeded at 1700 km after 3 billion years.*

differentiated, bringing potassium to the surface layers as on the earth.

A test of the latter possibility is soon to be carried out. The U.S. Ranger spacecraft will

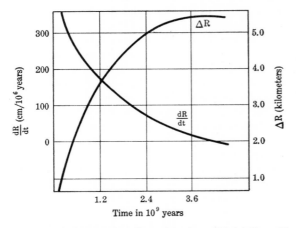

Fig. 4-23. Change of radius with time of initially cold (0°C) chondritic moon, as calculated by MacDonald. Radius increases by about 5 km during first 2 billion years because of high initial rate of radioactive heating. Radius reaches maximum after 4 billion years.

carry a gamma-ray spectrometer designed to look for gamma rays from the decay of potassium-40. This will determine whether the surface layers of the moon have an average or enriched content of this radioactive isotope, and thus whether there has been any large-scale volcanism of the surface-melting kind.

Moonquakes and magnetism

A related question is the stress caused by the internal heating. MacDonald's results for the initially cold moon of chondritic composition, shown in Fig. 4-23, indicate that the lunar radius would have expanded slightly more than 5 km during lunar history, but that it would have changed only slightly in the last 1.5 billion years. For each 1-km change in radius the surface area of the moon must change by 1 part in 1000. This would lead us to expect extensive cracks in the moon's surface. Even a moon considerably depleted in potassium should have some such cracks formed during its early history. Because there are not nearly as many as MacDonald's results require, we must question the assumption that the moon is chondritic.

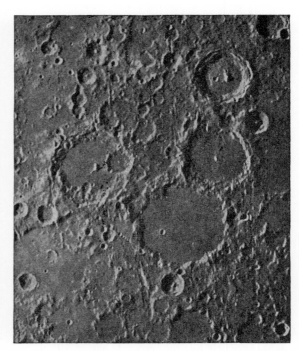

Fig. 4-24. Portion of Mare Imbrium is shown in photograph at left. Glancing angle of illumination brings out low-relief features. Wrinkle-ridges, sometimes interpreted as limits of lava flow, show very clearly. Semicircular chain of mountains, marking the boundary of Mare Imbrium, is presumably debris or part of old, churned-up surface. Urey suggests that grooves through mountains were formed by flying nickel-iron fragments when mare was formed. Photograph at right shows section of lunar "highlands" from upper central portion of moon's face in composite photograph. Irregular central peaks, attributed to rebound effect, can be seen in several of the craters. Also visible are series of grooves radiating away from mare below area shown here. 40 in. telescope, Yerkes Observatory. (Courtesy Lunar and Planetary Laboratory, University of Arizona)

Color Fig. 26. Here is a new kind of electron beam for machining—the plasma electron beam. Its electrons are generated in a cold-cathode gun (top) rather than in one with a hot filament (Color Fig. 25). Beam is quite collimated by nature but, as this experimental device shows, a magnetic coil must be used to narrow the beam for power densities high enough for machining. The plasma electron beam functions at a medium vacuum of 10^{-3} torr or better vs. the high vacuum of 10^{-4} torr required by the conventional e-b machines. See "Nontraditional Machining," in Chapter 3. (Courtesy G. E. Advanced Technology Laboratory)

Color Fig. 27. Main gallery of the Sodium-Graphite Reactor at Hallam, Neb., is dominated by 250-ton fuel-loading and -unloading machine with its "mast" rising 50 ft. above the floor. Reactor itself is below floor level (beneath the illuminated cylindrical structure at bottom, center). See "Nuclear Power Today," in Chapter 3. (Courtesy Atomics International)

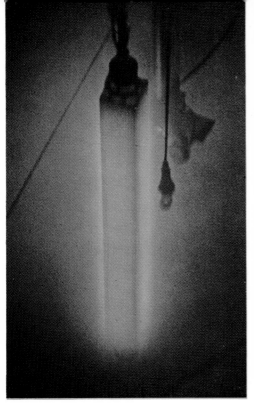

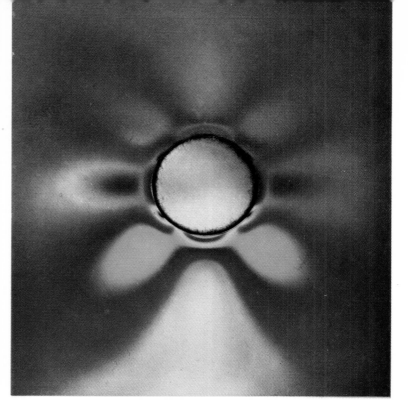

Color Fig. 28. Spent, irradiated fuel element is surrounded by blue glow of Cerenkov radiation produced by emitted particles coursing through the surrounding water. See "Nuclear Power Today," in Chapter 3.

Color Fig. 29. Dynamic patterns of strain around a hole in ½-in. Plexiglas under the fierce pressure of 5000 psi show up dramatically under polarized light with exposure of 0.1 μsec. See "Ultrahigh-Speed Photography," in Chapter 3.

Color Fig. 30. Coal pile nuclear style: 76 of these fuel elements power 170-MW Yankee reactor for 2 years. Virgin fuel is not radiation hazard to workmen. See "Nuclear Power Today," in Chapter 3. (Courtesy Yankee Atomic Electric Co.)

Color Fig. 31. With pressure-vessel head removed, top of Yankee can be made out through 25-ft. shield of water. Refueling is semiautomatic; fuel elements are transferred under water to chute that carries them to underground pit. See "Nuclear Power Today," in Chapter 3.

Since the inner part of the moon tends to heat and the outer part to cool, large stresses can be formed in the lunar interior. These stresses should result in deep-seated seismic disturbances. This will also be tested fairly soon. The Ranger spacecraft will contain a detachable lunar seismic package, which will send reports of lunar seismic activity to earth over a one- or two-month period.

The possibility that the moon may have a liquid core has interesting consequences for the related possibility that it may have a general magnetic field. Many people believe that the external magnetic fields of both the sun and the earth are generated by a complex series of convective motions within these bodies interacting with an internal toroidal magnetic field. In the earth, the convective motions are those of the liquid-iron core. This situation is illustrated in Fig. 4-25. Hence, if the moon has formed a liquid-iron core, it might be expected to have a significant magnetic field.

A preliminary investigation of the lunar magnetic field has been carried out by instruments on board the second Soviet cosmic rocket, which was launched in September, 1959. These measurements showed that the lunar magnetic field did not exceed 3×10^{-4} gauss down to within one lunar radius of the surface. (The earth's field is about 0.5 gauss.) This supports the idea

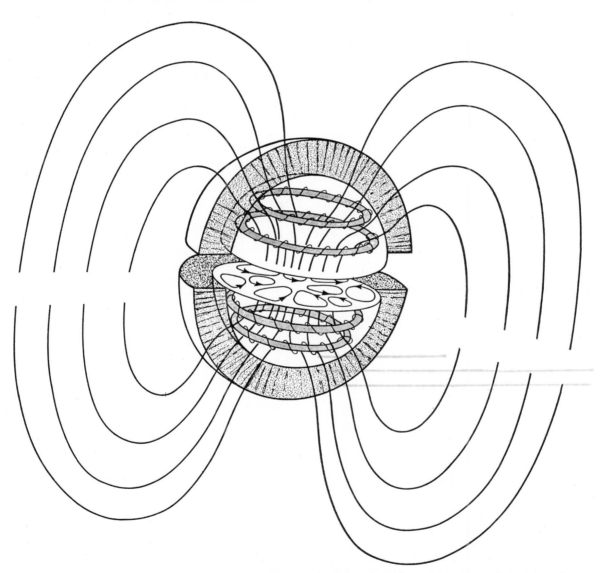

Fig. 4-25. Mechanism by which rotating body with liquid core can generate dipole magnetic field such as the earth's. Body has been cut along equator to show nonaxially symmetric convective motions which interact with toroidal field (heavy rings) to generate and amplify dipole field. Eddies in core in turn interact with dipole field to maintain and enhance toroidal field. Spirals indicate current which flows around toroidal field lines.

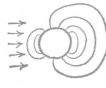

that the center of the moon has not melted. However, it has been suggested that the plasma flowing from the sun through interplanetary space may have pulled the magnetic lines of force of the lunar field back to the dark side of the moon, where the second cosmic rocket could not have detected them. This possibility, illustrated in the margin, remains to be investigated.

These plasma streams from the sun (the "solar wind") may also play a significant role in connection with the density of the lunar atmosphere. The most sensitive method observes whether signals from intense radio sources in space are refracted by the electrons in a lunar atmosphere when the moon passes through that region of the sky. From the absence of such refraction the lunar atmospheric density has been set at less than 10^{-13} of that of the terrestrial atmosphere.

Because the moon's gravity is low, most gases will easily escape from it, but the heavier inert gases, krypton and xenon, should be trapped. We would expect more of these gases than allowed by the above experimentally determined limit, if any extensive outgassing of gaseous fission products from the spontaneous fission of uranium-238 has taken place on the moon. However, such heavy atoms will easily be ionized by solar ultraviolet radiation, and then they should be captured and swept away by the solar wind. Perhaps this is another indication that the moon lacks a strong magnetic field; such a field would prevent this type of dissipation.

Volcanoes on the moon? Maybe

The internal temperature of the moon also bears implications for the possible role played by volcanism in the origin of the large-scale lunar surface features. The whole question of lunar volcanism is full of seeming contradictions; there is evidence both for and against.

The surface of the moon is packed with large numbers of craters in a wide range of sizes. These are circular depressions in the lunar surface surrounded by rocky walls; sometimes they also have a central peak that does not rise very far above the crater floor. There are also very large-scale features, of the order of a few hundred kilometers, called maria (anciently believed to be seas), that appear to be rather smooth dark plains perhaps composed of lava flows. In addition, there are smaller-scale features, a few kilometers in size, that one can describe as mountains, ridges, grooves, faults, and so forth. (Remember that only features with dimensions larger than half a mile can be resolved in photographs.) Many of these features can be seen in the full photograph of

the moon in Fig. 4-21. In addition some of these are shown close up, in Fig. 4-24.

These surface features have been extensively studied by geologists and classified in terms of their resemblance to various features on the surface of the earth. Many geologists do not stop here, but infer a structural similarity between the terrestrial features and their lunar namesakes. Because major terrestrial features tend to have been formed as a direct or indirect result of volcanic activity, such activity is then inferred to be operative also on the moon.

Conclusions of this kind can be accepted only with great caution. We have seen that radioactive heating has probably been unable to cause extensive melting in the moon, and the moon is too small a body to be melted by the release of its own gravitational potential energy. Under these circumstances the forces that molded the surface features on the moon may have little terrestrial counterpart. The resemblance of lunar surface features to well-known terrestrial structures may be superficial.

Most students of the lunar surface now accept the hypothesis that the lunar craters have been formed as a result of collisions of bodies with the moon. A hypothetical model for this event is shown in Fig. 4-26. On this model the shape of the craters is circular independent of the angle of approach of the colliding body. The central peaks, where they occur, are considered to be a rebound effect. Several meteorite craters have been found on the earth, and R. B. Baldwin has shown convincingly that the ratio of the depth to the diameter of a crater varies smoothly as one progresses in size from the terrestrial craters to lunar craters.

Yet it cannot be denied that there is evidence for considerable melting on the surface of the moon. The bottoms of the large maria have usually been interpreted as lava flows; the left photograph of Fig. 4-24 shows features which resemble a lava flow. And it has been suggested that certain rounded domes on the lunar surface have a volcanic origin. Some lunar craters appear to be flooded inside by lava. There are a few examples of small lunar craters that appear to be lined up in chains, which seems inconsistent with a random-impact hypothesis. Perhaps most important, because it suggests that some lunar volcanism exists today, is the spectroscopic observation by the Russian astronomer K. A. Kozyrev that gas containing carbon compounds has been emitted by the central peak of the lunar crater Alphonsus. However, the evidence for this is not yet clear or conclusive.

Urey has suggested that the lunar maria result from the collision of rather large bodies with the moon at relatively low speeds. This might allow extensive flows of lava to spread

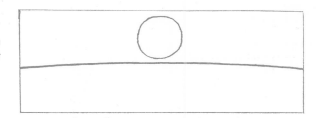

Fig. 4-26(a). *Many craters are believed to have formed by meteoritic impact. Here a meteor falls from the vertical direction at subsonic velocity.*

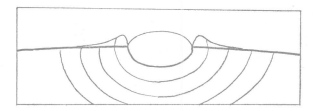

(b) Object only partly penetrates lunar surface. High pressure of impact generates pressure wave and displaces surface material.

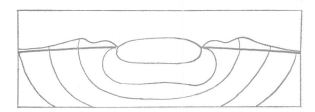

(c) Profile, somewhat later, shows ring of displaced material about area of collision. Heat generated by impact causes melting, both of meteor and of surrounding material.

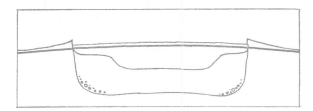

(d) Part of raised ring collapses, and lava from melted meteor flows over large area. Lava eventually solidifies filling crater to height greater than surrounding lunar surface, indicated by heavy line. Some unmelted debris may remain, but sinks to bottom as shown.

over the lunar surface shortly after the impacts. However, such regions of lava flow at the surface should long since have cooled.

We see, then, that there is strong evidence that volcanic activity has occurred on the moon. Yet studies of terrestrial volcanism lead us to associate volcanic activity with subsurface melting. But such melting is incompatible with a rigid moon, for which there is also strong evidence. Clearly, the resolution of this puzzle must await on-the-spot investigation.

One very important aspect of the crater-formation process is that it allows a relative chronology to be prepared for the events that have produced the major features of the lunar surface. As Fig. 4-24 shows, some craters lie on top of bigger ones, indicating that they were formed later. The density of craters in the maria is much less than that outside the maria; this allows us to establish when the maria were formed relative to the crater-producing process. Lava from some maria appears to have flowed into neighboring regions, thus establishing the

relative order of formation. Some of the older craters seem to have a softened outline relative to recent craters; perhaps they have been subjected to more surface erosion from micro-meteorites.

The absolute chronology of surface feature formation is harder to establish. However, a number of lines of evidence indicate that most of the surface markings on the moon have survived from the terminal phases of the accumulation process that formed the moon, when an intense bombardment is believed to have occurred. This should be a very valuable record to study when we get to the moon.

The lunar landscape

We will gain a much deeper insight into the lunar surface features when high-resolution TV pictures of it are first transmitted to the earth. These TV pictures will undoubtedly show a rather weird scene. From studies of the radar signals reflected from the moon, we have some very preliminary statistical information about

At full Moon: expect this,

but see this.

objects on the lunar surface in the range of size 10 cm to 2.5 m. It appears that about 10% of the lunar surface has irregularities on this scale. Most of the radar signals are returned from the central portion of the lunar surface, indicating that the lunar surface is remarkably flat. Figure 4-27 illustrates this flatness. Half of the returning radar echo seems to come from regions inclined at an angle of less than 5°.

The moonscape will probably have a soft, flowing, rounded appearance, the result of a novel form of erosion that has never occurred on the earth. Recent space flight experiments have shown that there is a relatively high density of small dust particles, or micrometeorites, in space near the earth. F. L. Whipple has estimated that about 2 kg of such particles have fallen throughout lunar history on every square centimeter of surface. This is not a simple process of deposition and accumulation. The dust particles will strike the surface with velocities of several kilometers per second, thus digging small pits and splashing material around. Over a long period of time this would wear down high points on the moon's surface. The dust may undergo vacuum sintering and solidify into a porous spongy material.

In any case, the churning of the lunar surface by micrometeorite bombardment will probably reduce color contrasts that one might expect to be associated with various kinds of rocks. Color measurements of the moon indicate a greyish landscape with little color variation from one region to another, but it will be interesting to see to what degree this also holds on a small scale.

We do have some preliminary and somewhat contradictory evidence concerning the microstructure of the lunar surface. One rather puzzling feature of this microstructure is that it does not produce any appreciable limb dark-

ening of the edges at full moon. This effect was first noticed and pointed out by Galileo. As the marginal sketch indicates, we would expect light striking the center of the moon disk to be mostly scattered back in the direction of incidence. But the light striking the limb should be mostly scattered away, causing the limb to appear darker. If we combine the absence of limb darkening with the additional observation that the fractional amount of light reflected by the surface is very low, we deduce that there is a strong tendency for light to be reflected back in the direction of incidence. No terrestrial rocks behave this way.

A likely explanation is that the surface is extremely porous, providing a directional effect; light can be reflected back in the direction of incidence through the holes by which it entered; light reflected at any other angle is likely to be absorbed. A close-packed fine dust seems excluded, but a porous sintered material might match the characteristics.

A. Dollfus has examined the polarization of light reflected from the lunar surface. The polarization is a maximum when the light is reflected at a considerable angle to the surface, and it vanishes at full moon. Dollfus has compared this behavior with that of various terrestrial rocks, and he finds that granular opaque substances, such as volcanic ash, have a similar behavior. Ordinary rocks and sands behave differently. Presumably the lunar surface does not resemble ordinary rocks and sand, but it may structurally resemble volcanic ash at the granular level.

W. M. Sinton and others have measured lunar surface temperatures from the infrared and microwave emissions from the surface, and they have tried to analyze the surface thermal properties from the rate of heating or cooling of the surface when exposed to or removed from

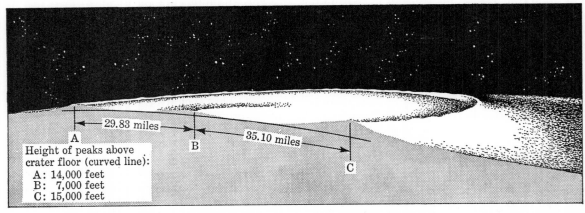

Fig. 4-27. Cross section of crater Theophilus reveals large ratio of breadth to depth typical of lunar craters. This sketch also depicts relative flatness and bleakness of lunar landscape. Except for inner crater walls, which are comparatively steep, all elevations are at low angle.

sunlight. It has been found that the lunar surface is a very good insulator. To account for the rapid fall of temperature of nearly 200°C following the onset of an eclipse of the moon, it appears necessary that a few millimeters of the top of the lunar surface have a much smaller thermal conductivity than the underlying rock. Perhaps this is the depth directly affected by radiation damage by energetic particles in the solar wind.

Another effect possibly induced by such energetic particles is the luminescence of the lunar surface. It was noticed by F. Link that there seems to be excess light emitted by the lunar surface during eclipses. This luminescence probably results from both ultraviolet and particle bombardment of the surface. But there is not enough data to indicate what material gives rise to this luminescence.

The pictures of the reverse side taken by the Russian rocket do show a puzzle, however. There seem to be far fewer maria on the far side of the moon than on the near side. There seems to be no simple explanation for this. Conceivably, it is a statistical fluctuation; the number of maria is, after all, small.

We can expect to learn much more when the Surveyor series of spacecraft is landed on the moon. These will contain drills designed to extract cores from the surface layers that can be subjected to extensive physical and chemical analyses. This is obviously a very necessary part of the preparations for a manned lunar landing. Our ignorance of the precise nature of the moon is so great that extensive instrumental investigations are needed before men can be risked in that environment.

An ancient record close at hand

All of the foregoing questions bear on a further puzzle—the formation of our own planet, and, in fact, of the whole solar system.

Although the earth sciences have long sought to reconstruct the history of the earth the results have been disappointingly meager. They show that we are constantly in the process of obliterating our past. For the surface of the earth is undergoing constant change both from wind and water erosion, and from the shifting and buckling of the land masses throughout the earth's history.

The oldest rocks so far discovered on earth were formed 3 to 3½ billion years ago, as determined by various clocks associated with the decay of radioactive elements trapped in the rocks. But similar radioactive dating methods show that the meteorites are 4.5 billion years old, and they also show that the earth seems to be part of the same general chemical system as the meteorites. Thus we cannot reconstruct from terrestrial evidence alone the behavior of the earth during its first billion years of history. We lack the means to study this crucial formative period that includes the formation of the earth, its chemical differentiation, the evolution of the atmosphere and the oceans, and the formation of the first continents. The record of these events has long since been erased.

Since life could not have developed on earth without the changes that erased the early record, we are singularly fortunate to have been provided with a carbon copy of that record close at hand and in a good state of preservation. Because the moon accompanies the earth in its orbit around the sun, we infer that it has shared the same external environment with the earth in the past. In particular, the mean surface temperature will have been about the same, and the moon has probably been subjected to essentially the same rate of bombardment as the earth by meteors and other chunks of space debris, both small and large. The moon appears to be pretty much a dead world, and hence most of the record written on its surface refers to a period of time for which the terrestrial record has been totally lost. By reconstructing the formation of the moon, we can learn a good deal about how the earth was formed. An intelligent race developing on an earthlike planet but without a lunar companion would find it immensely more difficult to investigate many of the details of its distant past.

Further reading

A handy reference book on the subject is *Structure of the Moon's Surface* by Fielder (Academic Press, 1961, $7.50). The first part contains an up-to-date discussion of what is known about the moon. The second part discusses the interpretation of surface features, but the reader should be warned that the author's own ideas are given a great deal of prominence. Also see MacDonald's article "Interior of the Moon" in *Science* **133**, 1045 (1961), which contains his calculations on the thermal and stress history of the moon. A fundamental examination of crater formation from the impact point of view may be found in *The Face of the Moon*, by Baldwin (U. of Chicago Press, 1949, $6).

There are two other excellent sources published by Academic Press (1962). The first, *Physics and Astronomy of the Moon*, ed. by Kopal, is the most advanced and exhaustive set of references available covering current investigations of the moon. The other, of special interest for the large number of Russian contributions which it contains, is *The Moon*, ed. by Kopal and Mikhailov. It contains the proceedings of the 14th Symposium of the International Astronomical Union, Leningrad, Dec. 1960.

Information on the U.S. plans for lunar exploration can be found in the *Hearings Before the Committee on Aeronautical and Space Sciences, U.S. Senate, 87th Congress* (U.S. Government Printing Office, $1.50). And the reader who is intrigued by the broader problem of the origin and history of the solar system, and the part which the moon plays in it, should see *The Planets: Their Origin and Development* by Urey (Yale U. Press, 1952, $5).

NEUTRINO ASTRONOMY

by Hong-Yee Chiu *

IN BRIEF: *The neutrino has been counted among the elementary particles of nuclear physics ever since 1931. However, since the neutrino has zero charge, zero mass, and only a very slight interaction with matter it was regarded as something of a curiosity. Now it is recognized that neutrinos can affect the evolution of stars. For stars whose interior temperature exceeds about 600 million degrees a new neutrino production process is important: the annihilation of electron-antielectron pairs to produce neutrino-antineutrino pairs. At 6 billion degrees the rate of energy loss through neutrino emission is about 10^{20} ergs/cm³/sec, sufficient to deplete the entire energy content of the star in little over a day. Such supernovas put out more than 10^{14} times as much energy in the form of neutrinos as our sun does in the form of light and heat. Equipment for observational neutrino astronomy is under design.—D.C.*

■ The neutrino is the most elusive of the particles in nature's menagerie. It has no charge, no mass, and so slight an interaction with matter that, once emitted from an atomic nucleus, it can roam the universe without absorption. For that very reason the neutrino plays an important part in astronomical processes. Born in the nuclear fires that provide the energy of all stars, moving with the velocity of light, the neutrino can easily pass through the entire mass of a star. Thus it provides a uniquely effective method for radiating away the energy of the hotter stars.

If our eyes were as sensitive to neutrinos as they are to light, the night sky would look very different. As Fig. 4-28 portrays, most stars would seem dimmer and smaller than they do at present. But some, the hotter stars, would be much brighter than they seem by light. And every hundred years or so, some star would, for a minute or two, flare up to a brilliance exceeding that of ten thousand galaxies—a supernova seen by its neutrinos is even more spectacular than by light.

* Hong-Yee Chiu is associated with NASA's Goddard Institute for Space Studies, and is Adjunct Assistant Professor of Physics at Columbia University in New York.

In fact we can't see neutrinos, but in recent years ingenious experimenters have learned how to detect them. Observational neutrino astronomy can now be considered. (That statement often causes smiles among those who know how elusive the neutrino is. But if the neutrino is a joke, it is at least a joke of cosmological importance.)

The little neutral one

To understand neutrino astronomy, we must first understand the neutrino. Its existence was first postulated in 1931 by Wolfgang Pauli, fresh from success in adding his Exclusion Principle to the axioms of quantum theory. Pauli was wrestling with a problem in nuclear physics that had brought into question the law of the conservation of energy. The phenomenon involved was beta decay, the emission of electrons by an atomic nucleus. Beta decay is unique among the modes of decay of a radioactive nucleus. It is the only one in which the emitted particles can have any of a range of energies. Since the decay results from transitions between two states of very definite energy we would expect all the beta particles to have the same energy—a sharp line spectrum. In fact we observe a characteristically broad spectrum lying entirely below that expected line (see Fig. 4-29).

If the conservation of energy is being violated, the degree of violation is not even the same for each nucleus that emits a beta particle. That is, in individual decay cases, sometimes the violation is strong and sometimes the violation is weak. It would seem that nature is not consistent and cannot make up its mind about the conservation of energy.

Pauli's solution was to hypothesize the existence of another particle, emitted along with the electron. The new particle had to be neutral in order to conserve charge, and it had to have a very small mass (as compared with the mass of the electron) and very slight interaction with matter to explain the fact that it has not been observed. It was Enrico Fermi who christened this particle the neutrino, meaning the "little neutral one." The name was soon adopted all over the world.

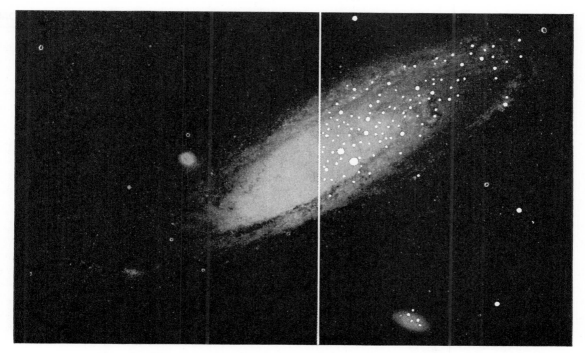

Fig. 4-28. For most stars, the amount of energy emitted in the form of neutrinos is only a few percent of that emitted in the form of light. But for those stars whose interior temperatures are above 600-million degrees, neutrino emission is the dominant mode of energy loss. These considerations guided the preparation of the right-hand half of this illustration, The Great Nebula in Andromeda. *(Courtesy California Institute of Technology)*

A more complete theory

Since Pauli's time our picture of the neutrino has become more and more precise but also more complex. On the one hand we can fix the physical properties of the neutrino more precisely: it has no mass (to within 10^{-3} electron masses), its spin quantum number is $\frac{1}{2}$, it carries no electric charge (to within 10^{-20} times the charge on an electron).

On the other hand we now recognize that there are four kinds of neutrinos. First of all there is an antineutrino; modern physical theory demands that there be an antiparticle corresponding to each particle, and the neutrino is no exception. These theories also tell us that if the electron is considered as a particle, then the neutrino which is emitted in beta decay must be an antiparticle. Thus Pauli's brain child is actually an antineutrino. We reserve the name neutrino for the one emitted in decays where positive electrons (positrons) are also emitted.

pronton → neutron + positron + neutrino

The other new kind of neutrino is the one produced in connection with the decay of pi mesons into mu mesons

pi → mu + neutrino

That these neutrinos are different from those emitted in beta decay has been demonstrated in an experiment completed in mid 1962 by Leon Lederman, Melvin Schwartz, and Jack Steinberger at Brookhaven National Laboratory. And of course these new neutrinos have their antimatter equivalents, making four types of neutrinos in all.

But these more esoteric considerations can divert us from answering some more basic questions about the neutrino.

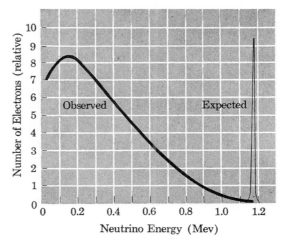

Fig. 4-29. Typical spectrum of electrons emitted in beta decay (this one is of bismuth-210) is observed to be broad. But what is expected is a narrow line spectrum at the energy corresponding to the energy difference between the two nuclei involved in the transition. This evidence first led Pauli to hypothesize that antineutrinos are carrying off some energy.

A common concern is to the effect that, if the neutrino has no mass how can it be said to exist at all. At our level of experience mass and existence are almost equivalent. But light waves have no mass. (Or at least no rest mass. By Einstein's principle of equivalency of mass and energy, photons and neutrinos both have an equivalent mass given by E/c^2.) So real things with zero mass are not unknown. Light seems very "real"—our eyes can "see" photons. But this is only a matter of the strength of the interaction between the particle and matter, and the way they interact. We should not expect nature to make all interactions of comparable strength any more than they should all be of the same type. So the zero mass and slight interaction of the neutrino are to be accepted. It is not for us to ask why.

Rather we can look at the pieces of the puzzle in the hopes of someday seeing a large whole among all the particles and forces seen in nature. Vaguely one senses certain hints of the patterns present here, but only vaguely.

In the absence of a universal, complete theory for all particles and forces the neutrino remains an ingredient in quantum theory. Its formal mathematical description requires the use of matrices rather than ordinary numbers or algebraic quantities. Though I use these mathematical tools in performing calculations I'm always conscious that they are just modes of description; they may reveal more about our way of looking at things than about the neutrino itself.

What is real is the result of experiments. Let's look at how the neutrino can be detected.

Cowan and Reines detect the neutrino

Given the very weak interaction between neutrinos and matter it is not surprising that no neutrinos have ever been seen in all the cloud chambers ever used to investigate processes in which neutrinos play a role. What *is* surprising is that with a sufficiently strong neutrino source, and with sufficient experimental ingenuity and sophistication, it proved possible to detect the shy and diffident (the phrase is the *New Yorker's*) neutrino.

The neutrino, or rather the antineutrino, was first detected experimentally in 1953 by two physicists Clyde L. Cowan and Fredrick Reines, then at Los Alamos. As a source of antineutrinos they used the biggest nuclear reactor they could find—one of the enormous production reactors at the AEC's Savannah River plant. The major ingredient in their detector was water, 1000 lb of it, to provide a target of hydrogen nuclei. Those protons are needed because the principal process by which antineu-trinos interact with matter is through their capture by protons

$$p + \bar{\nu} \rightarrow n + e^+$$

proton + antineutrino → neutron + positron

This is the inverse of the beta-decay process in which they are formed

$$n \rightarrow p + e^- + \bar{\nu}$$

neutron → proton + electron + antineutrino

Cowan and Reines doped the water with cadmium to capture the neutrons that resulted from the antineutrino capture process, knowing that when a neutron is absorbed by cadmium gamma rays are emitted. Two more gamma rays are emitted when the positron meets an electron in the water and they undergo mutual annihilation. The two sets of gamma rays are emitted within a very short time, of the order of several microseconds.

Cowan and Reines used electronic equipment such that an antineutrino event was recorded only when two sets of gamma rays of about the right energy were detected within several microseconds. This let them discriminate against the background of cosmic days, radioactivity inside the detector, and other sources of spurious signals. But the number of neutrinos detected was very few—although 10^{17} neutrinos passed through their detector outside the reactor shield wall every second, the observed rate of antineutrino-induced reactions was only 3 per hour.

Slow as this rate was, the evidence was convincing that the antineutrino had been detected. The experiment has since been repeated many times with improved equipment.

The neutrinos from the reactor are expected to be antineutrinos. The reason for this is that the products of fission are neutron-rich; nuclear stability is achieved as neutrons are converted into protons with the emission of an electron and an antineutrino. To detect them, Cowan and Reines' method is most suitable. To detect neutrinos proper, Raymond Davis of Brookhaven National Laboratory developed a method originally suggested by Bruno Pontecorvo. Their method depended on the fact that chlorine-37 nuclei are transformed into argon-37 nuclei by the absorption of a neutrino.

$$\nu + Cl^{37} \rightarrow A^{37} + e^-$$

within the nucleus

neutrino + neutron → proton + electron

A^{37} is beta radioactive with a half life of about one month. Measuring the amount of A^{37} thus produced in carbon tetrachloride exposed to neutrinos enables one to deduce the number of neutrinos that traversed through it. The amount of A^{37} produced even in a tank car full of carbon tetrachloride is very small, amounting to only a few nuclei. To extract those few from several thousand gallons of carbon tetrachloride is an incredible job. Davis achieved this separation by a clever method—using helium to flush out the argon produced and taking advantage of the great sensitivity of counting methods for measuring the radioactive A^{37}.

His experiment was originally designed to prove that antineutrinos and neutrinos are different particles by *not* observing any A^{37} in carbon tetrachloride exposed to the antineutrinos from a reactor. This negative result was achieved in 1956.

Although Davis cannot detect the antineutrinos from a reactor, his method can be very powerful in detecting the neutrinos that come from the sun. It can be a first tool for studying neutrino astronomy. But the Cowan-Reines method will have an important role, too, for antineutrinos are also emitted from stars. The techniques will supplement one another in observational neutrino astronomy.

The tools for neutrino astronomy are, in principle, at hand (see Fig. 4-30). We'll need detectors that are roughly 100 times more sensitive (and hence 100 times bigger) than those used by Cowan-Reines and Davis in the past. But these look feasible, if expensive. For at least one experiment—looking for antineutrinos from supernovas—an instrument developed by Reines, T. L. Jenkins, and the group at Case

Institute may possibly be adequate. Detecting stellar neutrinos is a formidable problem, but let us be optimistic and assume it can be done.

If the age of neutrino astronomy is at hand, what is it that we can hope to see? The answer lies in what goes on in the stars, especially the varied nuclear processes, for they produce the neutrinos we hope to observe.

Stars—gigantic nuclear furnaces

It is by now quite well established that nuclear fusion reactions are the principal source of stellar energy. No other source could provide the amount of power stars radiate. Gravitational energy is inadequate by a factor of hundreds, despite the great mass of stars. Chemical energy is inadequate by a factor of millions. Besides, the temperatures are too high to be the product of ordinary combustion, and hydrogen, the principal ingredient of most stars, cannot burn chemically by itself.

But the stars can burn hydrogen in a process of nuclear fusion. Just as two atoms of hydrogen can burn and combine with one atom of oxygen to form one molecule of water with the release of energy, so protons can combine to form the nuclei of heavier elements. Except in this case a fraction of the protons must change into neutrons, a process that, as we saw above, is accompanied by the emission of a positron and a neutrino.

I won't go into detail about the nuclear physics of hydrogen burning, which was done a long time ago by Hans Bethe. Rather I've set

Fig. 4-30. Astronomy in a mine! To reduce background from cosmic rays, Brookhaven solar neutrino experiment is installed 2300 ft below ground. Neutrinos from sun should transmute a few of the chlorine nuclei in twin 500-gal tanks of perchloroethylene at left. Radioactive argon-37 that results will be swept out with helium, using gear in center. (Courtesy Chemical Div., Pittsburgh Plate Glass Co.)

down in Fig. 4-31 the two principal hydrogen-burning nuclear-reaction chains. The first leg of the chain produces helium, whose very name reminds us that it was first discovered in the course of spectroscopic observations of a star, our own sun, Helios to the Greeks. When the helium becomes abundant additional nuclear combustion reactions are possible, producing the isotopes beryllium-7 and lithium-7.

HOW A STAR GETS ITS ENERGY

First hydrogen is burned ...

$$H^1 + H^1 \rightarrow H^2 + e^+ + \nu$$
$$H^2 + H^1 \rightarrow He^3 + \gamma$$
$$He^3 + He^3 \rightarrow He^4 + 2H^1$$

... later, when He is abundant ...

$$He^3 + He^4 \rightarrow Be^7 + \gamma$$
$$Be^7 + e^- \rightarrow Li^7 + \nu$$
$$Li^7 + H^1 \rightarrow 2\ He^4$$

Also carbon can be catalyst ...

$$H^1 + C^{12} \rightarrow N^{13} + \gamma$$
$$N^{13} \rightarrow C^{13} + e^+ + \nu$$
$$C^{13} + H^1 \rightarrow N^{14} + \gamma$$
$$N^{14} + H^1 \rightarrow O^{15} + \gamma$$
$$O^{15} \rightarrow N^{15} + e^+ + \nu$$
$$N^{15} + H^1 \rightarrow C^{12} + He^4$$
$$(\rightarrow O^{16} + \gamma)$$

KEY: ν = neutrino; e^+ = positron, that is a positive electron; γ = gamma ray; other nuclides as marked: oxygen-15 = O^{15}

Fig. 4-31. The reactions by which stars burn hydrogen nuclei (protons) thereby liberating energy and synthesizing heavier elements are tabulated here. Because nuclei require neutrons as well as protons to be stable, reaction chains are marked occasionally by a positron plus neutrino.

There's another cycle that is important in stars more massive than our sun; it's the carbon-nitrogen cycle shown in the lower half of Fig. 4-31. Here the carbon-12 nucleus acts as a catalyst in a cycle whose net effect is the conversion of four protons into one helium-4 nucleus.

The important point for our present purposes is that in either chain neutrinos are emitted. In the proton-proton chain about 3% of the energy produced is in the form of neutrinos; in the carbon cycle it is 5–7%. And once emitted these neutrinos sail with the velocity of light clear through the star in which they were formed, bearing evidence of what was going on deep inside. The other nuclear particles involved here, penetrating as they are, do not get very far within the dense star and contribute only slowly and indirectly to the energy that is radiated away at the relatively cool surface of the star.

Thus the detection of neutrinos from a star (our own sun would be a logical place to start) would be the first direct verification that the sun's furnace is nuclear. An experiment to do this is in the planning stage at Brookhaven. Beyond that, if we can find a way to tell the energy of the neutrino as well as its presence, we will be able to tell the relative contribution of various nuclear processes.

Figure 4-32 shows what we can expect; it's the neutrino spectrum from the sun, based on what we know of its mass and temperature distribution.

But still more exciting opportunities exist for neutrino astronomy—as a star grows hotter a new mechanism for the production of neutrinos comes into play. And, above 600 million degrees, this mechanism, I believe, rapidly becomes the principal mode of energy loss from the stars. Neutrinos dominate the evolution of

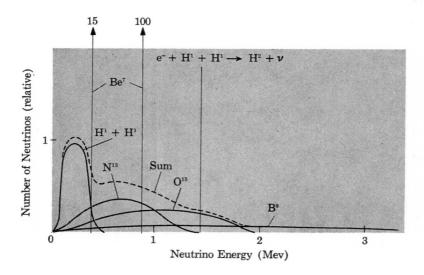

Fig. 4-32. Neutrino spectrum expected from our sun is a combination of broad humps and sharp lines. Most remarkable is the presence of intense lines resulting from the capture of free electrons by beryllium-7 nuclei. Hump at low energies is from a reaction in which two protons are transformed into a deuteron plus a positron and a neutrino. Other humps are positron-emitting decays (see table above). Remaining line is from a three-body interaction of electron and two protons. (after Hubert Reeves, NASA)

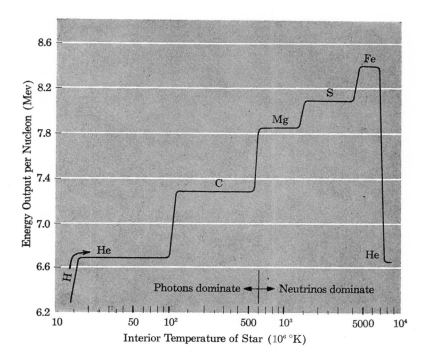

Fig. 4-33. Full range of nucleosynthesis in stars is shown in this staircase curve. Horizontal treads are stages during which gravitational forces contract the star and raise its interior temperature. Vertical portions represent periods during which the element whose symbol rests on preceding tread is consumed to form heavier nuclei. Contraction phases take 10^2–10^4 years, depending on mass and density of the star. Vertical steps take from 10^7–10^{10} years (for H burning to He) to 1–100 years (for burning Mg to S). Whole process is thought to end catastrophically in supernova as Fe is broken into He by high-energy gamma rays. (Courtesy Hubert Reeves, NASA)

a star from that point until its final burst of glory as a supernova (see Fig. 4-33).

The possible astrophysical implications of neutrino emission from stars had first been appreciated back in 1941 by George Gamow and Mario Schönberg, who considered the effects of neutrinos in beta decay and electron capture on stellar evolution. However, as subsequent analysis showed, those processes were not powerful enough as sources of neutrinos.

The new neutrino-production process is more than powerful enough.

A new neutrino process

The new mechanism that radically alters our view of how a star becomes a supernova is a process whereby neutrinos can be produced without reactions between nuclei, in the annihilation of electrons and their antiparticles, positrons:

electron + positron → neutrino + antineutrino

As recently as 1957 this process was unknown, electrons and positrons were thought to annihilate each other only through the emission of gamma rays

electron + positron → two gamma rays

But the same researches that led T. D. Lee and C. N. Yang to overthrow the concept of parity conservation and gain a much-deserved Nobel prize also inspired Richard Feynmann and Murray Gell-Mann of CalTech to a new unified theory of weakly interacting particles. And then Pontecorvo pointed out that this more complete theory could suggest new neutrino-emission mechanisms, some of which might be of significance in advanced stages of stellar

evolution. Their fundamental work in turn inspired Philip Morrison of Cornell and myself to calculate the probability of neutrino emission in the electron-positron annihilation. The result, which was startling to us, was that annihilation into neutrinos was only 10^{20} times less likely than annihilation to gammas.

For anybody but a nuclear astrophysicist a factor of 10^{20} working against a process would be more than convincing reason to ignore it. But there are lots of big numbers in the physics of stars. It turns out that there are so many electron-positron pairs in hot stars and it's so much easier for neutrinos than gamma rays to escape the star that the neutrino process dominates all other modes of energy loss above 600 million degrees.

But, to show how completely neutrinos can dominate the astrophysical evolution of a star, consider what happens when burning and stellar contraction have carried the star's temperature up another factor of ten—to 6 billion degrees. At this temperature electron-positron pairs are produced in such abundance that their density is close to 10^{30} pairs/cm^3, corresponding to a specific weight of 1 kg/cm^3 or 30 tons/ft^3. If this seems unbelievable remember that the density of matter in such stars is 10^4 kg/cm^3 and even the gamma rays are so dense that their equivalent specific weight is 30 tons/ft^3. Stellar conditions are like nothing on earth.

Most of the time the electron pairs annihilate and produce gamma-ray photons again, though photons of lower energy. But though neutrino-producing annihilations are much less probable, the pair density is so high that the rate of energy loss is 10^{20} ergs/cm^3/sec. That is, in one second neutrino-antineutrino pairs remove from each cubic centimeter of an incipient supernova an amount of energy equivalent to 1 kiloton of TNT.

Now, at the temperatures we're discussing the total energy density of the star is around 10^{25} ergs/cm³. This means the star can lose all its energy through neutrino emission in about 10^5 seconds, a little more than a day.

This might be a good point for me to con-

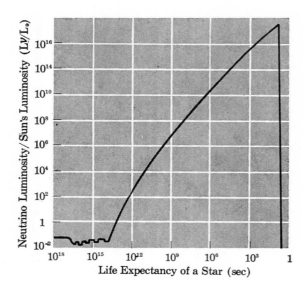

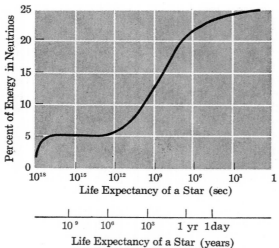

Fig. 4-34. Two measures of the neutrino's theoretical importance to stellar processes are shown here. Upper curve shows energy output in neutrinos of a heavy star relative to the total energy output of our sun. While the ratio is low in the early history of the star it reaches 10^{14} when the star is in an incipient supernova.

Lower curve is essentially the integral of the upper and shows that by the time a star becomes a supernova, ¼ of its total energy will have shown up in the form of neutrinos. Of course, these curves are based on theoretical calculations and presume the correctness of the new neutrino production process.

fess the conjectural nature of these theories. Theoretical physicists are as famous for their hindsight as for their forethought; hindsight may yet be needed in this field. Since the new theory depends critically on the validity of the new mechanism for producing neutrino-antineutrino pairs, Reines also has a project to determine experimentally the probability of that reaction.

To supply the energy radiated away so freely (see Fig. 4-34) the nuclear reactions have to proceed more rapidly and the star has to contract more rapidly. In the outer layers the temperature is still not high enough for neutrinos to leak away the energy produced, so they are heated very rapidly in the very rapid contraction process. Very soon all the nuclear fuel in the entire star is ignited. This causes an explosion, just like a hydrogen bomb, but on a fantastically large scale.

As part of the explosion a shock wave is produced in the central core of the star. This shock wave accelerates as it moves to the outer part of the star. Stirling Colgate of the Livermore laboratory has investigated this shock process and concluded that the wave can impart energies equivalent to acceleration through potentials of 10–20 billion volts. He believes that this mechanism, plus subsequent accelerations in collisions with interstellar magnetic fields, accounts for cosmic rays.

When the shock wave collides with the surface of the star, all members of the zoo of elementary particles can be produced. Most of these elementary particles are not stable and soon decay into protons or electrons. In this decay process, neutrinos of gigantic energy—ranging up to 10 or 20 billion volts—can be produced. All together, 10^{48} neutrinos of high energy may be produced in this shell.

These very-high-energy neutrinos can be detected from supernovas anywhere in this galaxy even at the present stage of detector technology. Reines has a project at the Case Institute of Technology to study the detection of such neutrinos.

The rate of occurrence of supernovas is around once per 100 to 300 years. The last one was seen in 1700. Therefore we expect, psychologically if not mathematically, to see one any time now. Personally I only hope the supernova holds off until after Reines' experimental apparatus is completed so that he can tell us whether it contains neutrinos.

Neutrino cosmology

If neutrinos are being produced in such abundance by stars and especially supernovas, where are they going? We know that very few are absorbed, the computed mean free path of neutrinos is about 10^{15} universes. Once produced, neutrinos will roam the universe practically forever. The red shift, which causes light from distant galaxies to be shifted toward the longer wavelengths, operates for neutrinos, too. Thus their energy is decreased and their quantum-mechanical wavelength made longer. Space is slowly filling with neutrinos.

Pontecorvo and Smordinsky have a theory that the universe began with neutrinos. If that were true we might say from neutrino we come, to neutrino we shall return. However we just don't know. We have arrived at the very frontier of astrophysics.

Further reading

A good general account of the neutrino is in an article of the same name by P. Morrison, *Scientific American*, Jan. '56, p. 58. Another article on neutrino astronomy is understood to be slated for publication by the same author in the same magazine. The possible role of neutrinos in stellar processes was first broached by Gamow and Schönberg, *Phys. Rev.* **59,** 539 (1941). Hong-Yee Chiu's own researches in this field are set forth in form more suited to the specialist but still accessible to the willing non-specialist in "Neutrino Emission Processes, Stellar Evolution, and Supernovae," *Annals of Physics* **15,** 1 (1961). For background on the problems of astrophysics try F. Hoyle's *Frontiers of Astronomy* (Harper & Bros., 1955, $5), also in paperback (New American Library, MD200, 1957, 50¢). Tougher but rewarding is M. Schwarzschild's *Stellar Structure and the Evolution of Stars* (Princeton, 1958, $6). The connections between nuclear physics and astrophysics are nicely laid out in "Synthesis of the Elements in Stars" by Burbidge et al., *Revs. Mod. Phys.*, **29,** 547 (1957). The experimental problems of neutrino detection are discussed by F. Reines in "Neutrino Interactions," *Annual Reviews of Nuclear Science* (Annual Reviews, Inc., 1960, $7); it is most valuable for its good bibliography.

Two more recent articles in *Physical Review Letters* (Vol. **12,** no. 11, pp. 300 and 302, 1964) by John N. Bahcall and Raymond Davis, Jr., further explore the feasibility of detecting solar neutrinos. A whole section in the International Cosmic Rays Conference held in Jaipur, India, December, 1963, was devoted to the discussion of neutrino astronomy. The *Proceedings* (Vol. **6** is on neutrino astronomy) are now available from the Secretary, International Conference, Tata Institute of Fundamental Research, Colaba, Bombay 5, India (the price is $5.00 or RS 20/). A recent article by Hong-Yee Chiu in *Annals of Physics* (Vol. **26,** no. 3, p. 364, 1964) discusses in more detail the collapse phase and the observation of remnants of supernovae.

MAN-MADE RADIATION BELTS

by Wilmot N. Hess *

IN BRIEF: *U.S. and Soviet high-altitude nuclear tests during the last half of 1962 injected copious numbers of fission-produced electrons into the earth's magnetic field. Here many still remain—with energies ranging up to several Mev, and at fluxes at least one or two orders of magnitude greater than the natural electron flux— to form a continuous, uniformly thick, persistent, and potentially quite troublesome belt of radiation all around the earth.*

Although this man-made belt has helped clarify many features of the natural Van Allen belts, it also has obscured—perhaps for many years—other aspects of the natural radiation environment. Moreover, it has increased cost and difficulty of providing long-lived, reliable power supplies for satellites and spacecraft. And it imposes new restraints on man in space. —S.T.

* Wilmot N. Hess is Chief of the Theoretical Division at NASA's Goddard Space Flight Center, Greenbelt, Maryland.

■ On July 9, 1962, at 0900 hours 09 seconds universal time, the U.S. carried out a nuclear explosion of 1.4-megaton yield—code-named Starfish—400 km above Johnston Island in the central Pacific. Within a few seconds brilliant aurorae were seen in Samoa and New Zealand, some 3000 miles to the south; in Alaska, a comparable distance to the north, observations indicated increased ionization in the lower or D-region of the ionosphere. Nearly a third of the way around the world in Maryland, at the same instant, radio receivers monitoring very-low-frequency transmissions also detected strongly enhanced ionization. Indeed, vlf signals reaching the Maryland receiver from a transmitter at Jim Creek, Washington, to take one instance, indicated that over the 3000-mile propagation path the ionosphere had in effect dropped from its normal night-time altitude of 90 km to 76 km—a drop of 15%— within 10 seconds after the burst. And everywhere, the earth's magnetic field trembled violently.

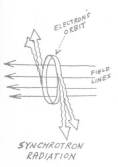

ELECTRONS ORBIT

FIELD LINES

SYNCHROTRON RADIATION

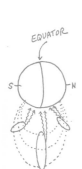

EQUATOR

S   N

Such representative effects of the blast, though spectacular, were relatively short-lived. In minutes to several hours, at most, conditions in the ionosphere apparently returned to normal. But as the hours passed into days, weeks, and months, less spectacular evidence of the blast's effects continued to accumulate to show that the effects—both useful and troublesome—will be with us for a long time to come.

Radio noise and silent satellites

Some 6 minutes after the Starfish burst, for instance, and roughly 6000 miles east of it, a new 22-acre radio antenna at Jicamarca, Peru, recorded an abrupt 9-fold jump in radio noise (Fig. 4-35), followed about 25 minutes later by a second, more modest noise peak, still 3 times more powerful than the pre-explosion background. After an hour or so and for the subsequent several hours the noise remained about 2½ times above normal background. Thereafter the excess noise decreased with agonizing slowness.

The intensity of the radio noise received in Peru has been followed for two years. One year

after Starfish, 15% of the original excess noise was left; two years afterwards, about 8% was still left. This noise should decrease slowly for the next year or so and then, near solar maximum in 1968, will probably pretty much disappear.

From the fact that this radio noise is strongly polarized there is little doubt that it is the kind of electromagnetic radiation, mostly less than 100 Mc/sec in frequency, that's called synchrotron radiation. Synchrotron emission results when charged particles such as electrons move in a circle around magnetic-field lines as dictated by classical electromagnetic theory (as shown in the margin). But emission only occurs, essentially, along the plane that contains the orbit of the electron. This taut geometry means that synchrotron radiation most easily reaches the earth's surface near the magnetic equator where magnetic-field lines are nearly horizontal (see marginal sketch) because here the orbital planes, being perpendicular to the field lines, intersect the earth's surface. But even at middle to higher magnetic latitudes—where magnetic-field lines become more nearly

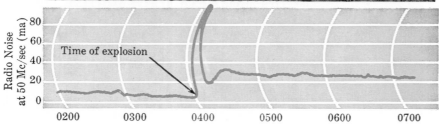

Radio Noise at 50 Mc/sec (ma)

80
60
40
20
0

Time of explosion

0200   0300   0400   0500   0600   0700

Eastern Standard Time—July 9, 1962

Fig. 4-35. Dipole antenna of U.S. National Bureau of Standards in Peru detected 9-fold jump in radio noise just 6 minutes after Starfish H-burst over Johnston Island, 6000 miles to west. Peak heralds passage over antenna of energetic electrons created by nuclear fission. These orbit around field lines in the earth's magnetic field, emitting characteristically polarized radio noise known as synchrotron radiation. More modest peak at 0430 denotes second passage of electrons over antenna after completing one trip around the earth. Thereafter, noise levels off to steady plateau about 2½ times pre-burst background as electrons spread in longitude, because they differ in energy and speed, to form continuous belt of radiation all around the earth. Observers believe excess synchrotron noise, which complicates the study of weak natural signals, will all but disappear by 1968.

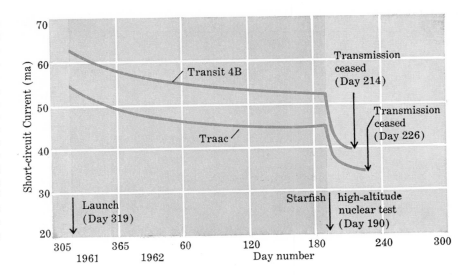

Fig. 4-36. Study by Johns Hopkins' Applied Physics Laboratory of output of solar cells on two satellites shows striking changes after Starfish high-altitude nuclear burst. Transit's solar cells showed ⅓ more deterioration in 24 days they survived after Starfish than in the 236 days since launch prior to the explosion. Story was pretty much the same for Traac and for joint U.S.-U.K. satellite Ariel, not shown here, all of which used blue-sensitive p-on-n type cells. (Courtesy Johns Hopkins Applied Physics Laboratory)

perpendicular to the earth's surface as they arch downward towards it—most of the synchrotron radiation still points roughly towards the equator.

After Starfish, as a matter of fact, only radio observatories located within 25° of the equator observed the polarized radio noise characteristic of synchrotron radiation. Furthermore, before Starfish the antenna at Jicamarca had searched its normal background of cosmic radio noise for synchrotron radiation with no success, although the antenna is so sensitive that a telltale polarized component amounting to only 1% of the background could have been detected easily, had it been present.

The synchrotron evidence, though indirect, strongly suggested that Starfish had injected energetic electrons into the earth's magnetic field where, gyrating around field lines, they continue to broadcast their presence.

Another, even more direct set of clues to what had happened on July 9, 1962, came from several earth satellites. Three days after the blast the joint U.S.-United Kingdom satellite Ariel began having transmission difficulties and since then has transmitted only intermittently. On August 2, Transit 4B of Johns Hopkins' Applied Physics Laboratory stopped transmitting. Its solar-power cells showed ⅓ more deterioration in the 24 days it survived after Starfish (Fig. 4-36) than in the 236 days since launch preceding the burst. APL's Traac satellite exhibited similarly rapid deterioration of its power supply (Fig. 4-36) and fell silent about 36 days after Starfish.

The expected had happened—in spades

But not all of the satellites in orbit following Starfish bit the dust, fortunately. The University of Iowa's Injun I—instrumented by Van Allen's group—which had been aloft over a year survived to tell the story of the following months in considerable detail. So did Bell Laboratories' Telstar communication satellite which went into orbit the day after the explosion. The counting instruments on these satellites, as well as those on the ill-fated Ariel and Traac, showed intense new fluxes of energetic particles in space shortly after the explosion, extending out from the earth's surface to as much as 4 to 5 earth-radii at the equator.

The expected had happened. The nuclear burst indeed had injected copious numbers of energetic electrons and relatively few protons into the earth's magnetic field, and here they had become trapped. An artificial radiation belt had been created, a belt analogous in many ways to the natural Van Allen belts, but more intense.

Meaning of the man-made radiation belt

How did it happen? How long will the man-made belt last? What's it good for—bad for? What is it like? What does it mean? All good questions. Let's take the last one first.

The newly trapped electrons already have enhanced our understanding of the earth's own striking and long-lived natural radiation belts, as well as the interaction of these with the solar flux. And we certainly can expect to learn more as time goes by. Conversely, they also have placed unfortunate limits on our ability to comprehend fully these environments as they were in their undisturbed state, at least for some years to come.

But perhaps most directly affected by the man-made radiation belt, ironically, are earth-satellite and space-exploration programs. The operation, lifetime, and design of solar-cell power-generating systems, as evident in Fig. 4-36, and the well-being of man in space, both hinge upon radiation fluxes encountered. Problems of shielding men and equipment become more difficult as radiation goes up. And if the extent of such intense radiation in space near the earth increases considerably, the difficulties attending exploration of these regions by either manned or unmanned satellites may well reach the point of no return.

It increased after Soviet high-altitude nuclear tests 3½ months after Starfish, for example, and it will increase in the event of any large future contributions.

Some unspectacular perspective on Starfish

Before we trace the Starfish electrons and their Soviet counterparts further along the trail of consequences let's get some perspective on events that led to Starfish.

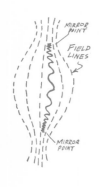

The creation of a band of trapped radiation by Starfish was no surprise, especially not to physicists at the Livermore Radiation Laboratory and elsewhere who in the middle fifties were attempting to tame the thermonuclear reactions of the H-bomb to produce industrial power. One of the major problems in this quest is to contain the intensely hot plasma—the cloud of protons and electrons—created in such reactions. Walls made of the most heat-resistant conventional materials won't do; they would melt. So instead intense magnetic fields are used—shaped into "magnetic bottles"—as shown in the marginal sketch. A physicist at Livermore, Nicholas Christofilos, scaled up such laboratory-sized ideas for a plasma-containing magnetic bottle to earth size and suggested that the earth's magnetic field similarly should be able to contain and trap energetic particles. He further showed that a nuclear explosion could serve as the source of particles to fill such a

terrestrial "bottle." These suggestions led directly to the U.S. high-altitude nuclear experiments of 1958, the Argus tests, planning for which was well advanced before the discovery by Van Allen of the natural radiation belt. In fact, the suggestion that a natural terrestrial belt might exist arose in Argus planning sessions, a speculation later dramatically confirmed by Van Allen's geiger counters aboard the Explorer I and III satellites.

Three small Argus explosions specifically designed to study the injection of particles into the earth's magnetic field were carried out over the South Atlantic in 1958 and each accomplished this modest aim. So by July 9, 1962, artificial radiation belts were no novelty.

Charged particles in a squirrel cage

But the Starfish belt turned out to be more intense and extended in space than the Argus belts—and herein lies its novelty.

The electrons introduced into the earth's magnetic field by the explosion (current estimates of their number range between 10^{25} and 10^{26}) neither simply lie dormant nor do they simply fall out. Being electrically charged particles, they are impelled by the magnetic field to perform an intricate and nearly endless dance. Figure 4-37 shows its basic steps, in somewhat schematic form.

As the electrons spiral clockwise around a field line (protons rotate counterclockwise) about a million times a second, they also move along it towards higher latitudes, where field lines descend towards the earth's surface.

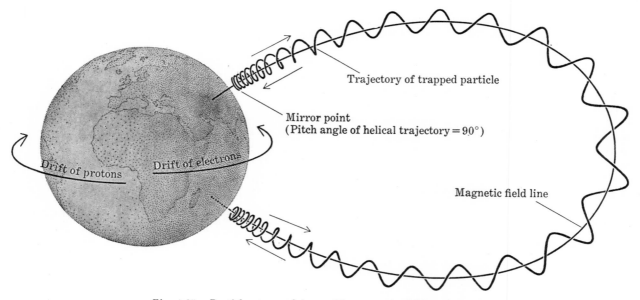

Fig. 4-37. Particles trapped in earth's magnetic field perform complex motion that's resolvable into three components—(1) spiraling around field lines, (2) bouncing back and forth along field lines, and (3) drifting in longitude—as fully explained in text.

Here the earth's field lines also converge and, therefore, the magnetic field grows stronger. A particle, in order to keep constant both its magnetic moment and its total kinetic energy, responds to the increased field by simultaneously performing four tricks: (1) it decreases its orbital radius of gyration; (2) it increases the angle at which its path crosses field lines (its pitch angle), thus flattening or tightening its helical trajectory; (3) it increases its orbital velocity perpendicular to the field line; (4) it decreases its velocity along the field line. Ultimately, when the particle reaches some critical point above the earth's surface where the field strength is appropriately great—some hundreds to thousands of kilometers up, depending on the particle's original direction of motion when first injected into the magnetic field—it can proceed no further along the field line, since all of its kinetic energy is invested in gyration around the field line. Here where its pitch angle is 90°, however, the converging magnetic field supplies a force that causes the particle to reflect back along the field line. Such a reflection point, or mirror point, also exists at the other end of the field line, of course, and the dynamics just described operate there too. As a consequence, most particles at higher altitudes are trapped in the magnetic field and constrained to round trips between mirror points, perhaps once every second, for a very long time to come.

Besides gyrating around a field line and bouncing to and fro along it, particles also drift in longitude around the earth. The reason for this is evident from the sketch in the margin. At the high altitude side of a particle's orbit, the side away from the earth's surface, the magnetic field is weaker than on the low-altitude side; therefore the particle's radius of curvature is larger there and the particle drifts sideways as shown in the sketch. Electrons drift east due to this effect and protons drift west. And particles with different energies, hence different velocities, drift at different rates; thus the time it takes a particle to complete one east-west (or vice versa) circle of the earth depends upon the energy of the particle. It's about an hour for a typical fission electron.

Spiraling electrons → synchrotron noise

The electrons Starfish introduced into the earth's magnetic field distributed themselves in a few seconds along north-south field lines at about the magnetic longitude of Johnston Island, creating the short-lived auroral and ionospheric disturbances in Alaska and New Zealand mentioned earlier. And in 6 minutes, remember, they had drifted 6000 miles eastward in longtitude to create the first burst of synchrotron radio noise at Jicamarca, Peru

(Fig. 4-35). Ten minutes after detonation electrons with the highest energy had drifted eastward almost entirely around the world to reach Wake Island—1600 miles *west* of the burst point—there to create synchrotron noise which reached maximum 25 minutes after the blast, as the maximum population of relatively less energetic electrons passed overhead. Finally, about 31 minutes after the explosion, the drifting electrons again were over the Jicamarca antenna to make the second radio-noise peak. And in a few hours they drifted around the earth several times, dispersing in longitude because of their different drift rates, to create a uniformly thick and persistent blanket of energetic particles all around the earth.

The natural context of Starfish

In order to put the Starfish radiation belt into its proper context let's briefly look at salient aspects of the natural belt. Figure 4-38 shows the distribution and flux of natural protons, divided into two groups—one of protons whose energies are greater than 30 Mev, the other of protons whose energies are lower, lying between 0.1 and 5 Mev. The higher-energy protons are quite penetrating, but their numbers are relatively few, so they are not much of a problem from the standpoint of radiation damage. For that matter, neither are the considerably more abundant lower-energy protons, because they are so easily absorbed by only modest amounts of shielding.

Not shown in Fig. 4-38 but present in the natural belt in considerable numbers are protons whose energies are about 10 Mev. They are both abundant enough and penetrating enough to damage too thinly shielded solar cells. This potential problem is largely eliminated, however, by general use of glass cover plates at least $\frac{1}{32}$ in. thick on solar cells.

The proton progeny created by Starfish is negligible compared with the natural proton population, so we'll say no more about it here. But, since Starfish's electron population is both considerably larger and higher in energy than the natural one, a fairly careful look now at the natural electron-flux maps (Fig. 4-39) will be useful for comparisons later. This figure also divides the particles into two groups—a relatively low-energy population of electrons whose energies exceed 40 kev, and a more energetic group whose energies exceed 1.6 Mev. The characteristics of the lower-energy electron population are not yet too well known, especially towards the inside of the radiation zone, just a few thousand km above the earth. The map, in fact, might be wrong by a factor of 5 or more in some places. And both populations of natural electrons fluctuate considerably over short pe-

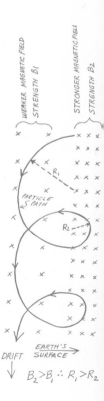

WEAKER MAGNETIC FIELD STRENGTH B_1

STRONGER MAGNETIC FIELD STRENGTH B_2

R_1

PARTICLE'S PATH

R_2

EARTH'S SURFACE

DRIFT

$B_2 > B_1 \therefore R_1 > R_2$

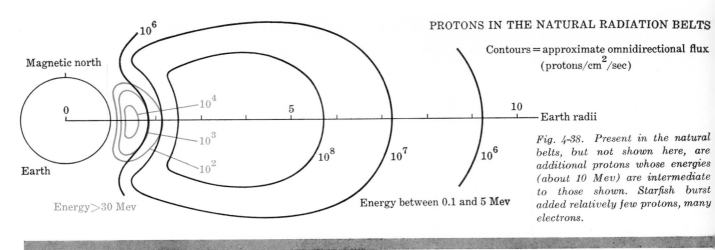

Magnetic north

10^6

10^4

10^3

10^2

Earth

0

5

10 — Earth radii

Contours = approximate omnidirectional flux (protons/cm^2/sec)

10^8

10^7

10^6

Energy>30 Mev

Energy between 0.1 and 5 Mev

Fig. 4-38. Present in the natural belts, but not shown here, are additional protons whose energies (about 10 Mev) are intermediate to those shown. Starfish burst added relatively few protons, many electrons.

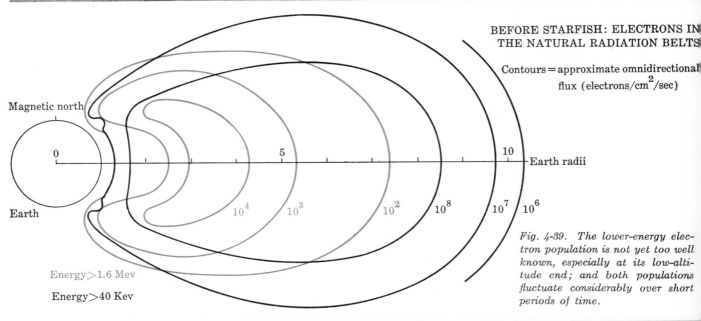

BEFORE STARFISH: ELECTRONS IN THE NATURAL RADIATION BELTS

Magnetic north

0

5

10 — Earth radii

Contours = approximate omnidirectional flux (electrons/cm^2/sec)

Earth

10^4

10^3

10^2

10^8

10^7

10^6

Energy>1.6 Mev

Energy>40 Kev

Fig. 4-39. The lower-energy electron population is not yet too well known, especially at its low-altitude end; and both populations fluctuate considerably over short periods of time.

riods of time, as well as during magnetic storms. The more highly energetic population, electrons above 1.6 Mev, rarely shows a flux more intense than 10^5 electrons/cm^2/sec. And in the natural belt there are few if any electrons whose energy is greater than 5 Mev.

Now let's see the Starfish contours.

Two views of Starfish, within a week

On July 10, the day after Starfish, there were four satellites in orbit that had electron detectors on board which gave useful information on the newly trapped particles: Ariel, Injun, Telstar, and Traac. Of these, Injun had been in orbit a long time and continued to function long after the explosion, so that it provided a very good before-and-after comparison of the radiation belt, but only for altitudes up to around 1000 km. Traac and Ariel detectors also provided a good comparison, as long as they lasted. Telstar, however, was launched the day *after* Starfish, so it could not give a before-and-after

comparison. This is quite unfortunate, because only Telstar goes to altitudes significantly above 1000 km (its apogee is 5630 km) to regions of space unavailable to the other satellites.

Thus Injun's counters mapped the new belt up to 1000 km and produced the first flux-contour picture of the Starfish electrons, and Telstar produced all of the information above 1000 km for the first three months afterward.

The experimental data from Injun and Telstar, organized for a few days after Starfish, are shown in Fig. 4-40. The highest electron flux encountered by either satellite is about 10^9/cm^2/sec, well above the natural flux shown in Fig. 4-39. These post-Starfish fluxes, however, unlike those shown in Fig. 4-39, are for the total population of electrons encountered, including all energies from > about 0.25 Mev up to several Mev. The existing data do not permit a distinction to be made here among electrons of different energy. The important

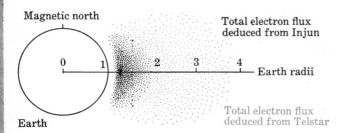

Fig. 4-40. Data from both Injun and Telstar satellites agree that the maximum flux of electrons of all energies >0.25 Mev, shown by most intense stippling, was about $10^9/cm^2/sec$, decreasing to about $10^7/cm^2/sec$ at outer edge of each distribution. Injun's detectors couldn't count lower-energy electrons abundant at higher altitudes as effectively as Telstar's could; thus its distribution closes at lower altitudes.

...AND ITS CLOSEST APPROACH TO THE EARTH

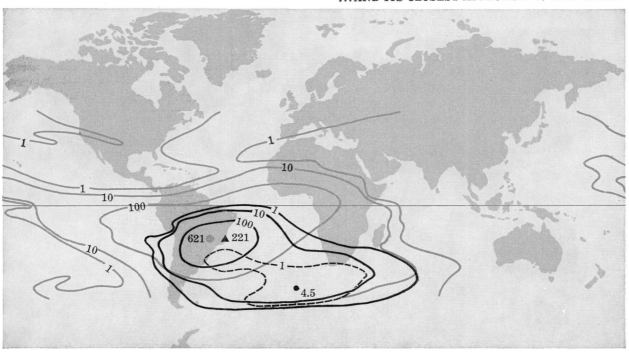

Maximum flux { ● 200 km altitude ------- / ▲ 600 km altitude ——— / ⬤ 1000 km altitude ——— } Contours of electron flux in units of 10^6 electrons/cm^2/sec

Fig. 4-41. Anomaly in earth's magnetic field, centered over the South Atlantic region and neighboring parts of South America and Africa, makes magnetic field lines lie closer to the surface in these regions. Consequently, electrons from Starfish burst—trapped in the magnetic field—also lie closer to the surface, as shown here for electrons that are definitely known to originate directly from Starfish bomb.

16 WEEKS AFTER: STARFISH ELECTRONS AND THE SOVIET TEST OF OCT. 28, 1962

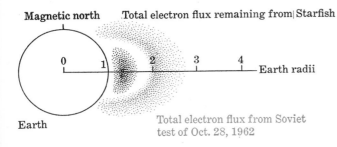

Fig. 4-42. By the time the Soviet test took place the extent of Starfish electrons had shrunk considerably; compare Fig. 4-40, above. But the flux of Starfish electrons remained as intense as it had been—$10^9/cm^2/sec$ at the center to $10^7/cm^2/sec$ at the edge of its distribution. The maximum flux of Soviet electrons was $10^8/cm^2/sec$; it similarly decreases to $10^7/cm^2/sec$ at the outer edge of its distribution. Another Soviet test a few days later neatly filled the gap that remained between flux fields shown here.

thing to note now is that, using Figs. 4-39 and 4-40, only the fluxes of pre- and post-Starfish electrons can be compared, and even these only qualitatively; the energy spectra of natural and injected electrons cannot be directly compared using these figures.

The Injun contours shown on Fig. 4-40 are compressed much closer to the earth than are Telstar contours of equal value. These differences have caused some controversy in the past, but we are now beginning to understand them. To understand the difference in the contours and, as well, to understand why pre- and post-Starfish energy spectra cannot be directly compared, we must understand the nature of the data used to construct Fig. 4-40.

The nature of Injun-Telstar differences

The counting rates of particle detectors aboard the satellites were multiplied by efficiency factors to convert them into electron fluxes. And these efficiency factors, in turn, were calculated on the *assumption* that the energy spectrum of electrons encountered was indeed an equilibrium fission-energy spectrum—as shown in Fig. 4-43—in which *all* of the electrons are assumed to result from the Starfish burst. Data available at the time showed this assumption to be essentially correct at altitudes up to about 1000 km. Thus, Fig. 4-41, which plots post-Starfish fluxes against a geographic base map for various altitudes up to 1000 km, shows all electrons that are *known* to have been

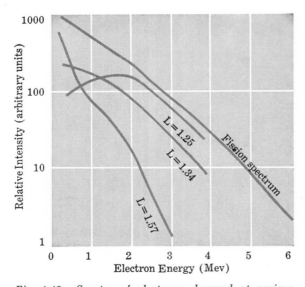

Fig. 4-43. Spectra of electrons observed at various distances from earth's center along equator (L, in earth radii) are much "softer" than pure fission spectrum that would prevail if electrons came directly from fission of H-bomb fragments. (Courtesy H. West, Livermore Radiation Laboratory)

derived directly from fission of Starfish bomb fragments.

But at higher altitudes the assumption of a fission-energy spectrum was an early guess, and we are now quite certain from later satellite data that this guess was wrong. At altitudes above 1000 km there are in fact many more low-energy electrons present than there should be (Fig. 4-43) if *all* the electrons came directly from nuclear fission. Or, expressed another way, the energy spectrum of electrons at altitudes higher than 1000 km is too "soft" to be a pure fission spectrum. What, then, are these higher-altitude, low-energy, but intense electron fluxes?

Most of us now believe they result from Starfish. And I personally believe they are fission electrons. But whether they are fission electrons directly from the burst, with their energy somehow diminished, or electrons from some other source, somehow triggered by the burst, is uncertain and may remain so forever. Indeed, because Telstar's launch date unfortunately followed Starfish, some workers still are not sure whether the low-energy electrons she counted at higher altitudes are from Starfish, or whether they were there—and simply undetected—beforehand.

The Injun-Telstar contour differences are more easily resolved. Because Injun's detectors could not count low-energy electrons at higher altitudes efficiently, Injun contours on Fig. 4-40 close lower. But Telstar's detectors could; therefore Telstar contours go higher.

If you're going to mess up, do it completely

On October 28, 1962, about 16 weeks after Starfish, the Soviet Union conducted the second in its series of high-altitude nuclear tests. Its results were very well documented by the Canadian satellite Alouette, by a Defense Department satellite, 1962 $\beta\kappa$, and by Explorer XV which had been launched just the day before to study the artificial radiation belts. Figure 4-42, which is drawn for the situation as of Oct. 28, shows the distribution and intensity of electrons from the Soviet test in comparison with remaining Starfish electrons, which had been partly depopulated by that time—presumably by slow leakage into the atmosphere past the mirror points of their trajectories.

Electrons at the inner edge of the new Soviet artificial belt had essentially a fission-energy spectrum. But at the outer edge—at higher altitudes—the spectrum was softer, in accord with the similar situation, previously noted, that existed for Starfish electrons. The October 28 electron population decreased with a mean half-life of about one week, agreeing with Telstar's observations of Starfish electrons at comparable altitudes. Then on November 1 a third Soviet explosion produced another artificial radiation belt of more limited extent that fit roughly in the gap on Fig. 4-42 (between the October 28 and Starfish electrons) neatly, so to speak, filling space around the earth completely. No USSR measurements have been reported on any of the artificial radiation belts, but U.S. measurements are continuing. It will be interesting to see what effects large magnetic storms will have, when they come, on the surplus electrons.

How long will the belts last?

Such storms certainly will alter the energy spectrum of the electrons as well as their distribution in space. And the residence lifetimes of the trapped electrons—a matter of considerable interest and speculation—also should be markedly modified. From a purely scientific standpoint the explosions of the past year have provided us with a unique opportunity for learning more than we otherwise could have about the lifetimes of electrons in the radiation belt. Before the explosions only indirect methods existed for estimating lifetimes, and these resulted in widely divergent values. Now we have direct measurements, some of which are shown in Fig. 4-44 for Starfish electrons whose energy $\simeq 0.5$ Mev.

The time spent by an electron trapped in the magnetic field seems to depend strongly on its altitude. Electrons between altitudes of 0.7 and perhaps 2.5 earth-radii at the magnetic equator (and progressively less as the magnetic-field shell at this altitude descends to the earth's surface—see marginal sketch) disappear much more rapidly than those that cavort below this altitude. For example, the mean lifetime of electrons only about 0.3 earth-radii above the surface at the equator is about a year. But at 1.5 earth-radii altitude the mean lifetime is only a few days.

Part of the difficulty in assessing the likely longevity of particles is that during the decay processes the energy spectrum of the electrons changes. Lower-energy electrons are more easily scattered at lower altitudes, where atmospheric density is greater, and are therefore lost first. Because of this the energy spectrum hardens with time until an equilibrium spectrum is developed which has an energy peak at about 2 Mev—pretty penetrating, as far as radiation damage to solar cells and people is concerned.

Power problems solvable—at a price

Electrical power for most space vehicles prior to Starfish has been provided by silicon solar cells. Most such solar cells have been *p*-on-*n* type, in which a layer of positive material overlays a base of negative material. A photon of

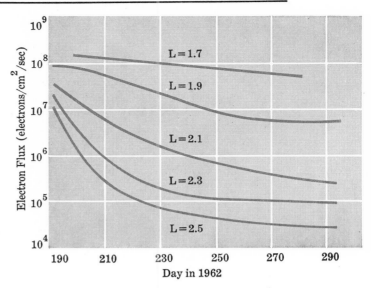

Fig. 4-44. As distance from the earth's center along equator (L, in earth radii) increases, the decay in flux of trapped electrons becomes exponentially more rapid than it is at lower altitudes. L = 1.7 may mark change from atmospheric to magnetic scattering of electrons. (Courtesy W. Brown, Bell Telephone Laboratories)

light striking such a cell creates a hole and a free electron, both of which then migrate either toward or away from the *p-n* junction, creating a potential difference that can be used for power. The average distance that the free electron and hole can travel without recombining is called the diffusion length of the cell; greater diffusion length indicates greater efficiency. Radiation from either electrons or protons introduces imperfections into the silicon's crystal structure which serve as recombination centers for migrating free electrons and holes. Thus, as shown in Fig. 4-45, under electron bombardment diffusion length is effectively shortened,

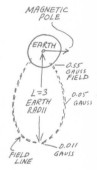

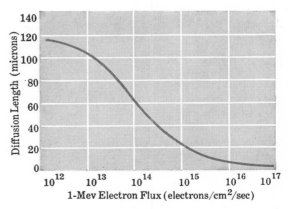

Fig. 4-45. Diffusion length is rough measure of the efficiency of silicon solar cells commonly used for power on satellites. Curve shown is for more radiation-resistant n-on-p solar cells.

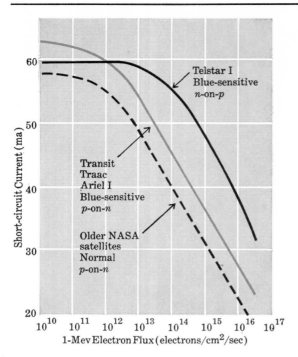

Fig. 4-46. Study by Bell Labs shows how various types of solar cells are damaged by 1-Mev electron irradiation. At electron energies >0.5 Mev, damage depends mostly on flux, not on energy. (Courtesy Bell Telephone Laboratories)

and efficiency of the cell goes down, leading ultimately to failure.

A conventionally designed satellite-power supply will malfunction if the solar-cell output drops to about 80% of its designed value. So from Fig. 4-46, an experimental curve which shows degradation in output of various types of cells under different fluxes of 1-Mev electrons, we see, for instance, that the cells used on Ariel will cease useful life at a flux of about 10^{13} electrons/cm^2/sec. Ariel's orbit took it into the high-flux region (10^9 electrons/cm^2/sec) created by Starfish about 5% of the time, so its solar cells were bombarded by roughly 2×10^{12} electrons/cm^2/day, indicating that its power supply should have lasted about a week before going into undervoltage. And that's just about how long it did last.

The ill-fated satellites—Ariel, Traac, and Transit—were equipped with p-on-n cells. But Telstar had more radiation-resistant n-on-p type solar cells (Fig. 4-46) and so stayed alive much longer. Injun also functioned long after Starfish, because its power supply happened to be so built that it could withstand larger percentage degradation and, therefore, more radiation.

Satellites clearly can be designed to have long

lives in the Starfish belt, or even more intense belts, at a price—by providing large margins of overdesign initially, by using more radiation-resistant n-on-p type cells, and by using thicker glass cover slides. But men cannot be redesigned.

A radiation barrier to man in space?

Within the intense heart of the Starfish electron belt right now, say at about 1000 miles altitude near the equator, and using the maximum effective shielding feasible, an astronaut in orbit for one hour would receive about 24 roentgens of radiation. A lethal dose is about 500 R. This means that manned flight in this region must be quite limited in time, as it will be in the Apollo flight-to-the-moon, for instance, thus clearing this hurdle.

But if more tests are carried out using large high-altitude explosions, trouble could result. It is entirely possible to make an artificial radiation belt much more intense than the Starfish belt, a thousand times more intense. This could make large regions of space a no man's land for a very long time, and it would severely limit unmanned satellites as well. We must avoid such a circumstance, but we should not "throw the baby out with the bath water." There are many extremely valuable geophysical experiments that can be carried out with only small high-altitude nuclear explosions. If such explosions are carried out properly, under international cooperation to insure safety, they should not produce any hazardous conditions and they should produce knowledge.

Further reading

This business of tampering with the cosmos is still new enough—perhaps fortunately in view of the results described in this article—that no comprehensive survey exists, other than the article in this issue. A few general articles have been written about the natural Van Allen radiation belt: by Van Allen himself in *Scientific American*, March 1959; by Hess in *Space Science Reviews*, **1**, No. 2, 1962, and by O'Brien in the same journal, **1**, No. 3, 1962. O'Brien also offers a review, in the May 1963 *Scientific American*.

The artificial belts are treated as exhaustively as they can be in two collections of original papers that cover the Argus experiments and the Starfish explosion, respectively, in the *J. of Geophysical Research*, Aug. 1959 and Feb. 1963.

Space Physics (Wiley, 1964) has a chapter on the natural radiation belt by O'Brien and another on the artificial belt by Hess.

ION ROCKETS

by A. Theodore Forrester and Stanton L. Eilenberg *

IN BRIEF: *A rocket moves by shedding weight— the weight it hurls backward to move forward. The less weight it discards, the more weight (payload) that's left to push around. And the lower the discard rate, the longer it can push with a given quantity of fuel. For the most part, these are the reasons why ion rockets are being developed for long journeys in space. In the ion engine, atomic cesium is ionized by stripping off its loosely bound valence electron. This positively charged ion is then driven out the exhaust with an electrostatic field. The engines don't develop much thrust and they gobble up awesome quantities of electric power, but they can run for a very long time on a small charge of propellant, and are capable of propelling spacecraft to very high velocities. Their eventual usefulness for space missions depends largely on whether they can be made to withstand several years of continuous operation and on the availability of a lightweight electric power supply.—C.J.L.*

■ Sometime in the not-too-distant future a package containing a new kind of rocket engine will be strapped to the nose of a conventional booster and lofted out into space. Once the package has coasted beyond the rim of the earth's atmosphere, the wraps will come off the engine and a blue-white beam of ions will begin to spew out the exhaust. (Color Fig. 34 shows such an experimental engine under test.)

The thrust on the package will be almost immeasurably small—less than that of a model airplane engine. Yet the new engine has importance far beyond that implied by the magnitude of its thrust. It was not designed to blast huge payloads into orbit; it was developed to expand man's arena of discovery beyond the moon and nearby planets—to satisfy his curiosity about the moons of Jupiter, the rings of Saturn, and the edges of the solar system. Envoys to these distant places cannot be driven along on the short-lived blasts of smoke and flame characteristic of chemical rockets. They require a new kind of propulsion system—one that urges the craft along with a gentle but steady thrust perhaps no greater than a few pounds (Color Fig. 35).

Let's take a closer look at the mathematical reasons behind the need for a rocket that

* Both from Electro-Optical Systems, Inc., Pasadena, California, A. Theodore Forrester is manager of the ion physics department and Stanton L. Eilenberg manages the ion engine program.

derives its power from something other than chemical energy. Any rocket is driven forward by expelling some of its mass out the rear. According to Newton's third law (action equals reaction), the magnitude of this propelling force is the same as that driving the propellant. That force is equal to the rate at which momentum is delivered to the expelled masses. This thrust is simply

$$F = \frac{\Delta m}{\Delta t} v_e$$

where v_e is the exhaust velocity and Δm is the mass expelled in the time Δt.

This equation shows clearly that at a given level of thrust, the rate of propellent consumption, $\Delta m/\Delta t$, is inversely proportional to the exhaust velocity. For any given quantity of fuel on board the rocket, the engine with the lowest propellant consumption rate runs for the longest time and consequently produces the highest total impulse ($I_{\text{total}} = Ft$). The performance of rocket engines is usually described in terms of the impulse per unit weight of expelled propellant—the so-called specific impulse

$$I_{sp} = \frac{F}{g}\left(\frac{\Delta t}{\Delta m}\right)$$

where g is the acceleration of gravity at the earth's surface. Notice that specific impulse is the thrust per unit of propellant flow rate ($g\Delta m/\Delta t$) and it is usually defined this way.

Although this is the customary way of defining I_{sp}, we feel (and other rocket scientists agree with us) that it is an unfortunate one. The g got into the argument because the definition is based on a reference unit weight (a property of a unit mass at the earth's surface) rather than on a reference unit mass (an invariant property of matter). That means this particular g—the acceleration of gravity at the earth's surface—must always be carried along in equations even when the rocket is on another planet or in free space.

Despite this objection, the direct relationship between specific impulse and exhaust velocity becomes evident when we replace the thrust in the equation with the thrust in the previous equation

$$I_{sp} = \left(\frac{\Delta m}{\Delta t}\right)\frac{v_e}{g}\left(\frac{\Delta t}{\Delta m}\right) = \frac{v_e}{g}$$

Therefore, the words "high specific impulse" are interchangeable with "high exhaust velocity."

The units of specific impulse reduce to seconds. In physical terms, this is the number of seconds an engine will deliver a pound of thrust on a pound of fuel.

Capabilities vs. requirements

To see the integrated effect of the thrust on the action of the rocket, we write an equation that combines the thrust equation with the equation of motion for the rocket

$$m\frac{dV_r}{dt} = -\frac{dm}{dt}v_e$$

The mass of the rocket is m and the rate that the rocket mass is decreasing $(-dm/dt)$ is the rate at which propellant is ejected from the engine. Solving for the velocity of the rocket and integrating gives

$$V_r = -v_e\int\frac{dm}{m} = v_e\ln(m_i/m_f) = I_{sp}\,g\ln(m_i/m_f)$$

where m_i and m_f are the initial and final masses and V_r is the velocity increment of the vehicle in a space free of gravitational fields and aerodynamic drag forces. Usually, such forces are present and this change of velocity is not actually achieved. We shall refer to it as the "velocity capability."

Any particular space mission, say an expedition to Jupiter, has a certain "velocity requirement" that must be matched against this "velocity capability." The escape from the earth, any change in orbit about the earth or sun (including those orbit changes that do not alter the gravitational energy—even those that decrease it), the effects of atmospheric drag—all these can be expressed in terms of velocity requirements. The rocket must equal or exceed these requirements; if it exceeds them, travel time is shortened.

This last explanation needs a minor qualification. It is not strictly accurate to speak of a fixed velocity requirement for a mission. It can change depending, for example, on whether the vehicle is accelerated quickly or slowly. However, it is approximately constant, and will be considered such for the purposes of this discussion.

Looking again at the equation for rocket velocity capability, it is clear that very large velocity capabilities require large values of I_{sp} or large values of the mass ratio (m_i/m_f). There are stringent limits on the mass ratio. For one thing, single-stage rockets with mass ratios larger than 15 to 1 are impractical. Staging improves matters some but this method is limited. In addition, if the mass ratio gets very large, it becomes difficult and expensive to make rockets large enough to deliver payloads to distant planets. Clearly, high values of specific impulse are desirable to achieve high velocity capabilities.

Limits on specific impulse

What are the means for achieving high values of specific impulse? Suppose we look first at the liquid- or solid-fueled chemical rocket. Its specific impulse—in fact, the specific impulse of any rocket—is ultimately determined by the kinetic energy imparted to the atoms in the exhaust jet. Writing the equation for specific impulse in terms of energy gives

$$I_{sp} = \frac{1}{g}\sqrt{\frac{2E}{m}}$$

For a rocket propelled by chemical energy, the maximum value of specific impulse is determined by combining the highest chemical reaction energy and the lowest mass for the reaction products. The best combination is the hydrogen-fluorine reaction, which gives a theoretical maximum of approximately 500 sec. In practice, this maximum is reduced to about 435 sec because of incomplete combustion, random motion of atoms, and nozzle losses.

If the exhaust is heated by a nuclear reactor, higher specific impulse is possible because the exhaust can consist of the lightest possible molecules (hydrogen) and these will have the highest velocity for any given temperature. Here, maximum specific impulse can be written

$$I_{sp} = \frac{1}{g}\sqrt{\frac{2kT}{m}}$$

showing that nuclear rockets are limited by allowable temperature limits for reactor and nozzle materials. With hydrogen fuel and temperature limits of about 2500°K, maximum specific impulse for a nuclear rocket is about 800 sec.

To achieve the higher exhaust velocities needed for higher specific impulses, we approach the problem as we would approach it in the laboratory: we turn to an electrically powered accelerator. Here, there are no limits (short of the relativistic one) on the velocity of the accelerated particle. Moreover, it is unnecessary to limit the propellant to light particles; even heavy particles can be accelerated to high velocity.

The aerospace industry is presently experimenting with three types of electric rockets. In order of increasing specific impulse they are: the electrothermal engine, an arc-heated jet similar to a plasma torch ($I_{sp} = 800$ to 1500 sec); the electromagnetic engine, a kind of MHD generator running in reverse ($I_{sp} = 800$

to 15,000 sec); and the ion engine ($I_{sp} = 2500$ to greater than 15,000 sec). In this article, we will focus on the ion engine.

The vanishing acceleration

The ion engine develops its thrust by accelerating ionized particles with an electric field. With this scheme, specific impulse can be as high as desired. For example, a cesium ion accelerated through 6700 V achieves a specific impulse of 10,000 sec, and much higher values are possible.

These gains in specific impulse are somewhat offset by the weight of the electric power supply. An ion rocket with a thrust of 1 lb and $I_{sp} = 10,000$ requires 218 kW of power. At present capabilities, minimum projected weight for a spaceborne power supply is about 10 lb/kW. This means that the electric rocket has to push a 2180-lb power supply around and therefore will have an acceleration limited to less than 0.0005 g.

Small values of acceleration are characteristic of ion rockets because power requirements (and consequently power supply weight) increase in direct proportion with specific impulse for a constant thrust. If specific impulse were 1000 sec in the example above, power (and hence weight) would drop by a factor of ten and acceleration would increase by the same factor.

Low power requirement and low propellant consumption are both desirable but unfortunately, they are at opposite ends of the specific impulse scale. Somewhere in between lies an optimum value. The optimum value is the one that gives minimum total vehicle weight and maximum acceleration for a given mission velocity requirement.

In an ion rocket the value of this maximum acceleration may appear impractically small compared to the 1 to 10 g of a chemical rocket. However, this small value of acceleration acts continuously, eventually building up a velocity greatly exceeding that of a chemical rocket. Consequently, mission times are appreciably reduced. For example, a mission that puts a satellite in a very eccentric orbit about Venus

ROCKET COMPARISON FOR TRIP TO MARS

	Chemical	Nuclear	Nuclear-ion
Payload (lb)	10,000	10,000	10,000
Reactor weight (lb)	0	5,000	10,000
W_{final} (lb)	10,000	15,000	20,000
Propellant weight (lb)	30,000	12,000	2,250
$W_{initial}$ (lb)	40,000	27,000	22,250
I_{sp} (sec)	450	1,000	10,000
Flight time (days)	220	260	330

takes 139 days by chemical rocket. The same mission can be accomplished in the same time with an ion rocket having a continuous acceleration of 10^{-4} g. Similarly, a fly-by excursion to Pluto would take 43 years by chemical rocket whereas a steady acceleration of 10^{-4} g would put it there in 3½ years.

In simplest terms, an ion engine is a large spaceborne ion gun, but an ion gun with a current density, total current, and lifetime staggeringly large compared with laboratory ion guns. There are other differences too. An ion rocket exhaust beam must be neutralized after it leaves the engine to cancel the space charge that would otherwise develop in the beam. This space charge would slow the flow of ions and eventually stall the engine. Further, the rocket engine must be capable of running for periods of a year or more at high power-efficiency.

Heavy atom, singly charged

Turning first to the problem of generating a dense beam of ions, it is clear that the first step is to choose a propellant that is easily ionized. The most likely candidates are the alkali metals—Li, Na, K, Ru, Cs—because of their single, loosely bound electron in the valence shell. Cesium has the lowest ionization potential and therefore provides the most efficient source of ions, both in terms of power lost and percentage of atoms ionized. It also has a low melting point (28.7°C) and a high vapor pressure at modest temperatures (300°C), both desirable for vapor production and feeding.

Cesium is also the heaviest of the lot. This is a fortuitous circumstance since, unlike chemical or nuclear rockets, there is sufficient energy in the electric field to accelerate a particle to any velocity, regardless of its mass. And a heavy particle is desirable for two reasons. In the first place, the energy of individual particles at a given velocity increases with their mass, and this reduces power losses in the ion generator since fewer ions need to be generated. In the second place, thrust per unit of exhaust area is greater with heavy ions.

This last reason follows from practical considerations. For a given exhaust velocity, a light ion needs a lower potential on the accelerating electrode than a heavy one. But fields on the order of 50,000 V/cm are desired for high thrust densities. Consequently, the electrode spacing required to achieve this field becomes impractically small in the case of a light ion. With a heavy ion, the spacing can be in the practical range of a few millimeters.

From atom to ion

Ion engine designers have relied largely on two methods for converting atoms to ions.

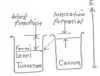

Consider first the surface-ionization process. The ionization of alkali metals at the surface of metals such as tungsten was experimentally studied in the 1920's by I. Langmuir. The principle of this mechanism is illustrated in the margin.

The sketch shows an energy diagram of a cesium atom close to a tungsten surface. Because the Fermi level (a level corresponding to the highest energy level in the metal) lies below the energy level of the cesium valence electron, that electron tunnels through the potential barrier into the tungsten leaving the cesium ionized. For cesium on tungsten, more than 99% of the impinging atoms can be ionized this way.

In practice, the metal surface is heated because the ionization process is modified by the presence of adsorbed atoms covering a finite area of the surface. Atoms have a finite sticking time before they are released as atoms or ions. This coverage of atoms, ranging from 0 to 100%, alters the work function of a tungsten surface from 4.7 eV for the clean surface to 1.8 eV for the completely cesiated surface. The degree of surface coverage depends on the arrival rate of atoms and the temperature of the surface. The relationship between the emis-

sion of neutrals, surface coverage, and atom arrival rate is shown in Fig. 4-47.

Porous tungsten electron-snatcher

It is possible to build a surface-ionization engine by feeding atoms directly to a hot surface, as illustrated in the margin. Unfortunately, incoming atoms scatter the accelerated ions. Moreover, the low-velocity incoming gas is dense enough to cause electrical discharge in the accelerator region. For these reasons, this configuration is not favored.

A more practical approach is illustrated in Fig. 4-48. Cesium vapor is fed through a porous tungsten disk and the cesium atoms are ionized as they pass through the pores. An analysis of this configuration shows that the pores must be exceedingly small—on the order of $1~\mu$ in diameter—to ensure efficient ionization. The metallurgical problems of making small-pore ionizer plates from refractory metals such as tungsten has received close attention in the ion-engine development program. Present techniques involve the controlled sintering of micron-size powders at high temperatures.

The performance of porous tungsten ionizers is an extremely variable quantity. It depends critically on pore size, pore spacing, uniformity of the material, and other factors. We are now studying the relationship between these factors with a special ion-emission microscope developed for the purpose. In this instrument, cesium atoms are fed through an ionizer plate and ions emitted from the surface are brought to focus on a fluorescent screen. The image is a highly magnified view (resolution is on the order of $1~\mu$) of the distribution of ion emission over a portion of the ionizer surface.

These studies have had some surprising results. For example, it was previously assumed that most ions come from the front surface rather than the pores. The ion-microscope images indicate that best operation corresponds to emission from the pores alone. Another surprising result is the existence of three distinct emitting states, which, under certain conditions, appear simultaneously on the same surface. Our understanding of these phenomena has since led to new analyses, which are expected to indicate an improved configuration for ionizers.

Electrons in the trap

Another way to ionize an atom—a more common way—is to strip its outer electron off with a bombarding electron. To take a simple example, suppose electrons pass from cathode to anode through a cesium gas. When an electron

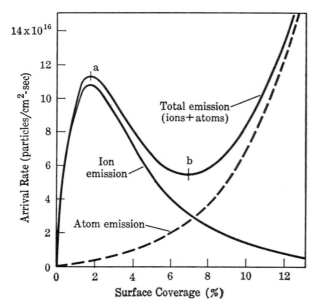

Fig. 4-47. Surface-contact ion engine must operate so that coverage of the ionizer surface by adsorbed atoms does not exceed that indicated by point a. Beyond this point, adsorbed atoms lower the surface's work function and reduce the number of ions emitted. Between points a and b, the system is unstable, and total emission (atoms plus ions) drops, because atoms arrive faster than they can be emitted. The degree of surface coverage depends on the temperature of the surface and the arrival rate. These curves are for cesium atoms on a tungsten surface at 1400°K.

strikes an atom it will knock the valence electron off leaving the atom ionized.

There are many ways to produce an intense electron-bombardment ion source. But one type stands out as so superior to all others for propulsion that it is unnecessary to consider other types here.

In this source (see Fig. 4-50) electrons enter a cylinder containing the gas to be ionized and are constrained to move parallel to the axis of the cylinder by a magnetic field. Actually, the electrons spiral about the magnetic lines of force. Because the cylinder is bounded on its

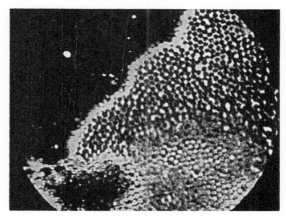

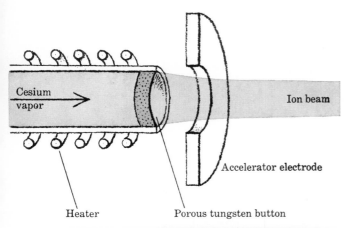

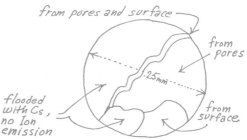

Fig. 4-49. Depending on the conditions, the emission from a porous ionizer may be entirely from pores or entirely from the front surface. Three stable states of emission (identified in the sketch) are shown in this ionizer image made with a special ion-emission microscope. There is nothing different about the tungsten or the cesium pressure in the three regions. Slight changes in temperature or feed rate can throw the entire ionizer into any of these three states. (Courtesy Electro-Optical Systems, Inc.)

Fig. 4-48. In one type of ion engine, cesium atoms are forced through a porous tungsten button to remove the loosely bound valence electron by surface-contact ionization. Pores in the button are so small (about 1μ in diameter) that it appears solid to the naked eye, yet helium passes through freely as shown in the lower photograph. (Courtesy Electro-Optical Systems, Inc.)

ends by electrodes at the cathode potential, the electrons cannot get out. They are forced to oscillate back and forth, working their way to the anode through collisions with atoms and probably with the aid of an electronic field oscillation that exists within the plasma. This entrapment greatly increases the opportunity for electrons to ionize atoms.

The power required to operate this type of ionizer is somewhat less than that for the surface ionizer, but with improvements in surface ionization, this difference appears to be vanishing. There is one distinct difference: The electron bombardment scheme will ionize any atoms or molecules that can be introduced as a gas or vapor. For propulsion applications, mercury and cesium appear to be the most favorable materials. Mercury has a mass advantage over cesium (atomic weight 200 versus atomic weight 133), but the ease with which doubly charged mercury ions are formed is a disadvantage.

The main disadvantages of the electron-bombardment source are the low ratio of ions

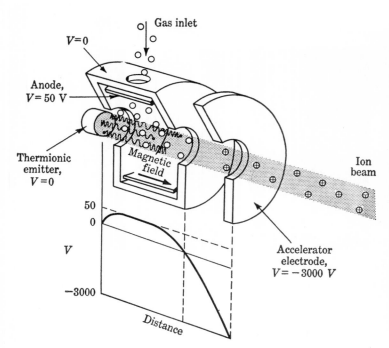

Fig. 4-50. *Bombardment ion source converts atoms to ions through collisions with electrons that have energies greater than the atom's ionization energy. Bombarding electrons come from a thermionic cathode, spiral into the vapor-filled cavity and are trapped there by the magnetic field and the potential hill at both ends of the cavity. Electrons eventually drain to the anode while ions diffuse to the cathode or the exit aperture.*

Fig. 4-51. *This electron-bombardment ion engine operates with a cesium propellant (some engines of this type use mercury), develops about 0.010 lb thrust on 2 kW of power. Electron emitters for neutralizing the ion beam are arranged around the inside of the exhaust tube. Mounted at the top of the exhaust tube is an "eye" that detects the number of neutral atoms carried out with the exhaust, thereby monitoring ionizer operation. (Courtesy Electro-Optical Systems, Inc.)*

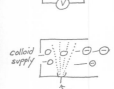

to neutral atoms compared with the surface ionizer, and the non-uniformity of emission over the area of a large ionizer. The consequence of these and other considerations is a lower thrust density for the bombardment engine than for the contact engine. Its advantages are its freedom from the need for special materials and construction techniques, and higher power efficiencies in the lower specific impulse range.

Heavier particles, lower losses

Both the surface-contact and electron-bombardment engines have been developed to the flight testing stage. There are other engines that have not yet progressed this far.

One of these is the colloidal-particle engine, in which the ion is replaced by a much heavier particle to extend the advantage cited above for heavy ions. The main problem in developing this engine is in the production of charged particles.

Several methods and types of colloidal material have been tried. Both liquids and solids have been tried as well as gases from which liquid particles are condensed. Oil on a surface has been subjected to electrostatic fields, which causes droplets to be drawn off and charged by induction forces. Solid alumina particles have

been treated in a similar fashion. Separate colloid formation followed by a charging process such as an electron-beam impingement or corona discharge has been suggested. A process by which a gas is caused to condense on charge ions has also been studied (see margin).

All of these attempts have met with, at most, limited success. It has been found difficult to maintain a sufficiently uniform mass-to-charge ratio for all particles. In addition, useful source flow rates are difficult to obtain in practice. To this date, there is no practical colloid-source ion engine in operation that compares in performance with engines using ionized atoms. However, its inherent advantage makes it worth the continuing pursuit.

Speed up, then slow down

Once the ions are generated, they must be pulled from the source and accelerated to the desired velocity. This is the function of the acceleration system. In principle, the acceleration system is simply a negatively charged electrode placed outside the exit of the ion source so that the positively charged ion sees a large negative potential in the downstream direction. In practice, the system is somewhat more complicated than this.

The rate that ions can be drawn from a single

ion-source aperture is limited by the space charge that develops around this aperture. As the flow of ions increases, the cloud of ions in the near vicinity of the source creates a large positive charge—the space charge—and this inhibits further ion flow. The current from an aperture can be increased only up to some reasonable limit on the order of a few milliamperes for cesium ions. To get beyond this limit and into the range of hundreds of milliamps, the engine must have many apertures and produce many beams.

To enhance the current density available from a single aperture, the potential on the accelerating electrode should be high. But there is little freedom to regulate this potential because it controls the acceleration of the ions and, hence, the specific impulse. We have solved the problem by placing a second electrode—a decelerating electrode—downstream of the accelerating electrode. With this configuration, the field in the accelerating region can be very large and the overaccelerated ion can be slowed to the desired velocity by the potential hill between the accelerating and decelerating electrodes.

Design of an accelerating system is a most exacting business. The size of the aperture in the accelerating electrodes, the distance between the electrode and the ionizer surface, and the shape of the ionizer surface all have an effect on current density, uniformity of emission, and collimation of the beam. In addition, electrode configuration governs the degree to which ions strike the acceleration electrode. If the engine is to operate continuously for a year or more, interception rates should be below one part in 10^5 to limit erosion of the acceleration electrode.

A gift of nature

Several years ago, the problem of neutralizing the exhaust to eliminate the large positive charge that would otherwise build up in the beam was regarded by many as the most difficult ion-engine problem. An appraisal of the problem showed that the task would be a formidable one. For complete neutralization, electrons would need to be injected into the exhaust with a density and velocity exactly matching that of the ions. This could be a complicated matter since the velocity of ions in the exhaust corresponds to an energy of 0.02 eV while randomly emitted electrons usually have an average energy five times as great.

Fortunately, nature chose to be benevolent. The neutralization problem solved itself when we exposed the ion beam to a heated electron emitter. The space charge created by the ions in the vicinity of the electron emitter auto-

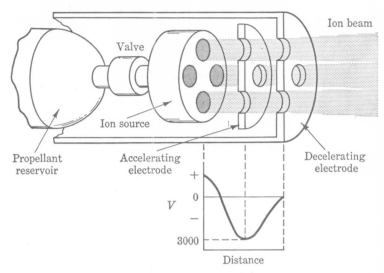

Fig. 4-52. A pair of electrodes—one to accelerate the ions, the other to decelerate them—surround the rocket exhaust. A high voltage between the accelerator electrode and the ionizer produces the electrostatic forces that draw a maximum number of ions into the beam. Overaccelerated ions are then slowed to the desired exit velocity by the decelerator electrode. The potential hill between accelerator and decelerator electrodes inhibits the backward flow of neutralizing electrons.

matically regulates the neutralization: When the space charge builds up, the higher potential between the emitter and the surrounding cloud of ions draws more electrons into the exhaust, where they are mixed, thereby reducing the space charge.

To make this scheme work, our engine needs one further refinement. The accelerate-decelerate system previously described as a means for increasing thrust density actually has a more compelling purpose. With the negative electrode interposed between the ionizer and the exit aperture, injected electrons travel downstream with the ions rather than being drawn to the ionizer.

Although experimental engines are being readied for their first flight tests, many questions remain to be answered. For example, we would like to know how ionizer efficiency will be affected by the deposition of atoms sputtered off the accelerating electrode. We would also like to know how much corrosion to expect when engine materials are exposed to cesium vapor at high temperatures.

For predicting the life of acceleration electrodes, we need to know how many atoms are ejected from a metal surface when an ion impinges on it with kilovolt energies and at various impingement angles. We would also like to know something about the probability of an accelerated ion colliding with a neutral atom inside the electrode system. This information is needed to predict electrode erosion rate.

Whence comes the power

The most pressing need remains the need for a lightweight power source. For the forthcoming flight tests, the power will be supplied by batteries. But interplanetary vehicles will need much more power.

Two nuclear-powered turbo-generator systems are expected to be available by the early 1970's. One is a SNAP-8, a 30-kW electrical system whose power can be transformed into a few tenths of a pound of thrust. The other is the SNAP-50 (or SPUR). It will deliver power on the order of a megawatt and this can be converted to several pounds of thrust. This power plant will be capable of propelling a vehicle weighing about 50,000 lb.

Both power supplies use a nuclear reactor and a turbine, with a liquid metal as the working fluid. Both are fraught with development problems. Liquid metals at high temperatures are extremely erosive, particularly in rotating equipment. Moreover, for minimum weight, the generators must operate at very high temperatures, increasing their susceptibility to bearing wear and structural failures.

A further complication lies in the conversion of raw power from the generator to the dc-voltage levels required for the ion engine. Other, possibly simpler, power systems such as thermionic converters show promise for the more distant future.

Further reading

Curiously, one of the most fertile sources for details on the fundamentals of ion rockets is in reports of work done over 30 years ago. Papers written by Irving Langmuir in the twenties and thirties discuss pioneering experiments with charged-particle beam devices, surface ionization, and plasma physics. For example, one key paper of current significance, which he wrote with J. B. Taylor, is "The Evaporation of Atoms, Ions and Electrons from Cesium Films on Tungsten," *Phys. Rev.* **44,** 423 (1933). All the papers are included in *The Works of Irving Langmuir,* 12 volumes (Pergamon, 1961, Vols. 1–11, $15 each; Vol. 12, $9).

Most of the recent work on ion rockets is reported in scattered technical papers. In two cases, the papers have been collected between hard covers: "Progress in Astronautics and Rocketry," Vol. 5, *Electrostatic Propulsion* (Academic, 1961, $5.75) and "Progress in Astronautics and Aeronautics," Vol. 9, *Electric Propulsion Development* (Academic, 1962, $10.50). Both, of course, are edited for the rocket expert. Review articles are published periodically in *Astronautics,* a monthly publication of the American Institute of Aeronautics and Astronautics. The most recent reviews of ion-propulsion devices are in the June 1962 and June 1963 issues.

SOLID FUEL BOOSTERS

*by William Cohen**

IN BRIEF: *The space trucks of the not-too-distant future are going to require launch vehicles with thrust levels of 7 to 10 million lb and above. First of these boosters, the Advanced Saturn, will be a cluster of five liquid-fueled motors each delivering 1.5 million lb thrust. Then scaleup problems get really complex. Boosters powered by solid propellants appear to offer a viable alternative: they are more readily scaled up. The fuel and oxidizer are mixed and cast in place prior to flight—obviating the need for complex mixing systems on the vehicle. Successful firings of motors 8 to 10 ft in diameter with thrusts up to 1 million lb have shown that present solid propellant technology is applicable to boosters. With the basic technology in hand, what's needed now is careful consideration of the implications of bigness: the next step will be to a new class of motors 22 ft in diameter producing 7- to 10-million-lb thrust, and adaptable to clustering for big boosters. Such a quantum jump will involve fabrication of large structures from new metals and plastics, the processing of large amounts of chemicals, the manipulation and transport of large weights. This means tapping the know-how of other, more established industries: shipbuilding, chemicals, and transport.—F.P.*

* William Cohen is Chief of Solid-Propulsion Systems at NASA's Office of Manned Space Flight.

■ Suppose you want to go to Mars. Or maybe you want to lead an expedition to the moon, establish a base, and occupy it for a year or two. You have your good reasons so we need not consider whether it is desirable; but is it possible? Yes, but difficult. And, as you soon discover, very expensive. When the weights and volumes of the things you need for a 2–3 year trip are added up, you discover that you will have a vessel, call it a spaceship, which will weigh 2 or 3 million lb.

The launch vehicle you need for this task will challenge the Washington Monument for height—nearly 500 ft. It will weigh about 15,-000 tons as it sits on the launch pad, about as much as a destroyer escort.

Now, what are the directions for getting to Mars? The first step is one of the most difficult. It reads as follows: Place your spaceship at a point in space about 100 miles above the surface of the earth and give it an escape velocity of 36,000 ft/sec. The velocity requirement seems a little high (it converts to about 26,000 miles/hr), but you have good ballisticians and have long accepted the stern facts of space mechanics.

How will you bring your several million pounds of payload to escape velocity? It is a question that generates considerable heat and noise, if I may use a rocket simile, because it involves quantities like cost, availability, and reliability. These three elements are intimately intertwined: cost and reliability can be traded against each other and to a certain extent availability has similar permutations. (By availability I mean the state of knowledge of science needed for very large space flights.)

The availability question seems to have one fairly clear-cut answer. Within the near future, say from now until 1980, it seems that chemical propulsion will be the only system available for high-thrust stages. The distinction I make is between chemical propulsion and nuclear or electrical propulsion.

The conclusion concerning chemical propulsion has considerable importance because it means that the launch vehicle will probably have three stages. This results from the fact that it is extremely difficult in the present and projected state of knowledge of materials and energy sources to devise a single rocket stage which will bring a useable payload to escape velocity or even to earth-orbiting velocity.

Oddly enough, the picture of the two upper stages for a planetary flight is fairly clear, while the selection of the boost stage is more difficult. The upper stages in all probability will make use of liquid propellant engines, burning liquid hydrogen with liquid oxygen, the engines individually producing thrust of about 1.5 million lb. Liquids are used for these stages primarily because the high thrust per unit flow rate of propellant (specific impulse) has much greater payoff than in the booster.

The first stage is less well-defined; its propulsion elements are the major subject of my discussion. The most important single piece of information about this stage is that it must produce extremely high thrust—up to 50 million lb of it. Great thrust means great size and weight. Millions of pounds of stage will be in-volved, possibly 15 or 20 million lb, and the propulsion package will probably be used once and thrown away. This places a premium on low-cost stages, and means that the energy content, or specific impulse of the propellants for booster stages is but one of the elements of importance in selecting the stage.

A bold adventure in rocketry

One of my colleagues at NASA, Milton Rosen, has written about the efforts to build large booster rockets in which liquid fuel and oxidizers make up the chemical "package." As he pointed out, the Advanced Saturn booster, on which the Apollo lunar flight hinges, is a cluster of five kerosene-oxygen engines. Each provides a thrust of 1.5 million lb, for a total of 7.5 million lb.

The engines whose technology I am discussing in this article are a new class of boosters—using solid propellants—*each of which* could equal or exceed the thrust of five of our largest existing liquid-propellant boosters. The dimensions and weight of these new boosters are correspondingly high: over 100 ft high (about the same as the Advanced Saturn booster), some 22 ft in diameter, and 3½ to 4 million lb in weight. Clustered together, these motors will enable us to construct boosters with thrusts in the 40–50-million-lb range needed for the heavy space vehicles of the future.

To put these numbers in perspective, the largest solid propellant motor now under development is a 1-million-lb thrust motor (Fig. 4-53) on the Titan III launch vehicle, which employs two of them. This motor has as its precursors solid-propellant engines on other military rockets whose names are familiar: Nike-Zeus, Polaris, and Minuteman.

A loyal, homely servant

How is it possible to leap ahead to a single, 7-million-lb thrust level engine? The answer lies in the inherent properties of solid rocket engines. They are basically simple devices consisting of a chunk of propellant, a nozzle, and a container. This violent oversimplification reveals why the thrust level of the solid rocket can be easily (well, relatively easily) increased. To produce more thrust, increase the amount of burning material, make the nozzle larger, make the container larger.

Isn't the problem the same for liquid engines? No. To increase thrust in the liquid engine, it is necessary to pump the liquids at a greater mass-flow rate. This requires larger pumps. The larger pump requires a larger power source to drive it. The greater flow rate of liquids requires larger controlling valves and pipe work. In the conglomerate, the liquid propulsion system, in

Fig. 4-54. Two characteristics of solid propellants: They're rubbery and they burn like sparklers. (Courtesy B. Poush, NASA)

order to grow, requires that considerable development and proof testing must be done on the turbopumps, the valves, and the other flow controlling elements.

The dimensions and performance of the new solid rockets are impressive but the elements of the rockets are prosaic. A piece of solid propellant can pass for a hard rubber eraser. Pick it up, twist it, and it feels like an eraser; it bends; it deforms (Fig. 4-54). Examine it closely and you see it is a rubber-like material filled with a crystalline solid. Hit it with your paperweight, rub it on the desk, tear out a piece with your fingernail, step on it—nothing happens. Apply a match, and it burns brilliantly with bright streaks shooting out, somewhat like a Fourth of July sparkler, releasing an acrid smell of hydrochloric acid.

The history of solid rockets is quite long, reportedly reaching back to thirteenth-century China. We are probably all aware of the use of Congreve rockets in the Napoleonic Wars in the 1800's and, as every book and paper on rocket propulsion rightly reminds us, it was the rockets' red glare in 1812 that showed that our flag was still there, with an assist from the bombs bursting in air. Modern solid rockets do not produce a red glare. They produce a rather smoky exhaust through which can be seen an intense incandescent core.

What's in a propellant?

Most of the solid propellants in use today, and those which will be used in the giant space

Fig. 4-53. This is a miniature space booster, despite its 1-million-lb thrust—the largest yet achieved using solid propellants. Two of them would lift 20,000 lb toward earth orbit. Fifty of them would launch a spaceship toward Mars. To make this jump in thrust level, a new class of motors, each delivering 7 to 10 million lb of thrust, is being investigated. Cluster 5 or 6 of them together, and you're on your way. But there's some big engineering to be done first. (Courtesy United Technology Center, UAC)

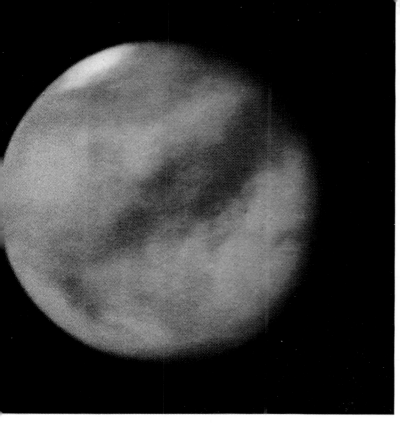

Color Fig. 32. *Remarkable resolution in this natural-color photograph clearly reveals major features of the Martian surface. Dark areas —called "maria," although they are not oceans—change in brightness, polarization, and extent through the seasons; they may be covered with vegetation, but inorganic covering cannot be ruled out yet. Bright orange areas are called "deserts," and probably are, possibly covered by the fine dust of the mineral limonite, a hydrous iron oxide. The white, generally cloud-covered polar cap waxes and wanes with the seasons. It may be sublimated deposit of water in the form of hoarfrost, plus maybe a little CO_2, but recent suggestion that it's nitrogen tetroxide — N_2O_4 — has merit. See "Mars," in Chapter 4. (Courtesy R. B. Leighton, Cal. Tech.)*

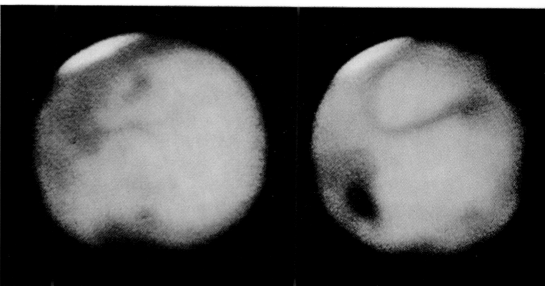

Color Fig. 33. *These unusually excellent photographs, like that in Color Fig. 32, owe part of their quality to the fact that Martian atmosphere was relatively free of diverse kinds of clouds and haze which sometimes obscure the surface. Visible rotation of surface markings provides measure of Martian day—24 h, 37 m, 22.7 s—accurate to ±0.2 s. See "Mars," in Chapter 4. (Courtesy W. S. Finsen)*

Color Fig. 34. Multiple beams emerge from an experimental ion engine being tested in a vacuum chamber. The engine is an early model having 19 beams, is capable of delivering 0.001 lb. thrust from 400 W (5000 V at 80 ma) of power. See "Ion Rockets," in Chapter 4. (Courtesy Electro-Optical Systems, Inc.)

booster rockets, are mixtures of an oxidizer, usually ammonium perchlorate, and a fuel. The fuel includes a rubbery material such as polyurethane, which has the prime purpose of holding the mass together, and frequently a metal such as aluminum in fine particle form. The major ingredient is the crystalline oxidizer, usually 60 or 65% by weight. Another 15% or so is metal, and the remainder is the organic binder. It is the burning of the metal particles that gives the exhaust its incandescent core.

The combustion of metal may seem an oddity to those not engaged in rocket development work, but there is no arguing with thermodynamics. The heat of combustion of a pound of aluminum is 7070 Btu, compared to 4570 Btu for a typical hydrocarbon binder (the same as for gasoline). In the area of gas dynamics, however, the metal components introduce complications. The metal oxide combustion products are in liquid or solid form, depending on their location in the motor. As could be expected, this does not make for a very efficient expansion through the nozzle. The composition of the solid propellant must therefore be carefully chosen to give the optimum energy release and good working gas characteristics.

It is well to note at this point, however, that secondary factors enter in the choice and apportionment of the propellant ingredients, because the finished solid propellant mass must have certain physical properties in order to be safe and reliable. For one thing, the amount of binder must be great enough to fill all the interstices between the solid component. If this is not done, the propellant charge mass, called a *grain*, will be porous. A porous grain is a hazardous grain. It can progress in its combustion to a much higher rate of reaction—detonation—a mode of energy release yet to be harnessed for comfortable rocket travel.

Another limitation on the apportionment of the ingredient is a requirement that the propellant mass retain rubbery properties. The property generally controlling is the modulus of elasticity. This comes about as follows: The ingredients of the propellant react to produce high-temperature gases and metal oxides, typically at 5500–6000°F. In order to protect the rocket motor case from this extreme temperature, the solid-rocket designers have rather cleverly arranged the structure so that the combustion takes place within the charge of propellant, proceeding radially outward—increment by increment—with the unburned propellant insulating the case. They are called internally burning grains, and have the appearance of a cylinder of rubbery material with a cavity along the center line of the grain.

The burning process in solid rockets in general takes place at fairly high pressure, typically 500 to 1000 psi. Thus the ignition of the motor exerts internal pressure on the propellant charge, stressing it in tension. Hence the modulus of elasticity must be kept low to prevent the propellant grain from cracking.

Mixing a giant propellant grain

The raw ingredients of the solid propellant are usually mixed together in ordinary chemical process equipment such as dry blenders and sigma-blade mixers. After mixing, the rubbery part of the propellant charge is still in its monomeric stage: the mixture of ingredients is a slurry and flows somewhat like a thick mud or thick cream. The slurry is poured into the prepared rocket motor case around a central mandrel which can have a variety of shapes, and the assembly is set aside to harden or cure. Usually the temperature is maintained at about 130°F for a few days. Then the motor is cooled, the mandrel is removed, and the solid rocket motor and its charge is essentially finished except for attaching the nozzle.

At this point the contrast between the liquid-propellant rocket and the solid-propellant rocket is most striking. Notice that the operations which bring the oxidizer and fuel compounds together have been carried out in the mixer, and that the mixer is on the ground. The oxidizer and fuel are now in proper proportion and in proper location with respect to each other, and they are rigidly locked into this position.

In the liquid propellant system, the oxidizer and fuel components are brought together in proper proportion and location by pumps, valves, orifices, and similar devices on the vehicle. If any of the numerous fluid pumping and control elements fails or malperforms, if the sensing, starting, and controlling circuitry become deranged during take-off or flight, the liquid rocket will falter or fail. In the case of the solid-propellant rocket, malfunction of the mixing plant can be detected and corrected, so that the rocket need not suffer.

This basic difference between the liquid- and solid-propellant rockets is in large part responsible for one of the major virtues of the solid rocket motor: relative ease of growth. In the solid rocket, growth in thrust level and total impulse is brought about by pouring more slurry into a larger container. In the liquid-propellant rocket, growth in thrust level means increase in size of the pumping and control devices. This almost always means new R&D.

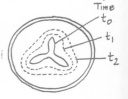

Controlling the thrust

But in the absence of pumps, turbines, and valves, how is the mass discharge rate—more specifically the thrust level—established? The answer is that the rate at which burning of the solid propellant occurs (always normal, to its surface) is carefully specified and controlled. This control, together with the exactly defined area exposed for burning (as determined by mandrel shape), establishes the rate of propellant consumption, the amount of energy liberated, and the rate of generation of working gas.

How can the burning rate be controlled so neatly? First, by control of the oxidizer particle size and secondly, by use of special burning rate additives. A range of burning rates, from 0.2 to 0.7 in./sec, is obtainable in propellants that also have the proper physical properties and good energy content.

I have mentioned earlier that rocket motors typically operate in the pressure range of 500–1000 psi. The burning rate of the propellant is a function of this pressure. A major part of the propellant development effort, therefore, is to define the relationship between the linear burning rate and the operating pressure, and to express it in terms useable by the design engineer. The most common (though not always the truest) description of the pressure effect is through an equation in the form $r = ap_c{}^n$, n

being the exponent of cavity pressure p_c. Most propellants in common use now have pressure exponents in the neighborhood of 0.3.

Enter—internal ballistics

Now the internal ballistic problem and design problem of the solid rocket begin to take shape. The rate of release of energy and the generation of working gas (plus the metal oxide) are established by the carefully controlled burning rate of the propellant and the closely defined burning surface. These two qualities, burning rate and area, are equivalent to the injector, pumps, turbogenerator, valves, etc., of the liquid-propellant engine.

As I noted above, the pressure generated in this cavity, or chamber, is dependent on the burning rate. Since burning takes place only at the surface, just how this area changes as burning progresses will determine the pressure profile with time, and hence the thrust. By using a star-shaped cavity, for example, an essentially constant burning area can be maintained even though the cavity enlarges as burning progresses (Fig. 4-55). Thus the chamber pressure, and hence the thrust, can be averaged out as steady value.

Such a propellant has what is termed a neutral burning characteristic. Other cavity shapes can give increasing pressure (progressive burning) or decreasing pressure (regressive burning). Other means of burning rate control include inhibitors applied to certain areas and the use of several different propellant grains in the same chamber, but these are details of propellant design I won't go into here.

By applying the law of conservation of matter, the internal ballistics of the solid rocket can be given formal expression: in a given unit of time, the mass of propellant consumed must equal the sum of the increase in gas mass in the combustion cavity and the mass discharged through the rocket nozzle.

If the increase in gas mass in the chamber per unit time is neglected, and if the simple exponential relation between burning rate r and cavity pressure p_c is introduced into the familiar nozzle equation (see margin), then the cavity pressure will be found to depend upon the burning area and upon the exponent n of the cavity pressure,

$$p_c \propto (A_b/A_t)^{1/(1-n)}$$

If, for example, the value of n for a particular propellant is 0.75, cavity pressure would vary as the fourth power of the burning area. Then, the pressure (and hence the burning rate and the thrust) would be quite dependent on small changes in the burning area. For this reason, propellants are generally selected that have low

Fig. 4-55. A typical solid propellant grain before firing (left) shows the internal cavity in which surface combustion occurs. As propellant burns away (right), pressurized combustion gases travel along the cavity, expand through a nozzle, and give the motor its thrust. Pressure is controlled by burning area. Here, star cavity is shaped so that burning area (and hence pressure and thrust) remains essentially constant. Combustion normally continues until propellant is consumed. In this case, it was cut off by creating a sudden expansion wave which dropped cavity pressure below that needed to sustain combustion. (Courtesy Lockheed Propulsion Co.)

NOZZLE EQUATION

Flow =

$A_t \rho_c \sqrt{\dfrac{gk}{RT_c} \left(\dfrac{z}{k+}\right)}$

$k = c_p / c_v$

values of n so that the effect of variations in grain geometry can be minimized.

Complex exhaust = complex computations

The design problem is not completed, however, until the amount of useful work obtained from the propellant is computed, a knotty problem common to both liquid and solid rockets (except when condensed phases are present in the exhaust of a solid motor). The problem is theoretically simple and practically difficult. Essentially, it involves the computation of enthalpy at two points, one inside the rocket motor and the second at the exhaust plane of the nozzle. The difference is the energy available for propulsion.

The difficult part of computations of this sort derives from the dependence of the various combustion chemical species (see margin) on the temperature. An iterative process must be used to establish the initial combustion conditions—the amount present of each of 10 to 15 chemical species and their initial temperature. The same iteration must be made to determine the exhaust conditions. When powdered metal fuel is included in the motor, there is an additional complication in computation: an estimation must be made of the thermal and kinetic equilibrium between the gaseous exhaust products and the condensed phases of the resulting metal oxide in order to compute the specific impulse with reasonable accuracy.

For both liquid and solid systems, a further degree of uncertainty in the computation is introduced by the lack of information on rate of recombination of the chemical species in the very fast transit through the rocket nozzle.

Part of the solid-rocket design problem, as I indicated earlier, is to make an optimum selection of the propellant ingredients within the limitations of physical properties, to maximize the energy release and minimize gas weight. In the liquid-propellant motor, this optimization is brought about by control of pumping rates. In the solid-propellant engine, the control and optimization is produced by a fine balancing of sometimes divergent factors, such as grain rheology and reactant energy content.

How good are solid propellants?

I have mentioned that the major ingredients of the solid propellants are a rubbery binder, an oxidizer such as ammonium perchlorate, and aluminum metal. Are these very good propellants? How good are they in comparison to the well-known liquid oxygen-kerosene combination, in comparison to the more advanced liquid oxygen-liquid hydrogen combination? The answer is that the solid propellants in general have slightly lower specific impulse than

the liquid propellants. This comes about because the ingredients are intimately mixed in the propellant and the most energetic solids turn out to be incompatible with each other in prolonged contact.

In the liquid system, by comparison, the reacting ingredients are stored in separate tanks and do not meet until their point of reaction in the combustion chamber. Indeed, the basic element of advanced research on solid propellants is the discovery of oxidizers and fuels with great energy availability, capable of living together in the heterogeneous propellant mass.

It should be clear that a single element, such as specific impulse, will not be the deciding element in the selection of large booster propulsion. The solid-rocket motors offer great virtues of simplicity, reliability, and ease of handling and preparation; virtues which may outweigh the somewhat lower specific impulse. In a general way, this situation is evident in the transition of the U.S. ballistic missile program from liquid propellant missiles to solid propellant missiles.

The implications of bigness

All of the foregoing emphasizes one key point: namely, that radically new propellant compositions and propellant processing methods are not needed for the very large solid motors to come. The essential novelty or difficulty accompanying the production of large motors derives, rather, from the dimensions and weight. I mentioned earlier that thrust levels of 7, perhaps even 10 million lb per motor are presently being planned. When these large solid motors are built, more than 3 million lb of propellant will be cast into each one as a single charge, much like the pouring of concrete in a dam. Moderate size batches weighing about 4 thousand lb will be mixed, transported to the casting site, and dumped into a deaerating hopper, thence through casting tubes over 100 ft long, to the bottom of the motor casing. Casting may continue for a number of weeks!

The dimensions of the inert components of the motor—case and nozzle—are impressive in comparison to prior solid rockets, or even to prior space launch vehicles. For example, one solid motor of this class can contain the entire Saturn I launch vehicle. Its case would be about 22 ft in diameter and the nozzle throat approximately 8 ft in diameter.

The manufacture of the components of this class of motors raises interesting problems of material selection as well as problems of welding, handling, and so forth. Materials used for smaller solid-rocket motors are of a class of high-strength steels, typified by alloys such as Ladish D6-AC, or AMS 255. To attain their

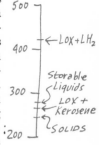

Typical specific impulses

$LOX+LH_2$

Storable Liquids

$LOX + Kerosene$

Solids

Typical specie reactions

$CO_2 \rightarrow CO + \frac{1}{2}O_2$

$H_2 \rightarrow 2H$

$H_2O \rightarrow \frac{1}{2}H_2 + OH$

$O_2 \rightarrow 2(O)$

$H_2O \rightarrow H_2 + \frac{1}{2}O_2$

etc...

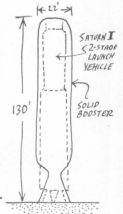

SATURN I 2-STAGE LAUNCH VEHICLE

SOLID BOOSTER

full strength, such steels must be formed first, then heat-treated at temperatures of approximately 1500°F in a carefully controlled atmosphere, followed by a quench with oil or air. Typically, yield strength in the neighborhood of 200,000 lb is sought.

As you can see, cases for the larger motors I am describing here cannot be made of these same materials because no heat-treating facility in the country could accommodate them (Fig. 4-56). Even if the construction of new heat-treating facilities were undertaken, it would be necessary to do considerable exploratory work because the technology of heat-treating the rocket grade steels does not yet extend to objects of these dimensions.

What alternatives are there? First, it might be possible to avoid the use of high-strength steel entirely: accept the thick walls and greater inert weight resulting from use of a non-heat-treatable steel, such as alloys known as HY-80 or T-1. These steels develop moderately high strength in the as-welded condition without requiring the heat-treat program. A second possibility might be to extend the filament-winding process used so effectively to build motors with reinforced plastic casings.

A third alternative lies in new high-nickel-iron alloys called maraging steels. These are solution-heat-treated in plate form and sub-

sequently brought to full strength by an aging process. The aging is done at a temperature of 900°F after the structure is formed, and does not require quench or controlled atmosphere.

The principal deficiency of these alloys, attributable to their relative newness, is a lack of information on the details of forming, welding, and aging of very large structures, as these large motor casings definitely will be. In spite of this temporary problem, the maraging steels will be used for the big boosters. The key new tooling requirement is a 900°F aging facility. The approach to this problem is to construct fairly rudimentary insulated structures, which can age sections of the finished cylinder each about 30 ft long. The individual sections will then be welded together and the weld zones locally aged by means of portable encircling heaters.

In some respects, the fabrication of the cases for these rocket motors is similar to shipbuilding. For one thing, it is quickly found that the case dimensions require tools and cranes available almost exclusively in shipyards. Furthermore, it is impossible to transport either the motor or nozzle by rail (the dimensional limitation on rail transport is about 160 in. in diameter), so that the manufacturing plant must be on the waterside. More about transporting these giants later.

At this point, a second major difference between solid rockets and liquid rockets is evident—a structural difference. The solid rocket motor carries its total propellant load within its casing, so the motor is a sturdy structure. The significance of this is that the solid-rocket motor can function as a major structural element of the launch vehicle. It can carry the axial and transverse loads produced in a launch vehicle with relative ease since it is controlled in design and in strength level by the need to contain high-pressure combustion.

In the liquid propulsion system, on the other hand, the situation is radically different. The engine is a distinct element, separate from tankage and from the vehicle structural elements. Liquid propellant tanks are almost always designed for moderate internal pressure, usually only for the head produced by the liquids under the maximum acceleration force, with the usual safety factors.

Fig. 4-56. Bigger solid-propellant motors mean bigger hardware. Largest motors fired to date are 10 ft in diameter. These casing segments, for the next generation of motors, are 23 ft in diameter. Five of them, each 100 ft long, would be needed to boost a planetary spaceship. This casing is experimental, not to be fired. It's being built to assay problems of manufacturing, propellant casting, handling, and transport. (Courtesy Aerojet General Corp.)

Nozzles are simple, but sadly abused

The rocket nozzle represents a third major difference between liquid-propellant and solid-propellant rockets. Essentially all liquid-propellant rocket motors are cooled by the passage of one of the liquids through tubes which form the nozzle and the combustion chamber. By contrast, all nozzles for solid rocket motors

(Fig. 4-57) are uncooled. Consequently, a major subtechnology has developed in the solid-propellant field for the research, investigation, and development of materials to withstand nozzle conditions.

In a solid-propellant rocket, the combustion products enter the nozzle at a temperature near 6000°F at a pressure of 600–700 psi, and travel at subsonic velocity. Within the short distance from the entrance to the nozzle throat, a distance of a few inches in smaller rockets to about 15 ft in the very large rockets, the velocity of the gas increases to the local sonic velocity. In going through this rapid exodus, the temperature and pressure of the combustion gas both drop. Beyond the throat expansion takes place, the velocity of the gas becoming supersonic, the static temperature and pressure dropping even further. The velocity of the hot gases leaving the nozzle is of the order of 8000 to 10,000 ft/sec. The nozzle, then, is a simple and fairly effective machine, but one that must face difficult conditions.

As we attempt to leap into space, a new facet of the nozzle problem is introduced. The burning duration for a rocket vehicle carrying men must be greater than the duration for a ballistic missile, roughly twice as long. Why? Because the human payload can stand only a peak acceleration load of about 16 g (and this only for a short time). The g-load is intimately intertwined with the aerodynamic load produced by the atmospheric pressure on the vehicle during its ascent. The aerodynamic load, in turn, is related to the burning time of the rocket motor. For the large solid booster with a human payload, burning time should be about 120 sec.

How can the solid rocket nozzle withstand prolonged heat transfer and thermal shock conditions? What about the erosive effect of liquid or solid aluminum oxide carried in the exhaust stream? The problem is met in two ways: on the one hand, through the use of materials with high melting points; on the other, through the use of ablative materials which melt, char, decompose, and in the process absorb heat (see "Ablation," page 535).

The small solid military rocket, with its short burning time, may use a simple nozzle of steel. The larger military rocket, with its longer burntime, may use refractory metals. The very large motors I am discussing here have nozzle requirements that stem from the difficulties of fabricating such big structures, and from the problems of temperature and stress. Thus fewer materials are available.

But there is a compensating factor when dealing with very large rocket nozzles. And this is that moderate change in nozzle diameter during firing has almost no effect on the per-

Fig. 4-57. The most complex hardware on any solid propellant motor is the nozzle. It's a composite structure of materials that must resist the hot, high-velocity gases of combustion, since there are no fluids on board for cooling. Here you can see the graphite throat—the area that takes the greatest abuse. As a booster, this motor is pretty small. Still, it's over 8 ft in diameter and delivers some half-million lb of thrust. At left is a tiny precursor, a solid-propellant motor of only a few hundred pounds thrust. (Courtesy Aerojet General Corp.)

formance of the rocket. For example, the erosion rate of a typical nozzle throat material, such as block graphite or a graphite-cloth laminate, will probably be 2- to 5-thousandths in./sec of burning time. In the 120-sec burning life of the booster, this will result in the removal of about ¾ in. of material from the nozzle throat, or about 3% increase in throat area. This will cause essentially no change in performance of a big rocket.

Big nozzles—a manufacturing problem

Very well, how should we make a nozzle with throat diameter of 90 in. and exit-cone diameter of 22 ft? The material selection is limited. Solid graphite or carbon might be used, since the erosion rate I mentioned above is tolerable. We find, however, that there is a limit to the size of graphite slugs available in this country, diameters above 6 ft requiring special equipment and facilities.

Refractory metals such as tungsten or molybdenum are effectively ruled out: first, because they would be difficult to obtain in the required dimensions, second, because of their weight, and third, because of their brittle characteristics.

In summary, it appears that the best materials for rocket nozzles for this class of motors are laminates of ablating materials (see margin). For the throat section and the parts immediately forward and aft, laminates of graphite cloth bonded with phenolic resins will be used. This kind of structure has been proved in motors with throats up to 37 in. in diameter,

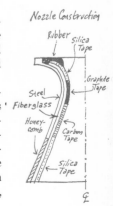

Nozzle Construction
Rubber
Silica Tape
Graphite Tape
Steel
Fiberglass
Honeycomb
Carbon Tape
Silica Tape

during burning times exceeding two minutes. The exit cone of the nozzle will be made of silica cloth bonded with phenolic resins, a structure well tested in many solid rockets and satisfactory in operation. The outer structure of the nozzle will in all probability be steel, although the aft part of the exit cone can be made of a lighter material.

Moving the behemoths

The nozzle of the future superbooster will present somewhat the same transportation problem as the motor case. The size (but not the weight) is too great for rail transportation, and barge or ship transportation will be required. I don't want to overemphasize the transportation problem, however. We should remember that much of the heavy transport in the U.S. is done now by barges and ships.

Nonetheless, the weight of the finished motor will surely exercise the ingenuity of transport and handling engineers: $3\frac{1}{2}$ million lb of motor, plus the necessary container, handling harness, and possibly temperature controlling system, gives a total of some 4 million lb to be handled. Barges or ships can carry the weight, but the difficulty will be getting the motor on and off the barges. A 4-million-lb lift by crane has never been made in this country. The largest cranes now available can individually raise somewhat over 1 million lb.

While larger cranes can be built, it is possible that other methods for handling the large motor will be better. Methods somewhat akin to dry-docking operations. The motor might be contained in a special caisson which would be maneuvered onto a partially submerged barge, the barge righted, towed to the receiving point, and then the process reversed.

No more assembly lines

In the rocket manufacturing plant very real changes in concept are required. The current practice in making small rocket motors is to move the motor through the various manufacturing steps. At one stop, the empty case is degreased and primed. The case is moved to another building, where liner and insulator are bonded in and cured, Another move takes the motor to the casting site, and so on. Clearly, with the very large motors, this flow of manufacture is not practical. In effect the machinery for preparing the motor case and for casting and curing the propellant will be brought to the motor which will remain in one location. Even the test facility will probably be integrated into the manufacturing site to avoid moving the loaded motor.

Visualize, if you will, the resulting integrated manufacturing and test facility. Its central feature might be a pit 100 ft deep and 50 ft in diameter. The pit concept for manufacture and test grows partially from the water method for handling and shipping the large motors as described above, for the pit can be flooded like a drydock and communicate by canals with water transport lanes.

The motor case is placed in the pit in the vertical position, nozzle end up. It rests on a concrete pad about 20 ft thick. And here we come to another of the fundamental differences between solid-rocket technology and liquid-rocket technology. For after the propellant is mixed and cast in place on-site, the motor can be tested, still in place, but upside down. This means that the 7-million-lb thrust can be taken by the earth through the massive but simple and relatively inexpensive concrete pad beneath it.

The corresponding static test stands for liquid-propellant engines are much more complex since in practically all cases they are fired to exhaust downward, requiring a rising supporting structure, and special flame deflectors to divert the exhaust. The cost difference between the two types is appreciable.

Think BIG!

The central point I have sought to make in the preceding pages is that solid-propellant rockets are well established; that they have built into them relative ease of growth to the sizes needed for very large boosters; and that consequently the central task is to focus on the engineering concomitant with such vast size.

Much of what I have discussed is established fact. The first 120-in. diameter motor was fired, producing a peak thrust of 250,000 lb, in 1962; in mid 1963 five of these "segments" were stacked and fired successfully, for a thrust of just over 1 million lb. This firing established beyond peradventure the arrival of the solid-fuel rocket in the big booster field.

What's next? The Air Force and NASA have worked out a careful program for the extension of these accomplishments (plus many for which I don't have space) to the very large boosters discussed in this article. This program involves essentially two steps: First, the manufacture and test of two "half-length" motors (70 ft long) of the 22-ft diameter class, each producing 3.5 million lb thrust. Second, the extension of these results to the construction and test of two "full-length" motors (130-ft long) with 7-million-lb thrust. At the same time, nozzle tests will be run using short, segmented motors of 13 ft diameter.

The technology implicit in this quantum jump in booster capacity has been outlined in the preceding pages. Its massive proportions clearly require undergirding that is more financial than

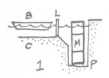

1

2

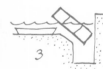

3

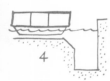

4

P— PIT
B— BARGE
C— CANAL
L— LOCK
M— MOTOR
IN
CAISSON

technological. Clearly, the program just outlined will cost tens of millions of dollars. Is it worth it? I firmly believe it is, for if the new class of solid boosters is fully developed, we will have a powerful, relatively uncomplicated tool available for large space flights when the need arises.

Further reading

For an easygoing introduction to solid propulsion, written for engineers, see Sutton's *Rocket Propulsion Elements* (Wiley, 1963). To place solid propulsion in perspective, read the state-of-the-art surveys at the beginning of the Propulsion Section of the *Space/Aeronautics R&D Technical Handbook* for 1962 and 1963. The Jan. 1963 issue of *Astronautics* (now *Astronautics and Space Engineering*) has a forward-looking series of six articles under the title "Large Launch Vehicles." The limitations of chemical fuels, both solid and liquid, are discussed in a lively manner in Johnson's "New Fuels," *Proc. of the Royal Society*, Aug. 1959.

First principles of thermodynamics and combustion in relation to rockets are well covered in a series of books, *High Speed Aerodynamics and Jet Propulsion*, ed. by Plase and Taylor (Princeton, 1956). See particularly Vol. 1, *Combustion Processes*, and Vol. 2, *Fundamentals of Gas Dynamics*. Detail on propellant grain design and properties of propellants will be found in Wimpress's *Internal Ballistics of Solid Fuel Rockets* (McGraw-Hill, 1950).

Invaluable for checking out the potential of various fuel and oxidizer combinations is Dobbin's compendium *Thermodynamics of Rocket Propulsion and Theoretical Evaluation of Some Prototype Propellant Combinations* (WADC TR-59-757 Project 3148, available to qualified contractors from ASTIA, Arlington, Va.). In preparing this "dictionary," Dobbins used data from *Selected Values of Chemical Thermodynamic Properties* by Rossine and Bichowsky, NBS Circular 500 (GPO).

If what you need is a single reference work, check *Aerodynamics, Propulsion, Structures and Design Practice* by Bonney, Zucrow, and Besserer (1956, $15), in the *Principles of Guided Missile Design Series* (Van Nostrand). The literature of the field can be tracked admirably in the *Journal of the American Institute of Aeronautics and Astronautics*.

ABLATION

by Irving Gruntfest and Lawrence Shenker *

IN BRIEF: *Re-entry of a space vehicle into the earth's atmosphere typifies a number of situations where a structure undergoes intense heating. How fast the interior temperature rises depends on the difference between the rate heat reaches the surface and how fast it is conducted inward. The problem of thermal protection is to make this difference a maximum. The solution is to obstruct the heat at the surface—i.e., give it something else to do. It can be made to melt, sublimate, or decompose the material so that the exposed surface recedes, or ablates. Organic plastics are well constituted to thus divert enormous quantities of heat because they contain plenty of hydrogen, the element that absorbs the most energy per unit mass. Properly reinforced against the shearing action of hot flowing gases, they make the best thermal shield yet devised. The problem now is to optimize their ablation performance to fit different heating situations.—F.P.*

■ The word "ablation" is a curious one. It means, literally, removal or separation. The surgeon uses it to indicate the cutting away of unwanted tissue. The geologist uses it to describe the removal of a particular rock type from an aggregate by mechanical means. More to our point here, it has been adopted by astronomers and astrophysicists to describe the erosion and disintegration of meteors entering the earth's atmosphere. The "removal tools" here are an unusual combination of intense heating and air friction that melts, vaporizes, and otherwise changes the surface.

In a very real sense, then, you can think of thermal ablation (we will drop the "thermal" hereafter) as an unusual type of nonequilibrium response to heating in which only the exposed surface is lost. Roughly speaking, in the process of ablation, mass is sacrificed for thermal protection.

Recoverable earth satellites, lunar or interplanetary vehicles, as well as long-range missiles, can be regarded as man-made meteorites. For a number of these it has been found most practical to insure the survival of the vehicle by covering its surfaces with materials that are sacrificed slowly and smoothly so as to protect the structure and payload from thermal damage.

In retrospect, however, the new technology of ablation is not altogether novel. In electric

* Both authors are at the General Electric Co. Missile and Space Division in Philadelphia. Irving Gruntfest is a physical chemist and staff consultant; Lawrence Shenker, a chemical engineer, is manager of the plastics technology group.

furnaces, or in carbon arc light sources, electrodes are continuously fed into the hot zone of the device and could be said to ablate. In nature, it is likely that the longevity of redwood and sequoia trees is due in part to the protection of their vital parts from fire damage by the unique thickness and ablating properties of their bark.

There is, of course, no material through which heat will not flow. The general laws governing the rate of flow of heat into a body were formulated long ago by Fourier. For a material whose properties are independent of temperature, the time required for it to warm up all the way through depends directly on the ratio of the volumetric heat capacity (usually written as ρc, the product of density and specific heat) to the thermal conductivity k.

Forgetting for the moment that for real materials both ρc and k turn out to be temperature dependent, the material that would withstand a hot environment the longest would be the one with the highest possible specific heat and the lowest possible conductivity. But what kind of material might this be? Atomic and molecular theories of specific heat show that the specific heat of a material depends on the number of atoms in a unit volume or unit weight. Since the smallest, lightest atom is that of hydrogen, one expects that the material of choice will contain a lot of hydrogen. Fortunately, some of the structural materials which are richest in hydrogen also have the lowest thermal conductivities. These are the organic plastics.

It may at first seem incongruous to think of these materials as having more heat resistance than the refractory metals and ceramics. Yet that is the way it turns out, at least in some technologically important situations. In others, designers have selected inorganic refractories, composites of organic and inorganic materials, and organic materials that contain no hydrogen at all. As the story unfolds we will point out some of the reasons behind these various choices.

The mechanics of ablation

In very hot environments any material will ablate. In a steady environment, the response of the material to heating often includes two transient phases, one of which is quasi-steady.

For example, if one surface of a large slab of solid metal is exposed to a very hot stream of chemically inert gas, its surface temperature will rise—the first transient phase. The rate of rise depends on the difference between the rate at which heat reaches the surface from the hot environment and the rate at which heat is conducted into the material.

A space-oriented anecdote, which we pass along without having scrutinized its origins, will give an idea of what this means. As the story goes, a large chunk of metal appeared in a salvage yard recently. To dispose of it, workmen began to cut it into smaller pieces with acetylene torches. The hottest flames available (3000°C) had no effect. Clearly, here was a relic from an unidentified flying object made of a refractory metal unknown in the free world. What is more, the "discovery" was concealed from the public and even from the scientific community.

As you might expect, the unknown metal was copper. No matter how hot the torch flame, the heat was conducted away from the point of application and dissipated so rapidly that the surface, though hot, never reached the modest 1083°C required to melt it.

If the torch had been bigger and had been held there long enough, surface melting would have occurred and hot liquid would have begun to drip or be blown off the surface. After this, the second transient phase would have set in—the surface of the chunk receding, or ablating, at a steady rate depending on the latent heat of fusion of the metal, its heat capacity and thermal conductivity as well as the heating rate.

If the same experiment were done with a material that sublimes rather than melts, similar transient heating and quasi-steady ablation would be expected. However, the ejection of vapor from the surface would interfere with the convective transfer of heat from the gas stream. This effect has been called "blocking action," and performs a useful function in thermal protection. In many practical situations, it can reduce the net transport of heat from the gas stream to the solid by more than 50%.

Useful ablation includes decomposition

This phenomenon can be further exploited. Some of the materials most useful in ablating heat-protection systems for re-entry vehicles do not merely melt or sublime in response to heating, but rather decompose to give large volumes of gas and a porous refractory residue. A typical material is a composite of nylon fibers and phenolic resin which, when exposed to a stream of hot gas, suffers two distinct, consecutive, transient processes followed by the development of a quasi-steady state.

In the first transient process, the surface temperature rises to the decomposition temperature of the composite. In the second, the material begins to char or carbonize and evolve gases of rather low molecular weight. The interface between the char layer and the virgin material now moves into the slab. During this period, gases generated in the course of the char-forming process at the moving interface diffuse through the char and absorb heat. These heated gases are ejected and exert a blocking action.

As the char layer thickens, the amount of heat reaching the moving interface is reduced by the insulating effect of the porous char combined with the cooling effect of the diffusing gases (see marginal sketch). Thus the rate of decomposition and gas formation at the interface is also reduced. As a result, the surface temperature of the char rises until *it* begins to ablate.

This second transient terminates when the rate of char surface ablation equals the rate of recession of the char-virgin material interface. The combined effect of heat exchange in the porous char and of blocking action at the heated surface as the evolved gases emerge is often called transpiration cooling.

The fact that the porous residue generated in the decomposition of the virgin composite is carbon makes it possible for a very hot surface to be presented to the environment. This not only can reduce the driving temperature gradient from the gas to the solid, but also can radiate back into the environment a substantial amount of the energy that it receives. This is the quasi-steady state mentioned earlier, and if it can be maintained long enough, the structure can emerge safely from its incandescent ordeal. Two samples which have survived such intense transient heating are shown in Color Fig. 36 with their char layers quite evident.

More than simple heat transfer

In order to complete this somewhat detailed but still qualitative description of ablation it is necessary to point out that chemical reactions between the environmental gas and the ablating material can usually be expected. Furthermore, the erosion of the hot surface need not be only thermal or chemical. Surface removal can also be caused by shear forces generated by the flowing environmental gas, pressure forces from the gas generated at the char-virgin material interface, or thermal stresses set up by the temperature gradients in the solid material. Keep in mind that the usefulness of an ablating material does not depend altogether on its rate of ablation but rather on its net ability to prevent heat from the environment from damaging the structure or payload on which it is applied.

Thus, we see that what started out to be a problem involving only convective heat transfer to a solid and conductive heat transfer in the solid has become more complicated. It also involves the effect of added combustible gases on the convective heating, radiative rejection of heat from the hot surface, receding surface,

flow of gas through a hot porous solid, and gas-producing chemical reactions at the char-virgin material interface. When the environmental gas becomes sufficiently hot to be luminous, radiative heating of the solid must also be taken into account. Furthermore, under these conditions the gas may dissociate and ionize, grossly changing its chemical and physical properties. The nature of these changes is the subject of much study at present.

In spite of this complexity, the ablation problem can be treated analytically with the help of modern high-speed computers. The analyses depend on the equations for conservation of energy, mass, and momentum, and use certain assumptions pertaining to the chemical processes at the char-virgin interface. These analyses have been quite useful for the correlation and extrapolation of experimental data, as well as for the design of vehicles. The theory developed here also advances our knowledge of the burning of solid fuels like coal which involves the behavior of a hot surface in a gaseous environment.

Different missions, different materials

We have belabored the complexity of ablation to make it clear that the details of the process can depend on both the nature of the material and the nature of the environment. The best material for one mission need not even be suitable for another. A few examples will make this clear.

One is shown in the re-entry photograph, Fig. 4-58 (also, see the example in Color Fig. 37). However, the explicit application of ablating materials did not begin with the intercontinental range missile. Ablating graphite fins in the rocket exhaust stream were used for the guidance of the German V-2's. No available metals were found to be adequate for this job. After World War II, the Hermes rocket project in the U.S. utilized a fiber glass reinforced plastic material for control surfaces. This not only eliminated a thermal-stress problem but also made possible a more slender, lower-drag configuration.

In the early development work on nose-cone materials for the Jupiter intermediate-range ballistic missile, investigators at the Redstone Arsenal ran many tests in the exhaust of rocket engines. Among the candidate materials were ceramics and metals, as well as various reinforced plastics. It became apparent that in this particular environment the reinforced plastics were by far the most efficient thermal protection materials, and the Jupiter nose-cone thermal shield soon consisted of all reinforced plastic. Monolithic refractory ceramics, including carbon or graphite, in the sizes required generally

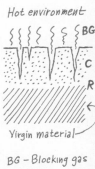

Hot environment

BG — Blocking gas
C — Char
R — Receding Interface

Virgin material

Fig. 4-58. Two man-made meteors trace their luminous way into the atmosphere. Thin single streak is the trajectory of a space vehicle penetrating successfully because it is protected by a thermal shield. Spent booster behind it is unprotected, thus breaks up and burns. (Courtesy J. Federico, GE Space Sciences Laboratory)

could not tolerate the thermal stresses generated in the test environments without cracking. Metals either melted, allowed too much heat flow to the interior, or had unreasonable weight requirements.

For the higher re-entry velocities and temperatures associated with the intercontinental ballistic missiles, it became apparent, both theoretically and experimentally, that a high glass- or refractory-fiber content might indeed not be the optimum solution. In many cases, therefore, the use of all-organic or high-organic plastic materials became fairly common. We have already touched upon the reasons for this, and will return to it shortly.

While these developments were taking place, the designers of rocket engines found that the ablative materials were extremely effective for protecting both the case and nozzle structures from the hot exhaust gases. This was particularly true in the case of solid propellant motors, where cooling with the liquid fuel was not possible.

Ablative materials are also used on the exterior of rocket engines and boosters to protect them from aerodynamic heating in the initial phases of flight. Solid propellant rocket engines, having high accelerations, reach high velocities at low altitudes and thus require substantial thermal protection.

The protection of launch pads or silos from the blast of rocket engine exhaust gases is another important application. This requirement is most substantial with liquid-rocket engines, which have a considerable burning time before lift-off starts. Here, the ablative concept of replaceable or thick coatings of plastic material on launch structures competes with cooling that uses huge volumes of water.

Re-entry conditions for satellites and space vehicles can often be even more severe than those encountered by ballistic missiles. The Mercury spacecraft were protected by a reinforced plastic ablative thermal shield, and the same principle is also being used in the shield design for the Gemini and Apollo spacecraft.

Simulating re-entry conditions

Direct studies of ablation during re-entry are unreasonably costly and inconvenient for the systematic evaluation of large numbers of potentially useful ablation materials. A great deal of effort has therefore been devoted to the development of laboratory simulations. Chemical flames, solar furnaces, regenerative gas heaters, and electric arc devices have been used as the heat sources. For simulating flow conditions, these heat sources are used in conjunction with wind tunnels of various kinds.

Simulation is important because the re-entry environments are unfamiliar and our intuition may be unreliable. The familiar sources of heat are combustion reactions. These reactions are reversible and at high temperatures the usual products—water and carbon dioxide—dissociate, absorbing much of the heat generated in combustion. Temperatures in the hottest chemical flames are thus limited to about 5000°C.

The temperatures in electric arcs, like those generated in re-entry, are not limited in the same way. In addition, the gas compositions can be controlled because the heating does not depend upon chemical reactions. However, it is found that as the power input to an arc is increased, the energy tends to make the "flame" bigger rather than hotter. Only by preventing this growth can the energy intensity be increased. When this is done, satisfactory temperature levels for ablation testing can be reached.

With these arc-heating devices for gases, commonly called plasma generators or plasma torches, one can nicely simulate a variety of re-entry environments and reach temperatures in the order of 20,000°C. They have also provided useful, new methods for fabrication of refractory coatings and structures, and for chemical synthesis (see "Plasma Torches," page 458).

We would like to emphasize the inadequacy of temperature alone as a quantitative index of the severity of an environment. Enthalpy, the integral of specific heat over a temperature range, is a preferable index because this is the property that can be expected to correlate with heat transfer. For example, low pressure gas at a very high temperature does not constitute a severe threat to a material because it has a low specific heat, hence its heat content (or enthalpy per unit volume) is low. Enthalpy is a useful index because it reflects the chemical nature of the gas, as well as its temperature and density.

What simulated ablation reveals

It's important to note at the outset that complete laboratory simulation of the re-entry environment has not yet been achieved. Nonetheless, many useful inferences about the performance of ablation materials have been made correlating laboratory results with flight test data and with analytical studies of the physics of ablation.

One of the earliest, and most important of these inferences was that the ablation rate cannot be correlated with high temperature stability. In those days, it was felt intuitively that refractory materials such as zirconia would not ablate as quickly as organic materials. We recall all too clearly the amused contempt which greeted early requests to test reinforced plas-

tics in ablative environments. The durability table below shows the surprising result. Ordinary glass-fiber reinforced phenolic resins ablated one-sixth as rapidly as zirconia, and the same resin with nylon fibers improved this even more.

DURABILITY OF MATERIALS

Material	Relative weight loss
Graphite	1.0
Phenolic + nylon fibers	1.48
Silicon carbide	2.1–7.8
Phenolic + silica fibers	2.7
Phenolic + glass fibers	2.7
Silica	2.9
Alumina	8.5–17.0
Aluminum silicate	10.0
Zirconia	16.0
Copper	75.0

Earlier in this article, we explained the excellent ablation resistance of the organic plastics in terms of the duration of the thermal transient —these materials have high heat capacities and can thus endure the hot environment longer. This result can also be understood in terms of energy absorption. The function of the thermal shield material is to *absorb* and *divert* energy from the structure and payload. This requirement is the reverse of that on a fuel which must *generate* and *deliver* energy. The chemical reaction which has the highest potential energy yield per unit weight is the recombination of hydrogen atoms.

By the same token, the dissociation of hydrogen molecules has the highest capacity for energy absorption. In effect, then, an ablating plastic can be thought of as an "antifuel." Materials with lots of hydrogen in them can function in this manner—absorbing enormous quantities of heat in their process of decomposition and dissociation. The heat absorption figures in the table of specific heats below show this clearly.

INTEGRATED SPECIFIC HEATS

Material	Heat absorbed (cal/g)	Relative gas vol.
Hydrogen gas	67,000	1.0
Organic plastic (CH_2)	24,000	0.21
Organic plastic (CH)	20,000	0.15
Graphite	16,670	0.08
Water	14,500	0.16
Beryllium	9,876	0.11
Beryllia	7,080	0.08
Fluorocarbon plastic	6,300	0.06
Cellulose plastic	5,760	0.10
Magnesia	5,500	0.05
Silica	2,800	0.05
Copper	1,600	0.016

We wish to make clear that ablative performance of a material depends vitally upon the nature of the thermal environment. At lower temperatures, the all-organic reinforced plastics are not as suitable as inorganic-reinforced plastics. For example, in the exhaust of an alcohol-oxygen rocket motor (about 2500°C), a phenolic plastic reinforced with silica fibers is almost three times as resistive to ablation as the same resin strengthened with nylon or glass fibers. Going somewhat lower, exposure in a hot-gas wind tunnel (about 1800°C) shows the phenolics reinforced with glass or silica fibers to be almost five times more durable than the nylon-phenolic composite.

The basic reasons for this reversal are that at the lower temperatures the combustion effects become more important, and that the surface of the inorganic materials can come into equilibrium with the moderately hot environment. For further specific comparisons among materials, we suggest you examine the additional reading cited at the end of this article.

The thermal erosion rates of organic plastics do not depend on their chemical composition alone. Plastics which form coke-like char on their surface in response to heating tend to erode more slowly. This is altogether to be expected because of the high temperature that can be sustained by a carbon surface. In addition, a plastic which gives a high yield of carbon on pyrolysis also gives a high yield of hydrogen or other low molecular weight gases

which are most effective as blocking agents. Among the common plastics, the phenolic resins give the highest yield of coke on pyrolysis, which probably accounts for their wide usage in the formulation of organic ablating materials.

The importance of reinforcement

Since in practical applications of ablation the recession of the surface depends upon mechanical as well as thermal effects, plastics reinforced with refractory fibers which can aid the retention of the porous char are often selected.

Among the inorganic fibers useful for this purpose are glass, high-silica leached glass, carbon, graphite, and varieties of asbestos. Organic fibers such as nylon or Dacron are used for the highest temperature environments and the highest heating rates, as noted above. However, their resistance to shear forces is limited and they may generate gases of decomposition before the matrix material is sufficiently degraded and porous to prevent pressure build-up in the composite. Thus, the char can pop off locally unless special provisions are made for venting.

Sometimes, ablative heat shields do not use reinforcement at all. One of the recent advances in ablation materials has been the development of compositions which can be cast or molded at low pressure, and which are equal to or better than phenolic resins in char yield. An example is the epoxy resin series to which special chemicals have been added. With such materials, costs of material and tooling, as well as time requirements for fabrication, are reduced. An example of such a nonreinforced thermal shield is shown in Fig. 4-59.

How hot is hot?

Thus far, we have explained the concept of ablation, and its complexity, and have indicated some of the steps that can be taken to use it. Our discussion would not be complete, however, without a brief look at the diverse environments in which ablative materials perform their protective tasks.

These are essentially two. The first occurs in combustion processes of all sorts, the most severe of which are to be found in rocket engines. Here, the gases which may cause damage are limited in temperature by the heat-absorbing dissociation of the combustion by-products. Although the temperatures are low (2000–3000°C) compared to re-entry conditions, there are factors that make ablative protection difficult to achieve. For one thing, engine configurations are often closed so that the beneficial effect of radiant heat loss is largely absent. For another, the by-products of combustion are often highly erosive and can thus

Fig. 4-59. Some ablative thermal shields do not require fiber reinforcement at all. This unreinforced 200-lb shield was cast using an epoxy resin that cures to a solid after it is poured into mold and heated. (Courtesy GE, Re-entry Systems Dept.)

adversely affect the buildup and retention of the porous char layer. These are complex ablation problems that have received much scrutiny.

Aerodynamic heating is the second important ablation environment, and our discussion of simulation techniques gave some indication of its severity. The source of heat here is the kinetic energy of the body to be protected. In the case of a re-entry vehicle, the potential energy of the carloads of fuel used to propel it into space is converted to kinetic energy, most of which must be dissipated when the body returns to earth. In most cases, only a small percentage of this total—less than 0.1% in the case of an ICBM—will reach the surface requiring protection. But even these small fractions can be quite formidable.

The most troublesome areas to protect are, of course, those which first impinge upon the stagnant atmosphere. On a given vehicle there may be many such areas where the gas molecules are abruptly accelerated to the velocity of the vehicle. As a consequence, the gas temperature of the gas and its heat content rise in a rather complicated manner which depends upon the flight mechanics, aerodynamics, and aerothermochemistry of the particular re-entry situation.

You can gain some idea of what this means in terms of vehicle temperatures and heating rates by scanning the typical "trajectories" plotted in Fig. 4-60 for a variety of re-entry vehicles. These are curves of altitude vs. velocity, upon which are superimposed dashed curves of constant heating rate. Each dashed curve is labeled with the temperature at which surface would be in radiation equilibrium with its environment. These are the highest temperatures the body can reach at that heating

rate—taking its emissivity as 0.9, a reasonable figure for char.

Notice that the highest heating rates occur for vehicles that retain their high velocities to very low altitudes—namely, the ICBM's. The ablation problem on such vehicles is severe, indeed. On the other hand, a manned orbital capsule is designed to decelerate at a very high altitude so that the maximum heating rate will be much lower, even though the total amount of heat to be diverted turns out to be higher.

Total heating time is, of course, a crucial factor: for a vehicle with a steep trajectory like a long-range weapon, this may be 20–30 seconds; for one like a manned vehicle returning from the moon on a shallow trajectory, the heating time might be 15 minutes or more. A maneuverable vehicle that could employ dynamic lift, like the proposed Dyna-soar spacecraft, would take even more time descending to earth.

Not one material, but several

From this brief description of diverse ablation environments, you can see that there probably exists no universal ablation material. For missile re-entry, where the heating rates are very high, the protective mechanism is the "pure" ablation described earlier: the quasi-steady state is reached in a few seconds, and protection depends on how effective transpiration cooling is in limiting attrition of the charred surface. The ablator is designed so that the surface recedes at about the same rate that the heat moves into the material (see sketch).

For a manned re-entry vehicle, the ablation situation is wholly different. The heating rate

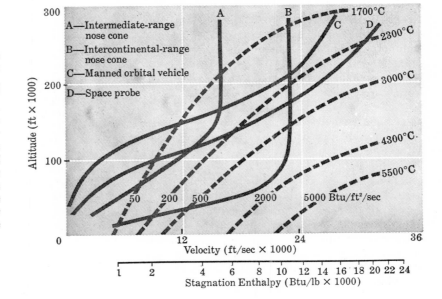

Fig. 4-60. Re-entry into earth's atmosphere is not a single heat protection problem but several, depending upon the type of vehicle and its characteristics. A ballistic missile slows down only at low altitude where air is dense, and is thus faced with a high heating rate (see dashed curves). A manned vehicle, by contrast, is decelerated at high altitude, encounters less dense air and hence a lower heating rate. Ablation materials are chosen accordingly.

A—Intermediate-range nose cone
B—Intercontinental-range nose cone
C—Manned orbital vehicle
D—Space probe

(as the curves show) is much lower, and even though the temperature of the surrounding gas and its heat content are quite high, the surface temperature has a limit. It cannot get hotter than the temperature at which as much heat radiates away as is brought to it by aerodynamic heating. If the surface char is stable at this temperature, the quasi-steady state ablation, involving gross loss of material we discussed earlier, never occurs. The design problem, then, is just how much heat will the thermal shield material conduct to the payload.

We have separated these two situations for the sake of emphasis. In reality, both may occur in different parts of the same vehicle—the leading and lee surfaces of a re-entry vehicle, for example (or the nozzle and skirt areas of a rocket engine, for that matter). Thus, it is not uncommon to find different types of ablative materials employed on the same body.

A look ahead

In the few years that the subject of ablation has been studied, the whole complexion of the heat protection problem has been changed. Indeed, the general ideas of ablation are not yet in the textbooks. The development of ablation materials is still in its infancy. When one compares the theoretically possible heat diversion capacity of various materials with those that have been achieved, improvement factors of ten appear to emerge as a tantalizing goal. Organic chemists are now engaged in "tailoring" materials to control such factors as char yield, char porosity, char strength, gas yield, type and orientation of inclusions, and methods of fabrication.

We think that ablating materials will grow in usefulness in rocket motors and in space-vehicle thermal shields as space technology evolves. As higher speed aircraft come into service, ablation materials may even be used in volume as expendable elements in much the same way as chemical fuels are used today. The supersonic aircraft that carries you in the future may pull up to a "reshielding station" as well as a refueling station to prepare for the next flight. Nuclear energy technology, too, depends on the survival of structures in very hot environments, and ablation may find its way into this field.

There is, however, an opposing view. It is that ablation is used only because scientists have failed to meet the challenge of discovering materials which are sufficiently stable in high temperature environments. Ablation will go out of style when such materials are discovered. We do not mind going on record with the view that solids much more thermally stable than carbon are not likely to be discovered. If

they are, however, we will be among the first to use them.

In conclusion, we regard ablation not so much as an example of a technological breakthrough as an example of what can be done with an interdisciplinary approach to a difficult technical problem. But the stimulus from this work need not only be the wider application of thermal ablation. Even now we find scientific interest quickening in the kinetics of decomposition, in heat transfer, and in high-temperature phenomena generally. Beyond this, we confidently expect the modes of thinking and analysis developed in ablation studies to be applied to other environments—such as corrosion and abrasion—where the transient survival of materials is the central problem.

Further reading

There is, alas, no book on ablation as yet. The literature of the field is, however, rich and varied. As a first step, you might learn more about the ablative environment by reading Allen's "Hypersonic Flight and the Re-entry Problem," *J. Aeron. Sci.*, **25**, 4 (1958). Then, you could study the special "High Temperature" issue of *Astronautics & Aerospace Eng.*, **22**, 1 (1963). To focus more closely on ablation, this ought to be followed by Schmidt's "Ablative Re-entry Cooling" in *Space/Aeronautics*, **37**, 2 (1962) and his "Ablative Propulsion Cooling" in *Space/Aeronautics*, **38**, 6 (1963). Then you are set for a look at the details of the char-forming process and the elegant analysis by which this intricate phenomenon is analyzed. For this, see Scala and Gilbert's "Thermal Degradation of a Char Forming Plastic During Hypersonic Flight," *J. Am. Rocket Soc.*, **32**, 6 (1962).

As to specific areas, if you want data on ablation performance, get the authors' "Re-entry Ablation of Reinforced Plastics," GE report No. PIB-15. This booklet of five articles can be obtained from: Manager, Product Information, GE Re-entry Systems Dept., Chestnut St., Philadelphia, Pa.

A thorough discussion of plasmas as sources of high temperatures is "Recent Advances in Electric Arc Plasma Generation" by John and Bade, *J. Am. Rocket Soc.*, **31**, 1 (1961). A recent thorough review of unclassified ablation studies sponsored by the Air Force is Schmidt's "Ablative Plastics for Re-entry Thermal Protection," WADC Technical Report No. 60-862, obtainable from OTS (Dept. of Commerce, Washington 25, D.C.). And for other references of historical and technical significance, see the selected bibliography accompanying author Gruntfest's treatment of ablation in the 2nd edition of the *Encyclopaedia of Chemical Technology* (Interscience, 1963).

COMMUNICATION BY SATELLITE

by Leonard Jaffe *

IN BRIEF: *The world-wide need for more long-distance communication channels is destined to be fulfilled by high capacity communications satellite systems. But so large are these systems, involving microwave stations on earth and stations or enormous reflectors in the sky, that an almost endless series of technical trade-offs are required. The system can't simply grow —almost all technical decisions must be made simultaneously. However, not all the technology for communication by satellite has yet been developed. Two passive and seven active NASA satellites have been sent aloft. With great success in launch techniques, they orbit at various altitudes up to 22,300 miles, providing invaluable data on how the earth and the sun perturb spacecraft orbits, and how reliable equipment will be when operating in the space environment. Ground stations of more than a dozen nations have tracked them with antennas of varying size, although one of their biggest challenges was to acquire and track at microwave frequencies with accuracies of a tenth of a degree.—E.H.*

■ Direct continent-to-continent communication began in 1866 with the laying of the first transatlantic telegraph cable. Sixty years later, in 1927, transatlantic telephone communication began via long-wave radio; its quality and reliability were far below land-line standards, but it was the best available for thirty years. In 1956, the new Atlantic cable began to provide high-quality telephone service, and today 300 telephone channels are available across the Atlantic.

Two things are impressive about this brief record: New technologies are being brought forth and are developing at an increasingly rapid rate. Every time communication channels have increased, they have been loaded to capacity almost at once; new means for communication have never caused the abandonment of the old ones.

The world is going to need many more channels for long-distance communication. There is the inevitable increase in conventional communication requirements. There is television, one channel of which occupies a bandwidth equivalent to 1200 telephone channels. There will be an immense increase in data transmission; an obvious example is the need for rapid trans-

mission of weather data. Where will the channels come from? How can they be obtained without further crowding the overcrowded frequency spectrum?

More cables can be installed, but their cost per channel is extremely high. On land a multitude of high-capacity channels can be provided

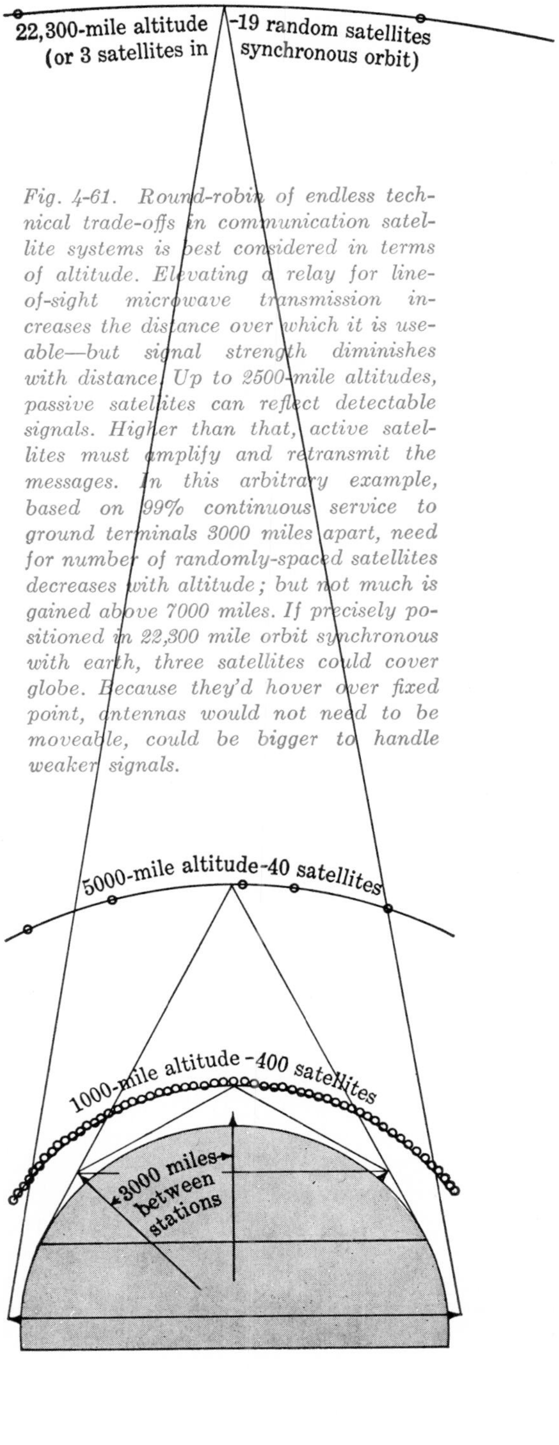

Fig. 4-61. *Round-robin of endless technical trade-offs in communication satellite systems is best considered in terms of altitude. Elevating a relay for line-of-sight microwave transmission increases the distance over which it is useable—but signal strength diminishes with distance. Up to 2500-mile altitudes, passive satellites can reflect detectable signals. Higher than that, active satellites must amplify and retransmit the messages. In this arbitrary example, based on 99% continuous service to ground terminals 3000 miles apart, need for number of randomly-spaced satellites decreases with altitude; but not much is gained above 7000 miles. If precisely positioned in 22,300 mile orbit synchronous with earth, three satellites could cover globe. Because they'd hover over fixed point, antennas would not need to be moveable, could be bigger to handle weaker signals.*

In the figure: 22,300-mile altitude (or 3 satellites in 19 random satellites synchronous orbit); 5000-mile altitude-40 satellites; 1000-mile altitude -400 satellites; 3000 miles between stations.

* An electronics engineer, Leonard Jaffe is Director of the Communication and Navigation Programs Division, National Aeronautics and Space Administration, Washington, D.C.

at relatively low cost by microwave radio. Microwave links, of course, are limited to line of sight distance; signals have to be transmitted from horizon to horizon by relay stations located as high as possible on towers or mountains.

Clearly, the next step is to raise relay stations even higher, putting them in an earth orbit to provide microwave communication at ocean-spanning distances. Within the next few years the new space technology is going to become the basis for a vastly expanded communications industry. Right now we are involved in making national and international decisions on the best ways to accomplish this.

The principle is simple. A powerful transmitter on the ground takes a message from the conventional land-based communication network; it sends it by line of sight to a transponder in orbit, which passes it along, again by line of sight, to a sensitive receiver several thousand miles away; from there the message is fed into another conventional network.

Deciding just how to do this is not simple at all.

Choices and trade-offs

Most large-scale systems grow out of small systems, and technical decisions about them get made step by step. But one of the essential facts about a system of communication by satellite is that it is large-scale from the start, for the cost of placing satellites in orbit is very large. Using microwave radio, satellites can provide a great number of channels at a cost per channel which is quite low compared, say, with ocean cables. For a few channels, they would be expensive. So decisions must be made at the very outset among an extraordinary number of alternatives. For instance:

Should the spacecraft in orbit be a passive satellite—simply a large object in space that can bounce signals from transmitter to receiver? Or should it be an active satellite—a radio relay that receives a signal and retransmits it?

What sort of orbit? Should the satellite be at 2000 miles, 5000 miles, 22,000 miles? The farther out we go, the greater the coverage each satellite can provide and the fewer of them are required—but the weaker the signal each satellite sends back.

Should the satellite be equipped to maintain itself in a precise orbit and to maintain a fixed orientation to the earth? This adds weight, but it also reduces the number needed and the signal-power requirements.

If the satellite is active, how much power should it transmit? More power increases the weight and shortens the life of the satellite; using minimal signal power makes it necessary

to use very sensitive and expensive ground stations.

What frequencies should be used for transmitting and receiving, and what kind of modulation should carry the signal?

How many satellites are needed? This depends on the kind of orbit, the kind of satellite, and the intended use of the system.

The list of choices goes on and on. And nearly every choice changes the factors involved in every other choice. Behind each technical decision is a long series of trade-offs of weight, of cost, of reliability, of service. My purpose in this article is to explain what is involved in some of the major choices and how they relate to each other in the design of a total communications system.

Experimental satellites first

Although the technical factors to be considered are well understood, there are still many unknowns about how equipment actually will perform in space. The primary task facing NASA was to launch a spectrum of satellite types into several types of orbits to gain experimental experience. These satellites were all launched, successfully, during the period 1960–1964:

Telstar I and II, wideband, active satellites built by AT&T, for intermediate altitude elliptical orbits.

Relay I and II, narrow and wideband active satellites built by RCA, for elliptical orbits at intermediate altitude.

Syncom I, II, III, narrow and wideband active satellites built by Hughes Aircraft Co., for synchronous orbits.

ECHO I and II, large, space-erected passive spheres, low altitude circular orbits built by the Schjeldahl Co. for low altitude circular orbits.

Ground stations for these experimental satellites were built during the period 1962–1964. The principal ones are shown in the table on p. 545. All of the organizations are participating on a voluntary basis without exchange of funds by the respective governments. NASA provides orbital data from its world-wide chain of tracking stations and gives technical assistance but not designs.

Characteristics of the signal

Let us start our examination of the choices to be made by looking at the signal to be transmitted from the satellite back to the ground receiver. That signal will be weak, so it is imperative to minimize the competition of noise. The ground antenna, pointing skyward, receives noise generated by the atmosphere and

Active Repeater Station

Sphere (Echo I & II)

GROUND STATIONS FOR COMMUNICATIONS SATELLITES

Location	Antenna	Operator	Capability
Andover, Me., U.S.A.	68-ft horn	AT&T	Television, voice, data
Nutley, N.J., U.S.A.	40-ft parabola	IT&T	Voice, data
Goonhilly, Great Britain	85-ft parabola	General Post Office	Television, voice, data
Pleumer-Bodou, France	68-ft horn	Centre National d'Etudes des Telecommunications	Voice, data
Rio de Janeiro, Brazil	30-ft parabola	Department of Posts & Telegraphs	Voice, data
Weilheim, Germany	85-ft parabola	Deutsche Bundesposte	Television, voice, data
Aveggano, Italy	30-ft parabola	Telespazio	Television, voice, data
Goldstone Lake, Calif., U.S.A.	40-ft parabola	STL/NASA	Television, voice, data
Takahagi, Japan	65-ft parabola	Kokusai Denshin Denwa Co., Ltd.	Television, voice, data
Kashima, Japan	98-ft parabola	Radio Research Labs.	Television, voice, data
Gothenburg, Sweden	84-ft parabola	Scandinavian Committee for Satellite Telecommunication	Voice, data
Mill Village, Nova Scotia, Canada	85-ft parabola	Canadian Dept. of Transport	Television, voice, data
Grinon, Spain	30-ft parabola	Espantelco	Voice, data

noise from outer space. This fact defines the frequency to be used—for atmospheric noise increases with frequency, while cosmic noise diminishes with frequency. A valley of minimum sky noise falls in the range of 1000 to 8000 megacycles.

This portion of the frequency spectrum is already used for common-carrier microwave links as well as for radiolocation and navigation systems. However, since relatively small amounts of power will be radiated or reflected from satellites, we are coming to the conclusion that it is possible to share the microwave bands with existing fixed point-to-point services on the ground. Moreover, since commercial satellite systems will themselves be used by the common carriers, it will be possible to centralize the responsibility for sharing frequencies and to have the same areas of the spectrum used for communication satellites and the ground microwave relay requirements.

It is significant that a tremendous addition to communication capacity is being created—hopefully without having to usurp any of the frequency spectrum. In sharing the spectrum, new regulatory considerations will arise. Limitations will have to be placed not only on the radiated power from the sharing systems but on the directions in which the systems are permitted to radiate this energy.

The signal power levels needed are set by the characteristics of the ground receiver stations. The ultimate in receiver sensitivity is already being approached through the use of maser techniques which come close to an internal noise temperature of 0°K. The over-all sensitivity can be raised significantly only by increasing the size of the receiving antenna. Here the governing factors are construction dif-

ficulties and cost. Fixed antennas could be made very large, but—unless a hovering or stationary satellite is used, the antennas will have to move to track the satellite in its orbit. The present practical limit for a movable antenna seems to be about 100 ft in diameter, and the largest now under construction for communication-satellite use are 80 to 85 ft.

Characteristics of these receiving antennas and of the most sensitive receivers, such as those using masers, indicate that the signal radiated from an active satellite should have a power of 3 to 10 watts. In the case of a passive satellite, this sets requirements for the power of the ground transmitter and for the minimum size and maximum height of the satellite. For an active satellite, this establishes a requirement for about 150 watts of power supply in the satellite.

Some of the high cost of ground equipment could be saved by radiating more power from the satellite. But this would call for more solar cells and also for more storage batteries to maintain power during passage through the earth's shadow. Perhaps more serious would be the reduction of reliability of the satellite as power output was raised. In the present state of the art, microwave transmitters must use vacuum tubes rather than solid-state devices, and the life of a tube goes down as the power it handles goes up.

There is a choice of modulation techniques to carry the signal—frequency modulation, amplitude modulation, or a variety of pulse code systems; FM has the advantage of requiring less power than AM, but it uses up a much wider frequency band. Conserving power seems much more important than conserving frequency, at present, so active satellites will probably transmit to ground via FM. However, to make it possible for several ground transmitters to have access to the same satellite simultaneously, single sideband AM might be used for the ground-to-space part of the microwave circuit.

It seems likely that an operational system will incorporate equipment using several different modulation techniques aboard the same satellite. The link from the U.S. to Europe requires wide-band circuits for television or to carry thousands of phone channels. But some less-developed areas might need just a few telephone channels capable of being received and transmitted by many ground terminals. We must provide for both kinds of operational requirements and a different modulation technique may be in order for each.

If two ground stations several thousand miles apart are to communicate via a particular satellite, the satellite must be in a portion of its orbit where it appears above the horizon for both of them as sketched in Fig. 4-65. For continuous service, another satellite must move into that portion of the orbit as soon as the first one moves out. Obviously, the higher above the earth the satellite is, the longer the period when it will be visible to both stations—and therefore the fewer satellites that will be needed.

Trade-offs on orbits

A little less obviously, if the satellites are neatly spaced one behind the other, fewer of them are needed than if they are orbiting at random intervals. But to maintain themselves in definite orbits with fixed spacings between them, satellites must carry propulsion and control equipment.

The ultimate form of a satellite communications system may well consist of a few well-spaced active satellites in a 22,300-mile orbit. At 22,300 miles a satellite circles the earth in exactly 24 hours—synchronous with the rotation of the earth. If the orbit is around the equator, therefore, it will stay fixed above one spot on the earth. If the orbit is somewhat inclined to the equator, the satellite stays close to a constant longitude, oscillating north and south in a figure-eight pattern.

The equatorial synchronous satellite system is a nearly ideal arrangement. Three equispaced satellites could provide complete coverage of the earth with the exception of the polar regions. Ground stations would not need movable antennas. The only departure from the ideal would be the time of travel of the signal up to the satellite and back—approximately 0.3 sec each way, causing a delay of 0.6 sec between the end of a remark and the receipt of a reply. This delay might or might not prove too annoying in two-way conversations; it is in excess of the delay permitted by existing international standards. Perhaps the standard needs to be re-examined. Of course, such delay would be unimportant in moving information in one direction for broadcast or in data transmission.

An operational synchronous system is barely not within the state of the art at present. It takes considerable rocket power simply to get into such a high orbit, and the boosters are costly. Moreover, the satellites would require added weight—for several reasons:

At that distance, we can no longer afford to radiate power in all directions; directional antennas must be pointed toward the earth. Such antennas themselves add weight. More important, the satellite will need elaborate stabilizing equipment to keep the antennas aimed. Even more serious is the weight and complexity of equipment needed to keep the satellite in an exact 24-hour orbit so that it really will stay in one place. The out-of-roundness of the earth introduces changes in orbital velocity; a satellite accelerates as it approaches a "high" spot, then decelerates as it leaves it. Furthermore, the moon tends to pull the satellite out of an equatorial plane, moving it into an inclined orbit.

Eventually these problems will be solved, but initially there is considerable interest in placing simpler active satellites in orbits from 5000 to 12,000 miles in altitude.

Active or passive?

Passive satellites off which signals can be bounced have obvious disadvantages. A satellite of the Echo type provides only a fraction of the traffic-handling capacity of an active satellite when used with the same-size ground equipment. Moreover, it takes a large number of passive satellites to provide world-wide coverage. That's because, to provide an adequate return signal, they must operate at altitudes less than about 2000 miles. These would necessarily be random orbits, since it would hardly be sensible to put active velocity-control equipment into a device whose very virtue is its passive character. And although the satellite itself may be cheaper than an active satellite, launching is expensive, since these satellites are heavy.

Nevertheless, the passive devices do have major advantages that make them worth considering. First of all, they are potentially very reliable. Some of the problems that became apparent in the Echo experiments seem solvable, leading to a passive satellite that should stay useful for decades. Thus a passive system might be cheaper in the long run than a system of active satellites which required frequent replacement.

The other advantage is flexibility. Active satellites have their complete capability designed into them at the outset. In the passive satellite case, additional capacity can be obtained by changing or adding ground equipment. Once placed in orbit, the passive system is free for anyone to use—anyone who can afford the elaborate ground equipment.

The first passive communication satellite, Echo I, is still in orbit, and much has been learned from it. By now it is reduced in size and wrinkled, so that its reflection characteristics are nonuniform. It wrinkled primarily because its plastic skin retained a memory of its folded condition in the canister that carried it aloft. If the "memory" of the plastic were eliminated, the only forces tending to collapse the sphere in space would be those resulting from solar radiation pressure and the impact of micrometeorites.

Echo II was constructed of two layers of ductile aluminum foil sandwiching a thin layer of plastic which provided greater strength. The foil takes on a permanent set when it's inflated, thus losing its memory. This structure is expensive in weight. The 100-ft Echo I sphere weighed 130 lb while Echo II, 135 ft in diameter, weighs 570 lb. This type of structure may be made lighter by removing substantial portions of the surface by etching or milling holes in the foil. Such a surface would still act as a solid reflector at microwave frequencies; the lighter structure would permit building larger satellites, and also reduce the surface area subjected to solar radiation pressure, which has dramatically changed the apogee and perigee of Echo I by as much as 500 miles. Another approach is to use a mesh structure imbedded in some plastic that would evaporate in the hard vacuum of space after the sphere had been inflated, leaving only the reflective mesh sphere in orbit.

There are also ways to strengthen the reflection by abandoning the spherical shape in favor of a shape that would reflect directionally toward the earth. The difficulty is that such a reflector has to be oriented again, only a passive orientation system would return the reliability advantages of the passive communication satellite.

One possibility is a passive orientation system utilizing the slight gravitational gradient of the earth. Any long object in space will eventually erect itself, pointing toward the earth's center if it is not tumbling, for whichever end happens to be lowest will experience a slightly greater gravitational effect and will be pulled toward the earth. It may be possible to orient a spherical segment in space, thus eliminating the necessity for placing in orbit that portion of a sphere which does not contribute to the reflected signal.

Problems of the active type

An active satellite is a far more complex affair. Most of the equipment it carries is shown in Fig. 4-62, including an antenna and receiver to pick up the ground signal on one frequency and a transmitter to amplify and re-radiate the signal on another frequency via another antenna.

Both AT&T's Telstar and NASA's Relay transmit to the ground on 4000 Mc. Telstar transmits ground-to-satellite on 6000 Mc, while Relay uses 2000 Mc for this link.

Radio equipment carried by the early active satellites is an excellent sample of the present state of the art for reliable communications. While all solid-state components would be best, there simply aren't any components available for the final power output stage of the transmitter that will provide the required 3 to 10 watts at these frequencies. The traveling-wave vacuum tubes employed are capable of handling the large bandwidths required and are much more efficient than triode vacuum tubes. Solar cells supply power to the electronics and whatever control systems are carried by the satellite;

SPHERE ETCHED WITH HOLES

MESH SPHERE

SPHERICAL SEGMENT GRAVITY STABILIZED

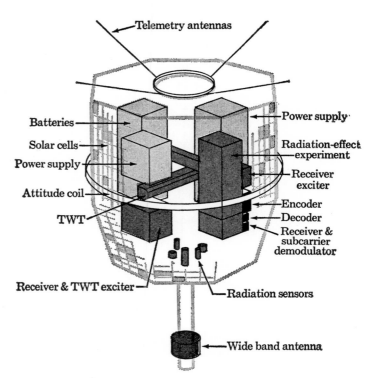

Fig. 4-62. Developmental Relay satellite has two transponders powered by storage batteries kept charged by external solar cells. Telemetry activates equipment, monitors radiation damage experiments. (Courtesy NASA)

batteries are used to provide stored energy when the satellite's solar source is eclipsed by the earth.

Solar cells have been shown to suffer degradation when bombarded by the high-energy protons and electrons that exist in space and in particularly heavy concentrations in the Van Allen radiation belts. Solar cells can be shielded from damage by electron bombardment with a small thickness of quartz covering the cell, but high-energy protons penetrate any reasonable amount of shielding. While this damage to solar cells has been measured by exposing them in accelerators, there is still a need for additional information on particle energy distribution in space and how this distribution varies with altitude.

The Relay and Telstar satellites orbited right through the heart of the Van Allen radiation belts and carried analyzers to measure the energy distribution and numbers of protons and electrons encountered. Radiation measurements were correlated with observed degradation of solar cells, diodes, and transistors carried in the satellite.

Much remains to be determined about how components can be damaged by micrometeorites and about the effect of the hard vacuum of space on components over a long period.

Prior to 1963, no active satellite of a *complex* nature had ever lasted longer than several months in space without a failure of some sort. The Vanguard I launched in 1958, is still beeping—but it contains only a very simple transmitter and a solar-cell power supply many times the required capacity to operate it.

Both the Relay and Telstar satellites were launched by a three-stage Delta rocket. Their orbits were elliptical—approximately 3000 miles in apogee and 500 to 1000 miles in perigee. Both are capable of carrying a television signal, one direction at a time. They are also capable of transmitting a dozen or so simultaneous two-way telephone channels.

In 1963 and 1964 three NASA Syncoms were placed in synchronous 24-hour orbit. The Delta vehicle can place a 125-lb pay load in an elliptic trajectory that will carry it up to 22,300 miles. By using about 70 lb of this pay load for another propulsion unit in the satellite—called an apogee kick stage—enough additional velocity can be added to propel the satellite into a circular orbit at that altitude.

As shown in Figs. 4-63 and 4-64, Syncom can be oriented and positioned in orbit by the thrust of simple gas jets. The satellite carries enough fuel to be capable of control for about one year. With only 55 lb available for the communications facility, Syncom can handle only a single telephone channel.

Choices on the ground

Ground-station facilities are very much dependent on the type of communication satellite system they will serve. For low-altitude systems in which satellites move rapidly across the field of view, two antennas are needed to maintain uninterrupted service. One antenna tracks until the satellite leaves the field of view. Meanwhile, a second antenna stands ready to acquire the next satellite as it comes by. If the ground station is itself a relay point, a third antenna is needed to retransmit to another satellite moving away.

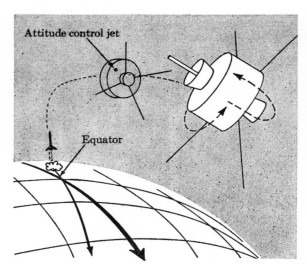

Fig. 4-63. Syncom was injected into elliptical orbit reaching 22,300 miles, then apogee kick stage rocket in satellite pushed it into circular orbit. Attitude jet precessed the spin axis. (Courtesy NASA)

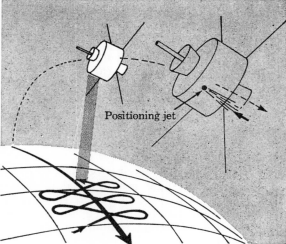

Fig. 4-64. To synchronize velocity of Syncom with earth's rotation, positioning jet slows or speeds it upon command from earth, also repositions satellite over Atlantic for experiments. (Courtesy NASA)

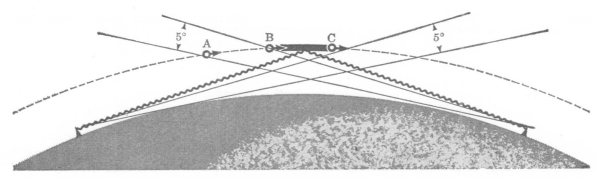

Fig. 4-65. To serve for communication, satellite must be visible to both receiving and transmitting station, must be at least 5 deg. above horizon for each. In diagram, section B-C is useful part of orbit. Station antenna tracks satellite from B to C. Second antenna tracks approaching satellite shown at A, which must pick up transmission when first satellite vanishes at C. A third antenna may be relaying traffic to another satellite.

There are many problems to be solved and techniques to be developed to position and track with these large antennas at microwave frequencies. At these frequencies, the antenna beamwidth can be as narrow as 0.1 deg. Pointing large antennas with these narrow beamwidths at rapidly moving satellites at great distances is no easy task. Acquisition of the satellite by the ground station will be assisted by equipping the satellite with a special tracking beacon radiating at a lower frequency, the beamwidth of the ground antenna being broader at lower frequencies.

Once a system of stationary satellites in 24-hr orbits can be established, nearly fixed antennas will be satisfactory. Theoretically, they'll simply look at one spot in space, but they must have some steerability to track the small relative motion of the satellite and to permit transferring operations to another satellite in the event one fails.

Geographically, ground stations should be as widely spaced as possible; this obvious-sounding fact has major technical and political

significance. It is technically and economically desirable to tie together large neighboring areas where possible by conventional means of communications distribution—usually ground microwave links. Once a ground terminal for communication by satellite exists on a large land mass, local distribution networks will feed the traffic out to the borders of neighboring countries. The need for conventional communications distribution systems will not be eliminated by communication satellites—indeed the need for local distribution systems will be greater with the advent of satellite systems. The technical and economic factors are not the only considerations, however, which will determine the position and number of ground terminals. National pride and area politics have always influenced the location and path of communication facilities in the past.

The next steps ahead

All our present planning for satellite communication involves the use of large fixed ground stations feeding the traffic into con-

TYPICAL COMMUNICATION SATELLITE SYSTEMS PROPOSED BY INDUSTRY

Type of Satellite			Orbit				
Wt. (lb)	Type	Altitude Control	Period Control	Alt. Miles	Inclination	No. of Satellites Required	Modulation Techniques
175	Active	None or spin stabilized	None	3,000	Polar	40–50 Random	Wide Index FM
450	Active	Active	Active	22,300	28°	3–4 Controlled spacing	PCM (Pulse Code Modulation)
30	Active	Spin stabilized	Active	22,300	Equatorial	3–4 Controlled spacing	AM
900	Active	Active	Active	6,000	Equatorial	10 Controlled spacing	PCM
—	Passive spheres	None	None	2,000	Polar	50 Random	Wide Index FM

ventional common-carrier networks. Looking farther into the future, we can speculate about the possibility of communicating via satellite with ships at sea, aircraft, or even roving land vehicles. The equipment they could carry would not be able to track moving satellites nor to receive the very faint signals we're working with now. Satellite systems capable of providing this sort of service would have to use space stations in stationary 24-hr orbits with kilowatts of power aboard—probably obtained from nuclear reactors.

Only when space stations of this sort and power supplies with tens of kilowatts of capacity become available can one begin to think about the possibility of satellite broadcasts direct to home receivers.

Further reading

The most elaborate examination of communication by satellite appears in the documentation of Federal Communications Commission hearings on the subject: "An Inquiry into the Allocation of Frequency Bands for Space Communications," FCC Docket No. 13522 (FCC Washington, D.C.).

A highly technical and extremely thorough study of a critical orbital problem was prepared for NASA by Frick and Garber, "Perturbations of a Synchronous Satellite Due to Triaxiality of the Earth" (Rand Report RM-2996-NASA, Jan. 1962, Rand Corp., Santa Monica, Cal.).

The technical aspects of "TV Broadcast from an Earth Satellite" were studied by R. G. Gould, Stanford Research Institute report RM-5 (Aug. 1961). Another SRI report by Wolfram analyzes "Time Delay Effects in Satellite Telephone Circuits" (RM-2, Dec. 1960).

An entire issue of the *Bell System Technical Journal* (July 1961) is devoted to a comprehensive report on Echo I. More recently (May 1962), the same journal carried a thorough technical article on "Interference Between Satellite Communication Systems and Common Carrier Surface Systems" by H. E. Curtis. The July 1963 issue of the *Journal* is a three-volume number devoted entirely to Telstar.

A comprehensive treatment of technical and economic factors is contained in a Rand report, "Communications Satellites: Technology, Economics, and System Choices," by Reiger, Nichols, Early, and Dews, Rand report RM-3487-RC (Feb. 1963).

THE NEW NAVIGATION

by Seymour Tilson *

In Brief: *Whether your aim is more profit and safety in transportation, or the exploration of space, you need more accurate and reliable navigation than ever before. One new system that promises these—Transit—uses the Doppler shift in radio frequencies transmitted from satellites to compute their orbits; fixes can then be made with respect to such orbits. But the system's potential is presently limited by imperfect knowledge of the earth's size, shape, gravity field, and ionosphere. The last also plagues modern versions of radio-ranging systems like Loran, which are going to pulse-delay techniques to raise accuracy and reliability, and to frequencies below 100 kc both to extend accuracy and to penetrate into the sea. Underwater work is obscured by security silence, but speculation about SOFAR, the ocean's remarkable sound channel, suggests some possibilities. With minor qualifications, Doppler radar everywhere is doing fine. So are inertial methods, most nearly self-contained of all, though at tremendous cost in complexity and, therefore, reliability. Neither their gyros' errors, nor our knowledge of gravity and astronomical constants in space make inertial methods alone suffice for long space cruises. But we still have man.—S.T.*

■ Finding your way from place to place anywhere within the accessible limits of the universe is not really terribly difficult—if you have unlimited time at your disposal. But time is money, as ever, and if we imagine it to equal fuel remaining aboard the plane on which you are a passenger, it may turn out to be life.

But let's be less dramatic. Imagine that you are not a human being at all. Instead you're a complex gadget, product of years of effort, vital extension of human mind and will—satellite in orbit, remote oceanographic research buoy, or heavily instrumented space probe taking your once-in-x-years' chance for a shot at Jupiter. Or maybe you're a nuclear-tipped ballistic missile, a manifestation of the universal sickness of the human spirit. In any case, you also, in ways unique to you, and in ways that have little directly to do with profit-and-loss but not, unfortunately, life-and-death, demand more accurate, more reliable, more efficient navigation than has ever been needed before.

In response, the many arts and sciences that

* Seymour Tilson is Associate Editor of *International Science and Technology.*

together comprise navigation are sharpening their tools and insights. They are hewing closer to that fine line that represents for any particular application the most efficient compromise among the sometimes conflicting needs for speed, safety, profit, and accuracy.

Not surprisingly, uncoordinated attempts to meet such diverse needs have made navigational science a complex mosaic of poorly fitting parts. Thus, our survey may reveal only random and ill-defined patterns. But perhaps it will also reveal those areas of misfit—and challenge—yawning between the parts.

Questions and answers—old and new

Every method of finding your way—new or old—seeks to answer one or more simple questions: (1) Where am I? (2) Which way am I going? (3) When am I going to get to where I want to be? (4) Am I going to get there?

Not every problem involves all four, of course. An earth-orbiting satellite, or a remote research buoy bobbing on the ocean waves, needs only a razor-sharp reply to the first. By way of contrast, and at a much less sophisticated extreme, centuries of navigating from atoll to atoll in outrigger canoe by natives of the Marshall Islands of the South Pacific has depended for success on their surprisingly subtle answer to "Which way am I going?"

Figure 4-66 is a facsimile of a Marshallese navigation chart; it's called a *rebelib* and covers the whole archipelago. The chart is made of sticks bound together with cord in an apparently abstract pattern, and is dotted with two sizes of cowrie shell. Larger ones locate islands; smaller ones mark nodes, meeting points of opposing wave patterns that refract around the islands. Trends and locations of the sticks, on the other hand, show major ocean waves and currents. All a Marshallese navigator need do is find the first node marking the apex of opposing wave trends that refract around the island he seeks. Thereafter he need only follow it, as one would follow a branch of a tree, till it leads to the main trunk and, ultimately, the island. What is his sensor? That primitive inertial guidance system—the seat of his pants.

My point in this admittedly anachronistic anecdote is not to ease you into inertial navigation; we will come to that presently. It is rather to stress two other critical ideas.

First, and most important, a workable navigation system needs the most explicit picture of the environment possibly attainable. The more explicit this picture, the less the need for increasingly costly and complex (and less reliable) equipment to remedy deficiencies in such

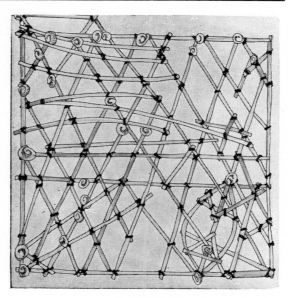

Fig. 4-66. Sticks on Marshall Islands navigation chart show trends of major ocean waves and currents. Larger cowrie shells locate scattered islands. Smaller shells mark nodes where waves refracted around islands meet each other. Navigator "simply" follows nodes to island he seeks.

knowledge. This theme recurs with almost tedius frequency—in the Transit-navigational-satellite effort for instance (Figs. 4-67 and 4-68), barred from reaching its superlative goals for accuracy, coverage, and reliability not so much by inadequate hardware, but by gaps in knowledge of the earth's exact size, shape, and gravitational field. And Transit shares with representative radio range-finding systems, even one like the new Loran (Fig. 4-70), inevitable degradation imposed by ignorance of the ionosphere's exact behavior. Though the environmental parameters may change, the same is true for acoustical efforts under the sea, for inertial systems anywhere, for horizon sensors and star trackers out in space.

The second point to remember is that any navigation problem is also a problem in logistics. Given enough time, and the promise of fair weather, neither our Marshall Islander nor his modern counterpart soon to be in space has crucial need for perfect accuracy. Just so long as he's pointed in the right direction, or has a big enough paddle with which to correct his misdirection, he's going to get where he is going, sooner or later.

Space between the planets promises fair weather. And sufficient time—to observe and think—also will be assured, to even the men who will go only as far as the moon. But for the moment let's come back to earth, where the weather isn't always fair.

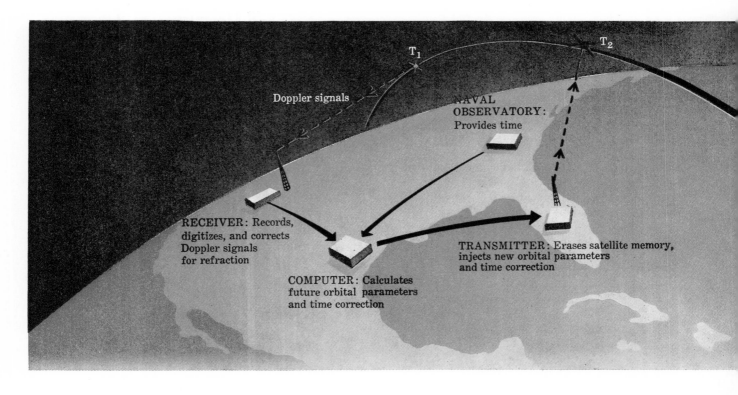

Doppler signals

NAVAL OBSERVATORY: Provides time

RECEIVER: Records, digitizes, and corrects Doppler signals for refraction

TRANSMITTER: Erases satellite memory, injects new orbital parameters and time correction

COMPUTER: Calculates future orbital parameters and time correction

Radio beacons in the sky—by and by

Here, two kinds of bad weather can bedevil the navigator. One is the conventional kind, which is bad enough. Still worse is the magnetic storm, which makes a shambles of compasses, communications, radio direction finders, and electronic aids to navigation in general. Coming to the rescue sooner or later, for ships at sea and for submarines that dare to surface—if not quite so effectively for aircraft—will be Transit, first operational navigation system based on the use of satellites.

Brainchild of the Applied Physics Laboratory of Johns Hopkins, Transit promises to provide fixes of latitude and longitude from anywhere on earth, and in any weather (conventional sense), to an accuracy that lies within either ½ or ¹⁄₁₀ of a nautical mile, depending on the elaborateness and cost of the navigator's receiving gear. That's pretty good accuracy as these things go; ordinary celestial methods yield a fix accurate to just 1 or 2 miles. Besides having unlimited traffic capacity—a desirable property it will share with every system that doesn't require two-way communication along overcrowded frequency channels—Transit claims to offer *relative* immunity to both man-made interference and magnetic storms.

The system (Fig. 4-67) uses the familiar Doppler shift in frequency (Fig. 4-68) observed when a receiver and transmitter move relative to one another. The amount of shift varies directly with the rate at which the length of transmission path between the two is changing. Observation of the shift in frequency of trans-

mission from an orbiting earth satellite from known points on earth permits the satellite's orbit with respect to these points to be calculated. Then the position of any other point on earth can be fixed by referring to the satellite's now-known orbit. To do this, in essence, you detect the point where the Doppler shift changes sign or passes through zero (Fig. 4-68); this places you vertically beneath the known path of the satellite overhead. But this is not as simple as it sounds; elaborate mathematical and Doppler curve-fitting procedures are involved, requiring huge amounts of time on even the largest computers.

Each of four satellites placed into orbits that are appropriate for optimum accessibility, longevity, precision, and ease of calculation will continuously transmit a harmonically related pair of radio frequencies which are controlled to 1 or 2 parts in 10^{10}, or better. Such extreme frequency stability is essential because—as a rough rule of thumb—measuring the Doppler shift of a 100 Mc/sec signal even to the nearest cycle, for example (which is a respectable 1 part in 10^8), would yield an error in position of at least 1 mile, well below Transit's accuracy goals.

It is to get higher accuracy too that a pair of frequencies is used, instead of a single frequency which would in principle do just as well. Use of a pair permits some correction to be made for ionospheric refraction of the signal. Even during the relatively short 20-minute maximum period when a passing satellite will be in effective range of shipboard receivers,

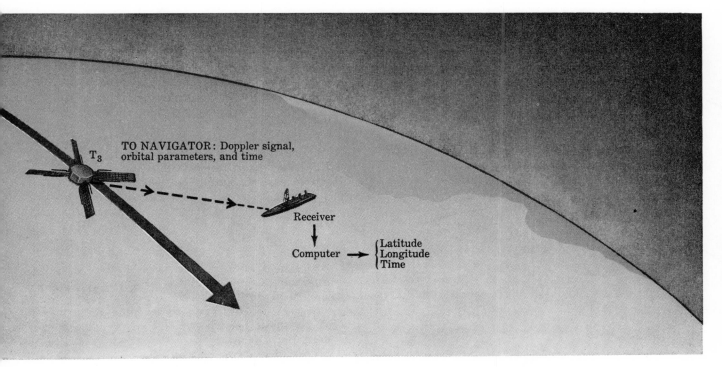

Fig. 4-67. Radio signals from Transit system's satellites, transmitted as a pair of harmonically related frequencies to permit some correction to be made for refraction of signals from a straight-line path by the ionosphere, go to ground complex which uses Doppler shift in them to compute the satellites' current orbital parameters. Updated values of these must be transmitted to the satellites every 12 hours, in present state of the orbit-prediction art. Navigator uses similar Doppler-shifted signals received from the satellite to get fix relative to the known current orbit.

such refraction can make the signal's path deviate rapidly, considerably, and erratically from the simple straight-line path shown in Fig. 4-68. If not so corrected the observed Doppler shift and ranges deduced from it would result in errors on the order of several miles.

The refraction correction currently in use seems to work well enough at middle and lower latitudes to retain the desired accuracy, even during magnetic storms when the ionosphere gets pretty frisky. It is still a matter of some doubt whether it will retain the system's design accuracy at higher latitudes, especially during periods of heavy auroral activity. Nor is this Transit's only remaining difficulty.

An orbit is a sometime thing

In the current state of the art, predicting the position of a satellite in its orbit to an accuracy much greater than about $\frac{1}{4}$ mile for a period much more than 12 hours in advance is impossible. Although this sounds pretty good it really isn't, if you recall that the desired final accuracy of navigational fix also lies in this range and that, therefore, the orbital parameters upon which the fix depends must be more accurate than this by a couple of orders of magnitude. In fact, in optimistic anticipation of the time when the orbit prediction art catches up,

Transit's hardware is being designed to permit its satellites' positions to be specified to within $\frac{1}{100}$ of a nautical mile. In the meantime, Transit expects to update the orbital parameters of its satellites about every 12 hours—with all of the possible slips 'twixt cup and lip that this makes possible.

Several intriguing factors contribute to the orbit-prediction problem: mechanical drag upon the satellite by the atmosphere and variation in the atmosphere's properties due to solar-induced photochemical, photoionization, and diffusion processes; radiation pressure from the sun on the satellite and perhaps even back-reflected radiation pressure from the earth; several kinds of electromagnetic effects that build up charge on the satellite; and even such minutiae as tides in the solid body of the earth!

By far the largest perturbing influence, however, and the one area in which more knowledge would pay off most handsomely is the earth's gravitational field. This is true, of course, not only for craft which orbit the earth, but also for even modest interplanetary orbits such as one from earth to the moon. The crude contour map of gravitational accelerations in the earth-moon system (Fig. 4-69) suggests the dominating influence exerted by the earth's field. It also suggests how important this single environ-

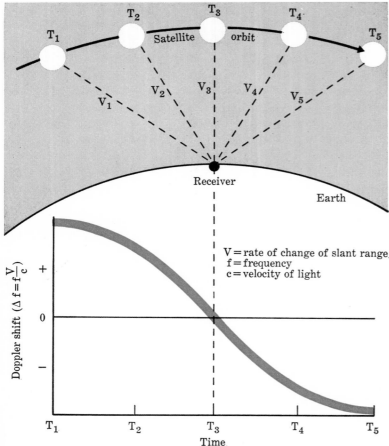

V = rate of change of slant range
f = frequency
c = velocity of light

Fig. 4-68. Stationary receiver below passing Transit satellite would observe symmetrical change in Doppler shift; theoretically would lie below point in orbit where shift passes through zero. But asymmetry induced by earth's rotation and ionosphere's refraction of signal necessitates curve-fitting procedures to get position fix.

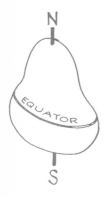

mental parameter is for optimizing the initial launch trajectories of lunar and interplanetary vehicles. (Not so incidentally, as we shall see shortly, the most nearly exact specification possible of the earth's gravitational field would also greatly benefit inertial navigating systems that are designed to operate within it.)

Besides inadequacies in the gravity picture, Transit's ability to accurately locate its satellites—as, indeed, any ground tracking system's similar ability to pinpoint either earth satellites, deep-space probes, or the point at which an orbiting astronaut will impact—is degraded by inadequately precise location of the tracking stations on the surface of the earth. Which brings us to briefly consider geodesy—the science that concerns itself with the form of the earth—and its almost incestuous relations with gravity.

Geodesy and gravity = ham and eggs

Since the earth's gravity field expresses the distribution of mass which creates it, it also indirectly but with infinite subtlety and exactitude expresses the form of that mass. Moreover, the shape portrayed by the gravity field is not the simple geometric one, ideal in its oblate sphericity; it is rather a truer dynamic one that includes not only the effects of shape, size, and mass distribution, but also those of the earth's rotation. As we have already noted, this dynamic gravity field is the principal contributor to perturbations in satellite orbits, which means that analysis of such orbits can in turn yield the most refined picture of the earth's field and dynamic form. Indeed, it is orbital data from satellites that indicate the earth to be in one heck of a peculiar shape—elliptical cross section at the equator, bulge in the southern hemisphere, and greater length along the axis from the equator to the north pole than to the south pole—all adding up to the by now familiar lopsided "pear-shape" exaggerated in the marginal sketch.

What's done to refine this homely picture in essence is to assume a best set of geodetic parameters; then calculate what any particular satellite's orbit should be on the basis of these factors; then observe what the orbit turns out to be, noting the difference between prediction and actuality. Evaluate this difference in terms of all perturbations responsible for it—but especially geodetic-gravity factors—adjust original assumptions accordingly, and try again, and again, and again.

Remember Transit? Her own orbital data, along with that derived from other satellites, will ultimately help improve the gravity-geodesy picture. But there is another serious limitation to Transit's usefulness that more immediately concerns many a potential user, especially one in an airplane.

A user in motion incurs a penalty

A user of Transit must take precious time, both while receiving his Doppler signals during the satellite's pass and while waiting for his computer to provide the final fix. This could amount to an hour or more, which isn't so bad, if you're not moving very fast in the meantime. But if you are, interpretation of the Doppler range-rate becomes more complex than suggested by the stationary receiver of Fig. 4-68. Furthermore, your fix is now perhaps an hour old, and some form of dead reckoning is necessary to yield present position.

Although not a crucial drawback, this does mean that Transit cannot aspire to be that golden calf of the navigation business, a com-

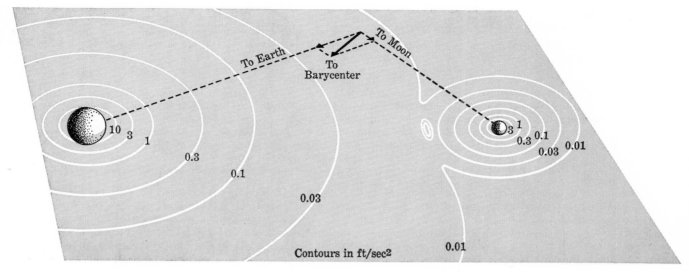

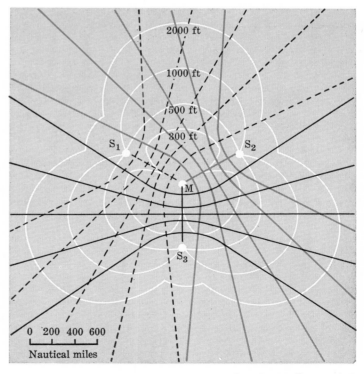

Fig. 4-69. Dominating influence that earth has on gravitational accelerations in space between earth and moon is suggested by this crude contour map. Beyond 0.01 ft/sec² contour the sun's field dominates. Improving precision in both initial-launch trajectories and cruise orbits of spacecraft depends on refining map, shown here not to scale.

pletely self-contained system. It also means that up-to-date versions of venerable radio systems like Loran (Fig. 4-70) will be around for a long time to come, especially in the most heavily traveled sea and air lanes.

Hyperbolas, hyperbolas everywhere

The newest version of Loran (designated Loran-C) is representative of several more-or-less similar systems that use radio signals to generate hyperbolic lines of position. Signal pulses identical in frequency and repeat rate are generated simultaneously by two transmitters—master and slave—located a precise distance apart (geodesy again!). The line on the earth's surface along which the two signals would be received with a constant difference in time of arrival is, of course, a hyperbola of possible positions. All that's needed to fix one's self uniquely on this hyperbola is the intersection of it with another hyperbola of different orientation. This is similarly generated by a second pair of transmitters, its master usually shared bigamously by the first pair.

This familiar basic principle of Loran assumes that all of the energy contained in a single discrete signal pulse emitted by the transmitter reaches the receiver along a path that hugs the earth's surface, as indicated in the marginal sketch by path G. But it doesn't, of course. Part of it instead takes a roundabout path, reflecting from various levels in the ionosphere (E, E_1, and E_2 of the sketch). Since these reflected paths are longer than the surface path, the signal received is stretched out in time; measurement of difference in time of arrival of the pulse pair from master and slave becomes fuzzy; and accuracy of the fix goes

way down. To make matters worse, radio reflecting levels in the ionosphere frequently rise and fall like a yo-yo on a string, but not, unfortunately, with its reliable regularity.

Recently, however, this problem has been diminished by introducing a time delay be-

Fig. 4-70. Master transmitter (M) of modern Loran-C star chain synchronizes pulses with each of slave transmitters (S). Sets of hyperbolas represent constant differences in time of signal arrival from each master-slave pair. Intersection of two hyperbolas yields position. Claimed accuracy shown by white contours.

tween the pulses generated by master and slave —usually 1000 microseconds. Proper time sampling of the received signal then more effectively resolves that part of the total signal which is crucial—the ground wave—from that spurious delayed part which arrives from the ionosphere.

Another recent trend in Loran-like approaches, still in the experimental stages, attempts to capitalize on several advantages inherent in going to the lowest possible operating frequencies. These offer considerably greater range, thus permitting greatly lengthened baseline distances between transmitters. This in turn is highly desirable because it cuts down on the necessary number of expensive installations and also sharply increases geometric accuracy. Loran-C itself is a step in this direction; it operates in the 90–110 kilocycle band. But the various experimental systems are aiming well below 100 kc. One more important attraction in this frequency range is that the lower the frequency the deeper it can penetrate into the sea.

Useful as this characteristic may turn out to be for submarines, in view of the drop in energy that accompanies it, long-range radio fixing under water is unlikely to replace either acoustic or inertial systems, or, for that matter, sooner or later sticking your head up for a fix (celestial sense, only). Before we leave electromagnetics to look into these other approaches to finding your way, a word on Doppler radar is in order.

Christian Doppler has come a long way

Based on the effect that Christian Doppler bequeathed to us (surely you recall: frequency shift → rate of change of range, or velocity, which once integrated → range), and operating in the microwave frequency region, Doppler radar is being developed or applied in almost endless variations for aircraft, ships, harbor and airport traffic control, missile and satellite tracking, and it undoubtedly will play a key role on spacecraft. But in our context—which is long distance or en-route navigation on earth or in space, not tracking, not guidance—it will probably be used most extensively in aircraft in the near future.

Here, a typical three-beam array such as the one in the margin yields either ground speed along the plane's track or distance from some reference point whose position is known. But accurately to relate either of these to the direction of the plane's track over the earth requires two added pieces of information: (1) some indication of the vertical (a need most emphatically shared by inertial systems intended for terrestrial use, as we shall see); and (2) some independent directional reference such

as a compass or an inertial device. For the latter, no existing variant of the compass is really good enough to achieve the full potential accuracy of Doppler radar. And although wedding Doppler radar to an inertial direction reference would be mutually rewarding, many barriers of cost and complexity remain to be overcome to accomplish this.

Sound in the sea—SOFAR, speculation

Neither Doppler nor hyperbolic attempts to answer "Where am I?" are restricted to using electromagnetic radiation. For underwater wayfinding crude acoustical analogs already exist— Doppler over-the-bottom speed meters, for example. But these are generally limited in accuracy by uncertainties about both the speed of sound and its propagation paths.

A possible breakthrough in limits imposed by such uncertainties may come from exploitation of SOFAR sound transmission (see "Underwater Sound," page 625). Its potential is extraordinarily rich, though since the early 1950's nobody connected with U.S. Navy undersea programs offers anything more than silence, a puzzled look, or pooh-pooh when asked about it.

SOFAR transmission relies on the existence of a remarkably efficient sound channel in ocean waters. The depth of this channel's axis varies from one part of the ocean to another; it lies where the velocity of sound propagation is least, about 4000 feet deep in the North Atlantic, for instance. If a sound source is on the axis, as in the sketch in the margin, any sound ray leaving it at an inclination from the horizontal of 12° or less propagates indefinitely far without terminating against either the surface of the water or the bottom, because it refracts back and forth across the axis of the channel.

The time it takes any particular sound ray to travel a given distance depends on its inclination. Travel time is least for rays which make the greatest angle with the sound-channel axis (their velocity is highest) and greatest for those slowest rays whose paths essentially coincide with the axis. So if you're let's say a thousand miles away from the source, as in Fig. 4-71, and listening with a suitable instrument placed on the channel axis, you will hear a series of sound pulses each of which comes from a ray that has traveled its own particular path. During the early part of this SOFAR concerto the time interval between successive pulses will be greatest. Then, exponentially building to a rousing finale, the interval will diminish to such an extent that pulses overlap—creating a crescendo of intensity—as rays whose paths lie closer and closer to the axis crowd upon each other. Suddenly—silence! The slowest rays riding essentially along the sound-channel axis itself have arrived.

The time that's elapsed between the sound's beginning at the source and its abrupt termination at a distant receiver can be measured to probably better than 0.003 sec. Thus, given a fairly accurate figure for sound's velocity along the axis of the channel in any particular part of the sea (known to be just about 4887 ft/sec in the Atlantic), the limit of error in locating yourself imposed by uncertainty in estimating time of arrival of the SOFAR signal is about 12 ft—over any distance to which the SOFAR channel extends. And indications are that it extends, at varying depth, everywhere the water is deep enough so that bottom topography doesn't intervene. Where it does—on continental shelves and slopes, for instance, or perhaps over the highest peaks of the Mid-Atlantic ridge—we can close the gaps in coverage with a little reasonable speculation.

One might guess, for example, that since the art of mapping the seafloor's topography with echo-sounders is well-advanced, both surface ships and submarines above a well-mapped area could navigate by echo reference to such underwater landmarks ("seamarks?"). The process would be essentially the same as a ship's or airplane's use of terrain-radar—or a pilot's use of his eyes over a familiar landscape in daylight.

In these connections, it would be interesting but unprofitable to speculate further on the hardware and system possibilities that undoubtedly are being explored. Heavy security wraps effectively muffle all sounds about such developments, if you will forgive me for the pun, except for an occasional "beep" or two in a press release. One such report seems to suggest that the age-old navigational concept underlying the use of precisely located lighthouses, fixed buoys, and aircraft omnidirectional radio beacons is being extended to the sea. The U.S. Navy is setting up (or perhaps has already set up) a sound beacon on the floor of the Atlantic, location quite specific but undisclosed. It's powered by one of the SNAP (Systems for Nuclear Auxiliary Power) series, strontium-90 thermoelectric generators, similar in principle to those that put the pep into Transit's satellites and automatic weather stations in the Arctic regions.

How nice that Newton passed those laws

Much more information of a generalized nature has been forthcoming about inertial systems for use in submarines, a high point of which was the inertially guided excursion of Nautilus under the Arctic ice to the North Pole way back in 1958. And after all we've said and

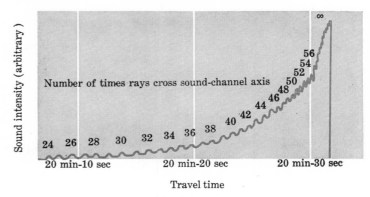

Fig. 4-71. Abrupt end of sound pulses that pile up with increasing intensity at receiver—here located 1000 miles from source on axis of ocean's sound channel, as shown in margin of page 556—signals arrival of slowest rays that travel essentially straight line along the axis. Measurement of time between signal at source and its abrupt end can be coupled with knowledge of sound's velocity along axis to yield distance, accurate to 12 feet!

done, there indeed remains but one—inertial—system for us to consider, before we leave the earth for outer space.

Inertial systems in redundance and variety are not only the seeing eye for Navy submarines and large ships; practically every known long-range ballistic missile, satellite, and space vehicle uses them or anticipates their use in one or another form and combination—at least during the brief but critical initial thrusting phase, and frequently also during later cruising. For more routine vehicles, civilian ships and aircraft, cost and complexity have so far combined to limit their general use. But even here the trend is to mesh inertial dead-reckoning devices with creatures like Doppler radar, and Loran and other radio direction-finding and fixing techniques. This trend is quickening despite the fact that enertial instrumentation offers formidable technological and mathematical challenges (or perhaps because of it).

What makes it worth the challenges, ultimately, is the fact that Newton's second law of motion, $F = MA$ (force = mass $\times$ acceleration) for all practical purposes is simple, exact, and universal. A navigating system based on it, therefore, essentially requires only a simple instrument (Fig. 4-72) to sense changes in velocity—or accelerations—continuously with respect to a known starting point. Ordinarily, since accelerometers respond in only one rectilinear direction, three of them are used jointly and mounted on the vehicle so as to sense acceleration in three mutually perpendicular directions. These are combined vectorially by computer into a single resultant. One integration of this offers present velocity, another yields distance traveled. Couple this to some directional reference and you have a system

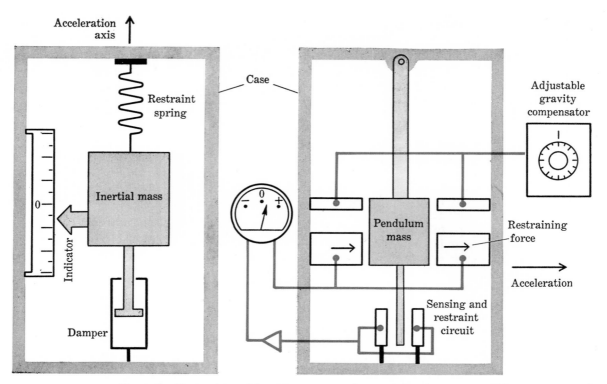

Fig. 4-72. Heart of inertial guidance system is an acceleration sensor which measures accelerating force that acts on mass (F = MA) either by elastic constants of restraining spring, left, or by electric circuit. In either case, acceleration due to gravity must be nulled out, essentially by applying its known value as bias.

that, in principle, offers the only means for continuously guiding any kind of vehicle whatsoever anywhere—under or on the water, in or far beyond the atmosphere—independently of weather conditions, magnetic field fluctuations, and either natural or artificial radiation contacts.

But in practice this idyllic principle is limited in accuracy by two factors. One, of course, is perfection of the instrument. There's no trouble on this score: accelerometers in being are very nearly perfect. Sensitivity thresholds approaching 1-millionth or less of the earth's gravitational acceleration are nearing realization and major instrument improvement efforts now aim to reduce size and electromechanical complexity —while increasing reliability—by going over to solid-state and molecular-electronic approaches. The second factor, however, is so serious a potential limitation that the whole remaining edifice of inertial navigation built upon the accelerometer has evolved just to do battle with it.

Ironically, it arises from another fact of nature that Newton also was the first to state clearly—the force of gravity is universal (as a reminder of this, you might glance back at Fig. 4-69). This force, like any other that acts upon a mass, imparts to it an acceleration. And accelerometers, extremely sensitive but not especially subtle, cannot distinguish gravitational acceleration from that induced by mo-

tion of the vehicle. (This, incidentally, is a concrete example of what Einstein meant by the principle of equivalence of gravitational and inertial forces when setting up the general theory of relativity.)

To cut gravity out of the picture, in the case of an accelerometer disposed to sense vertical motion, there is essentially only one available expedient. This in effect cancels g by taking its best-known value (which varies with location, of course) and applying it as a mechanical, electrical, or magnetic bias to either the inputs or outputs of the accelerometer. The same can be done to compensate for g in the two remaining accelerometers which sense horizontal components. But the doing of it in either case gets tricky, because there is no guarantee that either the "vertical" or the "horizontal" accelerometers will remain so oriented with respect to the earth's vertical during a vehicle's maneuvers and motion over the earth's surface. And applying appropriate biases to the accelerometers is possible, of course, only if their orientation relative to the local earth's vertical at every point in the journey is known.

That's what gyroscope-stabilized inertial platforms are for.

A pendulous platform to replace stars

Gyros operating on the familiar principle (which, in case it's not familiar to you, is reviewed in Fig. 4-73) serve the prime purpose

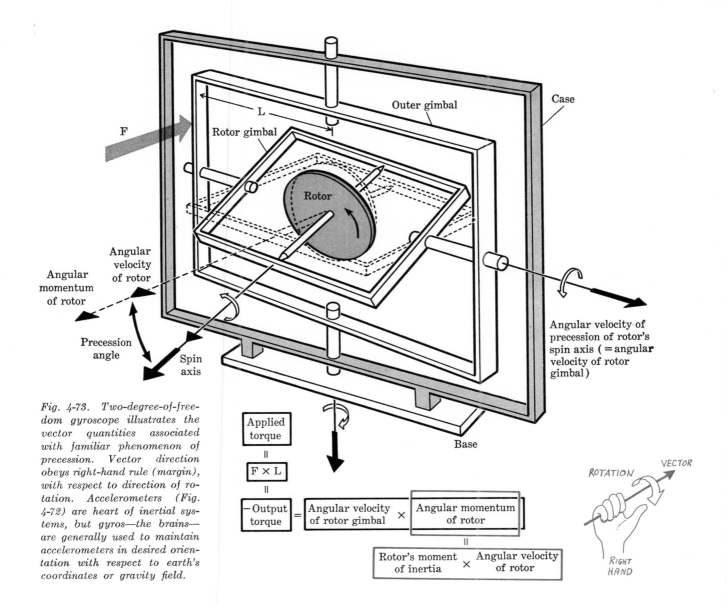

F

L

Outer gimbal

Case

Rotor gimbal

Rotor

Angular velocity of rotor

Angular momentum of rotor

Precession angle

Spin axis

Angular velocity of precession of rotor's spin axis (= angular velocity of rotor gimbal)

Fig. 4-73. Two-degree-of-freedom gyroscope illustrates the vector quantities associated with familiar phenomenon of precession. Vector direction obeys right-hand rule (margin), with respect to direction of rotation. Accelerometers (Fig. 4-72) are heart of inertial systems, but gyros—the brains—are generally used to maintain accelerometers in desired orientation with respect to earth's coordinates or gravity field.

Applied torque

=

F × L

=

— Output torque	=	Angular velocity of rotor gimbal	×	Angular momentum of rotor

=

Rotor's moment of inertia	×	Angular velocity of rotor

Base

ROTATION

VECTOR

RIGHT HAND

of holding in stable orientation—regardless of vehicle maneuver or motion—the platform on which the accelerometers are mounted. For a system to be used on earth, the platform is usually held normal to the local vertical to the earth. This changes attitude continually as the vehicle's position changes. This technologically not-so-simple expedient kills two birds at once: (1) the vertical accelerometer can be gravity-compensated without complications that would arise from any nonvertical orientation; (2) if all is going well and the horizontal accelerometers are held truly level, they don't feel *any* component of *g* at all. Usually all doesn't go this well, and for vehicles on a long cruise the gyros' inevitable precessional error—or drift—must be monitored. This is done by feeding back to them variable control torques which come from single integration of the accelerometer's distress signals; these indicate that the accelerometers are indeed experiencing the unwanted embrace of gravity and that, therefore, they

are departing from an attitude that's normal to the local vertical.

On a short hop such as that involved in ballistic missile guidance, for instance, the stable platform is *not* held locally level; it suffices merely to hold it to the attitude it had at the launch point. The effect of gravity along the way is simply precomputed, insofar as it's known, as a function of location with respect to point of origin, and electronically fed in at some point as a correction bias to the accelerometers. Gravity, once more.

There's nothing like shooting for the stars

Taking inertial systems off the earth and into space is conceptually simple enough. All that's needed is to substitute heavenly orientation and coordinate systems for earthly ones. The importance of the gravity bugaboo diminishes sharply out "there" because the gravitational influences of the planets drop off rapidly as the square of the distance from them. The background field generated by the sun's mass, for example, in the neighborhood of the orbits of the earth and moon (Fig. 4-69) is roughly only 10^{-3} of the value of g on earth. Thus, while not exactly negligible if you recall that the accelerometer art is pushing—of necessity—towards sensitivities approaching 10^{-6} of the value of g, gravity may perhaps prove to be less of a problem than excessive gyro drift.

Though gravitational accelerations in space away from the planets are slight, they change significantly with distance from the sun. And they, too, must be known well in order to calibrate instruments effectively. Thus the astro-

nomical constants on which they in turn depend must also be upgraded in precision.

Inertial use of gravitational fields points up the fact that all methods of navigating—anywhere—use force fields. On earth, for instance, we've long depended on the magnetic field, even with its vagaries. But the earth also has a temperature field in which rate of change of temperature depends on location, offering obvious navigational potential. And still more interesting is the earth's electrostatic field, in which the predominantly vertical potential gradient is about 100 to 300 volts per meter at ground level, over regular terrain in good

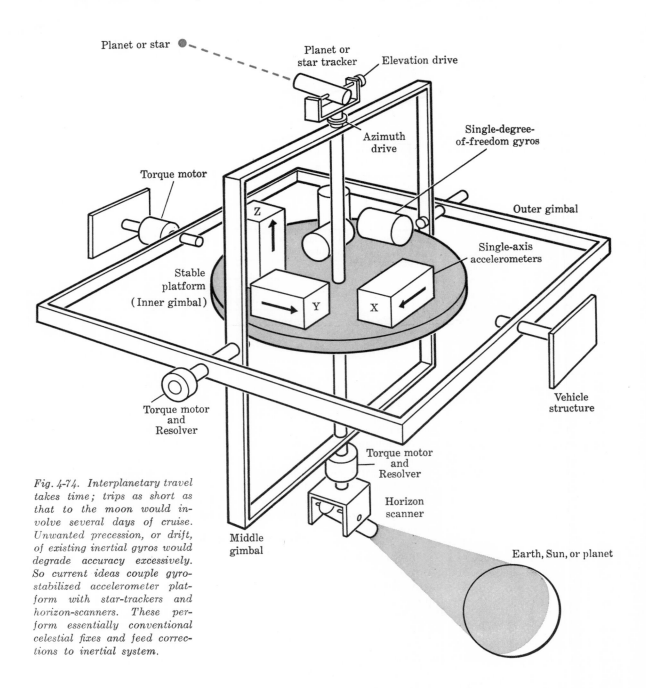

Fig. 4-74. Interplanetary travel takes time; trips as short as that to the moon would involve several days of cruise. Unwanted precession, or drift, of existing inertial gyros would degrade accuracy excessively. So current ideas couple gyro-stabilized accelerometer platform with star-trackers and horizon-scanners. These perform essentially conventional celestial fixes and feed corrections to inertial system.

weather. It drops with altitude to about 25 volts per meter at 3 km, for instance, and changes laterally with varying terrain, increasing to over 500 volts per meter on mountains. Uses, anyone?

Nor need such speculation about fields be restricted to earth. Magnetic fields exist in space, as do directional particle fluxes such as the solar wind and cosmic rays.

Exotic gyros for submarines and space

Though gyro drift rates are already remarkably low (probably well under 0.5 sec of arc per hour, but this is a guess because this sort of thing is classified) they may turn out to be too high over long interplanetary cruise periods that can extend from days to years. Similarly, whatever the exact accuracy score may be, it probably still is too close to marginal to insure the comfort of the navigation officer on a nuclear submarine that's cruising submerged for extended periods.

Much current development, therefore, aims to reduce drift rates still more than may be possible by merely improving conventional bearings that mount rotors and gimbals. Gas-lubricated spin-axis bearings for gyro rotors are becoming the vogue; and an electrostatically supported, so-called free, or gimbal-less spherically rotored gyro—operating in a vacuum—is already in use. The possibility of using magnetically supported rotors made of materials such as niobium which become superconducting under cryogenic conditions also is receiving much attention. And even more exotic, extremely accurate, long-lived gyros may be in the offing.

One, for example, is the nuclear gyro that proposes to capitalize on the perfect inertial properties of spinning atomic nuclei. This would bypass all the problems involved at the macroscopic level, such as getting near-to-perfect geometric alignment and balance, dimensional stability, structural rigidity, and so on. Such a device would also operate at cryogenic (liquid-helium) temperatures, so that once the magnetic moments of the nuclei were aligned they would have long relaxation times. Major problems are shielding delicate nuclear magnetic domains from outside influences, aligning the nuclei in the first place, and sensing changes in their direction.

A non-navigational but intriguing target for future geniuses of the gyro art to shoot at is a proposal by a group at Stanford to use a gyroscope that orbits the earth in a satellite to demonstrate the general theory of relativity. Calculations show the relativity effect would produce rotation of the gyro's spin momentum vector, or a precessional rate, that amounts to a specific but tiny 7 sec of arc *per year*. The gyro used would, of course, have to possess a

HERE'S HOW EASY IT COULD TURN OUT TO BE

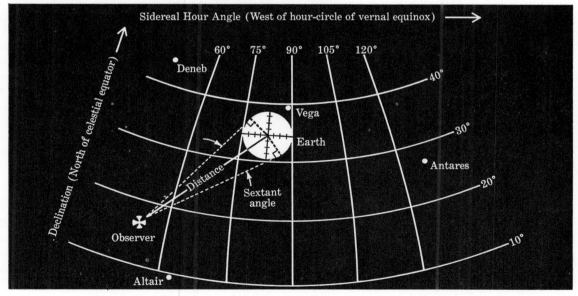

Fig. 4-75. Assuming the man who goes to the moon will be able to function (if not, why send him?), this is what he would see looking towards earth from 25,000 miles away. Using known values for the earth's radius and for positions of stars and visible artificial satellites such as Echo—arranged as in one proposed space almanac (Fig. 4-76)—all he needs to get both distance from earth and angular position is a sextant, chronometer, and the computer above his ears. And power to correct course, if needed.

5 JANUARY 1961											5 JANUARY 1961	
ECHO I FROM EARTH					STAR DISTANCES			EARTH FROM ECHO I				REMARKS
GMT	LONG	LAT/DEC	SHA	SPEED	GMT	ANTARES	SIRIUS	DISK	RANGE	DEC	SHA	
0h00m	W115.36	S08.46	011.01	14300	0h00m	26.19	18.59	113.23	684	N08.46	191.01	
05	104.90	19.99	359.30	14000	05	24.25	31.55	109.70	769	19.99	179.30	
10	93.25	30.23	346.39	13720	10	22.50	47.30	106.60	858	30.23	166.39	
15	79.54	38.62	331.43	13470	15	22.10	ALTAIR 32.50	103.60	944	38.62	151.43	
20	63.24				20	22.69	19.69		1022	44.50	133.88	
					25					47.17	114.24	
										36	094.43	
											76.55	

Fig. 4-76. This one evolved from a pilot class in space navigation conducted at the U.S. Naval Academy by Capt. P. V. H. Weems, perhaps dean of American practitioners of the ancient art of wayfinding. Nobody has yet found any bugs in principles he espouses.

drift rate well below even this fantastic figure, an attainment that probably lies far off in the future.

Checks, balances, and maybe an alternative

In the absence of more nearly perfect gyros most schemes that take inertial platforms into space couple them in some way to radiation-sensitive star-trackers and horizon-scanners, as indicated in Fig. 4-74. These devices are expected to perform essentially conventional celestial fixes on stars and planets, and feed such data to the inertial navigator as either periodic or continuous correction signals.

Be that as it may, I find I am particularly impressed by the arguments of such people as Captain P. V. H. Weems (U.S.N., Ret.) who, as a leader in the practice and development of sea and air navigation for the past half-century, ranks with great early American navigators like Bowditch, Sumner, Matthew Maury, Muir, and with contemporary giants like Moody, Ageton, and Lofquist. Compared with systems we have been discussing, his point is so simple, it's almost startling.

Assuming, first, that the man who will go to the moon within the next decade or so will be able to function and, second, that he will have adequate power available to maneuver the spacecraft, Weems points out he also will have time to observe and think—some 3, 4, or 5 days of it, in fact, in tranquil cruising time, free of the urgencies that accompany take-off and re-entry which are better left to the automatic controls anyway. And the man in cislunar space can look back to earth—as in Fig. 4-75— and *see* it, against the familiar and precise backdrop of the stars. Which means that with greater ease than when on earth—and with no need for a stable platform—he can spot his local vertical: it's his line of sight to the center of the earth's disk. He can get his distance from the earth by noting the angle subtended by its accurately known diameter (about 13° at a distance of 25,000 miles) and using simple trigonometry.

To locate himself with respect to earth and stars in angular position is an equally simple matter of observation and trigonometry. All he needs is a conventional sextant, an equally conventional and already sufficiently precise chronometer, a space almanac that arranges existing celestial data especially for his use, and a brain—all shelf items, except for the space almanac. Weems' proposal for one is shown in Fig. 4-76.

If such fixes show him to be wandering from the precomputed orbit he has with him, he must push the right guidance buttons, the sooner the better, to perform his traditional duty to conserve fuel. If all instead is well, he can relax, unlike his earthly counterparts, in the assurance that wind and current will not trouble him. With many others more versed than I in the wayfinding arts, I say, "This is just how simple it could turn out to be."

Further reading

Bowditch's American Practical Navigator and *Air Navigation* (U.S. Navy Hydrographic Office, No. 9 and 216, respectively) survey operating systems. Slater in the Nov. 1961 issue of *Astronautics* skims frontiers of the art. On Transit, see Kershner and Newton in the *J. Inst. of Navigation* (London), **15** (2), Apr. 1962; also Wyatt, ASME 62-AV-31, 1962. Influences on satellite orbits are detailed by Kaula in a review "Celestial Geodesy" in *Advances in Geophysics*, **9** (Academic Press, 1962).

Loran and other systems in aircraft applications are treated in *Electronic Avigation Engineering* by Sandretto (Int'l. Tel. and Tel. Co., 1958). Electronic distance-measuring techniques are treated in *J. Geophys. Research,* **65** (2), 1960. Also check the *Bibliography on Direction Finding and Related Ionospheric Propagation Topics* (NBS, Tech. Note 127, Oct. 1962).

Doppler radar is pretty well covered in a series of articles by Berger and Fried (*Trans. IRE,* ANE-4, Dec. 1957).

An easygoing introduction to inertial approaches is Slater's booklet *Newtonian Navigation* (Autonetics, Anaheim, Calif.). A stiffer one is *Inertial Guidance* by Draper, Wrigley, and Hovorka (Pergamon, 1960). For a broader outlook see Pitman's *Inertial Guidance* (Wiley, 1962).

Best point of departure for space may be two reviews in Nov. 1962's *Astronautics;* one by Legalley on guidance, the other by Szbehely on astrodynamics (the latter with excellent leads to other literature). *The Status and Improvement of Physical Constants Needed for Precision Trajectories* is the title of a RAND report (P-1559, Dec. 1958) by Herrick who is also writing the long awaited definitive book to bridge celestial mechanics and space navigation. Finally, see Capt. Weems' final report (1961–62) "Pilot Class in Space Navigation," U.S. Naval Academy, Annapolis, Md.

RADIO SEARCH FOR DISTANT RACES

by Bernard M. Oliver *

IN BRIEF: *It is now considered unlikely that intelligent life exists elsewhere in our solar system. But within some 16 light years are three stars which might have the kinds of planetary systems that could support life long enough for intelligent races to emerge. Within 1000 light years there are hundreds of thousands.*

Our technology—terrestrial technology—has reached the stage where an attempt to find and contact intelligent extra-terrestrials can be undertaken with a reasonable hope for success. If we use the optimum transmission frequencies and modes (as any intelligent race would), and if we can reach out far enough for a long enough time, our chances might be as high as 50%.

Among technically sophisticated races (those with radio telescopes) scientific semantics should not raise any insurmountable problems. But the whole thing depends on the longevity and effectiveness of the effort at both ends.—R.G.N.

■ Oddly enough, as further knowledge about our solar system has shown it to be barren of intelligent life except (debatably) on Earth itself, further knowledge in other fields has greatly increased our estimates of the density of intelligent life elsewhere in the universe, on planetary systems around other stars. There are, of course, a tremendous number of stars—about one hundred thousand million in our own Milky Way. And there are on the order of three thousand million galaxies in the known universe.

* Bernard M. Oliver is Vice President in charge of research and development at the Hewlett-Packard Co., Palo Alto, California.

A plentitude of planets

The feeling that in all this vast cosmos life must exist somewhere besides on earth is very appealing and plausible, but not scientific. The real questions are: How many stars have planets with the right conditions of temperature, gravity and so forth, and which are rich in the variety of heavy elements necessary for life (and just which elements are necessary)? Then, given a suitable planet, how likely is life to begin and to evolve?

Only a few decades ago, planetary systems were thought to be very rare. That is to say only about one star in a billion would have planets. Today planetary systems are thought to be produced as a necessary step in the evolution of typical stars. Stars begin their life cycles as huge masses of interstellar gas many times the size of the solar system. Typically, this extended mass of gas would be slowly rotating. As it condenses under its own gravity, conservation of angular momentum requires that the rate of rotation increase rapidly. By the time it has shrunk to about the size of the solar system (i.e., the orbit of Pluto or Neptune), centrifugal force will have flattened it to a lens of hot, ionized gas.

In order to condense to a spherical star, the whirling gas disk must lose most of its initial angular momentum. It can do this only by casting off from its periphery satellite gas masses and imparting angular momentum to these by magnetohydrodynamic interaction. This involves acceleration of the ionized (and therefore conducting) satellite by the magnetic field of the ionized spinning central mass. As each satellite mass is thus accelerated into orbit, the central mass contracts further. The process repeats, until the central mass becomes a star. The satellite masses then condense and cool to become planets and moons. In our solar system, over 99% of the total mass is the sun, while over 98% of the angular momentum is in the planets.

Since the galaxy as a whole is rotating, typical gas masses must go through this process to condense into stars. We conclude that planetary systems must be the rule, rather than the exception. In fact, several nearby stars show periodicities in their apparent motions which could be explained by the revolution of a planet of roughly Jupiter's mass.

The older stars, called Population II, were formed out of almost pure hydrogen gas. It is unlikely that they produced stable planets, or if so, that life could begin on them. But these stars convert their hydrogen to heavy elements in the course of their lives. When, in death, they explode as supernovae, they cast the heavy elements into space. There these elements mix with more hydrogen to form the gas masses out of which the second generation (Population I) stars like our sun condense. Planets of Population I stars are possible abodes for life.

Life is likely, but remote

A few decades ago, the origin of life was a complete mystery. Life was thought to be highly unlikely unless precisely the right conditions were present. Today the right conditions are believed to be present in at least one planet of almost every Population I star. The primitive atmosphere of a planet like the earth is believed to consist of ammonia, methane, water vapor, and other molecular gases. Upon irradiation with ultraviolet light such a gas mixture will form amino acids, the building blocks of proteins. On the primitive earth or any similar planet, these amino acids would rain down into the then fresh ocean to form a veritable consommé covering the planet.

Given a few phosphate radicals, it is not difficult to visualize the formation of large quantities of the molecules out of which deoxyribonucleic acid (DNA) polymerizes. Experiments have shown that once the first DNA polymer forms, a process of self-replication ensues. This is reproduction at its most basic, molecular level. Our sterile consommé will convert itself into a sea of genes, and even chromosomes.

Those who have studied the origin of life now feel that, given planets only approximately like the primitive earth, life is certain to start. On perhaps 1 to 10% it may develop into complex, and possibly intelligent, forms. Thus, during this century, while our expectation of finding intelligent extraterrestrial life has virtually vanished for the rest of our solar system, it has grown enormously for other stellar systems. We now contemplate a universe teeming with life, but this life is so remote from us as to almost preclude our ever establishing direct physical contact.

The nearest star, α-Centauri, is 4 light years away. Stars likely to have habitable planets exist about 10 light years from us. Within a radius of 1000 light years there are tens of thousands of candidates. By contrast our solar system is only a milli-light year in overall diameter. While man may roam the solar system with instruments (or even in person) during the next decades, to explore thousands of light years into space looking for other life still seems impossibly difficult. The only means of contact which appears feasible at this time is some form of electromagnetic communication.

Electromagnetically speaking

The engineering problem of interstellar communication can be divided into three major phases. There is the technical problem: Can we signal over these great distances and, if so, how can we best do it? There is the acquisition problem: How do we attract the attention of another race, or they ours? And finally there is the communication problem itself: How do we exchange meaningful information with a totally alien civilization?

The technical problem obviously depends on distance, and this depends upon the density of communicative races in our stellar neighborhood. A sincere effort to estimate this density was made in November, 1961 at a conference at the National Radio Astronomy Observatory at Green Bank, West Virginia. On the basis of quantitative estimates of the numerous independent factors involved, the conclusion was reached that if we can signal out to ten light years our chances of contact are extremely slim, perhaps one in a million. But if we can signal out to 1000 light years (and do so for an extremely long time) our chances of contact are good, perhaps 50%.

The ultimate range of an electromagnetic communication system is determined by three factors: the energy radiated per symbol, the directive gain of the antennas, and the noise. In the simplest (and a very nearly optimum) form of modulation the "symbols" would be pulses or spaces, and the messages would be encoded into these in some way.

Now the limiting amplification that can be used at the receiver is determined by the noise at its input: energy spread at random over the entire frequency spectrum. To "detect" a pulse, i.e., distinguish between its presence or absence, the signal energy must be comparable with or greater than the noise energy received during a pulse time. Thus the signal-to-noise (energy) ratio is a measure of detectability. If this ratio is unity, detection will be marginal and many errors will be made. If the ratio is 100 the detection will be almost unambiguous.

If we double the pulse length keeping the power the same, we double the pulse energy. We can receive these slower pulses with a receiver having a response time that is twice as long as before and therefore has half the bandwidth. This narrower receiver will receive half as much noise power and therefore the same total noise energy during the pulse. Thus we have doubled the signal-to-noise ratio by doubling the pulse energy and using a matched receiver. Of course we can now signal only half as fast. In an interstellar channel one would presumably use the highest economically practical power and very long pulses, since, at least initially, the communication rate is of little importance.

The size of the transmitting antenna (measured in wavelengths) determines its ability to concentrate the radiated energy into a beam directed at the receiver. The physical size of the receiving antenna determines how much of this energy is collected. In fact, the ratio of energy received to that radiated is simply $A_T A_R / \lambda^2 D^2$, where A_T and A_R are the *effective*

areas of the transmitting and receiving antennas, λ is the wavelength and D the distance between them. Thus the largest practical antenna should be used at both ends.

Let us now look at the spectral distribution of noise power. All bodies which can absorb and therefore reradiate electromagnetic waves are sources of "thermal noise," i.e., blackbody radiation in a single propagation mode. Resistors produce thermal noise. So do hot surfaces or gases at which an antenna may be pointed. Thermal noise at low frequencies has a spectral power density of kT watts per cycle per second. It is, therefore, convenient and customary to consider any noise source having a spectral power density, ψ, as equivalent to a thermal source at a temperature $T = \psi/k$. Figure 4-77 shows the effective noise temperature for three sources of noise germane to the present problem. Cosmic noise is received from all parts of the sky but is most intense toward the center of the galaxy. It is the noise which Jansky first heard and which started the science of radio astronomy. It falls off rapidly with increasing frequency, as indicated by Fig. 4-77.

Even an ideal amplifier—one without any thermal noise—would not be noise free. Quantum effects also produce noise. Referred to an amplifier's input, this noise is $h\nu$ watts per cps, giving an effective noise temperature of $h\nu/k$

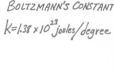

BOLTZMANN'S CONSTANT
$K = 1.38 \times 10^{23} \text{ joules/degree}$

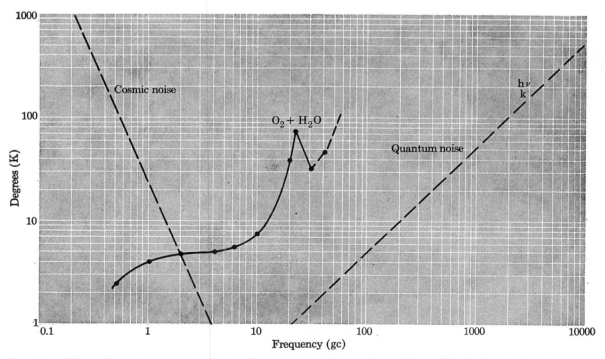

Fig. 4-77. *The optimum frequency for interstellar communication is dictated by masking noises. At low frequencies, the cosmic noises of radio astronomy set the limits of communication; at high frequencies, it's the inherent quantum noise of an ideal amplifier. For an earth-based antenna, there is also noise from atmospheric oxygen and water.*

as shown. Modern masers approach this ideal quantum-limited performance. This noise cannot be avoided by using photon detectors rather than coherent amplifiers, for then a similar "noise" exists due to randomness of photon count.

The total noise from these two (thermal and quantum) sources reaches a minimum of about 0.5°K around 8 gc (8×10^9 cps). This low temperature emphasizes the importance of avoiding thermal noise sources in our receiver. Eight gc would work just fine for interstellar communication if our receiver itself were in space. With an earth-based receiver, the atmosphere radiates noise into the antenna due to absorption (and reradiation) of energy by oxygen and water vapor. Taking this into account the quietest frequency range is about 2–10 gc with an effective noise temperature of 5°–10°K.

Above 50 gc, the strong resonances of O_2, H_2O, CO_2 render the atmosphere opaque. When it clears up again in the infrared, $h\nu/k$ has reached an effective temperature of several thousand degrees. Thus we have two likely regions for communication, one in the infrared and optical part of the spectrum, and a much quieter one in the microwave region.

Lasers versus microwaves

The advent of optical masers, or lasers, has focused interest on the possibility of using op-

tical frequencies for interstellar communication. Very narrow beams are possible with optical "antennas" of modest size. However, beam widths much less than a second of arc are impractical because of atmospheric turbulence and aiming problems. Such beams do not provide enough directive gain over present large microwave antennas to compensate for the increased noise at optical frequencies (noise temperature $\approx 20,000$°K). Thus the microwave region still seems best at the present time.

Figure 4-78 shows a performance comparison of two optical systems and one microwave communication system. The common ordinate for all these systems is signal-to-noise ratio (S/N), so their performances are comparable. For optical systems, this is the average number of photons received per pulse; for the microwave system, it is the ratio received energy per pulse to kT.

The present laser, with 10 joules per pulse at a wavelength of 0.7 micron, and equipped with 10-inch telescope "antennas" at both transmitter and receiver, would give the performance shown by the left line. An ideal quantum-limited receiver is assumed. We see that S/N falls to unity at a distance of 0.04 light year. Raising the radiated energy to 10^4 joules per pulse gives the performance shown by the middle dotted line: unity S/N at a little over 1 light year.

PLANK'S CONSTANT
$h = 6.624 \times 10^{-27}$ erg-sec

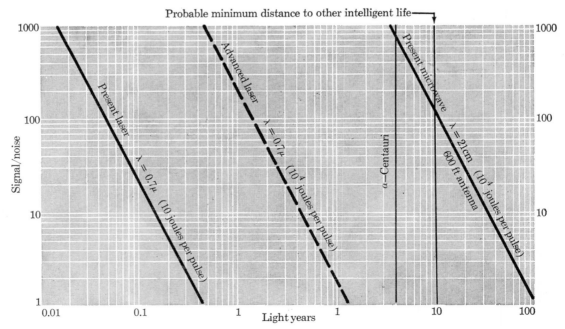

Fig. 4-78. A major criterion for unambiguity in a communications system is signal-to-noise ratio. A comparison of microwave and laser technology shows that even a 10,000 joule/pulse laser, operating at 0.7 micron with 10-inch antennas, offers smaller S/N over interstellar ranges than a 21-cm microwave system with 600-ft antennas. The same results would be obtained comparing the laser systems to a 10 gc microwave system. Ideal (quantum-limited) receivers are assumed.

The line on the right assumes a microwave system radiating 10^4 joules per pulse at a wavelength of 21 cm, with 600-ft transmitting and receiving antennas, and a receiver noise temperature of $10°$K. We see that unity S/N is reached at 100 light years. At ten light years S/N is 100. As a matter of fact, 10^6 joules per pulse (1 Mw for a sec) is certainly possible today, and this would give a S/N of 100 at 100 light years, unity at 1000 light years. The same results would be obtained with 230 ft antennas operating at say 10 gc.

We may conclude that the technical problem is barely within the present art, assuming equally effective cooperation at the other end!

Attracting attention

What about the acquisition problem? How do we attract the attention of the other race, or search for their signals? This is made difficult by sheer dimensionality. Whether we transmit or listen, or both, we must not only search in space, star by star, but also in time, over an extended period, and possibly in frequency as well. If we could eliminate one dimension of search, we could simplify the problem enormously.

If we (or the other race) had some means of generating extremely short pulses of extremely high power, say 10^{16} watts for 10^{-10} seconds, we (or they) could blanket the best part of the microwave region with energy. This is because a short pulse has a very broad spectrum. A very broad receiver sensitive from about 2 to 10 gc would then be indicated and would not require searching in frequency. Barring this, the high pulse energy can only be achieved by using the highest available power for long pulses. This requires a narrow band receiver.

Frequency search can also be eliminated, or greatly reduced, by transmitting on or near some natural frequency such as a spectral line. This is an inherent property of lasers and one of the strong arguments for their use. Project Ozma began with the ingenious suggestion of Cocconi and Morrison of Cornell that we listen on the hydrogen line frequency of 1420 megacycles (21 cm). They argued that since radio astronomers listen on this line a great part of the time, radio astronomers anywhere in the universe would be doing the same, and any intelligent race trying to communicate would choose this frequency or one nearby.

A good acquisition signal should differ markedly from all natural signals. It need not be a series of prime numbers as has often been suggested; mere pulses will do. But it should not be so efficiently encoded in the Shannon sense as to resemble thermal noise. (C. E. Shannon has shown that if the information in a signal is so coded as to make the statistics of the signal match those of thermal noise, the greatest transmission rate of information is achieved for a given power and bandwidth.) The acquisition signal can convey instructions for locating and receiving another signal, one more efficiently encoded. But *the acquisition signal itself should be attention-getting.*

After contact, rapport

How should we attempt to convey meaning? Since the nearest likely stars are 10 light years away, no answer can be received for at least 20 years. Certainly we should not waste time sending simple pulses till we get a reply. The other race would probably consider us so stupid they might not bother to answer. We should, I believe, send a repeated series of messages which constitute a course of instruction—facts about our civilization, our language, our science, and ourselves. The other race can then respond with a more sophisticated initial message, perhaps one indicating a more efficient means of communication.

In constructing these first acquisition messages we are justified, I believe, in making one very important assumption about any intelligent race: that they have eyes. Sight is such an important sense that it is hard to imagine technological development in a race devoid of it. Further, it has developed in a great variety of earth's life forms. Flies have eyes; so do scallops, and mice and men. Since pictorial matter provides a good, if not the best, means of conveying meaning in the absence of a common language, the initial signals should probably be pictorial. Other races would probably reach the same conclusion.

In addition, certain mathematical and physical relationships would be obvious and correctly interpreted by any race whose technology was sufficiently advanced to receive the message at all. For example, prime numbers are prime in any number system. The structure of atoms does not depend on who studies them.

Using these principles, Frank Drake, of the National Radio Astronomy Observatory, constructed an imitation message which he mailed to those who had attended the meeting mentioned earlier. No clues for decipherment were given, yet the majority of the group successfully got most of the meaning from it very quickly.

Let us assume that after years of futile listening we receive a peculiar series of pulses and spaces from ϵ-Eridani. The message is repeated every 22 hr and 53 min, apparently the length of their day. The pulses occur at separations which are integral multiples of a minimum separation. Writing ones for the pulses and

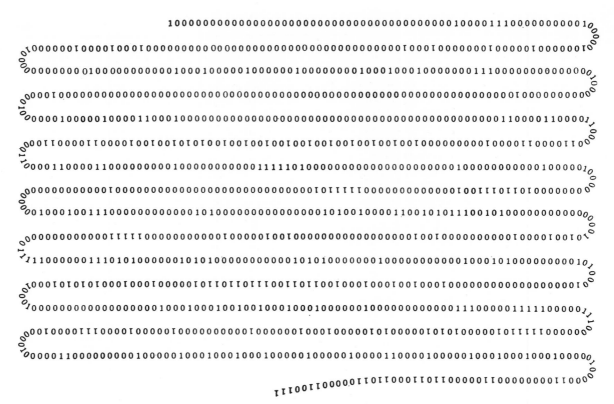

Fig. 4-79. Imagine that this simulated message has arrived as a series of pulses and spaces, here represented by ones and zeros. Some data could be contained in the transmission characteristics, e.g., the period of revolution of the planet of origin could be deduced from the message repetition rate. The entire pattern consists of 1271 ones and zeros. Since 1271 is the product of two primes, 31 and 41, it suggests arranging the message in a 31 × 41 array. The pattern on the facing page emerges.

filling in the blanks with the appropriate numbers of zeros we get the binary series shown in Fig. 4-79. It consists of 1271 ones and zeros. 1271 is the product of two primes 31 and 41. This strongly suggests that we arrange the message in a 31 × 41 array. When we do so, leaving blanks for the zeros, and putting down a dot for each pulse we get the nonrandom pattern of Fig. 4-80.

Apparently we are in touch with a race of erect bipeds who reproduce sexually. There is even a suggestion that they might be mammals. The crude circle and column of dots at the left suggests their sun and planetary system. The figure is pointing to the fourth planet, evidently their home. The planets are numbered down the left hand edge in a binary code which increases in place value from left to right and starts with a decimal (or rather a binary) point to mark the beginning.

The wavy line commencing at the third planet indicates that it is covered with water and the fish-like form shows there is marine life there. The bipeds know this, so they must have space travel. The diagrams at the top will be recognized as hydrogen, carbon, and oxygen atoms, so their life is based on a carbohydrate chemistry. The binary number six above the

raised arm of the right figure suggests six fingers and implies a base twelve number system. Finally, the dimension line at the lower right suggests that the figure is eleven somethings tall. Since the wavelength of 21 cm on which we received the message is the only length we both know, we conclude the beings are 231 cm, or 7 ft, in height.

This message certainly does not exceed Shannon's information limit. Better messages from this standpoint can easily be constructed. In fact, the earlier one, constructed by Frank Drake, used only 551 zeros and ones to convey a somewhat similar amount of information. But it is surprising how much we could learn about another race from only 250 pulses.

Further reading

"Some Astronomical Aspects of Life in the Universe" by Huang, in *Sky and Telescope*, **21** (1961), reviews the stellar conditions for genesis of life. Besides astronomers, many others are studying the likelihood of extraterrestrial life and so the literature is scattered throughout such journals as *Science, Nature, J. Aviation Med., Aerospace Med., Am. Scientists, Proc. Nat. Academy of Science*, and even *J. Am. Chem. Soc.* (where Miller's definitive work on production of organic compounds under simulated primeval atmospheres was reported in May, 1955).

A fine introduction to the larger questions of astrobiology is chapter 6 of *Basic Astronautics*, by Ordway, Gardner and Sharpe (Prentice-Hall, 1962, $16.00), which discusses current thinking on the conditions necessary for life and the general occurrence of these throughout the universe. The subject of communication with alien races is discussed more specifically in a collection of essays edited by A. G. W. Cameron, *Interstellar Communications* (Benjamin, 1963, $8.50).

Project Ozma, an attempt to detect communication from other stars, is described by Drake in his article in *Physics Today*, **14,** Apr.

(1961). The problem of interstellar semantics has also been considered, by Lapp in his *Man and Space* (Harper, 1961, $4.95), and a language has even been proposed by Freudenthal in *Lincos, Design of a Language for Cosmic Discourse* (North-Holland, 1960). But perhaps the most severe ultimate limitation on the population of sophisticated technologies throughout the universe is one that has been brought up by Bracewell, by Drake, and by Huang among many others. That is the mean lifetime of sophisticated technologies and the proportion of their demises which leave their planets uninhabitable. Von Hoerner's interesting (though pessimistic) treatment, "The Search for Signals from Other Civilizations" in *Science*, Dec. 1961, points up this pertinent heuristic.

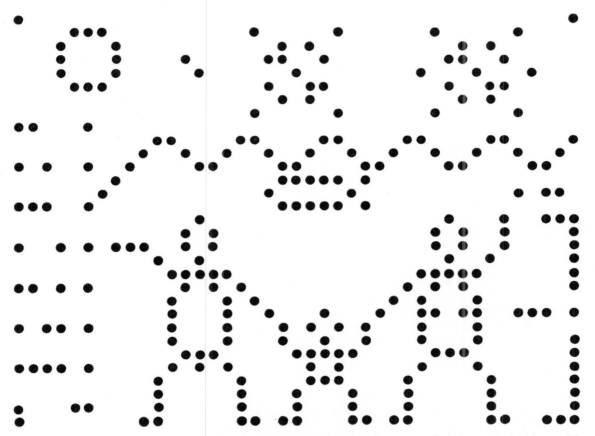

Fig. 4-80. The "message" Fig. 4-79 deciphered and rearranged. (It's reversed, left to right, but we would never know that unless we compared physical parity experiments or common star fields with the other race.) When a similar message was tried out on a group (uncoached) at the radio astronomy conference at Green Bank in 1961, most of them correctly read the intended message. You might like to try this message out on your own terrestrial friends.

Chapter 5

Earth Science and Oceanography

THE EARTH'S CRUST

by *Seymour Tilson* *

IN BRIEF: *No part of the earth offers as complete a picture of the planet's turbulent history as does its crust. And nowhere in the universe is there an equally accessible array of the resources necessary to men.*

Spawned at the dynamic interface between the solid earth and the solar-powered atmosphere-ocean system, the crust offers mute testimony to the strength and durability of the planet's internal sources of energy. Today these manifest themselves in the earth's magnetic field, in heat flow from the interior, and in continued volcanic and earthquake activity. In the past such internal energy—driving great convection currents within the mantle and core—has apparently built the continents.

A key link in the evolution of the continents has been the repeated creation through time of mountain chains that lumber in great arcs across the surface of the land. These have grown at sites marked hundreds of millions of years before by volcanic islands that swept in similar arcs across the vanished sea.

The overwhelming number of known metallic ore deposits are genetically related to the deeper parts—the "roots"—of mountain belts. Most undiscovered ores we seek also are to be found there.—S.T.

■ Any serious attempt to answer age-old questions about the universe and Man's place in it must begin with the story of the earth. It may not be the cosmic prototype for a planet, but it is still the only sample we have. And far more urgent than the facts of cosmology are the facts

* Seymour Tilson is Associate Editor of *International Science and Technology*.

of life. Little time remains in the race to meet humanity's mounting material needs. And nothing in the universe truly offers even the barest hope of meeting these needs—other than the rocks, minerals, soils, waters, air, and human ingenuity present on this prosaic planet.

The critical place on Earth, where Man's material survival and cosmological edifices must both find their roots, is the same place where the only life whose existence we are certain of began 3 or 4 billion years ago. Here—at the surface of the planet—the energy of the sun met the materials of the earth, and out of their flux came life. Out of it, too, came the waters of the sea, the components of the air, and the living skin—or crust—on the body of the planet. But while life could be created largely from the sun's energy and the earth's matter alone, creation of the atmosphere, the seas, and the crust took something more; it took the energy within the earth itself, the energy that causes us to describe the earth as a heat engine or a dynamo.

This article presents the story of the earth's crust, as seen by geology, geophysics, and geochemistry. It is a story pieced together painfully and slowly by a remarkable combination of scientific disciplines. And it is a story that is incomplete. But even so, the crust remains the only window into the vitals of the planet; and its resources are vital in the affairs of men.

The living skin on the body of the planet

Developing as it did, at the crucial boundary between the body of the planet and the energetic atmosphere of the sun, the crust bears the scars of the incessant battle between the two. The general nature of this crustal scar tissue, as it is exposed on the continents, is shown in Fig. 5-1. The section represents at most the upper 10 miles or so of depth in the continental crust. This is the region that has been made directly accessible to geological study through the revelatory work of deep erosion by nature, and the probing of Man in mines and deep wells. For information on the deeper parts of the continental crust, and the still more extensive areas of crust which underlie the oceans, we must for the time being mostly rely on indirect evidence and inferences of several kinds.

But within the next few years, if the engineering problems can be surmounted, the Canadians, the U.S., and the Soviet Union will drill deeply into the crust at several locations both on the continents and at sea. The samples retrieved from such drilling will provide invaluable checks and correctives for the body of inference built thus far by indirect though ingenious methods of study. The next few years will also see the international geophysical community accelerate studies of all kinds into the solid earth as part of its "Upper Mantle Project," loosely patterned after the successful IGY —which won huge insights into the ocean-ice-atmosphere systems of the planet. Funds, instrumentation, field observations and theoretical studies will be upped sharply. And integrated programs in solid-earth seismology, gravity, electricity and magnetism, heat flow, geochemistry, and geology—plus drilling of the Mohole and other deep holes, all of them to be sampled and logged for a dozen or more parameters—will throw new light on the dark interior.

The continents are a jig-saw puzzle

A glance at Fig. 5-1 suggests that the continental crust is a mosaic of many kinds and ages of rocks. Most abundant at the surface, but generally not very thick compared with the thickness of the crust, are the sedimentary rocks formed from the eroded debris of other more ancient rocks. At greater depths, or at the surface in places where erosion has stripped away the sedimentary veneer, are the much more abundant metamorphic rocks. These have formed mostly from original sediments that have recrystallized while in the solid state, under the influence of the higher temperatures and pressures that characterize the deeper or more dynamic parts of the crust.

Most abundant of all rocks—in fact, comprising 85–90% of the continental crust, and essentially all of the oceanic crust—are the igneous rocks. Of many kinds and shapes, they have taken their place in the continental mosaic by one of two means. Either they have intruded into the other rocks as molten masses called magma, which froze beneath the surface into a rigidity belying their original heat and fluidity; or they are volcanic rocks, formed where the magma reached the earth's surface before crystallizing as an intrusion, and poured forth as lava at modern or at long-vanished volcanic vents.

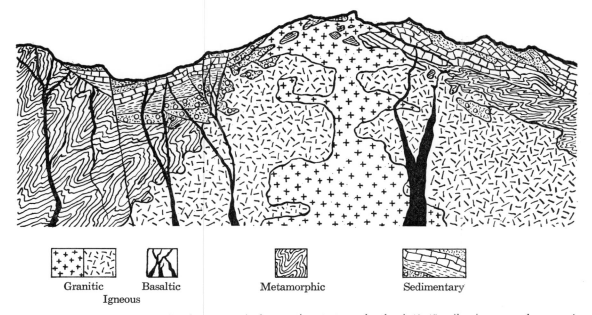

Granitic Basaltic Metamorphic Sedimentary
Igneous

Fig. 5-1. As geology sees it, the crust of the continents to a depth of 10–15 miles is a complex mosaic made up of many different kinds and ages of rocks. These have been folded at various times in the past, and broken along faults into blocks of diverse sizes and shapes. Compare Figs 5-4 and 5-8.

There are many hundreds of types of igneous rock, shading from one to another—yet they divide strikingly into two major groupings. The upper part of Fig. 5-2 will help to make this

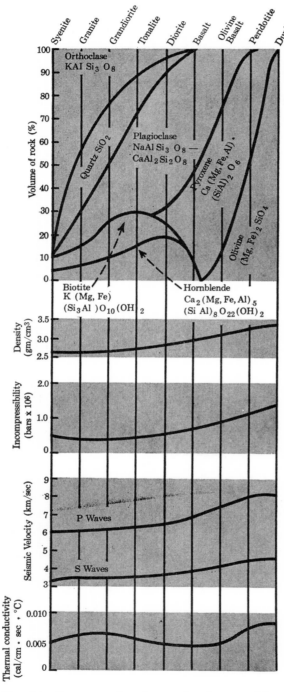

Fig. 5-2. Igneous rocks whose mineral composition is shown at top make up some 90% of the crust. Their physical constants, shown on lower graphs, are basis for inferences drawn from seismology about the deeper crust. Such data derived from laboratory work on rock samples is incomplete, especially at higher temperatures and pressures.

clear. The diagram displays the mineral composition (and indirectly the chemical composition) of the principal igneous rocks. Rocks of the granite, granodiorite, and tonalite groups—collectively known somewhat loosely as "granitic" rocks—essentially occur only on the continents, chiefly as vast intrusive bodies. And here they are overwhelmingly abundant. But the other exceedingly common igneous rocks—those of the basalt and olivine-basalt groups which are collectively described as the "basaltic" rocks—not only characterize the volcanic islands in all ocean areas (e.g., Hawaii); they also comprise the most abundantly occurring lava outpourings on the surface of the continents at many points in geologic time.

Here is our first major clue to the nature of the differences between the continental and oceanic parts of the crust. Presumably the chemical constituents and conditions needed to manufacture granitic rocks exist only in the continents, since granitic rocks are essentially absent on the volcanic islands of the world's oceanic regions. But the basaltic ingredients evidently are an intrinsic part of both the continents and the ocean floors. Where then have the enormous floods of basaltic lavas on the continental surface come from, repeatedly throughout later geologic time? Everywhere that erosion has exposed the feeder channels for the basaltic volcanic sheets, they are found to pass through fractures in the great granitic intrusive masses to the lowest levels that are exposed. Presumably, then, the source of the basaltic magma lies deeper within the continental crust than Fig. 5-1 will carry us.

This implies one of two sources for the ubiquitous basalts: they either derive from a world-wide crustal layer of basalt-like material, one that underlies the granitic continental plates as it similarly floors the oceans; or else they come from the earth's upper mantle. Geology cannot answer the question. Perhaps geochemistry can.

More oxygen in the crust than in the air

Vast numbers of analyses of rocks of all kinds from diverse geological environments have been made over the years. In recent years many of the newer methods of instrumental analysis (see "Tools for Analytical Chemistry," page 225) have greatly expanded the information available for the rarer and trace elements in the rocks. The average chemical composition of the crust in effect is that of the igneous rocks, because of their overwhelming abundance. Figure 5-3, which plots the abundance of the elements, is based on suitable averages for the predominant igneous rocks. Several striking relationships emerge from the chemical data of Fig. 5-3

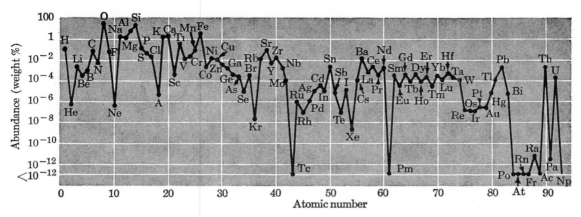

Fig. 5-3. *Logarithmic plot of the abundance of elements in the crust shows that only eight elements—O, Si, Al, Fe, Ca, Na, K, and Mg—are present in amounts greater than 1%; together they comprise about 99% of the crust. And of these, oxygen alone makes up about half of the total weight of the crust, silicon about one-quarter. (After Mason)*

and the mineralogical data in the upper part of Fig. 5-2.

Most surprising perhaps is the fact that a mere eight of the elements comprise just about 99% of the total mass! Of these eight—O, Si, Al, Fe, Ca, Na, K, Mg—oxygen is overwhelmingly the most abundant, making up close to half of the total weight of the crust. A quick look back to the top of Fig. 5-2 will explain this. The crust consists almost entirely of oxygen compounds, especially silicates of the most abundant metals noted above. Note too that the granitic rocks in essence are silicates of the lighter metals—K, Na, Al. On the contrary, though the basaltic rocks include fair amounts of light Mg, they also are distinctively higher in the heavier elements Fe and Ca. This chemical difference shows up, of course, in the density of the rocks as shown on the density curve of Fig. 5-2.

If we accept the prevailing idea that the crust passed through a molten or semi-molten stage sometime fairly early in the history of the earth, we seem to have a second clue to the nature of the deeper invisible part of the crust. The denser minerals characteristic of the basaltic rocks should have settled lower in the primordial crust than the less dense granitic materials—again suggesting logically that not too far below the visible granitic crust of the continents and the ocean waters lies a pervasive zone of basaltic rock.

The economic chemistry of the crust

Figure 5-3 also shows that many of the elements that are economically important are really rare in comparison with other lesser known or less used elements. Copper, for example, is less abundant than zirconium; lead is no more abundant than gallium; mercury is more rare than the so-called rare earths. In fact, many relatively unfamiliar elements are quite abundant—vanadium exceeds tin in the crust; scandium and hafnium are respectively more abundant than arsenic and boron.

Before we get too excited about new materials, however, we must distinguish clearly between the abundance of an element and its commercial availability. Many elements, though present in the crust in considerable amounts, are uniformly distributed through various common minerals, and so appear in trace amounts. They never occur highly concentrated in any one mineral. Rubidium, for instance, is more abundant than either zinc or cobalt, and about as abundant as copper; but Rb forms no minerals of its own—it always occurs as a trace substituent for potassium in potassium-rich minerals. On the other hand, some elements such as Ti and Zr do form specific minerals of their own. But these minerals, in turn, are themselves usually very widely—and uneconomically—dispersed in very small amounts throughout the most common rocks.

To summarize then—the commercial availability of a particular element depends upon three factors. First, the greater the ability of the element to form individual minerals in which it is the major constituent, the more available it will be. But even the common elements of industry, which are common precisely because they form their own minerals, much more often than not occur in diffusely distributed amounts throughout the rocks of the crust, rather than in those economically profitable concentrations we term ore deposits which are the second requirement for commercial availability.

However, the third factor may turn out to be most important of all. Availability of an element to industry depends very largely on the technology of extraction that we can develop. For example, the widely distributed deposits of ordinary clay minerals could be a far more readily available source for aluminum than are the much more restricted occurrences of bauxite. But extracting Al from clay minerals is technically difficult. The aluminum industry has only recently begun a serious effort to build a technology along this line. Another instance of the same technological handicap we face in exploiting even the ready at hand resources of the crust is the case of magnesium. There are extensive deposits of olivine-bearing rock (Fig. 5-2, top, dunite and peridotite) which contain up to 30% Mg, but there is no economical technology for extracting it. Thus Mg is extracted from sea water, where its concentration is a mere 0.13%. There are innumerable instances of the same sort which industry should bear in mind when considering potential outlets for its research energies.

Two kinds of crust on the continents

To a greater or lesser degree, depending on where one looks on the continents, the rocks are folded, flexed, and warped; and they are broken by fractures into blocks of various shapes and sizes. Along many of the fractures, fault movements have displaced the blocks relative to each other anywhere from a fraction of an inch to scores of miles.

But enough has been learned about this seeming chaos to let us recognize in the continental crust two major kinds of regional structure.

One is the stable continental platform that seems to comprise the keystone in the architecture of the continent. Here the life history of the crust seems to have been placid. Gentle warps, small scale folds, and fractures with displacements measured in hundreds of feet at most predominate. Here also the cover of sediments is wide but not very thick. And everywhere beneath the sediments, to the greatest depths we know, lies a complex mass of intricately deformed, chemically diverse igneous and metamorphic rocks that are called the crystalline basement. Where the sedimentary cover is absent the basement is exposed at the surface. It forms the great terranes of oldest rocks that appear to be not only the basement but also the nucleus or heartland of all continents. In these vast stable regions which comprise most of the area of every continent, deformation seems to be a function chiefly of differential vertical movements between adjacent portions of the crust.

The other kind of regional structure found on the continents presents a much more dynamic picture. These are the arcuate chains of mountains such as the Alps, Himalayas, and Rockies —100 mi. or more long and at most a few hundred miles wide. Here the sedimentary strata—originally deposited in horizontal layers

by the long-vanished waters of streams, lakes, and seaways—are intensely deformed. Layers are vertical or overturned. Folding is tight. Displacements along faults are such as to confirm the impression gained from the fold patterns that in these regions the crust—at least to depths of several miles—has been crushed by compression as if caught in a global vise. It's a startling picture: belts of sediments that were originally several hundred miles wide have apparently been shortened to as little as a few scores of miles! And still more startling surprises await us in the deeper parts of the mountain chains.

The clue to the continental crust

Wherever the mountain belts have been deeply eroded, their deeper portions bared to view by nature's scalpel, a remarkable transition is observed. The folded and faulted sediments characteristic of the higher levels grade through all degrees of transition into their metamorphic equivalents, as the core of the mountain chain is exposed. Nor is this all. In many places the metamorphic rocks themselves are observed to give way to great masses of granitic rocks which both intrude into and replace the metamorphic rocks.

Evidently as mountain chains made up of greatly compressed sediments form through many tens of millions of years at the earth's surface, a different story is taking place in the lower depths. Here, where the temperature and pressures are higher, the rocks undergo metamorphic recrystallization. And where the temperature becomes high enough, miles below the folds and faults growing above, the rocks can partially or completely melt. Such melting is expedited by the crustal fracturing which attends the deformation of the mountain belt: the release of confining pressure on the deeply buried rocks permits at least the lower-melting constituents of the rocks, already at temperatures in excess of their atmospheric-pressure melting points, to fuse. Thus the gross internal anatomy of a mountain chain in cross section is as shown in the margin. There is a central core of granitic igneous rock with various attendant satellitic shapes and rock types emanating from it. There is a crude halo of metamorphics more or less symmetrically arranged about the granitic keel; and near the surface are successively less and less deformed sediments.

Interestingly enough, the commercial ore deposits of many metals—gold, silver, lead, zinc, copper, tin, and others—frequently, though not invariably, occur in the satellite intrusions which are genetically related to the deeper "granitic" magmatic masses. This suggests that the chemical and physical mobility of the elements during the magmatic phases of mountain formation play an instrumental role in concentrating some elements into economically valuable ore veins.

But what might we expect to find as we went to deeper levels in the crust either by natural erosion, or by deeper mining? If we searched below the halo of satellitic veins and smaller intrusions? For many metals, the economic concentration in localized ore bodies would disappear. Indeed there might be large tonnages of each element in the granitic masses at greater depth, but likely it would be dispersed in an uneconomic uniform distribution throughout the granitic mass.

Again, the power of our extraction technology assumes importance equal to that of our discovery technology in the matter of mineral raw materials.

The continent is made of mountains

Recalling the earlier description of the stable continental platform, you will remember that beneath its thin veneer of gently deformed sediments lies the crystalline basement. And in all important essentials, this pervasive crystalline basement resembles the granitic-metamorphic roots of the mountain belts I have just described.

The mass of the continent, in other words, to a depth of perhaps a dozen miles, is made up of the deeply eroded cores or roots of now vanished mountain chains. And vanished though they may be, questions about how they were formed, what the energy source was, how the deeper sediments were metamorphosed, melted, replaced, and intruded into by granitic matter, must be answered if we hope to understand the dynamics of the earth.

The mountain belts provide the key to the puzzle of why there are two crusts—a continental one and an oceanic one. But to use this key, we must search the depths within the continents and under the sea. The aid of physics, chemistry, and engineering is indispensable in this search.

From mountains into mathematics

Let's pause for a moment to refine our definition of the term "crust." It has survived, of course, from an earlier time when it was believed that the interior of the earth was a liquid left over from the original molten earth and covered by a thin shell of crystalline rock. Now seismology has shown the earth to be solid in its response to the shock waves generated in earthquakes and explosions—at least to the depth of the mantle-core boundary 1800 miles below the surface; so the term has lost its original significance. But it is still used to designate the outermost solid shell of the earth, bounded below by the well-known Mohorovicic discontinuity. This boundary within the earth is marked by an abrupt increase in the velocity of seismic waves. The velocity of the compressional (or P) wave jumps from about 7 km/sec at the lower part of the crust to about 8.1 km/sec in the mantle beneath.

The best estimates of crustal thickness and structure call for a continental crust about 20 to 25 miles (35 km) thick. Of this, the upper two thirds has seismic wave velocities appropriate to rocks of "granitic" composition; the lowest zone is inferred to be basaltic. Under the oceans—whose average depth is about 5 kilometers (3 miles)—lies a much thinner crust consisting of perhaps a kilometer or so of oceanic sediments, and beneath this perhaps 5 or 6 kilometers (3 or 4 miles) of basalt-like crystalline rock. (See Fig. 5-4.)

The chain of deductions and observations leading to this crustal picture is fascinating. The entire structure depends on what are called "travel-time" curves.

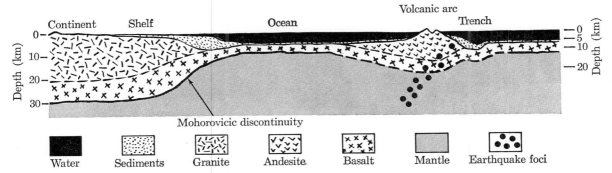

Fig. 5-4. Seismology pictures the crust as smoothly layered, in contrast with the great heterogeneity that geology has found to be the case (Fig. 5-1) at least for the visible upper half of the continents. The relatively thin crust under the oceans is the tempting target for forthcoming U.S. attempts to drill through it to the underlying mantle.

These are deceptively simple plots of the time it takes a seismic signal to reach a recording station versus the distance from the epicenter to the station. To get these curves, several assumptions must be made about the velocity and depth of penetration of the seismic waves. Seismic velocities generally increase with depth within the crust. But whether they increase continuously or in discrete steps is a moot point. Seismologists therefore can assume any one of a choice of structures for the crust, so long as the observational data on wave arrival times and epicentral distances are not violated. No unique solution to crustal structure is presently derivable from seismology alone.

If the velocity of the seismic waves is assumed to increase continuously with depth, the travel-time curves which result are erratically curved, cusped, and doubled back on themselves—generally difficult or impossible to interpret satisfactorily.

If, however, the crustal structure is interpreted as layered, so that velocities change in discontinuous steps as one goes deeper, the mathematical complexity of the travel-time curves is greatly reduced. In fact, it turns out that the travel-time curves can be drawn as a series of straight lines. Within each assumed crustal layer of Fig. 5-5 the seismic velocities are constant.

Once horizontal layering is assumed, solution of the seismic data for the thickness of the crust and for that of the layers within the crust becomes quite simple. Figure 5-5 shows an assumed two-layer crust, in which either an earthquake or a blast occurs at a focal depth D. At a seismic station a distance X away from the shock, three velocities of P waves will be received: the slowest is the wave whose whole path lies within the upper layer; next is the wave refracted downward and traveling the

horizontal part of its path along the top of the second layer; fastest is the wave refracted still deeper, the horizontal part of its path lying along the top of the earth's mantle beneath the two-layered crust.

Obviously, the geometry assumed for the crust, and for the wave paths in the crust, can yield values for the thicknesses of the crustal layers, L_1 and L_2, through simple equations.

The accuracy of the solution depends most of all on getting a value for the depth of the shock's focus, D. This is rarely obtained for a randomly occurring natural earthquake, because it requires the location of an observing station near the shock epicenter. But with the increasing density of seismic stations now being established, and with the increased use of blasts as the shock source, this difficulty is diminishing.

However, early hopes that explosion studies in which the exact position and time of the shock were known would lead to a final and exact interpretation of the earth's structure have not been borne out. Indeed, the chief conclusion of such modern work is that the earth is quite varied in its constitution, at least as far down as the Mohorovicic discontinuity. This had been the opinion held by geology, before early seismology had leveled the beautiful and intricate heterogeneity of the crust to a neatly layered structure.

Laboratory studies a key link

It is reasonable to suppose that a crustal layer of such relatively modest thickness compared with the dimensions of the earth (the crust represents 0.5% of the earth's total volume; 0.4% of its total mass) should resemble rocks that are abundant at the surface of the earth—in chemical composition (Fig. 5-3), mineral makeup (Fig. 5-2, top), and general physical properties (Fig. 5-2, bottom). A great deal of inference about the deeper nature of the crust depends on this surmise.

Below the level of visual observation, the diagnosis of the composition of the crust depends entirely upon the correlation of seismic wave velocities as observed in the earth with laboratory determinations of the elastic constants and wave velocities in rock samples of known chemistry and mineralogy. The seismic picture of the earth's internal *structure* does not, of course, depend upon the laboratory data: the calculation of seismic wave velocities in the earth as a function of depth in any given region depends only on the seismic records, and on the skill and general philosophy of the seismologist. But to translate these numbers into statements about which minerals and rocks can be found at each depth, or to use

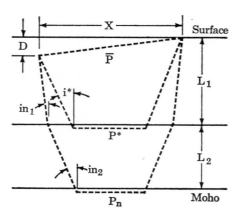

Fig. 5-5. Relative thickness of granitic and basaltic layers of continental crust is derived by simple trigonometric solution for values L_1 and L_2 from seismic wave geometry shown. See text.

them to deduce the physical properties of the deeper earth materials, demands laboratory results like those of Fig. 5.2. There are not nearly enough such studies, particularly at the high pressures combined with high temperatures needed to simulate conditions in the lower crust and mantle.

As it turns out, the seismic velocities observed in the crust are indeed compatible with the velocities that have been determined for lab samples of ordinary rock types. Moreover, most of the rock's physical properties correspond to the composition as well, varying in a fairly consistent way with the systematic variations in composition, as illustrated by Fig. 5-2. In general the properties plotted—density, incompressibility, seismic velocities, and thermal conductivity—all show a gradual rise in value towards the rocks of higher density and more basaltic composition.

Such correlation of higher seismic wave velocities with higher density in these silicate rocks forms the basis for the *assumption* that the deeper parts of the crust are indeed higher-density igneous rocks of approximately basaltic composition.

Seismology and geology reconciled

We find ourselves meeting basalt once again, this time as a seismically inferred layer that bottoms the continental crust and forms the essential part of the suboceanic crust, as shown in Fig. 5-4.

Until recently the seismic evidence was interpreted as showing within the crust two or more distinct layers—the granitic and the basaltic—each characterized by distinct seismic velocities. Since these observed seismic velocities in the crust usually were in the range shown by lab studies to apply to the common igneous rocks (Fig. 5-2), the seismologists found it easy to match rock compositions with the simply layered velocity structure. (This they chose to work with for the reasons of mathematical simplicity discussed earlier.)

But many geologists, and some seismologists, were unhappy about reconciling such a layered structure, Fig. 5-4, with the intense heterogeneity of continental basement structure suggested by Fig. 5-1. And some detailed seismological work on various continental crustal sections has indeed suggested that the simple concept of crustal layering which underlies the picture portrayed in Figs. 5-4 and 5-5, is probably unrealistic. The more realistic view is the one outlined earlier in the comments on visible basement structure where the continental crust, at least, appears to be a complex mosaic of rock types, ages, and structures to depths of 10–15 miles.

One reason for the apparent uniformity of observed seismic velocities in the crust, despite the heterogeneity that prevails there, is that there is a relatively narrow range of variation in the seismic velocities and other physical constants for a fairly wide range of rock compositions, as shown by Fig. 5-2. This is especially so over the composition range from syenite to diorite—precisely the range in types of rock that are dominant in the continental crust. It is probably true, however, that within the context of the heterogeneity that exists in the continental crust there is a gradual change in the gross composition of the material from the surface downward—a trend from predominantly granitic rock types nearer the surface to chiefly basaltic rock types further down. Thus the picture drawn from geologic observation is reconciled with the larger-scale structure inferred from seismology.

Mass deficiencies under the mountains

The reasonable reconciliation of geology with seismology is confirmed—with some exceedingly intriguing modifications—by the results of gravity studies. Gravity anomalies are simply the departure of the observed value of the gravitational acceleration from the value computed for it at any particular place. Units of acceleration due to gravity are usually referred to in terms of the *milligal*. One milligal equals an acceleration of 0.001 cm/sec². This is roughly one-millionth of the earth's average gravitational constant—980 cm/sec².

With instruments capable of detecting variations in gravity to a sensitivity of better than 0.1 milligals—or one-billionth of the acceleration caused by the total mass of the earth—gravity studies have deepened our understanding of the crust and upper mantle. But at the same time they raise a host of new questions.

Figure 5-6, for example, shows the profile of the land surface in the Alps, together with the Bouguer gravity anomalies across the same line. (The Bouguer anomaly is one that remains after corrections are made for latitude of the station, for its height above the sea-level reference datum, and for the mass of rock between the station and sea level.)

Quite apparently, the Bouguer anomalies are like an exaggerated mirror image of the overlying topography. And this turns out to be the case in most mountainous regions. In fact, the higher the mountains, the more negative the Bouguer anomalies usually are. The negative value of the anomaly means that the observed gravity values are lower than what would be expected on the basis of an assumed uniform distribution of mass everywhere beneath the earth's surface. In other words, there seems to

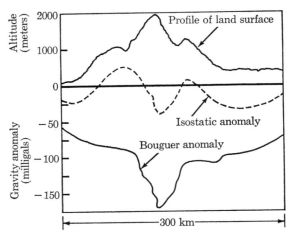

Fig. 5-6. Striking correspondence of the negative Bouguer gravity anomalies with the topographic shape of the Alps suggests a deficiency of mass below the mountains. Yet small value of the so-called isostatic anomaly suggests this shallow deficiency is compensated for at greater depth.

be too little mass beneath the major mountain belts.

If we look at the gravity picture along the trend of a modern volcanic island arc—one such as is shown in cross-section at the right side of Fig. 5-5—we again find belts of strongly negative gravity anomalies as shown in Fig. 5-7.

But the lesser pull of gravity here coincides not with the higher topography of the volcanic islands, as is the case in mountain chains, but instead with the deepest trenches on the ocean floor adjacent to the island volcanoes. Elsewhere throughout the oceans, as indicated on Fig. 5-7, the Bouguer anomalies are strongly positive.

From this comes the suggestion that the mass beneath the oceans is higher than it should be; and beneath the deep ocean trenches which parallel volcanic island chains mass is less than it should be—if the simple uniformity of Fig. 5-5 is really the case. How can these systematic variations be explained?

Mountains have roots and continents float

The negative Bouguer anomalies characteristic of mountain topography vanish when an appropriate correction is made, a correction that indeed assumes that surface irregularities such as mountain chains are compensated for—or balanced—by the invisible mass distribution at depth. Figure 5-8 suggests two ways such mass compensation at depth for the mountainous topography above may be achieved. Both concepts rely on the same simple assumption.

This assumption is that at some depth—called the depth of compensation—all segments

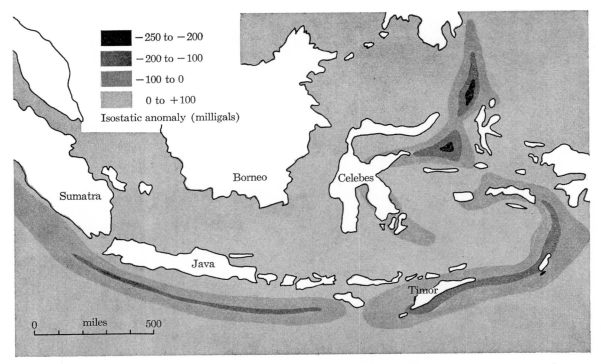

Fig. 5-7. Isostatic gravity anomalies along volcanic island arcs are even more strongly negative than the Bouguer anomalies (not shown). In contrast to the mountain chains (Fig. 5-6), this suggests that here the underlying mass deficiency is uncompensated.

of the crust exert the same pressure, regardless of whether the surface of the crustal segment is mountain, lowland, or ocean floor. Thus at this depth, which turns out to be about 100 km, adjacent segments of the crust and underlying mantle are in mass balance or equilibrium with each other. This concept of "floating" equilibrium of crustal segments above a constant pressure level at the depth of compensation within the mantle is termed "isostasy."

In the Pratt theory of isostasy shown in the upper part of Fig. 5-8, features such as mountains can be pictured as having been uplifted like fermenting dough. Here the density of the dough—or of the mountain—becomes less as it rises higher; so the fact that it exerts the same pressure at the depth of compensation as does an adjacent crustal segment results from density differences between crustal segments.

The lower part of Fig. 5-8 suggests a different alternative—the Airy hypothesis. Here it is assumed that the earth's crust under the mountains and other areas of higher elevation projects into the denser subcrustal (mantle) material below, somewhat analogous to the way icebergs float in water with $9/10$ of their mass submerged. In other words, the mountains have "roots" (not to be confused with our earlier usage of the term in connection with the granitic core of mountains). And, in a sense, the oceans have anti-roots of denser mantle material projecting upward closer to the ocean floor. Isostatic balance in this theory is achieved by crustal segments of uniform density which

"float" to varying heights—and depths—in the mantle below.

The peculiar thing is that either theory seems to work well for many kinds of geophysical and geodetic work. And in both theories, the depth of compensation turns out to be the same—about 60 miles (100 km). The theories thus confirm each other to a degree; they confirm the idea of compensation at depth for the major relief features of the earth's surface; they afford a calculated thickness for the earth's crust that accords with the interpretation of seismology; and they confirm the ideas gained from geology and seismology that the Mohorovicic discontinuity is not at the same depth everywhere.

Seismic work in fact has shown not only the differing depth of the Mohorovicic under the continents and the seas; it also has shown that under the mountain belts on the continents, the Moho goes to depths of as much as 25 to perhaps 35 miles (60 km)—well beneath the 20-mile average depth for the continent as a whole. Thus, the lower concept portrayed in Fig. 5-8—the Airy hypothesis—sometimes called the "mountain roots" theory, seems to best fit the geologic-seismic picture.

But what do theories of isostasy suggest about the case of Fig. 5-7, the great volcanic island arcs of the East Indies, West Indies, and Japan, where the anomalies are even more negative than along mountain chains—and where there are no mountains? Here, even after corrections based on isostasy are made, there is a large residual negative-gravity anomaly. In the

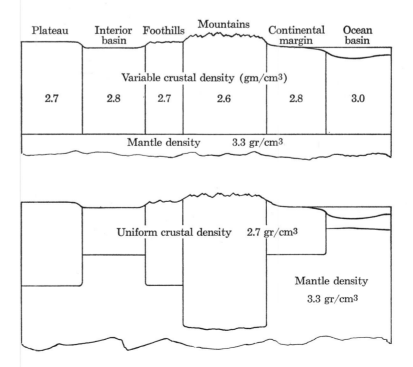

Fig. 5-8. Explanations for the gravity anomalies found in mountains depend on a single assumption. This is that at some depth in the mantle beneath the crust all sections of the crust—whether overlain by mountains or ocean floor—exert the same pressure; or, in other words, adjacent sections of the crust are in floating balance with each other. Pratt concept of such isostatic balance, top, assumes that crustal sections have common base, stand higher or lower at the surface because of density differences. The favored Airy theory, below, gives mountains "roots."

mountain belts on the contrary, as the isostatic anomaly curve of Fig. 5-6 shows, the residual anomaly after assuming isostatic equilibrium is essentially reduced to nothing.

Mountains begin with the root—maybe

The sketches shown in the margin offer the clue to this paradox. Where mountains exist with normal "roots" of less dense crustal rock projecting into the denser mantle, the isostatic anomaly—or the departure from equilibrium—is zero. But where a downwarp or downbulge of the crust exists in the absence of mountains, a condition of dynamic disequilibrium exists, as the negative isostatic anomalies suggest. And here, ultimately, the earth's crust will tend to rise—or float higher—until isostatic equilibrium prevails.

It may be in this way that the mountain chains, the key link in the evolution of the continental crust, themselves are born.

The favored theory for their conception and gestation is outlined in Fig. 5-9. This theory invokes the existence of great viscous subcrustal convection currents flowing within the mantle and, perhaps, the core as well. Such

currents are assumed to be driven by some sort of major complex of thermal cells within the earth. Where slow plastic-like flow in the mantle exerts frictional drag at the base of the crust, as shown in the upper part of Fig. 5-9, a crustal downwarp perhaps hundreds of miles wide and thousands of miles long is formed. Along its flanks deep crustal fracturing permits relief of pressure deep in the crust, and even in the upper mantle, where temperatures are high. As a result, local melting occurs and lavas travel through the fractures to the surface; the margins of the downwarp become the site of a chain of volcanic islands. And the downwarp, deepening through hundreds of millions of years —and manifesting a pronounced negative gravity anomaly during this phase—progressively fills with sediments derived from the volcanic islands, from the nearby continent, and from the precipitates of marine organisms in the seas that also fill it. Such a pattern of sedimentation indeed matches the deformed strata found in present-day mountain chains.

The succeeding steps in Fig. 5-9 tell the rest of the story. As the convection currents compress the lava sheets and sediments that filled

Δg=0

Mountain

Crust 2.7

Root

MANTLE 3.3

Δg<0

No mountain

Crust 2.7

Root

MANTLE 3.3

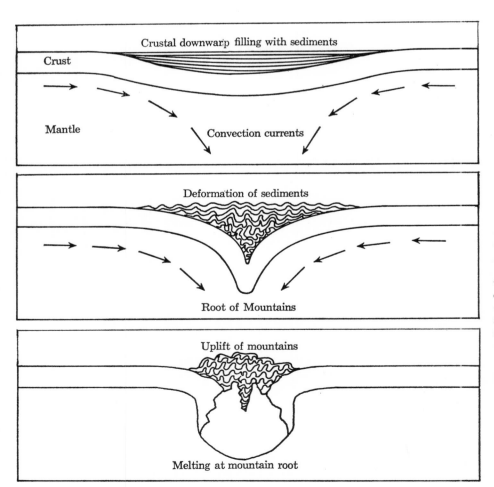

Fig. 5-9. Hypothesis of huge subcrustal convection currents pictures mountain building as beginning with crustal downwarp caused by frictional drag at base of crust. Sediments and volcanic lavas fill subsiding trough through period of active subsidence. As trough is pinched laterally by continued convection, sediments are folded and begin to rise into mountains at surface. Mountain roots are heated by depth in mantle, perhaps by compression, and pressure is relieved by deep fracturing of crust. Root may partially melt, yielding magma intrusion at higher levels.

the downwarp, in later stages a mountain chain becomes evident at the earth's surface. And 20, 30, or 40 miles below the compressed sediments, in the "root" of the mountain belt, some combination of higher temperatures appropriate to this greater depth, heat delivered to the root by the convection cell in the mantle below, heating due to the intensive compression, and pressure release due to deep fracturing of the crust yields melting and "granitic" magma formation on a vast scale.

We have, in the lower part of Fig. 5-9, a chain of mountains with granite roots. The ring forged by geology, physics, and chemistry is closed. This is where continents come from: this is why there are two kinds of crust.

Pretty theory, but lots of loopholes

The convection-current hypothesis looks good. It even offers an explanation for the recently discovered worldwide mid-ocean rift zones whose distribution is shown in Fig. 5-10. A schematic section across the rift chain is shown in the margin. The rifts are characterized by a median depression, flanked by a ridge on either side. They are also characterized by volcanic and earthquake activity. This of course suggests that the crust is in the process of actively splitting, allowing mantle-derived lavas to well up along the fracture zones and adding to the height of the flanking ridges. Subcrustal convection, as shown in the marginal sketch, seems an appropriate enough mechanism to do this.

But, of course, there are many unanswered problems. Seismic evidence postulates that the mantle is solid, at least in its response to shock waves. Yet much of the evidence of gravity demands some capacity for plastic flow in the mantle. And convection currents in the mantle, if they exist, must move with sufficient speed to do the work cut out for them in a finite though lengthy period of geologic time—perhaps a few hundred million years from the inception of the crustal downwarp to the completion of the mountain building process. Obviously, such questions carry us too far into the realm of speculation. But one or two others do not.

The earth as a heat engine and dynamo

Any theory that seeks to account for the growth and diversity of the earth's surface—that is, for the creation and distortion of the continental crust—calls in one way or another upon thermal energy. In the older view the thermal energy derived from the cooling of an originally molten earth caused the thin crust to wrinkle up to fit the shrinking earth within. The modern convection-current theory similarly

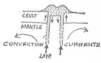

Fig. 5-10. Ideas of drifting continents and convection currents below the crust gain support from recently discovered worldwide mid-ocean fracture zones parallel to continental margins.

must go back to a nonuniform distribution of temperature within the earth to account for its convection cells and their location in space.

Presumably a dense enough network of temperature and heat flow observations—on the continents and the ocean floors—will reveal whether the thermal aspects of the convection hypothesis are indeed tenable. They also will help clarify the nature and sources of the earth's internal heat. How much is original, how much the product of radioactive disintegration of uranium, thorium, and potassium over long periods of geologic time? Tied to such questions are even larger ones—is the earth cooling and contracting? Or, as Urey and others suggest, is it heating up and expanding?

Also hidden in the rocks of the crust are some controversial clues to the nature and history of the earth's magnetic field. Their evidence points in no less than three directions at the same time. One is the possibility that the earth's magnetic field periodically reverses its polarity, decaying and building up again after each reversal in direction. Another suggestion arising from studies of rock magnetism is that possibly the entire earth has shifted its position relative to the position of its axis of rotation—and not once but several times: this concept is frequently described as polar wandering. And finally, new impetus has been imparted to the old idea of drifting continents by certain features of magnetization in progressively older rocks.

The older, generally more deeply buried crustal rocks also appear to offer the only true potential for discovering rich mineral deposits in the future.

The consequences of crustal history

There has been much speculation to the effect that our new resource frontier lies in the crust under the sea. Before indulging in a bit of speculation ourselves, let's clearly understand a few facts.

The deep sea floor is covered over vast areas with large but low-grade deposits of cobalt, nickel, copper, and rare earths. These elements are incorporated in nodules of iron-manganese minerals that encrust the surface and occur within the thin sedimentary layers of the ocean floor. The indicated gross tonnages of these elements, particularly of the manganese, is impressive—enough to last the U.S. for many centuries at present rates of consumption. But so far as the rocks beneath the sea are concerned, that's all there is. The sub-oceanic basaltic crust itself, in all likelihood, is as barren of rich concentrations of useful elements as are the known basaltic rocks of both the continents and the oceanic volcanic islands.

In other words, we are still very much at the mercy of our lack of knowledge about the dynamic and chemical history of the deeper parts of the continental crust. As noted earlier, ore deposits are genetically related to the processes, rocks, and structures associated with mountain building, crustal mobility, and magma formation and intrusion. If we don't "dig" those mountain roots in the intellectual sense, we are not likely to know where to dig into them for mining purposes.

As for the speculation, remember that the crust is made up (over 99%) of eight elements—O, Si, Al, Fe, K, Na, Ca, Mg. It is possible, indeed probable, that in the course of the planet's differentiation into crust, mantle, and core, significantly higher concentrations of many elements—iron and magnesium in the mantle, and iron and nickel in the core, for sure; platinum and gold in the core, for instance, maybe—did segregate at great depth in the plastic mantle and the liquid outer core. If convection currents are real, and if they do exert frictional drag against the base of the crust, then *maybe* concentrations of such elements are to be found not far below the Moho, wherever slow spots developing in the mantle's convective flow would tend to leave them behind.

The true nature of the heat engine and electromagnetic dynamo lurking within this prosaic planet awaits the studies of the next several years. These studies—of gravity, magnetism, seismology, heat flow, geology, high-temperature and high-pressure chemistry—can use equipment, brains, and money.

Further reading

Scientific, technical, and historical aspects of the proposed "U.S. Program for the International Crust and Upper Mantle Project" are outlined in detail in a mimeographed preliminary report (July 1962), available free from Dr. Lynn Hoover, NAS-NRC, Washington 25, D.C. Similar reports pertaining to Canadian programs can be obtained from the Department of Mines and Technical Surveys, Ottawa. An excellent review of all phases of the U.S. Mohole project, including names of people to contact, appears in the July–August 1962 issue of *Geotimes*, news magazine of the American Geological Institute, Washington 25, D.C.

The best single volume that treats the crust as a many-faceted entity is *The Crust of the Earth*, edited by Poldervaart, and published as Geological Society of America Special Paper 62, 1955. The Academic Press series *Advances in Geophysics* carries several outstanding review articles of interest, covering both theory and instrumentation. See particularly papers by Bullard, Byerly, and Jacobs in Volume 3 (1956), treating respectively heat flow, seismology, and magnetism. Volume 1 (1952) of the same series contains gravity review by Woolard. The Pergamon Press annual series, *Physics and Chemistry of the Earth* (Volumes 1–4), offers several cogent reviews by Urey, Ahrens, Hill, Verhoogen, Bullen, Cameron, Roedder, and others.

A stimulating introduction to geochemistry can be found in Mason's *Principles of Geochemistry*, 2nd edition, Wiley, 1958; and a comparable survey in depth of many phases of geophysics is *Physics and Geology* by Jacobs, Russell, and Wilson (McGraw-Hill, 1959). For a modern analytical treatment of geology, try *Principles of Geology*, 2nd edition, by Gilluly, Waters, and Woodford (Freeman, San Francisco, 1959). A deeper look at the gravity picture is afforded by *The Earth and Its Gravity*

Field by Heiskanen and Vening-Meinesz (McGraw-Hill, 1958). For more on seismology try Richter's *Elementary Seismology* (Freeman, 1958). The power of the physical-chemical approach to minerals and rocks is made amply evident in *Igneous and Metamorphic Petrology*

by Turner and Verhoogen (McGraw-Hill, 1960, 2nd ed.). See also "Underground Shocks" by Wilson, and "Mineral Supply" by Pehrson in the Jan. and Feb. 1962 issues (pp. 46 and 23, respectively) of *International Science and Technology.*

ENVIRONMENTAL ELECTRICITY

by Seymour Tilson *

IN BRIEF: *Variable fluxes of electromagnetic radiation and plasma, reaching the earth from the sun, interact with the earth's magnetic field and atmosphere to generate electric currents that pervade every terrestrial environment. Such externally induced currents range from a mere 1800 amp that continuously leak from the entire earth's surface to the air, to a more intense but intermittent flow of perhaps 500,000 amp in parts of the ionosphere when aurorae occur. These and other flows are quite feeble in contrast to an internal current of 10^9 amp, generated in the earth's liquid core by the same self-inducing dynamo action that supports the magnetic field. This current, however, is confined to the core by the poor conductivity of the overlying mantle. But external current systems—in the ionosphere, lower atmosphere, and earth's crust—are not closed circuits. Various mechanisms, such as the aurora in the ionosphere and lightning in the lower atmosphere, transfer electrons from one "component" circuit to another. Such electron-transfer mechanisms are not only important in the planet's over-all electrical budget; they also may have been critical in life's origin and evolution.—S.T.*

■ A more than casual observer of an aurora that occurred back in 1861 described it thus: "The darkness was so profound as to be oppressive. Suddenly, from the rear of the black cloud which obscured the horizon, flashed a bright ray. Presently an arch of many colours fixed itself across the sky, and the aurora gradually developed. The space within the arch was filled by the black cloud; but its borders brightened steadily, though the rays discharged from it were exceeding capricious, now glaring like a vast conflagration, now beaming like the glow of a summer morn. More and more intense grew the light, until, from irregular bursts, it matured into an almost uniform sheet of radiance. Towards the end of the display its character changed. Lurid fires flung their awful portents across the sky, before which the stars seemed to recede and grow pale."

* Seymour Tilson is Associate Editor of *International Science and Technology.*

His description is vivid, but far from overdrawn. An aurora (Fig. 5-11) is indeed one of nature's more flamboyant spectacles. It has

Fig. 5-11. Aurorae exhibit many forms besides the one shown here. All are controlled by the earth's magnetic field and by electric currents generated in auroral zones, as shown in Fig. 5-12. Electric field aloft also accelerates protons and electrons which excite air ions to emit visible radiation. (Courtesy S. Chapman and Danish Meteorol. Service)

every right to be, considering the strategic position it occupies in a complex chain of electrical events that extends unbroken from the sun to the core of the earth.

This chain has many links; some nearly as gaudy as the aurora and much more noisy, like lightning; others both silent and invisible, like the electric currents flowing everywhere— through space, the ionosphere, the lower atmosphere, the oceans, the solid earth—and even through you and me. Sometimes the flow is straightforward, a simple exercise in dc circuitry. More often it is subtle, recognized mostly on tenuous theoretical grounds, and the agency of energy transfer is a hydromagnetic wave in plasma, or some form of electromagnetic radiation. However its form and intensity vary in place and time, this chain of energy springs from—and is ultimately anchored in—just three sources. One, of course, is the sun. The second is the dynamo at the core of the earth. Here the earth's magnetic field is generated, whose lines of force arch far above its surface to grapple with the incoming solar streams. And the third is the resilient, changeable atmosphere, scene of the battle between solar and terrestrial forces, and stirred by the conflict to add its bit to the battle. As the sun's barrage of radiant energy and plasma varies through the days, seasons, and sunspot cycles, and as the earth rotates beneath the solar flux, the links in the chain are forged. Electrical phenomena tie every apparently discrete part of man's cosmic environment to every other part. In the form of lightning they may have accomplished the essential transformation between nonliving and living matter on the primitive earth, and in subtler ways they may have been a cogent factor in life's evolution after it began.

This survey will trace the flow of electricity across boundaries in space and time. To begin, let's go back to the aurora.

The aurora's visible radiations express the outrage, more formally the excitation to higher-energy levels, of the upper atmosphere's partially ionized oxygen atoms and nitrogen molecules, when energetic charged particles assault them. Most of these energetic protons and electrons ultimately come from the sun. But intense electrical fields that exist in the vicinity of the earth probably accelerate them to the energies they exhibit during an aurora. Such electric fields themselves are born in interactions between the solar flux and the earth's magnetic field.

Light up the sky!

Aurorae occur at heights of 50 to several hundred km, in the ionosphere, chiefly in zones that are crudely concentric about the magnetic poles at magnetic latitudes of 60° to 70°. These also happen to be the zones where the ends of the earth-girdling, horseshoe- or crescent-shaped magnetic field shells come to earth (Fig. 5-12). These shells, great magnetic containers, hold the huge numbers of energetic protons and electrons that make up the Van Allen belts. (See "Man-Made Radiation Belts," page 509.)

As you would expect, many attempts have been made to account for aurorae by invoking the discharge of Van Allen belt particles into the lower atmosphere, along lines of force in the magnetic field. This is an especially attractive line of reasoning, because aurorae correlate quite nicely in time with sunspots, solar flares, and magnetic storms. What could be simpler than to combine a "push" on Van Allen particles, by solar plasma that reaches the earth shortly after a flare, with a slackening or other upset in the restraining geomagnetic field, so "dump" the trapped particles, and—*voilà*—an aurora. But no hypothesis leading to "dumping" of geomagnetically trapped particles is free of serious difficulties. What's interesting and significant is that the leading contenders among theories do hold one idea in common: The separation of positively and negatively charged particles (protons and electrons) coming from the sun, along magnetic field lines far above the earth's surface, can create an electric field. And this field can account for auroral motions and forms. One theory of charge separation, portrayed in Fig. 5-12, ascribes the separation of geomagnetically trapped protons and electrons to gradients in the earth's magnetic field.

An appropriately oriented gradient in the geomagnetic field will separate the initially neutral plasma, trapped within magnetic field shells, into alternating sheets of protons and electrons. Separating the charges creates an electric field and a potential difference across the gap between oppositely charged sheets. As particles in the oppositely charged sheets move down along magnetic field shells during an auroral disturbance—from heights of several earth radii at the equator to ionospheric heights in the auroral zones—the electric field and potential difference also are carried downwards. Here, in the highly conducting medium of the ionosphere, the electric field and potential gap separating the proton and electron sheets lies perpendicular to the geomagnetic field. This generates a current that's perpendicular to both the electric field and the magnetic field, by a modification of the Hall effect.

This current is supposed to flow at a height of 150 km, at times of auroral and magnetic disturbances. It's known as the "auroral electrojet" and flows as a spherical current sheet

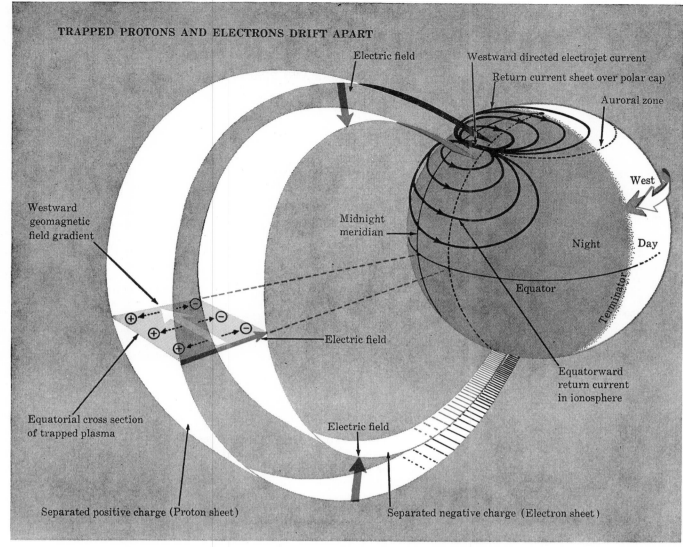

Fig. 5-12. Gradients in earth's magnetic field may separate the initially neutral plasma trapped in it, as shown at left, into alternate sheets of protons and electrons; this creates an electric field across gap between oppositely charged particle sheets. When solar storms drive particles down along field shells into the conducting ionosphere the electric field also moves down. Here it interacts with the magnetic field to generate currents that explain many features of aurorae. (Courtesy J. W. Kern, J. Geophys. Res.)

that spreads feebly over the entire hemisphere. But in the auroral zones it is most intense, amounting to perhaps 500,000 amp.

The name "electrojet" is appropriate because this transient, disturbed-time current is superimposed on—or an enhanced version of—the less transient current flows that always pervade the ionosphere. But these much more diffuse prevailing current flows, amounting at most to some 80,000 amp spread across nearly half of the earth's surface, vary diurnally and seasonally, even in the absence of aurorae.

An overhead dynamo and motor

Incoming solar radiation of various kinds and wavelengths produces the ionized layers of the atmosphere—termed D (50–90 km), E (90–160 km), and F (>160 km)—through a complex sequence of ionizing reactions, briefly summarized in Fig. 5-13. As a result the ionosphere contains equal numbers of positive ions and negative electrons, all embedded in the remaining un-ionized or neutral gas.

Wonder of wonders, when the tide of gravitational forces imposed by the sun and moon ripples across the earth, just as when thermal convection of the entire atmosphere occurs in response to earth-sun rhythms, both the neutral gas and the charged particles move. The mass of charged particles, of course, behaves exactly like a conductor would in moving through the earth's steady magnetic field. As the swarm of particles cuts lines of magnetic force, a current is induced in it. In fact it's

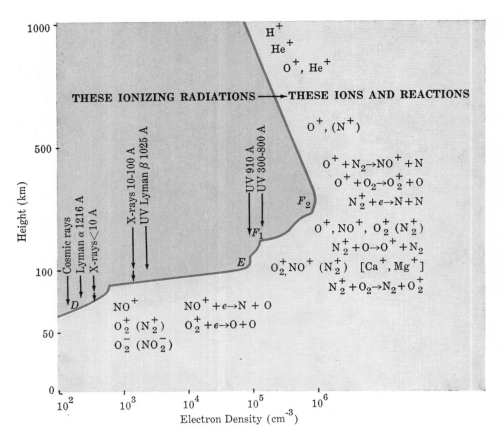

Fig. 5-13. Cosmic and solar radiations penetrate the earth's atmosphere to heights other than those shown here at the left. But at the heights indicated these radiations produce both the ionized atoms and molecules shown at the right (with the possible exception of H+ and He+ at the highest altitudes) and the free electrons whose density is shown by the curve. Free electrons plus negative ions are as numerous as positive ions; but changes in the electron density alone define the ionosphere's radio layers, labeled D, E, and F.

entirely appropriate to call that part of the ionosphere where this induced current is generated—probably the intermediate or E layer—an "atmospheric dynamo." But wonders cease not here.

Not only does the current in the "dynamo" region of the ionosphere induce changes at ground level in the main magnetic field, arising from the earth's own "core dynamo" (these changes being precisely what makes it possible to estimate the magnitude of the overhead currents); its flow also is accompanied by an electrostatic field. This field extends to other parts of the ionosphere, and on reaching the uppermost or F region—which hitherto has been minding its own business—causes currents to flow there also.

The earth's main magnetic field, meanwhile, acts on currents induced in the inoffensive F layer and makes the electron-ion plasma at these levels move bodily, independently of the tidal and thermally convective motions the plasma undergoes anyway. If the term "dynamo" is appropriate for the current-generating action that initially takes place in the E layer, the term "motor" is equally apt for the mass movement of the ionosphere at the F level. Furthermore, there also is an important "motor" effect in the "dynamo" or E region itself, since the currents flowing there also flow within the earth's steady magnetic field.

Had enough? OK, the point is this: the "fleas upon fleas upon fleas . . ." mutual induction and associated mass movement of portions of the ionosphere relative to each other, in general, explains the pronounced effects observed in the ionosphere during severe magnetic upsets. Its upper layers rise in altitude and the density of electrons in these layers decreases; the intensity of ionization in its lower layers increases abnormally; and its radio absorption and transmission characteristics undergo complex changes. None of these storm-time variations in the ionosphere is especially surprising, since they and the simultaneous variations measured in the magnetic field at the earth's surface are both, in a sense, manifesting changes in the output of the "ionospheric dynamo and motor."

And just to make sure we haven't put the cart before the horse, let me stress a crucial idea once more. Although we have said that ionospheric upsets occur during severe disturbances in the earth's magnetic field, it is in fact these very upsets—and the marked perturbations in quiet-time current flow in the ionosphere—which *cause* the observed magnetic variations. Inversion of cause and effect in talking about these things becomes unconscious and automatic, perhaps dangerously so, simply because the causative current aloft is deduced by laborious mathematical procedures from the observable magnetic effects below, at the surface.

Quiet currents in the deep blue sky

Such backward-tracing studies of quiet and stormy variations in the earth's surface magnetic field show that the ionosphere is more conducting, hence more completely ionized, by day than by night, in summer than in winter, and at times of sunspot maximum than at sunspot minimum. Figure 5-14 portrays the currents that flow in the ionosphere on magnetically undisturbed days—when the storm-provoking solar flares, aurorae, and other manifestations of disturbed days are absent.

At the equinoxes a maximum of about 65,000 amp flow through the ionosphere in each of two closed daytime circuits that are parallel to the earth's surface; one lies north of the equator, covers perhaps a third of a hemisphere, flows counterclockwise (viewing the earth from the equatorial plane, with the north pole up); the other lies above the southern hemisphere, is similar in extent, but flows clockwise in direction. When summer comes to the northern hemisphere—just as on a smaller scale when night yields to day—the ever-present solar and lunar tidal effects which power the "ionospheric dynamo" are aided by greatly enhanced thermal convection of the atmosphere in moving the conducting ions and electrons across magnetic lines of force. So, in June, the northern daytime circuit of 65,000 amp is enhanced to over 80,000 amp, and the circuit enlarges, spreading partly into the southern hemisphere at the expense of the equinoctial circuit there, which shrinks in intensity to some 30,000 amp. At times of maximum sunspot activity the currents show similar patterns. But current intensities are higher by 50% or more.

An important deficiency of such current diagrams as Fig. 5-14 is this. Although they represent the total current flow, integrated vertically throughout the full thickness of the current carrying layer, quite neatly and probably with fair accuracy, they fail to indicate either the height at which the currents flow or the vertical thickness of the current carrying layer. This inadequacy is being overcome as high-level measurements of magnetic intensity are carried out by rocket-borne magnetometers, and as radio-reflecting and related observations are carried out by ionosphere topside-sounding satellites. Such direct studies find the current carrying layer may lie at about 100 km, not far above the base of the ionosphere's E or intermediate layer. No great surprise in this, but what is remarkable is the very small thickness of the current layer—a few to several km at most! While these fragmentary early results do not eliminate the possibility that the iono-

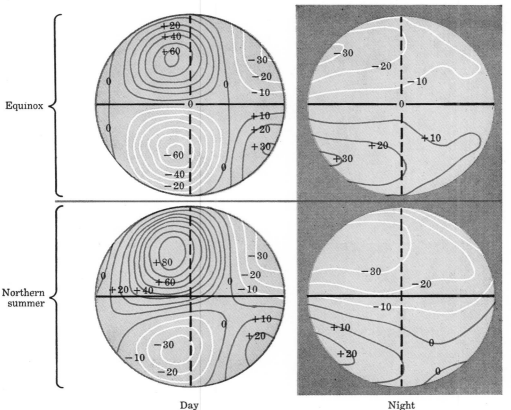

CURRENTS IN THE IONOSPHERE RESPOND TO THE SUN

Equinox

Northern summer

Day

Night

Fig. 5-14. 10,000 amperes flow between adjacent pairs of lines in this diagram showing current flow in the E layer of the ionosphere, at times when solar disturbances and associated terrestrial upsets such as aurorae and magnetic storms are absent. At times of maximum sunspot and related activity, current patterns in the ionosphere are similar to those shown here, but intensities increase by 50% or more. The view here is edgewise from the equatorial plane; geographic north is at top of the diagram. (Courtesy S. Chapman)

sphere may carry significant amounts of current transversely to its layers—either up into the higher parts of the magnetosphere, or vertically down into the lower atmosphere—they do make some proposals that have been made to this effect look more dubious. Which makes the nature of the electrical connection between the ionosphere and the lower atmosphere—except for a connection somehow related to aurorae, as we shall see—more problematical than ever.

Electrical currents in the lower depths

In another sense, however, there is a direct connection between the ionosphere and lower atmosphere, if only through the intermediate agency of the solid earth below.

The earth's surface can be regarded as the negative terminal of a huge battery that's continuously discharging electrons into the air. And the air, though a poor conductor, nevertheless can conduct electricity. Where to? Why, to the electrically neutral ionosphere that lies above. Although the number of negative ions plus electrons in the ionosphere is equal to the number of positive ions, the earth with its huge surplus of electrons (whose source we'll worry about later on) is estimated, over-all, to be about 360,000 volts negative with respect to the ionosphere, some 50 km above. This voltage difference drives electrons upwards.

Instead of thinking of the earth's surface as a battery terminal, however, it is perhaps more

suitable to think of it, and of the conducting layer of the ionosphere, as the oppositely charged plates of a gigantic spherical condenser—earth negative, ionosphere positive. Between the two lies the relatively insulating lower atmosphere. But the condenser leaks, because the atmosphere does conduct some electricity.

Its conductivity depends on the presence of ions which serve as charge carriers, particularly smaller ions with mobilities of the order of $1-2$ cm sec^{-1}/V cm^{-1}. These are created in ample numbers (Fig. 5-15) within the lowest meter of air by the combined ionizing radiations coming from radioactive rocks, the radioactive gases (e.g., radon) they release into the air, and penetrating cosmic rays. Ion production from such sources amounts to between 10 and 50 ion pairs/cm^3/sec in the first meter above the ground. (Not so incidentally, because both short- and long-lived fission products "falling out" of the atmosphere after atomic and thermonuclear tests also produce ionization at ground levels, it has been suggested that 1944—the year before Hiroshima—represented the last base year, for a long time to come, in which natural ion-production rates could be unambiguously studied.)

Another, less quantitatively important contributor to the air's conductivity is the complex of processes that goes under the deceptively simple name of the hydrologic cycle, or the precipitation cycle. Falling rain, for instance, generally carries the larger, relatively less mobile, mostly positive ions—which serve as condensation nuclei—back to earth. On the other hand, the evaporation and condensation steps in the cycle of water movement generally free electrons, which remain aloft when the rain or snow comes down.

Thus the lower atmosphere is not a perfect insulator. The average effective resistance of its entire thickness below the ionosphere is just about 200 ohm. Electrons from the earth, driven across this resistance by 360,000 V potential difference, constitute a continuous leakage current of about 1800 amperes, which comes from the entire surface of the earth. (This is roughly 9×10^{-6} amp/mile^2, pretty low by any standard, and why we don't sizzle up despite the average potential difference of maybe 250 V that exists between our heads and feet when standing upright.)

This continuous discharge of the earth-air-ionosphere "condenser" is enough to completely drain off the earth's surplus of electrons in anywhere from half an hour to an hour. But, somehow, it doesn't. The average potential gradient during fair weather in the lower atmosphere—which indicates the state of the "condenser's" charge—remains pretty well

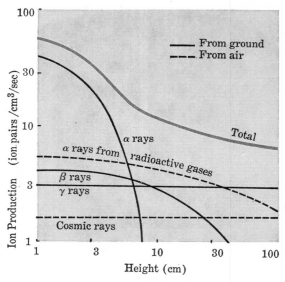

Fig. 5-15. Electrical conductivity of the lower atmosphere depends on the presence in air of sufficient numbers of small, mobile ions to serve as charge carriers. These are produced in ample numbers—some 10 to 50 ion pairs/cm³/sec in the lowest 1 m above the ground—by combined ionizing radiations coming from radioactive rocks, radioactive gases they release, and cosmic rays.

fixed, though it fluctuates slightly, with changes in the weather and in air pollution, and with aurorae and magnetic storms.

Which poses the leading question—how does the earth maintain its negative charge?

Thunderstorms—a different kind of dynamo

Most workers in meteorology and atmospheric electricity think that the earth's field is maintained by point discharges and lightning associated with thunderstorm activity in the lowest 10 miles of the atmosphere. Particular support is lent to this idea by the good correlation that's observed in diurnal variations of worldwide thunderstorm activity, potential gradients in the air, and air-earth current flow. Thunderstorms act as generators of electricity which is stored and dissipated in the region—coincidentally (?) the same one occupied by life—lying between the ionosphere and the earth's surface.

Point discharge results from the familiar fact that a charged body loses its charge fastest at its sharp points or corners. The earth's surface offers many such points—the tips of blades of grass, tree tops, church spires, grains of sand, and so on. When the voltage difference driving a point discharge is sufficiently high, the discharge—normally a quiet, continuous, invisible process—becomes intense enough to ionize the air and to excite some of the ions to luminosity, yielding a visible corona, or St. Elmo's fire.

During fair weather, point discharges usually carry electrons from the earth to the atmosphere. But when thunderstorms are around, the electrons flow the other way, and in much greater numbers than they leave it when the skies are clear. This reversal is understandable in view of the usual electrical structure of a thunderstorm (Fig. 5-16).

A thundercloud generally has two predominant regions of charge: its base is strongly negative, with a huge surplus of electrons, and its top is usually positive. Little is known about the behavior of the cloud top with respect to the inosphere—whether, as shown in Fig. 5-16 for example, it really does close the electron circuit that runs from earth to ionosphere to cloud top. Probably this picture is oversimplified, if not downright incorrect. At any rate, it's the nega-

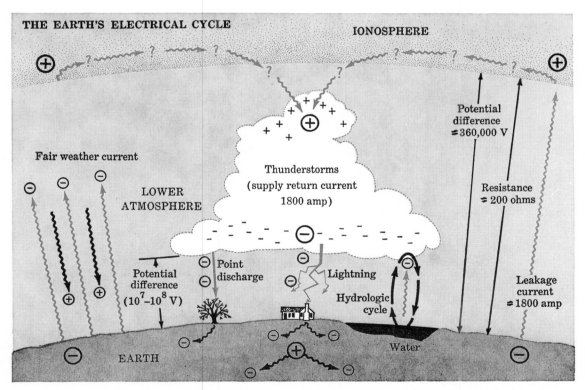

Fig. 5-16. Plus and minus signs in the larger circles show charge that prevails in various regions, with respect to charge prevailing in other regions similarly marked. Smaller encircled charge symbols, on the other hand, show paths followed by migrating charges. Although the ionosphere is electrically neutral, surplus free electrons make the earth 360,000 volts negative with respect to it. This potential continuously drives a total current of 1800 amp upwards from the entire earth's surface, in part via the hydrologic cycle; but this loss is more or less continuously restored by thunderstorms.

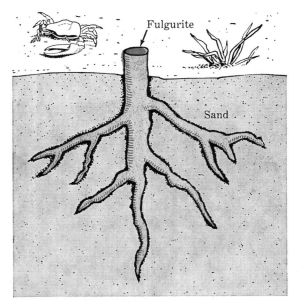

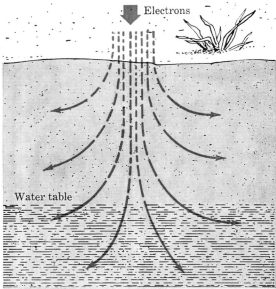

Fig. 5-17. The upper sketch shows a "fulgurite"—a branching fused tube of sand sometimes found where lightning has struck. Lower sketch suggests its origin, the flow of electrons into the ground, and their rapid dispersal laterally on reaching the highly conductive water table. A lightning stroke delivers perhaps 250 amp or more in <½ sec, probably can do the job.

tively charged cloud base that produces the electrical effects observed at the ground.

The overwhelming supply of electrons at the cloud's base repels electrons on the surface of the ground below, and these migrate away through the earth, altering telluric current flows, and changing potential gradients over an area much greater than that covered by the thunderstorm. Under the cloud the earth becomes much less negative than usual. In fact, it becomes

positive with respect to the cloud. As the cloud develops, the potential difference between cloud base and ground continually rises—to as much as 10^7 to 10^8 V! So impelled, electrons begin to leave the cloud; they travel through the air, and reach the ground through innumerable mostly invisible point discharges. But these may be insufficient to reduce the rapidly growing voltage gap. When the electric pressure gets too great (a potential gradient of about 15×10^3 V/cm is needed for dielectric breakdown of dry air at the temperatures and pressures of thunderclouds, less in the presence of water drops) the air resistance is completely overcome. A torrent of electrons—lightning—passes to the receptive earth below (Fig. 5-17). This "rain" of electrons helps restore their loss from the earth by point discharge and via the hydrologic cycle.

The average thunderstorm fires anywhere from 10–20 strokes of average lightning per second. Each discharge lasts less than a half second and releases $>6 \times 10^{16}$ ergs of energy. This amounts to a total release of electrical energy—from a run-of-the-mill thundercell—of perhaps 10^{18} ergs/sec, or 10^8 kW.

But don't be overly impressed by these numbers. The net current continuously maintained between the earth and the upper conducting layers of the atmosphere by this prodigious flow of energy, sometimes called the thunderstorm charging current, averages no more than a fraction of an amp! But it's an awfully important fraction, as we'll see in a minute.

The annual electrical budget

The exact way in which thunderstorms form and separate charge is unknown. Indications are that its generation is somehow related to the formation of precipitation, to the changes of state of water, and to the position of the 0°C isotherm in the growing thundercloud (see "Changing the Weather," page 603). But final answers still are lacking. The same is true of the relation of lightning discharge mechanisms to the over-all electrification and electrical budget of a thundercloud. These related questions are the most active areas in current research. Although no consensus has been reached on these very important details, fair estimates of the lower atmosphere's complete electrical budget nevertheless can be made, as shown in the table on the opposite page.

Such estimates agree that an average of between 3000 and 6000 centers or cells of lightning must always be active—all over the earth, at all times—in order to continuously return the 1800 amp of current constantly leaking from the earth. This number of lightning cells is demanded on the basis of measurements which

THE EARTH'S ANNUAL ELECTRICAL BUDGET
(10^{18} electrons/km^2)

Item	From earth	To earth
Fair-weather current	561	—
Hydrologic cycle	187	—
Point discharge	—	624
Lightning	—	124
TOTALS	748	748

show an average current per thunderstorm cell of 0.3 to 0.6 amp (our important fraction of a moment ago). And climatological data seem to confirm that the necessary number of thunder-cells is available. The budget looks balanced; all is well. But let's take a more careful look at the balance sheet.

Another item for the electric budget?

A key clue—one which, when it's more fully explored, may firmly link auroral disturbances to the transfer of negative charge from higher levels (the Van Allen belts?) down into the ionosphere, or still lower—may drastically change the electrical budget. It is based on observations made during *fair* weather that currents at the earth-atmosphere interface are abnormally high during aurorae. These currents correspond to a flux of 10^4 electrons/cm^2/sec, whereas the average fair-weather flux is only about 1.5×10^3 electrons/cm^2/sec. This seven-fold increase in the fair-weather conduction current may be caused, through a complex chain of events that needn't concern us here, by auroral electrons coming to rest in the upper atmosphere. Some such influx of electrons—either to the ionosphere, or at levels high in the atmosphere, but below the ionosphere itself—also is clearly called for by the anomalous behavior of the vertical potential gradient in the lower, weather-filled parts of the atmosphere. The normal change in potential as one ascends from ground level averages about 100 to 150 V/m. But this potential gradient decreases when there is an auroral display; the higher atmosphere apparently gains negative charge and, since the earth itself is also negatively charged, the electrical contrast between the two diminishes. This decrease is probably real, significant in the planet's electrical regime, but small, and does not exceed about 10 V/m.

But remember it! It may figure significantly in future attempts to close the atmosphere's electrical circuit.

If such studies bear out this implied correla-tion of auroral electricity with the atmosphere's electrical budget, the next story you read on this subject may be able to close the circuit between the outer atmosphere—the ionosphere and beyond—and the lower, weather-filled atmosphere more effectively than we can close it here. We can, however, look more deeply than we have so far into the parts of the circuit that lie below the ground.

Electricity under the ground

The telluric or electric field of the earth is associated with current sheets flowing in the earth. Earth currents (whose flowing electrons in large measure must account for the earth's prevailingly negative charge) originate mainly from sources near to or above the earth's surface: some currents are induced by the motion of water through the geomagnetic field; most are induced in the mantle and crust (see "The Earth's Crust," page 570) by currents in or above the ionosphere; a fraction are generated electrochemically by natural and manmade bodies in the rustal rocks; and some are just leakage currents from transmission lines, electric railways, etc. The earth's electric field is observed by measuring the difference in potential between electrodes placed in the earth, several hundreds to several thousands of meters apart. Green, List, and Zengel point out, in their review in the *Proceedings of the IRE* (Nov. 1962), that it is a weak field; its mean value may be zero and it reverses its direction in the course of a day. The range of diurnal variation for temperature zone locations is very small, maybe 5–10 millivolts/kilometer. These diurnal variations mostly result from the rotation of the earth beneath current cells such as those in the ionosphere (recall Fig. 5-14) which are fixed with respect to a line drawn between the earth and the sun. The apparent march of these cells past an observer on earth produces the local diurnal changes in potential gradient. Variations in the current flowing in ionospheric circuits also induce short-term temporal variations in the earth's magnetic field, of course. Indeed, such ionosphere-induced fluctuations in the magnetic field generate the major part of observed electric currents within the earth. Green and colleagues further note that until very recently the magnetic and the telluric (i.e., electric) fields of the earth have been studied separately, and attempts to relate one to the other have been inconclusive at best. These early studies measured only mean values and the relatively large, though absolutely small, easily observable diurnal or semidiurnal trends. But recent progress in the development of more sensitive magnetometers, low-noise dc amplifiers, and low-frequency filter components of small size has permitted measurement of the more strategically useful low-amplitude "micropulsations" of these fields at frequencies below 1 cps.

Measurements of micropulsations show the electrical and magnetic variations in the solid earth to be closely related to each other in amplitude or energy, closely related in time, and probably sharing a common origin—the injection of ionized plasma from the solar wind into the earth's magnetosphere.

When the solar wind blows

Solar wind is the popular term for the plasma streams, composed principally of protons and

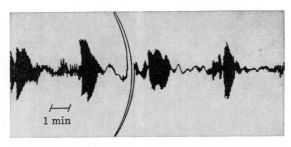

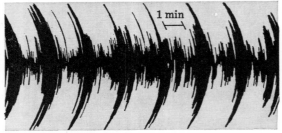

Fig. 5-18. "Pearls" shown are one kind of pulsation in the earth's electric field. They show up—on chart records of the potential difference measured between electrodes placed far apart in the ground—as regular, periodic episodes of increase in the normal potential gradient, of the order of a few tens of millivolts per kilometer.

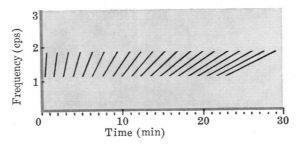

Fig. 5-19. Plot of observed pearl frequency against time, as above, shows that a pearl event actually is composed of several discrete frequencies. Analysis of such frequency dispersion features for pearl events lasting several hours suggests that pearls arise as trapped particles in the Van Allen regions drift repeatedly around the earth.

electrons, that are continually flowing outward from the sun and impinging on the earth's magnetic field. These particles, which travel with velocities of the order of 1000 km/sec, are normally deflected by the earth's magnetic field. But, as Green and his co-authors make clear, pulsations of the solar plasma are often able to penetrate the magnetic shield of the earth. And when they do they produce a number of effects, including aurorae and magnetotelluric micropulsations. It is believed that one of the mechanisms producing micropulsations is this injection of plasma into the earth's magnetic field high above the ionosphere; these plasma clouds propagate in various ways across and down the lines of the earth's field as hydromagnetic waves. Such waves travel down to the base of the conducting ionosphere with velocities ranging from a few hundred to a few thousand kilometers per second. Below this electron densities are too low and hydromagnetic propagation is no longer possible. The hydromagnetic wave is converted to an electromagnetic wave at the base of the ionosphere, and this may show up as a micropulsation at ground levels near the place where it originates.

Not all pearls come from oysters

Another mechanism that may create micropulsations has been invoked to explain an especially interesting class of micropulsations that has attracted much research attention lately, the so-called "pearl"-type. A pearl has two trademarks: (1) a short, apparently constant period, usually no more than one to several seconds; (2) frequent enlargement of amplitude at regular intervals ranging up to several minutes. The resulting pattern on a chart recorder (Fig. 5-18) yields the name for the phenomenon. Pearls apparently occur all over the world and their occurrence, like that of so many other of the electrical events we've discussed, correlates crudely but not invariably with the appearance of aurorae.

Plots of observed frequency versus time, as in Fig. 5-19, show that a pearl event is actually composed of several discrete frequencies, each either remaining constant or dropping slightly during an event that may last several hours. The frequency lines (or bands) of Fig. 5-19 show a fine structure consisting of a sequence of rapidly rising frequencies. But the beginnings of the frequency lines are often only 1–1½ minutes apart, and the endings slightly further apart, resulting in the fan effect shown.

On the basis of such frequency-dispersion features, it has been suggested that the equally spaced pearls might represent a bunch of geomagnetically trapped solar particles that drift about the earth in 1–5 minutes or so. Pearls presumably form by induction as the bunched particles drift over the recording station.

Magnetism from without?

An attempt has been made recently to ascribe the origin of the earth's main magnetic field—that copartner with the solar wind which partakes in and controls so many planetary electrical phenomena—to the cumulative effect of magnetic storms occurring throughout geological time. The idea is intriguing. In it, sun-driven magnetic storms presumably would induce unidirectional currents in the highly conducting nickel-iron core (most probable conductivity 10^3 to 10^4 ohms^{-1}/cm), because the earth's mantle, the rock layer lying between the core and outer crust, behaves as a semiconducting material. Under appropriate—and assumed—conditions governing distribution of conductivity, temperatures, and conduction-electron densities at depth, the semiconducting rocks of the mantle might not behave strictly according to Ohm's law. This departure would cause a partial rectification of currents induced at shallow depths in the earth during magnetic storms, as they gradually penetrated to the core. This would result in a net amount of current being left over in the core after a magnetic disturbance, and the magnetic field associated with such current would augment the field already present.

Various sophisticated mathematical arguments among the experts, however, indicate that it is extremely unlikely that magnetic storms, or any other transient variations imposed on the earth's field from without, can lastingly affect the earth's main field. Which leaves us, for the moment, with no alternative but to look into the core of the earth.

The core of the matter

The simplest explanation of the geomagnetic field, although the details of the explanation could not be more remote from simplicity, is that the earth is an electromagnet. Therefore its magnetic field must be caused by internal currents which, to account for the surface magnetic field (roughly one-half gauss), must be about 10^9 amp. These conjectural but undoubtedly real currents circulate mainly in the liquid, electrically conducting core.

They result from inductive interaction between the conductive liquid in motion and magnetic fields in the core. Where do these *a priori* magnetic fields in the core come from? Mostly from complex mathematical arguments that draw the magnetic energy from the kinetic energy of fluid motions in the core. And where do the motions come from? Mostly from thermal convection, driven perhaps by appropriate con-

centrations of heat produced by decay of radioactive elements, and modified by Coriolis forces arising from the earth's rotation. The motions also offer another possible explanation for the huge electrical currents: they may set up temperature gradients which in turn give rise to thermoelectric currents. Most of the generating job, however, probably is done by the "self-inducing" fluid-dynamo.

The dynamo theory smacks somewhat of circular reasoning, understandably. But a simple electromechanical analog for it may help. One is shown at the top of Fig. 5-20. All it needs is a push—an initial source of power—to make it run forever, neglecting friction, of course. But this model has a still more serious drawback. This mechanical disk dynamo shows no reversals of the external magnetic field it can theoretically produce. But the earth's magnetic field seems to have reversed polarity many times in the past—rapidly (geologically speaking), at irregular intervals, and for no clearly explainable reason.

So where does this leave the core dynamo? Roughly, in terms of another simple electro-

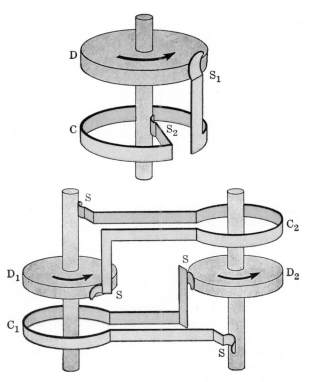

Fig. 5-20. Of the two models shown to simulate the self-inducing dynamo action in the earth's core that generates its magnetic field, the lower one is preferable. Its magnetic field reverses direction—like the earth's does—irregularly and unpredictably. D stands for rotating disks which generate electricity, C for fixed coils which generate magnetic field, S for sliding contacts.

mechanical analog, in the shape shown at the bottom of Fig. 5-20. (There's also a truer-to-life picture of the core dynamo in "The Moon," page 492.) This remarkable homopolar disk dynamo is a delight. It does show reversals of polarity when mathematically followed through time, reversals that are qualitatively similar to those shown by the earth's main magnetic field, in that they are equally erratic in their occurrence, and equally unpredictable!

Environmental electricity and evolution

At a recent meeting of the International Union of Geodesy and Geophysics (Berkeley, California, August 1963), Robert Uffen of the University of Western Ontario, Canada, suggested that such reversals in the polarity of the geomagnetic field may have been instrumental in the evolution of life. His theory, in essence, points out that whenever the field reversed it must have passed through zero, and remained nonexistent perhaps for several thousands of years. As a consequence, the protecting Van Allen belts of those times came tumbling down, like the walls of Jericho, permitting huge bursts of solar and cosmic radiation to come directly down to the earth's surface. Here these ionizing radiations would drastically alter genetic mutation rates, accelerating the normal snail's pace of evolution.

Now anyone can quibble about the details of any theory of cosmology; there's plenty of room for slack speculation in every one of them. And quibbling is not my purpose here.

It's just worth pointing out that Uffen's theory is an attractive one, and perhaps it can serve as the basis for a little speculation on our part. When the magnetic field reversed, there would indeed be no Van Allen belts. It's also likely that the resulting increase in the barrage of ionizing radiation would profoundly raise the rate of ion production in the atmosphere, both in the ionosphere (recall, Fig. 5-13) and near the ground surface (Fig. 5-15). In fact, it would seem that a much enhanced sort of ionosphere would develop right at ground level. Though no electric currents (Fig. 5-14) would flow in this ground-level ionosphere (because there would have been no magnetic field lines to be cut by ions and electrons moving in response to tidal motions and thermal convection), and the status of the aurora (Figs. 5-11 and 5-12) would be moot, it is likely that some reasonable facsimile of the lower atmosphere's thunderstorm-driven electrical circuit (Fig. 5-16) would persist. Or would it? Would the rates of point discharge and of lightning discharge go drastically up? Or down? And what would be the effects on life of extensive—or quite modest—changes in atmospheric and earth-surface electricity, then or *now?* I don't *know.* Do you?

Further reading

A clear, authoritative, and nonmathematical introduction to these matters is *The Upper Atmosphere* by Massey and Boyd, in its revised 2nd impression (Hutchinson, London, 1960). Then continue with *The Physics of the Upper Atmosphere,* edited by Ratcliffe (Academic Press, 1960, $14.50). Chamberlain offers an exhaustive and sophisticated exposition of all phenomena pertinent to the aurora—and they are many—in *Physics of the Aurora and Airglow* (Academic Press, 1961, $16.50).

Coming down from on high, into the lower atmosphere, a straightforward introduction is provided by Chalmers' *Atmospheric Electricity* (Pergamon, 1957, $10). Excellent collections of research papers, including a few of a quasi-review tenor, are *Thunderstorm Electricity,* edited by Byers (U. of Chicago Press, 1953, $7), and *Recent Advances in Atmospheric Electricity,* edited by Smith (Pergamon, 1958, $17.50). The most recent wrapup of activity in this area is the *Proceedings of the Third International Conference on Atmospheric and Space Electricity,* held at Montreaux, Switzerland, May, 1963 (Pergamon Press, in press).

Electricity at shallow levels in the body of the earth is reviewed in a chapter by Garland in Runcorn's *Methods and Techniques in Geophysics* (Interscience, 1960, $10). Also see "The Theory, Measurement, and Applications of Very-Low-Frequency Magnetotelluric Variations," by Green, List, and Zengel in *Proc. IRE* (Nov. 1962), as well as Wait's paper "Theory of Magnetotelluric Fields" in the *Journal of Research,* U.S. National Bureau of Standards, Vol. D, p. 509, Sept.–Oct. 1962. Deeper matters are treated in two recent reviews in the serial publication *Physics and Chemistry of the Earth,* Vol. 3, $15, and Vol. 4, $10 (Pergamon, 1959 and 1961). The earlier one is by Tozer, "The Electrical Properties of the Earth's Interior" (p. 414), and the later one is by Hide and Roberts, "The Origin of the Main Geomagnetic Field" (p. 27).

THE ORIGIN OF OIL

by Claude E. ZoBell *

IN BRIEF: *Virtually all petroleum has been found in porous marine sediments. It seems not to have migrated more than a few hundred feet vertically and rarely more than 10 or 20 miles laterally. Most commercial deposits required from 10^5 to 10^7 years to form.*

Many different theories have been advanced to account for oil's genesis. They fall into two groups, inorganic and organic. The inorganic theories fail to account for the almost overwhelming evidence that, like coal, oil formed from organic remains of plants and animals, at temperatures probably less than 150°C and at pressures no more than 1000 psi.

How it formed, however, is not known. Bacteria must have contributed to the process, along with radioactivity, inorganic catalysts, and other agents.—T.M.

■ The origin of oil is one of the great enigmas of geology. Geologists generally agree that petroleum is derived from the organic remains of plants and animals (see Fig. 5-21), but the reactions involved and the time required for the transformations are largely mysteries.

Petroleum is sometimes referred to as crude oil to distinguish it from vegetable, animal, or refined oils. This word, petroleum, is derived from the Latin roots *petra* (rock) and *oleum* (oil). The ancients coined the term because

* Claude E. ZoBell is Professor of Microbiology at the University of California's Scripps Institution of Oceanography, La Jolla, California.

Fig. 5-21. *Remnants of marine animals embedded in the oil-well core (left) and in the limestone of a petroliferous marine sediment (right) are evidence for the organic origin of oil.*

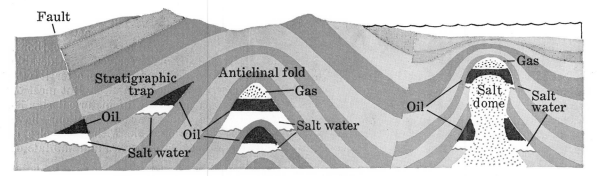

Fig. 5-22. *Though trillions of barrels of oil and its hydrocarbon precursors are entrapped in oil shales, tar sands, and other forms of sedimentary rock, most commercial oil fields are restricted to regions having one or more of the reservoir traps shown above. All of the traps are characterized by porous sediments in which gas and oil have accumulated in pools, roofed in by an impervious layer of rock called caprock. Stratigraphic trap (left) is formed where unconformity is overlain by shale. Anticlinal fold (center) is both overlain and underlain by shale. Salt dome (right) has oil at crest and flanks. (Courtesy American Petroleum Co.)*

Table 1. CHEMICAL CONSTITUENTS OF PETROLEUM

	HYDROCARBONS (i.e., COMPOUNDS OF CARBON AND HYDROGEN)		OTHER ORGANIC COMPOUNDS
	With plural (i.e., unsaturated) valence bonds	With single (i.e., saturated) valence bonds	
With straight chain (i.e., normal, abbreviated n-) molecules	Olefins (i.e., the alkene series) having the general formula C_nH_{2n}: Ethylene ($CH_2 = CH_2$) Propylene ($CH_3CH = CH_2$) etc.	Aliphatic compounds (i.e., the paraffin or alkane series) having the general formula C_nH_{2n+2} with $n = 1, \ldots 80$: Methane (CH_4) Ethane (C_2H_6) Propane (C_3H_8) etc.	Containing oxygen: Phenols Cresols Naphthenic acids Resinous compounds (e.g., menthol) Asphaltenes
With branched chain (i.e., iso-) molecules	—		Containing sulfur: Mercaptans Sulfides Disulfides Thiophenes
With closed ring molecules	Aromatic compounds (i.e., the benzene series): Benzene (C_6H_6) Naphthalene ($C_{10}H_8$) and/or derivatives of either	Naphthenic compounds (i.e., the cycloparaffin series) having the general formula C_nH_{2n} with $n = 3, \ldots 30$: Cyclopentane Cyclohexane etc.	Containing nitrogen: Pyridines Quinolenes Porphyrins

n- Octane

An iso-octane, 3-ethylhexane.

Another iso-octane, 2-2-4 trimethylpentane

Naphthalene

Cyclopentane

Cyclohexane

Benzene

petroleum is found mostly in rock, principally the porous sedimentary rocks, sandstone, limestone, and dolomite (see Fig. 5-22).

Properties of petroleum

Petroleum occurs in the gaseous, liquid, and solid states, depending partly upon the temperature. All three forms are generally commingled in various proportions.

Based upon the predominance of certain residues of distillation, crude oils are classified as paraffin-base or asphalt-base, or as mixed-base if they contain both paraffin and asphalt. But such a classification leaves much to be desired, because it fails to tell much about the chemical nature of petroleum.

Chemically, crude oils consist largely of various compounds of hydrogen and carbon known as hydrocarbons. Thousands of hydrocarbons, differing either in the number of hydrogen and carbon atoms or in the arrangements of these atoms, occur in crude oils (see Table 1).

Since hydrocarbons can be formed inorganically, some of the earlier theories proposed the formation of petroleum from mineral or inorganic substances.

First inorganic theories

In 1866, Berthelot expounded an hypothesis that free alkaline metals, such as calcium, as-sumed to be present in the interior of the earth, reacted with carbon dioxide and water at high temperatures to form acetylides and then acetylene ($HC \equiv CH$). As you can see, acetylene is unsaturated—that is, has atoms linked by more than one valence bond—so it does indeed have many possibilities of forming higher hydrocarbons. However, the required free alkaline metals are unknown in nature, so Berthelot's hypothesis is held untenable nowadays.

This may also be said of the carbide theory, which presupposes the existence of iron carbides or other metallic carbides within the earth. Conceivably such carbides could react with hot water to yield a variety of higher hydrocarbons. Therefore, this theory received considerable support for two or three decades after it was advanced by Mendeleyev in 1877. But most of us believe it is now only of historical significance, because the basic assumptions have proved to be incompatible with what else is known regarding the properties and habitats of petroleum.

You see, most crude oils contain a large number of compounds composed not only of hydrogen and carbon, but also a little oxygen, sulfur, nitrogen, or certain other elements. The presence of nitrogen compounds in petroleum is evidence for its organic origin, since plant or animal proteins are a possible source of certain nitrogen compounds. Of special significance are the porphyrins, which are ordinarily formed from chlorophyll, the green coloring matter of plants, or from the hemoglobin of animal blood.

In addition, most crude oils have the property of rotating the plane of vibration of a beam of polarized light passed through them. Those constituents are in excess that turn the plane or vibration of the oncoming light beam to the observer's right.

In nature, such dextrorotatory optical activity is confined almost exclusively to organic materials, thus supporting theories that oil has had an organic origin. The dextrorotatory optical activity of crude oils is attributed to the presence of decomposition products of phytosterol and cholesterol, sterols which are found in plant and animal matter.

This optical rotatory power of petroleum is permanently lost at high temperatures, suggesting that oil has had a relatively low-temperature origin and history.

Thermal history

Most likely the earth's surface temperature has been considerably less than 100°C during the history of petroleum. There was water on the earth's surface billions of years before the oldest known oil pools, while plant life preceded them by a billion years, and marine invertebrates were growing abundantly for a million or more years before the first oil pools appeared. Temperatures higher than 100°C would have precluded the presence of water and living organisms on the earth's surface.

The occurrence of petroleum in certain basins where the overburden appears never to have exceeded 5000 feet, despite the deformation of the earth's crust, erosion and other forces, indicates a formation temperature that has never exceeded 150°C. This value is derived by taking the earth's surface temperature as having a maximum of 100°C and an increase of 1°C per 100 feet with depth, the average temperature-depth gradient in the crust.

It might be argued that petroleum was formed at much greater depths, where the temperature is much higher than in the places where it is found at present. But we have seen that virtually all crude oils contain constituents so thermolabile that they are destroyed by temperatures ranging from 150 to 220°C. Among these thermolabile constituents are the chlorophyll derivatives and other porphyrins, which are destroyed by temperatures of less than 200°C. And, as I will describe a bit later, geologic evidence indicates that there has been relatively little vertical migration of oil.

In 1890 Sokoloff presented arguments for the cosmic origin of petroleum. He believed that it was formed by the combination of carbon with hydrogen during the consolidation of the earth, was then enclosed within the primeval magma, and thereafter found its way into subterranean pools.

Theory of cosmic origin

Proponents of this cosmic theory point to the occasional finding of hydrocarbons in meteorites. (But believers in the occurrence of extraterrestrial life cite the finding of bituminous materials in meteorites as evidence for life in outer space.) Be this as it may, the cosmic theory, like every other theory for an inorganic origin of petroleum, fails to account for its optical activity, content of nitrogenous compounds, porphyrin pigments, or its common association with biological remnants.

Moreover, if petroleum were of cosmic origin, we would expect to find much of it in old rocks, and in igneous or metamorphic rocks. But little oil is found in igneous or metamorphic rocks. Instead, more than 99% of oil and gas has been found in sedimentary rocks.

Time requirements

Crude oil occurs in marine sedimentary formation of the geological periods dating from the late Cambrian through the Tertiary, including the Pliocene epoch (see Table 2).

The most juvenile oil-bearing sands yet discovered are said to be about 5000 years old. Exceedingly rare, however, are commercial deposits of oil that are younger than 100,000 years. In fact, reservoir rocks are mostly older than a million years. Actually, more than 99% of the world's oil comes from formations that exceed 10 million years in age.

This much time, however, is not necessarily required for petroleum hydrocarbons to be formed. Small amounts of oil have been extracted from sediments that are only a few hundred years old. Oil might continue to form in sediments for thousands or millions of years, or for as long as the source material lasts. Moreover, marked changes take place with age in the properties or chemical composition of crude oil. In general, asphalt-base crudes are younger than paraffin base.

Part of the time is required for the formation and transformation of the petroleum hydrocarbons. Perhaps much more time is required for the development of structural or stratigraphic traps and for the migration and accumulation of oil in such traps.

Migration of oil

Being less dense than water or rocks, oil and gas tend to migrate upward, unless blocked by

Table 2. OIL-BEARING MARINE SEDIMENTARY FORMATIONS

Era	Period	Age (millions of yrs. before present)	How many oil fields exploit these formations?
		Present	
CENOZOIC	Pleistocene	1 + 0.5	50%
	Pliocene	13 + 1	
	Miocene	25 + 1	
	Oligocene	36 + 2	
	Eocene	58 + 2	
	Paleocene	65 + 2	
MESOZOIC	Cretaceous	135 + 5	30%
	Jurassic	180 + 5	
	Triassic	230 + 10	
PALEOZOIC	Permian	280 + 10	20%
	Pennsylvanian	310 + 10	
	Mississippian	345 + 10	
	Devonian	405 + 10	
	Silurian	425 + 10	
	Ordovician	500 + 10	
	Cambrian	600?	
PRECAMBRIAN		4500	

impervious structures. It is difficult to estimate how much oil might have escaped to the surface, but careful studies of stratigraphy, structure, porosity, reservoir boundaries, and other characteristics of oil fields indicate that oil and gas in subterranean deposits have, for the most part, migrated upward no more than a few hundred feet. In some fields a number of oil and gas pools lie one above another, with no evidence of vertical connections.

Downward movement of oil and gas is almost unknown except in a few unique formations where the deformation of the earth's crust has caused slumping to occur. In the sea, oil droplets and, to a lesser extent, adsorbed gas might sink when attached to sediment particles heavier than water, but it is difficult to account for much gas or oil being carried downward into sediments by this process. The preponderance of geologic evidence indicates that most petroleum was formed very near the depths where we now find it.

Although relatively restricted, the lateral migration of petroleum or its precursors seems to have been somewhat more extensive than vertical migration. Still, it is the consensus of most geologists that oil has generally migrated laterally only short distances, say up to 10 or 20 miles. Indeed, there is good geologic evidence that in certain pools petroleum was formed within a mile or two of the place where found.

Lateral migration may be influenced by structure of the formation, rock porosity, movements of water, temperature, pressure, seismic disturbances, and other conditions, any or all of which may have changed many times during geologic history. The chances of either liquid or gaseous hydrocarbons migrating laterally more than a few miles without either finding a trap or escaping to the surface are slight.

Accumulation of gas and oil in traps has probably resulted in part from these hydrocarbons' being carried there by water movements. As we saw in Fig. 5-22, the classical petroleum pool or reservoir consists of an impervious roof or dome covering a porous rock formation filled with a layer of gas on top, an intermediate layer of oil, and salt water on the bottom. The gas and oil, as a result of their buoyancy, displace water in the pore spaces in the trap. Much greater volumes of gas and oil probably move into the pool, both vertically and laterally, independent of water movements —buoyancy being the chief force which moves the gas and oil to the highest places in the reservoir rocks.

Although restricted largely to a few miles laterally and a few hundred feet vertically, there must have been some migration of petroleum to account for the amounts of gas and oil found in many basins, if organic matter is the progenitor of petroleum.

Organic origin of oil

We have already seen some of the many reasons for believing that most, if not all, components of petroleum have had an organic origin. Here are more:

Virtually no oil and little natural gas, with the possible exception of methane, has been found in purely inorganic formations. No oil has been found in formations predating periods when there was plant life on the earth. Throughout the geologic ages in which petroleum does occur, there has been a more than ample, continuous, and widely distributed supply of organic matter. Vast amounts of this organic matter, rich in hydrogen and carbon, have been deposited in many marine sediments. And petroleum deposits are nearly always associated with sediments having a relatively high content of organic matter and many microfossils.

Petroliferous sediments are characterized by an abundance of mineral skeletons or shells (termed *tests*) of prehistoric algae and protozoans.

Besides microfossils, the microscopic examination of petroliferous sediments and crude oils from many pools reveals the presence of petrified wood fragments, insect scales, spines, spore coats, fungi, small crustaceans, plant resins, and numerous other plant and animal relics (see Fig. 5-21).

I have already referred to the presence in petroleum of porphyrins, optically active substances, and nitrogenous compounds, all of which can be traced and attributed to the organic remains of plants and animals. Being present only in small concentrations, these organic residues and relics could conceivably have become entrained in petroleum from a foreign source as it moved through the rocks. The large variety of organic materials, however, and the evidence that most crude oils have been formed in or near the place where found, strongly suggest a genetic relation between petroleums and organic matter.

But what kind of organic matter?

Possible source organisms

Probably both plants and animals as well as bacteria have supplied source material for the formation of petroleum.

Most strongly suspected are minute one-celled plants known collectively as phytoplankton. Diatoms are the commonest example. The siliceous tests of diatoms are found in many oil-producing areas of the world. Diatoms and allied phytoplankton are most prolific in nutrient-rich, near-shore areas. It is in such areas that sedimentation is usually greatest. Phytoplankton is relatively rich in vegetable oils that are much like mineral oils in chemical composition.

While carbohydrates as well as the proteins of organisms probably contribute source material, it is the fats and oils produced by plants, animals, or bacteria, that are chemically most closely related to petroleum.

The tissues and excretions of many living plants and animals contain a large variety of hydrocarbons. The relevant literature documents the occurrence of 23 different paraffinic hydrocarbons ranging from CH_4 to $C_{35}H_{72}$, 34 different ethylenic hydrocarbons ranging from C_2H_4 to $C_{30}H_{60}$, beta-carotene and lycopene ($C_{40}H_{56}$), 60 different cycloparaffins, and 16 different aromatic hydrocarbons. The aromatics include compounds having a benzene, naphtha-lene, or anthracene nucleus with assorted side chains.

The concentrations of hydrocarbons occurring in most living organisms are relatively low. For most species that have been analyzed, the concentrations range from fractional to a few hundred parts per million of dry tissue. Much higher concentrations, however, occur in certain organisms. More than 10% of the dry weight of some of the rubber-producing plants consists of polyisoprene-type hydrocarbons represented by the formula $(C_5H_8)_n$. Among such plants may be mentioned the rubber tree, *Hevea brasiliensis*, the guayule plant, certain varieties of goldenrod, milkweed, and the Russian dandelion, kok-saghyz.

Unfortunately, not enough is known about the amounts and kinds of hydrocarbons occurring in the tissues and excretions of organisms to estimate their possible contributions to source beds of petroleum. It is significant, however, that sediments recently deposited in the Gulf of Mexico have been shown to contain from 30 to 450 ppm of liquid and solid paraffinic, naphthenic, aromatic, and asphaltic substances akin to petroleum. These substances are believed to consist of plant, animal, and bacterial derivatives. An extrapolation of the values indicates that a cubic mile of such sediments might contain more than ten million barrels of an extract resembling crude oil. While far from being enough to account for all of the crude oil in commercial deposits, the findings point to the possible importance of hydrocarbons from living organisms.

The fossil fuels

All forms of petroleum, including natural gas, are known as fossil fuels, because of their ancient origin. Coal is also a fossil fuel. Coal differs from petroleum primarily in consisting, in the purest form, largely of free carbon, whereas petroleum consists largely of compounds of hydrogen and carbon with no free carbon.

Petroleum as well as coal is believed to have resulted from the gradual elimination of oxygen, nitrogen, sulfur, and phosphorus from organic matter throughout the geological ages. In the formation of high-grade coals, hydrogen has also been largely eliminated from the original organic complex, while the hydrogen content of petroleum is much higher than the hydrogen content of the tissues of organisms.

Table 3 illustrates how petroleum differs from coal in elementary composition and how both differ from their presumed organic precursors. No one knows why.

Although the methods of formation remain a mystery, theoretically there are many mech-

Table 3. CONTENT OF FUELS AND OF ORGANIC
SOURCES

(Percent)	Carbon	Hydrogen	Oxygen	Nitrogen	Others
Petroleum (mean value)	85.4	13.5	0.4	0.3	0.4
Coal (high rank)	97.8	0.2	1.5	0.4	0.8
Organisms (marine)	51.4	5.7	29.8	12.1	1.0
Plants (terrestrial)	47.5	5.9	40.1	5.3	1.3

anisms by which the organic remains of plants and animals could be converted into petroleum.

Destructive distillation of organic matter

Nearly a century ago it was demonstrated that heating organic matter—either animal or vegetable—in the absence of free oxygen will produce a large variety of hydrocarbons and nitrogenous bases. Distillates prepared in this way from various organic materials resemble commercial kerosene, asphalt, or even crude oils in certain respects. Therefore, Engler, Day, and other scientists were led to postulate this as a mechanism by which petroleum is produced under natural conditions.

The postulate, however, fails to fit the facts learned during the last fifty years. Producing artificial petroleum from the destructive distillation of organic matter requires temperatures ranging from 320°C to 600°C, whereas we have seen that there is almost overwhelming evidence that most crude oils were formed at temperatures no higher than 150°C and some under 100°C.

When the evidence became known to proponents of the Engler theory for the origin of oil, they argued that oil might be formed at lower temperatures if given adequate time (centuries or millennia), proper catalysts, and other required but as yet unknown conditions. This may be true, but such low-temperature processes should not be called destructive distillation.

Inorganic catalysts

Catalysts are substances that initiate or accelerate a chemical reaction without permanently entering into or being consumed by the reaction. In the thermal cracking of oil in refinery operations, it has been found that a number of mineral catalysts cause the formation and transformation of hydrocarbons at temperatures and pressures much lower than without them. They include, for example, clays, quartz, iron oxides, aluminum silicates, nickel, platinum black, vanadium, and molybdenum compounds.

Such observations, coupled with laboratory experiments, have led to extensive speculation concerning the possible part played by inor-

ganic catalysts in the origin of oil. Petroliferous sediments generally contain surface-active, base-exchange, heavy metals, and other types of potential catalysts. Such catalysts are known to promote chemical reactions that are conducive to the conversion of organic matter into oil.

There is both experimental and geological evidence that inorganic catalysts influence the chemical composition of crude oils, but such catalysts alone can hardly be held responsible for the conversion of organic materials into petroleum.

The role of hydrostatic pressure

There is no evidence that pressure influences the chemical composition of crude oil, although there are relationships between depth of burial, temperature, age, and the characteristics of oil.

Hydrostatic pressure in the earth's crust increases with depth by an average of about 0.465 psi/ft. In extreme cases, the pressure gradient may be as little as 0.3 or as much as 0.9 psi/ft.

The pressure at any particular depth is influenced primarily by the weight of oil, water, and rock overburden. To a lesser extent, the pressure gradient is influenced by temperature changes, chemical reactions, tides, atmospheric conditions, earthquakes, faulting, and other phenomena.

As I said earlier, much oil is found in basins having an overburden of less than 5000 ft and a hydrostatic pressure of less than 2500 psi. Shear pressures, hydrodynamic pressures, and other localized or ephemeral pressure conditions could not be expected to increase this to any more than 5000 psi. Therefore, it seems safe to conclude that pressures higher than 5000 psi are not required for the formation of petroleum. As a matter of fact, oil has been found under conditions which indicate that neither certain crude oils nor their precursors have been subjected to pressures of as much as 1000 psi.

Part played by bacteria

Based on the premise that organic matter is the mother substance of petroleum, it is almost axiomatic that bacteria have contributed to the conversion.

Large numbers of living bacteria occur in organic-rich marine sediments, some species at depths of several thousand feet. Such bacteria reproduce and are physiologically active at hydrostatic pressures exceeding 15,000 psi and at temperatures up to nearly 100°C.

Bacteria catalyze numerous chemical reactions involving not only organic compounds and hydrocarbons but also molecular hydrogen and other inorganic substances. They attack virtually all kinds of organic materials and also bring about other changes in marine sediments that favor the formation, accumulation, and migration of petroleum.

Under most conditions, the organic remains of plants and animals start to undergo bacterial modification shortly after the death of the organisms. In the presence of free oxygen, much of the organic matter is oxidized or converted into carbon dioxide, water, sulfate, ammonia, and other simple substances.

Soon, however, all of the free oxygen is consumed by the bacteria buried in sediments, and conditions become anaerobic or reducing rather than oxidizing in character. Such anaerobic or reducing conditions modify the decomposition of organic matter and favor the formation and preservation of petroleum hydrocarbons.

For example, the anaerobic fermentation of organic matter nearly always results in the formation of methane, a common constituent of natural gas and crude oil. Anaerobic bacteria also liberate free hydrogen from certain organic compounds. Then reactions are also known whereby some species consume hydrogen in reducing carbon dioxide to methane according to the reaction:

$$CO_2 + 4H_2 \rightarrow CH_4 + 2H_2O$$

Also widely distributed in marine and petroliferous sediments are large numbers of sulfate-reducing bacteria consuming hydrogen:

$$CaSO_4 + 4H_2 \rightarrow CaS + 4H_2O$$

This fits the geological facts, because nearly all petroliferous formations show evidence of sulfate reduction and usually an absence of free hydrogen. It is generally agreed that bacterial activities account for sulfate reduction; organic matter as well as free hydrogen may be used in the process.

Sulfate-reducing as well as other kinds of bacteria use free hydrogen to build bacterial protein and other carbon compounds:

$$CO_2 + 3H_2 \rightarrow (-CH_2-) + 2H_2O$$

where $(-CH_2-)$ represents a building block of bacterial cell substance. Part of the latter (up to 0.42%) has been shown by laboratory experiments to be an oily substance consisting of paraffinic hydrocarbons and aromatic compounds.

A good many other hydrocarbons besides methane are also produced by bacteria, but the yields are very low. Whereas up to 40% of the carbon content of organic compounds can be converted into methane by certain bacteria, the yields of higher gaseous, liquid, or solid hydrocarbons are usually only a few parts per million at most. So, while academically interesting, the yields of liquid and solid hydrocarbons by any known bacterial processes are much too low to account for the origin of oil exclusive of other processes.

Whether (by as yet undiscovered conditions) bacterial processes may produce much higher yields of liquid and solid hydrocarbons, either directly from organic matter or by bringing about the polymerization of methane, remains in the realm of speculation.

The role of radioactivity

The natural radioactivity of petroliferous sediments could account for such a polymerization of methane.

Nearly 40 years ago the pioneer of radiation chemistry, S. C. Lind, and his associates demonstrated that the alpha-particle bombardment of methane resulted in the formation of higher hydrocarbons:

$$xCH_4 \rightarrow C_2H_6 + C_3H_8 + C_4H_{10} \cdots + H_2$$

Continued bombardment resulted in the formation of ethane, propane, butane, pentane, and higher hydrocarbons, along with free hydrogen.

Starting with any single gaseous hydrocarbon, activation by alpha rays resulted in the formation of all other members both higher and lower, along with the liberation of appreciable quantities of hydrogen.

These observations have been confirmed by other geochemists and extended to include a large variety of carbon compounds. The alpha bombardment of fatty acids, common constituents of living matter, has been shown to result in the formation of paraffin hydrocarbons, along with free hydrogen, carbon dioxide, and other products.

Field observations and calculations indicate that petroliferous sediments contain ample alpha-emitting radioactive substances to account for the hydrocarbons present if the latter are derived from fatty acids, methane, or possibly other kinds of organic matter.

Alpha particles are helium nuclei; the hypothesis is thus consistent with the fact that helium is found in many gas and oil wells in Texas and elsewhere.

You'll recall that in the polymerization of methane by alpha-particle bombardment, hydrogen was liberated. The presence of this free hydrogen would favor the hydrogenation of organic matter and the formation of hydrocarbons. However, free hydrogen is generally absent in oil fields and sedimentary rocks. This fact has been used as an argument against radioactivity only by those who have overlooked the other fact that free hydrogen is quantitatively consumed by certain varieties of bacteria found in marine sediments.

Although the circumstances outlined above fail to prove that radioactivity supplemented by bacterial activity has been responsible for the origin of oil, such processes could have been important contributing factors.

The actual factors have certainly been effective; the earth contains a lot of oil.

How much oil has been formed?

To tell how much oil has formed on earth is of course impossible. Even to learn how much oil is known to be in the ground is difficult, since other nations neither define nor report their reserves as the U.S.A. does. And, of what is known to be in the ground, only a part (called "proved reserves") is recoverable under current economic conditions and with present-day technology. Beyond what is known to be there, there's at least 10 and possibly 100 times more, in the form of tar sands, oil shale, and oil not now economically recoverable from reservoirs.

For what it is worth, I cite the estimate recently published in the *Oil and Gas Journal* that the world's reserves of crude oil are about 314 billion barrels of 42 gallons each. That's about 13 trillion gallons. The volume of Lake Superior is about 3 trillion gallons.

One wonders how much longer the balance will last. The world's annual consumption rate is now 9 billion barrels. Perchance oil in the earth is being formed as fast as it is being consumed. This possibility seems unlikely.

Further reading

Two excellent books on the earth science of oil are Levorsen's *Geology of Petroleum* (Freeman, 1954, $9) and Landes' *Petroleum Geology* (Wiley, 1959, 2nd ed., $9.50).

A survey of hypotheses and evidence is given in the review article "Origin of Petroleum—A Review," by Stevens, on p. 51 of *Bull. Amer. Assoc. Petrol. Geol.*, Vol. 40, 1956. On p. 645 of the same journal, but in Vol. 30, 1946, is another recommended article, by Cox, on "Transformation of Organic Materials into Petroleum Under Geological Conditions."

One of the best books on the chemical composition of petroleum is "The Chemical Technology of Petroleum" by Gruse and Stevens (McGraw-Hill, 1960, 3rd ed., $15.00).

The Gerardes have reviewed the extensive literature on the occurrence of hydrocarbons in plant and animal materials in a 47-page article "The Ubiquitous Hydrocarbons," *Assoc. Food & Drug Officials of U.S.*, Vols. 15 & 16, 1961–62.

In U.S. Patent No. 2,413,278, issued Dec. 24, 1948, Dr. ZoBell reveals a "Bacteriological Process for Treatment of Fluid-Bearing Earth Formations." The mechanisms of the "Bacterial Release of Oil from Sedimentary Materials" are described in an article by Dr. ZoBell in the August 2, 1947, issue of *The Oil and Gas Journal*. More recent observations are reported by La Rivière in two articles "The Production of Surface Active Compounds by Microorganisms and Its Possible Significance in Oil Recovery," *Antonie van Leeuwenhoek*, Vol. 21, 1955, pp. 1–27. While certain bacteria definitely release oil from oil bearing formations under laboratory conditions, introducing bacterial cultures in oil wells has not proved to be a satisfactory method of increasing the recovery of oil in this country, probably because of the growth of harmful bacteria which plug formations and corrode iron pipes. Lada (*Producers Monthly*, Vol. 23, 1959, p. 35) points out that controlling these harmful bacteria in injection waters contributes substantially to the secondary recovery of oil. According to Dostálek and Spurný (*Ceskoslov. mikrobiol.*, Vol. 2, 1957, p. 300), inoculating oil wells with bacteria increased the average daily output of oil by 6 to 12 per cent.

The results of a ten-year research project on the bacterial, chemical, and geological aspects of the "Transformation of Organic Materials into Petroleum" are published in the American Petroleum Institute's *Report of Progress— Fundamental Research on Occurrence and Recovery of Petroleum* in six volumes dating from 1943–1953.

Calculations of the content of hydrocarbons and other oil-precursor organic compounds appear in "Further Observations on the Paraffins and Primary Alcohols of Plant Waxes," by Waldron et al., in *Biochem. J.*, Vol. 78, 1961, p. 435.

A fuller account of microbial involvement in oil formation is given in the author's paper "Part Played by Bacteria in Petroleum Formation," *Sedimentary Petrology*, Vol. 22, 1952, p. 42.

The classic in that field is Beerstecher's *Petroleum Microbiology* (Van Nostrand, 1954, $8.50), now out of print.

The question of supply and reserves is covered in a good book, *Oil for the World*, by Schackne and Drake (Harper Bros., 1960, 2nd revised ed., $2.50, paper $1.75), and in the periodicals *World Oil* and *The Oil and Gas Journal*.

CHANGING THE WEATHER

by Louis J. Battan *

IN BRIEF: *Attempts to change the weather cluster around six objectives—(1) increasing rain or snow; (2) dissipating fog; (3) curbing lightning; (4) inhibiting hail; (5) hurricane control; (6) changing climate. Common to most such efforts is the seeding of clouds to aid nucleation of precipitation embryos that nature frequently fails to provide—ice crystals, in the case of supercooled clouds, or water droplets larger than 50 microns in clouds warmer than 0°C. Favorite seed materials, depending on temperature, are dry ice, silver iodide, plain water, or salt crystals. Dispersal methods include rockets, planes, and ground-based generators.*

The degree to which seeding increases precipitation, if at all, still is not proven, although dry ice can dramatically clear local openings in supercooled fog. Slight but significant first steps have been taken in altering electrical properties of clouds, and for hailstorms at least a satisfactory model has been constructed. But we still lack the means to act on the basis of this model and, in the case of hurricanes, even the model necessary for intelligent attempts at control is lacking. As for attempts to change climate, we would be fools to try anything until much less ignorant than now of possible consequences.—S.T.

■ In 1946, Vincent J. Schaefer, then at the General Electric Laboratories, dropped some small pellets of dry ice from a plane into a thin cloud comprised of water droplets. In a matter of minutes vast numbers of ice crystals formed in the cloud and grew rapidly. Some even became large enough to fall to the ground. This slight almost inconsequential snowfall began modern efforts to change the weather.

Most research efforts now cluster about one or more of six objectives: (1) increasing rainfall or snowfall; (2) inhibiting the fall of hail; (3) dissipating fog; (4) curbing lightning; (5) controlling hurricanes and other violent storms; (6) changing the long-term weather, or climate, over large regions. As we consider each of these let's keep some hard-nosed questions firmly in mind.

Has it been shown, beyond reasonable doubt, that weather can be modified?

What can we reasonably expect in the near future and in the far?

* Louis J. Battan is Associate Director of the Institute of Atmospheric Physics at the University of Arizona in Tucson.

Back to beyond the beginning

The first important step towards controlling precipitation—the step, in fact, that made Schaefer's experiment possible—came in the early 1930's when a Norwegian meteorologist, Tor Bergeron, discovered one of the two ways that nature makes rain. He observed that most clouds do not rain because the droplets of water in them are simply too small to fall. Their diameters average only about 20 microns, whereas diameters on the order of several hundreds of microns are the ticket for a one-way trip to earth. He also noted that droplets in common clouds ordinarily grow only very slowly by condensation alone, and that they stay liquid even when temperatures are far below freezing; we now know they can supercool to about −40°C in extreme cases, without freezing.

But Bergeron observed that when nature in certain circumstances managed to form some ice crystals in a cloud of such supercooled water droplets, the crystals, unlike the droplets, grew very rapidly and at the expense of the droplets (Fig. 5-23). Which is just what you would expect, since the saturation vapor pressure of ice is smaller than that of water at subfreezing temperatures. This simple process is the starting point for much of the precipitation reaching the earth's surface, but only the starting point. The ice crystals themselves must grow sufficiently large by sublimation so they can fall through the cloud, as in Fig. 5-24, and grow still further by sweeping out supercooled water droplets. Once they've made it this far they're truly on their way down, down, down.

When Schaefer attacked the stability of supercooled clouds with dry-ice pellets, which lowered the air temperature in their immediate vicinity to below −70°C, he of course produced the ice nuclei necessary to trigger the Bergeron process. Dry ice effectively causes ice nuclei to form in clouds at all air temperatures below 0°C, but many other ice-nucleating substances —natural ones such as kaolin, or synthetics such as silver iodide—depend for their effectiveness not on a brute-force approach of extreme undercooling but, instead, either on accommodating ice's hexagonal crystal structure with appropriate three-dimensional geometry of their own or on inviting surface properties.

More about seeding technology shortly. Let's go back to nature for a moment for a look at another rain-making possibility.

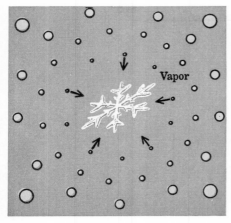 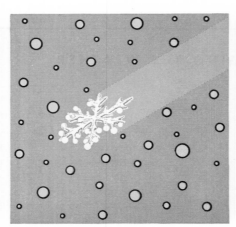 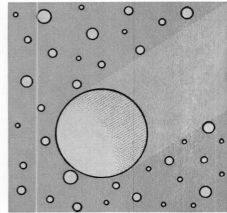

Fig. 5-23, left, shows how a snow crystal gets big enough to fall to earth, perhaps as rain if it melts enroute. In a supercooled cloud, any snow nucleus that forms grows larger as water evaporating from nearby droplets sublimes upon it. When it starts to fall, Fig. 5-24, it grows further by freezing unto itself droplets with which it collides. Fig. 5-25 shows nature's rain-making mechanism in nonfreezing clouds. Here, any water drop large enough to fall in the first place grows big enough to fall all the way by colliding and coalescing with smaller droplets in its path.

It rains from warm clouds too

At one time it was thought that almost all precipitation was produced by the Bergeron process; thus if clouds did not grow to altitudes where temperatures were below 0°C, rain was considered most unlikely. Yet in tropical regions small cumulus clouds (the white "cauliflower" clouds commonly seen on fair summer days in temperate regions) often produce substantial showers, even though their tops never reach subfreezing altitudes.

In this precipitation mechanism nature manages to form some water droplets of unusually large initial diameter—about 50 microns. Most ordinary cloud droplets are only about 5 to 30 microns in diameter because the condensation nuclei on which they grow are small—perhaps 0.5 microns. But over the oceans seawater droplets thrown into the air at wave crests and along shorelines evaporate, leaving behind vast numbers of salt particles to serve as condensation nuclei. And although most of these are tiny, less than a micron in diameter, a vitally important few are giants with diameters up to 5 microns. Simple condensation upon these, in air whose humidity is over 95%, yields cloud droplets whose diameters are greater than the crucial 50 microns needed to start them falling. Once in motion they grow to the still larger size necessary to reach the ground by colliding and coalescing with smaller droplets as in Fig. 5-25.

Since precipitation from nonfreezing clouds depends on the existence of at least some large water droplets, the obvious way to wring rain from them is to introduce some; or else to seed the cloud—not with dry ice or silver iodide, as is done for subfreezing clouds—but with giant salt nuclei.

In either approach, a critical factor is the rate at which the falling droplet grows by collision and coalescence. Not every collision results in coalescence, of course, and a key practical question we face is how to increase the so-called collision efficiency—or how to maximize the rate of coalescence.

Efficiency is low when the relatively stationary cloud droplets are small, because they flow around the large drop instead of striking it; efficiency also fails to reach its maximum when the falling drop and the droplets are about the same size, since all drops then move at about the same speed and seldom collide. Maximum merger takes place when the smaller drops are about 7/10 the size of the larger one, as portrayed in the marginal sketch.

The collision frequency is thought also to be affected by the presence of electric fields, but as yet no one has tried to modify precipitation electrically.

Curbing the lightning bolts of Jove

There have, however, been a number of attempts to modify natural electrical phenomena themselves by seeding with dry-ice nuclei. Some results indicate that when the upper part of a storm cloud is converted to ice crystals electrical fields in the vicinity rapidly increase from a few volts per centimeter to as much as 40 volts/cm. But it is still not clear to what extent these changes result from addition of ice nuclei rather than from natural evolution of the clouds. And the effects of seeding on severe lightning storms with their huge charges are even more inconclusive. On the other hand, there is no doubt that the electrical properties of small fair-weather cumulus clouds can be changed.

Bernard Vonnegut and his associates reasoned

that the small but measurable electrical charge of such small convective clouds comes from elementary space charges carried to the cloud from near the ground by thermal updrafts. To test this idea, they set a wire—14 km long and mounted 10 m off the ground—into corona discharge by applying high voltages. This raised the space charge in the area by about two orders of magnitude, from around 1 up to 100 elementary charges/cm³ over an area of about 50 km². By means of measurements made from airplanes (Fig. 5-26) they found that when a negative charge was released at the wire the clouds above became negatively charged; and the potential gradient both above and below the cloud—normally slightly positive in fair weather—was enhanced severalfold. What's more, reversing the polarity of the artificially created space charge not only reversed the polarity of the cloud's charge; generally it also reversed the sign of the potential gradient over the cloud from positive to negative.

Such experiments cannot yet be straightforwardly applied to larger thunderstorms in which natural charges and potential gradients are much greater. But additional tests, using larger quantities of charge over larger areas, are needed and are being planned.

From little seeds and acorns grow . . .

Returning now to our deferred discussion of seeding, the keys to its effectiveness are three: (1) the nucleating ability of the substance, depending on whether the aim is to produce ice crystals or giant water droplets; (2) the ability to disperse nucleating embryos in the desired locations; (3) the ability to achieve concentration appropriate to the modification task at hand. To induce snow, for instance, concentrations must be about 10³ nuclei/m³, while to suppress hail they must be much greater—about 10⁸ nuclei/m³.

Most ice-nucleation efforts aimed at increasing rainfall or modifying thunderstorms use silver iodide. Its prime advantage over other chemical reagents is that it leads to some ice crystals at a relatively warm −5°C. In general, as you would expect, the number of ice crystals produced by an influx of seed crystals increases with decreasing temperature, as well

as with the abundance of seeds. A good seeding generator can produce about 10¹⁴ ice-crystal nuclei per gram of silver iodide used at −10°C.

In spite of increasingly widespread use of

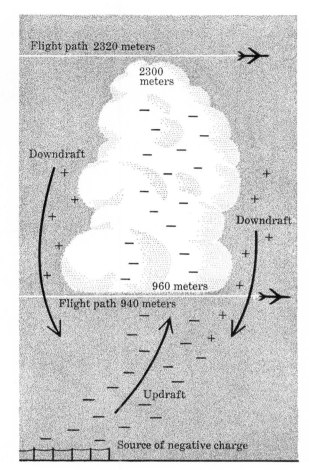

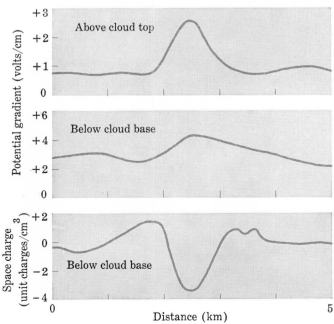

Fig. 5-26. Setting a long wire into corona discharge increases space charge in its vicinity from natural values under 1 unit charge/cm³ to about 100 charges/ cm³, in either positive or negative direction. As shown at top, updrafts carried charge of either polarity up to small fair-weather cumulus clouds, charging them similarly. Artificial charge also perturbed the natural potential gradient both above and below the cloud, as shown in graphs.

Figs. 5-27 and 5-28. Recently developed "Cloud-buster" (top) used 11 pounds of solid CO_2 to punch this 3-mile hole in deck of supercooled clouds in one hour. Carried aboard plane, the device expands liquid CO_2 through nozzle (not visible) and passes resulting dry ice and gas to cyclone separator (upright portion). Dry ice drops out of cylinder at top to pellet-forming wheel below, and goes overboard along a retractable chute. (Courtesy U.S. Air Force, Cambridge Research Laboratories)

Fig. 5-29. Airborne silver-iodide generator ejects fine spray of acetone-iodide mixture through a nozzle and ignites acetone by spark plug. Acetone continues to burn, dispersing iodide particles, as long as spray ejection of mixture continues. (Courtesy U.S. Forest Service)

silver iodide, however, for certain purposes dry ice still is the best available seeding material. For example, to clear supercooled fog or low clouds from an airport, it is important to be able to operate at the relatively warm temperature prevailing at such low altitudes, at a temperature as close to 0°C as possible. And dry ice, recall, will produce at least a few ice nuclei at all temperatures up to 0°C. But the upper limiting temperature at which silver iodide will work is -5°C. When dry ice is used it's usually dropped into the clouds from an airplane, as is done with the Air Force's Cambridge Research Lab's "Cloudbuster" (Fig. 5-27) which punched the remarkable 3-mile hole in a low supercooled cloud deck, shown in Fig. 5-28, in just about one hour!

In about 1955, Australian scientists under the leadership of E. G. Bowen developed some practical airborne silver-iodide generators. These instruments, as well as a similar one designed some years later by the U.S. Forest Service (Fig. 5-29), use nozzles to produce a fine spray of acetone-iodide solution. A spark plug ignites the highly inflammable acetone and, as long as it is sprayed, the flame continues to burn. Comparable airborne generators developed by the Russians use electrical power to maintain the burning chamber at a precisely fixed temperature to achieve greater uniformity in particle size and distribution.

Rockets, flares, and Roman candles

Recent years have seen growing interest in pyrotechnical devices for silver-iodide seeding. Schaefer first proposed using silver-iodide-impregnated flares in 1953, but the idea was not exploited. Major impetus to using rockets for cloud seeding came from northern Italy, where farmers have long used small pyrotechnic rockets—in startling numbers—in attempts to reduce the fall of crop-destroying hail.

In practice, firing starts when the thunderstorm that may drop hail comes over the hill and continues until it passes by. Ottavio A. Vittori, a well-known atmospheric chemist, tried to assess how the rockets might help; he was told by many eye witnesses that within minutes after the rocket launchings, the hailstones became "mushy." Vittori's proposal that possibly explosion of the rocket nose cone leads to cavitation in water and air pockets inside the hailstone (Color Fig. 38), causing development of many tiny cracks in the ice, is getting further study, as are other hail-suppression techniques that we'll mention later.

More than 100,000 rockets were launched in Italy during the 1959 growing season alone. The rockets used are little more than toys—about

3 in. in diameter, 5 ft long, and constructed mostly of cardboard. But they can reach altitudes of 1000 or 1500 m. At the summit of the trajectory, 800 g of gunpowder in the rocket head explodes. For many years only gunpowder was used, but starting in about 1958, tests were made with 200 g of the payload in the form of silver iodide.

Many other elaborate schemes for dispersing silver iodide are undergoing testing. Schaefer's idea of flares impregnated with silver iodide has been revived. Tracer bullets containing it have been fired from airplane machine guns. Still another new technique uses rocket fuels mixed with silver iodide. This has excellent potential because rockets can be launched into clouds with precision and in great numbers, if necessary, and into violent thunderstorms, or hurricanes where turbulence is too severe to risk airplane penetrations.

It is conceivable, also, that sound waves might cause rapid collision and coalescence among otherwise sluggish small water droplets in a cloud. As a matter of fact, laboratory tests have demonstrated that this can be done. Unfortunately, we cannot extrapolate these results beyond the laboratory, because the essence of the method is that standing sound waves must be set up. This does not seem possible except in special circumstances, such as across a canyon.

Can we make rain in meaningful amounts?

Extensive cloud-seeding activities by commercial rain-making firms were conducted from 1948 to 1953, particularly in the western United States. Notwithstanding the many claims of success, no one really knew if the seeding had any measurable effect on precipitation. Chief difficulty arose from the well-known fact that natural precipitation is highly variable in space and time, especially so in the more arid regions where rain-making efforts were numerous. To demonstrate quantitatively that cloud seeding can increase rainfall—to the 5 percent level of statistical significance, that is, to the level where chances of a wrong conclusion are only 5 out of 100—we must be able to distinguish natural changes of precipitation from those induced artificially.

To settle growing controversy about effects—controversy that reached into Congress—an Advisory Committee on Weather Control, appointed by President Eisenhower in 1953, used regression analyses of data collected by commercial rain makers to test claims and counterclaims. Its final report, December 1957, concluded that ". . . the statistical procedures employed indicated that seeding of winter type storm clouds in mountainous areas of the United States produced an average increase of precipitation of 10 to 15 percent . . ." But disagreement did not end there.

Though accepted by some meteorologists, particularly those in the cloud-seeding business, as positive proof that precipitation could be increased by small but important amounts, the report drew sharp criticism from a number of prominent statisticians, particularly A. K. Brownlee of the University of Chicago and J. Neyman of the University of California at Berkeley. They argued that data used by the analysts of the Advisory Committee were not collected so as to allow acceptable statistical tests of significance. They were especially disturbed by lack of a suitable randomization scheme for deciding when to seed. This meant that cloud seeders could have biased the results in the direction of showing that seeding increases precipitation, when in fact they might have been simply capitalizing—knowingly or not—on precipitation that would have occurred naturally.

Since the 1957 report and controversy, experiments in the United States and many other countries have incorporated statistical safeguards against biasing the results, chiefly by randomizing periods of seeding.

Experiments in Australia show a 20% increase in precipitation, but their widely publicized results have still not been published in sufficient detail to allow careful scrutiny by the scientific community. Tests in other parts of the world also suggest that in certain special situations it may be possible to increase precipitation. However, in the judgment of many scientists engaged in cloud-seeding research, a net, statistically meaningful increase of precipitation has not yet been demonstrated beyond reasonable doubt.

But there is no doubt at all that rain-making is merely one of our more modest headaches. Desirable as increased rain would be in some places, elsewhere the drastic effects of hailstorms, hurricanes, and other storms also merit—and are getting—attention.

Hail: the conquering villain

Hailstorms do millions of dollars of agricultural damage annually. Indeed, they are regarded as one of the major practical weather problems in many countries.

We've known for a long time that crop-smashing hailstones, an inch or more in diameter, grow only in thunderstorms containing large amounts of supercooled water. But just in the past 5 years we've learned that an additional essential feature such storms must possess, if hail is to grow to such large size, is a strong updraft of air that persists for as long as an hour. Color Fig. 38 shows a model of this kind of thunderstorm. Its key feature, from the standpoint of hail control, is the current of air that rises from lower levels at the leading edge of the thunderstorm and mostly leaves the cloud mass from the top front side.

In this updraft, large water droplets form by coalescence. Many workers believe that when these become sufficiently large and cold they freeze to form hail embryos; others think the embryos form by agglomeration of ice crystals. In either case, once a small ice particle forms it continues to grow by collecting supercooled cloud droplets as it is carried to higher regions of the clouds.

Some ice particles never make it to the cloud top; they fall out of the updraft as small nondestructive hailstones. Indeed, the smallest ones melt and reach the ground as rain. Others, however, the villains of our story, are alternately carried up and down by air currents moving in various directions within the storm. Throughout this merry-go-round ride, a stone remains in a region of predominantly supercooled water droplets and continues to grow at their expense. Finally, when the hailstone is so large that even the strong velocities in the updraft cannot support it, it falls all the way to the ground. The familiar and beautiful pattern of alternating layers of clear and opaque ice often found in hailstones (Color Fig. 39 shows large, natural stones) supports this cyclic picture of hail growth. When in parts of the cloud with high values of liquid water, the stone accumulates so much water that it can only freeze slowly, clear coarsely crystalline ice is formed. But when only small quantities of water droplets are intercepted, they freeze quickly, creating bands of finer-grained ice that are milky or opaque because of included water droplets and air bubbles.

The pyrotechnic rocket barrages we mentioned a while back seek to exploit the incipient weak spots inherent in such inclusions, but most other attempts to suppress hail try to prevent its formation. In most instances, silver-iodide seeding of the cloud is used, the object being to convert the supercooled liquid parts of thunderstorms entirely to numerous small ice crystals by overseeding. If enough silver iodide can be fed into the updraft at the leading edge of the storm, it can work. The trick, however, is to provide *enough*.

Estimates of quantities of silver iodide needed to overseed even a moderate-sized thunderstorm call for more than 100 pounds of silver iodide per cloud. This may not sound like much, but on a practical basis, for example, a recent Rus-

sian report estimates that in order to protect the Alazani Valley in Georgia, SSR—an area of about 2000 square miles—for a period of 6 to 8 hours, 40 tons of silver iodide would be needed. And this would have to be strategically dispersed. When you realize that the rates of silver iodide normally dispersed thus far are 10 to 1000 times less than this amount, you can see how far we have to go before we can hope that overseeding can eliminate damaging hail.

The key to formation of the very large stones appears to be the tilted updraft. It can persist for the better part of an hour. Perhaps if it could be interrupted, even momentarily, the incipient large stones would fall through the core of the updraft. How to do it remains the vital question.

Hurricanes, typhoons, and willy-willies

How to do it also remains the question to be answered for the most violent storms of all—hurricanes, typhoons, cyclones, or willy-willies—different names for the same thing, according to whether you're in America, Japan, India, or Australia. Hurricanes usually form over the oceans where and when the sea water temperature is highest. Heat from the water surface raises air temperatures, and evaporation transfers additional large quantities of latent heat to the air.

We don't know precisely how the hurricane vortex itself originates. But, somehow, a small initial disturbance in atmospheric pressures over the region of such thermal transfer causes the air near the surface to converge toward a particularly disturbed small region (Color Fig. 40), then to rise and diverge at higher altitudes. As the warm moisture-laden air rises, clouds form by condensation of the vast amounts of water vapor; this releases huge quantities of latent heat to the air.

When you think about modifying hurricane behavior, it is well to keep in mind the truly fantastic energies of these storms. The energy input needed to maintain a typical run-of-the-mill hurricane is estimated at about 3×10^{25} ergs/day. This is equivalent to exploding about 100 ten-megaton hydrogen bombs per day, making it distinctly unprofitable to consider approaching hurricanes by brute strength alone. When we more clearly comprehend the critical factors controlling development and movement of the storms, maybe adding just a small quantity of energy at the right place and at the right time can have major trigger influence.

But until then, attempts to influence the behavior of hurricanes which are not based on a well-understood physical model of the storm are of questionable value. What, for instance, would happen if particular quantities of heat were injected at a particular place and time? Nobody yet knows.

Seeding's fun, but thinking's better

To answer this question—which has not been answered by seeding experiments—mathematical models of hurricanes are being constructed. These use three-dimensional equations for air motions, plus equations to account for energy inputs by condensation and freezing and energy losses by evaporation. The boundary conditions for real hurricanes—dimensions, air velocities, air densities, and quantities of water vapor— are reasonably well known. As you would expect, the relevant equations are quite complex, but with acceptable simplifying assumptions they can be solved by numerical methods. Once a satisfactory model has been formulated it will be possible to introduce theoretical heat sources or sinks and quantitatively evaluate—prior to undertaking potentially risky experiments— what the effects will be.

Whether effects will be beneficial or devastatingly otherwise gets more serious as we increase the scale of control attempts. When we talk about rain-making or hail suppression, for instance, we refer to very minor atmospheric disturbances. And even if we could modify a hurricane several hundred miles in diameter the consequences—good or bad—in all probability would be relatively short-lived. But when we trifle with changing the climate, the average of weather conditions over long periods of time, and the prime determinant of the history, culture, and economy of a region, we may really be stepping out of our league.

Today hurricanes—tomorrow the world

Not too long ago anyone suggesting that changing the climate of the world was conceivable was regarded as having lost touch with reality. However, during the past few years, it has been seriously considered.

Since the chief factor governing the atmosphere's over-all circulation (see "Tomorrow's Weather," page 610) is the temperature difference between warm equatorial and cold polar regions, altering this could trigger changes in airflow patterns—and climate—over entire regions or, indeed, over the entire world. One proposal to do this that has received serious attention—first reported in October 1959 by P. M. Borisov, a Russian engineer—suggested that a huge dam be built across the roughly 50-mile-wide Bering Strait and that nuclear power be used to pump cold Arctic Ocean water through it into the Pacific Ocean. Cold water so removed from the Arctic basin would be replaced by inflow of warmer water from the At-

lantic Ocean, perhaps sufficient to heat the Arctic region enough to cause important climate changes. But in 1960 another Russian condemned this idea, showing that not only would the warming of the Arctic be very small in any event, but that even this slight warming might lead to a decrease of precipitation over the Soviet Union that could devastate the economy of the country.

Many other sweeping proposals—some completely impractical, others offering a glimmer of possibility—have been forthcoming, especially in the U.S. and the Soviet Union. Still unanswered is, "What climatic changes would be produced by warming the Arctic by even a small amount? And will the effects be beneficial or harmful? Most *scientists* concerned with these areas—the imaginative Russians included—recognize that before performing any tests to warm the Arctic, or to otherwise attempt "cosmic engineering," it is essential that we have a good idea of the consequences. It is conceivable that changes could be initiated which could not be reversed. Though it is indeed pleasant to contemplate converting deserts to gardens of green, it must be realized that creating the reverse is an equally probable outcome of proceeding in ignorance.

Further reading

For an easygoing introduction to matters meteorological, including techniques for modifying the weather and for the statistical evaluation of such efforts, see a pair of paperbacks written by L. J. Battan: *The Nature of Violent Storms* (1961) and *Cloud Physics and Cloud Seeding* (1962), both Doubleday Anchor Books. Considerably more advanced in level is a pair of books by B. J. Mason. The more comprehensive but older one is *The Physics of Clouds* (Oxford, 1957). The more recent one, *Clouds, Rain, and Rainmaking* (Cambridge, 1962), condenses and slightly popularizes its predecessor. To round things out as far as the physics of precipitation goes, see *The Physics of Rainclouds* by Fletcher (Cambridge, 1962), which emphasizes matters such as condensation and ice nucleation in theory and experiment. Then go on to a panoramic overview which is provided by the collected papers in *The Physics of Precipitation*, Geophysical Monograph No. 5 of the American Geophysical Union, 1960, also available as NAS-NRC publication No. 746.

The statistics involved in evaluating rainmaking are treated at length in the *Final Report of the Advisory Committee on Weather Control*, Vol. 2 (Govt. Printing Office, 1947). An astute critique of this report is Brownlee's article in the *J. Am. Statistical Assoc.*, **55**, 446

(1960). Vonnegut's work on modifying electrical properties of clouds is reported in the *J. Geophys. Res.*, **67**, 3909 (1962). And a comprehen-

sive analysis of problems involved in modifying climate over large regions is Wexler's article in *Science,* **128,** 1059 (1958).

TOMORROW'S WEATHER

by Thomas F. Malone *

IN BRIEF: *Today's score on predicting the weather in fair detail averages around 75% correct for periods of a day or two ahead. Increase the forecast period to a week, a month, or more, and accuracy and detail drop sharply. Better forecasts are coming in the next few years, though no one can surely tell how much better they will be.*

Some of the new tools available are in the hardware category—balloons, rockets, and satellites for gathering the essential high-altitude data on a global scale, and radar to probe storm structures, for example. The most impressive advances, however, are on the theoretical side—especially in the creation of simplified mathematical models which can replace the overly complex real atmosphere for forecasting purposes. These permit the forecasting problem to be cast into either of two sets of solvable equations. One approach, called the hydrodynamical method, is based on deterministic causal laws. The other approach takes a statistical path to the answer. In just a few years they have significantly bettered twenty years of human skill in forecasting basic weather patterns.—S.T.

■ Fundamentally the problem of predicting the weather reduces to this: Given the initial state of the atmosphere, as defined by the three-dimensional distribution over the entire globe of the so-called weather elements—winds, pressures, temperatures, humidities, clouds, precipitation, and so on—what will be the state of the atmosphere, in terms of these same elements, at any selected subsequent time.

In principle, the problem can be solved if four conditions can be met: (1) we get sufficient data over a large enough portion of the globe to be able to specify the initial state of the atmosphere in precise detail; (2) we thoroughly understand the physical processes by which the initial state is changed into the subsequent state; (3) we can cast these processes into quantitative form as a function of the passage of time and variation in space; (4) we can treat these quantitative expressions numerically to get the answer—what the weather will be at the selected time and place.

In practice, of course, none of these conditions can be fully met. But rapid progress is being made on the first two conditions with the aid of satellites, radar, and other modern technologies. These are rich areas of new development—a bit more about them later. Even more heartening and exciting, however, is the recent development and expanding use of mathematical models which substitute for the real atmosphere. Such models not only satisfy requirements (3) and (4) above; even more remarkably they also yield forecasts which have, in a short few years, matched or slightly bettered twenty years of human skill in forecasting the dominant weather trends! And this even though requirements (1) and (2) are far from being met.

Aided by the computer revolution, and by advances in several areas of mathematics and mathematical statistics, we are at last on the path to truly scientific weather prediction. Before we look to "tomorrow's weather," let's briefly view the most formidable obstacle in our path—the complexity of the atmosphere.

A witch's brew beyond compare

The atmosphere can be characterized by three deceptively simple statements: (1) it is thermally active; (2) it is thermodynamically open; (3) it is a hydrodynamic system. What do these mean?

Thermal activity results from the variable distribution of sources and sinks of energy throughout the atmosphere. The principal energy factors are incoming short-wave solar radiation, outgoing long-wave radiation, the latent heat involved in phase changes of water, and the flow of heat at the boundary between the lower atmosphere and the oceans or the land.

Saying that the atmosphere is thermodynamically open means that weather systems such as clouds, thunderstorms, and low-pressure areas are dynamic entities which are made up of constantly changing sets of individual air parcels. Matter, as well as energy, is constantly being exchanged between these systems and the environment external to the system.

When we term the atmosphere a hydrodynamic system we simply mean that it has the character of a fluid in motion. The fluid, of course, consists of a mixture of gases. As such

* Thomas F. Malone directs weather research for the Travelers Insurance Co., Hartford, Connecticut.

it is inhomogeneous, compressible, and viscous. Because it is influenced by the earth's rotation and by thermal activity and thermodynamic exchange, the atmosphere is in constant motion.

These motions, the winds which serve to diffuse, dissipate, and transfer energy throughout the atmosphere, are at once the heart of the forecasting problem, and the key to solving it.

A semblance of order from seeming chaos

As shown in a much simplified way in Fig. 5-30, wind patterns in the atmosphere vary greatly in scale. The largest pattern is the so-called planetary wave system. This circulatory system has wavelengths upwards of 1000 miles. It circles the poles at midlatitudes in an undulating current that is characteristically represented by the wind flow pattern at an altitude of about 20,000 feet. And it dominates, but does not absolutely control in detail, the distribution of the other motions which range on

down in size through the migratory cyclones (low-pressure areas) and anticyclones (high-pressure areas) of the conventional weather map, through still smaller-scale hurricanes, tornadoes, and other local wind systems.

These circulation patterns enable us to set out upon the complex path to our goal. Actually two converging paths are being followed in the search for quantitative and objective weather predictions: the *hydrodynamical* approach and the *statistical* approach.

The hydrodynamical approach has been directed toward the solution, by appropriate numerical methods, of the general boundary and initial value problem of the nonlinear partial differential equations of hydrodynamics and the associated equations of state, continuity, and thermodynamics.

The value of hydrodynamical approaches to forecasting the weather stems from their success in predicting the behavior of the planetary

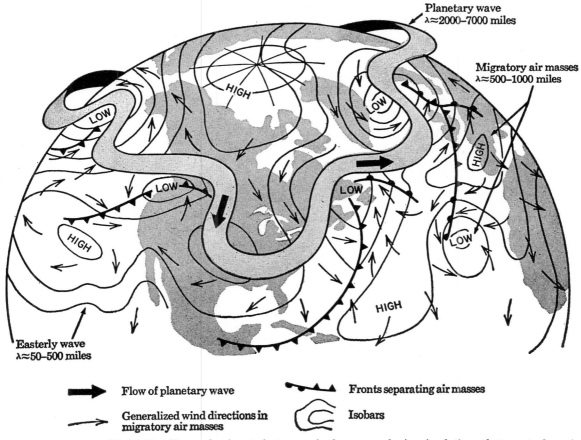

Fronts separating air masses

Isobars

Flow of planetary wave

Generalized wind directions in migratory air masses

Fig. 5-30. Three dominant features of the atmospheric circulation that control major weather patterns are, in order of decreasing size: (1) Planetary waves at mid-latitudes, averaging 20,000 feet in altitude, and strongly influencing the motion and timing of (2) Migratory air masses—the traveling cyclones, or lows, and anticyclones (highs) of the temperate latitudes which are shown on conventional weather maps; (3) Easterly waves that start as ripples on the migratory highs in subtropical latitudes. When fully developed as a circulation pattern, easterly waves can become tropical storms such as hurricanes.

wave systems. As mentioned above, these largest wind systems determine the distribution in time and space of the smaller-scale systems—especially that of the migratory high- and low-pressure air masses with their associated frontal weather. Attempts to extend the hydrodynamic method to the smaller-scale systems, however, and to the significant details of weather in the lower atmosphere have not as yet been particularly successful. Thus, after predictions of planetary wind flows high in the atmosphere have been made by hydrodynamical methods, it is necessary to infer the accompanying types of weather at the ground level in different areas by either synoptic means, statistical means, or both.

The statistical approach attempts to establish a functional relationship between a set of parameters characterizing the initial state of the atmosphere—in terms of any combination of the weather elements—and the probability distribution for the values of the same or other weather elements in some subsequent state. The immediate goal of this work is to determine relationships which will be valid for a weather situation which has not yet occurred and which will minimize the uncertainty in the probability distributions.

The advances in both the hydrodynamical and statistical methods have been made possible by the development of large-scale computers and concurrent work in mathematical physics and mathematical statistics.

Relatively greater attention has been devoted to hydrodynamical prediction than to statistical prediction recently, for two reasons: (1) at first glance it is intellectually more satisfying based as it is on deterministic, Newtonian, causal laws; (2) it is only within the past year or so that the basis for a unified statistical methodology has begun to emerge.

Hydrodynamical prediction

The roots of the hydrodynamic approach lie in von Helmholtz' work in basic hydrodynamics. Formulation of the problem we owe to V. Bjerknes' work right after the turn of the century. What Bjerknes said, in effect, was that the principles of the conservation of momentum, mass, and energy, together with the Boyle-Charles equation of state, comprise a mathematical, objective basis for meteorological prediction.

Conservation of momentum can be expressed in the form of the Newtonian equations of motion. These relate the acceleration of a small cube of air to the resultant of the four forces that act on the mass: (1) the force caused by differences in air pressure on opposite faces of the cube; (2) Coriolis force arising from the

earth's rotation; (3) gravitational force; (4) viscous forces.

The result of action of these forces on the mass can be expressed by three nonlinear partial differential equations. In a rectangular coordinate system, a typical equation is

$$\frac{\partial u}{\partial t} + u\frac{\partial u}{\partial x} + v\frac{\partial u}{\partial u} + w\frac{\partial u}{\partial z} =$$
$$(2\omega \sin \phi)v - \frac{1}{\rho}\frac{\partial P}{\partial x} + F_x$$

where u, v, and w are the components of velocity of the air along the x, y, and z axes, respectively; t is time; ρ is density; P is pressure; F_x is a component of the viscous force; and ϕ and ω are the latitude and the earth's angular velocity, respectively.

Conservation of mass can be expressed by the so-called equation of continuity

$$\frac{\partial \rho}{\partial t} + \frac{\partial(\rho u)}{\partial x} + \frac{\partial(\rho v)}{\partial y} + \frac{\partial(\rho w)}{\partial z} = 0$$

This simply states that any local increase or decrease in the density of the air must be exactly compensated for by a net import or export of mass in that region.

Conservation of energy is expressed by the first law of thermodynamics,

$$dQ = c_v \, dT + Pd\left(\frac{1}{\rho}\right)$$

where T is temperature, Q is heat energy, c_v is the specific heat for air at constant volume, and ρ is the air density, as before. This requires that any heat energy added to a parcel of air be used to raise its internal energy, work against external pressure, or both.

The last necessary equation, the Boyle-Charles equation of state, relates the pressure of air to its temperature and density, through the gas constant R for air: $P = \rho RT$.

This set of six straightforward differential equations contains exactly six unknowns—u, v, w, P, T, and ρ. Such a set is, therefore, solvable in principle, but no analytical methods are known to exist. However, the form of the equations makes it possible to express the instantaneous local time derivatives of each variable in terms of the space derivatives of the same set of variables. That means we can use finite-difference techniques, in successive iterative steps, to arrive at the values of the unknowns over any desired interval of time.

Thus, in principle, the state of the atmosphere at all times in the future is determinable by its state at a single instant. But until recently three major difficulties blocked attacking the prediction problem in this relatively straightforward fashion. First, we did not have sufficient observational data, especially for the upper air, to establish the initial conditions. This is being overcome by the flood of such observations now coming from greatly expanded upper-air sounding methods of several kinds— balloon flights and sounding rocket shots particularly. The second difficulty, which was the vast amount of computation necessary, has to some degree been ameliorated by advances in computer capability.

The third source of trouble was in a way the most serious. The general hydrodynamic equations described above contain not only the wave motions that are critical to deducing the weather-producing mechanisms, but also gravity (tidal-type motions) and sound waves; these constitute a sort of meteorological "noise" and they obscure the desired weather-making motion patterns. This paradoxical difficulty with the otherwise reasonably tractable hydrodynamic method has been the main theoretical problem in numerical weather prediction over the past ten years. It proved difficult to find a model which, while preserving the most essential aspects of the atmosphere's meteorological behavior, would at the same time not exhibit the other types of motion which are irrelevant to the forecasting problem.

Surprisingly enough, it is a relatively simple model—the so-called barotropic model—that is now the basis for most of the routine daily application of hydrodynamic prediction.

The barotropic model of the atmosphere

The barotropic model assumes that the atmosphere can be represented as a fluid in which the surfaces of constant pressure and constant density coincide. (This would be an idealized atmosphere in which the wind is invariant with height.) Basic to this assumption is the implication that the potential energy stored in the atmosphere in the form of temperature gradients cannot be converted into kinetic energy, i.e., no new storms can develop and existing storms will not die out. Nor does it provide for the existence of energy sources or sinks. Despite these seemingly hobbling restrictions the barotropic model is capable of producing predictions of the large-scale features of the planetary wave system that are remarkably good. The reason for this apparent anomaly is that these systems tend to conserve—or hold constant—a quantity called absolute vorticity and the assumptions involved in the barotropic model automatically require that this kind of vorticity be conserved.

The term "vorticity" brings to mind visions of whirlpools, but it is simply a measure of the

angular velocity of the infinitesimally small elements into which a fluid can be conceived to be divided. The term "absolute," when used to specify the kind of vorticity being dealt with, simply means that to the vorticity of the air *relative* to the earth has been added the vorticity of the earth. In practice, the relative vorticity can be determined directly from the field of wind velocity in the atmosphere, and the vorticity of the earth is determined by the angular velocity of the earth and the latitude. It may be most simply visualized by thinking of a mass of air overlying the North Pole. If the air is at rest with respect to the earth, its vorticity relative to the earth would be zero— and its absolute vorticity would be the vorticity of the earth which turns out to be twice the angular velocity of the earth. If the air mass were also rotating relative to the earth about the pole, as a solid body, in the same sense as the rotation of the earth and with the angular velocity of the earth, the absolute vorticity would be four times the angular velocity of the earth. Similarly, if the air mass were rotating *relative* to the earth in a direction opposite to the sense of rotation of the earth, but with the same angular speed, its absolute vorticity would be zero.

In purely physical terms, only the vertical component of the vorticity is considered in the barotropic model. The problem then becomes one of determining how the air flow pattern in the free atmosphere changes from its initial distribution when the vertical component of the vorticity is transported by the wind in a manner that conserves its value. In effect, what is done is to compute the value of the vorticity

$$\eta = \frac{\partial v}{\partial x} - \frac{\partial u}{\partial y}$$

from the pressure pattern (or its near equivalent, the height contours of a constant pressure surface) by finite-difference methods. The pattern of vorticity is displaced a short distance in accordance with the wind field and the new wind field which results from the constraint of constant absolute vorticity is calculated. This sequence of steps is repeated over successive small increments of time until the flow pattern a day or two later, or more, is obtained. The entire process can be programmed for a computer and an automatic map plotter.

The single most important product of the twice-daily computations on this model is a remarkably good representation of the planetary wave system in the middle troposphere (about 20,000 feet above sea level). These predictions for 24 hours in advance are prepared by the National Meteorological Center operated by the

U.S. Weather Bureau in Suitland, Md. From the general nature of the predicted circulation patterns on a hemisphere basis, "prognostic" weather maps showing the future position of storms and areas of fair weather are prepared by more or less subjective methods. These maps, in turn, constitute the basis for the prediction of the details of tomorrow's weather.

Potentially more effective models for atmospheric behavior are under theoretical development. Space limits us to only mentioning these so-called baroclinic models.

The need for statistical prediction

In view of the complexity of weather-producing mechanisms it is valid to question whether a deterministic Newtonian approach will ever be capable of coping with such complexity and variability. As Norbert Weiner remarks, in *Cybernetics*, "if all the readings of all the meteorological stations on earth were simultaneously taken, they would not give a billionth part of the data necessary to characterize the actual state of the atmosphere from a Newtonian point of view. . . . Using the Newtonian laws, or any other system of causal laws whatever, all that we can predict at any future time is a probability distribution of the constants of the system . . ."

There are several reasons why the statistical approach merits attention. The first is that complicated as is the system of non-linear differential equations that represents with any degree of completeness the physical processes that produce one day's weather from that of the preceding day, the atmosphere itself has performed the required integrations with great exactitude day after day for many years. The results of these repeated integrations are available in the climatological records of past years. A systematic examination of these solutions should shed some light on their integral form and place some limits on the information content required of data needed to specify an initial state in order to determine a subsequent state.

Moreover, meteorological prediction has objectives other than the purely scientific one of testing the adequacy of our quantitative understanding of the physical processes occurring in the atmosphere. The practical objective is to provide predictions that are useful in decisions related to human activities that are influenced by the weather. Since a completely deterministic solution to the prediction problem within the foreseeable future is unlikely, improvements in the application of weather predictions must be linked to the rapidly developing field of statistical risk. For this, predictions of probability distributions are required. The utility of such

forecasts depends on reducing the degree of uncertainty in the predicted probability distributions, and on the effectiveness with which these distributions can be related to other factors in an operational decision.

Advances during recent years in multivariate analysis, non-parametric methods, matrix techniques, decision theory, and the applications of probability theory, coupled with an almost explosive increase in the speed and capacity of electronic computers, have opened attractive avenues for combining mathematical statistics and meteorological predictions.

Nature of statistical weather forecasts

The customary approach to statistical prediction has been to develop linear equations of the form

$$y = a + bx_1 + cx_2 + dx_3$$

in which y is the single weather element (pressure, temperature, storm displacement, or other) to be predicted for some future time; x_1, x_2, and x_3 are weather elements known at the time the prediction is being prepared (not necessarily the same as element y—they may be present or past observations of any of the weather elements); and a, b, c, and d are coefficients determined by the application of the method of least squares to past weather data.

One of the best available methods for predicting the movement of a hurricane during the next twenty-four hours, for example, is an equation of precisely this kind. In this application y is the expected position of the hurricane tomorrow. The known quantities (x_1, x_2, etc.) are former positions of the hurricane and present and past barometric pressures at selected points over a large area surrounding the hurricane. The constants (a, b, etc.) and the particular known weather elements to be used as predictors are determined by processing vast amounts of data from past hurricanes to determine which combination empirically produces the best results. Since no combination will produce perfect predictions, of course, we also must know what the probability of an error of any given size might be for an actual prediction. This too can be determined as part of the procedure for developing the linear equation, and it is of considerable use in estimating the degree of danger which may exist when a hurricane threatens a particular location.

Yet another statistical technique known as multiple discriminant analysis recently has been developed to a highly promising stage by R. G. Miller and J. G. Bryan. The basic principle involved in its use in weather work can be illustrated by a simple example.

Suppose that one desires to predict whether

or not rain will occur or, more formally, to be able to discriminate between rain and no rain at some future time—say tomorrow. Two questions must be asked in examining past data: (1) what weather observations of pressure, temperature, cloudiness, rain, etc., on any given day will contain the most information on the likelihood of rain on a subsequent day; (2) how should these observations be combined to be most effective in discriminating between rain and no rain? Hopefully, one might identify a single weather element whose observed values day after day would tell whether or not there would be rain tomorrow.

To be a little unrealistic for purposes of illustration, suppose indeed that examination of past records indicated that the temperature today discriminated well between rain and no rain for tomorrow. Suppose, further, that rain *usually* occurred after a day on which the temperature ranged in value between 40° and 45°F, that it *usually* did not occur after days in which the temperature ranged from 70° to 75°F, and that there was a tendency for rain and no-rain cases to intermingle more and more as the temperature moved away from these ranges. Then the effectiveness of temperature as a discriminator for predicting the rain element tomorrow depends on two factors: (1) how far apart are the particular temperature ranges about which the rain and no-rain alternatives respectively tend to cluster; (2) how much do these alternative rain cases tend to disperse within their respective temperature ranges.

It is the ratio of the separation of these temperature ranges to the clustering of rain or no rain, as appropriate, within these ranges that is the statistical measure of the effectiveness of temperature as a discriminator. And it is also this ratio that determines which of the available observations of past temperature and rain conditions are to be selected for forecast purposes.

Expressed another way, the test for selecting any particular weather element as a discriminator for predicting the behavior of any other weather element is the degree to which such selection maximizes the ratio: Dispersion among classes/Dispersion within class. In the temperature-rain example given, the dispersion *among* classes refers to the spread between the hypothetical upper (70°–75°) and lower (40°–45°) temperature ranges. And the degree to which no-rain and rain, respectively, clusters within these temperature classes fixes the denominator.

Before leaving this simplified example, note that once the best discriminator has been determined from past weather records, it can then be used on current weather observations to make day-by-day predictions. Moreover, by changing the term "usually," used rather loosely in the above example, to a numerical frequency of occurrence of rain or no-rain, the numerical probability of rain for tomorrow becomes an integral part of the forecast.

In real life, no single weather observation is an adequate discriminator. However, it is possible to combine comparatively good discriminators linearly into discriminant functions, each of which defines a dimension in so-called discriminant space. This improves the discrimination as the process can be carried to several dimensions in discriminant space.

The end result is a set of discriminant functions which arrange in discriminant space the variable to be predicted, so that the probability of occurence of mutually exclusive groups of weather conditions can be readily determined.

New observational tools adding data

One of the most exciting new tools for observation and data-gathering is the meteorological satellite. The already operational *Tiros* series has been spectacularly successful in clarifying our picture of the cloud distribution associated with many different types of weather phenomena. Radiometers aboard the Tiros satellites—sensitive to bands in the visible portion of the spectrum, in the so-called "water-vapor" window (8 to 12 microns), and in the infrared (7 to 30 microns)—promise to provide long-desired data on the nature and amount of energy exchanged between the sun and the earth-ocean-atmosphere system. The gratifying success of the satellites has generated some first-order problems in data handling and interpretation that are as difficult as they are pleasant to contemplate.

Unlike the satellites which look at cloud patterns and radiation balances on a global scale, the use of radar in meteorology aims to diagnose conditions in detail, within about a 200-mile circle. The radar used lies in the 3 to 10 cm wavelength range and its use depends upon the reflective power of water droplets and ice.

It is particularly useful for detailing the four-dimensional picture of the morphology and growth of small scale weather systems—tornadoes, thunderstorms, and so on. Figure 5-31 shows a characteristic tornado pattern on a standard cps-9 radar.

Work in cloud physics is moving ahead rapidly at many laboratories around the world, particularly under Bowen's group in Australia. The problems here revolve chiefly about the related questions of the nucleation and the growth of water droplets and solid particles in clouds. Knowledge of these is the essential prerequisite to major advances in the embryonic

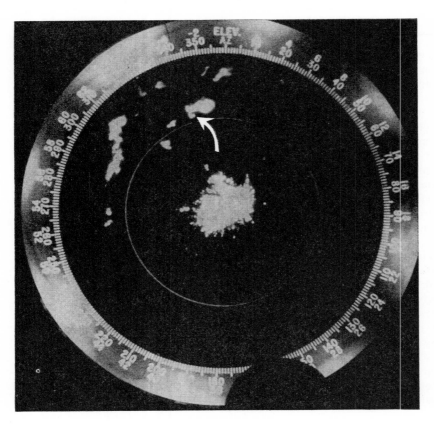

Fig. 5-31. Photograph of the plan-position indicator (PPI) of a CPS-9 radar shows an echo from a severe tornado 50 miles north-northwest of radar location. Arrow points to characteristic "hook" or "figure 6" shown by many tornadoes. Other echoes in the northwest are weaker showers and thunderstorms. Echoes in the center are due to terrain reflections.

steps we have taken in inducing rain artificially.

In another striking development, the mathematical models we have been discussing have found their physical analog in the remarkable development of so-called hydrodynamic models of the atmosphere. These are fluid systems which are subjected to appropriate thermal inputs. They are strikingly effective in reproducing the salient features of the global circulation pattern. In essence these are physical models for the atmosphere, and they offer rich opportunities in simulation and understanding of major circulatory processes in the real atmosphere.

The probability of weather control

A few words are in order on the question of weather control and climate modification: By weather control we mean conscious interference with predictable and ascertainable consequences in the normal life cycle of a specific weather system such as a cloud, a hurricane, or a tornado. By climate modification we mean positive intervention in the physical processes that influence a series of weather phenomena so that, although the consequences for any individual phenomenon may not be completely predictable and may even vary widely, the cumulative effect will be to modify the statistical collective of individual weather conditions that we have come to refer to as the climate.

Interest in the possibilities of weather control was stimulated by the experiment of V. J. Schaefer in 1946 that a supercooled cloud could be transformed into snow crystals. This demonstration set in motion a series of field experiments and basic research studies all over the world that have done much to elucidate the physical processes which produce rain and have provided strong evidence that under certain favorable conditions rainfall can be augmented artificially. A final assessment of the practical significance of the exciting possibilities that this work has opened up must await the completion of research investigation still under way. Meanwhile, studies and field experimentation are under way to explore the possibility of affecting the dynamics of hurricanes by seeding several cubic miles of supercooled clouds embedded in a hurricane with silver iodide and transforming them into ice-crystal clouds. While the heat of fusion thereby released is small by comparison with the kinetic energy of the hurricane, the thought is to seek strategically important areas of the hurricane in an attempt to set off a triggering mechanism that would in turn exert control on the mechanisms that influence the course and the growth of these systems. Some success has also been achieved in altering the electrical properties of clouds by modifying the space charge in the lower part of the atmosphere. The possibility of triggering the release of energy stored in the upper atmosphere in the form of atomic oxygen and free radicals by the use of suitable catalysts has been recognized. The most significant aspect of this work in weather control is *not* the results that have been achieved thus far but rather these three things: (1) the problem is being seriously considered, (2) there are sound scientific avenues along which to proceed, and (3) there is a rapidly developing technology of instrumentation and techniques for conducting field experimentation.

In the realm of modification of climate, there has been much speculation on the possible consequences of such projects as filling in or deepening the Straits of Gibraltar, damming the Bering Strait and pumping water from the Arctic region, or opening up passes in the Sierra Nevada to permit intrusion of moist air into the Nevada desert. Other proposals have been to spread carbon black over snow cover or create an ice-crystal fog over the Arctic to interfere with radiation balance and thereby influence the dynamics of air motion in high latitudes.

These speculations would remain nothing more than that, were it not for the development within the past decade of theoretical tools (such as electronic computers and hydrodynamic models) with which one can analyze the physical consequences of artificial perturbations and design meaningful experiments to be conducted in nature. The mastery of man's physical environment may one day take its place with the exploration of matter and the conquest of space as a new frontier of science.

I'm convinced that basic research studies carried on within a framework of international cooperation will be required to cope with the magnitude and difficulty of the problem and to mitigate the unforeseen difficulties that conceivably might arise should the effort be successful.

Further reading

By far the best concise survey of meteorology as an analytic and deductive science with fascinating challenges for the nonspecialist is Sutton's *The Challenge of the Atmosphere* (Harper, 1961, $5.95). Also designed especially for the potential outside contributor to weather science is Thompson's remarkably lucid account of hydrodynamic prediction, *Numerical Analysis and Prediction* (Macmillan, 1961, $6.50). The linkage between numerical prediction and computers is explored in detail by Phillips in the chapter "Numerical Weather Prediction," in Vol. 1 of *Advances in Computers,* ed. by Alt (Academic Press, 1960, $10).

The most up-to-the-minute account of statistical methods is *Statistical Prediction by Discriminant Analysis* by Miller. This is one of the American Meteorological Society's Meteorological Monographs, Vol. 4, No. 25. An older but thorough treatment of the applications of statistics to meteorology is the *Handbook of Statistical Methods in Meteorology* by Brooks and Carruthers (Her Majesty's Stationery Office, London, 1953, $3.50). Much additional material is scattered through *Bull. Am. Meteorol. Soc.*, the *J. Atmos. Sciences*, the *J. Appl. Meteorol.*, and the *J. Geophys. Research.*

RESOURCES FROM THE SEA

by John D. Isaacs and Walter R. Schmitt *

IN BRIEF: *We have, in the oceans, a huge physical-chemical-biological vat, with a volume of some 1.4×10^{18} cubic meters, mostly water, and some dissolved solids, 5×10^{16} metric tons of them. Each year, about 2.5×10^9 tons of solids are added, but a similar amount settles out on the bottom.*

Floating about in this solution is a bountiful chowder of plant and animal life, which could conceivably be made to provide for the protein needs of 30 billion people. The whole potpourri is in complex swirling and circulating motion, stirred up mostly by the power of sunlight, about 2.5×10^{11} megawatts of that.

The sea serves as a highway, a playground, a military shield—and as a cesspool. Moreover, there's an abundance of food, of energy, and of mineral wealth. Ascertaining how to get it out, and even what is there in detail, is the great challenge to an expanding world population.— R.G.N.

* John D. Isaacs is Director of the Marine Life Resources Department at the University of California's Scripps Institution of Oceanography, La Jolla, California. Walter R. Schmitt is a geophysicist at Scripps, studying resources of the oceans.

■ When the first drops of water condensed from the primitive atmosphere, they dissolved some soluble minerals, collected a few particles of insoluble ones, trickled down slopes, and set in motion a series of events that was to give rise to some of the most astonishing entities on earth, the oceans. Our purpose in this article is to discuss the significance of the oceans to another astonishing development, mankind, and to consider the meaning of the sea to man's burgeoning hordes.

In recent years, particularly since World War II, interest in the sea has been mounting for several reasons. We look upon the oceans

Fig. 5-32. About 2 months after becoming part of an artificial reef, this Chrysler was photographed. The photo on the right shows that 14 months after it hit the water, the encrustations and the intricate geometry had attracted a considerable marine community. This convertible model was originally used only by a little old lady-fish school teacher—in Santa Monica Bay. (Courtesy C. H. Turner, California Dept. Fish and Game)

as a great reservoir, harboring in abundance many things that mankind needs. For thousands of years man has taken food from the sea, collected a few minerals from its scenic shores, traveled it in search of adventures and new lands, and dumped his miscellaneous and many wastes into it.

Until very recently, this intercourse with the sea was a bonus to man, for the bulk of his needs, with the exception of intercontinental communication, was satisfied from the land. However, the unprecedented increase in his numbers threatens to shrink man's land base to a point where he is scouting for alternate resources. And which realm offers greater possibilities than the marine? The sea area is nearly two and one-half times the land area, and the average ocean depth is four thousand meters, while the average mining depth on land is perhaps a few hundred meters. Thus the sea offers ten to a hundred times more volume with much greater ease of penetration than does the land.

In addition to its use as a source of food, power and minerals, several other aspects of the sea are important—waste disposal, transportation, military use, recreation, aesthetics and scientific challenge.

Elsewhere, one of us discussed the ocean's capacity to receive mankind's wastes: "The oceans are huge enough to absorb, untroubled, all the trash, waste heat, and sewage the human race is ever likely to produce. Properly handled, many of these wastes can improve the food production of the ocean." But even oceans are not big enough to absorb civilization's atomic wastes indefinitely, unless they be locked in holes drilled into the bed of the ocean at great depths. Still the ocean does have a real and meaningful capacity to absorb atomic wastes, wholly adequate for the developmental period.

Our natural highway

The sea has been a bearer of people and armed fleets throughout human history. Yet only in about the last one hundred years has the sea begun to carry a considerable share of the goods produced in many countries. Shipping has thus become an important part of the economy of many countries, and is expanding still. Vessels larger than those now afloat are on the drawing boards, which incorporate new design ideas that may effectively bypass the size restrictions imposed by draft limitations. (See "High-Speed Ships," page 451.) Vessels, which for instance could transport fresh water from river deltas to the shores of arid regions, will require deep draft harbors.

Atomic explosives for the construction of these harbors have been suggested and, indeed, are probably necessary. Explosively generated natural harbors (Pago Pago is an example) are free from many of the ills that afflict the common estuarine ports; floods, debris, ice, and sedimentation are largely avoided. The broad deep blue man-made explosive harbors of Bikini and Eniwetok, now cowering in the Pacific under the censorious eyes of the world, are, in reality, the harbingers of a new freedom to the world's primitive rock-bound coasts.

Still larger carriers are potentially practical. New thin, strong, plastic membranes may permit the towing of immense quantities of light liquids, such as water. We are attracted by the idea of using icebergs, the formidable menaces of the high seas, in the service of man. In the Arctic Sea, ice platforms have been occupied for many years by scientific parties (of several countries) observing changing oceanographic and meteorological conditions, as these floating islands circle lazily about the North Pole. Moreover some icebergs represent gigantic stores of fresh water—some secondary bergs breaking off the Antarctic coast are of the order of 5 miles long, ½ mile wide and ¼ mile deep (one is equivalent to the annual water needs of Southern California), and are worth 60 to 200 million dollars at wholesale water prices. These bergs could be steered to the nearby arid shores by taking advantage of the oceans' currents and wave energy. As a matter of fact, these icebergs occasionally have made the journey unaided from the Antarctic to Peru.

Edibles for contemplation

"Sea food" is a catchall term for a great diversity of marine organisms, rare delicacies to some and staple foods to others. It is quite astonishing, really, that, of the multitude of life forms in the oceans, man uses so few. About a dozen kinds of fish comprise 75% of the catch taken from the world's seas. Thus, while a few species are overfished, most, among the approximately 20,000 known species of fish, are underfished or are not utilized at all.

Since World War II, sea food landings in the world have doubled; they now stand near 40 million tons annually. Some national diets are critically dependent on those landings. A statistical 81% of the Portuguese obtain all their animal protein from fish; the Japanese would need 186% more arable land to replace their fish protein; the Burmese would need 3570% more meat to replace their fish protein; the Indonesians would need 10,400% more milk to replace their fish protein.

Of course, agricultural productivity could be increased by tilling more arable land, but it would be practically impossible for many countries to replace much fish protein. And the trend is toward greater dependence. Naturally, man wants to know—particularly in the face of declining fish catches in some areas—whether the sea can sustain sufficient catch every year to make up the deficit between requirements and agricultural production for any reasonable number of people.

This raises a point of controversy: How many people shall ultimately inhabit the earth? Most predictions of ultimate numbers have already been surpassed or will be surpassed in the next generation. At the present rate of growth, world population will double in about 40 years. Some people have calculated the time

when the periphery of the expanding mass of human bodies will advance into space at the speed of light. But facetiousness aside, the earth is finite and can harbor only a finite population, human, animal, or plant. We have made our own prognosis from several pertinent factors; it appears that 30 billion people, give or take a factor of two, could lead fairly free and enriched lives on this earth.

It often has been argued that the oceans can contribute only a small part of mankind's eventual food needs. These calculations are all based on the appearance that, at the second trophic level (the first carnivores in the marine food chain), the oceans can produce only about $\frac{1}{10}$ of the human food-*energy* requirement. Clearly, no one would ever expect to supply the calorific requirements of the human race from the sea. It is a poor source of carbohydrates. More particularly, there is no foreseeable shortage of the calorific foods raised on land. This world is, and for some time will continue to be, a protein hungry planet, and particularly hungry for animal protein. It is here that the sea will provide, for the protein productivity of the sea at the second trophic level

Fig. 5-33. Japan's mountainous terrain encourages a fishing fleet of nearly 400,000 vessels. Whaling is important, too. A century after Moby Dick, the annual Japanese catch was over 18,000 whales. (Courtesy Consulate General of Japan)

is at the very least twice (and more probably 200 times) the animal protein requirements of 30 billion people.

This indicates that we have no need to harvest the phytoplankton, the primary producer of the seas' organic matter, as we do the plants on land. Herbivorous and carnivorous animals represent several trophic levels of a marine pyramid of biomass, in which each level constitutes only about 10% of the biomass of the level on which it feeds.

Not only will it be unnecessary to harvest phytoplankton, but it also appears to be a physical impossibility to do this at a significant level. If we filtered an amount of sea water equivalent to all man's present irrigation water (about 700 billion gallons per day) for plankton from the euphotic layer, each year's filtration would yield about 10% of man's present need for animal protein. Fish accomplish this harvest better. The economy of fisheries is crucial; it's the primary limiting factor in our efforts to utilize the sea more fully.

The net protein productivity of the sea is approximately 2×10^{16} g/year. This, of course, is not evenly distributed throughout the oceans but is concentrated in several fairly stationary regions as a result of their relative nutrient abundance. Several mechanisms keep the nutrient level high, for example, upwelling or river discharge. If it were not for these productivity nodes, fisheries would likely be nonexistent or at best deliver only very expensive fish. And just as on land, where man found it advantageous to cultivate (and improve) the naturally occurring grasses under favorable conditions, so, in time, will the cultivation of select oceanic areas make equally good economic sense. But agricultural practices cannot be readily transposed to the marine environment.

In this, we are not entirely dependent on our imagination. Efforts to cultivate aquatic organisms, especially in closed bodies of water, date back several hundreds of years. Rice fields lend themselves well to stocking with fingerlings, yielding over 150 lb of fish per acre yearly. Yields of up to 4000 lb/acre annually have been reported from some Southeast Asian countries where fish culture is seriously pursued. The mussel culture in the Bay of Taranto, Italy, has averaged a phenomenal 108,000 lb/acre yearly. This is an example of a rather widespread effect we call "dimensional emancipation"; the mechanisms are: (1) food is advected from outside, brought into the cultured area by currents and tides, and (2) the substratum that is provided permits the growth of large forms of filter-feeding animals that can consume microscopic plankton and detritus. This by-passes several inefficient steps through successively larger members of the food chain.

The dimensional emancipation we just mentioned is being used near Los Angeles in California's "Environmental Improvement Program." Old streetcars and automobiles are dropped into shallow water and quickly become populated by numerous fish. On a more grandiose scale, food-advection could be intensified in the many hundreds of atolls in the tropical oceans. Roughly 30,000,000 acres of lagoons, with reefal hide-outs, form ideal cultivation basins into which nutrient-rich water could be inexpensively circulated from deeper levels.

We said earlier that many species of fish are underexploited or unexploited. Several things combine to discourage their exploitation. One is taste. (People the world 'round are rather loath to change their dietary habits.) Another is distance from markets. Less than 10% of the world's fish catch is currently taken in the Southern Hemisphere, although here are larger areas of high fertility than those in the North Atlantic and North Pacific. A third reason is that some species do not congregate in schools, thus making their harvest laborious and uneconomical. Fourthly, government controls and international agreements concerning the fisheries interfere with the economics of their operation, and impose primitive methods on many fishermen. This is clearly exemplified in many U.S. fisheries.

One solution can be visualized for several of these problems. Floating protein-processing plants, assisted by several harvesting units, and operating much like the whaling fleets, would reduce waste, weight, and spoilage of the catch and utilize multi-species catches, even those of inedible sea organisms. Also, the technological revolution is increasingly giving the fisheries new mechanical and electronic devices, thus— where not in conflict with the laws—greatly enhancing the efficiency of their operation. It is clear, moreover, that multi-species harvesting will eventually become necessary for biological reasons. Continued harvesting of select species encourages the unwanted types. Harvesting of an entire trophic level probably is the only method that can achieve a steady state with respect to the desirable fish.

These immense operations will only be fore-runners to even more revolutionary equipment. Prototypes of manned underwater vehicles, robot manipulators, and other equipment necessary for subaqueous farming are already being tested. The third dimension of the sea is finally accessible to man. But the development of this new industry will depend upon economic factors. Probably some form of property right will have to be granted to the aqua-farmer. The shelf areas of the continents, gradually sloping to a depth of 200 m, will naturally be the initial "farmland" because of greater safety, abundant benthic life, etc. These areas, including shallow seas, comprise 7.6% of the seas and generally have fertile waters, because in shelf locations there is an effective recirculation of the slowly sinking nutrients back into the euphotic layer (that is, into the top 100 m layer, which is the only place where organic matter is produced). It appears that any attempt at fertilizing the sea must be patterned after these natural recirculation processes, for a simple calculation shows the cost of fertilizing with commercial phosphate and nitrogen fertilizers (even excluding the cost of transport and broadcasting) is ten to twenty times higher than the likely return from the increased harvest.

A number of oceanographic features could conceivably be harnessed to recirculate the nutrients. Nutrient-laden deep waters could be made to rise by heating with radioactive wastes or nuclear reactors, or by introducing fresh waste water (including sewage), or by deflecting horizontal currents, or by using that oceanographic curiosity, the salt pump. As shown in Fig. 5-34, this device exploits the temperature and salinity stratification of sea water, and is self-sustaining. These are some of the possibilities.

If we can thus increase the catch of desirable sea food to 150 lb/acre annually (the present maximum is 350 lb/acre yearly in the water off Peru, while the open Pacific averages about 0.5 lb/acre yearly), one third of the marine areas could provide all of the animal protein required by 30 billion people.

There are also suggestions that additional people accept seaweed into their diets, as, for instance, do the Japanese. Not only taste has prevented this. The digestion of seeweed apparently requires a special intestinal bacteria that the Japanese seem to have acquired over many decades. Perhaps suitable processing would make seaweed acceptable to more people than are now accustomed to it, but this is likely to be too costly. No complete tabulations of the present seaweed harvest are available, but we can estimate feasible seaweed production as 100 million tons dry-weight annually. Used indirectly, via the stomachs of cattle, this could raise current meat production 25%. Another use of the seaweed is as a fertilizer and soil conditioner. Both these uses have long been practiced on a small scale in many coastal locations.

In estuarine and tidal flats we find the habitat of another unexploited but potentially useful primary producer—the halophytic (salt

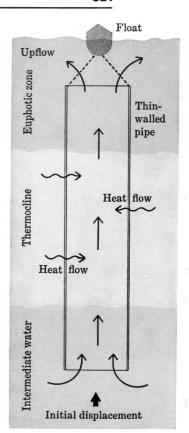

Fig. 5-34. *If a long open pipe with thermally-conductive walls is held vertically in the ocean, and the water in it is initially displaced some distance, the pump can then be removed and the water will continue to flow. This is because both salinity and temperature commonly decrease with greater depth. As deeper water is displaced upward within the pipe, that is, under heat exchange, it becomes lighter than the adjacent water outside the pipe by virtue of its lower salinity. Thus it will keep on rising by buoyant forces. The effect is reversible: water can alternatively be made to flow downward. The practical difficulty consists in finding a material both rigid enough for a large diameter pipe and conductive enough for the required heat transfer.*

tolerant) plants. Breeding greater usefulness into halophytes should enable us to raise crops in sea water, for every major group of higher plants has its halophytic members, and there is no doubt that salt tolerance is genetically controlled. Hence these plants incorporate the genetic information to solve one of humanity's most profound growing problems, the development of crops for soils too salty for existing crops.

Figure 5-33 illustrates a case in point; many peoples' nutrition is already inescapably linked to the sea. An expected ultimate human population of 30 billion will be able to supply its entire animal protein needs from selected regions of the sea, if the cultivation of these regions can develop unharassed, subject only to economic forces and our biological understanding.

Now, let us move on to the consideration of the sea's power potential.

Hot and cold running power

Two categories of energy have to be recognized in the sea, just as on land: Nonrenewable and renewable energy, which are called capital and income energy, respectively. The world's energy consumption has exhibited a trend away from renewable energy (75% of total consumption in 1860) toward nonrenewable energy (80%

of total consumption today). This trend bears significantly on the importance of the marine power resources for many thousands of years hence, since the sea harbors far more nonrenewable energy than the land, in the form of the potential fusion energy of its hydrogen and deuterium.

The power demand of the world in 2000 has been projected as 14 million megawatts. In Fig. 5-35, the ultimate fission and fusion of energy content of the oceans is shown in terms of multiples of that anticipated annual demand.

Thorium and uranium fission could, in principle, supply this 1.4×10^7 MW for some 700,000 years, whereas deuterium and hydrogen fusion can supply it for times that are greater than the age of the solar system. Although terrestrial sources of fissionable material are probably greater (and more economical) than the marine, the sea is clearly the predominant source of fusible deuterium and hydrogen.

Figure 5-35 also shows renewable power resources. Feasible tidal power can supply a tenth of one percent of the total need, but even

the entire tidal dissipation in all the oceans of the world represents only ten percent of the total need. Yet, if we apply the Carnot cycle to the thermal energy in the sea, i.e., if we could utilize the difference in temperature between the cold deep waters and the warm surface layers, the sea could provide 200 times the needed power, ignoring a slow change in equilibrium upon using this gradient. For perspective, Fig. 5-36 includes total hydropower, available wind power, total marine organic production, and the available solar energy. It is interesting to note that the principal input of renewable energy—solar energy—and the degraded forms of it—thermopower, wind power, marine organic, hydropower—decrease by orders of magnitude, as one would expect.

Power, naturally, also involves the construction of plants for its conversion. Figure 5-36 shows the numbers of several kinds of installations required to produce the world's power demand in the year 2000. You will note that it would require 140,000 Bay of Fundy installations, putting to work the highest tides in the world (we already saw that there's insufficient tidal power), and so forth.

If power could be reclaimed from the detonation of atomic bombs, it would require 2800 of the 100-megaton size per year. Even the highly imaginative Red Sea Project—which consists of damming up the Red Sea and waiting for it to lower some hundreds of feet from evaporation, then using the inflow as a perpetual hydroelectric power plant—would be required 350 times. It would require 175 Mediterraneans similarly treated. Please, though, observe the AEC's proposed 1.4×10^2 MW Desalination Fast-Breeder Reactor, which would be the world's largest reactor. Only 140 of these could supply this immense power bill.

Our conclusion to the power picture of the sea is that although important power plants may utilize the power of the sea, at best it can supply only a small part of the world's needs in the immediate future, unless new materials permit economical use of thermal gradients as power sources.

However, the situation with the mineral resources of the sea appears to be quite different.

Minerals in the marine mine

It is not quite clear where the dividing line between marine and terrestrial mineral resources should be drawn. To which do the submerged reservoirs of petroleum belong? Or should manganese and phosphorite nodules, lying on the sea floor, be taken into account after the Mn and P contents of the sea water from which the nodules accrete, have already

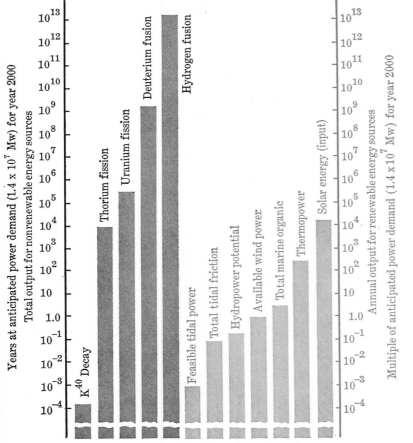

Fig. 5-35. It's anticipated that mankind's power needs for the year 2000 will be some 1.4×10^7 megawatts. Nonrenewable marine power sources are ranged on the left, renewable ones at right.

accounted for these elements? We shall not consider as belonging to the sea the resources below its floor, but we shall include the nodules on the ocean floor, as they constitute higher concentrations (with far greater chance for economic recovery) than in the brine from which they precipitate.

The oceans fill a total volume of nearly 1.4×10^{18} m³ and hold 5×10^{16} metric tons of dissolved solids, equivalent to a 45-m layer of dried salts covering the entire globe. Each year about 2.5×10^9 metric tons are added by run-off from the continents, amounting to 5×10^{-8} of the total. But a similar amount is being withdrawn every year, about 96% in the form of oceanic sediments and 4% as aerosols. Thus we have substantially a steady-state condition. Individual elements, however, are transferred at different rates, which explains why some elements are relatively sparse on land.

The concentrations of the elements dissolved in sea water range from 19 g/liter of chlorine to 1×10^{-13} g/liter of radium. Many other elements are not present or exist in concentrations too small to measure. The margin lists the approximate per-capita share for 30 billion people of several elements present in sea water.

The sea obviously is a fine source of bromine, potash, magnesium, and a remarkably fine source of salt water, and these are currently utilized. The high cost of extracting the other elements and their relatively high terrestrial abundances relegate most of these marine sources to a standby position. From among the metallic elements in the sea, whose abundances fall, by and large, between those of manganese and that of silver, we will likely be extracting a few metals profitably, but the main ones will continue much as they are now.

We can consider the sea a vast chemical vat, in which the multitude of interlocking and separate chemical reactions take place. Two of the resultant deposits, the manganese and phosphorite nodules on the sea floor, accumulate in concentrations sufficient to suggest the possibility of economic recovery, and in amounts sufficient to outlast high-grade terrestrial reserves. The tonnage of manganese nodules, which also contain several other metals in significant amounts, is estimated to be of the order of 10^{12} tons; that of phosphorite nodules is some 10^{11} tons.

Amounts of four of the manganese nodules' constituents—manganese, nickel, cobalt, and zirconium—in the Pacific Ocean alone exceed the terrestrial reserves of these elements by a factor of 10^3 or more. Also, these minerals accumulate there at rates 10 to 50 times greater than the world consumption of those elements

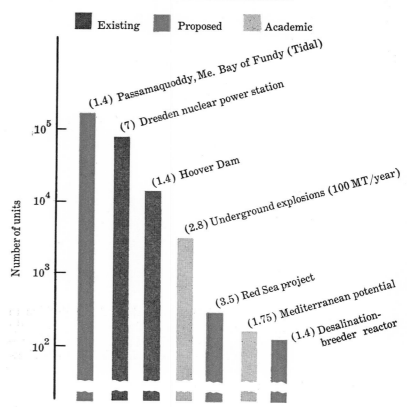

Fig. 5-36. *Even by feasible sea-power standards, that* 1.4×10^7 *MW is a lot of power. To fulfill the requirement with any of the power sources tabulated above would require the indicated numbers of stations.*

in 1960. Thus they constitute, unlike the mineral resources on land, a *renewable* mineral resource. This will be of crucial importance to future generations.

Finally, we offer a few thoughts on the subject of sea-water desalination. Politicians and newspapers have painted the picture that we are soon to suffer for water to drink. Existing and proposed desalination installations can all be justified on this premise: they produce fresh water at two to four times the cost of city domestic water.

Scientists in Los Alamos see a breakthrough in the use of nuclear power for desalination, using the breeder reactor we mentioned as a power plant. Yet even this process would not produce fresh water cheaply enough for Californian, let alone world-wide, irrigation. On top of this comes the cost of water transport. *Even if the sea were completely fresh water, it would not solve the irrigation problem for elevated continental interiors!* It therefore seems sensible to cultivate the wet areas of the world— lakes, swamps, salt marshes, and the sea—because, in the growing of crops, water is by far the heaviest of the required nutrients, some of which must always be brought in. Thus put into

Ocean Minerals/person
(for 3×10^{10} people)
5×10^7 *tons* H_2O
2×10^6 *tons* $NaCl$
7×10^4 *tons* Mg
2×10^4 *tons* K
3×10^3 *tons* Br
0.5 *tons* Mn
0.3 *tons* Fe
25 *lbs.* Ag
0.7 *lb.* Au

Fig. 5-37. *Virtually all the U.S. production of magnesium and about 80% of its bromine needs come from seawater. But the recovery of minerals from seawater entails handling huge volumes of water. This bromine plant at Freeport, Texas handles 2,000,000 gallons of seawater per day. Its initial capacity of 30,000,000 lbs/year was doubled in 1943. (Courtesy Dow Chemical Co.)*

perspective, it becomes clear that solutions to the water problem—which more specifically should be called the irrigation-water problem—will only in special situations involve desalination of sea water.

Afloat but not adrift

Man's interrelationship with the sea is fascinating and manysided, mundane and philosophical. Predominantly, the sea offers man suste-

Fig. 5-38. *This sea-going robot, with tv-camera (top dark cylinder), extendable tool-holder (just below camera) and maneuvering props, illustrates the technology needed to do major construction work 1000 ft. below the surface. (Courtesy Shell Oil Co.)*

nance, now and for his future numbers. But more important than its store of energy and minerals are the sea's nonmaterial resources to add meaning, security, and enjoyment to the lives of all.

The sea has been suggested as an excellent launch pad for some of man's most ambitious probes into space. Whether or not these schemes prove very feasible in its figurative sense, throughout history this suggestion has already proved eminently successful. For while the sea divides the continents, it unites the activities of their inhabitants in a thousand ways, a meeting place of scientists, scientific thought, and a challenge to those who are concerned for the future of man.

Further reading

Reflecting the bounteous nature of the oceans, is a copious and growing popular literature on the marine world. In particular, the authors recommend Frazer's *Nature Adrift* (Foulis, 1962), the general treatment *Natural Resources*, Huberty and Flock, ed. (McGraw-Hill, 1959, $11), and R. C. Cowen's *Frontiers of the Sea* (Doubleday, 1960).

In a more technical vein is Walford's *Living Resources of the Sea* (Ronald Press, 1958, $7.50), which includes maps and other data on the ecology and the influence of various environmental factors on the life of the sea. See also *Fish as Food*, by Bergstrom (Academic Press, 1962, $25), and *The Earth as a Planet*, Osborn, ed. (Doubleday, 1962, $12.50), and Putnam's *Energy in the Future* (Van Nostrand, 1953, $15). A recent symposium on the subject, sponsored jointly by Stanford and Arizona, resulted in *Applied Solar Energy* (U. of Arizona Press, 1955). Albert Defant's two-volume *Physical*

Oceanography (Pergamon Press) and John E. G. Raymont's *Plankton and Productivity in the Oceans* (Pergamon Press) thoroughly treat physical and organic productivity aspects.

Of course, no bibliography on this subject is complete without reference to the ubiquitous and classic tome *The Oceans* by Fleming, Johnson, and Sverdrup (Prentice-Hall, 1942, $22).

An extensive, updated version of *The Oceans*, edited by M. N. Hill, entitled *The Sea*, is available in three volumes (Wiley, 1962, 1963, 1964). A wealth of oceanographic data heretofore scattered among many U.S. government agencies is gathered and correlated at the interagency National Oceanographic Data Center in Washington, D.C.

UNDERWATER SOUND

by Robert A. Frosch *

IN BRIEF: *Finding a submarine by detecting the sound it either emits or reflects is easy. All it takes is a sonar system that can generate and/or receive sound whose power, frequency, bandwidth, pulse shape, and directional characteristics are capable of dividing the sea into resolved volumes about the same size as the submarine. Then the system must discriminate signals that might be caused by the submarine from quite similar echoes that may come from whales. This must be achieved in an environment that is full of noise and extraneous reflected sound. Add to the chowder the fact that sound energy—though better than any other kind for the job—does suffer losses from absorption and geometric spreading along its underwater propagation paths, and the additional fact that refraction can cause dead spots.*

Obviously the job is easy indeed, if you know all about the acoustics of the undersea concert hall. Do we? No. But much has been learned in the Navy's Project Artemis. And eventually this knowledge will find application in undersea navigation, communication, and exploration.—S.T.

■ Rich in potential resources of food and minerals, the world beneath the ocean waves also holds vital secrets about the earth's past, the origin and development of life, and the vagaries of the weather. Some even prophesy that one day its calm stormfree depths will become the major transoceanic freight route, plied by huge, fast, cargo-carrying submarines. But plying these same depths today are submarines carrying missiles that can deliver nuclear weapons.

Surveillance of the oceans for such submarines is an integral part of any modern nation's defense system. And if international disarma-

ment should become a reality, similar examination of the oceans can be expected to become a key ingredient of inspection.

Detecting and locating a submarine in the domain sketched in a simplified way in Fig. 5-39 requires using an energy source that has two essential attributes: (1) the energy must be able to penetrate the ocean over very long ranges, ranges preferably in the order of thousands of yards to thousands of miles; (2) the energy must be available at wavelengths equal to or smaller than the size of the submarine, so that suitably strong reflection signals are generated.

Only one form of energy meets both criteria besides being relatively easy to generate and to receive. This is acoustic or sound energy.

The Navy's Artemis program in underwater sound and very long-range sonar is aimed specifically at the submarine detection problem, and hence is tightly classified. But what we are learning about sound and its behavior in the sea will ultimately have extensive additional applications. Navigating and communicating underwater, locating commercial schools of fish and missile re-entry packages, air-sea rescue, and oceanographic research instrumentation will all benefit.

Of course much that we are learning is itself directly revelatory of the ocean's character. Eventually it may even be possible to routinely use acoustical phenomena to detail thermal, salinity, and biological layers in the oceans, and to trace ocean currents. Now we need to know more about the environment to understand its effects upon our sonar.

Systems = hardware + ocean + target

There are two kinds of sonar systems: passive and active. In the active method sound made by the system propagates through the water, losing intensity as it suffers absorption and geometric spreading losses. This sound reflects from the object of interest, and from other objects in the sea that are of less or

* Robert A. Frosch is currently Director for Nuclear Test Detection in the Advanced Research Projects Agency of the Office of the Secretary of Defense, Washington, D.C. When he wrote this article, he was Technical Director of the Navy's Project Artemis, and directed research at Columbia University's Hudson Laboratories.

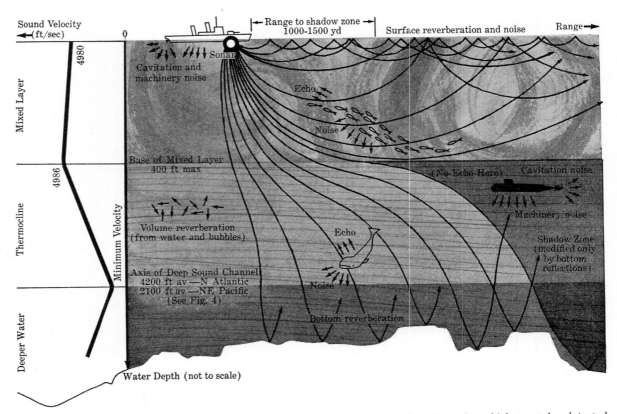

Fig. 5-39. *Sonar emits sound rays and listens for submarine echo which must be detected among false echoes, noise, and extraneous reverberation. Rays refract through layers of changing sound velocity, shown at left. In mixed layer, positive velocity gradient causes rays to refract up, concentrating high intensity sound over long range. Sound also penetrates well into the thermocline, but here negative velocity gradient causes downward refraction, spreading rays apart and reducing sound intensity. Reversal in direction of refraction at base of mixed layer leaves shadow zone, where submarine can hide. (Courtesy R. Kellner)*

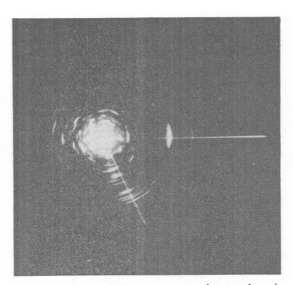

Fig. 5-40. *Sonar PPI-scope screen shows submarine echo on sweep beam that extends to right. Diagonal beam is track of ship's stern and shows multiple echoes of ship's wake. Clustered reflections around ship at upper left are noise and reverberatory reflections. (Courtesy U.S. Navy)*

no interest. The reflections then propagate, eventually to a receiver, and again absorption and spreading losses occur along the way. The receiver, which can have built-in directional characteristics, picks up three chief sources of acoustic energy: (1) the echo from the target; (2) reflections from extraneous objects (usually termed "reverberation"); and (3) ambient noise deriving from the sea itself. Figure 5-40 shows such signals on a PPI-scope.

Passive sonar is quite similar, the major difference being of course that the system itself produces no sound: it depends instead on detecting the sound produced by the submarine. The interplay of factors in a sonar system is simply described by the so-called sonar equations. These, chiefly for the convenience of being able to merely add or subtract signal gains instead of multiplying or dividing them, are usually written in terms of a dimensionless logarithmic unit—dear to electrical engineers—called the *decibel.* Thus, for example, the difference between two signal amplitudes that are expressed in any conventional units (volts, for instance) is defined in decibels as $20 \log_{10} \times$ Amplitude 1 in volts/Amplitude 2 in volts.

The equation for passive sonar is

$$S/N = I - H + D + G - C$$

This expresses the idea that the system's over-all signal-to-noise ratio, or efficiency, results from gains and losses—systematic and environmental—that change the original signal strength on its way to the receiver.

S/N is the ratio of the final received signal to the final received noise in decibels. I is the pressure exerted by the original sound source, in units of dynes/cm². Its value is derived as $10 \log_{10}$ of the sound pressure acting on an arbitrary spherical surface area which lies at a radius of 3 feet from the actual sound source. The quantity C is the sound pressure of the environmental noise in similar units. Subtraction of the logarithmic quantity C from the similar quantity I is, of course, equivalent to establishing a signal-to-noise ratio (I/C in decibels) which accounts only for the sound source and environmental noise, and which does not account for the remaining parameters affecting the output of the sonar system. These include H, the total signal loss in decibels caused by propagation path effects: $10 \log_{10}$ times the ratio of the original sound pressure (i.e., the value I) to the sound pressure reaching the sonar receiver. The value D is the receiver's directivity index, the ratio in decibels of receiving intensity on the main beam to the average receiving intensity in all directions. Just as a larger D enhances the over-all S/N ratio, so does G, the processing gain in decibels, also improve it.

The analogous equation for active sonar is

$$(E/N, E/R) =$$

$$I - 2H + D + G + T - (R, C)$$

This equation simply states the fact that the final received echo-to-noise ratio (E/N), or echo-to-reverberation ratio (E/R), equals the original strength of the sound source (I), sent out by the sonar transducer, minus the two-way propagation path loss—from sonar to target and back—(2H), plus the receiving directivity index (D), processing gain (G), and sonar target strength (T), minus the ambient noise (C) or reverberation level (R).

Two important differences distinguish the active case from the passive one. First, with active sonar the echo must be detected in the face of either or both interfering environmental noise and extraneous reflections from other objects (reverberation): passive sonar faces noise, to be sure, but reverberation is not involved. The second difference is the presence

of the target strength term (T) in the active sonar equation. This measures the effectiveness of the target as a sound reflector. It is $10 \log_{10}$ times the ratio of the reflected sound pressure measured three feet from the acoustic center of the target to the sound pressure arriving at the target.

The significance of the sonar equations

The sonar equations contain three kinds of terms. These are the *hardware* terms: source level (I), receiver directivity index (D), processing gain (G); the *ocean* terms: propagation (H or 2H), noise level (C), and reverberation level (R); and the *target* terms: sound level of the target (essentially I in the passive case), and target strength (essentially T in the active case).

Obviously, the system designer controls only the hardware terms. The ocean terms are set by the sea itself, and the system can only exploit these characteristics. And the target terms are determined by the target designer.

While the system designer *can* control the frequency, bandwidth, power, directionality, and pulse shape of the source, and the directional characteristics of the receiver—as well as the form of signal processing which he wishes to employ, along with display and decision techniques—he must deal with the pre-existing characteristics of the ocean for the propagation of his sound and for the noise and reverberation that obscure that target signal which he must detect.

Before we return to hardware questions, we must look into the acoustics of the sea.

Lighting the sea with sound

The major factor governing the propagation of sound in the sea is its velocity. Velocity increases with rising temperature, pressure, and salinity of the water. At the sea surface, at about 25°C, sound velocity is about 4980 ft/sec. Pressure raises the velocity 1.82 ft/sec for each additional 100 ft of water depth. And even more significant velocity changes are caused by temperature: 9.0 ft/sec velocity increase per 1°C temperature rise, at about 20°C, for example. On the other hand, salinity effects can be ignored here.

Though the temperature and pressure of the ocean vary with geographic position, they chiefly vary with depth. In general, temperature drops as the depth increases. At the same time the pressure increases as we go deeper. But in the top few hundred feet of the ocean the temperature profile results from the interplay of solar radiation, back radiation, evaporation, and the mixing activity caused by winds blowing over the sea surface. The temperature gradient with depth in this upper few hundred feet, therefore, strongly depends on variability in weather, season, and geography. At times this upper layer is well mixed and temperatures within it are constant. At other times, there is no mixed upper layer. Such capricious variability is crucial to our detection problem, as we shall see in a moment.

Beneath this occasionally present surface layer, temperatures decrease rapidly in what is called the "thermocline" (a zone of sharp temperature decline) to 0° to $-2°C$. Thereafter this temperature, at which sea water is most dense, remains fairly constant to the sea bottom. Such a vertical temperature profile characterizes only the mid-latitude regions of all oceans; it will vary in other regions.

The significant effect caused by this *temperature* profile is that the *sound velocity* structure in the upper few hundred feet above the thermocline correspondingly can be extremely variable in time and geography. But in the thermocline itself, and in depths below the thermocline, sound velocity gradients tend to be quite stable.

The left side of Fig. 5-39 illustrates a common condition prevailing when the surficial mixed layer is present. Although temperatures are constant, increasing pressure with depth causes the sound velocity to rise. Only at the depth where the thermocline takes over does the sharp drop in temperature outstrip the effect of increasing pressure, and here sound velocity drops sharply. Let's see what this means for sound propagation—the heart of our sonar detection problem.

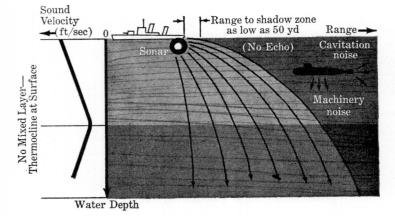

Fig. 5-41. Without mixed layer the negative sound velocity gradient that characterizes the thermocline starts at surface. The resulting downward refraction of sound rays creates a sound shadow zone at all ranges and depths that lie above the uppermost sound ray. Compare Fig. 5-39. (Courtesy R. Kellner)

How can we "illuminate" the shadow zone?

Sound rays emanating from a source, as shown on the right side of Fig. 5-39, are refracted as their velocities change—exactly as are light rays or seismic rays. In a water layer where the sound velocity increases with depth the sound rays will be bent continuously upward. On the contrary, in a water layer where the velocity decreases with depth (as in the thermocline) the rays will refract downward. Thus rays from the source whose initial inclination from the horizontal is sufficiently small will be confined to the mixed layer.

However, the fate of sound rays with large enough initial inclinations from the horizontal is quite different. Even though they are refracted upward while passing through the mixed layer they will nevertheless reach the bottom of it—where the sound velocity gradient becomes negative with depth. Here the rays bend downwards and they propagate still deeper, into the thermocline and below.

As a result, the ocean can be divided into three acoustical portions. In the first, the mixed layer itself, sound propagates to long ranges with relatively high intensity—the hearing is good. In the second region, directly below the mixed layer, propagation is also good, although rays spread apart as they proceed to greater depths, and the sound diminishes in intensity.

But no sound rays can reach the third significant area which lies below the mixed layer and farther away from the sound source than the uppermost limiting ray within the thermocline. This area is a sound shadow zone, or in the jargon of the trade, it is not "insonified."

Bad as this situation is, it can even be worse if there is no mixed layer. This is frequently the case in tropical regions, or during the summer in midlatitudes when there has been a long warming period of sunshine and very low winds. In these circumstances the thermocline essentially begins at the surface, and both the temperature and sound velocity gradients are negative. Thus all sound rays from a near-surface sonar source are refracted downward. And as shown in Fig. 5-41, the only ocean region insonified lies close to and immediately below the ship. All other ranges and depths are in shadow.

It must be emphasized that at reasonably high sound frequencies, that is, frequencies at which the wavelength is small compared with the thickness of the mixed layer, the shadows are truly shadows. Increases in either the power of sources or the sensitivity of receivers are of little or no use against targets in the shadow zones. The only sound there arrives

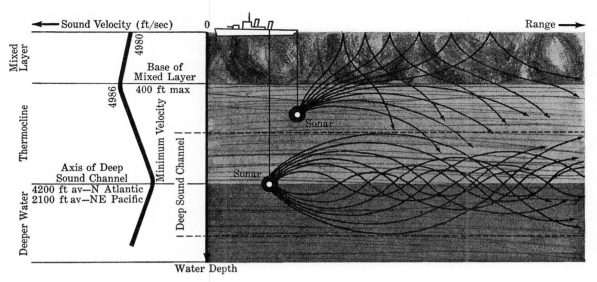

Fig. 5-42. *Sonar placed within the thermocline, as in upper part of figure, produces a pattern of refracted sound that eliminates the shadow zone (see Fig. 5-39) produced in the same sea condition when a shallower sound source is used. When source is still deeper, at sound velocity minimum, rays refract to follow variably wide sound channel whose axis lies at this depth. Concentrated sound which follows this waveguide propagates over enormous ranges in open ocean—12,000 miles in one experiment. (Courtesy R. Kellner)*

by diffraction, and even this falls rapidly in intensity away from the edges of the zone.

The only current remedy for the difficulty caused by the shadow zone is shown in the upper part of Fig. 5-42. If the sound source is placed below the mixed layer, rays within the thermocline are bent downward. But those that enter the mixed layer refract upward: they have long paths through the mixed layer and only bend back into the thermocline at respectable horizontal ranges. Such deep sonar permeates the shadow zones with sound. But spreading of the rays by refraction reduces intensity and raises power requirements.

Frequencies and hardware versus shadows

The above ray description for propagation is satisfactory for sound where the wavelength of the sound is small compared with the thickness of the mixed layer. But it is inadequate for frequencies at which the wavelength is comparable with the thickness of the mixed layer —for frequencies below several hundred cycles. In these ranges we must seek a more exact solution for the propagation of sound. This is provided by the scalar wave equation

$$\nabla^2 p - \frac{1}{c^2} \cdot \frac{\partial^2 p}{\partial t^2} = 0$$

where c is the velocity of sound, p the sound pressure, and t the time, solved for suitable boundary conditions. This solution treats the mixed layer as a waveguide, one which, however, leaks because the boundary at the bottom is not perfect, the velocity at the bottom corresponding to neither $c = 0$ nor $c = \infty$. Propagation is excellent in the waveguide, provided the frequency is not too low, or the wavelength not too large compared with the thickness of the layer. Beneath the layer, sound leaks from the waveguide and at very low sound frequencies the shadow region, therefore, does not truly exist. But the sound intensity below the mixed layer waveguide is quite low.

Even this treatment fails completely at extremely low frequencies, where the wavelength becomes equal to or larger than the thickness of the layer; sound propagates almost as though the ocean were homogeneous and unlayered—and there is no shadow zone. But ideal as this situation may appear at first glance, the frequencies at which this occurs are so low that it is difficult to build efficient sonar sources and directional receivers. This is because effective radiation and directionality can only be achieved by constructing devices several or many wavelengths in size. A ten-cycle transducer which might ignore the shadow zone produced at higher frequencies would have to be about 500 feet in size. Furthermore, at very low frequencies the scattering cross section of submarines would be too low for an active sonar, as would be the radiation effectiveness of a submarine being sought by passive sonar.

For these reasons surface ship sonar has usually operated in the multikilocycle range, where all of the difficulties of the shadow zone become acute. The submarine has a ready-made place to hide. The variable-depth sonar I discussed above is one solution, for relatively short ranges. But we must follow the sound deeper into the sea to find longer-range detecting possibilities.

SOFAR and the "deep sound channel"

Consider what happens to sound rays beneath the thermocline, as shown in the lower part of Fig. 5-42. Within the thermocline the influence of lowering temperature outstrips the opposing influence of rising pressure, and sound velocity drops. But below the thermocline—where the pressure effect exceeds that of temperature—sound velocity begins to rise. Consequently there is a minimum in the velocity-versus-depth curve. This minimum occurs at some depth in all oceans. It lies at approximately 700 fathoms (1 fathom = 6 ft) in the North Atlantic, and at 350 fathoms in the Northeastern Pacific. At other latitudes, seasons, and under varied geographic conditions its depth may be considerably less.

This velocity profile causes sound originating near the depth of the velocity minimum to remain concentrated near this depth. Figure 5-42 shows by the ray tracing method how sound rays are continually refracted back and forth across the axis of this natural deep sound channel.

Because of this refraction, which creates a

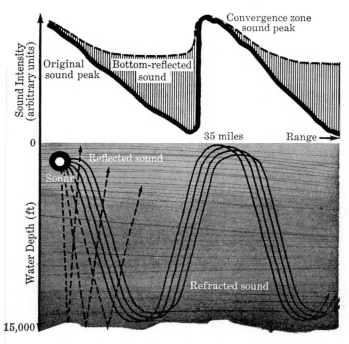

Fig. 5-43. When ocean is much deeper than axis of deep sound channel (see Fig. 5-42), sound rays refract to produce peaks in intensity at about 35 mile intervals along surface. Such peaks, however, can be partly or completely subdued if intensity of bottom-reflected sound is too high. (Courtesy R. Kellner)

waveguide effect, most of the sound originating on the channel's axis remains in the channel. Geometric spreading losses in intensity are extremely low; the channel acts as a superb "conductor" of sound at frequencies where losses due to absorption are negligible. Because the characteristics of the channel are determined by permanent characteristics of the ocean, sound velocities—and the dispersion of them along the axis—also are extremely stable in character.

These properties of the deep sound channel have obvious possibilities for the submarine search problem. Experiments also have been made with a prototype SOFAR, or sound fixing and ranging system. This system records the receipt time of sounds at the channel axis generated by explosive charges set off at the same or nearby depth. Several stations recording the arrival time of successive sound pulses can locate the initial point of the single-pulse charge by measurements of time difference, if velocities along the sound channel axis are known. Such a system, in fact, is now in use for locating missile nose cones when they enter the water at the end of their flight. A similar system has been proposed as a means of finding downed aircraft at sea. Moreover, the deep sound channel shows promise as a means of long-range precision navigation. It is always present over large regions of the ocean and is unaffected by weather, season, sunspot cycles, and other effects that plague electromagnetic navigation systems. The precise accuracy attainable with sound navigation has yet to be determined. Strikingly suggestive of the possibilities that may be exploited here, the longest path thus far for which experimental SOFAR reception has been successful was 12,000 miles—from Bermuda to the Indian Ocean—in experiments by the Lamont Geological Observatory.

Another feature of deep sound propagation that we would like to exploit is shown in Fig. 5-43. This is the phenomenon of sound convergence. Sound intensities literally pile up at the surface of the sea at ranges that are integral multiples of 35 miles in the North Atlantic, somewhat less in the Pacific. Between intensity peaks there are again shadow zones insonified only by those sound rays that initially radiate from the shallow source at inclination angles steep enough to make them hit and reflect from the bottom. All other sound rays refract to yield the convergence peak. Of course, if the water is shallower, more bottom reflection and less convergence peaking occurs: the shadow area more completely fills with bottom-reflected sound, and the convergence peak diminishes in relative intensity and may even disappear.

Fish and swish, the ocean is a noisy place

Noise and reverberation are continuing problems, though of course not unique to sonar. In distinction to most radar and radio systems, the internal noise of the hardware in sonar is not normally a problem. But self-generated noise—from the ship's own machinery, from propeller-caused cavitation of the water, or from hydrodynamic effects created by movement of the ship or the sonar gear through the water—sometimes causes difficulty. Even this can be minimized by suitable acoustical treatment of the ship and the sonar gear. The remaining noise in the signals received comes from the ocean itself.

Very little is known about the source of the noise, although shipping, breaking waves, and probably organic activity seem to be the chief factors. In particular areas porpoises, whales, snapping shrimp, and certain fish are notorious for their noise-making proclivities.

In general, the noise spectrum grows more intense with decreasing frequencies into the low infrasonic range (<10 cps). This noise is probably the same as the seismologist's microseismic noise, generated by weather effects at the ocean surface. Approaches to overcoming this ambient noise problem depend upon using the spectral or statistical properties of the noise sources, and more data is needed here.

Reverberation yields false reflections

When a short sound pulse is sent out from a source, even in the absence of a target, immediately upon the termination of the pulse reflected sound energy is received. This decays with time and may have many peaks—and it is usually even louder at the receiver than the ambient noise. Sources of such extraneous reflections—the "reverberation" of sonar terminology—include air bubbles, fish, masses of plankton, whales, perhaps the water itself, as well as the water's surface and the ocean floor.

In the case of large single objects such as whales, in fact, it is frequently difficult to make a meaningful distinction between reverberation and true target. Some responsible experts even claim that as many as 90% of the "submarines" that have been contacted by sonar have probably been whales, or other large marine forms.

A particularly interesting source of reverberation is the so-called scattering layer. It appears as a distinct reflection layer in many portions of the ocean in echo sounders (sonars used to measure the depth of the bottom). This layer frequently migrates in depth daily and with season, and the variation of the frequency peaks in its reflections indicates that the reflec-

tions are caused by the gas-filled bladders of fish or, perhaps, invertebrate organisms.

Since sources of reverberation exist throughout the volume of the sea and on the surface, a way to minimize them is to provide directional character to the sonar system, i.e., illuminate only in a narrow band of directions and receive only from these directions. By this means one can look at a small enough number of reverberators so that the total sound they reflect is not larger than the echo from the target within the beam. Another way to achieve the same effect is to use pulses and other signals that enable precise time resolution; this is equivalent to examining only a small interval in horizontal range.

By combining these means we can try to get a system whose range, bearing, and altitude resolution is such that the ocean is divided into small volumes, each precisely the size of the target scattering volume. If resolution is made finer, the target echo will be broken up into small pieces, and the target echo-to-reverberation ratio will be degraded. If the resolved box is much larger than the target, then an unnecessary amount of reverberation is being examined along with the target signal.

In order to provide directional sources and receivers suitable for overcoming reverberation, it is necessary to make radiating and receiving devices which are comparable with, or large compared to, a wavelength. The resolution of such devices is essentially proportional to the total radiating or receiving aperture. [One transducer—30 ft long, 50 ft high—already is active in the Artemis program.—Ed.]

Another possibility arises if the scattering properties of the reverberators are different from the scattering properties of the target, as a function of frequency. One might then be able to use a sonar frequency which minimizes reverberation while it enhances the reflection from the target.

Hardware considerations revisited

The parameters entering into the design of a source for an active sonar system are its frequency, bandwidth, directional properties, and acoustic power output. All sources are transducers, that is, they convert some convenient form of energy into acoustic energy. Some major categories of transducers are chemical (such as explosives), electromechanical (including piezoelectric and magnetostrictive devices, and motors of various sorts), and thermomechanical (in which heat energy is converted into mechanical motion). In addition, it is possible to convert hydraulic or pneumatic energy into acoustic energy.

The different types of transducers have different characteristics as acoustic motors. Explosives tend to be limited to short pulses of high energy, while the piezoelectric and magnetostrictive devices tend to be narrow band unless they are extremely carefully designed. Mechanical devices are usually very narrow band, and hydraulic transducers tend to be inefficient at high frequencies. As with all systems, the major source problem at the present time is that of combining high power with broad bandwidth.

Acoustic energy, once produced, must be coupled to the medium in such a manner that it can be radiated.

A fundamental limit here is the possibility of cavitation. At the radiating face the sound pressure is alternately compressional and tensional in nature. If the amplitude is extremely high, the tension can exceed the effective tensile strength of the water. While this is high for pure water, gas-free and under ideal conditions, in the sea the tension which water can support is often extremely low. This limits the power per unit area which can be radiated at the face of a transducer. But this limitation too becomes less stringent with increasing depth, as confining pressure increases the water's tensile strength.

Receivers are considerably easier to construct than sources. They are usually piezoelectric in fundamental principle. The main problem faced in receiver design is to construct a structure having directional properties. This can be particularly difficult at low frequencies, where directional structures which must be many wavelengths in size can become gigantic, as already mentioned. This is equally true for sources.

It is clear from the foregoing that the design of hardware for a sonar system is intimately connected with the particular characteristics of the ocean, target, and interferences. For this reason ingenious systems built around particular pieces of hardware are seldom successful. It is more useful to assemble carefully selected possibilities from a wide spectrum of available equipment into a system designed around the properties of the ocean. The addition of new and ingenious devices to the collection from which the system designer can choose is badly needed; but ingenious systems based upon misconceptions about the medium are useless.

Further reading

One of the best ways to ease into any subject is to read the classical references in the field. These frequently are written in a graceful style and with an economical lucidity that is lacking in later textbook rehashes of the material. The standard reference along this line is J. W. Strutt's (Lord Rayleigh) *The Theory of Sound* available as a Dover paperback reprint (1945). For a general elementary textbook, largely descriptive rather than analytical in approach, try *A Textbook of Sound,* by A. B. Wood (Macmillan, 1955).

As a brief introduction to the physical characteristics of the oceans, W. Von Arx's *Introduction to Physical Oceanography* (Addison-Wesley, 1962) does an admirable job of boiling a big subject down to manageable proportions. Essential to any work in this field are the results of a conference held at Easton, Md., under joint sponsorship of the Office of Naval Research and the NAS–NRC Committee on Oceanography. These are available as NAS–NRC publication number 600, 1959, under the title *Physical and Chemical Properties of Sea Water.*

For the all-important linkage of sound to the oceans two sources are available. Probably the more elementary, undergraduate level treatment can be found in *Introduction to the Theory of Sound Transmission with Application to the Ocean,* by C. B. Officer (McGraw-Hill, 1958). The more professional volume, a collection of papers by Maurice Ewing, J. Lamar Worzel, and others, is *Propagation of Sound in the Ocean.* This is available from the Geological Society of America as their Memoir 27, 1948.

Still the bible for sonar systems is W. Horton's *Fundamentals of Sonar,* published by the U.S. Naval Institute, Annapolis, 1957.

The periodical literature carries only scattered references to the specifics of the submarine detection program, chiefly because the work is tightly classified. Some material can be found, however, in the *Journal of the Acoustical Society of America,* and in recent numbers of the *Physical Review.* For details beyond these, one must deal with the Navy.

Chapter 6

Mathematics, Computers, and Control

ANALYZING NONLINEARITY

by Jack K. Hale and Joseph P. LaSalle *

IN BRIEF: *The common assumption of linear relationships is seldom more than a good approximation to the way nature behaves. The nonlinear differential equations that do provide a better description are generally not solvable analytically. However, many features of the solutions can be determined by a geometric approach developed by Poincaré and Liapunov. One represents the "state" of the quantity as a point on a phase plane—in which the position of the quantity and its first time-derivative are the two axes. Then the changing state of the system can be reflected in the motion of this point in the phase plane. One finds that nonlinear systems differ radically in their dynamic behavior from linear systems. In such a system the amplitude of an oscillation generally depends on its frequency, and it is possible to have completely isolated oscillations—that is self-sustained oscillations that take place only at one frequency and amplitude. The stability of any system is determined by its nonlinearities.*

Deliberate introduction of nonlinearity often leads to superior performance; for example, nonlinear control systems, which switch from one extreme of correction to another, achieve desired end results more rapidly than any linear system.—D.C.

■ Much of our understanding of nature and of the devices that man has built relates to change. Given the forces acting on a billiard ball, Newton's second law tells us how its velocity will change. Given the concentration of reactants in a processing vessel, the equations of chemical-reaction kinetics tell us how the concentrations will change.

Change of itself is usually of little interest, however. What we want to know, in almost all situations, is the state of the system at all future times. How will the billiard ball travel, and will it land in that side pocket? When will the reaction be 97% complete?

Differential equations are the basic mathematical tool for expressing what we know about change and its causes. In going from a differential equation to its solution we go from a knowledge of the way a quantity changes to a knowledge of how it behaves in time.

It's no accident that Newton, who gave us, in his second law, perhaps the central relation between change and its causes, also invented (contemporaneous with Leibniz) the differential calculus. Mathematicians who followed were primarily concerned with finding explicit solutions to the differential equations that arose when they applied his second law of motion to elementary problems of mechanics and physics. The few methods and solutions which they

* Joseph P. LaSalle is Director of Brown University's newly organized Research Center for Dynamical Systems in Providence, Rhode Island. Jack K. Hale is on the staff of the Research Center, and a Professor in Brown's Division of Applied Mathematics. They prepared this article while at the Martin Company's Research Institute for Advanced Studies in Baltimore, Maryland.

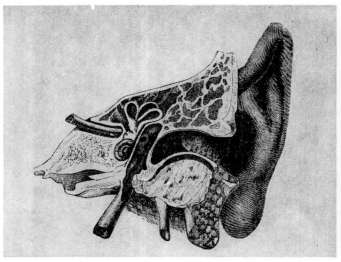

Fig. 6-1. Nonlinearity abounds in our world: The ear generates harmonics of strong tones. Microwave magnetrons oscillate in modes that vary nonlinearly with applied voltage. Watches convert a steady flow of energy into periodic vibrations. Transistor circuits oscillate at a unique amplitude. (Courtesy New York Public Library; Raytheon Corp.; Gruen Watch Co.; IBM)

found had profound scientific and technological implications, for they provided the basis for the development of mechanics and much of classical physics—and spurred the Industrial Revolution.

Yet those methods, powerful as they are, are a shaky basis for dealing with much of nature and of modern technology. Their weakness is that they generally assume the systems studied are linear—that effect is directly proportional to cause, that the extension of a spring is rigorously proportional to the weight hanging from it, that all resistors obey Ohm's Law, that PV is always equal to nRT. In the physical world, most springs, many resistors, and all gases at sufficiently high pressure behave differently, nonlinearly.

Correspondingly the differential equations that arise in modern technology are usually nonlinear. Sometimes it's because our measurements have grown so refined—as in determination of satellite orbits. Sometimes it's because conditions are so extreme—as in the very nonlinear shock waves. Sometimes it's because nonlinear devices are far superior to linear ones—the way the nonlinear tunnel diode outstrips its passive, linear resistor relatives with their meek adherence to Ohm's Law.

While, more and more, all of us need to consider nonlinearities, the training of most technical men reflects only the linear approximation to the real world. The usual college course in differential equations presents approaches used since the first quarter of the 18th century. We'd like at least to introduce you to the new mathematical phenomena that arise when the differential equations are nonlinear; clever application of nonlinearity can improve performance

of devices and systems in many fields (Fig. 6-1).

We'll be using the familiar properties of linear differential equations and their solutions as a stepping stone to entering the richer domain of the nonlinear. However, to avoid boring you with things you know and to introduce a technique that is invaluable for the understanding of nonlinear differential equations, we'll use a geometric point of view that may be new to you.

A new view of an old subject

Let's start by applying Newton's second law to the simple situation of a particle suspended at the end of a massless spring, whose extension is strictly, linearly proportional to the force applied (see Fig. 6-2). We can select as our origin for the coordinate the equilibrium position of the weight as it hangs at rest from the spring. Now if we displace the weight and release it, it will move in a fashion determined by Newton's law and the force of the spring. (In honor of Newton and because it's more convenient typographically, we'll use his notation $\dot{x}$ for the derivative rather than the dx/dt on which most of us were raised.)

$$\dot{x} \equiv \frac{dx}{dt}$$
$$\ddot{x} \equiv \frac{d^2x}{dt^2}$$

We have

$$\text{acceleration} = \text{force/mass}$$
$$\ddot{x} = F/m$$
$$\ddot{x} = -kx/m$$

Since we need not be concerned with units of measurement (a characteristic indifference among mathematicians) let's take k and m both equal to 1

$$\ddot{x} + x = 0 \qquad (1)$$

Now the general solution of this differential equation is well known, it is

$$x = A \sin t + B \cos t$$

A and B are disposable constants that we can adjust to satisfy the initial conditions of any and all problems. For example, if we displaced the weight to point $x = 2$ and released it while it was at rest, then $x = 2 \cos t$ much as shown in Fig. 6-2c, except that there we kept the k and m so that the period would be in more familiar form. With k and $m = 1$ the period is a mathematically convenient 2π sec.

Note that the period, and hence the frequency, is independent of the amplitude. Note that none of these periodic solutions is "isolated" —all amplitudes are possible. This is a characteristic property of linear equations.

We stress such obvious properties of the solutions because we'll find things are different for nonlinear systems.

Now let's look at our oscillating weight from the geometric viewpoint, a viewpoint that stems from the work of the Frenchman, Poincaré, and the Russian, Liapunov. We'll find that we don't need to solve the differential equation; all our information will flow directly from the equation itself.

We start with a purely formal step, and introduce a new symbol y for the velocity $\dot{x}$. Then, from Eq. 1, $\dot{y} = -x$. So Eq. 1 with its second derivative (a second-order equation) can be expressed as two equations involving first derivatives (two first-order equations)

$$\dot{x} = y \qquad (2a)$$

$$\dot{y} = -x \qquad (2b)$$

In the physical problem x and y express the "state" of the system—the position and the velocity of the weight, which are the minimum data required to define its motion completely.

If we introduce coordinate axes (Fig. 6-2d)

each point in the (x, y) plane represents a state of the system. This plane is sometimes called the "phase plane" or "state space" of the system. We can now look upon the differential equations (2a and 2b) as defining a flow in the plane. When we are given the differential equations, we are given the velocity of the flow at each point of the phase plane. This velocity of flow, which is now something quite different from the physical velocity of the system, can be represented by a vector $\mathbf{v}$ whose components are $\dot{x}$ and $\dot{y}$. This vector describes at each point (x, y) how—in magnitude and direction—the state of the system is changing.

In the case of our harmonic oscillator we know from the differential equations that the flow is perpendicular at each point to the radial line from the origin. Thus we know that the flow is circular in a clockwise direction about the origin. This we can confirm another way by showing that the time rate of change of the radius is zero.

$$d/dt \, (x^2 + y^2) = 2x\dot{x} + 2y\dot{y} = 2xy - 2xy = 0$$

For this particular system this is also the statement of the law of conservation of energy.

Since the speed of the flow is $(\dot{x}^2 + \dot{y}^2)^{1/2} = (x^2 + y^2)^{1/2} = r$, the radius of the circle, the period of the oscillation (the time to make one revolution of the circle) is 2π. The period does not depend on the amplitude of the oscillation, and the frequency is $1/2\pi$, confirming what we learned earlier when we solved the equation.

This geometric picture of the flow in state space is basic to the geometric or qualitative theory of differential equations. In the geometric theory one gives up the futile attempt to find general solutions of all differential equations and attempts instead to obtain as much information as possible about the flow, and the nature of the solutions defined by the flow, without explicitly solving the equations. Al-

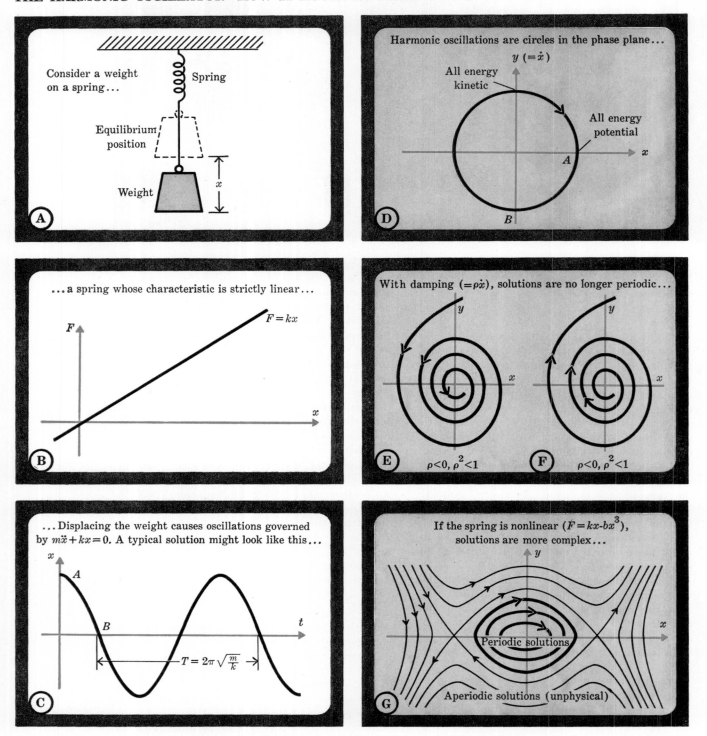

A Consider a weight on a spring... Equilibrium position / Spring / Weight / x

B ...a spring whose characteristic is strictly linear... $F = kx$

C ...Displacing the weight causes oscillations governed by $m\ddot{x} + kx = 0$. A typical solution might look like this... $T = 2\pi\sqrt{\frac{m}{k}}$

D Harmonic oscillations are circles in the phase plane... $y\ (=\dot{x})$ / All energy kinetic / All energy potential

E With damping $(=\rho\dot{x})$, solutions are no longer periodic... $\rho < 0,\ \rho^2 < 1$

F $\rho < 0,\ \rho^2 < 1$

G If the spring is nonlinear $(F = kx\text{-}bx^3)$, solutions are more complex... Periodic solutions / Aperiodic solutions (unphysical)

Fig. 6-2. The sinusoidal oscillations of a weight attached to a spring that obeys Hooke's law (extension proportional to force) are represented by circles in the phase plane, which has the position of the weight as one axis of coordinates, its velocity as another. As the weight oscillates in space, the point representing its state moves around a circle; two sets of corresponding points in the motion are marked A and B in frames C and D. What makes the phase-plane representation useful is that, without solving the differential equation that governs the motion, one can often generate the shape of the solution curves and thereby learn qualitative facts about the motion. It soon becomes easy to read behavior from the phase plane; consider the exponentially damped oscillation in E, or the exponentially expanding one in F. Weight attached to a nonlinear spring would yield solution curves like those in G. Note that the motion is no longer everywhere periodic, however some aperiodic solutions are unphysical (e.g., weight can't pass through spring support). (from J. J. Stoker's Nonlinear Vibrations*)*

though the differential equation of motion of the simple harmonic oscillator is easily solved (it is a linear problem), we obtained all of our information about the oscillations without exhibiting the solutions.

Putting on the damper

Let's use the geometric view to examine a more general form of the linear differential equation in which we take account of a damping or frictional force that is also a linear function, this time a function of velocity

$$\ddot{x} + 2\rho\dot{x} + x = 0 \tag{3}$$

Once again this second-order linear equation can be written as two first-order equations

$$\dot{x} = y \tag{4a}$$

$$\dot{y} = -x - 2\rho y \tag{4b}$$

Depending on the values of ρ we can distinguish three cases among the solutions:

- Oscillations that decrease exponentially in amplitude (or increase, if the "damping" is negative, reflecting an input of energy)
- Exponential variation without oscillation
- The critically damped case that is the boundary between these two.

We plot the paths of the solutions only for the oscillations of the first case as Fig. 6-2e and 6-2f.

Another (and our last) classic problem of linear differential equations is the forced harmonic oscillator, in which an external and periodic force is applied

$$\ddot{x} + x = a \cos \omega t$$

The paths in the phase plane can be shown to be ellipses, at least for those solutions that are periodic with $\omega \neq 1$.

To provide a peek ahead, Fig. 6-2g shows what solutions in the phase plane look like when our spring is nonlinear, in particular when its characteristic is $F = kx - bx^3$. Period now varies with amplitude and aperiodic solutions are possible.

By now the character of the geometric approach should be clear and particular examples of differential equations and their solution sufficiently numerous that we can ask you to accept some assertions about linear differential equations generally.

Superposition and provincial behavior

The most general linear differential equation of second order has this form

$$\ddot{x} + a\dot{x} + bx = F(t) \tag{5}$$

What makes it linear, by definition, is the fact that no term contains x or its time derivatives

to a power greater than the first; neither are there any products of x and its time derivatives. The most important property of linear differential equations and their solutions is the principle of superposition. That principle says that if x_1 is a solution of the above equation with $F = F_1(t)$ and if x_2 is a solution with $F = F_2(t)$, then $ax_1 + bx_2$ is a solution of the equation with $F = aF_1 + bF_2$ where a and b are any constants. An immediate consequence is that if $F = 0$, then *any* sum of solutions is also a solution. In particular any constant times a solution is also a solution. The foregoing facts of superposition are what underly the procedures by which one fixes the constants in general solutions of differential equations to match the initial conditions of a particular problem.

Another fact about linear differential equations may be expressed by saying that they are, so to speak, provincial—by which we mean that global behavior can be predicted from local behavior. The behavior of the paths of the solutions in a small region around the origin of the phase plane (or, indeed, any point in the phase plane) determines the behavior of the paths in the entire phase plane.

Nonlinear differential equations—those with higher powers of x and/or its time derivatives —do not obey the principle of superposition. Neither are they provincial—the behavior in one region does not necessarily tell you anything about the behavior elsewhere in the phase plane. Furthermore solutions need not be defined for all values of time, and there can be isolated periodic solutions.

Nonlinear is as nonlinear does

To make simple our comparison between linear and nonlinear systems let's start with a lower-order equation. Consider the linear first-order equation

$$\dot{x} = -x \tag{6}$$

and the nonlinear first-order equation

$$\dot{x} = -x(1 - x) \tag{7}$$

The general solution of the linear Eq. 6 is given by $x = ae^t$—where a is an arbitrary constant and is equal to the initial state of the system at time zero. On the other hand, if the initial state of the nonlinear system at time zero is a, then by direct substitution one can verify that the solution of Eq. 7 is

$$x = ae^{-t}/(1 - a + ae^{-t})$$

The plot in (one-dimensional) phase space and the behavior in time for the solutions of the two equations are shown in Fig. 6-3 for various values of a. As is observed from this

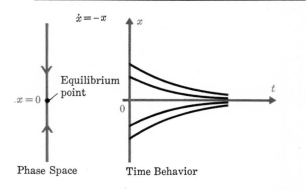

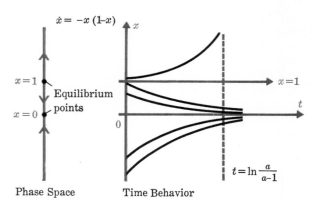

Fig. 6-3. The familiar exponential solutions of a linear differential equation (top) develop new features when even a single nonlinear term is added. Note especially the divergent branch (bottom). Correspondingly phase line has unstable equilibrium point.

figure, new phenomena occur even for the simplest nonlinear equations. For nonlinear systems there can be more than one equilibrium point, each of which is isolated. (An equilibrium point is one where there is no flow in phase space—velocity and position remain constant there.) Some solutions of a nonlinear system may become unbounded in a finite interval of time. Also, the behavior of the solutions of Eq. 7 with initial values greater than one is completely different from those with initial values less than one. None of these situations occurs in linear systems.

It is possible for linear analysis to yield some information about Eq. 7. We first study the solutions near the equilibrium point $x = 0$. Since the equation is $\dot{x} = -x + x^2$ it would seem reasonable that the equation $\dot{x} = -x$ is a good approximation near $x = 0$. An inspection of the curves in Figs. 6-3a and 6-3b shows this is actually the case. However, such an analysis of $\dot{x} = -x(1 - x)$ for all initial values is erroneous, since not all of its solutions approach zero and some are actually unbounded.

To analyze the behavior of Eq. 7 near $x = 1$,

let $x = 1 + z$ and study the behavior near $z = 0$. The new equation for z is

$$\dot{z} = z + z^2$$

Near $z = 0$, it again seems reasonable to take the linear approximation $\dot{z} = z$ whose solutions are $z = be^t$ where b is the initial state at zero. The linear analysis then yields the solutions of Eq. 7 near $x = 1$. On the other hand, the linear analysis would also say that all solutions are defined for all values of t, whereas we have seen that this is not the case—y goes to infinity at $t = \ln (a/a - 1)$.

Moral: linear approximation is often useful but has extreme limitations.

Nonlinear oscillators: hearts and triodes

We saw that it is impossible for linear equations to have isolated periodic solutions; but this is clearly not the case for nonlinear equations. Consider the second-order equation

$$\ddot{x} - 2\rho(1 - x^2)\dot{x} + x = 0 \qquad (8)$$

this becomes

$$\dot{x} = y \qquad (8a)$$

$$\dot{y} = -x + 2\rho(1 - x^2)y \qquad (8b)$$

where ρ is a positive constant.

Equation 8 is called van der Pol's equation. He studied it in connection with his work on the triode vacuum-tube oscillator and suggested that, for large values of ρ, this equation explains the shape of heartbeats.

To understand Eq. 8 we first observe that $x = 0$, $y = 0$ is an equilibrium point and analyze the behavior of nearby solutions by linearizing the equations so they resemble Eq. 4a and Eq. 4b. These linear-equation solutions leave the equilibrium point as t increases, as in Fig. 6-2f.

For large x, on the other hand, the term $2\rho(1 - x^2)y$ represents a frictional force and has a damping effect. As a result of this, one can show that the solutions of Eq. 8 are bounded and there is a curve C in the (x, y) plane across which the solution flow is from the outside inward. By our linear analysis, we can also construct a curve C_1 which lies inside C such that the solutions flow from the inside of C_1 to the outside. This is depicted in the margin; the arrows designate the direction of the motion along solution curves. Since there are no equilibrium points in the region between C_1 and C, intuition leads to the conjecture that there must be a closed solution curve (yielding a periodic motion) in this region. This is precisely the case as was proved around the turn of the century by Bendixson. By a more detailed argument, one can show there is only *one* closed

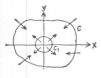

solution curve of Eq. 8, and all other solutions except $x = 0$, $y = 0$, approach this limit cycle as t increases (see Fig. 6-4).

Oscillations of the above type are called self-sustained, since they occur without the influence of any periodic external forces but arise simply from the internal structure of the system and the manner in which energy is transferred from one state to another. Such self-sustained oscillations can only be explained by a nonlinear theory.

A further contrast between linearity and nonlinearity is that nonlinearity can prevent resonance of the kind commonly discussed for linear systems. If the period varies with amplitude, as it does for nonlinear systems, then a periodic disturbance will become out of phase with the free motion, and the forcing function will be a hindrance to increasing amplitude.

How stable is stable?

Another thing that nonlinear differential equations can do for us is to help us understand the stability of systems. Often it is desirable to know how large a perturbation the system can withstand and still return to about its original condition. Sometimes the answer is easy to see—for example, in the classic case of a ball on a curved hilly track.

However, things are not always this obvious. In more realistic problems it is necessary to set up the appropriate differential equations and to inquire as to the stability of their solutions. That is if the values predicted by the solution stay "close" to the desired value the system is "stable." However, in more sophisticated investigations of stability it is necessary to distinguish at least three increasing degrees of stability: things are either stable, asymptotically stable, or asymptotically stable in the large.

Mathematically these three degrees of stability are defined as follows: Let C_1 be an arbitrary circle about the origin. Then if for each such C_1 we can find a smaller concentric circle C_2, which is so located that solutions which start inside C_2 remain inside C_1 (Fig. 6-5 left), we say that the origin is *stable*. If this is not the case we say that it is *unstable*. If there is also another circle C_0 about a stable origin such that solutions starting inside C_0 tend to *return* to the origin (Fig. 6-5 right), we say that the origin is *asymptotically stable;* and if *all* solutions tend to return to the origin, the origin is *asymptotically stable in the large.* For example, in Fig. 6-2d the origin is stable but not asymptotically stable. In Fig. 6-2e the origin is asymptotically stable and in Fig. 6-2f the origin is unstable.

Liapunov derived a method for determining

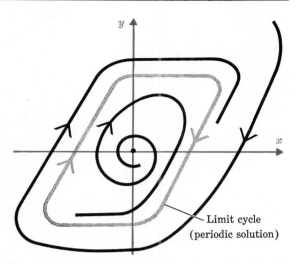

Fig. 6-4. Existence of a periodic limit-cycle solution to Van der Pol's equation is implied by the divergence of solutions near the origin, the convergence of solutions sufficiently far away.

the stability of the equilibrium points of a system that can be applied as soon as the differential equations that describe the system are known. His method does not require a knowledge of their solutions. In essence Liapunov's method consists of selecting a suitable function V in phase space such that (a) it has a minimum at the equilibrium point being investigated, and (b) the contours (surfaces along which the function is a constant) of the function surround the equilibrium point. Then if the flow of solutions in phase space can be shown to cross these contours from the outside towards the inside the equilibrium point is stable, at least for perturbations that keep

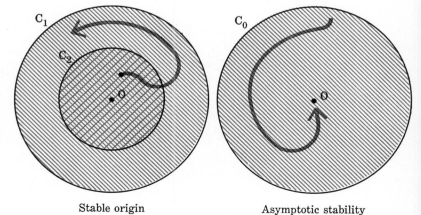

Stable origin   Asymptotic stability

Fig. 6-5. Casual definitions of stability do not satisfy the mathematician, who distinguishes at least three categories, two of which are shown here. By these lights a car shimmying along the highway, but not driving off the road, is stable, though not asymptotically so.

the state of the system within the largest contour for which the flow is always inward.

In carrying out Liapunov's method we actually check whether the Liapunov function, V, decreases along solution-flow lines. Since we required that V have a minimum at the equilibrium point, the fact that it decreases along solutions means these solutions are crossing the contours of V in the desired direction. Remember, we do this without solving the differential equation.

Of course, nothing comes for free in this life —the trick is to be able to find a suitable Liapunov function. We chose the example that follows so that V would have a particularly simple form; don't be deceived thereby, it's not always that easy.

Consider once again the second-order van der Pol's equation, Eq. 8. Letting $\epsilon = -2\rho$, $y = \dot{x} + \epsilon(x - x^3/3)$, we obtain somewhat different first-order equations

$$\dot{x} = y + \epsilon(x^3/3 - x)$$

$$\dot{y} = -x$$

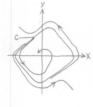

In contrast to the previous discussion, we will assume $\epsilon = -2\rho$ is positive. This is equivalent to reversing the flow in the phase plane, and the picture of the flow is now as in the margin. The origin is asymptotically stable, since every solution inside the old limit cycle tends toward the origin. However, if the system were to be perturbed to a state outside the limit cycle this would no longer be the case; solutions outside the limit cycle go to infinity. The region inside the limit cycle is called the *region of asymptotic stability,* and it is the size and shape of this region that determines just how stable the system is.

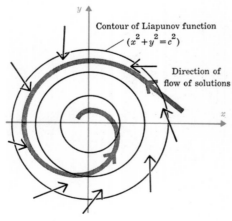

Fig. 6-6. The fact that all solution curves (and not just the one shown) cross contours of Liapunov function from the outside toward the inside proves that the origin is asymptotically stable. Full region of stability is defined by curve corresponding to limit cycle of Fig. 6-4.

It is possible to decide the asymptotic stability of the origin by omitting the nonlinear term $\tfrac{1}{3}x^3$ and examining only the linear approximation. But since the region of asymptotic stability for a linear system is always the whole space, the linear approximation cannot give any information as to how stable the system is. *The extent of the stability of a system is determined by its nonlinearities.*

In van der Pol's equation, the calculation of the limit cycle C (which determines the precise region of asymptotic stability) is extremely complicated. Fortunately the existence of a rather large region of asymptotic stability can be established without knowing C, by using Liapunov's method.

Recall that Liapunov's method begins with the selection of a function $V(x, y)$ which has a minimum at the origin. For our van de Pol's equation we take

$$V(x, y) = \tfrac{1}{2}x^2 + \tfrac{1}{2}y^2$$

At the origin $V(0, 0) = 0$ and everywhere else $V(x, y)$ is greater than zero.

Consider the rate of change dV/dt of V along solutions (see margin); from Eq. 8

$$dV/dt = x\dot{x} + y\dot{y} = (-\epsilon x^2/3) \cdot (3 - x^2)$$

Within the circle of radius $< \sqrt{3}$, that is, $(x^2 + y^2) < 3$, $x^2 < 3$ and $dV/dt \leqq 0$. In fact, within this circle $dV/dt < 0$ if $x \neq 0$. This tells us that for any circle $x^2 + y^2 = c^2 < 3$ the solutions cross the circle as shown in Fig. 6-6. This means that every solution starting inside $x^2 + y^2 = 3$ tends to the origin as t tends to infinity. We have not fixed the limit cycle C, but we have established a sizeable region within which there is asymptotic stability.

Liapunov's is the only general method available for the study of stability and has been widely used, particularly in the Soviet Union, to solve practical problems of stability. Success has been achieved in studying the stability of motion of rigid bodies, in investigating the stability of a large class of nonlinear control systems, and in determining the stability of nuclear reactors. The method and its extensions also play an important theoretical role in the study of differential equations.

There are some methods which guide one in the construction of Liapunov functions but effective use of the method requires ingenuity and experience. There are, as yet, no general schemes for using computers to decide the stability of nonlinear systems.

Bang bang for optimum control

If nonlinear mathematics can illuminate stability problems, it should not be surprising that they also contribute important new ideas to automatic control. After all the proper use of feedback involves an analysis of stability. Does the error tend to zero or does it not?

Nonlinear control permits us to go beyond the limitations of linear feedback and make corrections that depend not just on the difference between present and desired values of a variable but on more complex functions of the error. This permits more certain control over a wider range of variables.

However, we can ask still more of our feedback system—that it be optimal with respect to some further performance criterion. Frequently, for example, we want the system to achieve the desired condition in the least possible time. In many problems the best thing to do is to use the maximum force available but to switch its direction from forward to reverse according to which side of a certain curve in the phase plane (called the switching curve) the system state point resides. This is illustrated in Fig. 6-7.

The control law here is said to be "bang-bang." It jumps rapidly from + to − and at all times uses the maximum control available, which is intuitively what one expects. The control, although made up of linear pieces, is highly nonlinear on the whole and does what no linear control could do—it reduces the error to zero in finite time. Under linear control the error can only tend to zero exponentially. Nonlinear control can achieve performance far beyond that possible by linear control.

Where to from here?

This brief survey only suggests the considerable extent of present understanding of nonlinear differential equations. Actually most of the important questions that can be asked about second-order systems have been answered. This is not surprising since the geometry of flow curves in a plane is not too complicated. As soon as third-order systems are considered, however, the geometry becomes vastly more complicated; we are only at the beginning there.

Nonlinear control offers many unsolved problems, too. Given a performance criterion and a specified limit on the amount of control, it is not always clear that an optimum control law exists. If existence is established, methods must be devised for its computation.

Finally it is difficult to see how a system can be made truly adaptive (see "Learning Machines," page 658) without having the control law depend at least in part on a portion of the past history of the system. Such hereditary dependence in the problem takes one beyond the realm of differential equations; fortunately the pertinent mathematics has been under in-

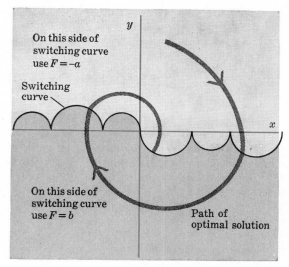

Fig. 6-7. How to stop a pendulum in the least time, given the ability to push towards the right with b units of force or towards the left with a units? Optimal control theory surprises your intuition by instructing you, some of the time, to urge pendulum along (segments of solution path between x-axis and switching curve).

vestigation since long before the conception of adaptive control.

Further reading

A very good elementary introduction to the modern theory of differential equations is a book by Birkhoff and Rota, *Ordinary Differential Equations* (Ginn, 1962, $8.50). For a discussion of the theory of nonlinear oscillations which is not too sophisticated mathematically and contains many physical applications, the reader should consult Minorsky, *Nonlinear Oscillations* (Van Nostrand, 1962, $16.75). A book by LaSalle and Lefschetz, *Stability by Liapunov's Direct Method* (Academic Press, 1961, $5.50), gives a self-contained and rather elementary introduction to the subject of stability as well as some applications to control problems.

A well-written treatment of oscillations of all sorts is contained in J. J. Stoker's *Nonlinear Vibrations* (Interscience, 1950, $8.50). Russian contributions to the field are summarized succinctly and critically in a chapter by J. P. LaSalle, and his mentor, Solomon Lefschetz, that forms Part 6 of *Recent Soviet Contributions to Mathematics* (Macmillan, 1962, $8.75), which LaSalle and Lefschetz also edited.

A unified treatment of oscillations is given in *Oscillations in Nonlinear Systems* by Hale (McGraw-Hill, 1963, $9).

The only books presently available in English on modern control theory are Pontryagin, Boltjanskii, Gamrelidze, and Mishchenko, *The*

Mathematical Theory of Optimal Processes (Interscience, 1962, $11.95), and Richard Bellman, *Adaptive Control Processes: A Guided Tour*

(Princeton University Press, 1961, $6.50). More elementary books on this subject will probably appear in the near future.

FINDING OPTIMUM COMBINATIONS

by Ralph Gomory and Alan Hoffman *

IN BRIEF: *One large and increasingly important class of problems in the domain of combinatorial mathematics involves selecting a combination that optimizes one of the variables of the problem—usually cost, time, or efficiency.*

When the number of combinations is large, the calculations are formidable, but with the development of high-speed computers, they are no longer insuperable. And new techniques render more and more problems "computable."

They have already proved extremely fruitful. The new optimization techniques have turned network planning—vital to a rapidly growing communications system—into an exact science. Transportation and assignment problems can be solved for maximum efficiency or minimum cost. And perhaps the best known product of combinatorial mathematics are the critical-path-scheduling techniques, which enable complex projects to be done on time, for the minimum cost.—S.J.B.

■ Combinatorial problems in the form of puzzles have a long history in mathematics, but comparatively recently these problems have begun to play a more important role. Combinatorial mathematics has emerged from the class of curiosities. Although the techniques it employs are frequently esoteric, the problems themselves may be quite concrete. In fact, much of the subject's charm lies in this juxtaposition of elegant method and practical problem.

Many of the problems involve finding an optimum combination of a large, but finite, number of elements For instance, one might seek the least expensive communication network linking a group of cities, or the least expensive means of distributing goods from various warehouses to the places where they are needed. As we will see, many—although by no means all—of the problems we will encounter seek to minimize cost.

This article will focus on some new optimization techniques. But finding optimum combinations is by no means the whole of combinatorial mathematics. The goal may instead involve finding the number of possible combinations, or

* Ralph Gomory and Alan Hoffman are at IBM's Thomas J. Watson Research Center, Yorktown Heights, New York, where they work in both theoretical and applied mathematical research.

in some cases, finding whether a particular combination exists! Nor are the types of problems considered here in any way exhaustive. Combinatorial questions abound in genetics, chemistry, statistical mechanics, and many other fields.

One striking difference between the environment in which combinatorial mathematics operates today and the environment of twenty years ago, is the difference between what is considered a tractable problem today and what could have been considered tractable in previous years. The electronic computer has made a profound difference. Most of the optimization problems discussed in this paper would have been dismissed by mathematicians of twenty years ago as either "solved" or "impossible." They were solved because, after all, the answers could be obtained in a finite, though large, number of steps. Or they were impossible because no one could ever hope in one lifetime to carry out all those steps. The computer has made some of these impossible problems possible, and mathematicians are trying to devise systematic procedures—called algorithms—to bring those that are still impossible within the realm of practical computability.

Optimizing trees

One particularly simple algorithm provides a solution to the communication network problem mentioned above. Imagine a large number, n, of cities spread out across the country. A communication network is to be built to link them all. Each city must be connected by wires directly or indirectly to every other. If the cost of establishing a direct link between the ith and jth cities is c_{ij}, we can compare the cost of any two proposed solutions. For instance the black network in Fig. 6-8 contains 10 points (nodes) corresponding to 10 cities. The lines (arcs) connecting them represent possible links between the cities; the numbers are the costs of the various links.

Let us pose the general problem: Of all possible networks linking the cities, which is the cheapest? Immediately, we can confine ourselves to networks that are trees, that is, networks that contain no closed paths (loops), for if a network contains a loop, one link of the loop can be removed, reducing the total cost

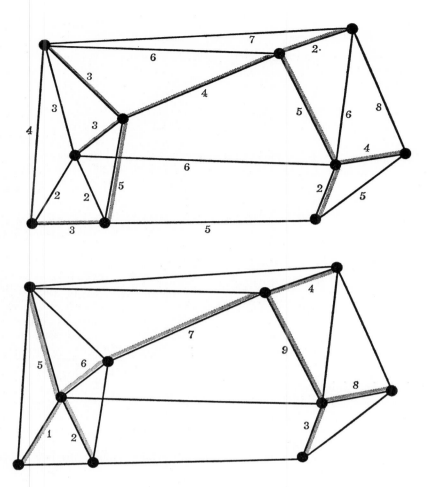

Fig. 6-8. Combinatorial techniques are used here to establish a least-cost communication network. The network represents ten cities and a set of links among them; the numbers are the costs of the links. Since cities need not be connected directly, we can restrict choice to trees, which are networks containing no loops. A systematic method, or algorithm, exists for finding the least-cost tree. Thus, while randomly selected tree, shaded links at the top, costs 31, algorithm selects links in the order indicated by the numerals at the bottom, producing the tree which has the minimum cost of 27.

by the cost of that link, and all cities are still connected that were connected before. Thus, the tree on the top in Fig. 6-8 (shaded area) links all the cities at a total cost of 31. So the question of the cheapest network becomes the question: Which tree has the lowest total cost?

Merely restricting ourselves to trees does not help too much for the trees are already fantastically numerous. (One can show that there are n^{n-2} of them.) Nevertheless, the best possible tree can be found by the following algorithm:

(1) Find the link of lowest cost. (If there are several with the same lowest cost, choose one of them arbitrarily.) This will be part of the final tree.

(2) Choose from among the remaining links the one with lowest cost that does not form a loop with the lines already chosen. Repeat this process, until all cities are connected.

This simple and rapid procedure, due to Kruskal, can be shown to give the least-cost connecting tree which is, as we have seen, the least-cost connecting network. Applying this calculation to our example we bring in the links in the order shown at the bottom in Fig. 6-8 and obtain an optimal tree which has a total cost of only 27.

Unfortunately, the simplicity of this procedure is almost unique. Many seemingly simple

problems involving trees or least-cost connecting networks have no solution procedure even remotely comparable. Consider the same map and the same cities and pose the problem of finding the cheapest single loop that passes through all of them. If the costs are now interpreted as the transportation costs of going from one city to the next, this would be the least-cost tour for a salesman obliged to visit all cities and return to his starting point. Unfortunately, this is still a very difficult problem for a large number of cities.

Transportation and assignment problems

There is, however, a certain class of problems which share some of the tractability of our first example. These problems, which include network flow problems and the assignment problem, are all basically variations on the easily stated transportation problem.

Imagine n cities to be supplied with grain from m granaries located in different parts of the country. The amounts of grain needed at each city are known, as are the supplies at each granary, and the total supply of grain in the granaries is enough to meet the demand. How much should be sent from each granary to each city in order that the total shipping cost is as small as possible? It is assumed that the cost of shipping along each route is proportional to the amount sent, but the proportionality constant (cost per ton) differs from one route to another.

Let a_i denote the amount of grain available at the ith granary, b_j the amount required at the jth city, and c_{ij} the unit cost per ton of shipments from i to j. Then our problem is to choose amounts x_{ij}, denoting the amount sent from i to j, which will minimize the total cost, subject to the constraints that the amount of grain shipped from a granary cannot exceed what is in it and that the amount of grain sent to a city must be at least equal to what is needed in the city. Expressed mathematically:

$$\sum_j x_{ij} \leqq a_i \text{ for each granary } i,$$

$$\sum_i x_{ij} \geqq b_j \text{ for each city } j,$$

where all x_{ij} are nonnegative. The total cost

$$\sum_i \sum_j c_{ij} x_{ij}$$

is to be minimized.

Thus our combinatorial problem leads to a system of simultaneous linear inequalities. If the inequality symbols were replaced by equalities, these would be the familiar simultaneous equations that are encountered in high school algebra.

There is one further difference. Here, we are not looking only for values of the variables x_{ij} that satisfy the inequalities, but are looking for that solution which minimizes the total cost. This is a special case of what is known as the linear programming problem: the minimization of a linear combination of variables, when the variables must satisfy linear inequalities. Fortunately, since the work of G. B. Dantzig in 1947, there exists a very effective algorithm, called the Simplex method, for obtaining the solution to linear programming problems. It is a completely algebraic method, but what it does can be described geometrically.

Each set of values of the x_{ij} which satisfy the inequalities can be thought of as a point in multi-dimensional space; the set of all points satisfying the inequalities is a convex, polyhedral figure in that space. Now, it is a theorem that the desired minimum will be attained at a vertex (or corner) of that convex figure. The Simplex method selects successive vertices, moving from vertex to neighboring vertex in the direction of decreasing cost, until one arrives at the vertex where the cost is as small as possible. The geometric properties of the figure insure that there is only one such minimum.

Of course, all of the steps of the Simplex method are carried out algebraically, but each algebraic step has its geometric equivalent. Dantzig's technique is so effective that it has been applied successfully to systems of inequalities of the same format with hundreds of sources and thousands of demand points.

Looking at a special case of the transportation problem leads to some new discoveries. Consider the case where the a_i and b_j are all 1. The constraints then become

$$\sum_j x_{ij} \leqq 1 \text{ and } \sum_i x_{ij} \geqq 1$$

An example of such a situation is where i refers to individuals, j refers to possible jobs to which these individuals may be assigned, and c_{ij} is a score that measures the skill of the ith person when doing the jth job. A reasonable way to allocate people to jobs is to favor the allocation where the sum of the scores for the man-job assignments actually made is greatest. This suggests using the transportation-problem format, where we attach the following meaning to the variables x_{ij}: if $x_{ij} = 1$, individual i is assigned to job j; if $x_{ij} = 0$, i is not assigned to j.

Of course, we also want to maximize, rather than minimize,

$$\sum_i \sum_j c_{ij} x_{ij}$$

but this is a trivial difference.

It is natural to ask what interpretation is given to a solution in which the x_{ij} are fractions. The answer is that this won't happen. Although in most linear programming problems the answers will not come out in whole numbers, the special system of the transportation problem has the remarkable property that the answers are whole numbers when the a_i and b_j are whole numbers. Since the x_{ij} are restricted to nonnegative values, it is easy to see that when the a_i and b_j are all 1, this will make each x_{ij} either 0 or 1.

These are just two instances of a huge class of problems. Aside from the Simplex method, other special methods have been developed, tailored for the assignment problem. By the use of the Simplex and these other methods, systems involving hundreds of jobs and people can be solved rapidly in digital computers.

Project planning

A problem related to the assignment problem deals with the optimal planning of complicated projects. One diagram frequently used to exhibit the inter-relationships in a complicated project is illustrated for a sailboat launching in Fig. 6-9. The circles indicate the jobs that must be done; the arrows indicate precedence relations, that is, which jobs must be done before others. In our figure, for example, the mast cannot be stepped before the boat is launched

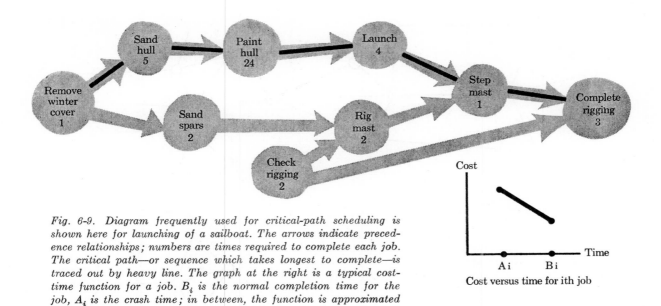

Fig. 6-9. Diagram frequently used for critical-path scheduling is shown here for launching of a sailboat. The arrows indicate precedence relationships; numbers are times required to complete each job. The critical path—or sequence which takes longest to complete—is traced out by heavy line. The graph at the right is a typical cost-time function for a job. B_i is the normal completion time for the job, A_i is the crash time; in between, the function is approximated by a straight line.

Cost versus time for ith job

and the necessary rigging attached to the mast. The time required to do each job is indicated by the numbers in the circles.

If we have a sequence of jobs, each one depending only on its immediate predecessor, like the sequence sand hull, paint hull, and launch, then the total time to do the jobs in this sequence is merely the sum of the individual job times. However, when there are several branches of the network, jobs may have to wait for each other.

It is easy to see that the minimum time required to complete the entire project is the largest total time encountered on any path from a starting point to the finish. The path along which this total is obtained is called the "critical path," and is indicated by a heavy line. The calculation of the critical path in a given network is itself a simple example of a type of problem we will encounter later under the heading Dynamic Programming.

So far we have assumed there is a fixed time required to do each job. Actually, it is often the case that by spending more money, a job can be speeded up. Suppose the project is to be finished at a certain definite fixed time T. Which jobs should be speeded up, and how much, so that the project is done on time and the least possible amount of money is spent? Certainly, at first one would want to speed up the jobs on the critical path, but beyond that, the way to proceed is not as clear. Again, we will introduce linear inequalities.

Let x_i be the time at which the ith job is started, and t_i the time it takes to execute. Then, if the ith job precedes the jth job, we must have

$$x_i + t_i \leqq x_j$$

If we write down all such inequalities, then any values for the x's and t's satisfying the inequalities give us a possible schedule. In addition, if we denote the last job by N, then

$$x_N + t_N \leqq T$$

with T as the finishing time referred to above.

Turning now to cost minimization, imagine that the cost-time relation for each particular job is given by a function like that diagrammed in Fig. 6-9. Here B_i is the normal completion time and A_i the fastest possible completion time. It is reasonable to approximate the cost for completing in some time between them by a straight line.

Thus, the cost C_i for a particular job is given by

$$C_i(t_i) = c_i - d_i t_i$$

which is simply the equation of the line in Fig. 6-9. To minimize the total cost, then, we must minimize

$$\sum_i (c_i - d_i t_i)$$

subject to the inequalities given above, and to

$$A_i \leqq t_i \leqq B_i$$

for all i. Since this is a linear expression, we again have a linear programming problem. Some of the special methods developed for the assignment problem can be used to great effect here, making the calculation quite practicable for projects involving more than a thousand jobs. The diagramming of complicated projects this way is now very common, and the use of the critical path in the minimum cost calculation is becoming widespread.

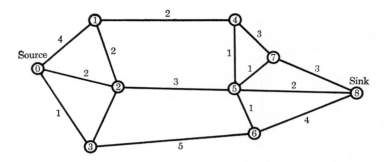

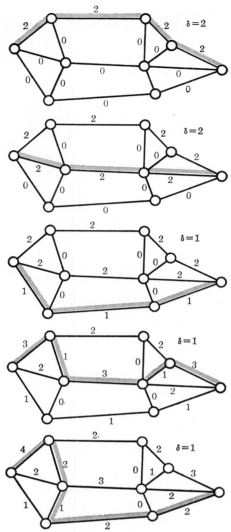

Fig. 6-10. Algorithm for determining maximum flow, applied to the network above, gives a maximum flow of 7. The nodes are labeled by the circled numbers; the other numbers are the capacities of the arcs. The sequence at the right illustrates the result of applying the algorithm; the numbers here refer to flows. We start with all flows = 0, and, applying the algorithm, trace out the path from source to sink shown by the shaded line at the top. We then send along this path the maximum additional flow, δ, that the capacities given above will permit. In this case, δ = 2. Retaining the new set of flow values, we proceed to trace out other paths, each time sending as much additional flow along the path as we can, until we no longer find a path that is not already at maximum. Here we find the maximum flow after five such steps. While order and number of paths are not unique, the maximum flow value is.

Network flow problems

Another problem closely related to the assignment problem is the problem of maximal flow. Consider the network in Fig. 6-10. The nodes are numbered, with two nodes distinguished as a source and a sink. The numbers next to the arcs are the assigned "capacities" c_{ij}. The problem is to send the maximal possible "flow" from source to sink. Intuitively, flow can be thought of as liquid flow through pipes with the flow through each pipe limited by the capacity; fluid is conserved at all points except the source and sink.

A more precise statement is that a flow is a set of numbers x_{ij}, where P_i and P_j denote points of the network, P_0 is the source, P_N is the sink. We impose the conditions:

$$\sum_i x_{ip} - \sum_j x_{pj} = 0, \; p \neq 0, N$$

(fluid is conserved at all of the nodes except at the source and the sink)

$$-c_{ij} \leqq x_{ij} \leqq c_{ij}$$

(flow does not exceed capacity), and also:

$$x_{ij} = -x_{ji}$$

which simply states that there is only one flow along a particular arc. The maximal flow is the one maximizing

$$\sum_i x_{iN} = f = \sum_j x_{oj}$$

Again we have a linear system and something to be maximized.

Before proceeding let us define a cut. A cut is any collection of arcs whose removal splits the network into two separated parts, one containing the source and one containing the sink. In Fig. 6-10, the arcs (1, 4), (2, 5), (3, 6) form a cut. The capacity of a cut is defined as the total capacity of the arcs in the cut. The cut (1, 4), (2, 5), (3, 6) has capacity 10; the cut (7, 8), (5, 8), (6, 8) has a capacity 9.

Clearly, the maximal flow value f possible in a given network is less than the capacity of any cut, for all the fluid going from source to sink must cross the cut, and could not exceed the sum of the capacities of the arcs in the cut. Hence, max flow $f \leqq$ capacity of a cut. This statement plays a role in the proof that the algorithm for finding maximal flows which we shall describe works. And the algorithm in turn plays a role in strengthening the inequality into the theorem: Maximum flow f = minimum cut capacity C, where the minimum is to be taken over all possible cuts.

The algorithm for maximal flows is as follows:

Start with all arc flows $x_{ij} = 0$.

(1) Place a check mark on the source P_0, go to Step (2).

(2) Select a point P_i with one check (if there are any—on the first round it will be P_0 itself), and go to Step (3). If there are no points with exactly one check, stop.

(3) For each unchecked P_j connected to P_i, check P_j if $x_{ij} < c_{ij}$. If P_N has been checked, stop; otherwise, go to Step (4).

(4) Put a second check on P_i, and return to Step (2).

This algorithm is simply a systematic procedure for tracing every possible path from source to sink and sending the largest possible flow through each path.

If this process ends in Step (3), so that P_N is checked, you have found a sequence of points leading from source to sink and connected by arcs such that $x_{ij} < c_{ij}$ for each arc (i, j). If $\delta = \min (c_{ij} - x_{ij})$ over all arcs in this path, this much additional fluid can be put over the path without violating any constraints; that is, for each arc in the path, a new flow $x_{ij} = x_{ij} + \delta$ is introduced, increasing the total flow by δ. So, if the process ends in (3), we have a bigger flow. We then erase all checks and start the checking process again with the new x_{ij}.

If, on the other hand, the process ends in (2), then the current set of x_{ij} values already gives the maximal flow. To see this, consider how the process can stop in (2). It stops in (2) because there are no single checks left; therefore every node has two checks or none. Call the set of nodes having two checks the S_1 and those having none S_2.

Since the source P_0 started with one check, it is in S_1 and since P_N never received one check [this would have stopped the process in (3)] it is in S_2. The arcs (i, j) connecting points in S_1 with points in S_2 must all have flows $x_{ij} = c_{ij}$, for if $x_{ij} < c_{ij}$, then when P_i was selected in (2), P_j would have received a check, but it did not. Certainly these arcs form a cut, and the flow f' across the arc equals the capacity (because $x_{ij} = c_{ij}$) and goes from points in S_1 to those in S_2. Since fluid is conserved at the nodes, all this flow reaches the sink; so f', the flow into the sink, equals C', the capacity of that cut. But,

$$f' \leqq \max f \leqq \min C \leqq C'$$

and, since $f' = C'$, we have

$$f' = \max f = \min C = C'$$

Thus, we have established the max-flow mincut theorem, and also proved that when the procedure stops in (3) the current flow is maximal. For the network in Fig. 6-10, we find a maximal flow of 7. Notice that the cut $(0, 1)$, $(0, 2)$, $(0, 3)$ has capacity 7, and is therefore a minimum cut.

The marriage problem

A famous combinatorial problem is the following: given n boys and n girls, some of whom are acquainted with each other, is it possible to pair off the boys and girls in n marriages so that each marriage is between a boy and a girl previously acquainted? This, of course, depends on the pattern of acquaintanceships. Consider, for example, a certain set of 7 boys and consider the girls who know at least one of these boys. If there are only 5 such girls, then the marriages could not happen. At least two of the boys could not find partners. More generally, if the marriages are possible, then it must be true that, if we select any k boys (from the group of n boys) the number of girls, each of whom is acquainted with at least one of the k boys, must be at least k. Otherwise, it would not be possible to arrange the marriages.

While it is obvious that the condition is necessary for the n marriages to be arranged, it is not clear that it is sufficient. However, it turns out that if this condition *alone* is satisfied, then the marriages can be arranged. There are several proofs of this theorem, which was originally found by P. Hall and E. Egervary. We shall show one which is based on the max-flow min-cut theorem.

The network needed for this proof is like the one in Fig. 6-11, containing nodes $B_1, \ldots, B_n$, one for each boy connected to the source S, and nodes $G_1, \ldots, G_n$, one for each girl, connected to the sink K. The arcs joining boys to source and girls to sink are all of capacity 1. The only other arcs present are arcs B_iG_j of infinite capacity which link the ith boy and jth girl, if and only if they are acquainted. We will now proceed to show, using our flow theorem, that if every k boys do know at least k girls, the marriages can be arranged.

In this network, the maximum flow will be from left to right, that is, units of flow go from the source to the B_i's to the G_j's and on to the sink. This gives a natural pairing of boys and girls; a boy and girl are to be married if there is a unit of flow through the arc joining them. They are clearly acquainted or there would have been no arc joining them. No two B_i are ever assigned in this way to the same G_j for the capacity of any girl-sink arc is only 1. Also the ith boy B_i is assigned only to a girl G_j whom he knows for these are the only ones to which B_i is linked. Consequently, a maximal flow of value p (where $p \leqq n$) will

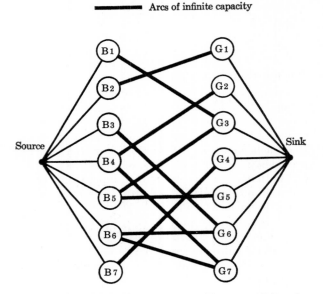

———— Arcs of capacity 1
━━━━ Arcs of infinite capacity

Fig. 6-11. Network used to provide a proof for the marriage problem is shown here for the simple case of seven boys and seven girls. Heavy arcs connect boys and girls who are acquainted. By applying the minimum-cut-maximum-flow theorem, conditions can be established sufficient to insure that all boys and girls can be married off, and in such a way that each couple is previously acquainted.

naturally yield an assignment of p boys to p girls. The question of when all boys can be so assigned is the question of whether $p = n$?

If $p < n$, then by our theorem, the capacity of the minimum cut also $= p < n$. What arcs make up the minimum cut? Certainly no arcs of infinite capacity can be included, so the cut consists of some p_1 arcs (all of capacity 1) from among those emanating from the source and $p - p_1$ others attached to the sink.

Consider the B_i *not* attached to cut arcs, they are $n - p_1$ in number. They are linked only to G_j that *are* on cut arcs for otherwise we would have an uncut path from source to sink and our cut arcs would not form a cut. The G_j that are on cut arcs are $p - p_1$ in number. So the $n - p_1$ boys are acquainted with $p - p_1$ girls in toto. If p is less than n, these boys form a set of $k = n - p_1$ boys knowing $p - p_1 < k$ girls. Thus the pairing process can fail only if such a set exists. But it will not fail (the marriages are possible) if every set of boys does know at least k girls among them as was to be proven. Note that our network flow algorithm actually gives us the maximal flow, and, hence, the marriages whenever they are possible.

The marriage problem has played a central role in much of the recent work on combinatorial optimization. First, some of the com-

binatorial algorithms have been based on applying the theorem which gives conditions on the acquaintanceships for the marriages to be arranged. It is sometimes hard to find the boys and girls, but they are there! Second, if one seeks to pair off the boys and girls in some specific way (the theorem tells us only when there exists some way), then one is led to develop algorithms whose principal ideas can be used in other contexts.

Integer programming

Since we have been so successful with our applications of systems of linear inequalities, we might push on and try to do all combinatorial optimization problems the same way.

Imagine that an expedition is to be formed from among the men of some community. The expedition is to be as large as possible because this improves its chances of success. On the other hand, the village must continue to function while the expedition is away. Thus certain conditions are to be imposed.

For example, the fire department should not be reduced below three members; there must be at least 35 people left, capable of working in the fields, etc. Again, we can impose these conditions by means of linear inequalities. Let us assign a variable x_i to each person who might be involved in the expedition. When the solution is obtained, we will interpret the values in this way: if $x_i = 1$, that person remains behind. If $x_i = 0$, he goes on the expedition. The fire department condition means

$$\sum_{i \epsilon F} x_i \geqq 3$$

where the sum is over the indices of men belonging to the fire department. Similarly,

$$\sum_{i \epsilon H} x_i \geqq 35$$

with the sum in this inequality over the indices of people who qualify as fieldhands. (These groups, of course, may overlap.) We could go on listing each of our requirements as an inequality.

Maximizing the size of the expedition is equivalent to minimizing the number of people left behind. Therefore, the objective is to minimize

$$\sum_i x_i$$

where the sum is now over all values of i. Again, we have a linear programming problem. However, if we proceed to solve it using the Simplex method, we will have an unpleasant surprise. Our solution may very well look like this: $x_1 = \frac{1}{4}$, $x_2 = \frac{3}{4}$, $x_3 = 0$, $x_4 = \frac{1}{2}$, etc. The answers will, in general, not come out to be zero and one, which are the only values of x_j we can interpret.

We have, thus, come up with a very severe and common limitation to the use of linear inequalities for combinatorial work. It is very often the case, as it is here, that we must insist on integral or even 0, 1 answers. The problem of obtaining a solution in integers is called integer programming. During the past few years, special methods for integer programming resembling the Simplex method have been devised, and some useful calculations performed with them.

These methods do not yet appear to be as efficient as the general Simplex method for problems in which the integrality requirement is not present, and (because of the intrinsically more complicated geometry of integer programming problems) probably never will be. The search for improved methods of integer-programming calculation is a very active area of mathematical investigation.

Cutting stock problem

Another complication that occurs in the attempt to use the concepts of linear programming in combinatorial optimization, is that the number of different kinds of combinations may be enormous, and this may be reflected in the fact that the number of variables or the number of inequalities may be too vast to write down. Just as in the problem of finding the minimum tree, however, this difficulty may be overcome in some cases. One such case is the Cutting Stock Problem.

Assume that a paper machine produces large rolls of paper of some fixed width W. The paper company cannot sell these rolls to its customers for they need rolls of smaller widths, W_1, $W_2, \ldots, W_n$. Let us assume that the customers need amounts D_i of width W_i. The paper company would like to supply these demands, using as few big rolls as possible.

If we formulate this as a linear programming problem, we have to take into account all possible ways in which the standard roll can be cut up. The variable x_j will indicate the number of rolls cut up in the jth way. Specifically, the jth way gives a_{ij} rolls of width W_i, and we will consider every possible way. Our linear programming problem becomes,

$$\text{Minimize } \sum_j x_j$$

$$\text{subject to } \sum_j a_{ij}x_j \geqq D_i$$

that is, the number of rolls of each width is at least as many as the customers want.

Now, there are two things wrong with this formulation. One is the familiar integer diffi-

culty. We cannot interpret a value of x_j like $73\frac{1}{2}$ as we have no way to cut up $73\frac{1}{2}$ rolls according to a given pattern. However, this difficulty is more apparent than real, since orders are approximate only and extra rolls created by rounding a non-integer solution (74 instead of $73\frac{1}{2}$) are often acceptable.

There still remains the problem of size. There may be, in a moderately large problem, millions of cutting patterns, too many to allow the matrix even to be written down, much less calculated with.

Recent developments in linear programming have enabled us to deal with these enormous problems, and take into account every possible way of cutting. The reason is that the columns of the matrix, that is, the cutting patterns, are not given arbitrarily, but by some sort of systematic rule. In the cutting stock problem, the rule is quite simple. Any set of n nonnegative integers a_{ij} can form a column, provided only that

$$\sum_i a_{ij}W_i \leqq W$$

In other words, anything will do as a cutting pattern as long as it doesn't cut more paper from a roll than there is in it. This enables one to carry out the steps of the Simplex algorithm without listing all possible cutting patterns at the start, because the computer can find the best new vertex, using this rule to generate the columns of the matrix that are needed.

Dynamic programming

A different optimization technique is that based upon a recursive calculation (dynamic programming). A recursive calculation is one in which the calculations for one set of conditions are given by a formula based on the result for simpler conditions, in some logical order.

Consider the problem of job setup. A machine is to do a large variety of jobs, but must be reset for each one. The time it takes to reset for job j, following job i is t_{ij}. The question is, in what order should a large number of jobs be done in order to minimize the time spent resetting?

To solve this problem, we consider a subset, S, of jobs. Let $F(S, a) =$ total time it takes to do jobs in S ending up at job a, where a is a job in S. What is the order of doing jobs in S?

We can develop a recursion formula by considering another set T which contains all of the members of S except a. The formula is

$$F(S, a) = \min \{F(T, b) + t_{ba}\}$$

where b is a member of T and we minimize over all possible choices of b. This formula will generate the best order of doing the jobs.

This same recursive calculation can be used in many situations. The traveling salesman problem mentioned above can be solved by a much more complicated recursion, although in that case the computational load becomes prohibitive if there are more than about thirteen cities in the network.

Like most of the methods discussed above, dynamic programming is a relatively recent development. Nevertheless, most of the modern theory of inventory management is based conceptually on the recursive point of view.

Further reading

There have been a number of recent books on combinatorial mathematics, all of which require considerable mathematical background. *The Theory of Graphs*, by Ore (Am. Math. Society, 1962, $9.20), is an excellent introduction to the subject of its title, and probably the one with least mathematical prerequisites. *The Theory of Graphs and Its Applications*, by Berge (Wiley, 1962, $6.50), is devoted principally to problems involving networks, and *Flows in Networks*, by Ford and Fulkerson (Princeton U. Press, 1962, $6.00), is entirely on that topic. The last book is especially valuable for persons interested in actual algorithms involving network problems.

The best current source on linear programming is the book, *Linear Programming and Its Extension*, by George Dantzig (Princeton U. Press, 1962, $11.50). For dynamic programming, see *Dynamic Programming*, by Bellman (Princeton U. Press, 1957, $6.75). The application of linear programming to business problems is discussed in an article by Henderson and Schlaifer, "Mathematical Programming: Better Information for Better Decision Making," *Harvard Bus. Rev.*, May–June 1954, p. 73.

Another excellent source of information is *An Introduction to Combinatorial Analysis*, by Riordan (Wiley, 1958, $8.50). It is devoted mainly to "counting" problems. The approach it takes is somewhat different from the one taken here, and it provides an introduction to another important area of combinatorial mathematics. Another fine book is *Combinatorial Mathematics*, by Ryser (Wiley, 1963, $4.00), which is less interested in counting problems and more in the question of whether or not certain combinatorial arrangements exist.

CRITICAL PATH DIAGRAMMING

by Gale Nevill and David Falconer *

IN BRIEF: *In all project planning and scheduling, the jobs necessary to accomplish the project must be determined. This is usually easy to do. Finding how they interrelate and constrain each other is not so easy. The critical path method does this graphically by assigning to each task an arrow and constructing a network of these such that a task cannot begin until its necessary predecessors are complete. Once the network, or arrow diagram, is complete, and time estimates assigned to each job, the longest sequence of jobs—the critical path—can be found. This controls the duration of the project. From the network, tasks can be found that can be done concurrently, thus saving time. Slack time drawn from tasks further down the line can be used on earlier critical jobs. The article focuses on simplified CPM techniques applicable to small projects containing up to 40–50 tasks, and applies them to a typical example project.—F.P.*

* Colleagues at Southwest Research Institute, San Antonio, Texas, when they prepared this article, both authors have returned to the academic world: Gale Nevill is with the Department of Engineering Science and Mechanics at the University of Florida, Gainesville; David Falconer is obtaining his Ph.D. in mathematics at the University of Texas.

■ The rather odd-looking, cannon-like device illustrated in Fig. 6-12 is, in reality, a special-purpose shock tube built recently at the Southwest Research Institute. Closed at one end, the tube has a thin and relatively weak diaphragm across it at some intermediate point. At its simplest, operation of the tube involves a buildup of pressure at the closed end; then the diaphragm is pierced, allowing a shock wave to travel down the tube toward the open end. Here, a structural model is placed so that the influence of the shock wave on the model can be observed and measured.

This installation is an example of a small, fairly modest research and development project which had to be designed, built, and put into working order on a very rapid time schedule. In planning and scheduling this project, we employed a simplified version of the so-called critical path or network methods so spectacularly successful in recent years on very large projects—the use of PERT (Program Evaluation and Review Technique) on the Navy's Polaris program, to cite one example.

This attack on the problem proved highly successful, for we were able to order the various jobs on the project so as to cut the total

Fig. 6-12. This $20,000 research shock tube was designed and built under the supervision of the authors. Even on such a small project, they found critical path methods helpful. This shock tube is composed of fairly simple elements: flanges at right constrain a large diaphragm, usually made of soft aluminum or Mylar. Pressure is built up in section of tube to right. Buttress at far right absorbs impulse when diaphragm is pierced and pressure released. Frame at left carries model whose behavior under resultant shock wave is being studied. (Courtesy Southwest Research Institute)

time by 50% over that required to perform the same series of jobs sequentially. We have used this method on a number of other small R&D projects and have found it to be of real value. Our purpose in this article is to present a clear picture of the concepts and techniques in critical path methods and to show, through the example of the shock tube, how they may be applied to small projects—those involving less than 40–50 individual tasks—in which the planning is done by the technical supervisor himself. We hope that in this way you will be stimulated to give this method a try on your own research and development planning problems.

The idea and its advantages

Essentially, the critical path method of project planning involves identifying the major tasks to be performed, deciding the rough order in which they must be performed, and—by a graphical model—optimizing their performance. The graphical tool that provides the basis of the method is termed an activity network, and is somewhat analogous to a road map on which times to accomplish the project tasks or activities are plotted instead of distances.

Such a network contains many paths or sequences of activities through which one must progress from the start of the project to its end. The length of any path is simply the calendar duration found by totaling the time estimates for the activities comprising the path. The *critical* path is the longest of these alternate paths; it is critical because it controls the project completion date. Identifying the critical

path simply requires adding up the time estimates along each possible path and then comparing them.

The critical path is useful for planning in the following ways: It indicates which activities could be accelerated to advantage and clearly shows which jobs should be monitored most closely while the project is underway. If any job which is on the critical path is delayed, the completion date of the entire project is pushed back. However, time lost by slippage of such an activity can perhaps be regained by expediting a succeeding job on the critical path. Hence, by using information derived from critical path planning, it is possible to monitor the project effectively and, when slippage does occur, to decide selectively which activities to speed up.

There are other advantages to be gained. One, alluded to above, is the clear picture you get of the technical constraints and interrelationships among the various project activities. Another is that the planning and scheduling aspects of the project are separated, allowing for more effective treatment of each. The method also forces you to think in a disciplined way about the tasks to be performed, their resource requirements, and their interrelationships. Once into such an analysis, you can quickly see when some arbitrarily imposed completion date is not feasible, and when work scope or resources must be adjusted to achieve an imposed date. Finally, the network can be invaluable in fighting unreasonable demands on project personnel by higher management.

Although the concepts of the critical path method (CPM) can be expressed in mathematical terms, such an approach is not necessary for understanding it in its simplified form as applied to small projects. We will present here a phenomenological approach that should make clear the basic ideas and, at the same time, allow you to try the method yourself without the burden of detailed pre-study. If you find the method yielding results, that is sufficient time, we feel, to go back to the original sources (see the bibliography following the article), or to extend the method to more ambitious projects by means of computer programming techniques.

Preparing the activity network

First, we must—as in most planning—prepare a list of all jobs which must be accomplished to complete the project. In the jargon of management science these are called activities. For each we consider three questions: (1) What immediately precedes the activity? (2) What immediately follows it? (3) What can be done concurrently with it? Usually we prepare a formal list of answers to the first and second, and jot down for future reference any pertinent thoughts on the third. In doing this, it is very important to obtain the best possible information, and usually the best source is the person who will perform the activity or one who has carried out a similar activity—an obvious point, but one too often ignored.

Armed with the activity list and as much information as possible about each activity thereon, we move to the heart of the critical path method and its first unique feature: arrow diagramming, or network preparation. The basic idea is to select an activity, call it X, and represent it by an arrow:

The length of the arrow has no significance. Next, we attach to the head of this arrow those activities, say Y, Z, and W, which immediately follow it and attach to the tail all those activities, say U, and V, which immediately precede it:

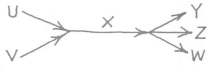

The points at which two or more arrows interconnect are called nodes and represent events or milestones in the project. To complete the network, we continue connecting arrows until all activities in the project are included.

A convenient way to start the network is to pick an activity that has no predecessor, then continue using its successors until a job is reached that has no successor. This process is repeated until all activities have been charted. In order to show definite starting and finishing points for the project, the network must originate at a single node and terminate at a single node. Thus, all activities without predecessors originate at a common node. Likewise, the heads of all arrows with no followers terminate at a common node.

During network preparation, several things invariably occur. We discover that some activities have been overlooked and that some should be broken down into several. Some jobs that seemed unrelated actually have a crucial interdependence, or vice versa. In the shock tube project, for example, the flanges could not be designed until the diaphragm they supported was selected. Preparing the network is probably the most significant part of CPM planning on smaller projects: It sheds much light on the organization of a project and, when the network is complete, the project activities list has often changed quite significantly.

Once the network has been drawn, we can determine at a glance the interrelationships between any job and the others. For example, in the arrow diagram sketched above, the predecessors and successors of X are readily seen: job X cannot begin until jobs U and V are completed; and once they are, nothing else prevents X from proceeding.

In order to accommodate more complex task relationships, however, further refinements are necessary. For example, consider a network node of the following, quite common form:

Here, jobs leaving the node must *all* have the same predecessors and those entering the node must have the same followers. Putting it differently, any two jobs leaving a node either have all predecessors in common, or none in common. Likewise, two jobs entering a node either have all successors in common or none in common.

These logical requirements can be generalized in three rules:

(1) All jobs entering a node must have identical successors,

(2) All jobs leaving a node must have identical predecessors, and

(3) A node must describe the complete relationships between the entering and leaving jobs.

There is one situation in which these rules require supplemental help. Suppose we wished to express a task relationship which has the following two components:

and:

We might be tempted to draw this as:

This way, however, the rules are violated because the interrelationships are incorrectly shown since the start of activity Z does not depend on termination of Y.

To circumvent this logical difficulty, we introduce the dummy activity—one in which work is not done, in which neither time nor money is expended. Its only purpose is to show the proper interrelationship between activities; it usually appears as a dashed line. The logical difficulty in the previous illustration may be resolved as follows:

This sketch shows that W is dependent not only on Y but also on X, through the use of the dummy job X', whereas Z is dependent only on X.

It is possible to develop inadvertently a logical loop—a closed sequence of tasks which, if followed, would lead to repetition of the same tasks over and over. This seldom occurs in a small network but is quite easy to create in a large one. Its existence can be determined by trying to number the nodes—under the restriction that the number at the head of an arrow must be larger than that at its tail. When the network cannot be numbered this way, then there is a logical loop. This is a consequence of the topological properties of such networks. The easiest numbering approach is to count the nodes, then number the last one first by setting its number equal to the node count, and then number the diagram backwards by trial and error according to the restriction noted just previously.

From planning to scheduling

Thus far only the planning phase, which CPM isolates, has been considered. The simplest approach to the scheduling phase is to make a single time estimate for each activity and put each of these down against the corresponding arrow. Then individual path durations can be computed and the critical path, or sequence of activities, can be identified. If you want to be more elaborate, statistically based time estimates for each activity can replace single time estimates in the scheduling process as will be shown later in the article.

Two additional scheduling concepts must be considered. One is *free float,* the maximum slippage in an activity that can be tolerated without affecting the completion date of any other activity. The other is *slack time* (also termed total float), the maximum slippage in an activity that can be tolerated before the overall project completion date is affected. Knowing the existence and location of slack time and free float helps you to reallocate resources, perhaps to shorten the critical path or perhaps to make up time lost by slippage on the critical path. This is one of the most important operational advantages of a network model.

Slack time is easily computed from two other quantities. The first of these is the *earliest possible start time* for an activity. This is determined by the longest sequence of necessary preceding tasks from the start of the project to the start of the activity in question. The other quantity is the *latest possible start time* for an activity, which is the critical path time minus the longest path from the start of the activity, *through the activity,* to the end of the project. Slack time is the difference between the latest and the earliest possible start time. Activities that lie on the critical path, of course, have zero slack time (sometimes even negative slack time if a total duration has been imposed on the project that is shorter than that predicted by the critical path computation).

All the planning discussed so far has been on the basis of a diagrammed activities list that yields nodes or events. Instead, you can start with a list of events or milestones. Each milestone then corresponds to a node in the network. By connecting the nodes, it is possible to work backward and determine the activities. However, we have found the activity approach more useful to us on small projects. The chief value of the milestone approach seems to be for large projects where management is primarily interested in the passage of important events, rather than in the various tasks required to go from event to event.

The shock tube design project

Let us now turn to the application of these concepts to the planning and scheduling of the special purpose shock tube shown in Fig. 6-12, and discussed at the beginning of the article. Our first step in the CPM planning for this facility was the activity list. The first activity was, logically, a preliminary study that covered the various possible shock tube configurations and the operating parameters, leading finally to the specifications from which the facility could be constructed.

Following this came the design and construction activities which we conveniently divided into five basic groups. These, together with their various sub-activities, are listed in the first column of the activity list, below. The next two columns show our decisions as to which activi-

ties must precede and which must follow each of the activities in the first column. The last column gives the time estimate for each as finally included in the network. A brief analysis of four of these activities will give you a feel for the method, the language you have to live with in employing it, and the project itself. After following these through, we suggest you pick another activity at random from the list and check it through yourself for practice.

First off, the preliminary study activity P has no immediate predecessors. Thus the tail of its arrow must be at the node representing the start of the project. It seemed that activities $A1$, $B1$, $C1$, and $D1$ should all follow P immediately. Activity $A1$, the design of the slab and buttress, could not begin until the basic facility specifications were established, so P

ACTIVITY LIST FOR SHOCK TUBE PROJECT

Activities in this column . . .	*Must be preceded by these activities . . .*	*and must be followed by these activities . . .*	*The total time in days for each activity is . .*
P Preliminary study	—	A1, B1, C1, D1	6
A Foundation			
A1 Design slab and buttress	P	A2, A3, A5	7
A2 Grading and forms	A1	A7	6
A3 Acquire reinforcing steel	A1	A4	4
A4 Fabricate reinforcing steel	A3	A7	6
A5 Design tube supports	A1	A6	1
A6 Fabricate tube supports	A5	B8	2
A7 Place reinforcing steel	A2, A4	A8	1
A8 Pour concrete and set	A7	B8	4
B Tube			
B1 Select tube	P	B2	2
B2 Acquire tube	B1	B6	8
B3 Design flanges	C1	B4	3
B4 Acquire flange material	B3	B5	4
B5 Machine flanges	B4	B6	6
B6 Weld flanges to tube	B2, B5	B7	5
B7 Post-weld machining	B6	B8	10
B8 Assembly on foundation	A6, A8, B7	D3	1
C Diaphragms			
C1 Study and selection	P	B3, C2, C4	7
C2 Acquisition	C1	C3	12
C3 Preparation	C2	E1	3
C4 Striker design	C1	C5	3
C5 Striker fabrication	C4	E3	5
D Controls and instruments			
D1 Selection	P	D2	3
D2 Acquisition	D1	D3	10
D3 Installation	B8, D2	D4	2
D4 Checkout and calibration	D3	E1	2
E Facility checkout			
E1 Static pressure test	C3, D4	E2	2
E2 Determine diaphragm burst pressure	E1	E3	10
E3 Calibration with striker	C5, E2	—	5

was listed as immediately preceding *A1*. Upon completion of *A1*, activities *A2* (grading and placing of forms for concrete), *A3* (acquisition of reinforcing steel), and *A5* (design of tube supports) could begin, so we listed these to follow *A1*.

Or consider activity *B6*, the welding of the flanges to the tube sections. First, the flanges must be machined, so activity *B5* should be listed as preceding *B6*. Further, it would be necessary to acquire the tube elements (activity *B2*) before welding the flanges to them. Postweld final machining would probably follow immediately on completion of the welding step, so for activity *B6* we listed *B2* and *B5* as immediately preceding, and *B7* as immediately following.

Finally, look at activity *E1*, the static pressure testing of the facility. This depended on the completion of *D4*, the calibration and checkout of instruments and controls, but it also required a test diaphragm. Hence, both *D4* and *C2* were put ahead of *E1*. Similarly, activity *E3*, the calibration of the facility using the striker, depends not only on *E2*, selecting the burst pressure, but also on *C5*, the striker fabrication step. Since we had no other activity listed that followed *E3*, its arrow was terminated at a node representing the end of the project—the point at which the shock tube was considered ready for operation.

With the interrelationships of the activity list complete, we constructed the network that

graphically represents it. This was, as always, somewhat a trial and error process. The result is Fig. 6-13. From it we could immediately answer questions about activity concurrence. As examples, it is seen that activities *D1*, *A7*, *A5*, *B6*, *C2*, and *C4* could all take place at once, as could *B1* and *C1*. On the other hand, *B6* and *C1* could not, since *B6* depends upon completion of *C1*. Clearly, it is important to know what jobs can be done concurrently so that resources of men and machines can be allocated properly.

Adding in the time factor

The activity network of Fig. 6-13 can be of considerable visual value in itself to a project planner or monitor. However, the inclusion of time estimates for the various activities makes it much more useful. We have found that simple, single time estimates are very satisfactory for small projects. This is the estimate you get by asking the man likely to perform the task what time, based on his experience, the job would be likely to require. For example, time estimates for machining jobs on the shock tube project were based on discussions with the machine shop foreman as to acquisition time for materials, availability of machinists and machines, and the like.

More sophisticated estimating schemes suitable for R&D projects have been devised. The most popular one is that used in PERT which utilizes a statistical concept. For example, assume that an activity will be performed 100

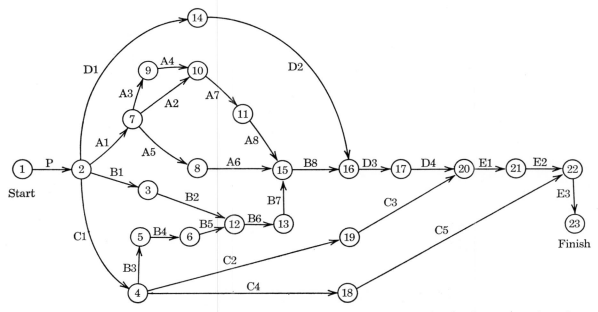

Fig. 6-13. Network model, or arrow diagram for shock tube development project shows tasks from activity list in proper sequence. Numbers in circles are nodes, points that represent milestones in the project and from which the existence of a logical loop in the network can be predicted.

times. In most of these the calendar duration will be about the same. In a few instances, however, the task will be finished in a shorter time; in a few, the task will take longer. The shortest time is the optimistic time estimate t_O. The longest is the pessimistic time estimate t_P. The period that the activity would usually require is the most likely time t_L. The *expected time* t_E (50% probability of completion by a given date) is based on an assumed beta distribution of project durations and can be calculated as

$$t_E = \frac{t_O + 4t_L + t_P}{6}$$

One question that may arise is: How do you estimate when only limited manpower and other resources are available? Usually, you either know the personnel who will be available or you know that additional help will be obtained. In the former case, we recommend making time estimates based on best utilization of available personnel for each task, without regard to the demands of concurrent activities. You may have to adjust your plan later to mesh with these, however. In the latter case, just assume that the manpower required will be available and that adjustments will be made if time or cost requirements so dictate.

For the shock tube project, we made simple single time estimates for each activity assuming a fixed manpower supply. These, in working days, are tabulated in the activity list. Esti-

mates of cost requirements are not included here since usually only the prediction of total cost obtained from the sum of the time estimates is desired. It is possible to extend CPM to find the least-cost means of effecting a required reduction in overall project duration but the problem becomes very complex and involves determining the different cost-duration relations for various activities. We will not go into this except to point out that in small projects this can sometimes be accomplished by inspection.

The activity network with time durations included in color for the various tasks is shown in Fig. 6-14. With these it was possible to calculate the expected durations for various paths, or task sequences. For example, the path in lightest color would require an estimated 40 working days to accomplish, while the dashed color path takes an estimated 46 days. The path shown in deepest color would take an estimated 63 working days. This one is the critical path, since it is the sequence of tasks that takes the longest time to accomplish in the project.

Slack time could now be calculated for the various activities. For example, for activity *A2* the earliest starting time was found to be $7 + 6$ or 13 days after Start. The latest possible starting time was $63 - 33$ or 30 days after Start (the figure 33 is the longest time from node 7, through activity *A2*, to node 23). Thus, the slack time for *A2* is $30 - 13$ or 17 days. Or consider a critical path task: The

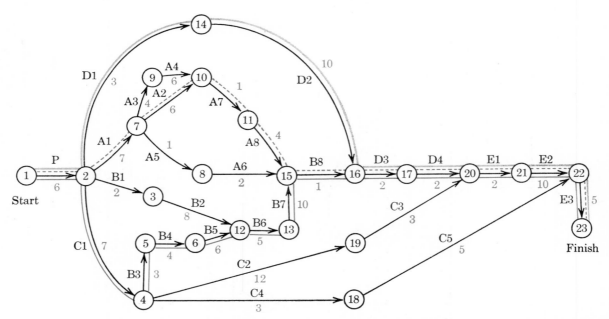

Fig. 6-14. The same network, with time estimates for each activity marked by colored numbers, allows duration of each possible path, or sequence of tasks through the network, to be determined. Longest path is that shown in deepest color. This critical path sets the minimum length of the project.

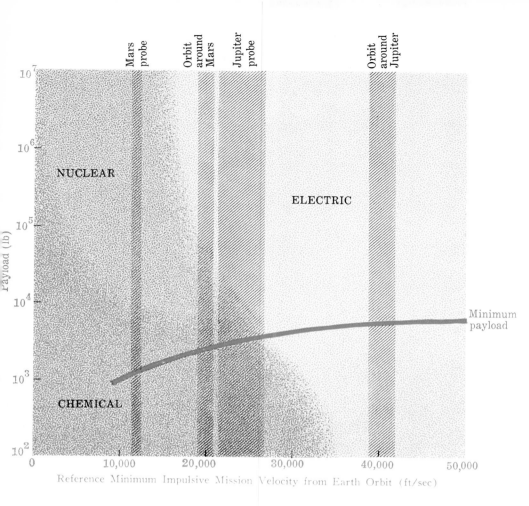

Color Fig. 35. The requirements of any mission are customarily expressed in terms of velocity— escape velocity plus maneuvering velocity plus retarding velocity, etc. Long missions have large velocity requirements. Because they spend propellant frugally, electric rockets have a large "velocity capability" and are able to send large payloads on long missions. See "Ion Rockets," in Chapter 4.

Color Fig. 36. Ablation is a pyrolytic process, as these charred test specimens show. Convective heat from the hot environment that would normally be conducted into the body, raising its interior temperature, is diverted into decomposing the exposed surface. Hot gases flowing around the body erode the exposed surface while the interface between char and virgin material recedes inward. Ablation thus provides heat protection to interior by slowly sacrificing surface. The char plays an important part in the ablation mechanism, as text explains, and different materials char differently. Under same exposure, plastic reinforced with inorganic fibers (left) chars much deeper than the same plastic reinforced with organic fibers (right). Magnification is about 4×. See "Ablation," in Chapter 4. (Courtesy F. Smith, GE Space Sciences Laboratory)

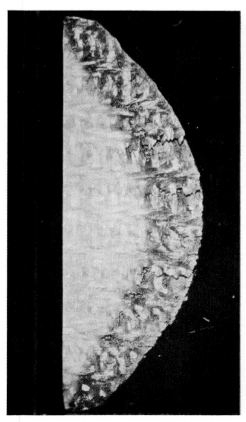 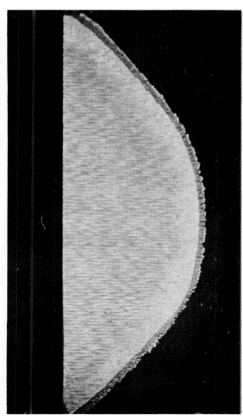

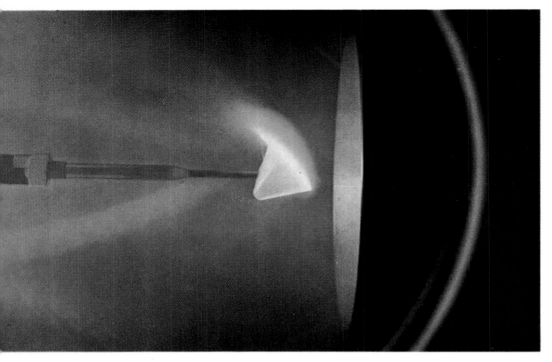

Color Fig. 37. Re-entry in miniature. The gas around a model space vehicle glows as its enormous kinetic energy is converted to heat. The high-velocity gas impacting the model flows from the shock-tube nozzle at right. Experiments of this sort show what the heating rates are likely to be in actual flight. Model is 2½ in. across; temperature exceeds 10,000° C. See "Ablation," in Chapter 4. (Courtesy GE Space Sciences Laboratory)

Rear

Front

Air currents

Rain   Hail   Snow

Color Fig. 38. Key feature of this hailstorm model is the current of air that rises from lower levels at the front side of the storm. In this updraft, which can persist for the better part of an hour, water droplets grow by coalescence, form hail embryos, and these continue to grow by collecting supercooled water droplets as they get caught in the updraft and make repeated round trips. Ideas for interrupting the updraft, anyone? See "Changing the Weather," in Chapter 5. (Courtesy J. Eggleson)

flange design *B3* had an earliest possible start date of 13 days after Start and a latest possible start date of 63 − 50 or 13 days, and hence a slack time of 13 − 13 or 0 days.

Using the network information

With the important factors such as path durations, concurrence relationships, slack times, and so on, available, we could make full use of the network for scheduling activities and for resource distribution. However, this general problem is too broad and involves too many combinations of limitations, restrictions, and the like to permit optimization by a set of simple rules. Indeed, development of such rules is one of the most pressing needs in the CPM field today. There have been a number of rote methods or algorithms proposed to handle the many contingencies in this problem. However, we feel that for small projects these are prohibitively complex and that an intuitive approach using the network is preferable.

Just what can we do with the information now available to us? Consider the scheduling of the start of various activities. This should be done so as to take advantage of the slack times. For example, with a limited manpower restriction on the shock tube project, we began activity *C1*, the study and selection of diaphragms, immediately after the planning task. This was because *B3*, the design of the flanges, depended on diaphragm selection, and there was no slack time on job *B3* (since it lay on the critical path) that could be used to advantage in selecting the diaphragms. Generally, in a project of this size, the appropriate adjustment of jobs and personnel to do them is readily accomplished from the network, which can also be very useful in scheduling additional help for rush periods during the project.

The end product of CPM planning for such a project as this would be a revised network in which all predictions reflect the various constraints and limitations that are unavoidable. As the project progresses, however, it is often necessary to change the diagram and estimates frequently. This monitoring involves the insertion of actual time durations for activities as they are completed, the revision of estimates where necessary, and the recalculation of slack times. The new slack times are then used to guide changes in plans, redistributions of resources, and so on as necessary.

What course of action did the network suggest on the shock tube project, and what was the result? First, the manpower available turned out to be insufficient to make our required completion date. Part time help was procured to do the noncritical tasks under foundation and diaphragms (groups *A* and *C* in the activity list). Controls and instruments were selected and acquired (tasks *D1* and *D2*) by personnel taking advantage of slack in other task groups (principally *B*, *D3*, *D4*, and *E*). The result was completion in 70 working days. This we considered a vast improvement over the estimated 140 days required to do all the tasks sequentially, without regard to possible concurrent accomplishment.

Further reading

Reference articles and publications on this subject abound. As a beginning we suggest you obtain three company brochures: "Critical Path Method" from GE's Computer Department (Phoenix, Ariz.), and "General Information Manual: PERT" from IBM's Data Processing Division (White Plains, N.Y.), provide a general introduction. The problems of limited resource treatment are discussed in the third, "The Critical Path Method: Resources Planning and Scheduling" by J. E. Kelley, Jr., of Mauchly Associates, Inc., Ambler, Pa.

Next, here are several useful magazine articles: Fundamentals are discussed in some detail in "Critical Path Planning and Scheduling" by Glaser and Young, *Chem. Eng. Prog.* **57,** 11 (1961), and in a series of five articles "Network Models for Project Scheduling" by Christensen, beginning in *Machine Design,* **34,** 12 (1962). "Critical Path Scheduling" by Lynch, *Prod. Eng.* **32,** 37 (1961), includes an example of small project planning. The cost of implementing a Program Evaluation and Review Technique (PERT) program is discussed in "How to Plan and Control with PERT," *Harvard Bus. Rev.* **40,** 2 (1962). If you are mathematically inclined, examine "Critical Path Planning and Scheduling: Mathematical Basis" by J. E. Kelley, Jr., *Oper. Res.* **9** (1961).

Turn to page 642, to "Finding Optimum Combinations," to find some of the mathematical techniques suitable for computerized CPM programs.

Finally, some special items: A 35-minute color movie, "Breakthrough," which describes the use of PERT on the U.S. Navy Polaris program, is available through IBM and the Navy's Special Projects Office, Washington. A circular slide rule for calculating t_E is available for $1 from Merchandising Methods, P.O. Box 2089, San Francisco, Calif.

LEARNING MACHINES

by A. E. Brain, G. E. Forsen, N. J. Nilsson, and C. A. Rosen *

IN BRIEF: *In many practical problems, it is inconvenient (to say the least) to follow an analytical route from empirical data to a useable interpretation of a phenomenon. A computer which is intended to handle such problems without following the analytical route must treat its own output as an undefined function of its input. By training on sample problems, it alters its own structure until its output responses match some externally imposed criteria. It can then match patterns of input data to these required responses.*

A simple workable model consists of three layers of relay-like devices, with the middle (the associating) layer of elements randomly connected to elements of the other two and arranged so that each relay in the hierarchy fires when it receives signals from a majority of its inputs. Then, between the middle layer and one of the other two, the connections are run through "volume controls." We train such a machine by turning up the volume of the active elements when the response is what we want and lowering the volume of the active elements when the response is "wrong." In this way, the machine and its instructor evolve a model which tends to give the "right" answers. The whole thing sounds vaguely Darwinian.—R.G.N.

neuron   Synapse

neuron

if signal from 1 exceeds threshold of 2, 2 fires

3 fires if 1 OR 2 fires

3 fires if 1 AND 2 fire

3 fires if 1 BUT NOT 2 fires

■ The anthropomorphic term, "learning machine," seems to conjure up a specter of a purposeful automation. This is probably more a consequence of the decidedly unchallenged imagination of the human mind than of its also unchallenged analytical capabilities. Nevertheless, there is in modern technology a growing interest in the kind of electronic system to which this tag is attached. We offer this engineering interpretation:

A learning machine is a trainable computer whose internal operation is progressively modified, by application of a simple set of training rules, to favor some result. Since this internal reorganization is effected automatically, without recourse to mathematical analysis, these machines are often referred to as self-organizing systems.

Protoplasmic gadgetry

A prime (naturally occurring) example of such a self-organizing system is the biological brain. Indeed, some of the most important work in

* A. E. Brain, G. E. Forsen, N. J. Nilsson, and C. A. Rosen are colleagues at Stanford Research Institute's Applied Physics Laboratory, Menlo Park, California.

this field has been done by psychologists who see these new machines as devices with which to construct models of human behavior and by neurophysiologists who identify certain elements of machine structure with neurons and are interested in assemblages of such elements insofar as they model the logical properties of biological neurons. Further, because of these similarities, a very considerable body of information relevant to machine design is to be found among the literature on the simulation of biological neural networks.

Most current information on neurons has been gleaned largely from research on the neuron chains connecting the brain with sense organs and muscles. Most neuron models preserve these features of actual neurons:

(1) all-or-none firing (called threshold operation)

(2) excitatory and inhibitory connections (called synapses)

(3) many-branched connecting fibers (called axons) which synapse on many other neurons.

After a suitable neuron model has been selected, networks of these models are postulated. Then, by a combination of mathematical analysis and computer simulation, the postulated network is studied, and the biological implications are inferred from the results of the models. Conversely, there's some reason to believe that the designer who bases the organization of his machine on neurophysiological findings may gain some of the advantages inherent in the structure of living brains. But the real significance of this *apparent* similarity is still very questionable, for the functional differences between biological neural nets and artificial ones are many and profound. Among the most obvious, we can list:

(1) the number of neural elements. There are generally many orders of magnitude more neurons in a biological system than in the most sophisticated man-made systems.

(2) the complexity of operational functions. Artificial "neurons" can simulate all-or-none operation and only about a half dozen of the many other operational features of biological neurons; most of those features have yet to be described.

(3) the organizational rules. Biological brains are enormously complex. Their detailed internal structure and dynamics are largely unknown. All artificial neural nets proposed to date have been simplified to permit formulation of the mathematical model.

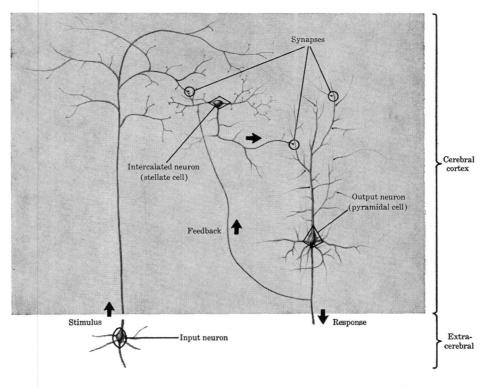

Fig. 6-15. Neurophysiologists generally agree that some 10^{10} neurons control the basic functioning of human brains. Shown here are an intracortical stellate (center) and a pyramidal (right) neuron, which sends response signals outside the cortex. In this biological network, the fired pyramidal neuron sends a feedback signal back to the stellate to prevent refiring the pyramidal. This results in a refractory period, during which the pyramidal cannot be fired. In some neuron models, such time-dependent properties are omitted in favor of instantaneous action. The artificial neuron (bottom) is from an audio perceptron. Such elements have also been called variously response-units, majority logic elements, Adalines, and threshold logic units. All perform the basic function of comparing the sum of several inputs with a threshold level. (Courtesy Bob Demarest)

The engineering view

Viewing things in a somewhat different light, the engineer recognizes that a certain machine logic is appropriate to a large class of problems (a major one of which is general pattern recognition); he is ultimately interested in the synthesis of useful devices. That is our view, and so, while we must often hearken back to our neurological prototypes, our concern will be with the two questions: (a) How can one build a computer, which *without a prescribed mathematical analysis*, improves its ability to perform operations with experience? (b) What applications are there for such learning machines? As is usually the case, the second question seems easier to answer than the first. And,

as is also usually the case, the accomplishment of the machine will probably suggest further applications.

In some situations, the input to a system is either not uniquely specified or is imperfect, and what is required from the machine is an educated guess regarding the classification of the input (the pertinent experience—the education—has been accumulated during the training program). Learning machines seem to be appropriate. For example, suppose we have a machine for recognizing the letters of the alphabet and the numerals, and it is required to change over to the processing of italic rather than roman type, or gothic style instead of sans-serif; a trainable machine could make the

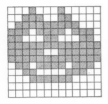

$$m = 13^2 = 169$$

▨ = 1

☐ = 0

changeover merely by retraining on a sample of the new style, without the need for an analysis of the new problem.

An example in somewhat similar vein is speech recognition; even a single speaker shows considerable variation of pitch, speed, and emphasis over a series of trials. Learning machines for recognizing printed characters and speech could find wide application in business accounting. The problem of constructing a machine to read handwriting is appreciably more difficult since the range of variation to be accommodated is so much greater; however, a successful machine could, in principle, greatly reduce the cost of sorting mail.

The translation of foreign journals is fundamental to the development of modern science, and the input to any mechanical translation system necessarily involves reading printed pages, frequently in a strange symbolism. So long as there is sufficient information in the training sample, the trainable machine can "learn" to classify the symbols correctly without requiring any criteria for decision-making from the operator.

Another interesting possibility is a machine which has been trained on a number of unambiguous patterns, say photos of cloud formations, previously categorized by general meteorological agreement. After training on the sample, there resides, within the machine, a set of criteria by which it can rapidly categorize cloud patterns that might otherwise need considerable deliberation by meteorologists. Such a machine is actually under study.

Recognizing the uses for pattern recognition

However, the potential applications of learning machines are not restricted to visual and speech patterns. A machine might have a number of discrete sets of input signals, derived from different sets of sensors. Thus, tactile, radiation, sonic, etc., information could be sampled spatially and temporally, and presented (after suitable preprocessing) to a large learning machine. These complex input signals could form patterns which have previously been "taught" to the machine, with prescribed output signals assigned to each such pattern. Some of these output signals could operate other equipment, others might change some aspect of the environment such as temperature, light, etc.; still others could emit signals which, in turn, are part of the input patterns of other similar automata.

If sufficient capacity were built in, we'd have a machine in many ways matching a highly trained man who is not expected to do much thinking. Of course, the man can also be imaginative and creative, but the machine can

be quicker, tireless, more specialized, better matched to other machines, and able to work in an environment inimical to man.

Other still more intriguing structures (and results) are possible. One such is appropriate to the many processes so complex or so poorly understood that their workable mathematical formulation is not feasible. In some cases, the important variables are not known. In others, some quantities chosen as variables are extraneous, and in still others, there are too many pertinent variables to be measured. An important future application of machines which can weigh features of their inputs can be foreseen in which complex meteorological or medical or economic processes are imitated or modelled by suitably organized learning machines.

Essentially, machines might use the input data and *known* outputs, to "learn" the right answers, and in so doing, to generate analogs to the functional relations, i.e., to "model" the process. This "learning" can be continuous, new input data and dependent outputs being fed into the machine as they become available, with consequent slow but continuous improvement in the approximation to the actual process performed by the modeller. If provisions have been made for modular enlargement and for the periodic "purging" of unreliable or relatively unimportant data stored in the adaptive modules, the machine grows in size and power until it does, in fact, model the process to a highly useful degree. Perhaps, after such a program, its state would then give us insight into the original process.

The machines described above are relatively direct extensions of present research efforts. Fundamental questions are now being raised. Partial answers or even good guesses to these questions could increase the sophistication and power of these machines enormously.

When these powerful computers (or, rather, their optical sensors) first see light of day, they will stem from the first principles enunciated in an historically important paper written by McCulloch and Pitts in 1943.

Hearking back

In "A Logical Calculus of the Ideas Immanent in Nervous Activity," McCulloch and Pitts applied symbolic logic to the analysis and synthesis of networks of neural elements. Assuming networks to be composed of simple threshold elements, these pioneers set out to ". . . calculate the behavior of any net, and to find a net which will behave in a specified way, when such a net exists."

What they showed is that any logical proposition that can be stated about a number of input variables can be implemented by a neural net.

McCulloch and Pitts also proposed a learning mechanism based on the concept of an *alterable synapse*, that learning requires "the possibility of permanent alterations in the structure of nets. The simplest such alteration is the formation of new synapses or equivalent depressions of threshold." They then went on to suggest conditions under which the effective number of synapses could be changed by experience and use.

This idea (of a changeable synapse) is basic to most learning machines. The effect can be generally pictured as a changing strength or conductivity of the synaptic junctions. This suggestion, incorporated into a neurophysiological theory by D. Hebb in 1949, precipitated the study of several neural net models with variable synaptic "weights."

Hebb proposed, "When an axon of cell *A* is near enough to excite a cell *B* and repeatedly or persistently takes part in firing it, some growth process or metabolic change takes place in one or both cells such that *A*'s efficiency, as one of the cells firing *B*, is increased. . . ."

It is still not certain just what this metabolic change is. Hebb's idea was that: "When one cell repeatedly assists in firing another, the axon of the first cell develops synaptic knobs (or enlarges them if they already exist) in contact with the soma (cell body) of the second cell."

An engineering analogy to the variable synapse would be a variable gain control linking the output of one neuron with the input of the next. The variable gain control can be looked on as the *adaptive element*, which changes the relative emphasis or "weights" of the various synapses as a function of experience. Training a learning structure then means adjusting its weights, preferably automatically. Its behavior will depend on the training and on how the "neurons" are interconnected.

Connections and the weighting game

In 1954, Farley and Clark reported on the results of a fascinating experiment in which neuron-like elements were randomly interconnected by adjustable weights. The network was simulated on a digital computer, and the weights were varied during the experiment so that the network "learned" to give arbitrary, prescribed responses to two different input patterns. In a second experiment, the network learned to give the prescribed responses to "noisy" versions of the inputs as well. This historically important work incorporated many of the features that were used in some of the later networks.

Using the basic principle of adaptable weights coupling randomly connected neuron-like elements, a psychologist, F. Rosenblatt, proposed (in 1957) a machine capable of sorting visual patterns. The α-perceptron was an outgrowth of an attempt by Rosenblatt to study neurological phenomena using neural-net models as subjects. The basic element of his model is a binary threshold logic unit (TLU) similar to those used in the earlier neural nets. The TLU sums a number of weighted inputs, and compares this sum with a threshold value that it has previously been given. If the sum of the input signals exceeds the threshold value, the TLU emits a "one"; if not, it emits a "zero."

Perception by machine

In the α-perceptron (see margin, page 662) the binary TLUs are arranged in three layers. The first layer provides the inputs to the rest of the machine. This input, or sensor, layer might be stimulated (turned on) by optical patterns (with photocell sensors), audio signals, or other sensory data. Those *S*-units are not connected together in any way; they act in parallel and simultaneously to convert raw sensory data into binary form. In some machines suggested by Rosenblatt, the *S*-units form a two-dimensional array suggestive of a biological retina, but the arrangement is unimportant in considering the logic of the machine.

The second TLU layer consists of association units (*A*-units). Each of these receives inputs from a selection of *S*-units. No *A*-units are interconnected. Each *A*-unit is a threshold device with inputs weighted so that:

1. Unconnected *S*-units have zero weight
2. An excitatory input has a weight of +1
3. An inhibitory input has a weight of −1
4. If enough *S*-units are turned on by the stimulus, signals to the *A*-unit exceed the *A*-unit's threshold; the *A*-unit becomes active. Any input pattern then will activate an identifying set of *A*-units, just which ones is fixed by: the *S*-units excited, the *S*-*A* connections, and the *A*-unit thresholds. So far, everything about the network is predetermined; we have no provisions for adaptation or memory. In the original proposal, at least, all these parameters were considered fixed.

The third layer consists of response units (*R*-units). Each *R*-unit receives adjustable weighted inputs from all the *A*-units. If this weighted sum exceeds the fixed *R*-unit threshold, it is made active; otherwise it isn't. (As simple α-perceptrons, we'll assume only one *R*-unit.) Training this machine means adapting the *A*-*R*-unit weights so that the *R*-unit responds to a certain set of the input patterns, but not to others.

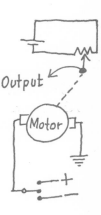

Pattern recognition might be a typical chore for an α-perceptron. Suppose we have a group of patterns. We want the machine to separate the patterns into two classes "A" and "B." For each pattern in class "A" we want the R-unit to fire; for each pattern in class "B," we want no response. We need a scheme (a training method) for adapting the weights between the A-units and R-units in an iterative manner as the various patterns are presented to the machine. Rosenblatt proposed several such schemes, some of which are guaranteed to converge on solutions—if solutions exist.

How to train perceptron machines

One method is the *error correction procedure.* The patterns are presented to the machine in any sequence, so long as each pattern recurs in a finite time. The weights start with any convenient values. If the response to the pattern is correct, no changes are made, and the next pattern is presented.

If the R-unit does not respond to a pattern appropriately, those weights with inactive A-units are not changed; weights with active A-units are either increased or decreased by small amounts, as needed to rectify the error.

After the weights have been changed, the pattern is presented again. If the response is right, the next pattern is presented. If the error persists, the weights are adapted again, and so forth, until the desired response is evoked. We have selectively and iteratively reduced the influence of units which tend to give unwanted responses and enhanced the influence of those units that tend to give the desired responses. (See example in Fig. 6-16.)

If some structure of fixed size, of the form in the margin, admits of a solution to such a problem, this procedure is guaranteed to converge upon a solution in finite time. Convergence is reached when all patterns are classified correctly. Mathematical proofs of the convergence of this procedure have been given.

The learning ability of α-perceptrons has been tested by experiments on an actual model and by digital computer simulation. The analog model, called Mark I, has 400 S-units. These are a 20×20 array of photocells mounted in the focal plane of a camera. They are randomly connected to 512 A-units so that any S-unit can have up to 40 connections originating from it. The A-units are then connected to 8 R-units through weights (motor-driven potentiometers). Since there are 8 (binary) R-units, the input patterns can be separated into 2^8 categories.

Mark I was trained to recognize all 26 letters of the alphabet (when they were presented in a standard position). For this experiment, five of the eight output units were used to give a coded response. The machine categorized all 26 letters after having been trained on only 15 samples of each. A further experiment illustrates that this machine resembles its biological counterpart in another important way. Its response is the weighted majority decision by many A-units operating in parallel. Failure of a few units may degrade performance but will not, in general, disable the machine. An α-perceptron with 240 A-units was trained to discriminate between the letters "E" and "X." Failure of the A-units was simulated by randomly removing some of them from the trained machine. The decline in performance was slight even after a substantial fraction of the A-units had been removed. There is, of course, also the possibility that retraining can restore a machine to its previous performance. Thus, periodic "repair" would be effected by periodic "retraining." Similar machines have already exhibited unusual reliabilities, even with faulty components, cold solder joints, miswirings, etc.

It was also shown that Mark I could learn to discriminate between the "E" and the "X" even when the training samples were "noisy." Noise was introduced by adding extraneous random dots to the photographs of "E" and "X" and by allowing a little variation in the position of the letters. The machine was then tested with noisy "E" and "X" patterns (on which it had not been trained). The test scores (100% correct for small noise levels) indicate that the α-perceptron can make simple generalizations. This kind of learning depends on overlap between the test pattern and the training patterns.

While the α-perceptron can make simple generalizations, it does not seem capable of much more than that. This is not surprising, considering the relative simplicity of its structure! The next question is: How can we build more complicated nets which learn more difficult problems faster with fewer components?

Taylor's approach and Madaline's motto

A promising approach was proposed by Taylor in 1959. His idea was to propagate analog values through the learning machine, right up to the final decision element. In one version, the (two-dimensional) input pattern—a variable intensity image—is sampled by $(2^m - 1)$ A-units. Here m is the number of resolvable spots in the pattern. Each A-unit accepts weighted combinations of spot intensity. When its threshold is exceeded, the A-unit emits an output proportional to the input excess over the threshold value. Otherwise the A-unit output is zero. A subsequent layer determines which A-units have the highest output. This categorizes the input pattern. Taylor proposed several such structures whose potential has, unfortunately, not yet been realized.

Widrow's Madaline (multiple adaptive linear neuron) is a recent (1961) approach to a learning machine built up of threshold logic units (TLUs). Its logic is based on the idea that what one TLU can't learn, a group of TLUs can. This comes about by using a structure much like that of the α-perceptron. Both machines are three-layered networks of threshold devices with binary outputs. Each machine has one layer of adaptable weights—the α-perceptron has them between the A- and R-units, Madaline, between the S- and A-units.

The TLUs in Madaline all have outputs of $+1$ or -1, so that decision-making by the R-unit(s) is accomplished just by summing the outputs of the A-units and comparing the results with zero (which is the threshold). Training Madaline is like the procedure described for the α-perceptron. Patterns are presented to Madaline one at a time. If the majority of TLUs in the second layer respond correctly, no changes are made. If the majority respond incorrectly, then from among the incorrectly voting TLUs, we find the ones whose outputs are closest to zero. Those nearest to being right then have their responses altered so that a majority will be correct. One alters the responses of *only enough* TLUs *to make the majority respond correctly.*

Both these structures are special cases of a more general machine—one which has yet to be developed—with two layers of adaptable weights—between the S- and A-units *and* between the A- and R-units. When such a machine can be trained, Madaline will have an adaptive vote-taker (giving more weight to the outputs of some of the voting TLUs), and the α-perceptron can have an adaptive preprocessing system. The two machines would then be very similar. A central need in this field is for designers to learn how to handle such a general structure. Let's see what general hints we already have about it.

Black boxes and data spaces

First, let us consider a general learning machine as a "black box" with m input leads and n output leads, and see what the machine could do for us. We already know how to get it to recognize patterns: We just divide the pattern into a two-dimensional array of numbered squares. We associate one input line with each numbered square, so that any input pattern can be looked upon as an input code word of m ones and zeros. What we really want is that the output—an output code of n ones and zeros —will represent some arbitrary classification

for the input pattern. We have seen that, starting with a layered network of threshold logic units, if we "reward" (increase the gain of) the connections associated with our favored response and decrease the gain of the others we'll have a *classifier.*

However, a black box of this type can perform other functions depending on the values given to m and n. If we have as many output leads as patterns, and if the output contains a single *one* on a specific line (the remaining outputs being zeros), then we have a *selector.*

Our black box can also add. We just divide the m input leads into two groups, so that each group represents a coded binary number, and require the output signal to be the binary representation of the sum. Presto, the black box is now an *adder.* Then again, it might become a multiplier. Obviously a trainable code converter could be quite handy; it might very well operate as an adder in one situation, and, after retraining, operate as a multiplier, or an arbitrary classifier, which can perform these and other functions in combination. Of course, we pay a price for all this versatility: many fixed operations can be carried out more efficiently using conventional digital and analog computer techniques.

Many other properties of devices like those we are discussing can best be understood by use of a geometrical representation, as shown in Fig. 6-17. There, input patterns are represented by points in an input space (S-space) and output responses by points in a response space (R-space). In these terms, the learning machine problem is: Find an adaptable structure and an adaptation procedure to take us from S-space to R-space. Thus, a single TLU, the simplest neural-net pattern classifier, is able to transform points (vertices of an S-space cube) into points in R-space (vertices of an R-space cube) by separating the S-space into regions.

Biology also has indicated some interesting principles by which layered neural net structures can be organized.

Pointers from physiology and other lines

Along biological lines, recent physiological research has shown that animal vision involves preprocessing tests such as line, spot, motion, and contrast detection. These tests seem to be fixed in the animal and, in particular, do not change as a result of learning.

In some of the problems to which a learning machine might be applied, the input data is also amenable to some sort of fixed preprocessing. For example, in character recognition problems it might be useful to know whether or not the input pattern was composed of straight lines,

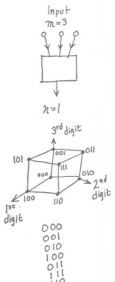

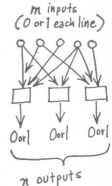

Here is a simple example of the process a simple machine might go through in solving a simple but real problem — learning to discriminate between the letter P and the letter E*

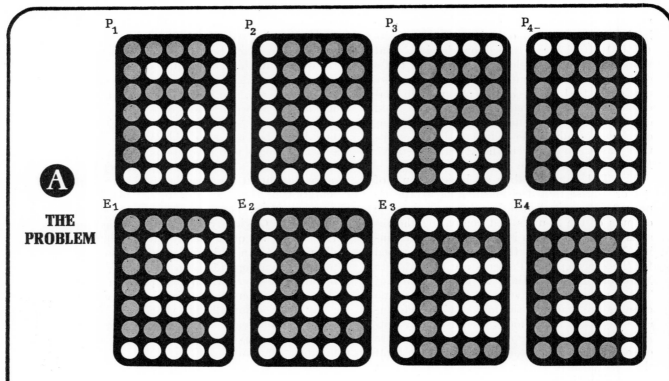

(A) THE PROBLEM

Our machine has 35 sensors, S-Units, arranged in a grid on which we can project our two letters in any of four positions. In each position, the letter forms a signal which stimulates some of the S-Units.

(B) THE WIRING

A-unit number 1 is connected to these nine S-units

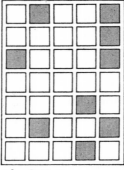

A-unit number 2 is connected to these nine S-units

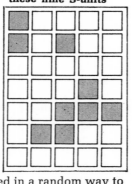

The S-Units are connected in a random way to association units, A-units. There are 10 A-units in our imaginary machine, each connected to 9 S-Units. The diagrams above show the particular S-Units to which the A-1 and A-2 association units are connected. Similar diagrams could be drawn for the other 8 A-Units.

CHANGING VALUES OF WEIGHTS APPLIED TO

Trial No.	1	2	3	4	5	6	7	8	9	10	11	12	1
	P_1	E_1	P_2	E_3	E_4	P_1	P_2	E_2	P_3	E_3	E_4	P_1	E
A–1	0	0	0	1	1	1	1	1	–1	–1	–1	–1	–1
A–2	0	0	–7	–7	–7	–7	–7	–7	–7	–7	–7	–7	–7
A–3	0	0	0	0	–8	–8	–8	–8	–8	–2	–3	–3	–3
A–4	0	0	0	0	0	0	0	0	–2	–2	–2	–2	–2
A–5	0	0	–7	–6	–6	1	1	1	–1	–1	–1	–1	7
A–6	0	0	–7	–6	–6	–6	–6	–6	–8	–2	–2	–2	–2
A–7	0	0	0	1	–7	–11	–4	–3	–5	1	0	–12	–4
A–8	0	0	0	1	1	–3	4	4	2	2	2	–10	–2
A–9	0	0	0	1	1	1	1	1	–1	5	5	5	5
A–10	0	0	0	1	–7	–7	–7	–7	–7	–7	–8	–8	–8
Threshold	10	10	10	10	10	10	10	10	10	10	10	10	10
Total	10	10	–4	12	4	–10	0	8	–12	2	12	–13	8
Machine says	P	P	E	P	P	E		P	E	P	P	E	P
Correction	–20		8	–24	–8	20	1	–16	24	–4	–24	26	–16
Unit correction	–7		1	–8	–4	7	(1)	–2	6	–1	–12	8	–5

(D) LEARNING

* Adapted from Cornell Aeronautical Laboratory.

Fig. 6-16.

	P_1	P_2	P_3	P_4	E_1	E_2	E_3	E_4
A–1	2	5	3	1	3	4	3	2
A–2	2	1	3	3	4	2	2	2
A–3	3	3	4	3	2	2	4	3
A–4	2	3	3	2	3	4	3	2
A–5	4	4	2	2	4	5	1	1
A–6	3	5	4	2	4	4	3	2
A–7	5	5	4	3	3	5	4	4
A–8	4	4	1	4	3	4	3	5
A–9	3	4	4	3	2	4	2	3
A–10	3	4	3	2	2	2	4	1

Each A-unit is stimulated by this many S-units

	P_1	P_2	P_3	P_4	E_1	E_2	E_3	E_4
A–1	0	1	0	0	0	1	0	0
A–2	0	0	0	0	1	0	0	0
A–3	0	0	1	0	0	0	1	0
A–4	0	0	0	0	0	1	0	0
A–5	1	1	0	0	1	1	0	0
A–6	0	1	1	0	1	1	0	0
A–7	1	1	1	0	0	1	1	1
A–8	1	1	0	1	0	1	0	1
A–9	0	1	1	0	0	1	0	0
A–10	0	1	0	0	0	0	1	0

These A-units do or do not exceed threshold

THE LOGIC

If you compare the first two illustrations, you can see that when the letter P is projected in its first position, forming signal P_1, it stimulated 2 of the S-Units which are connected to A-1 and also 2 of the units connected to A-2. Similarly, in position P_2, it stimulates 5 of the S-Units connected to A-1. The upper left-hand matrix shows how much stimulation each A-unit receives from each P or E signal.

Now we apply a threshold to the A-Units. If it is stimulated by fewer than 3½ S-Units, an A-Unit has zero output. If it is stimulated by more than 3½ units, it produces a unit output. The resulting response pattern is shown in the matrix at left.

-UNITS ON SUCCESSIVE TRIALS

	15	16	17	18	19	20	21	22	23	24	25	Solution ↓
	E_2	P_3	E_4	P_1	P_2	E_2	P_3	P_2	E_3	E_4	P_2	W_1
0	-2	-2	-2	-2	1	-2	-2	-1	-1	-1	-1	-1
2	-12	-12	-12	-12	-12	-12	-12	-12	-12	-12	-12	-12
3	-3	-3	-2	-2	-2	-2	-2	-2	-2	-3	-3	-3
2	-2	-4	-4	-4	-4	-7	-7	-7	-7	-7	-7	-7
3	1	1	1	2	5	2	2	3	3	3	3	4
7	-6	-8	-7	-7	-7	-4	-7	-6	-5	-5	-5	-4
4	-3	-5	-4	-7	-6	-3	-6	-6	-5	-5	-6	-6
2	-1	-3	-3	-6	-5	-2	-5	-5	-4	-4	-5	-5
5	6	4	5	5	5	8	5	5	6	6	6	6
8	-7	-7	-7	-7	-7	-4	-4	-4	-3	-3	-3	-3
0	10	10	10	10	10	10	10	10	10	10	10	10
5	7	-2	3	-2	-10	11	0	-6	0	1	-1	
E	P	E	P	E	E	P		E		P	E	
0	-14	4	-6	4	20	-22	1	12	-1	-2	2	
1	-2	1	-3	1	3	-3	(1)	1	(-1)	-1	(1)	

Now we are ready to train our imaginary machine. All ten A-Units are connected to a response unit. We are able to apply adjustable positive or negative weights to the outputs of the A-Units. If the total weighted response, plus a threshold of 10, is positive, we consider that the machine has detected a P. If negative, an E. We want to adjust the weights to values at which the machine will always respond correctly. We start with zero weights. At the first trial, in the table above, we show the machine a P in position P_1.

We know from the matrix in the third illustration that units A-5, A-7, and A-8 are sufficiently stimulated to exceed threshold. But with zero weights, the only output is 10. This is positive. So the machine says P. The machine is right. So we leave the weights at zero.

For trial 2, we show the machine the E in position E_1. Units A-2, A-5, and A-6 fire. The total is still 10. The machine still says P, and it is wrong. We adjust the weights on the three operative A-Units by enough to make the total −10 instead of +10. That is, we add −7 to each, giving us the weights for trial 3.

For trial 3, we use a P in position P_2. Units A-1 and A-5 through A-10 fire. The weighted total is −4. This is wrong, and we change the weights by −1 to give a total of +4.

And so on. This particular set of trials is very efficient; the machine happens always to be wrong and so learns something from each trial. And by the 26th trial we have achieved a set of weights which will give correct results for all possible P and E signals. We have trained the machine.

Fig. 6-16 (cont.)

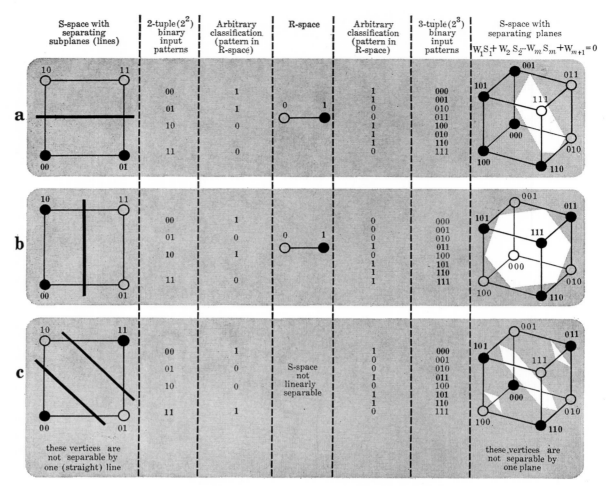

Fig. 6-17. CUTTING UP DATA SPACE WITH HYPERPLANES

A geometrical construct gives intuitive insight into some possibilities (and limitations) of neural nets. The possible combinations of m binary digits (0 or 1) correspond to the vertices of a hypercube in m-dimensional space. (Examples at left and right edges above are for two and three-dimensional space.) These possible combinations are also tabulated above as m-tuple input patterns.

Similarly, each output is a dimension in an R-space, diagrammed center above. For simplicity, we show a 1-dimensional hypercube. The job of the machine is to transform points from S-space to R-space. It does this (if it can) by cutting S-space into regions, so that vertices are divided into two R-space classifications. Thus, in Fig. 6-16, sorting 8 patterns means dividing a 35-dimension S-space so 4 points are separated from the rest.

The simplest separator is a hyperplane (a line, in 2 dimensions, etc.). A TLU implements a hyperplane: vertices of an S-space cube which evoke a 1 lie on the opposite side of the hyperplane from those that evoke a 0. A single TLU can transform vertices of an m-dimensional cube to those of a 1-dimensional cube in R-space if and only if a single hyperplane will do the separating. The figure discloses the problem: Sometimes no single hyperplane can sort out the vertices

asked for. Then a single TLU can't be trained to solve the problem. Usually m >> 3; then it's very hard even to tell whether a set of vertices is linearly separable.

We could try to use several TLUs in parallel. Their outputs can be charted in a new A_1-space. If the vertices in A_1-space are linearly separable, outputs of the A_1-units go to an A_2-unit which gives the answer; we have a 3-layer machine. If not, A_2-space is cut to generate A_3-space, etc. Finally, we'll reach a linearly separable A_{n-1} space so the A_n space will be R-space. Each slice is made with a layer of TLUs like this:

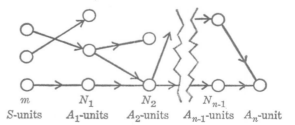

The trouble is: Nobody knows how to adapt the weights of such a multilayer machine. We can also try curved hypersurfaces, but they introduce other problems . . .

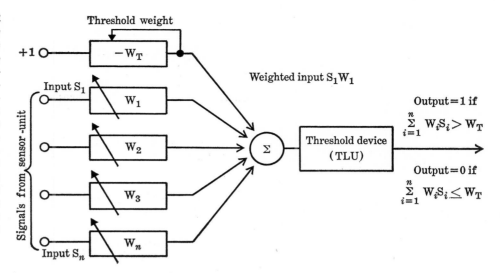

Fig. 6-18. Training a neural net machine means adapting the weights W_i so that the quantities $W_i S_i$ compared to the threshold result in selectively activating the appropriate TLUs to give the "correct" response for any given input pattern. The problem is to group the input patterns according to required response. Adjustment of weights (W_i) also corresponds to orienting the hyperplane which separates the data space in the figure opposite. W_T represents the hyperplane's distance from the origin.

convex shapes, curved lines, etc. The preprocessed data, reflecting these features can then serve as the input to the learning machine, which then operates on a new "feature space." If the number of tests required is reasonably small, preprocessing can reduce the dimensionality of the problem.

If a set of discriminating tests cannot reasonably be established, the test selection must be included in the adaptive part of the machine. One could, for example, think of each A_1-unit as implementing a particular test. When the input weights to the A_1-units are subject to adaptation, the tests implemented by the A_1-unit are evolved rather than pre-set.

Some interesting tests can be run on networks of threshold logic units with fixed weights and thresholds. For example, it is quite straightforward to devise TLU operations on a retinal field of S-units which detect the presence of straight lines, edges, convex spots, corners, etc. In the last few years a considerable amount of work has been done on this type of preprocessing in machines.

Another biologically inspired approach is heuristic in nature. In examining a complicated problem, a human usually first attempts some "first-state" tactics which seem to be appropriate. He then determines which of these is most likely to lead him closest to the final answer. The most likely candidate is selected and the process is repeated to find a good second-stage tactic, and so on. Applying this process to the construction of digital computer programs is called heuristic programming. Heuristic programming has met with considerable success in mechanizing this process, in digital computer programs for chess-playing, theorem-proving, and the like.

Methods of statistical decision theory have also begun to provide promising results. One assumes that the input patterns belong to ensembles which can be characterized by simple (usually Gaussian) probability distributions. The training patterns are then used to determine (i.e., to "learn") the unknown parameters of these distributions. Once the parameters have been estimated, optimum decision procedures can be employed to guess the categories of new input patterns.

As is usual in such a technological development, the engineering implementations of many of the promising ideas that have been offered hinge on the bits (no pun) and pieces that make up the hardware.

Bits and realizations

Four basic logical operations are used in the present organization of trainable (learning) machines:

Addition—a set of signals (usually having binary values *1* and *0*, or *+1* and *−1*) are added to give an *analog* sum.

Threshold—the analog sum is compared with a reference, with a threshold level.

Gating—if threshold level is exceeded by the summation signal, an auxiliary circuit is fired—the behavior is that of a relay.

Adaptation—an adjustable signal is stored and can be read out without being destroyed. The signal adjustment is made during the machine training program.

The threshold logic unit (TLU) described before can include all four functions. It takes a weighted sum of several binary inputs. A threshold value is subtracted from the sum. If the remainder is positive or negative, then a +1 output or a 0, respectively, is gated on. Some TLUs in Madaline use plus and minus ones for inputs and outputs. Trinary logic can also be employed, e.g., + or − responses are gated only when the absolute magnitude of the remainder exceeds a certain amount. Otherwise, a "don't-know" condition exists, and the output is zero.

Summation can be done easily with a resistive adder, multiple windings on a transformer, the total response of a photocell with several light beams incident on its surface, or pulse counter.

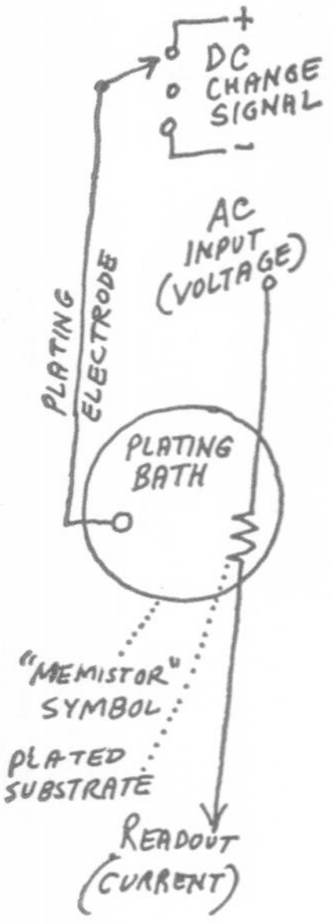

Threshold and gating are often found as the combination of a nonlinear device (diode, "square-loop" magnetic core, chemical reaction, relay, etc.) and a bias signal whose amplitude, frequency, duration, etc., determine the threshold level.

A fixed, weighted connection can be a resistance, or the number of turns on a transformer winding (which allows negative valued weights), or the aperture of a lens, or the number of pulses in a pulse train.

An adaptive weight is a weighted connection between two points whose value can be changed in small amounts by a (usually external) sig-

nal. An early adaptive weight is the motor-driven potentiometer used in the Mark I perceptron. The stored weight is the instantaneous resistance; the servo-motor changes its value, as shown in the margin of page 661.

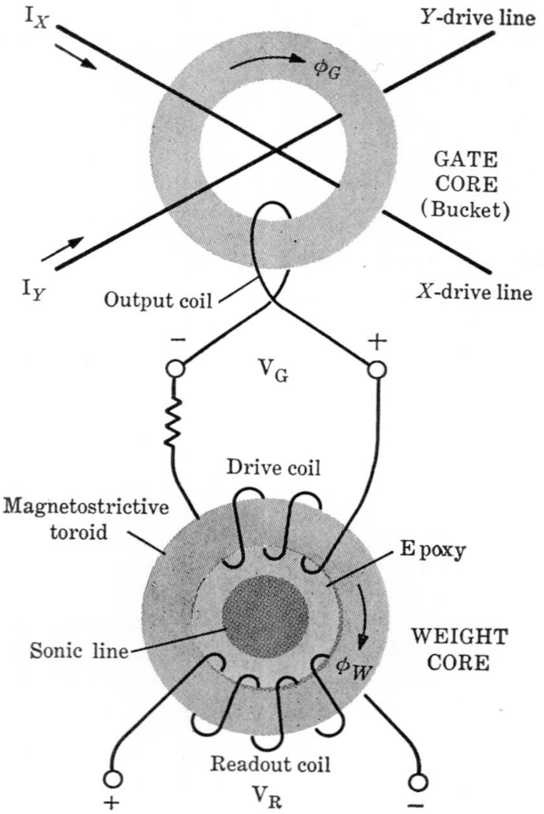

Another adaptive element is the "Memistor" or plating cell used in Widrow's Madaline at Stanford University. A conductive film is plated on a substrate. The storage parameter is film thickness, hence the conductance of the film. The thickness can be changed by a dc signal of proper polarity applied to the plating electrode; it can then be sensed nondestructively by ac.

Various solid state schemes have been developed. Some use partially switched flux in toroidal magnetic devices. The storage parameter of these devices is the difference between magnetic flux oriented clockwise and that oriented counterclockwise in a toroid. This flux is switched in direction with respect to the sensing (readout) winding. The change of state is accomplished by applying a magnetic field that exceeds a magnetic threshold for a short time. Effort is being made to use *only* wire and magnetic devices in order to increase the speed and reliability of logic circuitry.

Although their application to quasi-analog storage is fairly recent, magnetic devices have been highly developed. They are also comparatively inexpensive and are generally compatible with semiconductor circuitry. Another feature of magnetic devices is that power is required only to *change* their storage. No externally applied energy is needed to maintain states; hence their capacity for memory is retained even in the face of power failure.

Several methods of non-destructive readout, of sensing the flux state without permanently changing it, are feasible. One way is to sense the amount of flux switched around the major aperture of a MAD (multi-aperture device) by switching the unblocked portion of flux around a minor aperture. A similar core can provide a 3-circuit gating function. The combination was used in the Minos I here at the Stanford Research Institute. Other magnetic weights have been developed at Melpar and at Ford's Aeronutronic Div.

Flux levels can be sensed by sound energy if the material is magnetostrictive. Some ferrite materials and nickel-iron alloys generate a magnetic field on application of mechanical stress. Sonic excitation of them can produce a useful readout voltage at low impedance levels. The approach in Fig. 6-19 is being developed for Minos II, a machine being built at SRI for the U.S. Army Signal Corps.

But despite important and necessary advances like these, learning machine develop-

Fig. 6-19. *Short pulses are generated by a gate core or bucket, when current is passed through its drive lines. These pulses change the flux in the weight core, so that when it is mechanically stressed by the magnetostrictive toroid, the weight core generates a voltage in its readout coil. Often n such TLUs share m inputs, and are arranged in an $m \times n$ array of weights and gate pairs that can be controlled by $m + n$ terminal signals. This feature is handy when m and n are large. The system also has the advantage of isolating the many weights in a large system.*

ment has barely begun; as yet we have developed only a few major concepts and applied them to relatively simple structures. The surprisingly powerful results shown by the first elementary machines have made it easy to overpredict and to skip consideration of the painfully slow intermediate steps. Yet each of these may be fundamentally as important as the initial concepts, and any meaningful "card-reading" must weigh them carefully.

Several major technical advances will have to be made before general and widespread utilization of learning machines is possible. It will be necessary:

To develop very inexpensive adaptive elements and the auxiliary gear needed to use thousands, or even millions, of those elements in single machines. To learn better ways to filter essential data from an overwhelming mass of available input data; this is primarily important for visual and oral pattern recognition. To learn to connect and use cascaded layers of adaptive elements; in particular we need simple training procedures (if such exist) which guarantee convergence of the training sequence when two or more such cascaded layers are being trained.

But when those techniques become available and well understood, a wide choice of interesting applications will become possible. Promising and important work, which may very well help solve those problems, is going on along various lines besides neural networks (and even in other disciplines). In some final synthesis, perhaps the enormous power of the stored-program computer, coupled with these new techniques and organizations, will relieve man of many routine mental burdens and help him to a better understanding of both himself and his environment.

Further reading

Human nerve cells, which serve as a model for at least some learning machines, are discussed in all detail in J. Eccles' *The Physiology of Nerve Cells* (Johns Hopkins, 1957, $5.75). Another text is *The Nervous System*, a lucid discussion by G. M. Wyburn (Academic Press, 1961, $5.00).

The logic of neural nets and the concept of alterable synapses were first set forth by McCulloch and Pitts in their paper, "A Logical Calculus of the Ideas Immanent in Nervous Activity," *Bull. Math. Biophysics* **5**, 115 (1943). Farley and Clark's early experimental work on digital-computer simulation of networks of neuron-like elements is reported in their paper "Generalization of Pattern-Recognition in a Self-Organizing System," *Proc. Western Joint Computer Conference*, p. 86 (March, 1955).

Rosenblatt's researches with perceptrons are recounted in his book, *Principles of Neurodynamics: Perceptrons and the Theory of Brain Mechanisms* (Spartan Books, 1961), $6.50. Another good review of perceptrons is "The Perceptron: A Model for Brain Functioning" by H. Block, *Revs. Modern Phys.* **34**, 123 (1962).

The convergence of trained perceptrons is discussed mathematically by A. Novikoff at a symposium on the mathematical theory of automata held at Polytechnical Institute of Brooklyn in April, 1962. Proceedings are available from Polytechnic Press (1963, $8). The training procedures and convergence properties of Madaline-type structures are reviewed in "An Adaptive Logic System With Generalizing Properties," by W. Ridgway III, which appears as Stanford Electronics Laboratories Report TR 1556-1, April, 1962. Proceedings of the Armour Research Foundation's 1962 symposium of Self-Organizing Systems cost $12 (Spartan Books).

A very good general survey is P. B. Andrews' "A Survey of Artificial Learning and Intelligence," which was published in 1962 as IBM Research Report #612. Other good review papers appeared in the January, 1961 Computer Issue of *Proc. IRE*, **49**, No. 1 (1961). Of particular interest are papers by M. Minsky and J. K. Hawkins, and a paper by A. E. Brain on the use of multi-aperture magnetic cores as memory units. Another new device that has been built for use as an adaptive element in learning machines is the Memistor, developed by M. E. Hoff and B. Widrow of Stanford University. Data are available from Memistor Corp., Mountain View, Calif.

Work at the Stanford Research Institute has resulted in an operational learning machine, called MINOS II, which has been described in a paper entitled "A Large, Self-Contained Learning Machine," by A. Brain, G. Forsen, D. Hall, and C. Rosen, presented at the 1963 Western Electronics Convention, San Francisco, California. Copies are available from the authors. This research has been supported mainly by the Data Transducer Branch of the U.S. Army Electronics Research and Development Laboratories, Fort Monmouth, New Jersey. Additional research support has been provided by the Information Systems Branch of the Office of Naval Research and the Air Force Systems Command (RADC).

FLUID COMPUTERS

by O. Lew Wood and Harold L. Fox *

IN BRIEF: *The idea of a computer operating on jets of water or air in this day of electronic sophistication seems at first glance to be too silly to even consider. Yet the flow of fluids has recently been shown capable of performing the same logic functions as the "flow" of electricity and with a good deal less sensitivity to environmental factors such as radiation, heat, and vibration. The interaction of fluid jets with each other and with the walls of the devices containing them provides a stable system for digital processing. Also standard criteria for material selection for the devices ensure their stability, as well as the possibility of cheap, mass-produced logic systems.*

One of the major impediments to widespread application of fluid computers, however, will be their inherently low speed. This limitation will not bar them from areas where a human being is part of the control "loop," of course, or where extremes in response-time are not as essential as high reliability and freedom from variations in control under varying conditions.

At the least, this new method of performing logic functions deserves a good hard look, before deciding against it as inapplicable.—H.W.M.

* O. Lew Wood and Harold L. Fox collaborate on the fluid logic development project at Sperry Utah Co., Salt Lake City, Utah.

■ If you ask the nearest electronic computer operator for his comments on the use of fluid computers, you'll likely hear: "Why fluid computers? I'm having enough trouble with the one I've got, without worrying about one that leaks besides!" Without realizing it, he will have answered the question: "Why fluid computers?" Even with the best computer room facilities, air conditioning, and pampering, the maze of electronic components does give seemingly unending trouble. Fluid computers, on the other hand, using any of a number of liquids or gases, have the potential of high **reliability** even under adverse environments.

If the electronic computer gives trouble in an optimum environment, consider the added problems that result when it is wired into a rocket booster or installed in a chemical plant for process control. Yet it is exactly in applications such as these that higher computer reliability is required, where adverse conditions exist, such as the severe radiation environment of nuclear-power systems and outer space, the vibration and shock of missile launching or airborne use, and the heat and cold of a lunar base.

Need for reliability provided impetus

The never-ending search for high reliability elements has recently led to a new field of fluid logic and proportional devices. Originating at the U.S. Army's Harry Diamond Laboratories (formerly Diamond Ordnance Fuse Laboratories) and dubbed "pure fluid amplifiers," this new class of computer and control elements could replace electronic and electromechanical devices and systems in a number of applications. Interest has been growing on the part of government agencies, academic institutions, and industry, centering as much on fluid data-handling and computing systems as on fluid amplifiers for control purposes.

While most of the work done to date is still in the laboratory stage, some interesting devices have been built, and others will be. One of the advantages is that no transducers will be needed in many applications—pneumatic inputs from sensing elements can be fed directly into the logic circuits, and the output used directly to power control valves, automatic typewriters, or accounting machines. Punched tapes can be used to control input jets to operate ma-

Fig. 6-20. Fluid flip-flop of plastic, made at Harry Diamond Laboratories, illustrates typical configuration and size. Multiples are also possible. (Courtesy Harry Diamond Laboratories)

chine tools or automatic-processing equipment.

Current emphasis on fluid device development is for use in the extreme environments mentioned, but the future refuses to be environmentally limited. "Fallout" from more sophisticated applications may even provide the technology for competitively priced desk calculators, or a fluid computer to run the household of the future.

Mass production the answer

Such examples immediately raise the economic question: Can fluid computers be designed and produced in competition with tomorrow's solid-state integrated circuitry? We feel the answer is yes. Research and development costs, as such, will be no lower for fluid circuitry than for new electronic circuitry. However, just as an injection molding machine can make $1.98 replicas of "Old Ironsides" from a $35,000 mold, replicate arrays of fluid-logic circuitry can be produced using similar fabrication techniques. With mass production and the use of suitable plastics, the cost of fluid computers should compare favorably with the cost of their electronic counterparts. Other mass production techniques will also be developed for applications requiring materials such as glass, metal, or ceramic.

That the costs can be competitive must be proven to the skeptic, so to demonstrate the potential low costs, consider a comparison between the building blocks of fluid and electronic computers. First, let us discuss the development of the basic units for a fluid computer.

An introduction to the world of pure fluid devices can well begin with the invention by Nicola Tesla of a fluid "diode" in 1916. In Tesla's words, ". . . I believe that I am the first to discover or invent any means which permit the performance of the above function (valving) without the use of moving parts . . ." Tesla's "diode," shown in the margin, permits flow to occur in the "easy" direction (top to bottom) with little flow interference, but restricts flow in the "hard" direction (bottom to top) due to the clever means of dividing the flow which results in self-interference.

Tesla vs. Coanda

It is improbable that Tesla's fluid diode will prove as useful in the fluid computer as devices based on the effect observed by the Roumanian engineer, Henri Coanda. The "Coanda effect," as illustrated in the margin, is at the heart of one of the early fluid-device inventions. It occurs when a jet of fluid is expelled near an inclined (or offset) adjacent flat or curved plate. The free jet leaving the orifice

entrains fluid from its surroundings. The entrained fluid is more easily replaced on the "open" side of the jet than it is on the side with the adjacent plate. The results are threefold: the evacuation of fluid near the plate; the formation of a vortex or "bubble" of fluid at low pressure; and the establishment of a transverse pressure gradient along the jet. This pressure gradient serves to bend the jet over toward the plate as it proceeds downstream. (Almost any fluid can be used, although the bulk of the present experimental work has used water or air.)

Although usually a phenomenon associated with an adjacent plate on only one side, the Coanda effect was put to use in a pure fluid flip-flop amplifier developed in 1959 by Bowles and Warren of the Harry Diamond Laboratories. A flip-flop is, of course, a device with two control inputs (set and reset) and two outputs (Q and Q'). When a signal is applied to the set input, there is an output at Q that remains until the reset input is pulsed, at which time the output switches to Q'. The two outputs are mutually exclusive—when there is an output at Q, there is none at Q', and vice-versa.

The configuration of this pure fluid flip-flop is shown in Fig. 6-21. Let us assume that the flow in Fig. 6-21a is coming from the power input and has "attached" to the left wall of the interaction region by the Coanda effect, and that the flow thus issues from the Q' output. As long as no control flow issues from the set input, the device exhibits a stable Q' output flow and a vortex or bubble of low pressure is formed between the free jet and left wall of the interaction region. However, the set control input provides a means for introducing fluid into or near the bubble of low pressure. Flow from the set control input can thus destroy the low pressure vortex, detach the flow from the left wall, and move the free jet closer to the right wall of the interaction region, where the Coanda effect takes over. In this condition, the flow issues from the Q output, as shown in Fig. 6-21b. This condition is also stable—the jet remains attached to the lower wall and proceeds through the Q output after the set control flow is terminated as is shown in Fig. 6-21c. When the reset input is pulsed, however, jet again issues from output Q'.

Fluid, yet stable

Thus, the fluid flip-flop provides us with a "memory element"—it has two stable states and can, hence, remember a "one" (presence of flow) or a "zero" (absence of flow) for binary logic. Besides being a logic element, albeit an unconventional one, the fluid flip-flop

TESLA'S VALVULAR CONDUIT 1916

EASY DIRECTION

HARD DIRECTION

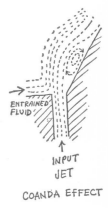

ENTRAINED FLUID

INPUT JET

COANDA EFFECT

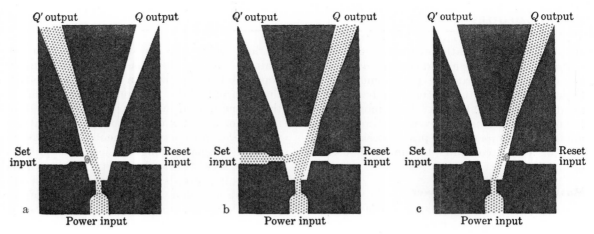

a   Power input

b   Power input

c   Power input

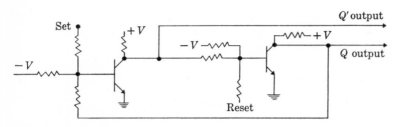

Fig. 6-21. Pure fluid flip-flop devised by Harry Diamond Laboratories uses Coanda effect to produce bistable switch. In (a) the jet from the power input has attached itself to the left wall, and the vortex exists near the nozzle of the set input. In (b) a control flow issues from the set input, destroying the low-pressure zone and providing momentum to move the power jet toward the right wall, where it attaches, again the Coanda effect. This attachment is stable, existing until an input from the reset nozzle returns it. (Drawing at left shows the electronic counterpart for purposes of comparison.)

is also an amplifier, since the power output flow is much larger than the control flow.

Other useful fluid logic devices can be produced, using the basic flip-flop. One such device is a NOR gate which has two or more inputs and one output. When a signal is present at any one or more of the inputs, there is no output signal—an output signal occurs only when there are no input signals present. Figure 6-22 illustrates a pure fluid NOR gate with two inputs, developed by Bauer of Bowles Engineering Corp.

Interestingly, when only one control input is present, the NOR gate forms an inverter—the output is a "one" when the control input is a "zero" and the output is a "zero" when the control input is a "one."

Comparisons, anyone?

Now, how do these fluid flip-flops and NOR gates compare with equivalent electronic devices? Let us consider first the simple electronic flip-flop shown in Fig. 6-21. It requires eight resistors and two transistors. A fluid flip-flop is formed from a single fluid logic element. The electronic NOR gate, shown in Fig. 6-22, consists of one transistor and four resistors. Again, only one fluid logic element is required for a NOR gate. Also, since the basic computer building blocks such as flip-flops, NOR gates, and inverters are inherent in a single fluid logic element, as we saw above, no added expense is incurred in assembling individual components

to form them. In addition, the long-standing reliability hazard of interconnections in electronic circuits is reduced or eliminated using fluid-logic building blocks, because there are no separate fluid components to fail and no fluid interconnections to make between separate components.

Still need some connections

However, we must admit that to get some of the more complex circuitry required for a computer, fluid-logic elements must be interconnected. An example of this is the AND element shown in Fig. 6-23. It is composed of two inverters, with one output of the first element capable of driving the input of the second element. When no control flows are present, the power flow issues from output A as is illustrated in Fig. 6-23a. If a control signal is applied at control input A, the input jet is forced over and drives the second inverter as depicted in Fig. 6-23b. The jet then exits from output B unless there is a control signal present at control input B. Thus, to obtain an output signal at the AND output as shown in Fig. 6-23c, control input signals A and B have to be present simultaneously.

How to build one

With the discussion of fluid logic elements and simple circuitry must come the question of how these are assembled to form a computer. We have described only pure fluid digital devices, although many fluid analog devices and analog computers, such as pneumatic proportional controllers and valves, have been developed for industrial process control. Our discussion of a fluid computer will be similarly directed to a fluid digital computer. In any ideal control system, there will be a variety of operations which may be represented by a generalized block diagram (see "Modern Process Control," page 729). At the heart of these operations is the data-handling "black box" or computer system. A look into the generalized digital "black box" reveals five standard functions as shown in the margin—Input, Output, Memory, Control and Timing, and the Arithmetic Unit.

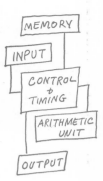

Where the first level of design and assembly for the electronic designer is the buildup of flip-flops, NOR gates, and other logical circuitry from active and passive elements such as resistors, diodes, transistors, ferrite cores, and capacitors, the fluid-logic designer begins with a "one-level headstart," with an array of logical components such as AND gates, inverters, and flip-flops, "piped" together to form a standard unit.

Piping up the building blocks

One such standard unit of interest to the computer designer is a fluid triggerable flip-flop shown in Fig. 6-24. A triggerable flip-flop is a device with one control input and two outputs that change each time the control input is pulsed. This device is constructed from two fluid flip-flops. The lower element in the figure is continuously powered and the upper element is pulse-operated. A small fluid feedback to the interaction region of the pulse-operated element serves to direct the incoming pulse to the appropriate control port of the lower element. The net result—each new incoming pulse causes a change in the output of the lower element and a triggerable flip-flop is achieved. The designer's interest in this unit can be understood when one realizes that such a device is a partial summer. When two binary bits are added together the sum consists of a partial sum plus a "carry" or "borrow" which must be properly distributed with the partial sum in order to produce the desired sum. The sum is the algebraic sum and includes all cases for the addition or subtraction of signed numbers. Because the triggerable flip-flop produces the partial sum of the two binary digits, it can be used for the "heart" of the arithmetic unit. Figure 6-25 illustrates a universal register circuit—one which can "add," "subtract," count up or down, or shift data to the right or left—which has a triggerable flip-flop as its "heart."

"Heart" goes flip-flop

The triggerable flip-flop heart consists of the two elements labeled "elements of the partial summer." If a reset pulse is introduced into the reset control duct of element P_1, the right-hand element P_2 of the partial summer will be "reset" or placed in the "zero" state with flow issuing from the lower output. Assume a binary digit is now introduced into the partial summer through the element P_3 by use of the buffer register. Assume another digit to be added is read into the buffer register and introduced into the P_3 element. Considering that there is one such circuit as shown on Fig. 6-25 for each digit of a binary number, one digit of such a number is

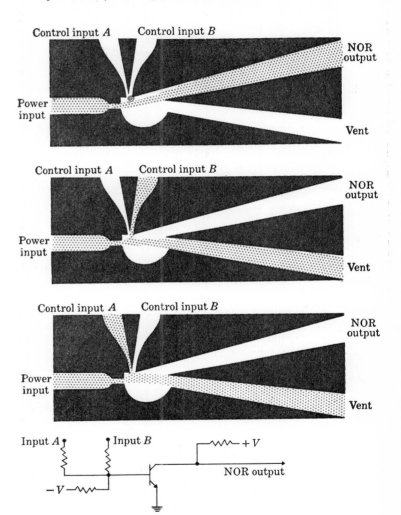

Fig. 6-22. In two-input NOR gate, presence of round chamber at bottom prevents attachment by the Coanda effect, except at the upper wall. Thus, the device is "biased" to the NOR output as long as no control output is present. If output issues from either control nozzle (or both), the flow will be diverted to the vent, to return to the NOR output as soon as flow from the control input ceases. (Bottom drawing is electronic counterpart.)

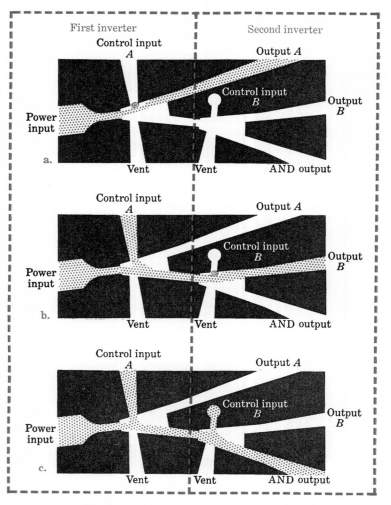

Fig. 6-23. *Typical of the way simple fluid-logic components are interconnected to form more complex elements is this AND gate. Vent opposite each control input serves to bias the flow toward the upper output in each case; thus, the jet issues from the AND output only when both control elements are flowing.*

stored in the arithmetic circuit and another digit is introduced through P_3. The partial sum of the two digits introduced through P_3 now appears at the upper output of the element P_2. The combination AND-OR gate at the right of the figure serves to properly distribute the "borrow" or "carry" to adjacent stages. This distribution of the "borrow" or "carry" is controlled by supplying a signal "carry timing" or "borrow timing" as appropriate. The inverters associated with the B and C timing pulses are of special design. That is, the incoming Sum′ signal is inverted if the B or C timing control signal is present before the Sum′ signal arrives. If the Sum′ signal arrives first, it is not inverted. This insures that the "borrow" and "carry" occur when needed.

The OR Gate at the left-hand side of Fig. 6-25 serves to receive the "borrow" or "carry" at element P_4 from an adjacent stage and corrects the partial sum during the next time period of the operation of the computer. The result is that the final sum appears in the add-subtract register (consisting of all P_2 elements) at the end of this additional time period. Thus the entire operation of adding one number from the buffer register to a number already in the add-subtract register is accomplished in two time periods. In terms of the computer designer's language this is a two-bit time parallel adder.

This collection of logical circuitry can be modified to perform counting functions and shifting functions, useful in multiplication and division, by the addition of a few simple connections.

In a similar fashion to that pursued for the arithmetic unit, logical circuitry can be designed for providing any of the other computer functions. A flip-flop with appropriate feedback can be made to oscillate and become the heart of the timing and control function. Compatible fluid input and output equipment can be constructed. And, finally, a memory system can be added. The total of these functions provides all that is necessary for a fluid digital computer.

To paraphrase the old question, "If you're so smart, why ain't you rich?," "If fluid computers are so easy to make, why don't we see them around?" Answers to both questions are similar—problems exist in the proper application of knowledge. For the fluid computer designer, it is not enough to be able to make logic elements and then to design circuitry which uses these elements. He must also (1) properly interconnect these various elements, (2) provide interconnections that do not degrade the switching speed, (3) fabricate the elements, together with their interconnections, in logical arrays, (4) make the arrays of such a size that power requirements are low, and (5) provide for all of the above with consideration of the problems of signal transmission through fluids.

Insuring that the functioning of downstream fluid devices is not affected by changes in operation of the upstream units is one of the key problems in the interconnection of these components. There are two notable fluid devices which interconnect easily. One is the turbulence amplifier developed by Raymond N. Auger of Fluid Logic Systems, New York City. The turbulence amplifier is constructed from two collinear small diameter pipes (approximately thirty mils or less in diameter) whose ends are separated by a gap of approximately ¾ inches. A low pressure flow connected to one pipe provides a laminar flow across the gap and the second pipe serves to collect a large portion of the laminar flow. Control inputs are arranged at an angle to the laminar stream. The presence of a small control flow causes a transition from laminar to turbulent flow with a consequent large decrease in flow at the output. The device serves as a multiple input NOR gate. In addition, one turbulence amplifier can drive several other similar amplifiers. As the output is isolated from the input, the devices are simple to interconnect. The turbulence amplifier has the disadvantages of low power output (although for some applications, this is an advantage), long recovery time after switching (7–10 msec), and sensitivity to sonic and mechanical vibration.

The other device which interconnects easily is a very promising high power pure fluid amplifier developed at the Sperry Utah Company and termed the axisymmetric focussed-jet NOR gate. The device utilizes a fluid dynamics phenomenon which developers of ground effect vehicles strive to avoid. That is the tendency of an inwardly directed annular jet of high aspect ratio to collapse and focus to a circular jet along the axis of symmetry. In the focussed-jet NOR gate the circular jet is captured by an output duct. Inherent in the focussed-jet NOR gate, therefore, is input-output isolation so that one device can also drive several other devices. This isolation alleviates the interconnection problem. Other advantages of the axisymmetric focussed-jet NOR gate include high gain and high switching speed, ease of fabrication and sealing, and amenability to mathematical analysis. All of the critical dimensions of the axisymmetric device can be fabricated with turning or boring techniques. This allows the holding of much tighter tolerances on the axisymmetric device than are possible on planar devices. As the flow in the focussed-jet device is radially symmetric in nature, transient and steady state flow can be investigated with a two parameter approach using the Navier-Stokes equations (fluid-flow equations). In contrast, the flow in planar devices requires a three parameter approach. One will appreciate the reduction in the number of parameters required when he realizes that for the first time it is practical, by using two parameters with suitable computer techniques, to study the flow phenomena in pure fluid devices. This analytical approach will speed the development of pure fluid computer and control technology because the cut-and-try empirical approach to device design can be greatly reduced or eliminated.

Problems transient but troublesome

In a general sense, most of the problems that arise must be considered in terms of acoustics. Also, considering these problems from the

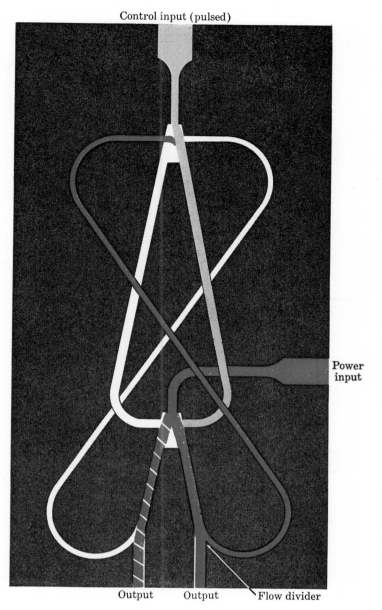

Fig. 6-24. Feedback from flow divider in each output arm of triggerable flip-flop provides control function to direct the main control input into the proper channel to switch the output. If control input pulses are regular, the unit will operate as an oscillator at either output with a frequency of half the input pulse frequency.

standpoint of an electronic analogy, they are mostly problems of transients. Electronic devices face similar problems, but there is in electronics a long history of experimental investigation of electrical and electronic transient measurement, transient filtering, transient isolation, transient suppression, and even many theoretical investigations of the general problems of transients. This is not so in fluid dynamics. Because of the difficulty of theoretical treat-

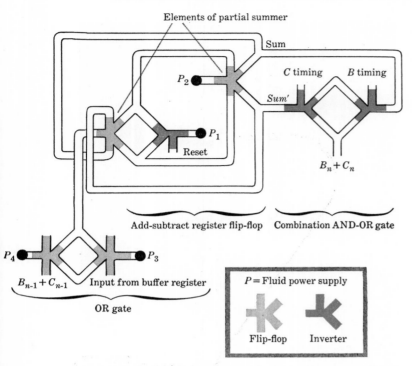

Fig. 6-25. *"Universal" register circuit uses a trigger-able flip-flop, a combination AND-OR gate, and an OR gate—all pure fluid devices—to add, subtract, count up or down, or shift data to the right or to the left.*

ment of the Navier-Stokes equations, most of the advances in fluid dynamics have been made with experimental and theoretical treatment of quasi-steady-state or steady-state flow. Only a very small portion of the extensive fluid-dynamics literature treats transient problems. And almost none of the literature, of course, treats fluid transient problems from the stand-point of the complex interconnections of pure fluid circuitry.

Still sticking with our electronic analogy, "noise" or unwanted signals arise from many sources in a complex array of pure fluid devices; also, a complex piping arrangement will be full of bends and turns, walls and channels, which will act as undesirable reflectors and conductors of this noise. The faster the "switching speed" of a fluid device the more noise, in general, it will produce. Thus, a high signal-to-noise ratio is necessary at the control port of an element with a high-switching speed to provide a useful output.

Precision measuring instruments needed

To resolve the transient flow or noise problems in designing a fluid computer, the designer must be able to measure both the signal and the noise and to discriminate between them.

This obviously requires flow measuring equipment which has a high-frequency response. In addition, if we are talking about small devices, the requirement for instrumentation can only be met by very small devices or transducers for sensing fluid velocity and fluid pressure. It should not be particularly difficult to make the type of instruments required in this day of ultraminiaturization, but it is well to bear in mind that the instrumentation should be able to measure flow in a pipe or a duct in three dimensions. In contrast to most of electronics, we are concerned not only with flow values down the pipe (or wire) but also with the components of flow perpendicular to the main flow.

The hot wire anemometer is, to date, the best all-around "multimeter" available to the fluid dynamicist. However, this instrument is not easily made in the small sizes that are required for use with pure fluid devices. For example, if it is desired to measure air flow fluctuations at a frequency of 10,000 cps, then we must use a basic platinum or tungsten wire that is about two ten-thousandths of an inch in diameter. The anemometer's circuitry then must heat up a small length of this wire ($\frac{1}{16}$ in.) and sense the change in current in the wire caused by a change in heat removal which, in turn, is caused by a change in air flow across the wire. Additional problems arise due to the change in temperature of the fluid being sensed.

However, problems of instrumentation and of the interconnection of arrays of fluid logic and proportional devices are being solved and will continue to be solved. We can expect that there will develop out of current research not only the solutions to the problems of new types of computers, but also some fine contributions to the growing field of precision instrumentation of fluid measurements.

Why greater reliability?

We mentioned earlier that one of the main justifications for fluid computers would be their inherently greater reliability when compared with electronic types. The question naturally arises as to why this should be the case, and from what aspects this greater reliability should stem. Let's first consider the usual areas of trouble in electronic logic systems, and then see how they compare with those in fluid systems, using the flip-flop circuit discussed earlier as a specific case in point. The number of expected failures for the various components involved, as given by Earles and Eddins in *Reliability Engineering Data Series—Failures Rates*, are as follows:

Component (number)		Failure rate *	Number of failures *
Transistors, Si	(2)	0.01/10⁶ hr	0.02/10⁶ hr
Resistors	(8)	0.005/10⁶ hr	0.04/10⁶ hr
Solder joints	(20)	0.0001/10⁶ hr	0.002/10⁶ hr
			0.062/10⁶ hr

These figures combine a generic failure rate (GF_r) with an application factor (K_A).

These data must, of course, be modified by factors relating to the environment in which the equipment will operate—whether the temperatures will be abnormally high or low, whether radiation is present and how much, and whether the equipment is subjected to shock or vibration. These environmental factors were estimated and are listed in the table below; the failure rates must be multiplied by them to get true failure rates.

Environmental conditions

Laboratory	1
−50°C	5
+150°C	10
Missile vibration	900
Nuclear reactor	1000
(partially shielded)	
Single A-bomb blast	100
(5 miles from 20 megatons)	
Single solar flare	10
(in cislunar space)	
Cislunar space	2

The experience on which we base our reliability estimates for pure fluid-logic elements must of necessity come from other fields. However, there seem to be only three modes of failure possible in fluid computers: failure of connectors between "sheets" of components, obstruction of orifices or passages by particles in the fluid, and complete or partial failure of the material from which the components are formed, whether by separation, creep, warp, or other physical deformation. No other failure modes are evident. If the fluid components are not clogged from particles or improperly vented by fracture of the material or failure of connectors, they will work as designed.

Perhaps the most likely material failure mode will be in the separation problem of sealing two plates together. The best failure rate applicable appears to be that of phenolic gaskets, at 0.05 per 10⁶ hr. Using the same conservative failure rates as in the electronic counterpart, a failure rate for fluid components from this factor should be 0.1 per 10⁶ hr.

Reliability experience indicates that the problems of sealing will be much worse than those of cracking or rupturing, so we can assume a failure rate for these aspects of 0.01 per 10⁶

hr; which gives a failure rate for "improperly ducting" the fluid of 0.11/10⁶ hr.

Failure from contamination of the fluid can be predicted from experience with internal combustion engines with their filtering arrangements and should not exceed 1.0 per 10⁶ hr, or one magnitude worse than that from fluid escape, especially if recirculation of purified fluid is practiced.

The other mode of failure, that of pneumatic joints, is one on which good data exist. Again as published by Earles and Eddins, this amounts to 0.02 per 10⁶ hr per joint.

Assuming now a logic plate containing 100 fluid logic elements, constructed according to today's state of the art from material which is satisfactory for the environment in which it is used, we can apply the following failure rates.

Item	Failures
Fluid connectors (100)	2.00/10⁶ hr
Contamination of board	1.00/10⁶ hr
Fracture or separation	0.11/10⁶ hr
Total for one board (100 components)	3.11/10⁶ hr
Average predicted failure rate per component	0.0311/10⁶ hr

The situation becomes even more striking when environmental factors are considered. For example, with proper selection of materials, a field which is reasonably straightforward these days, the failure rate should no more than double with each 100°C increase in temperature, up to 1000°C; this factor should also hold for reduced temperatures down to perhaps −200°C.

Turning to the effects of radiation environments, the effects should be negligible, again assuming proper choice of materials, but to be conservative, we will allow a factor of 10 in multiplying failure rates when using fluid components in the vicinity of nuclear reactors. Even in the case of vibration and shock, it is much easier to protect packaged fluid components than electronic devices, so a conservative factor of 10 should be suitable. These environmental factors result in an expected failure rate for fluid compared with electronic elements, as shown in Fig. 6-26, for a guided missile fire control computer. (A larger number of fluid logic are needed for this relatively sophisticated computer because of the faster switching speed of the electronic elements. Calculations are based on a signal "fan-in" "fan-out" of four for the fluid units. Electrical switching speed is assumed to be 100 times that of fluid switching speed.)

ENVIRONMENT	FAILURE RATES/10⁶ hr		
	Electronic	Fluid	Ratio
Laboratory computer	2.6	41.4	1:16
Temperature			
+150°C	26	83	1:3
− 50°C	13	83	1:6
+250°C	large	124	5:1*
−150°C	large	165	5:1*
Radiation			
cislunar space	5.2	41.4	1:8
solar flare	26	83	1:3
nuclear blast	260	207	1.2:1
nuclear reactor	2600	414	6:1
Vibration			
missile guidance	2340	414	6:1

* *Conservative estimate.*
Note: Colored ratios indicate superiority of fluid elements.

Fig. 6-26. Missile fire control system comparison.

How about speed?

As we have already stated, one of the limitations on fluid computers lies in the maximum fluid-jet velocities attainable in small passages. In general, these maxima are limited by sonic choking of orifices (at about Mach 0.7) in gases and by the velocity which results in cavitation or the formation of "vacuum bubbles" in liquids. In addition, of course, manufacturing techniques will limit the smallest practical size which can be mass-produced in the materials normally used, probably to channel dimensions about 10 mils width and 20 mils depth. For air at atmospheric pressure, a good rule of thumb for propagation time down a duct or pipe is not faster than one millisecond per foot.

Response speeds will obviously be inversely proportional to the channel dimensions and directly proportional to jet velocity. (Reducing the channel dimension introduces an element of risk, of course, in increasing the possibility of plugging the lines with particles, but this can be reduced by device assembly in clean rooms, and the use of adequate filtering and recirculation systems.) Acoustic principles and the basic physical principles mentioned will limit the "switching speed" of a single fluid-logic element to a maximum of about 100 kc.

What about actual elements now in existence? There are fluid-logic elements which switch in about 100 microseconds, and arrays of elements connected in the form of computer functions that will operate with a clock pulse frequency of about 100 cps. For the future, the computer clock rate will almost certainly be limited to about 10 kc, or one order of magnitude slower than the fastest switching speed of the elements.

Where will it all end?

Of what value will be the fluid computer with a clock rate of less than 10,000 cps? One obvious area of potential use is the large field of applications for computer and control systems where man is in the loop, provided that not too many calculations are required in an interval equivalent to the time of human response. Since the fastest muscular response of man is about $\frac{1}{10}$ of a second, the response loop from a stimulus through man's senses to a muscular reaction is about the same magnitude. With man in the loop, the control circuit probably need not respond any faster than 100 times/sec (or one order of magnitude faster than man). As a matter of fact, there are many servosystems which need not respond any faster than man himself. For example, in steering a ship, the wheel-house-to-rudder control loop places no burden on the speed of operation of the control system.

The day may well come when the electromechanical calculator will be replaced by a similar-sized (or smaller) fluid calculator. The replacement may be brought on by both economic and reliability reasons, for the fluid calculator should be less costly to produce than the electromechanical device which it replaces—and also more reliable. The college engineer may be easier to spot by his puffing at a computer rather than by his swinging a "slip stick." The less reliable office machine data-handling equipment will be exchanged for office machines in which fluid circuits have replaced most of the electromechanical parts. The car you drive, the typewriter you use, the machine you use for putting postage on your letters, are all candidates for future applications of fluid circuitry. And so are the servomechanisms, the process control equipment, the machine-tool controls, the low-speed computers in high schools and colleges, the training simulators, as well as a hundred and one other applications.

Further reading

The field of fluid-logic devices for computer and control systems is still in its infancy, and, as yet, there are no textbooks covering the subject. The first major symposium on fluid-logic devices was held in October 1962 at the Harry Diamond Laboratories (Washington 25, D.C.)

and summarized in the *Proceedings of the Fluid Amplification Symposium,* published by HDL. Also available from HDL is the *Proceedings of the Second Fluid Amplification Symposium,* held in May 1964. The American Society of Mechanical Engineers sponsored a symposium on fluid-jet control devices at their Winter Annual Meeting in New York in November 1962. Papers given were bound by the ASME as *Fluid Jet Control Devices* and edited by Brown of MIT. Two recent survey papers discussing fluid-logic devices are, "Fluid Logic Devices and Circuits" by Mitchell, Glaettli, and Mueller of IBM Zurich, presented to the Society of Instrument Technology, London, February 1963, and "A Survey of Fluid Devices for Automatic Control Systems" by Fox and Wood, given at the 6th Region IEEE

Technical Conference, San Diego, Calif., in April 1963. Those interested in the reliability study by Earles and Eddins should note that it was published by Avco Corp., Wilmington, in April 1962.

For an elementary treatment of digital computer design, see the book by Phister, *Logical Design of Digital Computers* (Wiley, 1958, $9.50), or the book by Richards, *Arithmetic Operations in Digital Computers* (Van Nostrand, 1955, $10).

Finally, to gain a better understanding of the basic fluid-dynamics phenomena upon which fluid-logic elements are based, the book by Schlichting, *Boundary Layer Theory* (McGraw-Hill, 1960, $17.50), will give a thorough treatment. This book requires a good degree of ability in reading mathematical literature.

OPTICAL INFORMATION PROCESSING

by Lewis C. Clapp and Huseyin Yilmaz *

IN BRIEF: *Until recently, the enormous information capacity of optical signals eluded practical application, except for a few functions as elements of electronic and electromechanical information-processing systems. New means of exploiting the potential for extracting information from optical images, or for using light as a carrier of information, are now at hand because of the stunning pace of progress in further development of lasers, fiber optics, pattern recognition techniques, and spatial filters. Many of the missing links seem to be available now for more sophisticated reconnaissance and detection systems, optical logic and storage elements leading to extremely fast computers and optical communication systems.—E.H.*

■ When I was a student of physics in college, I thought optics was already a closed subject. As the lecturer described how light is reflected by mirrors or is separated by a prism, my mind would drift away to other fields that I felt were more exciting. I was intrigued by thoughts of computers and radar systems, fascinated by microwave communications and prospects of bouncing radio waves off the surface of the moon. Optics then seemed to be a worn-out science rapidly being superseded by electrical engineering.

Today, less than ten years later, as I look at the areas of electronics I once thought the

new frontiers, I am painfully aware of many severe technical problems each of these fields still faces—and I am surprised to see now that optics offers a great potential for solving such problems from wholly different angles. The photon holds promise of practical information-processing systems that would not be possible with the electron alone.

There is now good reason to believe that the introduction of optical techniques will lead to calculating machines more than 1000 times faster than present systems. Our radio communication bands are becoming seriously overcrowded, and there, too, optical techniques offer a solution: a new and very wide-band portion of the electromagnetic spectrum for communication purposes.

Another kind of information-processing problem stems from aerial reconnaissance. Aircraft and satellites generate an enormous number of photographs as they pass over an area under surveillance. Very often details are not clear or are even out of focus. With optical processing, it is possible to enhance the image and also to construct machines that automatically recognize previously taught patterns and call them to the attention of the operator or photo-interpreter.

Many of the components for optical information processing are products of the present generation. They did not exist before 1940, and many are just emerging from the laboratory now in more practical form. These devices represent the new optics. With them we are now on the verge of new techniques for the processing or manipulating of information.

* Lewis C. Clapp is currently working on optical computers at Bolt, Beranek and Newman, Cambridge, Massachusetts. Huseyin Yilmaz works on field theory and is developing a cognition and perception theory at Arthur D. Little. He is on the faculties of Northeastern and MIT.

By "optical processing of information" we refer specifically to information systems that handle data in some form of light during the process. This may be partial optical processing as in vision, where the signal is in optical form only to the point of detection; or we may consider a complicated lens system that manipulates light, finally allowing it to impinge on a photographic plate.

The properties of light

To process information being carried in the form of light, we must manipulate the variables of the light wave. It's characteristic of electromagnetic waves that they consist of a vibrating electric field at right angles to a vibrating magnetic field; both of these are perpendicular to the direction of propagation. Thus, light is a transverse vector wave, unlike acoustic waves which are characteristically scalar and longitudinal.

The polarization of a light wave is specified by the direction in which the electric field is vibrating. In plane-polarized light the electric field vibrates only in one plane; in randomly polarized light the polarization varies at random, and the electric vector at any instant can point in any direction.

A polarizing filter can be placed in the path of such a light wave to pass only those components which vibrate in a specified direction, producing linearly polarized light. With more complicated types of filters, light also can be polarized so that the electric vector rotates to the right or to the left, either rotation resulting in circular or elliptical polarization.

Another light property of great current interest and usefulness is degree of coherence. Coherence is a measure of the correlation between the phases of all the wavelets of the total wave front. When the phases are totally uncorrelated, the wave is said to be incoherent. In classical optics, we usually deal with incoherent light sources. The light of an ordinary incandescent lamp, for example, is incoherent because the radiation emitted from one portion of the tungsten filament is completely independent of the radiation from any other portion of the filament. This is true of most other sources of radiation including stars and fluorescent lamps, but in the past few years, we have created strong sources of coherent light using the laser and similar devices.

Simple optical techniques can be used to accomplish fairly complicated operations such as addition or multiplication. Consider the arrangement of two masks shown in the margin: it can multiply. Each mask—open in some spots, opaque in others, and with various degrees of light transmission in between—can

represent values between zero and one. A point at which the mask is totally transparent represents the number one, while points that are opaque represent zero. Partially transparent points denote intermediate values. For example, the first mask is divided into four quadrants that represent ½, 1, 0, and ½. The quadrants in mask 2 represent ½, 1, 1, and 0.

If a beam of light passes through the masks and impinges on a screen, the light on the screen represents multiplication of the mask densities. Similarly, optical addition can be achieved by placing the masks in parallel and superimposing their outputs.

A simple optical multiplication network like this illustrates one aspect in which optical signals are superior to other information processing techniques. It is difficult and costly to transmit data in parallel by most electronic methods. Optical methods permit a great number of bits of information to be transmitted in parallel. A slide projector instantly puts the entire image on the screen, but the same image on the face of a TV tube has to be constructed serially, bit by bit and line by line. If the information in a 9.5-in.-square photograph with a resolution of 1000 lines/mm were converted to a serial representation and written on magnetic videotape it would take 10,000 hr. to record the information bits at 15 in./sec.

Fuzzy photos and particle paths

A fundamental operation in information processing is to extract information from the total signal, particularly in the presence of extraneous noise. The detection of minute details in a fuzzy or blurred photograph is a classic problem of this type. In the past decade, some ingenious optical techniques have been developed for improving poor images to the point where details completely hidden in the original can be recognized clearly in the resulting image.

French physicists at the University of Paris, under the direction of André Maréchal, have devised a method of enhancing photographs by optical filtering. A photographic negative illuminated by coherent light acts as a diffraction grating, creating a pattern which is a harmonic analysis of the spacing between light and dark area in the photograph. If only the higher spatial frequency components are retained and the low-frequency contribution is suppressed, details of the image are accentuated. A schematic of the experiment is shown in the margin.

The next ambitious step beyond image-enhancing devices is the construction of machines that recognize patterns. They are an extension of image enhancement techniques

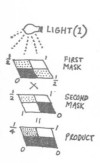

LIGHT (1)

FIRST MASK

SECOND MASK

PRODUCT

Source

P = ORIGINAL

F = FREQUE DEPEND FILTER

N = ENHANC IMAGE

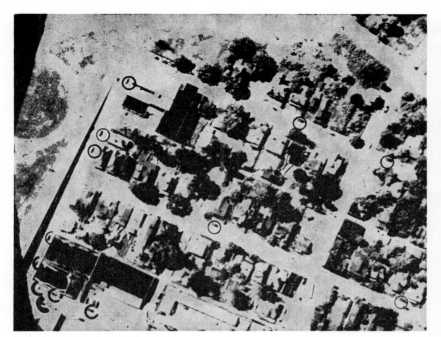

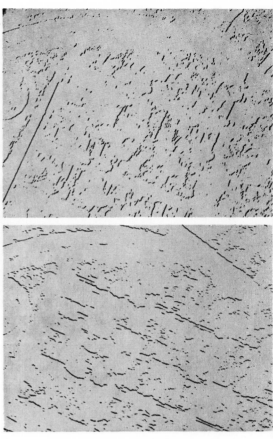

Fig. 6-27. A major problem in photo-interpretation is, still, finding significant patterns. By subjecting this photo to a computer-like process of decision-making filters, intersecting lines were found. Results of vertical and horizontal decisions at right. All lines that enclosed oblongs of a certain area were denoted autos pointed north-south or east-west. Two-toned cars that appear as adjacent double squares would not have been missed if additional masks were used. (Courtesy Ford Aeronutronics)

in the sense that salient features of the signal often must be refined until they are separated from the surrounding noise so they can be compared with an image previously taught to the machine. Someday, computers may not only be able to read printed pages directly, but also scan photographs transmitted by a Tiros satellite to make a prediction of the world's weather without any intermediate human intervention.

Although the general pattern recognition problem is still far from a complete solution, a number of intermediate techniques have been relatively successful. At the Aeronutronic Division of Ford Motor Co., Joseph K. Hawkins has developed a technique for recognizing specific objects in a photograph. First Hawkins enhances the boundaries by employing spatial filters similar to those used in the Maréchal experiment. With the boundaries crispened, the image is processed in a series of steps, each identifying a particular aspect of the desired object.

For example, look at Fig. 6-27, where the problem is to find all the automobiles pointed in North-South or East-West directions. The first step filters the image through a mask that passes all lines that are oriented N-S. Similarly, the image is filtered by a mask that passes all E-W lines. The two resultant images are superimposed, producing a map of all the intersec-

tions of N-S and E-W lines. Further processing through another series of decision-making filters isolates all the places on the photo where intersecting lines form a box of specified area and shape.

These processing operations are programmed in advance in computer-like fashion so that the occurrence of a specific object in any photograph could be detected. Thus we could find all the automobiles—small oblong boxes—in the photograph. In this example several automobiles were missed because not enough decision-making filters were used to determine that two-toned cars formed adjacent squares which added up to oblongs of the size and shape being sought.

Another example of a practical pattern-recognition system is the photo-interpretive program for the analysis of spark chamber photographs developed jointly by Massachusetts Institute of Technology and Bolt, Beranek and Newman. The pattern (Fig. 6-30) of sparks in the chamber at any moment indicates the paths of subatomic particles. The spark patterns which are photographed during the experiment must be scanned to locate significant events, but only a small fraction of all the photographs produced contain significant information. In the MIT-BBN program, the image in each frame is examined by a cathode-

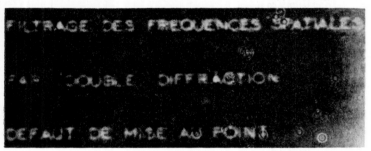

Fig. 6-28. Reconnaissance photos are often taken under difficult conditions. A spatial-filtering technique developed at the Institut d'Optique in Paris enhances image detail through harmonic analysis of the spacing between light and dark areas. When the lower spatial frequency components are suppressed by a circular filter, details emerge. Crispening of the image in this fashion is pre-requisite to automatic photo-interpretation and character recognition. This spatial-filtering technique applied to restoration of document detail above shows dramatic improvement. Original document is at top. Occluded image of it (center) was restored by spatial filtering (bottom). En anglais: SPATIAL FREQUENCY FILTERING BY DOUBLE DIFFRACTION UNFOCUSED. (Courtesy Institut d'Optique)

ray tube and a digital computer. The scope functions as a flying-spot scanner, momentarily displaying a point—as a flash of light—at selected coordinates. A system of lenses projects an image of this point onto the frame of film at corresponding coordinates. If the film is transparent at this location, the light passes through and falls on a photomultiplier tube which alters the state of flip-flop circuits in the computer. Thus the computer constructs an internal "map" of the entire film image.

The program first searches this for the

"image" of a spark; when one is found, it takes control of the scanning process and predicts the approximate location of the next spark in the track, thus reducing the total area to be examined in succeeding photographs. This task is performed by the computer at the rate of 5000 frames per hour, as opposed to a human rate of about 50 frames per hour.

In many such pattern-recognition programs, the optical image is converted into electrical impulses very early in the process. Processing would be faster and more flexible if the entire operation were completely optical and did not require any photoelectric conversion. The major problem, as we shall see, is that of light amplification. With the optical tools available up to two years ago, there were no reliable and easy ways to amplify an optical signal without first converting to electric pulses. Since each information-processing operation, such as passing the signal through a filter, reduces the amplitude of the signal, there is clearly a limit to the number of processing steps that can be executed before amplitude restoration is required. Despite this barrier, several groups, such as Cornell Aeronautical Laboratory, are investigating machines with a minimum of opto-electric conversions.

Character recognition, detection, and identification of letters and numbers, is a special case of the general pattern-recognition problem. Techniques have been developed independently at Arthur D. Little, Inc., and the U.S. National Bureau of Standards which recognize characters by determining the center of gravity of a pattern and the distribution of higher moments about it. These methods of specifying a character surmount background noise and also locate characters regardless of their position on a page. IBM, Farrington, Sylvania, and many other companies now offer machines that read typed or printed material with certain restrictions. Some of these devices also get passing grades in recognizing hand-printed characters; however, reliable recognition of cursive handwriting is still a wide open field. A few organizations seem remarkably close to perfecting such a machine, although I seriously doubt whether they will ever be able to recognize my own illegible scrawls. (Try the margin.)

Information through light pipes

While lenses, prisms, mirrors, and filters still do a good job of manipulating optical signals, they alone cannot explain the sudden increased interest in optical signal processing. Improvement of the old and an astonishing rate of discovery of new techniques has given additional impetus. An example of sudden progress is seen

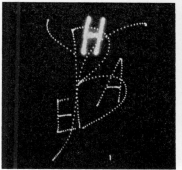

Fig. 6-29. Computers can be taught to recognize letters in a jumbled image. Each character acts as noise which must be suppressed to identify another. In this CYCLOPS program by Marill of Bolt, Beranek and Newman, computer is taught coordinates of each letter element by tracing it on scope with light pen. Recognition program locates, identifies, brightens letters. (Courtesy L. C. Clapp)

in fiber optics. For many years we've known that long fibers of glass act as light pipes. In fact, several patents were granted to early investigators who suggested various image-processing schemes using such fibers. However, none of these devices worked very well, because all the fibers in a bundle touched each other, permitting cross-talk. Then, in the early fifties, Hopkins in England and Van Heel in Holland independently thought of coating each fiber with a glass of lower refractive index than the central portion or core. As light traveled down the axis of such a coated fiber, it would be reflected back into the central portion of the fiber whenever it struck the boundary.

Progress in fiber optics has led to the development of an intriguing optical device for recognizing complex audio signals such as spoken words. R. D. Hawkins of the Sperry Gyroscope Co. calls his invention a SCEPTRON (Spectral Comparative Pattern Recognizer). The SCEPTRON consists of several thousand optical fibers of varying lengths, supported at one end but free to vibrate when excited by soundwaves. Light enters the fiber at the fixed end and emerges at the free end where it passes through a mask to a photocell detector, as shown in the margin.

A pattern of light and dark points on the previously prepared mask represents the word to be recognized. This word is recognized only if the amount of light coming through the mask exceeds a certain threshold value. The soundwave causes vibration of those fibers with a corresponding natural frequency. Thus,

the amount of light that passes through the SCEPTRON depends on the sound and on the mask. Masks are made by generating the desired audio signal so that light from the moving ends of the fibers projects a pattern on a photographic plate.

One attractive feature is that a great many of the units can be packed in a small space, while the major limitation seems to be the lengthy and cumbersome process needed to teach the device a single syllable.

Thousands of units would be needed to recognize even simple conversations.

Fiber optics can be used in a variety of other image-processing applications. By carefully arranging the order of the individual fibers, a bundle can be constructed that will invert an image. By making the fibers at one end smaller than the fibers at the other, image magnification can be achieved.

The laser as an optical processor

Recent production of fiber-optic lasers are having an important effect on optical signal processing. There are many who regard the invention of the laser as the most important step along the road to direct processing of optical information. The bandwidth of a system in which light is the information carrier is thousands of times greater than a similar microwave network. Since the information-carrying capacity of a communication network is proportional to the bandwidth, a single laser system has the bandwidth to replace all the present communications systems between the East and West Coasts of the U.S.A. This will not

TRACK

← SCAN

LASER

RED
FILTER

← ω

NON-LINEAR
MEDIUM

A

← 2ω

UV
FILTER

B

← 2ω

DETECTOR

*A = fundamental
and first harmonic
generated in
material*

*B = filter allows
only harmonic
to pass*

Fig. 6-30. Spark-chamber photographs record the tracks of high-energy particles, but visual scanning of thousands of images is too time consuming. This film-reader at MIT is computer-controlled. Frames are examined at rate of 5000 per hour. (Courtesy Bolt, Beranek and Newman and MIT)

be possible, however, until the techniques for modulation and demodulation are improved.

A second potential advantage of the laser for communication of information is the extreme narrowness of the beam. This means that most of the transmitted energy can be picked up by the receiver of a point-to-point communications system. Laser communication networks are very promising for long-distance space applications. However, close to earth clouds and atmospheric scattering greatly limit their performance.

It has been suggested that the large bandwidths and resolution properties of coherent light could lead to optical radar systems with greatly improved resolution in range and velocity. For instance, a laser-based radar system emitting a pulse every nanosecond could measure velocities as low as 1 ft/sec. Hughes Aircraft is now working on the so-called Colidar (coherent light radar) optical ranging system which employs a pulsed ruby laser and may have an ultimate range of thousands of miles in outer space. On earth, atmosphere attenuation has limited the useful range of this experimental system to about 20 miles. A similar system is also being developed at the U.S. Army Electronics Research and Development Laboratory.

The laser should inject new life into many of the classical information-processing schemes

that were once abandoned for lack of a suitable light amplifier. Nevertheless, not all light-amplification problems are about to be resolved. The laser only amplifies a beam of light; we would also like to have devices that amplify an entire image.

Light as an information carrier

If light is to be a carrier of information, means must be found to modulate it. Almost a hundred years ago Alexander Graham Bell experimented with gas flames modulated at audio frequencies. Later the German Army used this communications concept in a device called the "Lichtsprecher" which enabled battle front conversations that were difficult to intercept. However, modulation techniques appropriate to such low frequencies cannot be expected to work for the 10 kMc bandwidths sought with laser systems.

The laser itself provided the key to this problem. For many years it has been known that parameters such as the dielectric constant of many materials were nonlinear. However, it was virtually impossible to demonstrate such nonlinearities because they produce small effects which are proportional to the intensity of the applied optical signal. The laser provides a beam with optical fluxes—in the order of megawatts per square centimeter—which are intense enough to exploit the optical nonlinearities in many materials.

The optical polarization induced in a given material is a function of the strength of the electric field of the signal:

$$P = XE(1 + a_1E + a_2E^2 + \cdots)$$

Note that if only the first term of the equation is retained, we have the relation between the polarization and the electric vector that is taught in elementary physics courses. Although the coefficients are all small, a large value of E can make these nonlinear terms quite important. For instance, the second term contributes to the total polarization a term which oscillates at twice the fundamental frequency (see "High Energy Lasers," page 135). A typical experimental arrangement for the production of these higher frequencies is shown schematically in the margin.

A more striking effect is observed by combining radiation from two different lasers, each oscillating at different frequencies, in a suitable medium. The emerging radiation is found to contain components oscillating at frequencies equivalent to the sum and difference of the original frequencies. The frequency difference can be made so small that the resulting radiation is microwave rather than optical. The arrangement used in these experiments is somewhat symmetrical. It is possible to reverse the effect and modulate one laser beam by microwave radiation. The result is an amplitude-modulated beam of light. Thus we have the techniques for modulating and demodulating a beam of light, an essential requirement for an all-optical communication system.

It has been almost two years since the first successful optical mixing experiments were announced. In a step beyond this work, the General Telephone and Electronics Corp. has demonstrated a laboratory model communications system for transmitting and receiving television pictures (see Fig. 6-31).

Similar experimental arrangements have been demonstrated by a number of other organizations. The Westinghouse Electric Corporation recently demonstrated an optical communication system in which the information signal was used to modulate the frequency rather than the amplitude of the optical beam —resulting in an FM optical communications system.

The digital computer can be regarded as a special type of communications network. Signals generated at one point must travel to another part of the computer where they are processed and interpreted. This action in turn generates other signals.

An optical computer

Optical radiation offers the computer engineer too an opportunity to try some bold innovations. My own group (author L.C.) is trying to take advantage of the basic nature of light to develop optical computers that perform complex operations faster, for example, the addition of two large matrices in a single instruction time.

Although engineers have been developing a wide variety of electronic devices that might serve as components of a fast digital computer, devices which must communicate with each other in, say, a nanosecond (10^{-9} sec), even at the speed of light cannot be more than about a foot apart (see "Nanosecond Computing," page 687).

Though increased transmission speed is one of the reasons for considering the marriage of optics and computer technology, its real value for faster computers lies in harnessing the extremely short switching processes that occur in nature. Except for certain subnuclear reactions, the fastest processes known to physicists are interactions between light and atoms or molecules. The wavelength of optical radiation is comparable to the size of the atoms, which makes light an excellent probe for

Fig. 6-31. Laser beam carrying microwave signal of video information was demonstrated in laboratory of General Telephone and Electronics Corp. In a similar experiment with audio signals, IBM used a gallium arsenide injection laser. Until recently, practical modulation of light was a major problem in its use as an information carrier. (Courtesy General Telephone and Electronics)

triggering processes involving individual atoms. Many light-induced atomic transitions occur in 10^{-12} sec. We look forward to eventually producing computer elements with switching times within this magnitude.

Storage and logic

In a digital computer, data are most conveniently stored as binary representation of two distinct physical states—a sequence of "ones" and "zeros." One optical method for storing these binary digits (bits) is based on the energy distribution of the atoms in a laser. Under normal conditions, most of the atoms are in the lower energy states (see marginal sketch). This energy distribution can be altered by permitting light of the proper frequency and intensity to pass through the laser material. Pumping radiation inverts the populations of two levels from the normal distribution. When a cell is in the normal distribution, we can designate it as storing a binary "zero." The same cell in the inverted condition stores a binary "one." Optical radiation can cause the laser to change state or can be used to sense the state that it is in. We have all the requirements necessary for a storage device.

However, there is an important difference between the optical storage devices just described and the memory units currently employed in digital computers. In conventional memories, both states are quite stable. Unfortunately, the optical element in its inverted state is only metastable; gradually its atoms return to the normal distribution. This relaxation time will vary depending on the specific materials, from microseconds to seconds. Therefore, it will be necessary to periodically regenerate the data before they are lost. Nevertheless, this seems like a small price to pay for attaining an ultrafast computer.

A second difficulty is cost. Even if we do store data in a ruby laser it may be the world's most expensive bit! Despite the speed advantage, it is hard to justify a storage cost of $1000 per bit while present storage only costs a few dollars per bit.

There are two approaches to a solution: We can develop techniques for storing many bits in a single crystal or we can try to miniaturize the laser systems. But right now the trend in laser research is directed toward achieving greater power output. Because power is proportional to the cavity volume, the larger structures are receiving most of the attention.

One of the most interesting investigations of small computer elements is being carried out at the American Optical Co. This work stems from the discovery by Elias Snitzer that a glass fiber doped with active ions like neodymium also exhibits laser behavior. Recently Charles Koester at A.O. has demonstrated that two lasers can be serially connected, as shown in Fig. 6-32, so that the first laser can control the activity of the second. When an opaque mask is placed between them, the second or controlled laser emits radiation (oscillates) independently of the first. If the mask is removed, radiation from the first induces transitions in the second laser which alter its energy balance. Oscillation in the controlled laser then ceases. As the second laser is being driven from its oscillating condition, the radiation from

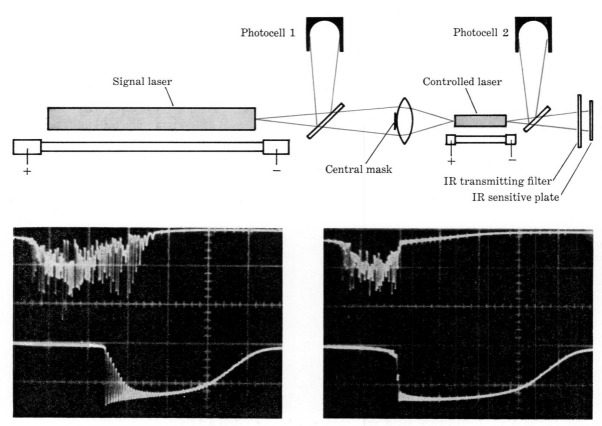

Fig. 6-32. *Feasibility of optical flip-flops for computers is shown in experiment by Charles Koester of American Optical. With mask in place (scope picture at left) each laser operates independently. When it is removed, light from signal laser quenches stimulated output of controlled laser by forcing its atoms to a different energy state. Upper scope trace is controlled laser. (Courtesy American Optical Co.)*

the first is being amplified by the second. This principle might be used to construct a pulsed type of optical flip-flop—a bi-stable storage device.

The appropriate spacing between the energy levels of the material is crucial for proper operation of the memory devices discussed above. It may not be possible to find the proper materials in nature. Does this mean that the optical computer ideas might have to be abandoned? There is some reason to believe that this will not be the case. Chemists at the Woolwich Polytechnic Institute in London report the ability to optically pump and stimulate emission from organic molecules imbedded in a rigid glass matrix. One day it may be possible to specify the energy levels needed and then produce tailor-made laser crystals with the desired specifications. This would vastly differ from the current pattern in laser research, where the bulk of the effort is expended in searching for just the right kind of material to test out a new idea.

A computer must contain logical or switching elements in addition to storage elements. The properties of light can be used to create novel types of logic elements. One intriguing scheme for implementing logic is based on the polarization of light. For example, imagine that data are represented by beams of light which are linearly polarized either in the horizontal or vertical direction. The sketch in the margin shows how a circuit can detect the simultaneous occurrence of two vertically polarized beams. The two beams under examination are combined, passed through a 50% transmitting filter and then through a sheet of polarizing material oriented so that only vertically polarized light can pass. Only when both beams are vertically polarized is enough light detected to produce an output signal.

With the elements and techniques of optical information processing now more firmly within our grasp, we stand on the verge of constructing optical computers that may be 1000 times faster than any electronic machine we can build today.

Further reading

Since optical signal processing is a field with a promise rather than a past, there are very few sources that the reader can look to for a comprehensive summary of the state of the art. A good start might be the *Proceedings of Symposium on the Optical Processing of Information,* edited by Pollock (Spartan Books, July 1963). A second symposium, co-sponsored by the Office of Naval Research, was held in Boston, November 9 and 10, 1964. Proceedings will be published in 1965 by M.I.T. Press, Cambridge.

A great deal of material about classical optics will be found in Strong's *Concepts of Classical Optics* (Freeman and Co., 1958, $9.50), a good account of fiber optics.

The entire January 1963 issue of the *Proceedings of the IEEE* was devoted to lasers, optical mixing, and quantum electronics. Many of the papers there are quite technical and some readers may prefer to read Lengyel's excellent book on *Lasers* first (Wiley & Sons, 1962, $6.95).

Some good papers on optical computers can be found in the *Proceedings of the 1963 Pacific Computer Conference* sponsored by the IEEE. I particularly recommend the survey paper by J. T. Tippett and the account of fiber optic lasers by C. J. Koester.

Those interested in optical character recognition should process the book, *Optical Character Recognition,* edited by Fischer, Pollock, Raddack, and Stevens (Spartan Books, 1962, $10). Interesting papers on image improvement techniques can also be found in journals like *Applied Optics,* published by the Optical Society of America (Washington), and *Optica Acta.*

"Optical Harmonies and Non-Linear Phenomena" by Franken and Ward is a technical but particularly excellent review article in *Review of Modern Physics,* Jan. 1963.

For a description of PIP (Photo-Interpretive Program for the Analysis of Spark-Chamber Data) by Rudloe, Deutsch, and Marrill see Communications of the ACM (June 1963).

NANOSECOND COMPUTING

*by Douglas L. Hogan, Ronald L. Wigington, and Raymond W. Sears, Jr.**

IN BRIEF: *Computers almost a thousand times faster than present-day machines are on the* *horizon. At such speeds, solution times become more reasonable for many problems in mathematics, pattern recognition, statistical correlation, and real-time control of rapidly occurring events. The jump in speed, from microseconds to nanoseconds, has been completed at all levels of the computer hierarchy by interrelated advances in fast physical phenomena, materials*

* Douglas L. Hogan is a systems expert and logical designer, Raymond W. Sears, Jr., a circuit and equipment designer, and Ronald L. Wigington, a researcher in fast physical phenomena and instrumentation. All three are members of the Department of Defense team that has been directing research and development toward nanosecond goals.

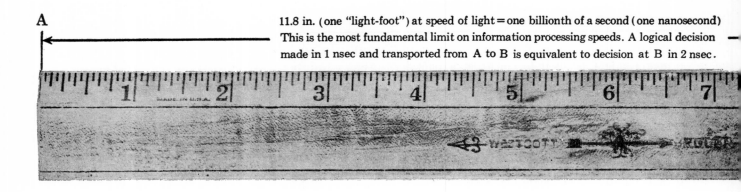

A

11.8 in. (one "light-foot") at speed of light = one billionth of a second (one nanosecond) This is the most fundamental limit on information processing speeds. A logical decision made in 1 nsec and transported from A to B is equivalent to decision at B in 2 nsec.

development, and logical design. Semiconducting devices and thin magnetic films show the greatest immediate promise, but the payoff in the long run may be devices based on superconductivity at very low temperatures, though their fabrication problems are still formidable. Above the device level, though, the physical and logical relationships within a computing system are coming hard against a fundamental limit to information-processing rates—the speed of light.—E.H.

■ Computer users are constantly seeking machines faster than those they have. Their quest for higher and higher speeds is more than a simple search for another technological Everest to conquer. The redoubtable peaks to be scaled are extremely complex problems in mathematics, pattern recognition, and statistical correlation whose solution times still lie outside reasonable reach of today's most rapid computers. Even for simpler problems well within the capacity of available machines, more computations per dollar per unit of time is an ever-present economic goal.

The computer industry is now on the verge of completing a most significant jump in computing speed—from microseconds to millimicroseconds (nanoseconds)—having succeeded in translating fast physical phenomena into fast computing techniques in which operations occur in the time light travels one foot.

Even if these computers merely manage to work serially, processing one digit of information at a time, rather than handling many digits simultaneously in the parallel fashion of most machines today, they will solve problems with a fraction of today's hardware complexity and power consumption.

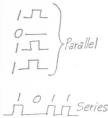

Achievement of nanosecond speeds requires a number of interrelated advances—finding faster physical phenomena, developing clever logical design to avoid the geometrical limits of the light-foot, new ways to attack problems with the resultant faster computers.

Another revolution in computer technology has indeed occurred, but the advances have not been uniform on all fronts. We three have

been in the thick of it for the past few years, and, while we should be accustomed to it, we find it exciting to reconsider these advances.

Horse and buggy speeds

Five or six years ago, the state of commercially available digital computer technology was typified by vacuum tube computers. We called these "high-speed" then—memory cycle times (minimum time for successive accesses to the stored information) were of the order of 10 μsec, transfer times (of energy between bistable elements) of the order of 1 μsec, and electronic switching and response times (time required to change from one of two states to the other) of the order of $\frac{1}{3}$ μsec. These were loosely referred to as "megacycle machines"; because the timing information had a fundamental frequency of that order.

As positive feedback developed between computer users and computer designers the very existence of progressively faster computers suggested new methods of solving problems put to computers. These methods, in turn, demanded greater computer capability. Computer users were facing the inescapable fact that even on "high-speed" computers, problems involving simulation of random processes and solution of complex systems of nonlinear differential equations would still require a considerable portion of the lifetime of man and machine. Many problems, such as missile guidance and tracking, involve "on-line computation." These use a computer to make decisions on the progress of a physical process and to exercise control over it, but many problems were not solvable because of the short fixed time allowed for calculations. We also suspect that faster real-time control would benefit industrial processes.

By brute force alone, the speed of known computing techniques might have been improved by a factor of ten or so. But what the users really wanted was a huge jump in capability similar to the transition from electromechanical (relay) to electronic (vacuum tube) machines—an improvement in speed by a factor of approximately 1000.

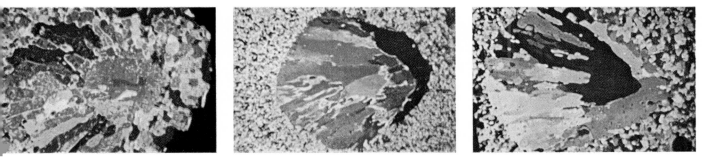

Color Fig. 39. Cyclic growth of large hailstones suggested by the model of Color Fig. 38 is supported by photomicrographs of natural stones such as these, taken in polarized light. When in parts of cloud where supercooled water is abundant, hailstone picks up so much water that freezing is slow, leading to coarsely crystalline, radiating blades of clear ice. When little water is intercepted, quick-freezing creates layers of finer-grained ice, with included water droplets and air bubbles. See "Changing the Weather," in Chapter 5. (Courtesy R. List (ZAMP) and V. Schaefer)

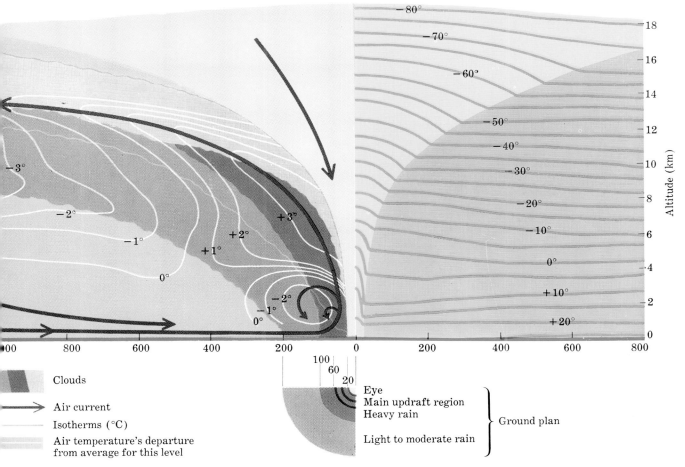

Color Fig. 40. Intelligent attempts to control the path or intensity of a hurricane must await development of a model better than this relatively crude physical picture showing a few major features. Such mathematical models, now in the works, use three-dimensional equations for air motions, plus equations to account for energy exchange by condensation, freezing, and evaporation of water. Once a satisfactory model exists, control proposals can be evaluated before undertaking potentially risky experiments. See "Changing the Weather," in Chapter 5. (Courtesy J. Eggleson)

Color Fig. 41. You're facing the reheat furnace (above) at the beginning of the 2800-ft. hot strip mill shown in Fig. 6-62. Steel slabs weighing almost 20 tons, are "watched" by a computer as they are heated to a prescribed temperature. They are rolled, under computer control, by the roughing stands into the thinner, still fiery slabs seen emerging at right. Sensors at strategic locations report back the slab's temperature, width, and location. As it is squeezed and flattened the measurements are compared with what the computer has predicted at each stage to make the ideal product. The computer readjusts the controls for each successive stand, perhaps changing the roller openings or speeding the mill. At right, a bar enters the finishing stands. It emerges as a silver ribbon speeding toward the coilers below at 34 mph. Its physical characteristics are affected by how it's cooled after rolling. See "Modern Process Control," in Chapter 6. (Courtesy International General Electric)

Fig. 6-33.

Historically, the approach to speeding up computers had been simply to improve the speed of the individual decision-making devices from which computers are constructed. These improvements were gradual, except for the transition from electromechanical millisecond to electronic microsecond events.

We knew that a thousand-fold increase in component speed alone would not produce a computing system capable of *solving problems* 1000 times as fast because delays are introduced in the processing of information by the physical and logical relationships of each device and subsystem, and by the relationship between man and machine.

Representation of information

An electronic computer is a remarkably intricate hierarchy of decision-making devices. From the sheer simplicity of "yes" or "no" answering devices, we can build magnificent machines capable of solving enormously complex problems. Quite coldly perhaps, hardware-oriented engineers view a computer as a collection of physical elements, each with a few physical states. In the aggregate, these produce a large number of possible physical states of the total system. From another point of view, their logician colleagues regard the physical state of the computer system at any particular time as a representation of some logical state in the solution of a particular problem.

Most physical elements from which a computer can be constructed have two easily identifiable states, and can represent the "zeros" and "ones" of a two-valued or binary logic. Each element can represent a single bit (binary digit) of a binary number. Some examples of physical quantities whose elementary states can be used to represent binary variables are magnitude or polarity of voltage, frequency of a signal, or an energy state.

Operations on the binary numbers are controlled by sequences of two-state logic. The physical transition from one state to another must correspond to a logical transition in the problem solution. The transition in the total state of the machine is the aggregate of transitions of the two state elements.

The processes causing transition require energy transmission from one element to another and they also require nonlinear interaction between several signals at the receiving element.

For example, in the marginal sketch, one input, S, gives a small response, R_1, whereas two inputs $2S$, yield a response, R_2, indicating a change in the state of the device, C. This shows a simple two-input AND function.

Elementary operations of two-state logical variables can be described by such logical expressions as AND, OR, NOT, etc. The result of the AND function of several independent variables is *1* if, and only if, all the independent variables are *1*. The OR function produces a *1* if any one of the independent inputs is *1*. The NOT function changes a *1* to *0* and vice versa.

Quite simply, then, a logic circuit responds to separate input signals representing two distinct physical states, and produces one of two distinct physical states, or a bit, at its outputs. We're interested in speeding up the electrical analogs of logic functions.

The computer hierarchy

For reference points to measure and compare speed, let us examine in greater detail the computer hierarchy. At the lowest level, physical phenomena are used in various devices—diodes, transistors, magnetic cores, etc.—to achieve input-output characteristics from which circuits can be synthesized. Circuits are needed to realize the complex terminal properties—that is, to represent logic functions—not possible with devices alone.

So, at the circuit level, the emphasis begins to shift from electrical quantities to consideration of logical entities. From logic circuits can be synthesized certain functional logic blocks—a group of circuits that operates on words or groups of bits, adding them, comparing them, etc.

These blocks, in turn, are combined to form subsystems—memories, arithmetic units, con-

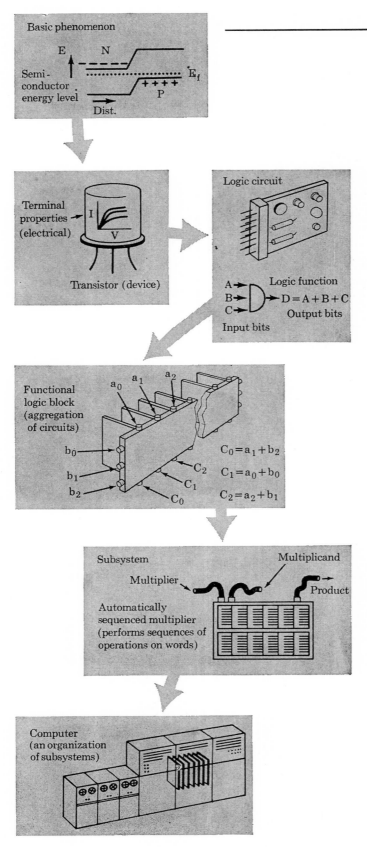

Basic phenomenon

Semiconductor energy level

E
N
E_f
P
Dist.

Terminal properties (electrical)

Transistor (device)

Logic circuit

A
B
C

Logic function
$D = A + B + C$
Output bits

Input bits

Functional logic block (aggregation of circuits)

a_0 a_1 a_2

b_0
b_1
b_2

C_2
C_1
C_0

$C_0 = a_1 + b_2$
$C_1 = a_0 + b_0$
$C_2 = a_2 + b_1$

Subsystem

Multiplier
Multiplicand
Product

Automatically sequenced multiplier (performs sequences of operations on words)

Computer (an organization of subsystems)

Fig. 6-34. A computer is a hierarchy of assemblies that increase in complexity at every level. Each assembly is characterized by the physical and logical nature of its inputs and outputs.

trol units, etc., which perform sequences of operations on sequences of words. In actuality, a computer is a collection of such subsystems which have the classical ability described by von Neumann: "to execute the basic operations . . . according to the logical pattern in which they generate the solution of the mathematical problem." So, once the decision-making criteria have been set, a computer operates automatically, changing its own logical pattern of operation to meet each new logical condition arising during the solution process.

As modern computing and information processing machines have become widespread, aggregations of such machines, each deserving to be called a computer in the sense of von Neumann's definition, have been operated collectively in *supersystems* to enable the solution of multiple problems to be achieved simultaneously.

While the great supersystems of computers like SAGE and BMEWS are not part of this article, it is nonetheless true that we need each computer in the network to be as fast as it can be. On a scale not quite so grand, it is becoming more common to connect small computers to larger ones to handle the peripheral processing for them. In a sense, this repeats the essential pattern of the hierarchy.

Faster phenomena

Part of our quest, then, is for a compatible set of fast phenomena to build devices and circuits with desirable characteristics. We want amplification over a wide range of frequencies (one measure of high information-rate transmission capability). We're looking for sharper thresholding—a large ratio of response to an input signal on opposite sides of the designated "threshold level." This makes for more certain responses to the perennial questions in computer operation: "Is it a zero or is it a one?" "Is there a signal or is there none?" We also need shorter device propagation delays (the time required for an input to the element to result in a useable output).

Semiconductor junctions form the backbone of today's computer technology. Four major properties of such semiconductor junctions have been used: rectification, amplification, capacitance variation, and tunneling. The simplest of these is the rectifying action of the *p-n* junction. Diodes have been constructed for switching and shaping pulses with rise times of tenths of a nanosecond and durations of the order of 1 nanosecond.

Transistor action—control and amplification—is achieved by the combination of two junctions. Gain-bandwidth products (the product of amplification ratio and the frequency range over which they are effective) of 2 to 3 gc (a gigacycle is 10^9 cps) have been achieved in present-day transistors. Some laboratory models have greater gain-bandwidth products for communication uses, but for switching applications, transistor designs may not extend beyond a few gc bandwidth because of inherent speed-limiting factors.

In a semiconductor junction, capacitance varies as a function of voltage. The action is much as if one were able, by electrical means, to rapidly vary the spacing (and hence the electrical capacitance) of a parallel-plate capacitor. This phenomenon can be used for manipulation of digital information—for example, by modulation of a radio-frequency carrier to represent information. Varactor diodes have been constructed having a gain-bandwidth product greater than 100 gc. Unfortunately, as used in an RF carrier technique, the information rate is only 1–2% of the gain-bandwidth product of the device.

The fastest junction phenomenon now known is tunneling. Quantum mechanics predicts that a particle approaching a potential-energy barrier has a finite probability of appearing at the other side of the barrier at the same energy even though the height of the barrier is greater than the energy of the particle. A semiconductor junction provides such a barrier for current carriers under certain circumstances. A properly formed junction exhibits the current-voltage characteristics shown in the marginal sketch. This characteristic is clearly nonlinear and can be used for amplification because of the region of negative resistance, where current decreases with increasing voltage. The tunneling process has a fundamental time constant of less than 10^{-13} sec and thus the tunnel diode is a prime candidate for high-speed switching.

Faster with ferromagnetism

In addition to semiconductors, faster devices are promised by phenomena in the strongly magnetic ferromagnetic materials. Here the interest is shifting from ceramic ferrite cores to thin films of ferromagnetic metals—iron, nickel, cobalt, and their alloys.

Two properties of ferromagnetics are of interest. The first is magnetic remanence, that is, that some magnetic field remains in the material after the magnetizing current is removed. The second is extreme nonlinearity. The hysteresis loop in the margin on page 689 shows how very nonlinear magnetization can be.

The properties of a thin film of ferromagnetic material are quite different from the properties of the same material in bulk form. Crystals of ferromagnetic material, randomly oriented in a bulk sample, are magnetically aligned by the thin geometry of the film, and by fabricating the film in the presence of a magnetic field. The magnetic alignment of the crystal results in a preferred axis of magnetization, a magnetic uniaxial anisotropy. Magnetization in one direction along the preferred, or easy, axis is identified as a "1" and in the other direction as a "0." Application of two magnetic fields, one perpendicular to the preferred axis and one opposite to the existing remanence, causes all the magnetic dipoles of the film to rotate in unison. Reversal of the direction of magnetization in thin magnetic films by such "rotational" switching has been predicted in the order of 1 nsec., and has been achieved experimentally in 1–2 nsec.

Cold logic

Another phenomenon closely associated with magnetism is superconductivity. At a few degrees Kelvin a number of materials (Sn at 3.73°K, Pb at 7.22°K, Ta at 4.40°K, Nb at 8.0°K, and many others) lose all their resistance to the flow of electric current. The temperature at which a particular material becomes superconductive can be lowered by application of a magnetic field. Increasing the magnetic field can thus destroy an existing superconductive state, allowing logic to be performed. The ratio of resistances in the resistive and superconductive states is theoretically infinite; experimentally, it has been determined to be greater than 10^{21}. In fact, circuits can be so arranged that one current can be controlled by a smaller current in a separate superconductor, thus providing amplification.

The speed-limiting factors in transitions from one state to another involve both electrical and thermal mechanisms. The propagation of a magnetic field through the material to cause the superconductive state transition might take 10^{-11} sec in a film 1000 A thick. This fundamental limit is nowhere near those imposed by circuit limitations. Thermal problems arise because energy is dissipated during switching and must be removed to prevent thermal quenching. This thermal time constant can be of the order of 10^{-9} sec in thin film geometries.

Still on the horizon

The instrumentation art has lagged behind what we have needed for our investigations of high-speed phenomena and devices.

Phenomena being investigated not only operate on a time scale never before measured easily, but also at combinations of voltage, current, and impedance levels which have not been previously encountered.

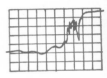

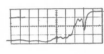

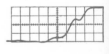

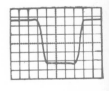

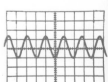

At the present time, though, oscilloscopes exist which will resolve risetimes of less than 0.1 nsec of millivolt signals and which can be synchronized to repetition rates well over 1 gc. The experimental instrumentation for this soon may be commercially available. These oscilloscopes are based on a sampling principle, a sort of an electrical stroboscope. Also, there are instruments in wide use for measuring nanohenries, picofarads at low impedance levels, and a host of other special parameters important to high-speed operation.

The ingenious engineers

Even with the discovery of fast phenomena, and with instruments that yield useful design data, the specific techniques to obtain nano-

second digital operations, with the notable exception of transistors, represent completely new technologies and ways of thinking. This is significant when it is realized that the time and effort spent in inventing the new technologies has been very small compared with the time and effort expended simply in extending transistor technology.

With circuit improvements, we can get response times between 1 and 10 nsec. We feel that transistors have now been pushed close to the limit of their speed as primary gain elements in digital circuits.

The three-terminal nature of the transistor is a very important property, since the input to a transistor is therefore largely independent of the output. The isolation between input and

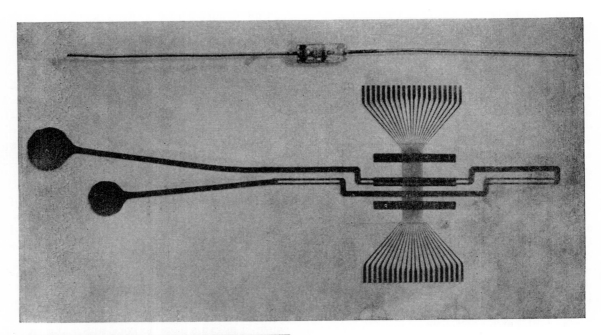

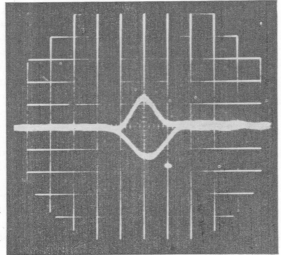

Fig. 6-35. Experiment with magnetic film shows a memory can be made extremely small. Bits are 5 mils apart on 1-in. film strip. One vertical wire in assembly passes over each bit location. Scope picture shows "0" and "1" outputs from a single bit location in the experimental magnetic film memory pictured above. Each vertical line is 1 millivolt; each horizontal division is 1 nsec. (Courtesy Sperry Rand Univac)

output simplifies design problems since the effect of a circuit upon previous outputs is independent of the conditions at its own output.

We had noted tunnel diodes as prime candidates for nanosecond circuits because of their extremely short basic time constants. Though they can perform all functions needed for computer circuits—amplification, thresholding, rectification, and bistability—a single tunnel diode cannot efficiently do all of these simultaneously. The two-terminal nature of the element makes it difficult to synthesize combinations that perform all the necessary circuit functions.

Although practical techniques for general nonlinear synthesis do not exist, human ingenuity plus precise numerical analysis with the aid of computers has resulted in practical tunnel diode circuits which operate in less than 1 μsec. RCA has developed a group of logic circuits (shown in Figs. 6-36 and 6-37) based

on a set of tunnel diodes types each tailored to perform a different circuit function.

Hybrids are another approach.

Several types of circuits combine tunnel diodes with other basically different solid state elements to synthesize logic circuits. In a circuit developed by Chow, Cubert, and Sear of Sperry Rand Corporation, ordinary rectifying diodes perform thresholding, tunnel diodes provide bistability and some amplification, and a so-called "enhancement diode" provides additional gain during switching. This circuit operates in less than 1 nsec.

Another hybrid circuit described by Hwang, Piel and Raillard of G.E. uses a tunnel diode to provide gain, thresholding, retiming, and signal standardization and a transistor to provide isolation between inputs and outputs. Since no gain is required of the transistor, it does not limit circuit speed.

Still another hybrid circuit was described

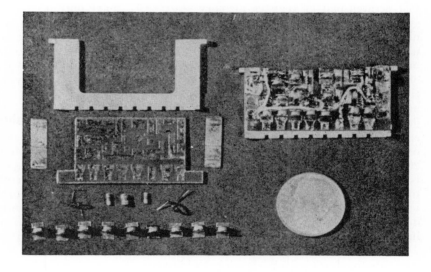

Fig. 6-36. Tunnel-diode logic circuit, shown actual size, is an assembly of several devices. From the bottom: tunnel diodes, resistors and inductors, power-supply filter capacitors flanking wafer with etched wiring, metal frame. (Courtesy RCA)

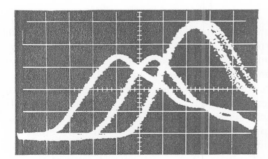

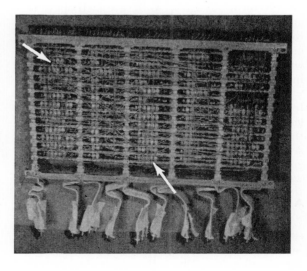

Fig. 6-37. Distance means loss of time, so logic must be balanced against geometry to achieve nanosecond speeds. Here miniature coaxial cable interconnects circuits to speed signals in the frame of circuits, above. Arrows 6 in. apart show points where wave forms of the signal passing from one circuit to another were measured with oscilloscope to show the delay in propagation and circuit response. (Courtesy RCA)

by D. W. Murphy of IBM. Clever combinations of connections of transistor building blocks lead to a large family of possible basic logic functions. The output signals are in the $\pm \frac{1}{4}$ volt region and thus a pair of tunnel diodes, which operate well in that range, can be used as power amplifiers and transmission line impedance matching devices. These give a circuit operation times of 1 to 3 nsec, but the logic operations performed are more complex than simple AND, OR.

Since a tunnel diode can be biased bistably and driven from one stable point to the other, it is a natural candidate for memory application; that is, memory in the normal sense of a block of stored information rather than the transient storage that occurs in all sequential logic networks. The present method of assembly from individual components limits this application of tunnel diodes to memories of a few hundred words at most. However, it does provide the fastest means at present for small fast scratch-pad or register memory.

Here let us consider some of the clever techniques that have made thin magnetic films useful in computers now, despite limitations presumably surmountable in the future. One obvious use of the short rotational switching time of thin magnetic films is for high-speed memory. Best results have been obtained by depositing one or two small spots of film for each bit. These "film-cores" may be circular or rectangular with dimensions in the order of 20–30 mils $\times$ 1000 A thick. An array of spots is deposited in a single operation, but it's still impossible to control the properties of individual spots so as to be able to make coincident-current selections of each bit as we do in conventional toroidal core memories.

To get around this obstacle, a "word-organized" approach is used: As shown in the margin, all bit locations of a word are activated at once by a current passing over them. The rotation of magnetization of each spot induces an output in the corresponding sense line. Rewriting into each cell is controlled by a steering current in each digit line.

Even more can be accomplished with this technique. Each film spot can act as an AND gate; the two drive currents are inputs and the sense line receives the output. A single sense line linking several spots acts as an OR gate. Thus, using arrays of thin magnetic films, we can construct logic blocks.

A cryogenic long-shot

Cryotrons and other structures based on superconductivity were originally conceived as logic elements, but their properties are ideal for memory, too. Since the same element can

be used for both logic and memory, these functions are easily intermixed. Consequently, some of the most powerful ways suggested to use cryotrons involve memories in which logic operations, oftentimes several simultaneously, are also performed.

As we pointed out in our discussion of "cold logic," a cryotron is simply a current diversion switch which can be designed to have gain. Current in one electrical path can divert currents from one or more paths to other paths, giving us logic functions. These currents are super currents; they flow in a closed loop unless diverted, providing memory properties.

Superconductive devices require mass fabrication of thousands, even millions, of identical components whose collective functional operation is determined by their pattern of interconnections. The problems of precise fabrication of multiple layers of superconductors and insulators with reproducible properties are formidable. The predicted nanosecond speeds have only been approached—one of the fastest circuits built is a flip-flop (bistable circuit) operating in 7 nsec operation time. Although this field has not progressed as fast as early optimism predicted—it still remains a research activity, not development—the potential payoff is enormous.

Limits of the light-foot

Perhaps the most fundamental problem that has been encountered in using high-speed phenomena is the speed of light, which sets the minimum time required to transfer information from one place to another. The speed of light in vacuum is 11.8 in./nsec, easier to remember as 1 ft/nsec, and in any real electrical circuit the propagation rate of information along wires will be typically $\frac{1}{2}$ to $\frac{2}{3}$ of this. At every level of the hierarchy of computers, there exist logical loops. For example, at many points during a computation, information will need to be drawn from a memory that is some distance from the place at which the calculations are being performed, and the information in one word in the memory may tell the location of the next word to be used. The second memory access cannot begin until the results from the first access are obtained. Information transfer around such loops, which must be completed before succeeding operations can begin, is limited in speed by the physical length of the loop.

Clever logical design can shorten or eliminate some of these loops, but an organization to eliminate all of them has not yet been found. The effect on logic design is clearly stated in a paper by Hwang, Piel, and Raillard of GE's Electronics Laboratory in Syracuse: "A logical decision made in 1 nanosecond and trans-

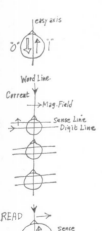

ported one foot is equatable to a logical decision made in two nanoseconds and used on location. This does *not* mean that ultra high speed computers must be built in a shoe box, but rather suggests that logical designers should use space-time relationships as well as Boolean functions . . ."

Further delay is caused by stray inductances and capacitances introduced by the structure of devices and circuits. Even though a change of state has already taken place, there is a delay before enough useful output appears at the terminals because energy is stored in the stray inductances and capacitances. Classical electric circuit theory is based on lumped elements in which devices—inductors, capacitors, resistors—are viewed as properties lumped at a point.

Design and analysis based on these lumped-element concepts lose their validity when the spectrum of wavelengths involved in the signals extends to dimensions small enough to be comparable with the physical size of the structures involved—what formerly could be treated as a point now has dimensions. While 5-ft waves may seem a smooth sea when seen from the deck of the Queen Mary, conditions appear quite different from a 12-ft rowboat. Since frequency has gone up faster than size of structure has decreased, the distributed nature of real components and interconnections has become highly important.

Furthermore, power that cannot be transferred into a load because of imperfect matching to the interconnection paths is reflected back down the path toward the driving end, possibly disturbing the "sending" element and even causing more reflections. If it is necessary to wait for such multiple reflections to die out, time is wasted.

Undesired coupling between points can occur through other stray inductances and capacitances, and unwanted signals may appear from other points on the common paths of a network connecting two particular points. These difficulties increase at higher frequencies. As a consequence, transmission-line engineering (the mechanical as well as electrical engineering of distributed electrical structures) must permeate all phases of the electrical analysis and design of ultra-high speed computers, from power-supply distribution to signal-path routing.

Construction techniques required to actually build anything operable in the nanosecond range are a long story, beyond the scope of this article. Very simply, there is a multivariable design problem in which conflicting electrical, logical, topological, and materials problems must be resolved. And the intricacy of it is compounded by the very tight relationships among the various factors. Controlling uniformity and dimensions of many spots on thin magnetic films, or mass fabrication of enough identical cryotrons to be useful, is a formidable task for the cleverest of mechanical engineers.

Nanosecond test beds

Nanosecond techniques for computing are now in a state of consolidation. Many ideas are being subjected to the trials of building test subsystems and small test machines. Significantly, small computers and subsystems are now being built—not just circuits.

The most extensive demonstration of any of the nanosecond techniques is a small general-purpose computer built to test thin magnetic film elements by Univac Division of Sperry Rand. The three major magnetic subsystems include a high speed memory of 1024 words of 24 bits each, and two logic arrays—a search memory of 128 words of 24 bits each, and a shift matrix of 24 words of 24 bits each.

The high-speed memory was designed for a cycle time of 50 nsec. The effective cycle in the machine environment will actually be limited to 100 nsec by transistor logic needed for word selection. The search memory is designed to compare the content of its input register with all of the 128 words stored in it in 100 nsec and to give the location of the matching word, if any. The shift matrix, also designed to operate in 100 nsec, reproduces the input word, shifted from 0 to 23 places. The complete machine has been assembled, and debugging of subsystems is in progress.

Two subsystems of reasonable complexity (379 logic circuits and 160 bits of memory) have been constructed by RCA to demonstrate the feasibility of using tunnel diodes for nanosecond logic and memory. A "wired in" sequence allows the logic system to perform operations typical of those done in a computer, such as transferring information, counting, shifting, etc. The system is capable of detecting and correcting its own errors. The memory subsystem consists of 32 words of 5 bits each, mechanically constructed and electrically loaded to simulate 1024 words of 24 bits each. This subsystem has been operated with a cycle time of approximately 30 nsec.

Sub-assemblies of counters, adders, and short sequence generators have been constructed by the Electronics Laboratory of General Electric to demonstrate hybrid transistors-tunnel diode circuits. An assembly of about 100 units, operated at a pump rate of 0.2 gc, provides a processing time of 2.5 nsec per logic operation.

At the present time there is no sound information about the reliability of nanosecond computing systems. Their components may be expected to be as reliable as present devices, based on failures per component per unit time. So we get many more computations between failures. In the near future, data from the various demonstration units should provide a broader basis for prediction of reliability.

The next generation of computers

Some data processing problems require simple operations on vast amounts of input data, and in turn produce vast amounts of output results. Or, extremely complex calculations are performed on small amounts of input data, and in turn produce very little output.

Most real problems lie between these extremes, so we're concerned with how fast we can solve them, not simply how fast the components will operate. Extrapolation of the organization of the "megacycle machine" would be of little help in improving speed for performing operations with large amounts of input or output. Unfortunately, neither would such an extrapolation produce a 1000 times increase in solution speed of many complex problems having very little input and output.

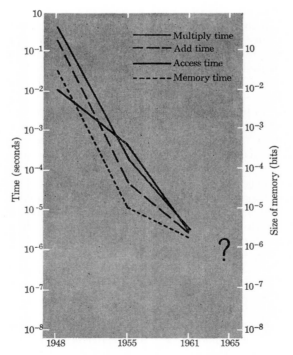

Fig. 6-38. Computers are getting faster. Within a year, approximately, speeds might be characterized by add times of 25 nsec, multiplication times of 60–80 nsec. Memory cycle times may approach 20 nsec for memories of up to several hundred words and 100 nsec for 4000–65,000-word memories.

Total problem-solution time includes preparation of a problem for machine solution as well as the time required for actual computation. In many cases, preparation represents an effort measured in man-years. Even if computation time were zero, the saving would not be significant. Fortunately, efforts are being made (independent of development of nanosecond techniques) to reduce preparation time through automated programming techniques and improved machine organizations. Hopefully, these efforts will lead to better methods of logical assembly of the computer hierarchy and its associated programming system.

Nanosecond techniques probably will appear first in machines constructed primarily with low-speed hardware, reducing speed mismatch of logical operations within and between levels of the computer hierarchy. Simpler fast-carry networks and high-speed multipliers, and larger high-speed scratch-pad memories may be designed for computers still having microsecond memory cycles. Although nanosecond components are expensive at the present time, these uses will provide improved performance at little increase in cost, or equivalent performance at less cost. We can begin today to use limited numbers of nanosecond circuits effectively while we continue to attack problems of assembling and operating large numbers of items in a complete system.

The first systems which could really be called "nanosecond" computers will probably be serial computers. The "megacycle computers" were largely parallel machines, operating on the n bits of a word in a single memory cycle time of several microseconds. Nanosecond techniques can be used in a serial organization to accomplish the same effective operation as a "megacycle" machine with considerable saving in the amount of hardware.

Certain computer subsystems, though not all of them, can be made simpler by a serial design. For example, a parallel adder for n bits has approximately n times the active hardware of a serial adder. Other attributes of serial organizations are reliability, low power consumption, and high computing density (more answers per unit volume). These will be most significant in real-time control systems, especially where the computer must be carried by a vehicle such as a satellite.

Beyond nanoseconds?

"Brute force" improvements upon presently available nanosecond hardware may increase circuit speeds by a factor of 5.

Is it appropriate to expect yet another technological revolution in speed of computation? Should we go on to the picosecond range (10^{-12}

sec)? One might reply that too much remains to be done in making use of the speed we already have or are about to get. Perhaps first we should learn how to use microsecond hardware and its immediate refinements really effectively.

However, every researcher worthy of the name will continue to seek faster computing techniques. Although the known physical laws which appear to be limitations to these will not be repealed, human ingenuity may find ways to overcome them. While advocating realism for the short term view, we prefer to retain some measure of optimism that our present limitations in the nanosecond range—or in any faster realm—are now more a matter of knowledge and viewpoint than of fundamental physical laws. Whether or not optical phenomena, microminiature vacuum tubes using electron emission from a cold rather than heated cathodes, and solid-state devices based on thin films, or some other as yet undiscovered phenomenon or technique will open new possibilities for making even higher speed computing both possible and useful, the reader is invited to make his own guesses.

Further reading

Current developments in basic high-speed physical phenomena are covered by *The Physical Review, Physical Review Letters,* and the *Journal of Applied Physics.*

A basic book on high-speed measurement is by Lewis and Wells, *Millimicrosecond Pulse Techniques* (Pergamon, 1959, $8.50). Most up-to-date information in measurements is found in the *Trans. IRE Prof. Group on Instrumentation* and the *Review of Scientific Instruments.*

Device and circuit descriptions appear in the *IRE Proceedings* and the *Transactions of the Professional Group on Electronic Computers,* the proceedings of the *Solid State Circuits Conference* sponsored annually by the IRE, AIEE and the University of Pennsylvania, and the *IBM Journal of Research.* Good recent examples from these sources include: "The Enhanced Tunnel-Diode Logic Circuit," by B. E. Sear, J. S. Cubert, and W. F. Chow in *Proceedings, 1963 International Solid State Circuits Conference;* and from *Transactions of the IEEE Professional Group on Electronic Computers,* "A High-Speed Arithmetic Unit Using Tunnel Diodes," by W. G. Daly and J. F. Kruy (Vol. EC-12, No. 5, p. 503, 1963), "System Design of a Small Fast Digital Computer," by H. Schorr and N. E. Wiseman (Vol. EC-12, No. 5, p. 698, 1963), and "300-Mc Tunnel-Diode Logic Circuits," by M. Cooperman (Vol. EC-13, No. 1, p. 18, 1964). The June 1962 issue of the *RCA Review* contained several articles in the high-speed field. The proceedings of the 1961 *Magnetics Conference* in Belgium contains useful information. AIEE special publication *S-136 Gigacycle Computing Systems* contains a mixed set of papers relating to devices, circuits and systems.

Pertinent papers, presented at the International Federation for Information Processing Congress—62 in Munich, are available from North-Holland Publishing Co. of Amsterdam.

Three motion pictures, all free, provide highly palatable basic material on computers: *The Information Machine* (10 min.), Modern Talking Picture Service, 10 Rockefeller Plaza, N.Y.C., N.Y.; *Memory Devices* (27 min.), call local Bell Telephone business office; *Electronic Computers and Applied Mathematics* (23 min.), Colburn Film Distributors, Box 470, 668 N. Western Ave., Lake Forest, Ill.

AUTOMATED DESIGN

by Börje Langefors *

In Brief: *If a computer is given a design specification that can be programmed, it can design mechanical cams or electric motors, can even instruct men or machine tools. Computers can also systematize cut-and-try design of complex shapes like ship hulls or intricate structures like bridges for which there is no simple way of programming an entire design. The designer must tell the computer about form, structure and content of the object. In Scandinavia, design description has been through special computer languages. In the U.S.A., graphical inputs to the computer enable it to "see" the designer's sketch. Both approaches make it possible to store sets of design data in the computer—families of hull curves, cross sections of roads, building floor plans and patterns of use —so that a designer can simply modify a general design description while the computer, which has stored the rules for a specified design, calculates the interaction and displays the total result in drawings or tables.—E.H.*

* Börje Langefors manages the Systems Development Bureau of Svenska Aeroplan Aktiebolaget (SAAB) Computer Division in Linköping, Sweden. He is also Sweden's council member in the International Federation for Information Processing.

■ Design has always seemed to be a personal, creative activity. To suggest that it can be automated at all often has a stunning effect upon designers.

Fig. 6-39. Every highway interchange poses such an enormous variation in design problems that a computer semingly would be of little help to a civil engineer. You can see typical constraints here: limited land area, existing buildings, drainage, grade changes from level to level, vertical clearances through underpasses, horizontal clearance, flow through lane changes. Yet this intersection in the Miramar area of San Juan, Puerto Rico, is one of many designed with the computer working on the entire problem, rather than on bits and pieces. MIT helped develop the COGO (COordinate GeOmetry) program used to design these Puerto Rican highways. In Europe, new roads being built in Sweden, Norway, Finland, and Germany are designed with the aid of a computer program developed by AB Nordisk ADB and the Swedish Board of Roads. (Courtesy Puerto Rican Economic Dev. Admin.)

Yet the electronic computers that they find so valuable for numerical calculations have begun to invade both ends of a wide spectrum of design activity that has been ostensibly the province of the human—from conception of shapes and structures, to production orders to factory workers or control signals to fabricating machinery.

Computers have developed designs that range from airplanes to architecture, from electrical circuits to clothing, from ship hulls to highways. The results have exhibited the constraints of an experienced human designer's feel for form and aesthetics and his canny knowledge of the possibilities and limitations of production facilities.

For several years there has been tangible evidence that the computer's contribution can extend beyond preliminary design to the very beginning of the production cycle. One can enter the design parameters for, say, an electronic circuit of specified functions into a computer and receive not only a circuit diagram and component values as an output, but also a production wiring diagram or layout suitable for fabricating an etched circuit board.

More surprising than such a "cookbook" design is the involvement of the computer in what designers have jealously considered thought processes. Yet it turns out that many steps taken by a human in so-called creative design are, in reality, definitions of forms and the

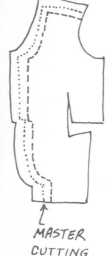

MASTER
CUTTING
PATTERN

successive stages in which they are modified. While the graceful curves of a sleek hull are a source of pride to the naval architect, the fairing of ship lines indeed may be a series of computer modifications of his preliminary design to suit construction constraints and the requirements for smooth flow.

Streamlined hulls and other complicated shapes cannot conveniently be built up in a simple way on the drawing board from straight lines and circle arcs. But these familiar problems can be handled easily, though tediously, by numeric methods that give coordinates for a set of points along a curve. The mathematical character of this drawing function obviously lends itself to computation.

But not all design problems seem so easily programmable. There are many design ideas whose form is first defined by drawing. So we have the problems of how to describe the design in a language the computer can understand or to have it "see" a sketch of a design idea so that it can begin to help.

If we can formalize parts of the design function so they can be entered—by sketch or by simple language—into a computer where their equivalent data representations can be manipulated more rapidly and precisely than by man, then a human can concentrate on parts of the design activity which cannot be formally treated by mathematical analogy.

This combination of man and machine can

enormously reduce the lead time for the design activity of a project. For it opens up new possibilities of integrating more of the critical data about the design process into management information systems, thus leading to improved preliminary cost analyses for a new product, and more realistic production scheduling. Ultimately, automated design affects the entire company information system.

A typical information processing operation—whether the processor is a computer or a human—involves the input, the processing system, and the output. The input specifies the problem to be solved. The output gives the solution to the problem, as "understood" by the processing, and analysis of how well the design meets specified requirements.

In a human, the design process is a mixture of imagination, know-how, design rules learned by formal education and by experience, tentative calculations, and repetitive modification of layout. This does not appear to be something that could be programmed.

However, notice that much of the design process consists of establishing procedures which will solve part of the design problem using information available to the designer from his memory, handbooks, files of his company, etc. Much of this information can be stored and specified in computer programs.

The better we understand a design process, the more of it can we hand over to a computer until it may take over the control of the design task. The human designer, as the modifier of an automatic system, will work on improving system information—programs and quantitative knowledge of various objects—rather than solving the specific design problem being processed. Designers will design the designing system which designs the actual objects.

Programmable design operations

Long before we considered programming an exact sequence of design operations on a computer, programmable design operations existed in the sense that a simple formula would give a direct solution. The depth of a cantilever beam can be calculated from length and width. The correct diameter of a pipe can be determined from length and pressure drop. But most design problems are dependent on so many design parameters in such an *implicit* way that a simple formula cannot describe the solution. A civil engineer can give a formula for a road cross section, even an interchange, but not an entire highway system.

The human designer feels his way through the tangled parameters by applying his knowledge and experience in an intuitive cut-and-try procedure. For this reason, many design oper-

ations are regarded as creative and intuitive, requiring a high degree of skill and are therefore unprogrammable. But often it is only the complexity of calculation that has led to this manner of working. Computers can handle complexity if we can program the steps to be taken.

Trends toward production simplification and reduction of inventory carrying costs, introduce standardization. Fortunately, this constrains design choice to a defined set of components instead of requiring individually designed parts for new objects. One manufacturer of industrial measuring instruments explodes a customer's functional specification into production orders based entirely on the variable relationship of standard parts listed in the computer memory.

Some objects, like mechanical cams, can be designed by programmed computation without using drawings as input specifications or as directions for production. Numerical tables and text printed by the computer are often used now, but the increasing use of numerical control of machine tools emphasizes the trend toward computer outputs of tape data to operate production machinery. Cam forms are well defined mathematically by the function they are to perform. The complete design of a cam also calls for specified rules for the choice of raw material and the dimensions. Thus the design of these simple objects already makes use of standardization.

Small electric motors are much more complicated examples of products which are designed today in a completely automatic way. For a given specification, the computer chooses standardized iron cores for stator and rotor design, as well as rotor axles and casings. It also makes some engineering computations for the wire dimensions and the windings. The input to such an automatic design procedure is simply a table form in which the desired performance data are filled in by an engineer. The computer output need only be a list of standard parts and data on wire, the configuration of the windings, and the turns to be wound.

Systematizing "cut-and-try"

Computers can do design work even in more complicated problems where a direct computation of dimensions or standardized choices cannot be used. This is the case for some static structures. If they are redundant or have different types of loading, no direct computation of local dimensions of their parts can be done.

If the construction has its structure and geometry already defined, it is possible to let the computer establish the internal stresses that result from an applied set of external

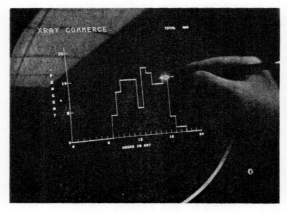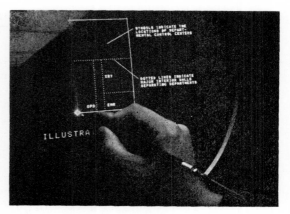

Fig. 6-40. In hospital planning, an architect must balance operational patterns (left) with physical constraints of a building plan (right). He can observe, say, how changes in x-ray room traffic affect movement through the building, for a computer can display data on the interaction of each modification. (Courtesy Bolt, Beranek and Newman and American Hospital Assn.)

loads. In an increasing number of cases, it has been possible to program the computer to change the local dimensions of the construction in a way that will lead to a more even distribution of internal stresses. A good example of this is the intricate pattern of flush rivets in an aircraft wing. The computer can do a new stress analysis followed by a new modification of rivet sizes and spacings and repeat this procedure until a best design is obtained. In this way, the computer takes over a job that is today considered as a typical activity of designer's intuition or his cut-and-try attempts. It rapidly tries many calculated solutions from a fairly general problem statement and a reasonable point of departure chosen by the human designers.

Often either or both the structure and the shape of the object are not known beforehand or are not computed from specified rules. Rather, it is one of the main tasks of the designer to work this out. This he does by making lay-out sketches during a creative phase of his work. Intuition, based in an undefined way on his skill and training, is then at work.

It is here that our comparison of design activity and information processing operations comes into play. Even in this intuitive phase of creative design work a significant proportion consists of information processing of some sort. Although such processing is not systematized today, it could be formalized into computer programs.

It is interesting to note that such "totally

Fig. 6-41. (a) A designer may normally be using a shape like curve S_1 which he adjusts from object to object by varying the Y-scale. He has chosen $Y_{max} = \frac{1}{3}$ for his actual design and asked the computer to display this. Then he finds that he wants to make a change, so he draws the corrected curve S_2. The computer now determines the difference $S_2 - S_1 = d_{21}$. The designer now has not only two curve shapes but a whole family of curves. Thus, while $S_1 + d_{21}$ gives him S_2, he can for instance from $S_1 + 1.3\,d_{21}$ obtain another curve. After some experiments he learns to design and think in terms of S_1 and d_{21}. If, later on, this still does not satisfy him, he draws another curve, S_3 say. Computer now establishes the best approximation to S_3 by the combination $S_1 + \alpha d_{21} = S_3{}^*$ for some α, and computes the difference $d_{3.21} = S_3 - S_3{}^*$. He now has available S_1, d_{21}, and $d_{3.21}$ as terms in his language for describing curves for his specific design. He talks in these intuitive terms. The computer uses the mathematics necessary. (b) You can describe a ship hull form by cross-section contours and their lengthwise placement along keel. Spacing can be varied for long, sleek form or a short, blunt one and different scales used for cross-section height and width, but ship family is still the same. Within one family, you can specify performance and capacity, design a ship automatically. Once hull-form data are in the computer, it can design internal hull stiffeners, check space for machinery installation. (c) The structure formed by these beams can be described by a matrix that specifies the end connections for each member. (d) The form at far left is described by its structure: two rectangles and a semicircle, each specified by a matrix. The same form, center, can be described by coordinates of straight lines, semicircles, etc. Computer can store coordinates or numerical "type" codes for various curves. Symbols for elements of same form are logically related in MIT parlance in plex shown above. Note similarity to type code matrix. To describe forms and structures to a computer with sketches and matrices, as shown in this figure, you do not need a knowledge of programming or of how computers work.

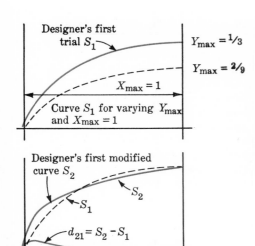

Designer's first trial S_1

$Y_{max} = 1/3$

$Y_{max} = 2/9$

$X_{max} = 1$

Curve S_1 for varying Y_{max} and $X_{max} = 1$

Designer's first modified curve S_2

S_1

S_2

$d_{21} = S_2 - S_1$

Designer introduces a 2nd modification S_3

S_3^*

$d_{3,21} = S_3 - S_3^*$

(a)

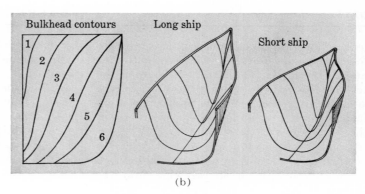

Bulkhead contours   Long ship

Short ship

(b)

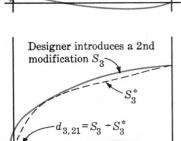

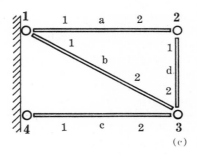

	1	2	3	4
a1	✓			
a2		✓		
b1	✓			
b2			✓	
c1				✓
c2			✓	
d1		✓		
d2			✓	

(c)

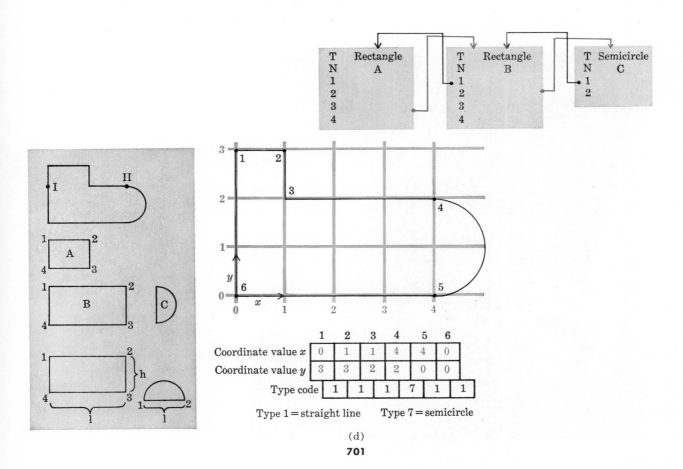

	1	2	3	4	5	6
Coordinate value x	0	1	1	4	4	0
Coordinate value y	3	3	2	2	0	0
Type code	1	1	1	7	1	1

Type 1 = straight line   Type 7 = semicircle

(d)

701

creative" work as designing an arts master-piece does make use of system information at hand to the artist. This can be seen from the fact that, as a rule at least, most successive works of art reflect elements and composition of ideas already exhibited in earlier works by other artists.

Although it is no problem to feed data into a computer, it is not quite as trivial to feed the information of design sketches into the computer—and have the computer "understand" it. What is demanded here is a convenient way for the designer to have a conversation with the computer about his layout and the modification of it. This may be indicated by analysis results returned from the computer, also in the form of sketches.

There is experimentation in the United States, for example at MIT, to enable a computer to read a sketch drawn with a "light pen" on the surface of a cathode-ray tube connected to the computer. Similar, but less direct, methods have been developed in Sweden.

In Scandinavia there is also an entirely different approach: to develop a "form language" by which a designer can describe his concept of shape in terms of functions that have intuitive meaning for him in connection with the class of objects to be designed. He need not think in mathematical terms during this conversation with the computer, yet his statements

of *form*, *structure*, and *contents*—which virtually define an object completely—have a mathematical meaning to the computer. This development lets the computer also teach the designer by showing him what basic form elements he is unconsciously using. Such work already has been applied to such diverse fields as naval architecture, aircraft structures and clothmaking, thus indicating the broad applicability of the underlying concepts.

Both these directions of development—graphical inputs and descriptive language—have had to solve the problems of storing information about shape and structure and of manipulating such information.

Telling the computer about form

To describe the form of a curve or of a three-dimensional body to a computer, we may simply list the coordinates of a large number of its points. This method is not usable in a design phase, however, where a designer must describe his thoughts about a shape and its successive modifications in a way which aids his creative activity. His natural way is, of course, to work by drawing. Without drawings, he would have to define shapes by data.

The shape of a ship hull can be described by a large number of cross sections, each described by the coordinates of a large number of points. Even if the volume of the hull is to be kept

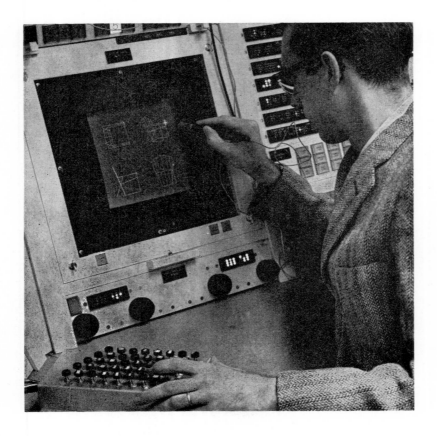

Fig. 6-42. Sketchpad with a computer is literally that. While the designer draws with a light pen, his left hand manipulates controls for scale, constraints of length, types of curves, attachment points for lines, etc. Note the "wire frame" appearance of the rocking chair. A line drawn in one view is simultaneously seen in three other views. Spot of light on one view produces equivalent spots on the other views. These drawings all can be rotated simultaneously around a chosen axis of any view. (Courtesy MIT Lincoln Laboratory)

fixed there is an intractably large number of displacements of these points possible. Suppose you want to define a set of such displacements which leads to minimum drag. Two different principles combine to make this virtually unmanageable problem solvable.

The many-to-one principle helps in this way: although the hull shape determining drag can be varied by displacing a great many points in a variety of ways, the resulting drag varies as a single point being displaced along a single curve. To obtain a certain drag value, we have to find simply one of an almost infinite number of hull-point placement sets.

The second principle, the principle of restrictions for feasibility, means that if one hull point is displaced by a certain amount, then the neighboring points also must move in a way that conserves smoothness of the hull. This vastly reduces the number of possible point-displacement combinations. Only a few of the many still left need be considered because of the principle of many-to-one.

So a single, smooth curve can be described as the sum of a finite set of "component curves" with shapes differing enough to describe the point displacements or desired form modifications. Very few component curves are needed to describe a streamline.

A designer gets to know which class of component curves are common to the objects he wishes to design and he can describe the shape he wants by specifying to a computer the amount of each of the component curves. Let me show you how.

Computer chalk-talk

Rather than making written statements to a computer, it is still today more natural for most designers to draw a sketch. The graphical man-machine communication system called *Sketchpad*, developed at MIT's Lincoln Laboratory, is a fascinating example of this technique, for construction of a drawing with a light pen and a computer is really a model of the design process.

The designer sits in front of an oscilloscope screen flanked by a set of buttons and controls. Using a light pen—a hand-held photocell—he "draws" on the screen while the computer tracks its arbitrary motion over the scope surface and generates a series of points which appear as lines in the wake of his pen. Since the computer program and the controls really control the scope display, these can apply geometric constraints to the points and lines of the drawing. A combination of "form language" and sketches can be advantageous.

Assume that he roughly sketches a curve like S_1 in Fig. 6-41a and the designer indicates to the computer by a coded symbol on the control panel that it is a segment of a parabola. It can be smoothed or "normalized" by the computer which generates the correct coordinates for such a curve. The designer can also prescribe the precise height and width of the curve. Once he is satisfied with a curve, he can have the computer store it as system information for recall at the touch of a button.

Now suppose he wants to modify curve S_1, changing it to S_2. After the computer normalizes S_2, it computes S_2-S_1. The resultant modification is the difference d_{21}, which you see as a curve at the bottom of the graph. This is also stored as system information so the computer can generate the whole family of combinations of S_1 and S_2.

The next time the designer presents a rough sketch to the computer, say, S_3, the computer will try to approximate it by combinations of S_1 and d_{21} giving the smallest possible difference from S_3. The computer may report this difference $d_{3.21}$ on the screen so the designer may decide whether it is acceptable.

Once a designer gets accustomed to the set of component curves S_1 and d_{21} or $d_{3.21}$ he can directly describe the curve he wants by giving these to the computer via a keyboard and watch the curve appear on the screen.

While the shape of curves can be drawn or described mathematically, the structure of an object has long been described primarily by drawing. By its structure we mean the way it has been built up from different parts such as sheet metal, bars, and bolts. Its contents are the material of which the parts are made.

Describing structure

Structure most obviously enters the design game in cases where shape is of no significance. In electrical networks below radio frequencies, a formula is normally applied to a given network structure to determine the loading or power drawn from the branches of the network and thus to check contents—how heavy a cable, how large a transformer, etc. But first, the problem of describing the network structure to the information processing system had to be solved so this computation could be performed automatically.

Network-like design also occurs in other objects. In the static constructions of civil engineering or aeronautical design, however, form as well as structure has to be considered. Simple matrices appropriate to the connection or mesh of an electrical grid are no longer natural entities for describing such construction.

This difficulty is circumvented by the introduction of even more elementary matrices called "coincidence matrices." The concept of coincidence matrices turns out to be so general in scope that it can serve as a tool for defining structure in all design problems. An indication of the generality of this concept is that while coincidence matrices were introduced in Scandinavia for static structure problems and then used for general design, they were introduced independently in MIT's design automation program. In the United States they were not referred to as matrices.

To see how a coincidence matrix can describe a simple network-like structure, consider the simple example in Fig. 6-41c. The configuration of the four joined beams can be uniquely described by a table or matrix with one column noting each junction point and two rows noting the end points of each beam.

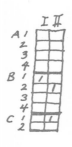

Structure and form combine to give the overall shape of an object, and this, too, can be described in matrix fashion. Note that the contour of the form at the far left in Fig. 6-41d consists of a square, a rectangle, and a semicircle. These are described in a matrix which notes the measurements, say, length and height, of the rectangle and points at which they make contact (see margin).

This same form and structure can be described by a coincidence matrix of codes, Fig. 6-41d, for each of the simple component types—straight lines, circles, and parabolas. The codes also represent the coordinate values of various component curves. Coincidence matrices associated with such curves can easily be stored in the computer memory and can be any of the basic curves or difference curves for a class of design objects. In fact, the component type codes may also identify a part of a surface already computed or a cross-section line between two such surfaces.

As you can see, a computer can store information in matrices which specifically describes the components in a structure—their measurements, shape, connection points, cross-sections, etc. Similarly, the MIT development of computer-aided design is based on a concept of "n-component elements"—a single unit of information about a problem which describes one attribute of an element in a structure just as a coincidence matrix contains pairs of data defining components of form or structure as shown in Fig. 6-41.

In MIT parlance, an interconnected set of n-component elements—a structure—is called a *plex*. Consider a line as an element of a plex. The components of the element are a *type*—"this is a line"—a *name* like L_1, and points which indicate the ends of the line. In this hierarchy, the points can be elements with type and name components and two additional components which specify the x and y coordinates of each point in a coordinate system. In effect, these data are a model of a line.

So, as in the matrix description of structure, there is a logical connection of the data which describe the structure of a plex. This logical relationship is the computer's conception or map of particular structural properties. Compare the form and structure of Fig. 6-41d in the matrix and when described as a plex by n-component elements.

A computer in the Haystack

You can describe an object to a computer in matrix form by a keyboard input of symbols for each column and row, though you would have to work out the matrix in advance. Or you could sketch a simple diagram with a light pen which the computer can set up as a matrix or plex. When a structure is complex, it is possible to combine these two ways of talking to a computer by drawing diagrams for parts of an object and putting in a coincidence matrix to define how the substructures you have diagrammed are to be put together in the total structure of the object you are designing.

For example, the designers of MIT-Lincoln Labs' *Sketchpad* have drawn bridge shapes with enough constraints to make them geometrically accurate. Then, each member of, say, a pin connected truss is made to behave like a bridge beam. It is assumed that each bridge beam has a cross-sectional area proportionate to its length. The calculated forces in the beams show as numbers in the bridge picture on the computer output screen. With his light pen, a designer can change various loading conditions and supports while the computer calculates new distribution of forces.

Or take another example—the design of large radar antennas. Often the brute strength construction methods for large movable antennas produce serious problems because excessive weight deforms what should be a precise parabola. Take the 120-ft diameter radar antenna called Haystack, built for USAF and Lincoln Laboratory. In its design, the reflector had to meet tolerances of ± 0.075 in. maximum total deviation at any point on the quarter-acre structure.

For example, the reflector support consists of 1300 members which form five concentric and trussed rings interconnected by tension rods and strategically placed compression members. In effect, these are used to preload the structure to minimize deflection. The stiffness and deflection analysis of this complex structure was performed by manipulating large matrices that take into account the contributions of each member. All the design analyst had to furnish as input were the x, y, and z coordinates of joint locations, section properties, and end restraints of the individual members, plus boundary or support conditions for the total structure and applied loading conditions.

One might think of linkages as pin connected trusses. It is possible to sketch such linkages on the screen as a computer input and then to move a driving link—by turning a knob on the scope control—so that the designer can observe the complex motions that are generated even by the simplest of linkages.

Both the truss and the linkage are examples that lead to some understanding of what we mean by describing content to a computer. In these cases, content can be defined as the material of each bar as it affects the elasticity of the bar. If you know the form and structure of a truss and the elastic content of its parts, you can determine the elasticity of the entire structure . . . which was one problem in the design computation for the Haystack antenna.

There are many design problems for which no mathematical language exists to describe a total problem and a procedure for its solution. Yet solutions to sub-problems can be calculated and these affect the over-all problem. For example, engineering a highway system involves traffic analysis, layout of intersections, cut-and-fill for various road contours, perspective sketches of the road as seen by drivers from different seat heights, etc.

Consider the calculations of perspectographic sketches to show the road from a driver's view. The problem input is data from three previously calculated tables: road profiles by height and radius of a set of road sections, the contour of the road as seen from above, and the terrain cross section at different locations. As you can see in the margin, the computer produces successive sketches on a scope screen that show the road slopes and curves as they would appear from a running car.

In the same vein, architectural design is also a series of structured problems. One phase of hospital planning involves the movement of patients, nurses, physicians, and supplies through horizontal and vertical paths to and from emergency rooms, x-ray facilities, operating theaters, wards, etc. The interdependence of these activities is often vital and requires collaborative research into their optimum relationship.

A more systematic approach to hospital planning is being developed for the U.S. Public Health Service by a group at Bolt, Beranek and Newman in Los Angeles, working with the American Institute of Architects and the American Hospital Association. Architects are usually oriented more to physical arrangements but must be responsive to the projected operational patterns desired by the physicians and hospital administrators who are the clients for their designs.

The BBN computer program, called *Coplanner*, allows planners of either orientation to observe on a screen the effect of the interactions between a physical design and an operational pattern.

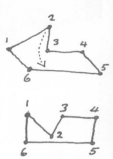

Drawing scales can be changed, plans and layouts can be modified with a light pen, as shown in Fig. 6-40, and the sketches can be stored in the computer memory for subsequent recall and modification of the data they represent. A planner can easily review the effects of,

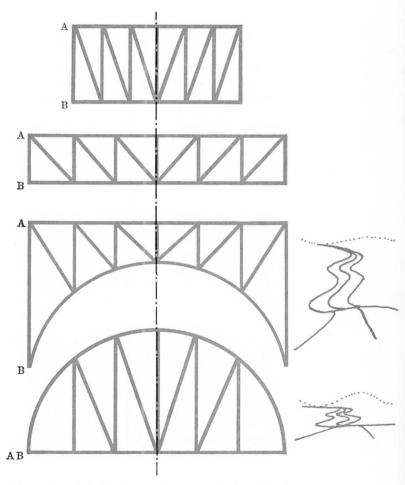

Fig. 6-43. A designer can play a practical game of cat's cradle with trusses and linkages. He can modify structures while the computer indicates forces in each member, or displays motions of linkages. He can try variations via light pen or a computer language for civil engineers called STRESS.

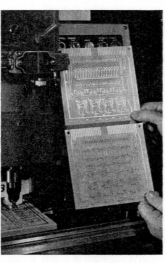

Fig. 6-44. Newest Honeywell computer, H-200 was designed on Daddy H-800. H-800 checked logic, described circuits, allocated interconnection points, routed wires, produced punch cards to run wire wrap machines, helped program tape-controlled drill. (Courtesy Honeywell EDP)

say, a policy change in the use of the x-ray room which would keep it operating during lunch hour.

The computer already has stored data on the arrival of patients in x-ray each day, where they come from in the hospital and whether they come by corridor or elevator, on foot, by wheelchair or stretcher, and how long various x-ray tasks take. Simply by a light pen modification of the arrival pattern shown in the graph in Fig. 6-40, the effects can be shown on graphs of the other data just mentioned. Or a physical plan of the hospital can be modified with a light pen and the effects of these changes would be shown in data graphs. Suppose you expand a floor, or put a high traffic-generating facility like a pharmacy into the floor plan. This would change the traffic load on elevators serving that floor.

It becomes apparent that the design information in a computer affects or is affected by the total information system of an organization and leads quite sensibly toward the integration of these two information systems. Customer requirements affect design while data produced by design processing can be made available for cost analysis, sales projection, production scheduling, for automatic control of machine tools, for controlling transport of parts, for myriad management inputs.

Indeed, as in Fig. 6-44, the company information system may be operated on a computer-designed computer.

Further reading

Some Scandinavian experience is documented in SAAB Technical Notes (TN), available from Svenska Aeroplan Aktiebolaget, Linköping, Sweden: "TN 49-Algebraic Topology for Elastic Networks" (1961), "TN 7-Approximate Solution of Simultaneous Equations by Means of Transformation of Variables" (1962), "TN 48-Analysis of Plates and Shells by Matrix Methods" (1961). Asker has written on "The Spline Curve" in *Nordisk Tidskrift för Informationsbehandling* (BIT), Copenhagen, 1962. Automatic matrix systems for structural analysis are described by Asplund in *First Draft of Structural Mechanics* (Chalmers Tekniska Högskola, Inst. för Byggnadsstatik, Gothenburg, 1962).

Excellent descriptions of the MIT Lincoln Lab approach appear in an entire section of the *Proceedings of the AFIPS Spring Joint Computer Conference 1963* (Spartan).

Computer languages for automated design include, among others, STRESS (Structural Engineering System Solver) described by Fenves in MIT publication T63-2, May 1963. There is also COGO for civil engineering problems. Documentation on COGO I is available from IBM in New York. An interpretive matrix processing system called SAMBA has been worked out at SAAB by Bruno Hellström. SAMBA is supplemented by substructure matrix generators called SUGGEST, whose exponents include A. Sundstrand of SAAB and A. Ohlsson of Facit Electronics, Stockholm.

Feder surveys "Automated Optical Design"; Brunelle and Willey tell about computer design of a sextant in *Applied Optics*, Dec. 1963.

"The Design of Highway Interchanges" is discussed by Manheim and Alexander in MIT publication R62-1 (March 1962). "Planning Roads by Computer" appears in *Discovery*, Sept. 1963. "Fairing of Ship Lines on a High-Speed Computer" by Theilheimer and Starkweather appeared in *Mathematics of Computation* (Oct. 1961). *Planning for Hospitals: A Systems Approach Using Computer-Aided Techniques* available from AHA, 840 N. Lake Shore Dr., Chicago ($7.50). Sessions on automated design will be featured in the triennial IFIP Congress 65 in New York, May 24–29, 1965.

ASSURING QUALITY

by E. G. D. Paterson *

IN BRIEF: *There's no magic quality control that isn't common to most engineering. Of course, the QC-man has some special tricks to his trade, particularly statistical ones—control charts that suggest (before the fact) when a process may be getting out of hand and sampling techniques which gage the (probable) quality of items never inspected.*

Nowadays, however, even those statistical techniques are common engineering property, so that the quality engineer draws on the same technologies as the designer and the manufacturing engineer, plus a liberal amount of the kind of horse sense that comes of continuous exposure to the user's as well as the sources' views of a product. Besides this broad overview, the thing that sets the QC-specialist apart from other engineers is the impartial insight he can provide from his unique vantage point.

The result is that the questions (and the problems and arguments) relating to quality control mostly center about that vantage point, and about the quality engineer's role in his company organization, his legitimate responsibilities, and authorities.—R.G.N.

■ Within view of our kitchen window is a simple structure, designed, built, and used by two adolescent workmen. Conceived with a minimum of technological planning, constructed with simple materials, tools, and skills, at a cost measured in pennies, it rests in the crotch of a large tree in the backyard of one of our neighbors. Known as a "tree-house," it boasts the barest of facilities. And yet, in the eyes of its owners, it is a close approximation to perfection. A whimsical touch—a ventilator—appears on the roof. Unintended and unrecognized as such by its incorporators, it represents what, in today's technical terminology, we call redundancy. We might also call it "over-design"; the production process itself has insured adequate, uninterrupted ventilation.

In contrast with this is a large, imposing, dome-shaped structure located in a secluded valley in southern Maine. Together with a few smaller buildings, it houses the main ground station for the Telstar satellite, a part of a

* E. G. D. Paterson, recently retired Director of Bell Telephone Laboratories' Quality Assurance Center in New York, is now a consultant in quality and reliability engineering.

Fig. 6-45. Tree-house technology has advanced slowly enough so that the skills necessary for originating and controlling quality are widely disbursed—no specialists here, QC or otherwise. (Courtesy E. G. D. Paterson)

communication system which also includes other ground stations in England and France. (One gets just a glimpse of one phase of the achievement when he learns that a received signal power of some 10^{-12} watts serves to point a 380-ton antenna assembly in ever-changing elevation and azimuth to within $\pm 0.2°$.) It is the only system of its particular kind, and thus beyond direct comparison. The fact that it works at all attests to its quality.

For the simple product (such as our tree-house) of the individual artisan, quality, and its attainment, generally have been, and continue to be, well recognized, automatically coordinated, and easily effectuated. Deficiencies were easily isolated, their sources assigned, their elimination assured. There was no need for specialists, quality or otherwise. In fact, the only one, in most industries before World War II, who might possibly be characterized as a quality specialist was the inspector, and his job was essentially the passive one of making comparisons and sorting. However, today's quality specialist is a technical expert concerned with all aspects of quality and their implications; inspection serves him as measuring stick and guide post.

The "mother" of invention

As early as the twenties, the introduction of complex automated systems into communications emphasized the need for a specialized, technical approach to assuring quality. Recognition of this need and the development of techniques to fulfill it, led to what is now "quality control"; its inauguration awaited neither the "electronic" age nor the pressure of dissatisfaction with quality.

Subsequently, when the need to control quality arose in other areas, comprehensive and effective methods were already available. We can credit the Bell System for the concept and development of this new quality activity, but it was predominantly the government which, some twenty years later, pushed QC's large-scale adoption in the U.S.—a forced adoption in some instances.

Today, the quality man's true role is that of a helper rather than creator—a helpful means to an end sought by all. Some QC people are prone to impute to quality control responsibilities for design and production; functions which long preceded their own efforts, and which are still the primary sources of quality. In this article, I want to direct attention to those particular activities by which the quality engineer supplements the primary sources of quality.

Quo vadis, QC-man?

A newcomer who tries to assess the present-day quality practitioner's domain, responsibilities, and techniques is likely to be confused. There is no official definition for the various functions under which the quality man operates. Quality itself is defined as an attribute or characteristic—that which makes a thing what it is. In a practical sense, it is wanted or expected; in industry, it's usually a functional capability, whether or not we define it in a neat technical package. Any combination of such qualities derives from materials and the ways they are treated.

The designer must choose such materials and treatments as will (conceptually) ensure a product which is economically satisfactory to the user, and describe (specify) his choices clearly, completely, and unequivocally. The manufacturer's function is to implement these specifications explicitly and economically. When those basics are performed adequately, quality is automatically forthcoming; then nothing is left for QC except to measure how well the functions have been performed and to facilitate their fulfillment.

With complexity, the choices and functions multiply; specialties and specialists develop. Each imposes a new problem of coordination —à la mode, a new interface. Effective use of this heterogeneous complex of know-how requires coordination, a difficult process to which the quality specialist contributes in large measure—although his role may not be commonly recognized as that of a coordinator.

Any organization which presumes to control quality must define it, set a goal for it, measure it, evaluate it, isolate its deficiencies if they exist, and take steps to ensure their elimination. These are the formal functions of quality control. Because those functions require special tools and techniques, we assign them to an independent engineer, a quality specialist. This doesn't mean he provides the quality; he merely judges whether the quality has been attained, and if not, why not, and what must be done about it. Practice varies widely in industry—and quite properly so. After all, economic realities apply to quality control, just as to design and manufacture.

Objectives: subjective and objective

Qualities can be separated into two categories: those which are objective (and more or less specifically measurable) and those which are subjective and are measurable, if at all, only qualitatively. Where subjective qualities, such as appearance, flavor, and comfort, are involved, they must be translated into characteristics which *are* definable and measurable— at least in the sense that different observers are likely to agree upon their status in any given instance.

Illustrative is a homely but impressive incident: Many years ago, I had installed a "high fidelity" speaker system at home, carefully explaining to my wife in lay, but enthusiastic, terms its wide range and flat response. Her reaction to the demonstration which followed was sympathetic, simple, and significant: "I'm sorry, but the piano doesn't sound much like a piano."

It took years to find out why. In those days, we weren't using square waves to resolve the steep-attack problems of percussion, and we didn't know much about harmonic and intermodulation distortions. People are still trying to understand, measure, and produce the subjective quality, "sound-like"—and acoustics is one of the oldest branches of physics.

Fortunately, most qualities of interest in technology can be objectively resolved in terms of mass-length-time units or their equivalents. Qualities of importance in the finished product are, or should be, stated in the design specifications; that's the design function, whether one is designing a piece-part, or a system.

Charting this variable called quality

One of the first, certainly the earliest, documented, specialized QC technique arose from the recognition that it is economically practical to apply statistics to the variability inherent in all production processes. In other words, inspection can be used for more than just sorting. The idea was that "assignable" (nonchance) causes of process variation could be detected *statistically*. In the exposition of this technique, the terms "quality control" and "control chart" appeared for the first time.

The control chart is a scheme (like the one in Fig. 6-46) whereby we set statistical limits (control lines) for a controlled variable in a process. The limits are set empirically so that if the observed values in the process fall within them, we can (in a practical sense) attribute the variations to causes which are not economically separable and removable. If the process values were distributed in accordance with a known distribution, say the normal law, then we could predict the proportion of the observed values which, on the average, would lie within a given range. For example, if we *knew* that we had a normal distribution, we could say that, in the long run, 99.73% of the points should fall inside the 3σ limit lines—unless the distribution changed. Points outside these limits indicate "lack of control."

Actually, we rarely know the true nature of the distribution, so we cannot be sure of the precise meaning of an "outage." There is always a limitation of this kind in statistical inference; we must base our final decision on our judgment. Experience has shown that limits of $\pm 3\sigma$ are likely to prevent looking for trouble unnecessarily, and that limits of $\pm 2\sigma$ are likely to prevent overlooking a significant change in process when it really occurs. The quality man also uses other criteria, such as "runs" and "trends," to aid his judgment.

Thus we have a tool to help us decide whether a process is in such a state of "control" that we cannot improve its results (quality) without a fundamental change in the process. On the other hand, until we have reached such a state, we have not done all that can be done to optimize that particular process. This procedure, and its later elaborations, gave rise to statistical quality control (SQC).

To take a specific case, many characteristics of transmission wire—its breaking strength,

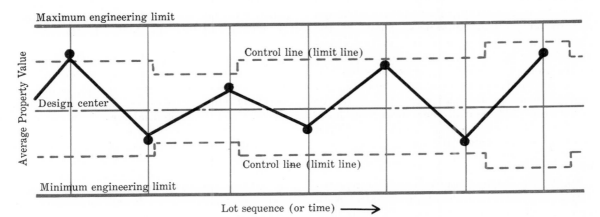

Fig. 6-46. On control charts, such as this, average properties of each of a series of lots is plotted against lot number and compared against control limits (which are well within design limits), to detect budding troubles. By theory, control limits should be inversely proportional to the square root of sample size.

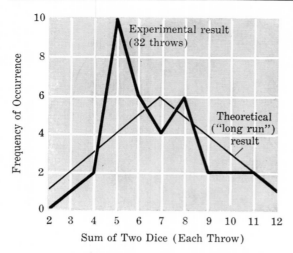

Fig. 6-47. As anticipated, comparing the author's 32 experimental throws of a pair of dice with the theoretical distribution leaves some doubt as to whether the dice are slightly loaded.

the adhesion strength, and other properties of its insulation, etc.—are determined by measurements on short samples. Before control charts, it was common to test short specimens from the ends of a finished coil, and judge the whole coil accordingly. But, in many respects, wire production is a continuous process; the ends of an arbitrary coil length represent one-unit samples of the whole process, rather than the coil. Unless we know that we have "control" of the *process*—the stability of the speed of extrusion, etc.—we know relatively little about the remainder of the coil.

With the control charts, we can reduce the sample size (for one wire, only one part in 20×10^6 is currently tested) and use less insulating compound. Even with this greatly reduced sampling, we know more about the true quality of the wire than we did formerly.

Control charts also help the designer to recognize the variability inherent in his design and to set realistic tolerances. They are the cheapest and most informative quality-assurance data available. Knowledge that a product comes from a controlled process supplies the maximum, and sometimes almost the only, real confidence as to its quality. Since variability is a rule of life, control-chart principles have been widely applied—from minimizing billing errors to the assurance of "honest" dice.

Inspection by proxy

Unlike the quality control chart, many statistical methods used for quality control were first developed elsewhere. Scientific sampling, in particular, had been employed in biology and agriculture, but scarcely, if at all, in industry. Concurrently with control charts, sam-

pling techniques were introduced, especially for inspection purposes. While many of its aspects had advanced prior to the advent of quality control, inspection was still largely a rule-of-thumb procedure. It was customary to select "10% of the lot" (or some such arbitrary sample) and use it to evaluate the lot without rationalizing the "risk" in so doing. Now probability theory enables us to weigh the risk of accepting substandard quality (there is always some "consumer's risk") against the risk of rejecting good quality (the "producer's risk").

In a sense, practically all inspection involves sampling. (We measure the diameter of a shaft by a few readings; the instantaneous output of a generator is a sample in time.) In the earliest method, we base our conclusions on a single sample. However, we can take advantage of the cumulative information afforded by combining successive small pieces of information from successive samples. In such a scheme, what we do next depends upon what happened previously—in the previous samples. Figure 6-48 shows one such arrangement.

Combining these techniques with others, such as environmental and life-testing, we can isolate and evaluate various factors. No longer may we assume that the "universe" of a particular resistor or egg beater is adequately characterized by a few prototypes. Furthermore, since the designer knows his requirements will be met, he can be realistic in specifying tolerances.

Some of the major troubles with the quality of World War II ordnance arose from unrealistically tight tolerances, specified in the hope that the resulting (expectably nonconforming) product would be useable. Early in those days, some suppliers were dismayed to learn that tolerance limits were actually meant to be verified and enforced. The uneconomical, and unfair practice of specifying ±0.001 in., with the hope of getting ±0.003 in., had put the quality structure into disrepute.

New inspection methods have evolved: pneumatic and electronic gages, nondestructive testing, closed-loop process control, automatic screening, automatic process data analysis, and others. Often the potential error in a measurement is of the same order as the variability in the product to be measured. In such cases it is sometimes necessary to specify wider tolerances for the product because of this "measurement noise." One practice, for example, is to require that product tolerances be at least twice the measurement error (e.g., if our microwave power measurements are only good to ±2%, then output-power tolerance for a device would be ±4% or more). In such a no man's land,

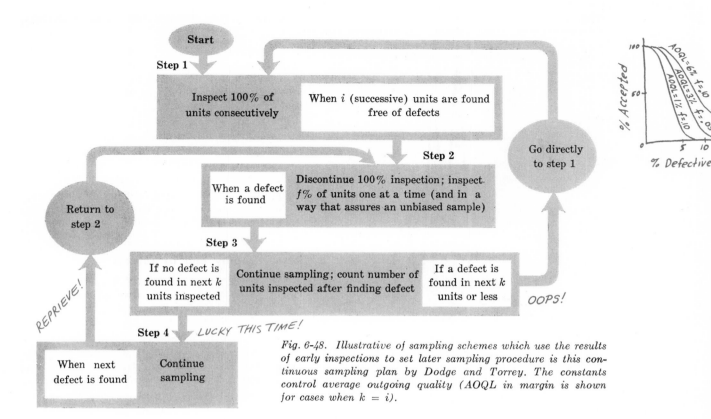

Fig. 6-48. *Illustrative of sampling schemes which use the results of early inspections to set later sampling procedure is this continuous sampling plan by Dodge and Torrey. The constants control average outgoing quality (AOQL in margin is shown for cases when k = i).*

SQC helps establish inspection procedures and acceptance criteria.

The precision of estimates concerning a population increases as the square root of sample size, so most SQC applications are restricted to situations where sufficient test or performance results are available to provide a reasonably well-defined distribution. In such cases, we can (from a sample) estimate, closely and reliably, the averages and boundaries of qualities of *unexamined* products. I use the terms "averages" and "boundaries" advisedly; we never really know the actual quality of untested items.

Because many of today's problems—especially reliability forecasts—involve complex systems or devices produced in small numbers, an urgent question is being asked: "What can be done about a sample too small to provide a usefully narrow distribution, or a numerically determinable high degree of confidence of successful performance?" My answer is: Frankly, not enough to satisfy us as we would be satisfied with large samples, but quite a bit inferentially in those instances where the full play of quality control is effective.

From limited data, the conclusions we can draw vary greatly. Shewhart used a term "the degree of belief" (P'_B) which, although devoid of any precise mathematical and physically verifiable justification, indicates a confidence of likelihood derived from what some of us refer to as "horse-sense." (Since Dr. Shewhart demurred at my use of the word "horse-sense" in this context, I clothe it in respectability, defining it "rational conviction derived from pertinent educated experience.")

Because of his background, the quality engineer is likely to be particularly aware of the circumstances which form the bases of quality judgments—of which P'_B is one. He should know better how, where, and in what respects to inquire, and how best to use the answers he gets. He plays the part of a quality historian, a genealogist of the antecedents whose offspring provided the limited data in question.

Holding high standards—and compromising

Despite its origin in an R&D organization (Bell Laboratories) and its growth and continued close association with the broad activities of its birthplace, quality control is often defined and treated as a part of manufacture (probably because the bulk of the literature and much of the practice is limited to manufacturing). Such a circumscription is an unwarranted limitation on the intent of Shewhart, who conceived the term; it also tends to stifle what should be QC's earliest and one of its most important functions—the economic reconciliation of the interface between design and manufacture.

When the manufacturer transforms the paper description of a designer's concept into a physical reality, the process is largely be-

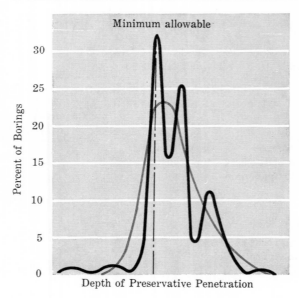

Fig. 6-49. Two foibles of an inspector show in this comparison of his inspection reports (in black) and the expected distribution of depth of preservative penetration in a large number of telephone poles. Note the appearance that preservative tends to penetrate in multiples of ¼ in., skipping odd ⅛-in. marks, and the very small population of marginally unacceptable poles.

yond the designer's control, even though it is the final outcome with which he is concerned. Since it is an immutable fact of life that concept and reality differ, the quality engineer must decide in what respect and to what degree differences can be tolerated. Before the start of manufacture, he must establish standards for the product that represent the economically compromised interests of design, manufacture, and use. Quality is what comes off the shelf, not what is specified on paper.

Sometimes the standards call for an average product quality better than that specified for an individual unit—for example, we might specify a tighter tolerance for average conductor resistance than we do for an individual cable pair. More frequently, however, the standards will reflect the sound over-all economy of permitting deviations from design requirements; e.g., we expect a few bad nails per barrel.

When standards contemplate departures from the ideal implied by the design, provision must be made and standards established in terms of limits for these departures. I remember a case where it proved to be most economical to ship a relatively expensive product as much as 2% defective, and then reinspect it at the point of installation (with suitable provision, of course, for test gear and spares).

When product quality is sampled, there is always some hazard of accepting some nonconforming material. Even 100% inspection is generally not 100% effective, and, of course, 100% inspection is not possible for the many important qualities whose verification involves destruction. Then too, inspectors exhibit such human foibles as fatigue and the tendency to shy away or "flinch" in the area close to a feature of nonconformance—especially when the measurement mechanism is imprecise, e.g., depth of preservative penetration in timber as shown in Fig. 6-49. We can also see (by the "peaks") a tendency to read to the nearest large subdivision.

Rating quality and its sources

One of the oldest quality standards used in rating is in the form of "percent defective," which limits the proportion of the product falling outside the specifications. While this is a simple standard, it conveys little information about composite quality; it does not differentiate between serious and trivial deficiencies, nor can it meaningfully portray the combined quality of different types of items.

Among the newer quality-rating schemes is "defects-per-unit," a measure of the relative number of *defects* rather than the relative number of defectives. These rating schemes are often applied to the entire periodic output of a plant, to assess relative product quality and to indicate budding, but still subtle, sources of quality trouble.

Perhaps the best, certainly one of the most versatile, quality standards is expressed in terms of "demerits-per-unit." For each departure from specifications, demerits are assigned to the product, depending upon the importance of the requirement and the degree of departure. We might, for example, assign 10 demerits for a poorly soldered connection or a marginal transistor characteristic, 100 demerits for an intermittent open circuit or a shorted resistor, etc. Or, we might assign a dollar amount to each deficiency, to indicate depreciation of product value. Either way, we have a method for weighting quality, a necessary component of any effective quality evaluation procedure.

Whatever form they take, the standards have a primary influence on the manufacturing program, which must meet them effectively and economically. Obviously, they have a direct bearing on the customer.

Feedback from customer complaints

Setting appropriate standards is a task impossible of successful attainment without the feedback implicit in any comprehensive quality-control practice. The basic and final measure of the quality of any product is, of course, its performance in service.

No matter how brilliant the design, how effective the manufacture, or how well the product meets quality standards based on the design requirements, a dishwasher which fails to wash dishes properly is of unsatisfactory quality. The real need is for quality control to look beyond design and manufacture, to implement some form of customer-oriented, operational feedback. The original, and still most common, sources of feedback are customer complaints, especially for those shortcomings which appear only after actual service.

This delayed feedback is usually supplemented by quicker-response environmental tests, accelerated life-tests, "field trials," etc. Still, many failure phenomena have been disclosed through user complaints—environmental cracking of plastics, silver migration in insulation, cathode poisoning, "whisker" growth, many types of fatigue and corrosion susceptibility, systems incompatibilities, etc., to mention a few within my personal experience. Not only does the QC engineer need the information furnished by complaints but, because he is in the best position to objectively assign responsibility for their sources and to prosecute their elimination, the technical aspects of the complaint activity are also a part of his function.

Looking things over

Long ago we knew that we needed some comprehensive procedure, some broad-scale review, to see that the intent of the design is properly reflected throughout product development—for example, in the clarity and completeness of the design specifications themselves. To satisfy this need, a step-by-step analytical review was inaugurated. In this quality survey, all quality-affecting aspects of the product—from design requirements to service history—are examined critically.

Although this procedure was a part of quality control (or quality assurance) as originally developed, it isn't as widely practiced as some other QC activities. Nevertheless, it is potentially one of the most valuable, since it includes a soul-searching critical examination of QC itself. It is interesting that in one large enterprise, of the important problems brought up for correction thus far, over half have related to design. The design engineers are both helpful and favorable to this phase of quality control. As consultants to the quality engineer, they obtain an intimate and comprehensive picture of how their brain children are actually being reared.

The survey follows the precept that, while

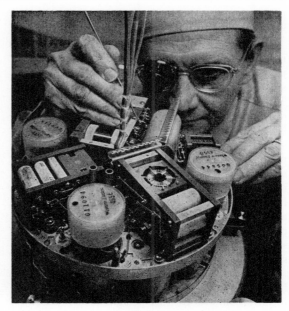

Fig. 6-50. No space capsule this, and no mil-spec item either. Except for hardware differences, this scene, inspection of a repeater amplifier, could have been taken any time during the several-decades-long history of underwater telephone cable systems. (Courtesy Bell Telephone Laboratories)

the mathematical tools and graphical evidence of quality control are largely statistical, the groundwork involves analyses and implications of cause systems which underlie the statistical results. It has proved valuable where relatively novel, complex, costly, high-reliability products must be put into service promptly. For example, the underwater components of a transatlantic cable system—its cable and repeaters—undergo a continuous quality survey during manufacture. This helps assure the intended interpretation of the unusually detailed design specifications, the maintenance of suitable records, and the many other factors affecting quality and reliability. The rigor is well worth the effort: It costs about $250,000 to locate and repair a deep-sea failure.

Reliability as a quality with a future

Whether regarded as a separate activity, or properly incorporated within design, one aspect of quality has attracted considerable attention during recent years. Discussion (even dissension) is rife regarding the relation between reliability and quality control. To QC people in industries where reliability is not only a paramount consideration but a fait accompli, it seems strange to hear some statements that have been made, statements to the effect that we can in fact "attain high quality without reliability." Anomalously, these things were said just when much of the literature laid the blame for unreliability at the door of "poor quality control."

Unlike most qualities, the ability to function in the future cannot be determined directly until after the fact. Indeed, the very act of supplying this attribute determines reliability. The fact that we cannot presently measure it directly drives us to a second definition of reliability—one which enables us to measure or at least to estimate it. Thus we have two definitions of reliability: the classic one denoting a quality; the other denoting a probability, i.e., a prediction. The whole prediction process, however, is still an often incomplete and uncertain procedure at best, and it would be completely worthless without QC to ensure some semblance of integrity to the empirical constants employed.

The fact (belatedly recognized by some reliability practitioners) is that the bases of reliability inhere in the design itself. In practice, however, many of the features which determine reliability (soldering, wiring, assembly, workmanship) are often neglected in its measurement, are frequently left almost entirely to the conscience and control of QC.

Let us bear in mind that, historically, the pressure for reliability arose because of the plethora of unreliable, complex military systems. Since the likelihood of failure increases with the number of critical parts, unreliability was associated with complexity. While complexity is obviously a factor, history rebuts the premise that reliability is fundamentally governed by complexity. The mundane task of getting us to work in the morning, for example, often involves a complex system including an extremely large number of subsystems and components.

Fortunately, it is not complexity, but lack of sufficient know-how which leads to unreliability. Complexity will always be with us; insufficient know-how can be overcome. In this atmosphere, quality control and reliability—and design, production, and so forth—are similarly directed; there must be close cooperation among them all, however we slice the organizational pie.

Further reading

Still the classic reference on this subject is Shewhart's *Economic Control of Quality of Manufactured Product* (Van Nostrand, 1931, $8.25) which delineates the formal bases of what has become current QC practice. A good alternate starting place is the more recent elementary text by Grant, *Statistical Quality Control* (McGraw-Hill, 1952, $8.50), which includes many illustrative problems and examples.

The management and administrative views of QC are covered in Feigenbaum's *Total Quality Control* (McGraw-Hill, 1961, $12.50) and the *Quality Control Handbook*, ed. by Juran (2nd ed., McGraw-Hill, 1962, $22).

An excellent treatment of the control-chart method can be found in the ASTM manual on *Quality Control of Materials—Special Technical Publication 15-C* (at $2.50 from ASTM), while a feeling for sampling methodology is one of the bonuses of a perusal of *Sampling Inspection Tables* by Dodge and Romig (Wiley, 1959, $8), in which they explain the theory and provide tables for various sampling plans.

While the literature on the QC of particular product areas is, of course, scattered among many journals (an example is the ASTM journal *Materials Research & Standards*), the monthly *Industrial Quality Control* (the journal of the ASQC) and the Hitchcock periodical *Quality Assurance* are of special interest and contain many papers of pertinence to this article. For still more information, see the 45 or so references in E. G. D. Paterson's critical review, "Reliability and Quality in Communications," in the March 1964 issue of *Industrial Quality Control*.

STATISTICAL VIBRATION ANALYSIS

by Ira Dyer *

IN BRIEF: *Time was when vibration analysis was pretty simple: knowing the force field and the structure's characteristics, you calculated the response of one to the other by classical methods devised by Rayleigh and Timoshenko. Now, the complex structures of contemporary interest are excited by environments that are random in nature and cover a wide range of* frequencies all at once. Instead of just one resonance, or mode, clearly definable and sometimes controllable, we must now cope with many modes that—piled one upon the other—may cause unwanted effects: the missile buffeted by the acoustic energy of its engines, the building lashed by the hurricane's energy, the ship tormented by that of the stormy sea. The answer is to look at the energy of the vibrating system, to examine the behavior of the sum of the modes, rather than that of the individual*

* Ira Dyer is a Vice President of Bolt, Beranek and Newman, Inc., Cambridge, Massachusetts.

modes. By examining the modal response over the whole frequency range, and by applying concepts based on statistics, we can rather quickly discern whether our structure is safe.—F.P.

■ Recently a new method of structural vibration analysis has been developed. To many it may come as a surprise that structural vibration is a subject for inquiry or new approaches. Didn't Lord Rayleigh say all that had to be said about the physics of vibration back in 1877? And didn't Timoshenko say all that had to be said about vibration engineering?

The classical techniques taught so well by Rayleigh, Timoshenko, and many others have been side-stepped recently, not because they are wrong, but rather because they are not well-suited for the investigation of some contemporary problems. In the design and operation of space vehicles, marine vessels, and tall office buildings, as examples, we meet vibration problems that defy solution by these techniques.

The elements common to contemporary problems that have given rise to difficulties are (1) the random nature of the forces we must deal with, (2) the complex nature of the structures themselves and (3) the interest in high-frequency behavior, that is, in the response of a structure at frequencies much higher than its fundamental. A space vehicle, for example, is subject to intense noise radiated by its booster (see sketch in margin): the noise is a random-in-time force that is most energetic at high frequencies. Although sleek looking, the space vehicle is structurally complex, being an assemblage of curved plates, frames, stringers, and cross-beams. And finally the load of the space vehicle, including electronic equipments, may be very sensitive to the effects of vibration, particularly at high frequencies. The task of the designer, specifier, or tester is to understand this rather complex situation, and for this the classical techniques of vibration analysis have not been adequate.

Precisely why do the classical techniques fail? After all, they are based on physical principles that we still believe. Recall that the classical approach entails determination of the resonant motions or modes of the structure (as sketched in the margin and shown in the interesting photographs in Fig. 6-52). The exciting force is then resolved into the various possible mode shapes and the amplitude of vibration for each mode results. For random forces distributed over the structure, all of the modes may be excited, so that the spectrum of response will be rather broadband.

Fig. 6-51. *The modern sky-scraper, with its glittering facade of glass, is actually a complex structure on which wind, rain, and hail play a forceful tune. The vast expanses of glass—clamped as they are in their soaring mullions, and abraded by swirling dust—have been known to vibrate flexurally to the point of failure. This is but one of many vibration problems where the random nature of the force field is stimulating designers to look at statistical methods of vibration analysis. (Courtesy Heka)*

If we had the patience and adequate knowledge of the force field and the structure, we could calculate the response. We would get a

Booster Noise

Booster Exhaust Stream

One Mode

Another

One More

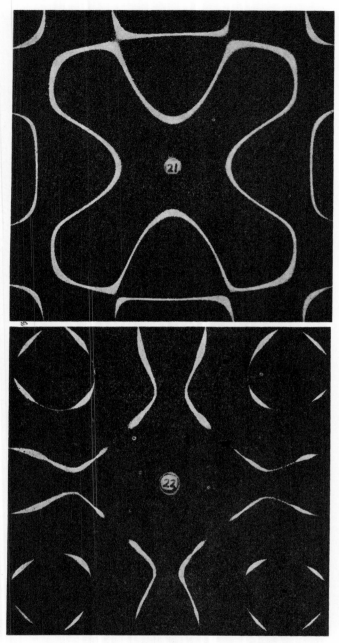

result something like that sketched in the margin. Now here's the difficulty—we almost never have adequate knowledge of the force field and the structure to predict the details of the response, particularly at the higher frequencies. Thus the failings are not so much related to the classical techniques themselves, but rather to our inability to provide the primary data.

With patience and a great deal of labor, however, we could predict the trends of the vibration response well enough. In today's technology, patience and labor can be circumvented by high-speed digital computers. But it seems wasteful and perhaps physically misleading to use calculation tools capable of providing detailed information, when all that we expect to use is an average or trend of the details.

A statistical theory of vibration

In recent years a statistical theory of structural vibration has been developed. In a straightforward and simple way this theory provides the trends we seek, and once learned, is easier to apply than the classical theory. Its simplicity also encourages physical interpretation and the development of general design guides. In essence the theory is built around the idea that when the response is composed of many modes, it is easier to describe the behavior of the *sum* of the modes, than to describe the behavior of the individual modes.

Statistical theories are used often in physics, and it is perhaps helpful to draw some analogies. Consider the kinetic theory of gases. Just as we forego the details of *individual* molecular motion to describe, say, the pressure of a gas, so we shall forego the details of *individual* modes of a structure in favor of the behavior summed over a large number of modes.

Molecules in a gas possess kinetic energy that on the average can be related to the gas temperature and to the number of degrees of freedom. Similarly, the concept of "temperature" has been introduced into vibration problems as a measure of the average vibrational energy of modes of the structure, while the number of modes is a measure of the number of degrees of freedom.

Black-body radiation was analyzed statistically by Rayleigh and Jeans on the basis of the number density of electromagnetic wave modes

Fig. 6-52. These patterns are not the tracing of some bemused textile artist. Rather, they are tiny sand bars that delineate contours of repose on a sheet of metal that is being forcibly vibrated at its center while its edges hang free. The sheet responds to vibrations in a different manner, or mode, at each different frequency of vibration. Sand sprinkled on the surface drifts into the nodes, forming contours—called Chladni patterns after their discoverer. Shown here are but two of many patterns revealed over a wide range of frequencies, yet they represent vibration modes that are but 200 cps apart. Exciting the plate (or any structure) with random, broad-band vibrations in effect superimposes all these myriad resonances, rendering the description of the motion all but impossible by classical methods. By statistical techniques, however, useful information about the response of the structure

can be gained, as explained in the text. (Aluminum panels above are 11¾ in. square × 0.090 in. thick. Top panel is pulsed at 1.92 Kc; bottom panel at 2.13 Kc.) (Courtesy R. Fisher, MIT)

in a cavity, and by assuming that on the average each mode has the same energy (equipartition). Planck also used the modal density, but assumed a quantized distribution of modal energy to obtain the first success of quantum physics, the prediction of black-body radiation.

Sound waves in large rooms may be described statistically also. In fact, architectural acousticians design the gross features of concert halls, not by solving the wave equation, but rather by using energy relations that follow from statistical concepts.

Although the prediction of black-body radiation and the beginnings of architectural acoustics as a science came in the early 1900's, statistical techniques do not appear to have been applied systematically to structural vibration until recently. Of course any system supporting wave motion may be analyzed statistically, but it makes sense to do so only if the system is large compared with wavelength and if the results we seek are averages of the motion. Many contemporary structural vibration problems are such that a statistical approach does indeed make sense.

The three forces that count

Let us examine the bases of this approach. To do this, we will first review the nature of resonant vibration in structures and then examine briefly the obstacles that make the analysis of a multiresonance system so difficult with the classical mode-by-mode approach. This will make it easier to understand the statistical method and to appreciate more fully its power and utility in many applications.

We recall that three internal properties of a structure are of importance in determining its motion in response to external forces: its inertia, its stiffness, and its dissipation, commonly known as damping. When the internal forces of inertia and stiffness just balance each other, as they may do at particular frequencies, the structure is said to resonate, and it takes on a particular vibration pattern or mode. Because we are interested in random external forces having a broad bandwidth, many resonances or modes may be excited simultaneously. At resonance, the structural motion or vibration is controlled by the one remaining internal force, the dissipation force. This force is proportional to the velocity of vibration, and the constant of proportionality is termed the resistance.

To determine the vibration of a structure, we must know the external force as well as the internal force. For a particular mode, the relevant external force is determined by resolving or weighting the actual force by the modal vibration pattern. If the spatial pattern

of the external force (at any given time) is very much different from that of the mode we're interested in, the resolved force is very much smaller than the total external force, and the mode will not be excited strongly.

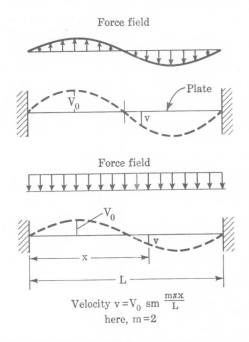

$$\text{Velocity } v = V_0 \text{ sin} \frac{m\pi x}{L}$$
here, $m = 2$

On the other hand, if the spatial patterns of both the force and the mode are identical, or nearly so, the resolved force is equal or close to the total external force and the mode will, indeed, be excited strongly.

The sketches above show this in a crude way. In each, a flat panel is clamped along its edges and is subjected to an external force in the spatial pattern of a pressure. Each will resonate because there is energy in the force field at the resonance frequency of the plate (as well as at other frequencies). But the first panel will have a large velocity amplitude V_0 because at each point the force field and the panel velocity "fit" or match closely. At the other extreme, if the pressure is uniform at any instant of time, as in the lower example, the force over half the panel opposes the motion, thus inhibiting it. Amplitude V_0 will be large in the first instance and small in the second, though both panels are at resonance.

Clearly, for each mode the resolved external force must equal the internal dissipation force. From this fact we could, in theory at least, find the vibration energy of each of the modes —which would, in turn, lead us to the sum of energies for all the modes and thus characterize the vibration. Let us pursue this mode-by-mode approach a bit further.

To write the energy of just one mode, we recall that it is proportional to the inertia (mass) times the vibration velocity squared, and that the velocity is, in turn, proportional to the external force divided by the structural resistance. Thus, the energy per mode can be expressed, in word form, as follows,

$$\text{Modal energy} \propto \frac{(\text{Mass}) \times \left(\begin{array}{c}\text{Resolved external} \\ \text{force at resonance}\end{array}\right)^2}{(\text{Resistance})^2}$$

The question that this equation presses upon us is: how would we express the "resolved external force at resonance"? We have discussed spatial force resolution already, so that the question is, in essence: "How do we express the force at resonance?" For the answer, we have to consider the random nature of the force field. That is, we have to take into account the time-dependent (i.e., frequency-dependent) character of the exciting force. Having done this, we can then return to the spatial aspects.

Describing a random force field

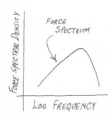

If the external force exciting the structure is random in nature, it is distributed in frequency, as sketched in the margin, and is expressed as a spectral density, that is, in terms of mean square force per unit frequency. If we were to integrate the spectral density of the force over all frequencies, we would then have the total mean square force acting on the structure. Right now, though, we are interested only in the external force for the one mode we are considering. Thus, we must integrate the spectral density of the force only over the range of frequencies relevant to the mode. This range is called the mode bandwidth, and it can be shown to be proportional to the structure resistance of the mode divided by mass. Expressed in terms of force spectral density, the energy per mode then takes the following form.

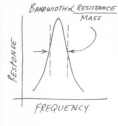

$$\text{Modal energy} \propto \frac{\left(\begin{array}{c}\text{Resolved-force} \\ \text{spectral density}\end{array}\right)}{(\text{Resistance})}$$

We see that the modal energy depends upon but one structural parameter, the resistance, and upon the external force, resolved or weighted by the mode vibration pattern, as discussed earlier.

Now structural resistance is not easy to determine; one is almost always forced to guess its value for any particular design. You could conclude that the tenuousness of our primary data on resistance is reason enough to abandon the mode-by-mode method of analysis and to embark upon a calculation scheme based on statistics. But stronger reasons exist for the new approach, as we have noted previously and shall discuss now.

The real villain when it comes to analyzing random vibrations mode-by-mode is the resolved force—as we saw in the resonating flat panels discussed a moment ago. The resolved force is an extremely complicated and sensitive function of the spatial details of both the force field (say, the acoustic field emitted by a rocket engine) and the vibration field (say, the vibration of the missile skin itself). The energy of the two modes closely spaced in frequency may therefore have vastly different energies, so that unless the resolving or "fitting" is done precisely, the response calculated at a given frequency could be grossly in error. The statistical approach side-steps this problem completely, as we'll see in a moment, by considering the average behavior of a number of resonances, or modes, rather than the individual behavior of each.

The average is a vital statistic

In applying the classical approach to vibration analysis of a complex structure in a random force field, most of the labor would be devoted to the determination of the resolved force mode-by-mode. It is dreadfully difficult to compute for one mode, and almost impossibly difficult to compute for the multiplicity of modes met in a practical situation. There may be thousands of them present, and even the best computers could barely make a dent in the calculations needed.

If we consider, instead, the *average* energy of at least several closely spaced modes, we can get a vastly simpler description of the behavior. In fact, researchers have found simple expressions by which the average energy can be calculated in problems as diverse as those associated with boundary layer excitation of submarine hulls, rain falling on schoolhouse roofs, and rocket engine noise effects on space vehicles. An example would be the first expression on the opposite page, for the average energy of a panel structure when excited in flexure by sound. On the other hand, calculating the individual modal energies in such cases in order to obtain an average is an impossibly difficult task.

In short, the average modal energy, like the average energy per degree of freedom in kinetic theory, obscures some of the modal details, but enables easy calculation of the trends we seek. This is because the average energy of a structural mode is insensitive to the precise nature of the structure—kinds of stiffening, edge fixity, attachments, and the like. A small perturbation in a structure may affect particular modes significantly when viewed individually, but when viewed statistically the perturbation may have a small or even vanishing effect.

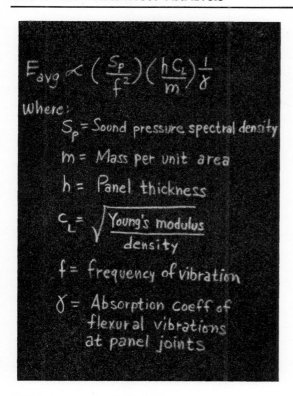

$$E_{avg} \propto \left(\frac{S_P}{f^2}\right)\left(\frac{h\,C_L}{m}\right)\frac{1}{\gamma}$$

Where:

S_P = Sound pressure spectral density

m = Mass per unit area

h = Panel thickness

$C_L = \sqrt{\dfrac{\text{Young's modulus}}{\text{density}}}$

f = frequency of vibration

γ = Absorption coeff of flexural vibrations at panel joints

But the sum is really what we want

Now that we see the virtue of working with the average energy in a finite frequency interval (or bandwidth) which contains several modes, and now that we have straightforward methods for calculating that energy, we may ask: What good is it?

The answer is that we can use the average energy (which we'll call E_{avg}) as a means for calculating the total energy in each observational bandwidth, just as Rayleigh and Jeans did for black-body radiation. If a number of modes ΔN occur in a frequency interval Δf, the total energy in that bandwidth is simply $E_{avg} \times (\Delta N)$, as shown in the following sketch.

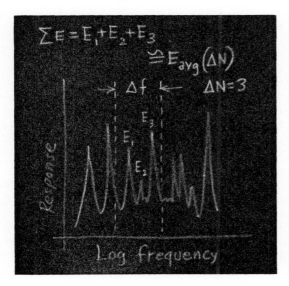

The total energy in the vibrating structure is then the sum of all the various bandwidth totals. However, we learn more about the response of the structure if its total energy is displayed as a function of frequency rather than as a simple sum. So we create what is termed the energy spectral density by dividing the total bandwidth energy $E_{avg}(\Delta N)$ by the bandwidth Δf. Thus, the energy spectral density (which we'll call S_E) is this,

$$S_E = \Sigma E/\Delta f = E_{avg}(\Delta N/\Delta f)$$

Since the average energy E_{avg} can be calculated, all we require now is the ratio $\Delta N/\Delta f$, which is termed the modal density.

It has been found that the modal density can also be calculated—from equations that are, in general, even simpler than those derived for the average energy, particularly at the higher frequencies in which we're interested. Indeed, it turns out that the modal density is usually a simple function of the structure's properties.

For example, it can be shown that for a flat panel structure vibrating in flexure, the modal density $\Delta N/\Delta f$ is simply proportional to the surface area of the panel divided by its mean thickness, regardless of its shape or edge fixity. Equally simple results for $\Delta N/\Delta f$, also proportional to total surface area, have been obtained for other structural systems such as finite cylindrical shells. Since most structures can be approximated by an assemblage of panels or shells, these simple expressions for modal density have real importance—for the total modal density of the structure is simply the sum of the densities of the structure's components.

For flat panel:
$$\frac{\Delta N}{\Delta f} = \frac{\sqrt{3}}{C_L}\left(\frac{A}{h}\right)$$

Modal density can be perhaps made clearer by giving it some physical significance. The graph in Fig. 6-53 displays the results of a simple experiment on a flat aluminum plate of given dimensions. By exciting the plate with a vibration shaker at increasing frequencies, and by counting the number of different resonances as they appear, the cumulative number of modes can be plotted as shown. The modal density is, then, simply the slope of the resulting "curve." In this case, the curve is a straight line and the modal density is a constant. We see that the slope of the measured curve is in good agreement with that predicted by theory.

It is revealing to note that this relatively small panel has about 250 modes up to 100 cps and, by extrapolation, about 2500 modes up to 10,000 cps! It might be possible to view all these modes by creating a whole series of Chladni patterns like those pictures in Fig. 6-52. But this would be only a qualitative approach, and a tedious one at that. A detailed quantitative account of all these modes by

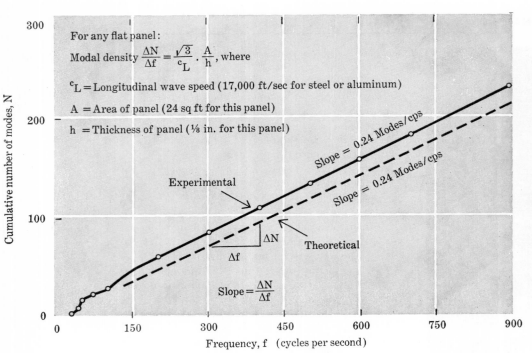

For any flat panel:

Modal density $\frac{\Delta N}{\Delta f} = \frac{\sqrt{3}}{c_L} \cdot \frac{A}{h}$, where

c_L = Longitudinal wave speed (17,000 ft/sec for steel or aluminum)

A = Area of panel (24 sq ft for this panel)

h = Thickness of panel (⅛ in. for this panel)

Slope = 0.24 Modes/cps

Slope = 0.24 Modes/cps

Experimental

Theoretical

ΔN

Δf

Slope = $\frac{\Delta N}{\Delta f}$

Cumulative number of modes, N

Frequency, f (cycles per second)

Fig. 6-53. A vibrating plate has many resonances, more than you'd think, over a wide range of frequencies. This diagram shows just how many accumulate as you go to higher and higher frequencies in exciting the plate. There are far too many resonances, or modes to analyze by classical techniques. But by employing a method based on statistics, which uses the slopes (actually the mode densities in various frequency intervals) of cumulative mode diagrams like this one, you can predict a structure's vibration response quickly and easily. See text for details.

classical calculation techniques is clearly prohibitive in time, effort, and expense. But by using the statistical approach just described—multiplying the average energy by the modal density—we can quickly and simply get the energy spectral density and reveal the nature of the vibration over the entire frequency range.

The sum is what we can measure and use

When the analyst examines the vibration response of a complex structure by the statistical methods outlined above, he usually does not seek a spectrum of energy density. Rather, he is more interested in motion parameters easily derived from energy. Principal among these is acceleration, for this is a quantity that we humans sense readily and—for that reason, among others—one that we build instruments to measure. Actually, we generally measure mean square acceleration, so this is the motion quantity whose distribution in frequency we seek.

Accordingly, by taking the energy sum as proportional to mass times velocity squared, and velocity proportional to acceleration divided by frequency, we can write the mean square acceleration by simply multiplying the energy by a quantity proportional to f^2/mA. Here, f is the frequency, m the mass per unit area, and A the area of the vibrating surface. Thus, we can calculate from the energy spectrum the spectral density of acceleration, S_a, as

$$S_a \propto E_{avg}(\Delta N/\Delta f)(f^2/mA)$$

Recall that the modal density $\Delta N/\Delta f$ is proportional to the surface area A. Therefore it turns out that the spectral density of the acceleration is independent of the *size* of the structure, as shown below for a flat panel. This

For a flat panel excited by sound:

$$S_a \propto \left(\frac{S_p h C_L}{\gamma m f^2}\right)\left(\frac{A}{C_L h}\right)\left(\frac{f^2}{mA}\right)$$

or

$$S_a \propto S_p\left(\frac{1}{\gamma m^2}\right)$$

is a vital point, for in the classical approach, size is an ever-present and critical parameter.

In broadest terms, the calculated spectral density of acceleration is used as a first rough view of the vibration response of a structure. Suppose, for example, it is the vibration of the skin of a new space vehicle that concerns us. We would calculate the acceleration spectral density and then compare it to that *measured* on other designs that had proven successful.

Typical measured acceleration spectra in response to rocket engine noise for two different parts of the Army's Jupiter space vehicle are plotted in the graph in Fig. 6-54. If the calculated spectrum of mean square acceleration for the new design, when drawn in alongside, proved to lie well above these curves, then it

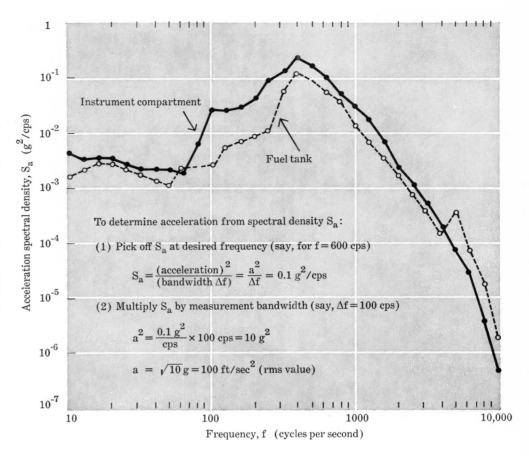

Fig. 6-54. These spectral densities of acceleration are what the vibration analyst seeks, either by calculation or from measurements, to give him clues to the response of a complex structure to a random force field. The magnitude of surface motions may be excessive; or, there may be peaks at frequencies (as shown here at 400 cps) that might cause trouble. These spectra were measured on a Jupiter missile at take-off. They, and similar experimental spectra for other complex structures, can form standards against which the calculated response (see text) of new, untried structures can be compared.

To determine acceleration from spectral density S_a:

(1) Pick off S_a at desired frequency (say, for $f = 600$ cps)

$$S_a = \frac{(\text{acceleration})^2}{(\text{bandwidth } \Delta f)} = \frac{a^2}{\Delta f} = 0.1 \ g^2/\text{cps}$$

(2) Multiply S_a by measurement bandwidth (say, $\Delta f = 100$ cps)

$$a^2 = \frac{0.1 \ g^2}{\text{cps}} \times 100 \ \text{cps} = 10 \ g^2$$

$$a = \sqrt{10} \ g = 100 \ \text{ft/sec}^2 \ (\text{rms value})$$

would be a signal either to stop and test comparable components (or models) of the new structure, or (if our experience were broad enough) to initiate a redesign of the structure.

Comparing calculated and measured spectra

You may ask: is it valid to compare spectral densities calculated by the statistical method to those measured with instruments? The answer is yes. Vibrations measured on large structures at high frequencies (where much of the excitation caused by random force fields shows up) are proportional to the sum of the modal energies in the measurement bandwidth, rather than to the energy of an individual mode. This is so because present-day measurement systems have frequency bandwidths that usually encompass at least several structural modes.

Spectra of the surface motion on complex structures are the meat and potatoes of vibration analysis. It is not our purpose to discuss these aspects in detail. However, you can appreciate that if the surface resonates strongly in certain frequency ranges, the consequences could be manifold: the surface might act as a driver itself, radiating acoustic energy to the detriment of delicate electronic components nearby; or, the vibration might be transmitted through the substructure to other regions; or, the surface material could—after sufficient time—fail by fatigue. Each of these, and others,

must be examined closely in any practical situation.

The utility of the statistical approach to vibration analysis of such structures lies in its enabling us to predict whether we will, indeed, be faced with such problems in some part of the frequency range. The power of the method lies in its ability to provide these insights for any structure, no matter how large, simply and quickly. The exploitation of these attributes has just barely begun.

Further reading

As was noted above in the article, statistical theories have been used in physics for many years, most notably in the area of gas kinetics. Architectural acousticians have been applying them in one form or another for perhaps two decades. Their extension to what we might call "hardware" began in 1955 when the first attempts were made to analyze the vibration of aircraft structures in response to jet engine noise. A summary of this first work will be found in "New Methods for Understanding and Controlling Vibrations of Complex Structures" by Heckl, Lyon, Maidanek, and Ungar, a report for the Aeronautical Systems Div. of Wright-Patterson Air Force Base [Document ASD TN-61-122 (June 1962) also carries ASTIA No. AD-281798].

It was not until the 1960's that rigorous

treatment of the subject began to appear in the technical literature, principally the *Journal of the Acoustical Society of America*. Five important papers from this source are cited below: The complex problem of force resolution is treated by Smith in "Response and Radiation of Structural Modes Excited by Sound," **34**, No. 5, 640 (1962). Modal density equations for shells are derived by Heckl in "Vibrations of Point-Driven Cylindrical Shells," **34**, No. 10, 1553 (1962). To see how a thermodynamic or heat-flow analogy can be applied to vibration problems, see Lyon's and Maidanek's "Power Flow between Linearly Coupled Oscillators," **34**, No. 6, 623 (1962). In Heckl's "Measurements of Absorption Coefficients on Plates," **34**, No. 6, 803 (1962), an analogy to architectural acoustics is used to characterize the localized damping at boundaries of structures in terms of absorption coefficients. Statistical methods are extended to complex, built-up shapes in Maidanek's "Response of Ribbed Panels to Reverberant Acoustic Fields," **34**, No. 6, 809 (1962).

Although there exists no "handbook" treatment of the statistical approach to vibration analysis, the following two references are of an applications nature, and may help in this respect: The first is "Estimation of Sound-Induced Vibrations by Energy Methods" by Franken and Lyon in the *Proceedings of the 31st Symposium on Shock, Vibration, and Associated Environments*. To request a copy, write to Mr. W. W. Mutch, Code 4021, U.S. Naval Research Laboratory, Washington 25, D.C. The second is "Response of Space Vehicle Structures to Rocket Engine Noise" by our author Ira Dyer, Chap. 7 of Crandall's *Random Vibrations*, Vol. 2 (MIT Press, 1963).

To review the classical methods of vibration analysis, get Lord Rayleigh's *Theory of Sound*, Vols. 1 and 2 (Dover, 1945), and Timoshenko's *Vibration Problems in Engineering* (Van Nostrand, 1955). For a summary of how statistical methods were employed in the black-body radiation problem, on which their use in acoustics was based, see p. 164 of *Introduction to Modern Physics* by Richtmyer and Kennard (McGraw-Hill, 1955). And if you are intrigued by the Chladni patterns in our article, see Waller's fascinating monograph, *Chladni Figures—A Study in Symmetry* (G. Bell & Sons, 1961).

PREDICTING SYSTEM RELIABILTY

by Harold M. Gordy *

IN BRIEF: *Although the causes of specific failures may be deterministic, the aggregate of all that determinism is best described statistically.*

After an initial wear-in (or "burn-in" if it's electrical) period, and until the onslaught of increasing failure rates with age and use, subsystems usually settle down to a relatively low, steady, time-independent failure rate, one described by an exponential hazard function.

For series systems, where all subsystems must function for the system to succeed, the statistics provide a ready means for predicting reliability. But then arises the thorny question of the confidence of the prediction—and all the polemic, craft, and witchcraft that goes with it.

Still, all is not bleak confusion; the math suggests ways to better the odds of series systems, by replicate subsystems (redundancy), by using switchable and repairable redundancy, and voting logic, and whatever else designers and "equipment actuaries" can come up with.—R.G.N.

■ When we buy an automobile, we see what we buy. We can even try it, test it, so to speak.

But when a governmental agency or a commercial airline buys a piece of complex electronic equipment, they buy it sight unseen. They buy it long before anyone knows what it looks like. More important, its ability to perform its required functions for a given mission is unknown.

Millions of dollars may be spent, and many hairs turned gray, before the reliability of the system can be measured. In fact, it may never be measured with any degree of confidence. Now, any customer wants to know something about what he is buying. The government, or a commercial company, would like to predict important parameters of a complex system before it spends money.

Some characteristics of systems are easy to predict; they follow well-defined physical laws, or they can be estimated closely from laboratory simulation. Reliability, unfortunately, is a maverick. It has no dimensions, but is a pure number. And even this pure number is not really pure. It describes not what can be expected from any given system, but only what can be expected, on the average, from a homogenous population of similar systems. Still reliability predictions are commonly applied

* Harold M. Gordy is Corporate Manager of Reliability and Quality Control at Giannini Controls Corp., Duarte, California.

Fig. 6-55. The Russian Baltic Company's "Ilia Mourometz" series planes could boast of a reliability feature not available on modern aircraft. Not only would these Sikorsky-designed planes fly with a couple motors aflame and limp on one engine, but provisions were made for members of the crew to leave the cabin during flight and, holding on to rails, climb along the wing to replace spark plugs and make minor repairs (including firefighting). With such features and heavy armament (for 1916), these planes made a total of 400 raids with only one plane lost. For aficionados, this bomber is a 1916 Model E, with four Renault motors totaling 880 horsepower. (Courtesy Sikorsky Div., United Aircraft)

to very small populations and to populations which are not very homogenous.

Is it any wonder that, until a few years ago, the prediction of reliability was considered witchcraft? Yet it was a necessity to be able to predict reliability, for a lack of reliability might render a system useless, and this can be very annoying. So, the first prediction methods for reliability were born.

By the early fifties, several commercial companies had cooperatively established a group to study this question of reliability. Early studies of data gathered on failures of complex military equipment indicated that failures in these systems seemed to occur randomly with time.

But, over long periods, the failure rates remained constant with time. That is, for "burned-in" equipments, the number of failures per unit of time did not vary with operating time. These two facts led to the postulation of an exponential hazard function for the reliability of equipments. The hazard, of course, was failure.

Now, what the ultimate user usually wants to know is the chance that his equipment will function for a certain mission time. A function that describes the probability that equipment will survive over a time, t, is:

$$R = e^{-t/\theta} = e^{-\lambda t}$$

R is Reliability, the *probability* that a given equipment will survive without a failure for a time, t, and λ is the constant failure rate, and θ is the inverse of failure rate, the "mean-time-to-failure."

Normal hazards and actual ones

This hazard function is not the only one that can occur for complex equipments. Where a system consists nearly entirely of parts that wear out, and each part has a wear characteristic almost like every other part, then the function will no longer be exponential; it will be normal, and will be described by:

$$R = \frac{1}{\sigma\sqrt{2\pi}} \int_t^\infty e^{-(t-m)^2/2\sigma} \, dt$$

where t is the time at which reliability is measured, m is the mean of the familiar normal distribution and σ is its standard deviation. What this formula says is that, if wearout is the controlling cause of failures, then the re-

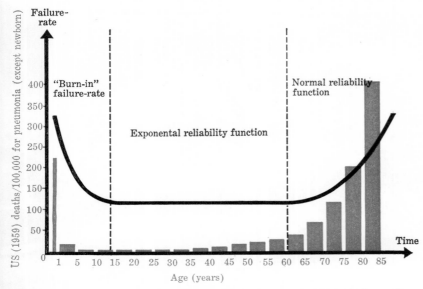

Fig. 6-56. Populations of subsystems, biological as well as mechanical, tend to follow this general history. Early in the game, the faulty, marginal cases are weeded out and failure rates are high. Then comes a period of relatively reliable operation, then increased failure with age and wear. Here, the biological failure is pneumonia.

liability of the equipment depends on when it is used. The reliability tends to worsen with every operating hour, and woe to the poor user who gets the equipment when it is well into mean life.

Of course, the normal hazard function is more familiar than is the exponential, for most of our everyday "equipment" fails from wear-out. Our automobile repair bills mount with time, the washing machine gradually becomes a full-time repair job, and our temper goes up with the failure rate of our appliances.

The normal hazard function also applies to electronic equipments in which parts are not replaced before they fail. However, in the case of modern electronic equipments, usually the mean of the normal distribution does not occur until long after the equipment is outmoded. Thus, in most complex electronic systems, we are operating in the flat portion of the curve of Fig. 6-56, i.e., the exponential hazard function is a good approximation of reliability over the entire useful life of the equipment. This (and the fact that the mathematics of complex systems predictions is much more tractable using the exponential function) led to the adoption of this function for purposes of prediction.

Actually, if the lifetime of a system goes beyond the point where wearout begins, then a combination of constant failure rate and normal distribution (increasing failure rate) best describes the system's failure rate.

If quite a few parts in the system tend to have failure mechanisms causing early failure, the failure rate will be higher at first than the mid-life constant failure rate. This leads to the composite "bathtub" curve shown. The early failure characteristic can be avoided.

Usually, lots containing parts with potential early failures are "burned-in," that is, operated, until the potential failures are weeded out. Then, as an added precaution, the whole system should also be burned-in, to minimize any tendency for a high initial failure rate. With the high failure-rate part of the curve thus excluded and with the normal function end of the curve already out of the picture, we shall concentrate our attention on systems whose unit subsystems have the constant failure rates described by the exponential hazard function.

On chains with failing links

How do we predict reliability using the exponential method? An example is in order. Suppose we have a simple set of units, each with its own failure rate, λ_1, λ_2, λ_3. If a failure of any of these units causes a system failure, we have a series system:

$$-[R_1]-[R_2]-[R_3]-$$

Then the reliability of the system becomes the product of the reliabilities of the units, for probability of survival of one unit *and* a second *and* a third is the product of their probabilities:

$$\text{system reliability} = R_S = R_1\,R_2\,R_3$$

But $R_1 = e^{-\lambda_1 t}$ and the same applies to the other units, so the reliability of the system then becomes

$$R_s = e^{-\lambda_1 t} \times e^{-\lambda_2 t} \times e^{-\lambda_3 t} = e^{-(\lambda_1 + \lambda_2 + \lambda_3)t}$$

So, now we can predict the failure rate of the system by adding the failure rates of each of its units. Given the mission time, we can predict the reliability of the system; that is, we can calculate the chance of its survival for a period t.

Of course, we have neglected to say how to arrive at the unit failure rates. But if many of the units are used in the system, and a failure of any one still causes system failure, then, $\lambda_S = n_1\lambda_1 + n_2\lambda_2 + n_3\lambda_3$, where n_1, n_2, and n_3 are the number of units with failure rates λ_1, λ_2, and λ_3, respectively. If we look at unit 1 as a capacitor, unit 2 as a resistor, and unit 3 as a transistor, then (adopting some typical numbers) we can predict system reliability from part failure rates:

Let the capacitors fail at the rate of 0.3 parts/10^6 hr, the resistors at 0.01 parts/10^6 hr, and the transistors at 0.1 parts/10^6 hr. If there are 2000 capacitors, 10,000 resistors, and 1000 transistors, then the system failure rate is: $\lambda_s = 800$ failures/10^6 hr $= (2000)(0.3) + (10,000)(0.01) + (1000)(0.1)$. The system reliability, for a one hour mission, will be $R_s = e^{-\lambda_s t} = 0.9992$.

That's the easy part. The really difficult thing is to determine the part failure rates. For years after this method of reliability prediction was proposed, the failure rates of parts was little more than a guess. Finally, field reports on operating systems provided rough estimates of component failure rates, by types. This made the guessing game of reliability prediction a bit more exact, although data taken from the two different sources may, even today, differ by an order of magnitude. Reliability prediction thus depends on that questionable virtue, engineering judgment.

Common sense and uncommon stress

It was soon recognized that the use of average failure rates for part-types was outrageously inaccurate. After all, if 999 resistors in a system were operated at 125% of their power rating, and one at 20% of its rating, we could hardly expect average failure rates for resistors to apply. So we knew, albeit vaguely, that stress on the parts affected their failure rates. This didn't help much; it complicated an already vague area by demanding some quantitative relationships between stresses and failure rate. Without these relationships, we were stuck with reliability prediction using average failure rates.

So, plodding reliability engineers tested, gathered data from part manufacturers, and invented stress functions describing changes in failure rates due to temperature, power dissipation, etc. Of course, failure rates always increased with greater stress. Now if we wanted the failure rate of a particular transistor in a circuit, we computed its total power-dissipation, estimated its surface temperature, and entered a magic curve, like the one in Fig. 6-57, to retrieve the failure rates. By combining failure rates for each circuit in a system, we could predict basic system reliability.

As reliability engineers working on electronic equipment, we thought we had a discovery. We could predict the potential reliability of electronic equipment. While I was explaining this prediction method to a group of design engineers, one of them, who happened to be a mechanical engineer, really deflated me.

"Listen," he said, "mechanical engineers have

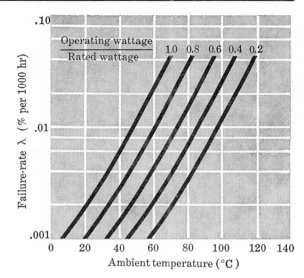

Fig. 6-57. A family of failure-rate curves, like this one for resistors, enables designers to predict failure rates as a function of an environmental stress (in this case, temperature) for various operating stresses (here, ratio of operating to rated power).

been predicting reliabilities of structures for years."

I was annoyed by the interruption. Yet, it occurred to me that what he said was true. I knew the method, even before he explained it to me; I remembered it from my strength of materials courses. It was quite simple. First, you tested, to destruction, all the materials to be used in a structure, by applying more and more stress to each of several samples. Then, you plotted the stress needed to "kill" each sample. When you plotted the stress to destroy vs. the number of samples, you obtained the parameters of a normal distribution of the failure stresses.

Now, by static and dynamic force and torque determinations for the structure, the highest stress level, i.e., the critical stress level, could be obtained, given the cross sections of material. Plotting the critical stress as a divider on the normal strength curve (as in Fig. 6-58), you divide the area under curve. The area to the left of the critical stress line represents the percent of samples which you'd expect to fail in the worst environments anticipated. Naturally, then, the reliability is the area remaining under the curve.

Not only was this method good for reliability prediction; it generally represented a demand for structural improvement so that, say, the 5σ point in Fig. 6-58 became the highest critical stress point (and the chances were some 99.9999% in favor of the integrity of the structure). Once the reliability of all the structural pieces is determined, then, by multiplication,

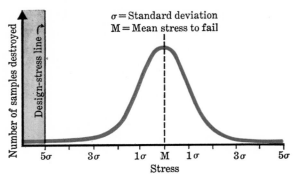

Fig. 6-58. Plotting the number of failures against the stress required to cause failure give a distribution like this. As the stress imposed on a part decreases (the design-stress line moves left), the shaded area under the curve diminishes and the chances for the part's survival improve.

we can obtain the reliability of a complex structure, provided that it consists of many nearly independent structures, such as a missile airframe and booster combination.

I shamefacedly admitted that my mechanically minded friend was correct. Then he added the barb:

"And the prediction method of structures doesn't require any magic numbers either. It's easy to get accurate predictions, by testing a few samples."

I differed violently at this point, noting that the definition of environment was not so exact as all that, and that structural interrelationships were often neglected in such predictions —and that the result was often higher-than-predicted stresses, and disaster!

As an example, I brought forward the disasters which befell several airliners of the same type because of unforeseen amplification of vibration by their structures. But this was only defensive maneuvering; on the whole, he was right. Structural reliability *was* easier to predict than was the reliability of complex electronic equipment, and so a number of the prediction methods made their earliest appearances in structural design. Only recently have we attempted electronic reliability prediction.

The reliability of reliability predictions

It behooves us, at this point, to pose the question all cynics ask, when we mention reliability prediction by parts-count and stress-relationship methods.

"Just how accurate *are* those failure rate vs. temperature characteristics? In fact, how accurate are the average failure rates?"

The answer is that nobody really knows the confidence levels of each point on any of the popular characteristic curves. That is because they are a conglomeration of data taken from field experience or many-component parts tests. There are very few characteristic reliability-stress curves which are "pure"; that is, taken from test data under controlled experimental conditions. But I do know of a company that tested the verity of its predictions against field reliability experience.

They calculated the theoretical reliability of each of several systems, then compared the theoretical reliabilities with actual field data. The discrepancies averaged 30% (positive and negative) in several systems; the maximum error found among those reliability predictions was ±75%. This may not seem good to those used to structures standards, but it indicates that more than luck is involved.

The best predictions seem to come from failure-rate characteristics taken from laboratory tests of large samples, where the results are "weighted" by a field-use factor. But, in any case, the predictions are not exact; we would like a better method. Any suggestions? To date, we have no more accurate way to predict the reliability of electronic equipment.

The growth of technology being what it is, the complexity (in numbers of parts) of systems has become rather large. Predictions showed that, for some very complex systems, the expected reliability was far below that required. Also, for some missions, such as space vehicle orbits, with unattended radio or radar operation, mission times involved were long. This raised the MTBF (that is, the mean-time-between-failures) requirements for even the simplest systems to unattainable values—for series systems.

When this happened, reliability engineers remembered that electric power transmission and distribution is very reliable, much more reliable than could be expected from a series system. But regional power systems are *not* series systems. When one generator fails, another is switched in to carry the load, whether in addition to its normal load or as a "standby" generator. Such systems continue to operate. This and similar situations suggested redundancy, the use of more than one part or unit to do the job of only one, in order to improve the system reliability.

Reiterating reliability with redundancy

As an example, let us assume that we have a system of two "black boxes," each with a failure rate, λ, connected like this:

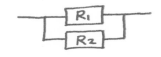

We further assume that both units are operating at all times, but that the output of one is sufficient to assure successful system operation; we have "parallel non-switched redundancy." Now the reliability of one of the units is: $R_1 = e^{-\lambda_1 t}$, and the probability of success of the second unit is: $R_2 = e^{-\lambda_2 t}$. Since $\lambda_1 = \lambda_2$, the reliability of the combination is the probability that *at least one will* continue to operate; $R_s = R_1 + R_2 - R_1 R_2$.

Assuming an exponential hazard function,

$$R_s = e^{-\lambda t} + e^{-\lambda t} - (e^{-\lambda t})(e^{-\lambda t}) =$$
$$2e^{-\lambda t} - e^{-2\lambda t}$$

Now, it may not seem obvious at first, but the hazard function of the parallel system not only has changed from the series system function; the new function is no longer completely described by a simple parameter, such as MTBF or failure rate, over all time. The failure rate of such a redundant system is not constant. The system above was simplified by equal failure rates for the redundant units, but you get the idea.

Just to extend our thinking, consider three units operating in parallel redundancy, each with the same failure rate,

$$R_s = (R_1 + R_2 - R_1 R_2) + R_3$$
$$- (R_1 + R_2 - R_1 R_2)R_3.$$

I won't bother to substitute the exponentials, but the system reliability turns out to be:

$$R_s = 3e^{-\lambda t} - 3e^{-2\lambda t} + e^{-3\lambda t}$$

The advantages of redundancy are obvious. The disadvantages are represented by the additional weight and volume—and cost—necessary to provide the redundant components.

The advantages of redundancy, or replication (to use a word with less of the connotation of uselessness), are not limited to electronic systems with exponential hazard functions; the method is good for any type of equipment, if the reliability of the individual units can be expressed as a probability.

Using the idea to get somewhere

For instance, if the reliability of a truck tire over a certain haul is estimated to be 0.96, and a truck has four tires, all of which must succeed in order for the truck to complete its run, then the estimated probability of success for the truck is: $P_s = P_{st}^4 = (0.96)^4 = 0.85$.

However, if the two tires on the rear axle are replicated, as is done with many trucks, and the truck can complete its run with one tire out on either side or on both sides of the

rear axle, then the probability of success looks like:

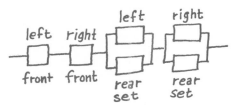

Mathematically, it's:

$$P_s = (P_{st})(P_{st})[P_{st} + P_{st} - (P_{st})(P_{st})]^2$$
$$= P_{st}^2(2P_{st} - P_{st}^2)^2 = 0.92$$

That looks complicated, but it really isn't. The probability of total success is equal to the probability that both front tires will succeed (because failure of either one fails the truck) times the probability that the left rear wheel-set will not fail (each wheel is replicated once) times the probability that the right rear wheel-set will not fail (same replication as the left wheel-set). Using the same probability of success for each tire as we did for the four-tire truck, the probability of success for the replicated model thus becomes 0.92. (Remember now, we have tacitly assumed 100% confidence in our original 0.96 figure for tire-reliability. In complex systems, that's how we keep the mathematics tractable.)

We now know quantitatively what our instinct told us before: truck-tire replication improves chances of successful truck operation. What may be less obvious is this: If, when a tire fails on the rear axle of the replicated model truck, it is immediately detected and replaced, then the probability of a rear-axle failure in toto is reduced to the almost infinitesimal chance that both rear tires on one side will fail simultaneously.

This is actually the practice in electrical generation systems. When one generator of a set fails, and the other carries all the load, the failed one is repaired or replaced as soon as possible. The chances of the second generator going out while the first is being repaired or replaced are very small. Furthermore, as the repair time of a replicate unit goes down, the reliability of the system approaches unity.

Of course (although it has been done), the chances of repairing one unit of a replicated set of aircraft units during flight are quite small, so the model for replicated systems *without* repair usually holds for such systems during their flights. On the other hand, if we have a ground-based system with several units to do the job of one and if a frequent maintenance procedure guarantees rapid replacement

REDUNDANCY

of failed units, we can expect reliable (though sometimes expensive) operation.

I won't bother to derive the probability models for replication greater than three units. The general formula for multiple replications *without repair* is:

$$R_s = P_s = 1 - (1 - R_u)^n$$

where R_s equals system reliability, still the system probability of success, R_u is unit reliability, and n is the number of replications (assuming the unit reliability is the same).

Switching in the redundance

What we have covered so far pertains to operating replication only. However, if one unit is *not* operating while another unit is operating, and the first unit is switched into operation only when the second unit fails, the model becomes somewhat different.

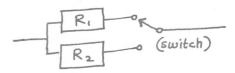

Assuming that each unit follows an exponential hazard function, then a two-unit standby replication of the type that I just described, is represented by

$$R_s = e^{-\lambda t}(1 + \lambda t)$$

and the general formula for multiple standby replication is:

$$R_s = e^{-\lambda t}\left(1 + \lambda t + \frac{\lambda^2 t^2}{2!} + \cdots + \frac{\lambda^n t^n}{n!}\right)$$

But this model assumes 100% reliability for the switch, whose reliability is in series with that of the operating units.

By no means have we covered all aspects of reliability systems analysis. Alternate modes of operation for the system will have a salutary effect on its reliability. There are many cases where there is a combination of series and redundant units which requires special treatment, using methods of Boolean algebra. Whether certain parts generally fail by opening or shortening may possibly influence the system reliability model. And, as I've mentioned, there are schemes which provide for repair of failed units while the alternates carry on. Still other arrangements are possible and/or have been proposed.

Voting for reliability

If we have available the outputs of three or more similar units, these can be compared, and an answer chosen which represents a ma-

jority vote of the unit's answers. Such a system can be represented as:

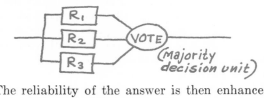

The reliability of the answer is then enhanced over a single unit's answer. For the case of a 2-out-of-3 voting system,

$$R_s = 3e^{-2\lambda t} - 2e^{-3\lambda t}$$

assuming that all systems are identical.

The general principles hold for any grouping of units which can be described by a probability of success. If we can predict the reliability of the smallest functional parts of a complex system, we can then project this prediction, through the use of systems analysis, into a prediction for the entire system. These methods can also be used to improve reliability; that is how reliability engineers (and a few brave design engineers) are now using them.

Besides, we can always hope that someday there will be two motors in every washing machine, one waiting patiently at standby to take over when the first one inevitably fails.

Further reading

Watch out. The literature on this subject is almost as unreliable as it is profuse. As with any needed and rapidly developing field, and especially, it seems, because it's probability-based, the picture is rife with pseudo-panaceas, polemic and promiscuous promotions of pet schemes. But things are looking up. A good journal source has been the *Proceedings of the Professional Group for Reliability and Quality Control* of the IRE. (The group is still functioning during its incorporation, with the rest of the IRE, into the newly formed IEEE.) The best recent symposium was the Ninth National Symposium on Reliability and Quality Control held in San Francisco in January 1963, under the sponsorship of IRE, AIEE, ASQC, and ASME (*Proceedings*, $5).

An excellent book for the beginner is Lloyd and Lipow's *Reliability, Management, Methods and Mathematics* (Prentice-Hall, 1962, $15), while he who wants a thorough treatment for the professional should see Bazavshy's *Reliability Theory and Practice* (Prentice-Hall, 1961, $11.65) or Sandler's *System Reliability Engineering* (Prentice-Hall, 1963, $7.50), and for the reader who wants to get mathematical about it, there's the somewhat stiffer *Redundancy Techniques for Computing Systems* by Wilcox and Mann (Spartan, 1962, $10).

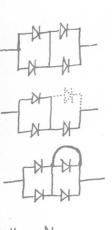

all = (diode)

The operating side of the business is best represented by "the law," Rome Air Development Center's *Reliability Notebook*, PB 161894 (OTS, $4) and MILHDBK 217 [Weps] (Naval Supply Depot, Philadelphia, Pa., free of charge). The engineer serious about getting down to cases should seek these out. They're both (of course) unclassified, but more readily available to government contractors than to others.

MODERN PROCESS CONTROL

by R. E. Finnigan, P. M. Uthe, A. E. Lee *

IN BRIEF: *The advanced state of the control art is belied by the narrowness of its applications in the process industry. Despite great advances in control techniques and equipment for aerospace and military systems, few of these improvements appear in even the newest plants. Not enough is known about the dynamics of most processes to develop the mathematical definitions from which integrated systems can be engineered to control all the process variables simultaneously. When they can, integrated controls, supervised by a computer, often produce vast improvements in throughput and product quality. But marrying computers to controls is still a costly experiment for most processors, for few are capable of engineering the total system; they tend to turn back this responsibility to instrumentation and control manufacturers. However, these suppliers, in turn, have to put more emphasis on hardware for the widest markets than on advanced techniques that require new sensors and actuators. Technological fall-out from aerospace controls is slowly increasing; by the late 1960's, its impact will be strongly felt.—E.H.*

■ *Question:* Is industry today using the available automatic control technology to improve productivity, quality, and profits to the fullest extent possible?

Answer: Surprisingly, no—its potentialities still are virtually untapped and it will require several decades to utilize everything already known today.

We base this on more than a year of visiting 150 process plants and engineering organizations, examining them in the light of our many years of experience in control engineering. Two of us had long been involved with control as applied to aerospace and military systems where much of this new technology has been reduced to practice. The third has had many years of practice in industrial process control engineering.

* The authors prepared their study of industrial process control at Stanford Research Institute in California, where A. E. Lee directs economic research. After completing this article, R. E. Finnigan and P. M. Uthe joined the Integrated Controls Department of Electronic Associates, Inc., Palo Alto, California.

We've analyzed the vexing technoeconomic factors in industry that hold back control applications to the fullest extent of the art, but the most advanced techniques of process control will ultimately produce an impressive payoff in quality, throughput, and safety.

We find that great technological breakthroughs are *not* needed, but the process industries, in particular, will have to make major changes in their approach to control. These changes will require new types of specialists, revisions to the philosophy of plant design and operation, and adoption of design and construction procedures.

One of the biggest deterrents to more rapid changes is that industrial plants are one-of-a-kind from a control systems standpoint. Not all of the controllable factors have been defined mathematically.

It is rare for equivalent processes to have numerically identical parameters from a control viewpoint. It turns out that even supposedly identical boilers for steam generating plants are often found to have different dynamic characteristics. One answer is that myriad variations in processes and process vessels make it difficult to justify the extensive research and engineering needed to produce identical processes from control systems of the type found in the aerospace industry.

By process industries we are referring to those industries that continuously or semi-continuously process gases, liquids, and solids. Typically these include chemical, food, steel, pulp and paper, and steam power plants. The process industries have control-system design objectives quite different from those of aerospace. Rather than maximizing performance while limiting size and weight and regarding cost as a secondary factor, industrial processors seek adequate performance at minimum cost. Usually, instrumentation involves off-the-shelf hardware to minimize design and startup time and permit the use of standardized application procedures.

Unfortunately, what's available off-the-shelf for aerospace control is not usually suitable for industrial environments. Industrial equipment must perform reliably far beyond the

Compares ideal finished product
with actual finished product and
operating conditions that made it

Computer
(optimizer)
Model of ideal
process conditions

Readjusts demands for
better operating conditions
based on last measurement
of process and product

Optimizing loop

Main control loop

Regulate
process
variables
to hold
within
demand limits

Controllers

Initial
demands
and limits

Sense process
operating conditions,
properties of finished
product, and properties
of product at each step

Sensors

Desired
process
condition
(fixed computer program)

ACTUATORS → PROCESS

Fig. 6-59. Supervisory or optimizing control is one of the more advanced control techniques applied in aerospace systems and now being adapted to industrial processes. While each variable is conventionally regulated to hold certain values or set-points, computer compares observed result with model of what's wanted, orders changes in set-points during process, much like foreman at right in 18th century plate glass factory below.

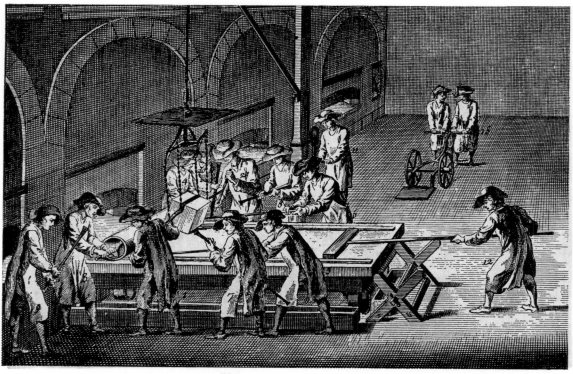

few critical minutes of a missile launching, to endure years of constant use exposed to high temperatures and pressures, highly corrosive process fluids, and fatiguing vibration. Often the measurement devices must be protected from the very environment whose properties they are trying to measure, thus reducing dynamic response and accuracy.

No wonder, then, that our investigations frequently uncovered an air of suspicion and even disenchantment with newer control technology. "We're in business to make chemicals (or steel)," we heard, "not only to advance technology."

When significant cost savings or other major advantages of new controls are easily recognizable to the potential user, they're adopted with alacrity. One steel company, which has capitalized on advanced control system techniques, first increased production of steel strip within ±2 mils-tolerance from 37% of total steel rolled to 85% by installing an analog multivariable control system and then, with digital computer control, achieved 94% useable product.

The electric utility industry, by use of modern integrated control systems, has safely enabled plant capacities to increase from 50 megawatts to 500 megawatts. This rapid advancement in steam-plant technology has caused the reduction in critical response times required of the control system and operators from several minutes to a few seconds. But these benefits of advanced control technology today still turn out to be more the exception than the rule.

Tuning the loops

Then where do the process industries stand today in the use of control systems?

The majority of control systems in use today involve combinations of single-variable control loops. Each control loop is assembled, tuned, and operated independently of all other loops. But the various sub-loops may interact when many of them are combined to control a process. Control would be more effective if it could be integrated—if it could keep multiple variables from interacting in an uncontrolled way.

When you drive a car, you're the integrating control over speed and direction. A locomotive engineer doesn't control direction—the tracks do that—he only controls speed. He cannot optimize speed and direction simultaneously because each of these variables is independently controlled.

Typically, the data about each control loop are picked up by sensors in the process plant and transmitted to recorders, indicators, and controllers at a central location. Controllers measure the difference between actual and desired conditions of, say, temperature, pressure, or flow, and send signals to appropriate actuators back in the plant to correct these conditions. The plant operators have had lots of "seat-of-the-pants" experience and know what demands and limits should be set on each loop to achieve the desired end-product from the plant.

The trouble comes when the specifications of the end-product are changed—a different grade of gasoline, another type of paper. It also comes when the plant is started and each loop must be brought up to a steady-state condition; the loops have different reaction times, and their interactions differ under various conditions. The fact is that too little is known even about the static conditions of a process when the variables are all being held to their desired set-points. Even less is known about what happens to all the variables under changing conditions.

Conventional single-variable control systems are actually a collection of compatible components adjusted for each variable by trial and error, rather than integrated systems that exercise unified control over all variables at once. Thus far, in the vast majority of cases, integrated control systems are used by the process industries only when processes are uncontrollable or unsafe under conventional control. Seldom have they been used simply to improve product quality, throughput, or cost of operation.

Advanced automatic techniques

It is significant to note that literally hundreds of thousands of military and aerospace control systems have been built since the early 1940's using mathematical techniques for quantitative design and analysis of feedback control systems. Some of the mathematical disciplines for the solution of modern control problems are: vector analysis, numerical analysis, advanced algebra, differential and integral equations (linear and nonlinear), Laplace transform and Fourier analysis, complex variables, probability and statistics, information theory, and operations research.

Mathematical techniques are used to describe basic components, the interaction of components, and detailed operating characteristics of the process, as well as in the design and analysis of the control system itself. More important, the use of advanced mathematics permits the "optimization" of the control system strategy and hardware. As used in control theory, optimization is a relative term implying the "best possible" within real-world constraints and indeterminates.

We will not go into details of the classical methods of control systems analysis here, but merely note that these methods provide for quantitative synthesis and analysis of linear systems where the steady-state and transient behavior often serve as the design criteria. Almost without exception, military and aerospace systems have employed continuous (full time), dynamic (transient as well as steady-state) analog control of the process or weapon system. In analog control systems we usually control an easily measureable and transmittable quantity—such as voltage, current, or pressure —which is proportional to (or an analog of) the desired control variable. The variable is generally a physical quantity such as position, temperature, velocity, heading, etc.

In the last few years, a number of expressions have been coined to designate systems derived from even more advanced concepts. More common descriptors are "optimum," "optimizing," "adaptive," "self-adaptive," "self-adjusting," "learning," "self-organizing," and "self-improving." (See "Learning Machines," page 658.) Frequently, identical terms are used to designate different systems.

The type of advanced system that is getting the most attention today is supervisory or optimizing control. To understand how this works, you should recall that conventional controllers have certain demands set into them and operate to close the difference between real and desired values. These demands are based on experienced predictions of what the set-points should be to achieve a desired result.

With supervisory control, the predicted set-points of a number of controllers are automatically produced by a computer, based on a mathematical model of the process that should produce the ideal product. In the steel strip mill shown in Fig. 6-62, in Color Fig. 41, and in Color Fig. 24, the operator tells a supervisory computer that a specific type of steel, so thick, must emerge from the rolling line at a given speed. The computer also gets information from sensors that measure temperature, thickness, and width of the slab to be rolled. From the specifications of the finished product and the information about the slab, the computer sets the initial demands—a model of control system conditions—into the multivariable controller that will maintain screwdown of the rollers, gage control, and individual stand speeds.

When the first slab emerges from the end of the line as steel strip, the computer compares its finished specifications with the specifications for the ideal product. On the basis of calculated deviations from the ideal, the computer improves its model of the process.

Electronic supervisors

Computers are interwoven with the technology of modern control. They are used to analyze control systems, to design them, and to operate as part of them.

The multipurpose analog computer, an equation-solving device, can be used as a multivariable controller operating simultaneously on each process variable. Each computer component performs a single mathematical function such as addition, integration, multiplication, etc. A program for solving a simple differential equation is shown in Fig. 6-61.

You'll find analog computers used as multivariable controllers for stable and optimized

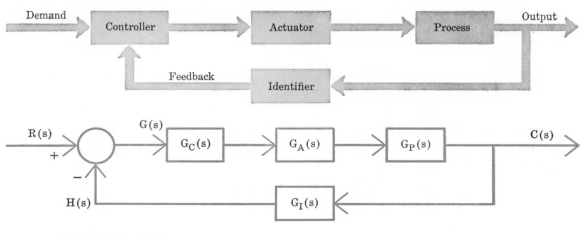

$$\frac{C}{R}(s) = \frac{G_C(s)\ G_A(s)\ G_P(s)}{1 + G_I(s)\ G_C(s)\ G_A(s)\ G_P(s)}$$

$$s = \sigma + j\omega$$

Fig. 6-60. Control systems that are essentially linear can be represented by transfer functions of each sensor, actuator, and controller. Desired ratio of over-all system output to its input is achieved by adjusting transfer function of controller.

control of distillation columns or nuclear reactors. They are most easily and inexpensively applied to those processes which can be described by linear mathematical equations, though you also can get modular computing elements with nonlinear capabilities.

Computing time in an analog machine is independent of the number of control variables involved, but complex mathematical control functions require more computing equipment. Solution of partial differential equations or discrete iterative selection processes often proves so complicated that the number of computing components becomes prohibitively large for analog equipment.

When only a few variables are to be controlled, the analog computer (multivariable controller) is eminently suitable, usually costing about $1000 per variable. Only when you get near 100 variables does a digital computer enter more serious economic consideration.

The modern process control digital computer is neither a glorified version of a business machine nor a scaled-down version of a scientific computer. It has been designed specifically for process control and more than 175 have been installed in the U.S. alone—but few are actually being used to control a process. Most of the digital computers presently in operation are used for process monitoring, alarming, computing, and logging. While the analog computer shines in dynamic simulation and control, the digital computer excels in modeling, data reduction, scanning and comparing, accurate computing, and general data processing.

The "one sample at a time" operating mode of presently available digital computers is incompatible with the continuous and multivariable characteristic of the modern process. In practice, this basic incompatibility is often focused at the interface between computer and conventional analog measurement and control components. This interface is bridged by analog-to-digital converters and digital-to-analog converters which tend to be expensive and of lower accuracy than the computer.

As presently used in process control, the digital computer operates sequentially on each process variable. For this reason, computing time is dependent upon the number of variables and computer operations required.

If memory and input-output capacity are not fully committed, additional control functions can be incorporated without the addition of more computer equipment. Unfortunately, most computer purchasers underestimate equipment requirements.

Theoretically, the digital computer should be very valuable in supervising process startups and shutdowns, and it should ultimately

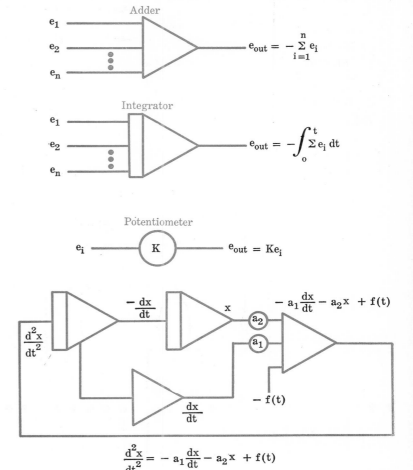

$$e_{out} = - \sum_{i=1}^{n} e_i$$

$$e_{out} = - \int_0^t \sum e_i \, dt$$

$$e_{out} = K e_i$$

$$\frac{d^2x}{dt^2} = - a_1 \frac{dx}{dt} - a_2 x + f(t)$$

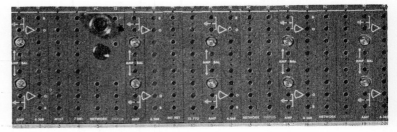

Fig. 6-61. Analog computing components in diagram perform single mathematical functions, can be connected via patch panel at bottom to solve equations.

see considerable use in industrial plants (such as steam-generating stations) for this purpose. Because of the great number of manual operations presently required in starting up complex processing, these plants will have to be redesigned *for* computer control before a digital computer can be employed effectively.

Digital control computers are designed to be more reliable than business or scientific machines. But few data have been published on control computer mean time between failures. About 40 days of failure-free operation are being realized now and at least one computer

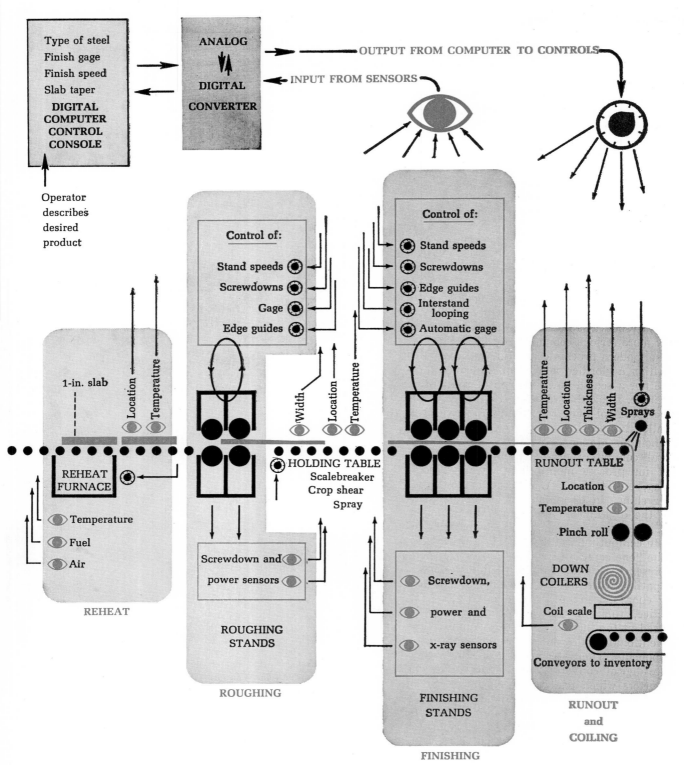

Fig. 6-62. *In May 1963 new Spencer Works of Richard Thomas & Baldwin, Wales, England began rolling steel under supervisory control of GE digital computer. Entire process was first simulated on an analog and digital computer in a U.S. control engineering laboratory. Supervisory computer tracks each slab from time it enters reheat furnace. It has been programmed with customer specifications for desired product: grade of steel, thickness, temperature as it is finished and coiled.*

Comparing these with mathematical model of process, the computer calculates how equipment in entire hot strip line must react at each stage of process and keeps changing set-points of multivariable analog control system. Steel mill near Detroit has been under similar computer control for 4 years, though total supervisory loop is shorter, doesn't include reheat furnace. See Color Fig. 41 and Color Fig. 24 for additional details.

has operated on-line without failure for more than 240 days. It is standard practice to operate these computers with little or no preventive maintenance. Most control computers are self-checking and fail-safe; in the event of a failure, they usually turn control back to the conventional controllers.

Prices for digital control computers range upward from $100,000. Today, typical installed cost is about $300,000, but special control requirements can easily double this. Furthermore, since a considerable amount of application engineering is required to implement a digital computer process control program, an equal investment for technical manpower also may be required. Normally, the equipment purchaser and supplier share these costs.

Control systems engineering

It is common practice today to design and construct a modern process plant to satisfy an economic performance objective. After the plant has been built, months and even years are spent in manually adjusting the system to achieve better performance—usually increased throughput at some required quality level.

A more modern approach to process and control system design might enable this plant to be brought on line within a shorter time period, to operate with significantly greater economic benefit than otherwise is possible, and to undergo major improvement during its lifetime. Modern process and control system design focuses on the uniqueness of the process, while conventional design focuses on the capability of already available controls, instrumentation, and other process equipment. Though the conventional controller has been applied to a great number of processes, the modern multivariable control system cannot be readily applied to any process other than the one for which it was synthesized.

So broad is the scope of modern control systems engineering that no single individual can be sufficiently competent in all the technical and economic areas involved. The solution of a control system problem may involve process specialists, control and instrumentation engineers, economists, and applied mathematicians. Modern process control is truly multi-disciplinary with no one technical specialty being of overwhelming importance. Program direction is often assumed by the technical specialist who has the major problem; generally, it is better to assign program responsibility to an individual who grasps the fundamentals of each of the technologies involved.

Effectively applied, the technology of control systems requires considerable thought and analysis about process control objectives and designs before production hardware is procured. In fact, this is the reason technological manpower costs may exceed hardware costs.

If one starts from process definition, a manpower to equipment cost ratio of more than two to one is usually anticipated. A distillation column controlled by a multivariable controller (analog computer) may incorporate $20,000 in instrumentation and controls, but may involve $40,000 in technical manpower to design and apply it. Such a system has raised the return on investment for one petroleum company by 50% over previous designs.

Stumbling blocks to modern control

What, then, are the stumbling blocks which limit what can be accomplished by processors today and which determine the time constant of their advance to more modern control?

Although many of our industrial processes have been with us for years, the dynamic characteristics of the majority of them are still relatively undefined. Oddly enough, we know considerably more about the complicated dynamics of missiles and rocket engines and nuclear power plants.

Within the past several years, a handful of processors have formed sizable analysis groups to improve the control of existing processes and assist in the design of new ones. Several such groups move around a company examining the various processes and upgrading the control systems. Some groups use a mobile digital computer for on-line process analysis and data reduction. These specialists must have a familiarity with the processes, with the instrumentation used to analyze them, and with mathematical techniques of process analysis and modeling. They must be able to choose parameters based on these process models which will provide stable and accurate control. In the application phase, they must be familiar with modern techniques of control engineering and with all available types of hardware. Because the process industries have been slow to realize the importance of such analytical work, the type of specialists required is rare in industry today, and will continue to be until control systems engineering becomes a recognized discipline taught in the universities.

Throughout the process industries the most critical equipment need is for better sensors to provide both primary and secondary measurements. Primary measurements are those used for direct dynamic control of the process; secondary measurements are those used for monitoring, evaluation, safety, etc. To provide adequate dynamic control, primary measurements such as temperature, pressure, level, and flow must possess good accuracy, high stability, reasonably fast response, and extremely high reliability. Secondary measurements such as stream composition analysis (often with gas chromatographs), stack gas analysis, process efficiency measurements, etc., do not require the same order of reliability and speed of response as primary measurements but they do require high accuracy and stability.

The lack of accurate and reliable sensors is limiting our ability to control many of our present processes, and retards making such major improvements in the processes themselves as going from batch to continuous operation. This is particularly true where unusual fluids are being processed. For example, it is difficult to measure accurately the temperature of molten steel, the consistency of pulp for paper, the properties of processed food slurries, such as sugar or salt, or the yeast level during beer processing.

Many of these measurements presently have to be made in the laboratory because of the lack of sensors which can make such measurements "on-line" during the actual process. This frequently necessitates a batch operation to allow time for such measurements and to permit operator supervision of each batch. Continuous processes requiring accurate, on-line instrumentation save money for the processor because they eliminate costly storage tanks and increase throughput.

In addition to not having sensors available to measure many process characteristics, those which we do have are often inadequate in terms of accuracy, speed of response, stability, and maintainability. Despite the recent interest in electronic instruments, most of the instrumentation in the process industries today is pneumatic. Pressure is usually measured by conventional diaphragm or bellows-type transmitters. High accuracy, high-response strain-gage transducers, for example, have not yet come into common use for pressure measurement.

Temperature is still measured with bulb-type thermometers or large thermocouples insulated from the process in thermowells rather than by accurate and fast miniature thermocouples or resistance thermometers. These slow and often inaccurate sensors penalize industrial control systems, make even the most modern electronic controls less effective.

In considering the sheer variety of instruments required by the process industries and the severe environments in which they must work, it is not surprising that instrument companies find it economically infeasible to attempt to meet all the industry's needs. It would involve development of many special-purpose instruments. The development costs are high

and the market is usually narrow. So, the processor is forced to do without the needed instruments or develop them himself. The largest processors can maintain a staff of qualified instrument engineers, but, this certainly is not feasible for the typical company.

Many of the sorely needed sensors are presently available from our aerospace programs. But most of these have yet to be engineered to meet the daily punishment of severe environmental conditions in process plants. High cost and lack of assurance about long-term reliability have discouraged any great demand for them by the process industries.

Rather than pursue the limited market for special-purpose sensors, numerous manufacturers are producing and marketing sophisticated control systems including analog and digital control computers, employing, wherever possible, multipurpose equipment which can be used in many applications. There simply is not enough activity toward the development of a measurement technology which provides for more quantitative design of the needed instruments and which makes better use of the considerable aerospace research and development. Until more processors recognize that there is a critical need in this area and are willing to invest their time and money accordingly, the performance of available control systems will be limited by capabilities of its measurement equipment.

Computer-process interface problems

It is important to recognize that the marriage of the control computer to the industrial process is still an experiment. Rarely is a computer applied as a result of adequate systems engineering by the processors and their engineering firms. Usually it is superimposed on the process almost as an expensive afterthought rather than integrated into the process control system in the design and checkout phase. Often this results in the superposition of a sophisticated control computer on a Model-T control system.

A number of processors have already invested millions of dollars over 3 or 4 calendar years (in some cases more than 50 man-years of engineering time) in attempting to put a digital computer in control of a process. (The first computer-controlled hot strip mill took 18 months to shakedown.) When they have only limited success, the computer ends up as a fancy data logger and performance monitor. On the other hand, less sophisticated analog computers for on-line control of petroleum and chemical processes have been successfully put to work in less than 6 months, paying out their total investment in periods as short as two months out of savings in the cost of processing or from improvements in product quality.

What are the problems which complicate computer control? Can a processor determine in advance whether or not he should attempt computer control?

Initially, a major problem was the unreliability of the digital computer itself, which had a very low "meantime between failures." This has since been corrected by using all solid-state and magnetic components.

But marrying a digital computer to an analog process involves the mating of equipment that is somewhat incompatible. The digital computers currently in use are serial machines which operate on only one variable at a time; each variable must be in some digital form. Hence, digital computers need high-speed conversion equipment for both the input and output of process information. To keep track of what all the variables of the process are doing (as many as 2400 are monitored in some processes) the computer must sample these quantities at very high rates, rapidly operating on the information to determine required settings or to take necessary corrective actions. But process sensors produce a variety of low-level inputs; sampling them at high rates and with a satisfactory signal-to-noise ratio has been a major problem in many applications.

Possibly the knottiest problems arise in the search for a completely new approach to process control. Before computers (B.C.) the processor solved most of his control problems by finding the proper instrumentation and control equipment or, in many cases, by bringing in an equipment manufacturer who tuned what hardware he had to the process. The user did not rely on new techniques to solve his control problems.

With more sophisticated hardware like digital control computers, the equipment itself can introduce many more problems than it solves. The user must learn to program the machine (or at least to write computer flow diagrams).

He must understand his process and its present control systems so he can describe them to the computer. Programming the computer to control a process which is not thoroughly understood and whose dynamic behavior may vary from one day to the next with change in ambient temperature, humidity, etc., is a problem which can require many man-months of expensive engineering time. Also the user must design circuits which convert his present instrumentation signals to levels compatible with the computer, taking care to assure proper isolation between the two. In short, the user must learn to use systems engineering techniques in all phases of the computer implementation program.

But some users seem to feel it is advantageous to have the engineering firm or the equipment manufacturer marry the computer to his process; many a control computer sale has depended on providing this service free or at nominal cost. As with most everything else, the purchaser gets just what he pays for when buying control computers. Those who have obtained "free" software such as process control system studies, computer programming service, and application engineering service, very often end up with expensive control computer installations which cannot be economically or technically justified. In many cases, those same processors would have gained more if they had invested in training their engineering staff in more modern control techniques or in securing the services of special consultants.

No general, well-defined method of specifying a digital computer for process control has yet been derived. We think a possible approach might be to solicit equipment bids on the basis of a functional block diagram (an expanded computer flow chart) with information concerning required reliability, environmental resistivity, service guarantee, delivery dates, etc., included in the normal manner. This technique would force the purchaser (the processor) to think through his requirements in functional

INSTRUMENTATION AND CONTROL COSTS

	Basic Equipment	Required + Application Engineering
Conventional controls (per loop)	$750-$1250	$450-$1250
Stream analyzer or other special sensor	$1000-$65,000	$2400-$160,000
Integrated control (per loop, no digital computer)	$1200-$1500	$2000-$3000
Added costs for digital computer control	$175,000-$1,100,000	$200,000-$1,100,000

Fig. 6-63. Control components for advanced control systems need to be integrated by applications engineering more expensive than the hardware itself. (Courtesy Stanford Research Institute)

detail before committing himself to a specific computer system. The computer manufacturer could more clearly determine what types of computers are needed and would no longer be forced to play the role of process engineer or even control systems engineer. The computer purchaser could easily protect his proprietary interests through use of functional flow chart specifications. The use of symbolic language could even prevent the computer supplier from knowing what the pertinent plant produces.

A crystal ball on control

We think the immediate future of process control will parallel the immediate past. We foresee new techniques and new hardware emerging in an evolutionary way. There's too much inertia to be overcome for us to believe the heralds of a revolution in control.

We doubt that mathematical techniques of control system design and analysis will be generally accepted and used in the process industries until the 1970's. But managements of the more progressive processors will support experimentation with modern control techniques—especially control computers.

As attempts are made to improve process control, the system imbalance between sensors and actuators and the controllers will become increasingly obvious. High performance sensors and actuators will be adopted, even though they will cost more.

We believe that a major shift of electronic instrumentation will take place, spurred by the requirements for faster control system responses and compatibility with computers. As these advanced equipments become available, the analog computer, the advanced continuous sensor, and the high-performance control actuator will be engineered as a system to accomplish high stability of operation over a wide band of operating conditions. These integrated control systems will be highly reliable and will be self-checking.

The digital computer will be used for the supervision of the process primarily through the analog computer control system. This supervision will incorporate adaptive features and will intermittently test the process to determine a better operating point for greater economic return. Product analyzers will probably feed directly to the digital computer while most other process feedback will be obtained from the analog control system. The computer will also collect and compile production and accounting data but will *not*, for many years to come, be supervised by a master computer at the corporate offices.

Plant operators and technicians will be closely coupled to the analog system while

management will be concerned primarily with the digital computer, for it is here that profit and loss will be balanced. For plant managers this may involve some change in present thinking, for the digital computer will be used increasingly to optimize *profit* per day, not throughput per day.

This evolution in process control will be accompanied by other advances. Process plants will cost less to build because they will be designed for high reaction and flow rates with less intermediate storage capability and less intrinsic safety margin. The new hot-strip mills and high-capacity steam plants are indicators of what is to come. Typically, throughput is up 500% in the last ten years.

To reduce engineering costs and, in some instances, permit automatic, unattended operation, many processes will become "packaged." This is already happening in gas and sewage processing. Plant startup time and the time needed for first-level optimization will be much less than today. Many chemical plants today are started up within nine months of contract award. More operating manpower will be required (engineers and technicians) but fewer accountants and men to schedule production will be needed. Operators will be trained on simulators.

As all of this comes about, the process industries will cease to lag the technical state of the control art. Indeed, to gain greater increases in productivity, they will start pushing the state of the art in many other areas—metallurgy, reaction chemistry, and structural design.

Further reading

For a good basic text on servomechanisms, the classic is *Principles of Servomechanisms* by G. S. Brown and D. P. Campbell (Wiley, 1948, $8.50). An excellent and widely read text on feedback control systems, though for the advanced engineer, is J. G. Truxal's *Control System Synthesis* (McGraw-Hill, 1955, $14). For a fine source of modern mathematical design techniques, see *Control Systems Engineering* by W. W. Seifert and C. W. Steeg, Jr. (McGraw-Hill, 1960, $15). A survey of the field has been accomplished in Volumes I, II and III of *Automation, Computation and Control* by E. M. Grabbe, S. Ramo, and D. B. Wooldridge (Wiley, 1961, Vols. I and II, $18.50 each, Vol. III, $19.75). This covers most techniques and gives many applications.

Mathematical Theory of Optimal Processes has been translated from the original Russian edition (1962); available from Office of Technical Services, U.S. Dept. of Commerce ($7). A systemized theory of optimal automatic control systems is presented in *Optimum Second Order Relay Servomechanisms,* translated from the Polish (1961) ; available from OTS ($5.60).

Industrial firms wishing to adapt instrument designs and process techniques of Oak Ridge National Laboratory can get assistance from the Office of Industrial Cooperation, U.S. Atomic Energy Commission. A similar service is available from NASA's Office of Industrial Applications.

Some papers on the technical and management aspects of process control were presented at the 17th Annual Instrument Society of America Conference held in New York City in October 1962 (available from Instrument Society of America, Pittsburgh, Pa.).

Process control falls within the purview of many technical societies: IEEE, ASME, ACS, and ISA. These four sponsor a Joint Automatic Control Conference each year.

Internationally, the field is covered by the International Federation for Automatic Control, whose members cooperate with UNESCO in preparing a quarterly *International Bibliography of Automatic Control* (Gordon and Breach, New York, $25 per year). U.S. periodicals to follow are *Automation, Automatic Control, Control Engineering, Chemical Engineering, ISA Journal, Instruments and Control Systems.* In the U.K. there is *Automatic Control and Automation;* in Germany, *Regelungstechnische Praxis;* in the USSR, *Automatika.*

A detailed analysis of the effects of process dynamics in the case of consecutive reaction systems is given in *Adaptive Optimization of Continuous Processes* by Box and Chanmugam in *I & EC Fundamentals,* a relatively new American Chemical Society publication (Vol. 1, No. 1, Feb. 1962). The authors describe an adaptive optimizer they have designed.

Index